IDENTIFICATION GUIDE TO NORTH AMERICAN BIRDS

PART I

Identification Guide to North American Birds

Part I
Columbidae to Ploceidae

by Peter Pyle

with the collaboration of
Steve N.G. Howell
David F. DeSante
Robert P. Yunick
Mary Gustafson

*A compendium of information on identifying, ageing, and sexing
"near-passerines" and passerines in the hand.*

Illustrations by Steve N.G. Howell

Slate Creek Press
Bolinas, California
1997

Identification Guide to North American Birds. Part I.
Copyright© 1997 by Peter Pyle. All rights reserved
2nd printing 2001

ISBN: 0-9618940-2-4
Library of Congress Catalog Card Number: 97-69065

Cover designed and illustrated by Priscilla Yocom and Steve N.G. Howell.

Printed in the United States of America by Braun-Brumfield Inc., Ann Arbor, Michigan.
Second printing by Sheridan Books, Inc., Ann Arbor, Michigan

Special thanks to Priscilla Yocom, Duncan McCallum of Braun-Brumfield, and Kathy Brown of
Sheridan Books, Inc.

Designed and produced by Peter Pyle, Priscilla Yocom, Steve N.G. Howell, and David F. DeSante
for Slate Creek Press, P.O. Box 219, Bolinas, California, 94924.

A product of:

The Institute for Bird Populations
P.O. Box 1346
Point Reyes Station, CA 94956

4990 Shoreline Highway
Stinson Beach
CA 94970

In memory of my brother
Robert Lewis Pyle

and of those ornithologists of a bygone (but hopefully not forgotten) era:

S.F. Baird
E. Coues
J. Dwight Jr.
R. Ridgway
H.S. Swarth
H.C. Oberholser
J. Grinnell
A.J. van Rossem
A.H. Miller
A.R. Phillips

Table of Contents

Acknowledgements

Most importantly, I would like to apologize to my family, friends, and colleagues for being so elusive and unrelaxed during the three years it has taken to perform this revision. Completion of the project otherwise would not have occurred.

Many have assisted with this in various ways. Foremost among these are the four collaborators listed on the title page. Without the help of the three coauthors of the first edition (Pyle *et al.* 1987) there would not have been a first edition, and therefore no revision. Robert P. Yunick continues to provide inspiration with his many publications on ageing and sexing. David F. DeSante, besides providing unconditional morale support, has been of tremendous help with the publication and distribution of the first attempt, and will be so again for the second. And Steve N.G. Howell, besides continuing to be a regular field *compadre* (on both sides of the border), was of invaluable assistance in the museum specimen collections and greatly helped to ensure that the illustrations (and text) were as correct as possible. In addition, Mary Gustafson not only reviewed the entire text for accuracy, but has been a pleasure to work with in ensuring that the species accounts (including acceptable age/sex-code criteria, alpha codes, and band sizes) met Bird Banding Laboratory standards.

A potential sixth collaborator (before he retired from the National Museum of Natural History) was M. Ralph Browning, who reviewed the geographic variation sections for the "near-passerines" and provided many useful comments on the general format of this section. I am also indebted to Kenneth C. Parkes for reviewing the introduction, providing many useful tips, and ensuring, especially, that the information on molt and molt terminology was accurate. Christopher W. Thompson also reviewed several of our recent papers on molt, keeping us in line when our terminology strayed.

I am much indebted to Elizabeth F. Gilbert, Mary Gustafson, Michele Hammond, and Steve N.G. Howell for proofreading the entire manuscript and pointing out many errors; those remaining undoubtedly were introduced by the author at a later stage. Jon R. King, David F. DeSante, Philip Ashman, Will Richardson, Ken Convery, Joel Ellis, and F.R. Gehlbach read certain portions or accounts, or provided additional assistance with the illustrations. I also thank David Cothran and Steve N.G. Howell for assistance with specimen measurements.

I greatly thank Priscilla Yocom, who typeset the entire manuscript, including the scanning, layout, and labling of all illustrations and the incorporation of all bar graphs. This was an enormous task, done in a very competent and efficient manner.

The people at The Institute for Bird Populations (IBP) helped in many ways. My thanks to Brett Walker for extracting wing chord data from the Monitoring Avian Productivity and Survivorship (MAPS) program, David F. DeSante, Eric Ruhlen, Hillary Smith, and Kenneth Burton for frequent commentary on the species accounts, and Eric Ruhlen, Dan Rosenberg, Eric Feuss, Danielle O'Grady, Kenneth Burton, Dan Froehlich, and David F. DeSante for technical help with softwear. This is IBP contribution # 78.

Likewise, many folks at the Point Reyes Bird Observatory (PRBO) continued to be of assistance; I especially thank Grant Ballard, David Cothran, Dan Evans, Geoff Geupel, Karen Hamilton, Denise Hardesty, Michelle Hester, Anne King, Elizabeth McLaren, Jackie Miller, Nadav Nur, Gareth Penn, Dave Shuford, William J. Sydeman, Sophie Webb, Laura Williams, and, especially, the many volunteer banders at the Southeast Farallon Island and Palomarin field stations. This is PRBO contribution # 743.

I thank members of Powdermill Nature Reserve (Bob Mulvihill and Bob Leberman) and Long Point Bird Observatory (Paul Prior and Jon D. McCracken) for providing data or feedback on sections of the guide, the library staff at the California Academy of Sciences (Anne Malley,

Theresa Meikle, Leslie Segedy, Susan Campinelli, Tom Moritz, and Larry Currie) for much assistance with references and for allowing me to roam freely among the stacks, and the curators and assistants at the many specimen collections for permitting me to examine the specimens under their care. These include Luis F. Baptista, Karen Cebra, and Kathleen Burke (California Academy of Sciences), Ned K. Johnson, Carla Cicero, and Barbara Stein (Museum of Vertebrate Zoology), Kimball Garrett (Natural History Museum of Los Angeles County), Philip Unitt (San Diego Natural History Museum), Walter Wehtje and Jon Fisher (Western Foundation of Vertebrate Zoology), John Hafna and James Northern (Moore Laboratory of Zoology), and Mary LeCroy (American Museum of Natural History).

Many people have assisted in various ways through correspondence and feedback to the first edition. These include David Agro, Per Alström, Philip Ashman, Stephen F. Bailey, Richard C. Banks, Luis F. Baptista, Grant Ballard, Louis R. Bevier, Susan R. Blackshaw, Rhys V. Bowen, M. Ralph Browning, Paul A. Buckley, Kay Burk, Ken Burton, Phil Capitolo, Allen T. Chartier, David A. Christie, Jane P. Church, David Cimprich, Charles T. Collins, Douglas M. Collister, Rita Colwell, Ken Convery, Albert E. Conway, Chris Corbin, Jon Curson, Robert W. Dickerman, Jochen Dierschke, Mark S. Dugdale, Jon L. Dunn, John B. Dunning Jr., Lee Elias, Steve Emslie, Richard A. Erickson, Mario Diaz Esteban, David L. Evans, Shawneen Finnegan, Richard A. Forster, Charles M. Francis, Mary A. Fuith, Steve J.M. Gantlett, Kimball L. Garrett, Elizabeth F. Gilbert, Lex Glover, Geoff Geupel, William Hamilton III, Ives Hannay, Keith Hansen, Denise Hardesty, Matt T. Heindel, Tom and Jo Heindel, David Holmes, Mark A. Holmgren, Denver W. Holt, Paul Holt, Peter H. Homann, Kim Hollinger, C. Stuart Houston, Gordon E. Howard, William H. Howe, David J.T. Hussell, James I. Ingold, Jerome A. Jackson, Alvaro Jaramillo, Andrea Jesse, Elly Jones, Durrell Kapan, Kenn Kaufman, Charles E. Keller, C.A. Kemper, Jon R. King, M. Kathleen Klimkiewicz, Alan Knox, Walter D. Koenig, Lisa M. Krajcirik, Anthony Lang, Jeri M. Langham, Robert C. Leberman, Paul E. Lehman, Tony Leukering, Catherine Levy, Curtice Marantz, Peter P. Marra, Tom Martin, Guy McCaskie, Robert G. McKinney, Jon D. McCraken, Joseph Morlan, Jenna Mueller, Robert S. Mulvihill, Ron Mundy, Bill Murphy, Christopher Norment, Robert Pantle, Kenneth C. Parkes, Michael A. Patten, Allan R. Phillips, Frank A. Pitelka, Bill Principe, Glen Proudfoot, C.J. Ralph, Cynthia A. Renk, Will Richardson, Nick Riddiford, James D. Rising, Chandler S. Robbins, Don Roberson, Craig Roberts, Sievert Rohwer, Eric Ruhlen, Martin Schaefer, Fred S. Schaeffer, N. John Schmitt, Thomas W. Sherry, Kristen M. Shields, David A. Sibley, Hillary Smith, David Spector, Richard W. Stallcup, Jim Statz, Jim Steele, Hannah B. Suthers, Lars Svensson, Pat Tabler, Ian Tait, Dan Tallman, Christopher W. Thompson, Olivier Tostain, Charles H. Trost, Robert C. Tweit, Phillip Unitt, Mary K. Waddington, Brett Walker, George E. Wallace, Sophie Webb, Claudia P. Wilds, Oriane Williams, Ernest J. Willoughby, Kenneth P. Winkler, Joseph M. Wunderle, and Gregor Yanega. Of these, the following provided unpublished manuscripts: William H. Baltosser, Luis F. Baptista, Rhys V. Bowen, Allen T. Chartier, Douglas M. Collister, Jon Curson, Mark S. Dugdale, Jon L. Dunn & Kimball L. Garrett, David J.T. Hussell, Frank R. Moore, Robert S. Mulvihill, Ron Mundy & Jon D. McCraken, David A. Sibley & Steve N.G. Howell, George E. Wallace, Ernest J. Willoughby, and Joseph M. Wunderle.

The personnel of the USGS/Bird Banding Laboratory (BBL) and Biological Resources Division (BRS), and the Canadian Wildlife Service (CWS), including M. Kathleen Klimkiewicz, Mary Gustafson, Ellen Hayawkawa, Lucie Metras, Chandler S. Robbins, John Tautin, Bill Howe, Danny Bystrak, and Sam Droege were helpful and encouraging about having this guide represent their standards for age and sex code acceptance. As part of this assistance, I was able to review and incorporate all of the correspondence on ageing and sexing in the BBL folders. The information that banders have contributed was extremely useful in updating the accounts. Those that contributed in this manner (° denoting those that contributed for at least five species) include: Curtis S. Adkisson, Oliver L. Austin Jr., James Baird°, K.E. Bartlet, Don Beimborn°, R.

Bertin, Charles H. Blake°, Dorothy L. Bordner°, Clait E. Braun, David Brewer, David F. Brinker, Jerram L. Brown, Edward E. Burroughs, Peter F. Cannell, Paul M. Catling, Mary H. Clench°, W. Chapman, Charles E. Cochran, Robert R. Cohen, Charles T. Collins°, Ralph W. Condee, W.D. Corser, Richard D. Crawford, Richard S. Crossin, Rebecca M. Dellinger, David F. DeSante, Margeret T. Donnald, Mary E. Doscher, Christina Dowd, Paul E. Downing, Elizabeth H. Downs, Erica H. Dunn, Stephen W. Eaton, Charles A. Ely, R. Engs, Thomas C. Erdman, David L. Evans°, D.M. Fairfield, Erma J. Fisk°, Annette B. Flanigan, John J. Flora, Eric D. Forsman, Dottie Foy, Frederick R. Gehlbach, Frank B. Gill, Maurice G. Goldberg, Alfred H. Grewe Jr., Alfred O. Gross, George A. Hall, Paul B. Hamel, Fran Hamerstrom, Harold T. Harper, Elva H. Hawken, Kathlyn Heidel, Richard A. Hill, Bill Hilton Jr., Larry L. Hood, Deborah V. Howard, John P. Hubbard, Elgen B. Hurlbert, David J.T. Hussell°, Jerome A. Jackson, Joseph H. Jeppson, Morgan Jones, M. Kathleen Klimkiewicz°, Robert L. Jarvis, John H. Kennard, Warren A. Lamb, Wesley E. Lanyon°, Robert C. Leberman°, Albert C. Lloyd, Trevor Lloyd-Evans, Willetta Lueshen, Steven L. Loch, Frederick E. Ludwig, Dottie Malec, Marlyn Mauritz, George R. Mayfield Sr., M. McEntee, Katherine McKeever, Elaine Meese, Wilde R. Mellancamp, Will D. Merritt Jr., Sophia C. Mery, L. Richard Mewaldt°, John B. Miles, Clark Miller, Daniel E. Miller, Burt L. Monroe, Robert A. Montgomery, John N. Mugaas, Mickey Mutchler, David M. Niles, Val Nolan Jr., Russell T. Norris, Robert T. Orr, Robert T. Paine, Kenneth C. Parkes°, Hapgood Parks, J. Michael Patterson, Robert M. Patterson, Donald E. Payne, Robert B. Payne, Leonard J. Peyton, Richard M. Poulin, Amadeo M. Rea°, James D. Rising, Chandler S. Robbins°, Oscar M. Root, Chris N. Rose Sr., Stephen M. Russell, K. Salata, Mike San Miguel, Robert R. Sargent, John Sarvis, Frederick S. Schaeffer°, Mark C. Shieldcastle, Brian Sharp, Jay M. Sheppard°, Paul A. Shirokoff, Rob Simpson, Charlotte E. Smith, Roy B.H. Smith, Trudy Smith, William P. Smith, Bruce A. Sorrie, Doris H. Speirs, F. Gary Stiles, Wendell Taber, Ann T. Tarbell, Robert C. Tweit, Laurel F. Van Camp, Mary K. Waddington, Lawrence H. Walkinshaw, Ron D. Weir, Charles M. Weise, John S. Weske°, George C. West, Francis M. Weston, David Willard, Kevin Winker, Arthur J. Wiseman, D. Scott Wood°, Merrill Wood°, Paul W. Woodward°, and Robert P. Yunick°. Of these, M. Kathleen Klimkiewicz, Erma J. Fisk, and John S. Weske should be especially acknowledged for the amount of information and thought contributed.

Finally, I am indebted to Rowena Forest for love and for understanding my need to work.

Peter Pyle
Midway Atoll
13 May 1997

Introduction

Since the first edition of this guide (Pyle *et al.* 1987) was published we have made some progress in our understanding of the molts, ageing, and sexing of North American birds; however, we still lag behind the Europeans in these areas, by as much as ten years according to recent estimates. As with the first edition, this revised and expanded version attempts to bridge this gap, at least partially. More importantly, it again attempts to reflect the state of our current knowledge in these areas, providing a baseline for the further development of our understanding, and pointing out many areas in need of additional study. As with the first edition, a primary objective of this guide is to call attention to unsolved problems.

Three major changes will be found in this second edition: 1) It includes all North American (north of Mexico) "near-passerines", or doves through woodpeckers in the order of the American Ornithologist's Union Check-list (AOU 1983), 2) short descriptive summaries are presented for all currently recognized subspecies, and 3) the sections on molt have been substantially expanded, incorporating many recent findings, and increasing the detail on feather replacement to the level of the wing coverts. As a consequence of the last change, the sections on ageing have also been expanded, with a greater focus on molt limits among the median, greater, and primary coverts. Much of the new information in these areas was gained through extensive specimen examination (see **Acknowledgments** and p. 38) and is in need of critical testing in the field. Several minor changes to the content and format of this edition will also be evident. These include increased information useful for species separation in the field, the addition of a section on hybrids, the presentation of bar graphs indicating temporal periods of reliable ageing and sexing, and a greatly expanded list of references.

As with the first edition, the author strongly encourages users to publish contradicting, additional, or supporting information, or to contact him (at PRBO, 4990 Shoreline Hwy, Stinson Beach, CA 94970 USA), so that it may be incorporated into future editions. Such feedback was a vital component of the current revision process (see **Acknowledgments**). In addition, as the title ambitiously states, a second part is planned to include (in the same format) information on North American waterbirds, diurnal raptors, and gallinaceous birds. Any unpublished information or leads to funding will be greatly appreciated.

SCOPE

Totals of 395 species and 857 currently recognized subspecies, of near-passerines and passerines, are treated in this guide. Most or all species which regularly breed or have bred at least once in North America (north of Mexico) are included, plus at least two other regular vagrants from tropical America. Only three introduced species and no extinct species are included. The information presented in the accounts of many migrants is applicable on both their breeding and their tropical wintering grounds. Species taxonomy and order follow those of the AOU (1983), as modified by the AOU (1985-1997). See the section on **Geographic variation** for methods used to determine subspecies taxonomy.

BIRD TOPOGRAPHY

The names of soft parts and feather tracts follow those most widely used in the current ornithological literature (Figs. 1 & 2). Primaries are numbered **distally** (innermost to outermost) and secondaries **proximally** (outermost to innermost), as in Figure 1 (see also Fig. 13). In the terminology of this guide, "p6-p9" (*e.g.*) indicates primaries 6 through 9, whereas p6 – p9 indicates p6 minus p9, a measurement used in determining wing morphology (see below). Here, the term "**flight feathers**" refers to the primaries, primary coverts, secondaries, and rectrices. "**Middle secondaries**" refer to the secondaries immediately adjacent to the tertials (*e.g.*, s3-s6 in passerines). **Wing feather edging** refers to the edging and fringing on the wing coverts and tertials.

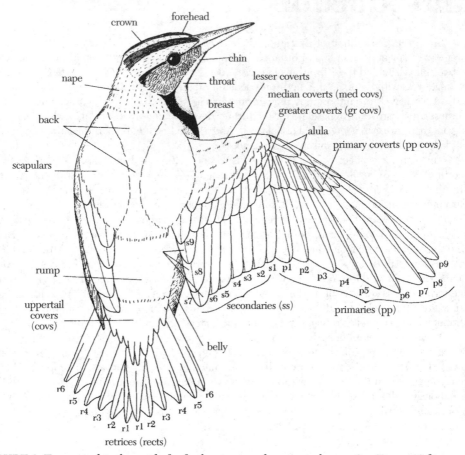

FIGURE 1. Terms used in this guide for feather tracts and anatomical areas. See Figure 13 for more details on wing feather terminology.

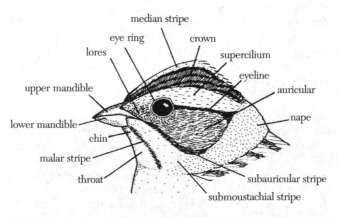

FIGURE 2. Terms used in this guide for areas of the head.

IDENTIFICATION, AGEING, AND SEXING TECHNIQUES

The accurate identification, ageing, and sexing of North American near-passerines and passerines generally is complicated by a high degree of variation in size, plumage, and molt patterns found within each species, subspecies, and age/sex class. In this guide, a format which summarizes the distinguishing features of each group, in a directly comparative manner, was chosen over the popular (but oversimplified) dichotomous-key approach, because it better represents this variability and the complexity of the subject. It also emphasizes two important aspects of accurate identification, ageing, and sexing that should always be kept in mind by users of the accounts:

1) **Determinations should be based on a synthesis or combination of all available characters (whether or not they are definitive), all of which may or may not coincide with those of one particular species, subspecies, or age/sex class.**

2) **Intermediate individuals and exceptions will always occur which are not reliably placed in a particular species, subspecies, or age/sex class by in-hand criteria alone.**

An understanding and acceptance of these concepts is crucial to the accurate identification, ageing, and sexing of birds in the field or the hand. Variation within groups, and degree of overlap between groups, can be represented statistically by "bell-shaped" curves (Fig. 3A). Assuming "normal distributions" (consistent variation around means) the distribution in size of a species, subspecies, or sex group can be represented directly, and the plumage conceptually, by these curves. If two groups overlap in a certain character, the proportion of birds falling in overlap zones can be represented (Fig. 3B). Near the tails of the bell-shaped curve lay the "outliers", such as individuals with abnormally small or large measurements or individuals with plumage anomalies that may cause them to appear more like other species or groups. Statisticians and certain ornithological groups (*e.g.*, the Canadian Wildlife Service [CWS] and Bird Banding Laboratory [BBL] when assessing the age and sex codes assigned by banders) are satisfied with 95% accuracy. Within a bell-shaped curve, the cutoffs for 95% of a population can be estimated by the mean ± twice the standard deviation (Fig. 3A). Ranges representing 95% of the variation within a group or sample are much more useful than the "true" ranges of a sample when assessing such criteria as measurements or wing morphology formulas, as true ranges may or may not include anomalous individuals.

Throughout this guide, ranges in measurements and plumage appearance are presented based on the concept of 95% confidence intervals. Thus, 5% of the individuals will be expected to fall outside of the ranges given, 2.5% at each end, the mean can be calculated as the midpoint between the given extremes in range (see Fig. 3A), and one standard deviation will equal approximately a quarter of the range. In addition, a variable proportion of individuals (up to 50% in some cases) will fall into overlap zones between groups (Fig. 3B), and will not be reliably aged, sexed, and/or iden-

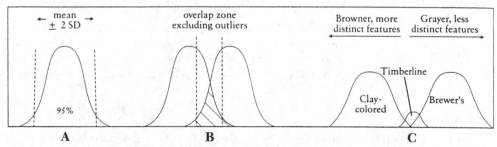

FIGURE 3. Bell-shaped curves, including 95% confidence intervals (as calculated by the mean ± twice the standard deviation), an example of an area of overlap between two similar populations, and an example of its use in *Spizella* sparrows (see pp. 566-568). Variation in both measurements and plumage descriptions in this guide are based on 95% confidence intervals (see text). Figure from Pyle and Howell (1996).

tified with any one or all of the criteria given for a particular group. By understanding these concepts and by combining all criteria with in-hand experience, users of this guide should be able to make determinations with well above 95% accuracy. References to the combination of criteria and to the potential for intermediates in specific cases occur throughout the species accounts.

MEASUREMENTS

Size often is useful for identifying, ageing, and especially, for sexing birds in the hand. In this guide, ranges of wing chord (**wg**) and tail length (**tl**) are given for every species as an indicator of sex, and for many subspecies in which geographic variation includes size. Bill measurements also are given frequently, where useful in subspecific determinations or sexing. For several species, published discriminant function analyses (see Brennan *et al.* 1991) or other formulas are referenced, which use a combination of size criteria to separate sexes or other groups within a species. Measurement data should always be considered when identifying, ageing, or sexing a bird in the hand.

In many owls, females average larger than males, whereas in most other species treated in this guide, males average larger than females. The extent to which the sexes overlap in size depends both on the species and the particular measurement being considered. Wing chord is the easiest measurement to take and serves as a useful representative of the size of a bird, at least within a certain group. Overlap in wing-chord lengths between the sexes can range from almost complete (*e.g.*, in woodpeckers, Wrentit, and some vireos) to little or none (Dickcissel and many icterids). With most North American near-passerines and passerines there is 60-80% overlap. Wing chord, therefore, varies from being practically useless to entirely reliable for sexing, and most often will reliably separate 20-40% of the individuals (see also Selander 1972, Payne 1984). Other measurements, such as those of the tail and bill, also can be useful, although the amount of overlap tends to be greater with these measures than it does with wing chord. The difference between the wing chord length and the tail length (wg – tl) also can be useful in specific and subspecific identifications.

Certain measurements vary with age, but to a lesser extent than with sex. In most passerines and many near-passerines, juvenal primaries tend to be slightly (5-10%) shorter than adult primaries. In some families (such as blackbirds and nightjars), however, the wing chords of fully-grown juveniles can average 10-20% shorter than those of the adults. Thus, the wing chords of juveniles, and of birds that retain their longest primaries during the first prebasic molt, will be slightly to moderately shorter than birds with adult primaries. Because of the individual and sex-related variation found in bird size, measurements are not recommended for ageing; however, the tendency for juvenal primaries to be slightly shorter than those of adults may sometimes be used to help sex known-age birds and vice versa. Individuals with juvenal primaries often have wing chords falling in the bottom portions of the ranges of each sex, while wing chords of adults will be longer, falling in the upper portions of the ranges. Of course, this reasoning should never be used as a sole means of ageing a bird. On the other hand, by considering age, the percentages of birds that can be sexed by wing length (and other measurements) may be increased (see Blake 1965a, Alatalo *et al.* 1983, Mewaldt & King 1986, Francis & Wood 1989).

When using measurements for identifying, ageing, or sexing near-passerines and passerines, it is important that the measuring techniques be the same as those used to obtain the published measurements with which you are comparing yours. In the following sections, the methods of obtaining the measurements used in this guide are outlined. All linear measurements given are in millimeters (mm).

Wing Length

At least three methods of measuring the wing length have been described in the literature. The wing chord, or "unflattened" wing length, is the measure most frequently used and published in North America; the "flattened" wing length is widely used with museum specimens and was previously popular in Europe; and the "maximum flattened" wing length or "maximum chord" is the measure presently used as a standard by ringers in Europe. Depending on the species and

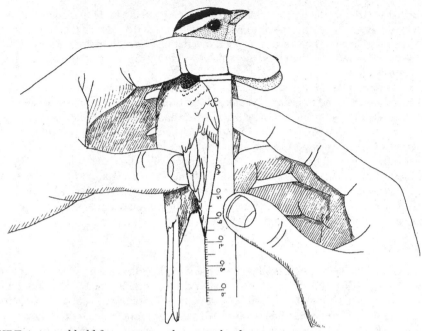

FIGURE 4. A good hold for measuring the wing chord.

handling conditions, the flattened wing length is 0.5-2% longer than the wing chord, and the maximum flattened length, in turn, is 0.5-3% longer than the flattened length Another method, that of measuring the distance of the eighth primary from its insertion, currently is being practiced in Europe (Jenni & Winkler 1989). See Nisbet *et al.* (1970), Spencer (1984), Svensson (1992), and Gosler *et al.* (1995) for analyses and discussions of the advantages and drawbacks of each method.

In this guide, measurements of the wing primarily refer to the wing chord (wg), as this is the length most frequently used by North American banders and most widely published for North American near-passerines and passerines. In a few accounts (e.g. the *Oporornis* warblers) the flattened wing length, "wg (flat)", is used because previous major studies of these species have used this wing measurement method. A primary concern with the wing chord method is the potential for non-conformity between different species, handlers, and handling conditions (Svensson 1992). When performed properly and in a standardized way, however, the wing chord method should result in consistent and reproducible measurements (Arendt & Faaborg 1989). It also is the easiest method to use with larger birds (Baker 1993).

To measure the wing chord of a live bird, it is best to have a thin ruler with a perpendicular stop at zero. Alternatively, one's thumb or forefinger can, with care, serve as a stop. The ruler should be inserted under the wing, and the bend of the wing (carpal joint or "shoulder") should be pressed snugly against the stop. A source of potential variation with wing measurements is the amount of carpal compression applied by the pressure on the stop by the bend of the wing (Yunick 1986). It is recommended that the bend of the wing be pushed against the stop with no more pressure than the wing itself applies when the ruler is moved in a posterior direction. Once the wing

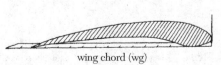

wing chord (wg)   flattened wing (wg [flat])

FIGURE 5. Profiles of wing measures used in this guide.

is in place, make sure that the line between the carpal joint and the tip of the longest primary lies parallel with the edge of the ruler. Gently lower the wing tip to the ruler so that it touches it, and read the wing chord length (Figs. 4 & 5). To achieve a flattened wing length, gently press the wing flat against the ruler with the thumb on the wing coverts (Fig. 5) and read the resulting, slightly longer measurement.

When measuring the wing it is important to make sure that the longest primary is not missing, broken, or growing, and to realize that older and more worn primaries in spring and summer will result in a slightly shorter measurements (by 1-5%) than freshly grown ones in fall and winter (Francis & Wood 1989, Rogers 1990). In addition, damp wings will be slightly flatter, hence longer, than dry wings (Svensson 1992), and museum specimens will show a slightly shorter wing length (up to 3%) due to shrinking during drying (Yunick 1990, Barajas & Phillips 1993, Winker 1993); this effect may be more substantial on birds with a greater amount of natural concavity to the wing. Data on wg – tl also tend to be longer in specimens than on live birds (Yunick 1990). These effects should be taken into consideration when measuring damp or wet birds, or comparing data from live birds with those from specimens.

Tail Length

Although it has received less attention than the wing length, the length of the tail also is of use in identifying, sexing, and ageing near-passerines and passerines. The tail length is defined as the distance between the tip of the longest rectrix and the point of insertion of the two central rectrices. Ideally, this distance should be measured with calipers, especially on museum specimens. But calipers can be difficult to use with live birds in the hand, and accurate and more reproducible measurements can be achieved with a ruler.

Two methods of measuring the tail with a ruler currently are practiced. In both cases, it is imperative to use as thin a ruler as possible, with the end of the ruler coinciding with zero. One method is to hold the ruler parallel to the tail and insert it between the tail and the undertail coverts (see Svensson 1992). The other method is to hold the ruler perpendicular to the tail and insert it between the two central rectrices (Fig. 6). In both cases, the zero end of the ruler should be pushed firmly against the root or point of insertion of the feathers. Both of these methods have been tried on a series of live birds and the differences found between the two were negligible (PRBO, unpublished data). The latter method (inserting the ruler between the two central rectrices) perhaps is easier and more consistent than the former method but, with practice, either technique should yield accurate and reproducible results.

As with the wing, it is important to make sure that the longest rectrices are not missing, broken, or in molt, and to realize that older and more worn feathers will result in a shorter measurement (by up to 15% on very worn tails) than fresh feathers. Note also that, if the longest rectrix is not the innermost, an attempt should be made to reduce the bias caused by the slight angle between the insertion of the central rectrix and the tip of the tail (particularly if the longest rectrices are the outermost).

Another measurement of the tail that is useful for separating certain species is that of the furca or "tail-difference", the difference in length between the outer and central rectrices (r6 – r1 in passerines; e.g., see Fig. 167). A clear plastic ruler placed flush with the closed

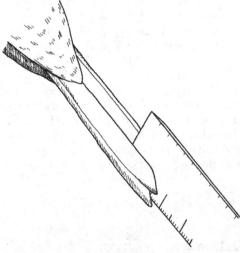

FIGURE 6. Measuring the tail between the central rectrices.

tail is the best way of achieving this measurement. As with the tail length, be sure to measure along the axis of the tail rather than at the slight angle that occurs when these feathers are in their natural position.

Bill Length

As with the wing, at least three methods of measuring the bill length currently are employed, depending on the point at the base of the bill from which the measurement is taken. In this guide, the term "**bill from nares to tip**" commonly is used and refers to the distance between the anterior end of the nostril and the tip of the bill (Fig. 7). This probably is the most consistent of the methods, although the length of the nostril itself may vary somewhat, affecting this measurement to a slight degree. The exposed culmen ("**exp culmen**") also is referred to commonly, especially in the subspecies accounts. The exposed culmen indicates the length between the tip of the feathering at the base of the bill, and the bill's tip (Fig. 7). A third method, the "total culmen" or length between the bill tip and the notch at the base of the upper mandible, where it enters the base of the skull (see Svensson 1992, Baker 1993), is perhaps the most accurate measurement; however, it has not been widely used in North America and is referred to rarely in this guide.

Since the length of the bill actually is a chord measurement (notably on species with curved upper mandibles) it is best to use calipers (Fig. 7); however, with care, a fairly accurate measurement can also be achieved with a ruler. Begin by making sure that the bill tip is not broken or deformed. Place the tip of the bill against the inner jaw (it is easier with calipers constructed of thick material) and gently slide the tip of the outer jaw to the anterior edge of one of the nares or to the feathering along the culmen. The exposed culmen measurement is taken from the tips of the feathers along the central ridge (culmen) of the bill, not the nostril feathers or those on the sides of the forehead (Fig. 7).

When using bill lengths, it should be kept in mind that slight seasonal variation may occur, the bill generally being slightly longer in the summer than in the winter (Davis 1954, 1961; Packard 1967a; Johnson 1977; Morton & Morton 1987).

Bill Depth and Width

All references in this guide to bill depth and width indicate measurements taken at the anterior end of the nostril. Again, calipers should be used. For the bill depth, place the outer jaw on the point of the culmen even with the anterior ends of the nostrils and bring the inner jaw up to the lower mandible such that the calipers are oriented at a 90° angle to the axis of the bill. When obtaining this measurement on a specimen, be sure that the bill is fully closed. To get the bill width, open the calipers to the point where they stop at the anterior end of the nostrils when they

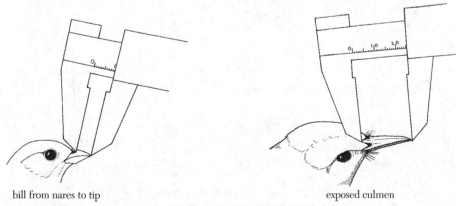

bill from nares to tip   exposed culmen

FIGURE 7. Measuring the bill (from nares to tip) and the exposed culmen.

are gently moved toward the base of the bill. Again, the calipers should be oriented at a 90° angle to the axis of the bill.

Tarsus

The length of the tarsus is referred to in only a few instances in this guide because it is a relatively difficult measurement to perform on live birds and because variation in tarsus length between similar species and sexes is comparatively slight. Again, the measurement is best obtained with calipers. It is the length between the intertarsal joint and the distal end of the last leg scale before the toes emerge (Fig. 8).

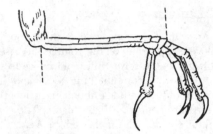

FIGURE 8. The tarsus.

Mass

Because bird mass (often called weight) varies substantially with geography, condition of the individual, stomach contents, and season or period within the life cycle of each particular species, this measurement is not as useful for ageing, sexing, or identifying birds as are the above linear measurements. In a couple of instances, however, masses are given in this guide as a useful character for sexing, or are referred to as part of discriminant function or other multiple-variable analyses. The most important considerations to make when weighing birds are how much fat is present (see Leberman 1967, Rogers 1991), and whether or not females have eggs in the oviducts, both of which can substantially increase a bird's mass (Reese & Kadlec 1982). Dunning (1993a) provided sample masses in grams (gms) for most North American birds, and Clench and Leberman (1978) provided analyses of the masses of eastern North American passerines by age, sex, and season. These should be referred to when considering bird masses.

WING MORPHOLOGY

Wing morphology (or "wing formula") refers to the shape of the wing, reflecting three aspects of the primaries of birds: the relative lengths, hence position of the tips of each primary; the occurrence and length of notches on the inner webs of each primary; and the occurrence of emargination to the outer webs of these feathers (Fig. 9). Because of such factors as distance of migration and foraging behavior, wing morphology usually differs slightly among otherwise similar species and, thus, can be very useful for separating these species in the hand. The finer details of wing morphology, furthermore, have been found useful in certain species for subspecific identifications (Unitt 1987, Mulvihill & Chandler 1991, Pyle 1997a) and ageing and sexing (Phillips *et al.* 1966; Chandler & Mulvihill 1988, 1992; Mulvihill & Chandler 1990, Pyle 1997a), and are undoubtedly useful for such determinations in other species, as well.

In this guide, the use of wing morphology is limited primarily to the positions of the tips of the outer primaries (usually p9 and p10) or longest primaries (often p8) relative to the positions of the tips of the other primaries, the tip of the longest secondary (often one of the tertials), or the tips of the primary coverts.

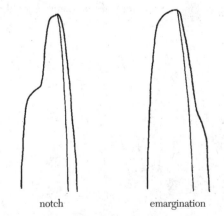

notch   emargination

FIGURE 9. Examples of notched and emarginated primaries.

It should be noted that the illustrations of these wing morphology features are drawn with the wing open such that the relative positions of the primary tips are clearly shown. When performing wing morphology measurements, however, it is important that the wing be closed and in its natural position (Fig. 10).

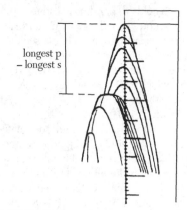

When determining the distance between primary tips, it is easiest to measure the distance between the tip of the longest primary and that of each of the primaries being considered, taking the difference between these lengths to calculate distances between respective primaries. The measurements are best achieved by placing a transparent ruler (or, with more difficulty, a pair of calipers) next to the wing in its naturally closed position and putting the tip of the longest primary at zero of

FIGURE 10. A good way to measure the distance between primary tips and the longest primary to the longest secondary.

the transparent ruler (Fig. 10) or calipers. Always make sure that none of the primaries is broken, missing, or growing. If, during molting, an incoming feather is still in its sheath, it may not be fully grown and should not be used in wing morphology analyses.

In this guide, the measurement between the tips of two primaries, *e.g.*, the 9th and the 5th, is abbreviated as "p9 – p5". A positive value in this case indicates that p9 is longer than p5, and a negative value indicates that p5 is longer than p9. The measurement "p5 – p9" produces the same distance but with the opposite sign. In most cases, values of wing morphology are presented in terms of 95% confidence intervals (Fig. 3) based on these distances, which are more useful for identification than such vague terms as "p9 usually ≤ p5" (Pyle 1997a).

A more complete knowledge of wing morphology has developed in Europe (see Svensson 1992) than in North America, in part because of the relative prevalence of difficult-to-identify species found there. Further study in the use of wing morphology in North American near-passerines and passerines for determinations of species, subspecies, age, and sex, is encouraged (see Pyle 1997a).

SKULLING

The art of skulling, and the usefulness of skull pneumaticization for ageing passerines in the hand, have improved steadily since Miller (1946a), Norris (1961), and Baird (1964) first described and modified the process (see also Wiseman 1968a). Skulling is now recognized as being the most reliable technique for ageing passerines during the fall months and, for many species, is proving useful through the early winter and even into spring. Although many near-passerines do not seem to complete pneumaticization of the skull as adults, the relative sizes of "windows" in the skull have been found to be age-specific in certain species (D.W. Johnston 1958, R.F. Johnston 1962) and possibly is so in many others, as well, despite physiological reasons (related to brain size) that cause the skull pneumaticization process to slow substantially when a juvenile near-passerine has reached full size (Jenni & Winkler 1994). Banders are strongly encouraged to become proficient at skulling and to skull birds throughout the year, so that a better understanding of the exact timing, variation, and reliability of the pneumaticization process for ageing each passerine and near-passerine species can be achieved.

Skull Pneumaticization

When a fledgling passerine leaves the nest, the section of the skull overlying the brain (frontals and parietal) consists of a single layer of bone. From this time until the bird is four to twelve months old (depending mostly on the species), a second layer develops underneath the first, the two layers being slightly separated by spaces or air pockets, and joined by small columns of bone (Dwight 1900a). The process by which this second layer, the air pockets, and the columns develop is called skull pneumaticization.

The pattern and rate of skull pneumaticization varies both within and among passerine species. The pattern generally follows one of the two progressions illustrated in Figure 11, but may show other variations (see Yunick 1979a, 1981a; Jenni & Winkler 1994). Smaller species tend to show the peripheral pneumaticization pattern and larger species the median line pattern (Yunick 1981a), although much variation occurs, both among species and among individuals within a species. Individuals of certain species may show either pattern, and the exact shapes of the unpneumaticized areas or "windows" will also show substantial individual variation.

Generally, the skulls of smaller species become pneumaticized more quickly than those of larger ones, but this may vary somewhat depending on the family. Wood-warblers, for instance, show a faster rate than flycatchers of similar size. The rate of pneumaticization also depends more on the age of the bird than on the season, yet both factors are involved. Pneumaticization slows, for example, in stressful times, such as during fall migration and winter, and is more rapid in southern populations than northern ones. Thus, the time of the year when the skull becomes fully pneumaticized depends on the

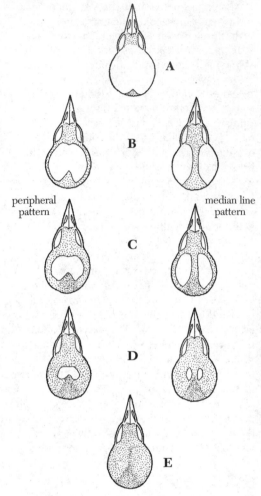

peripheral pattern

median line pattern

FIGURE 11. The two common sequence patterns of skull pneumaticization. See text for details.

species, the age of the bird, and the amount of stress an individual endures during the fall and early winter months. These factors, hence the rate of pnematicization, can vary interannually (*e.g.*, Wiley & Piper 1992).

Any passerine found with large windows in the pneumaticization of the skull (Fig. 11**A-C**) can be reliably aged as a first-year bird. In most North American passerine species, the skulls of the earliest first-year birds become completely pneumaticized in October and November, and in the latest birds between November and February. The date when the earliest birds complete pneumaticization is important in ageing, as this is when adults can no longer be aged reliably by skulling alone. However, completely pneumaticized skulls should still support other ageing criteria indicating adults for at least a month following the initial dates given in the species accounts.

In some (perhaps many) species, small unpneumaticized windows (Fig. 11**D**; see also Fig. 204) are regularly retained by some first-year birds until spring and even early summer. This is seen most commonly in long-distance migrants such as flycatchers, swallows, thrushes, and vireos, but can also occur in residents, particularly those that winter in colder climates. Birds with windows greater than two or three millimeters in diameter are reliably aged as first-year through

June. Birds with these windows in July-August, and birds with smaller windows should not necessarily be aged first-year because a variable proportion (depending on the species) of adults will never show complete pneumaticization. In addition, it should be noted that windows in the occipital triangle at the base of the skull, can occur more frequently (if not ubiquitously) in adults (Collier & Wallace 1989), and should not be regarded during the skulling process. It must also be stressed that birds without windows after the indicated date of earliest completion, are not necessarily first-year birds.

Thus, extent of skull pneumaticization is reliable for ageing first-year birds through October to June, and adults through September to November, depending on the species.

Skulling

Unpneumaticized areas of the passerine skull usually appear pinkish while pneumaticized areas appear grayish, whitish, or pinkish white, with small white dots indicating the columns of bone. The color and/or contrast (when present) between these two color patterns can usually be seen through the skin of the head, especially after the head has been wetted to allow parting of the feathers.

To skull a small bird, start by holding it in one of the two positions shown in Figure 12. A third method, in which the bird's head is held tucked against its chin and the thumb is run against the feather tracts from the base of the skull, presently is gaining in popularity. The hold illustrated in 12**A** or that described above may be the easier to use than that of Figure 12**B** because the skin can more readily be moved around the skull, allowing a larger area of the skull to be viewed through a smaller area of skin. With experience, however, all three holds can be used with equal effectiveness.

In order to see the skull, the feathers need to be parted such that a small opening of bare skin is created. This can be accomplished without wetting the feathers but is more easily done if a small amount of water or saliva is applied; do not use detergent or alcohol solutions. Those with extensive experience in skulling will be able to part the feathers and see the skull simply by blowing or by licking their thumb or finger. Beginners, until they are familiar with the appearance of the skull in its various stages of pneumaticization, should wet the feathers a greater amount in order to create larger viewing areas. In cold weather, however, substantial wetting should be avoided so as not to chill the bird.

It usually is easiest to part the feathers by running the thumb or finger forward over the crown, against the direction in which the feathers lie. In the late summer and early fall, when most young birds are just beginning the pneumaticization process, it is good to start at the rear of the skull and work up towards the crown. Later in the fall, the parting should be made higher up on

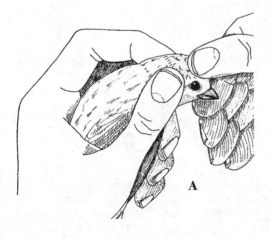

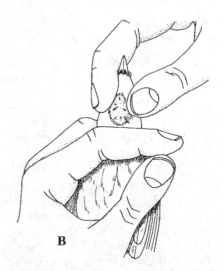

FIGURE 12. Two good holds for skulling.

the crown (in the areas just above and behind the eyes) where the last unpneumaticized windows usually occur (Fig. 11**D**). With thick-skinned birds (see below), an opening made on the side of the head or neck (where the skin is more transparent) and moved up to the crown will often improve viewing conditions. When the skulling process is finished, the feathers can be smoothed back into place.

Once an opening between the feathers has been created, gently move the skin around so that a larger area of the skull can be examined. If the skin is still dry, wetting it will make it more transparent. Hold the bird under a fairly strong light bulb or in shaded or indirect sunlight to achieve the best lighting conditions for viewing the skull. Direct and strong lighting may reflect off the skin too much, hindering the viewing process. It often is helpful to move the head around as different angles of light can make it easier to see through the skin. Finally, banders may find it helpful to look through a mounted loupe or other magnifying device.

Look for entirely pinkish skulls in very young birds (Fig. 11**A**; June-July), for contrasts between the pneumaticized and large, unpneumaticized areas (Fig. 11**B-C**; most frequently in August to October), for smaller windows (Fig. 11**D**; November-January or later), or for the entirely grayish or pinkish-gray skulls, with white dots, indicating complete pneumaticization (Fig. 11**E**; all months). Small windows (Fig. 11**D**) should be looked for carefully at all times of the year, indicating a first-year bird in late winter to early summer or, in some species, an adult at any time of the year. Care should be taken in separating young birds with very little pneumaticization (Fig. 11**A**) from adults with complete pneumaticization (Fig. 11**E**). With experience, the difference in color, and the presence of white dots on the completed skull, are readily detected.

Any of several factors, however, can make it difficult or impossible to see the pneumaticization of the skull. In larger passerines or those with large bills (notably the corvids, grosbeaks, and icterids), the skin of the head often is too thick to adequately discern the pneumaticization pattern, particularly when no contrasts can be seen. Birds of northern populations will increase the amount of fat in the skin during the winter, which can further hinder visibility, and thick, dark, or otherwise opaque skin occasionally is found on individuals of all species. The skin of molting birds becomes flaked and less transparent, and injury-related blood hemorrhaging sometimes is encountered which can partially or totally obscure the pneumaticization pattern or cause the skull to appear unpneumaticized. Finally, in some birds, the demarcation line between pneumaticized areas and windows is very subtle and only discernible after close scrutiny.

Despite these pitfalls, the pattern of skull pneumaticization of most individuals is readily seen and provides a reliable means of ageing passerines during at least the fall. As with all ageing techniques, the information provided by skulling should always be combined with all other ageing criteria for accurate determinations.

MOLT

A complete understanding of the timing, sequence, and extent of molts is an essential aspect of the accurate ageing and sexing of birds in the hand. Several good summaries are available on the subject of bird molt (see Dwight 1900a, 1902, 1907; Watson 1963; Palmer 1972; Payne 1972; Ginn & Melville 1983; Jenni & Winkler 1994). Readers should consult these treatments for an overall understanding of the mechanisms and finer details of bird molt. Here, molt is summarized and discussed as it pertains to ageing and sexing near-passerines and passerines in the hand.

Molt and Plumage Terminology

Molt and plumage terminology currently is a debated topic, with different nomenclatural systems being popular in Europe and North America, and disagreement within both continents concerning the best terminology to use (Humphrey & Parkes 1959, 1963; Stresemann 1963; Amadon 1966; Wilds 1989; Willoughby 1991, 1992; Rohwer *et al.* 1992; Jenni & Winkler 1994; Thompson & Leu 1994; Parkes 1995a). Much of this confusion stems from the complex and variable nature of the molts themselves, as no system is without flaws. In this guide the terminology of Humphrey and Parkes (1959, 1963), with modifications suggested by Rohwer *et al.* (1992) and Thompson & Leu (1994), is followed. This system attempts to standardize the terminology of homologous molts between age groups or related species, rather than basing them on the terms of the breeding season or time of the year, thus promoting understanding of the evolutions of molts in a context independent from other annual events. It is important to note, however, that annual events such as seasons and breeding phenologies often need to be considered in determining homologies.

The Humphrey-Parkes (H-P) system has distinct advantages over traditional terminologies in the tropics, in the southern hemisphere, and among certain non-passerines, where molt strategies are complex and can be unrelated to breeding or time of year. In north temperate latitudes and among passerines, however, the H-P system has a high rate of correspondence with traditional systems, which explains the reluctance of some ornithologists to adopt it. In the following sections, widely used traditional terminology is mentioned along with H-P terms, indicating corresponding nomenclature *in the majority of cases.* This is not to imply that the terms themselves are homologous. It also should be emphasized that, for most birds, our understanding and determination of molt homologies is still in its infancy (Jenni & Winkler 1994). It is hoped that the adoption of the H-P system in this guide and elsewhere will motivate researchers to determine molt homologies among birds, and to further refine and designate the H-P terminology, both generally and on a species-specific basis.

Prebasic Molt

All species treated in this guide have a molt strategy that includes a single "predominant" replacement of feathers during the year. In the majority of north-temperate birds this molting period occurs just after the breeding season (whether or not an individual breeds), and is termed the **prebasic molt.** In birds that have reached their maximum (adult) plumage stage, it is referred to as the "definitive" or **adult prebasic molt,** and in juveniles (birds in **juvenal plumage;** see below) it is referred to as the **first prebasic molt.** If plumages or other criteria allow for the identification of molts during the second and subsequent years, these can be termed the **second prebasic molt, third prebasic molt,** etc. Most species treated in this guide reach definitive plumage after their second prebasic molt, such that all subsequent prebasic molts necessarily are termed adult prebasic molts. In traditional terminology, the "postbreeding molt" or "postnuptial molt" often corresponds with the adult prebasic molt, and the "postjuvenal molt" often corresponds with the first prebasic molt.

The first prebasic molt results in the **first-basic plumage** (often corresponding with the "first-winter" or "first non-breeding" plumage of traditional terminology), and the adult prebasic molt results in the definitive- or **adult-basic plumage** (often corresponding with the "adult-non-breeding" or "adult-winter" plumages of traditional terminology). Note that, in this guide, the traditional term "adult" continues to be used as a synonym of the term "definitive" of the H-P system, especially when referring to molts or individual feathers, because it is felt that the reasons given by Humphrey and Parkes (1959) for using "definitive" over "adult", while perhaps a bit more than just semantic, do not justify the disruption of established terminology.

In certain species, adult feathers and definitive plumage correspond with first-basic feathers and plumage, if these are replaced during the first prebasic molt and are indistinguishable from the feathers of subsequent plumages. Alternatively, if the **second-** or **third-basic plumages** or feathers (resulting from the second- or third-prebasic molts) can be separated from definitive plumages (as in many non-passerines), these terms are used instead of "definitive" or "adult". If these plumages and molts cannot be separated from subsequent plumages and molts, the term "adult" is used.

In most north-temperate passerines and near-passerines, the first and adult prebasic molts usually take place from July to September (occasionally as early as May and as late as December or later), just after the breeding season. In these cases the molt usually occurs on the summer grounds and often in the breeding territory, but sometimes takes place during fall migration or on the winter grounds. It can also start on the summer grounds, be **suspended** during fall migration, and be completed on the winter grounds. In some species, particularly among the near-passerines, the prebasic molts can be **protracted** or suspended over winter, completing during the spring, just before the next breeding season. Protracted and suspended prebasic molts, involving the continual replacement of a single generation of feathers, should not be confused with strategies that include a prealternate molt (see below). In most of the species treated in this guide, the first and adult prebasic molts differ in extent, timing, and/or locality. These differences result in many useful criteria for ageing.

With one or two exceptions, the adult prebasic molt in passerines is **"complete"** (includes all body and flight feathers), whereas in juveniles it most often is less than complete. In some near-passerine families (*e.g.*, doves, owls, nightjars, and woodpeckers), the adult prebasic molt can be less than complete, including most (if not all) body feathers but not all flight feathers. In the complete molt (Fig. 13) of all North American passerines and most near-passerines, replacement of flight feathers of the wing proceeds in a **typical sequence** (the "basic sequence" of Ginn & Melville 1983), beginning with the tertials and the innermost primaries (p1-p4; Fig. 13). Among the primaries, the sequence of replacement proceeds **distally,** toward the outermost primary (p9 or p10; Fig. 13). After the tertials have been renewed, the remainder of the secondaries are replaced, beginning with the outermost (s1), and proceeding **proximally** through the middle secondaries and toward the body (Fig. 13). Thus, the numbering of primaries and secondaries (see also page 1, Fig. 1) follows the typical sequence of feather replacement.

Usually, s6 is the last flight feather replaced during a complete molt, although sometimes the replacement of s6 can precede that of s5. Replacement of the rectrices occurs during molt of the primaries and secondaries, usually beginning with the central rectrices (r1) and often proceeding **centrifugally** (from the inside outwards in both directions), toward the outermost rectrices (r5 or r6). In the blackbirds and meadowlarks, it proceeds **centripetally,** from the outer to the inner rectrices (K.C. Parkes 1972, pers. comm.). In many species and individuals, especially among the near-passerines, the rectrices may not be replaced in sequence; often, in these cases, the outermost rectrices will be the next pair renewed after the central rectrices. Replacement of

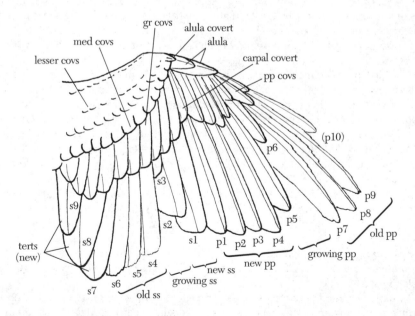

FIGURE 13. An example of a wing during complete molt in typical sequence, including wing feather terminology (see also Fig. 1). The marginal coverts are here termed "lesser coverts" following widespread current usage, despite the fact that, historically, lesser coverts referred to a separate tract (Winkler & Jenni 1996).

all wing feathers normally occurs symmetrically, the same feathers being replaced on both wings at the same time, whereas rectrices can be replaced symmetrically or asymmetrically.

In some near-passerines, notably among the cuckoos, owls, and kingfishers, the replacement of primaries and secondaries can proceed in different directions from several molt centers along the wing. Replacement of the primaries in many owls, for example, proceeds centrifugally from p6 or p7, at the same time or later proceeding distally from p1, while two or more centers can also exist among the secondaries (see p. 67). In cuckoos, the secondaries are replaced proximally from s6 to s9, and **centripetally** (inward from the outsides) within s1 to s5. In this guide, irregular flight-feather replacement sequences among near-passerines are summarized in the family sections preceding the species accounts.

In contrast to the adults, juveniles of the majority of North American passerine and near-passerine species normally do not have a complete first prebasic molt. In many species, only the body feathers, none, some, or all of the wing coverts, and perhaps 1-3 tertials and the central rectrices are replaced during a **partial** first prebasic molt. In other species, some or all of the primaries, outer secondaries, and outer rectrices can be replaced during **incomplete** molts. The juvenal primary coverts often are the last feathers replaced during incomplete, first prebasic or subsequent molts. Earlier broods and southern populations of a species often molt more feathers than later broods and northern populations, and this can vary overall from year to year.

During partial first prebasic molts, a variable number of lesser, median, and greater coverts can be replaced, usually in a fairly predictable sequence, beginning with the lesser coverts and inner feathers and ending with the greater coverts and outer feathers (see p. 207 and Fig. 133 for details). When most or all of these coverts have been replaced, one or more tertials (usually beginning with s8 but sometimes beginning with s9 or s7) and one or two central rectrices can often be replaced. Depending on the length of the breeding season, extent of the geographic range, and other factors, the amount of intraspecific variation in the replacement of these feathers can be limited or quite extensive.

Incomplete first prebasic molts also are quite variable, both among and within species. In some species, this variation ranges from none to all of the flight feathers, depending on the individual or population. In many species, incomplete molts result when the typical flight-feather replacement sequence (Fig. 13) is **arrested,** such that consecutive, juvenal outer primaries (among p5-p10) and/or consecutive, juvenal middle secondaries (among s2-s6) are retained (see Fig. 137). Certain near-passerines may also arrest irregular replacement sequences during incomplete molts (see p. 39, p. 67, and p. 163).

Another pattern found in many passerines and some near-passerines that have incomplete first prebasic molts is called the **eccentric** replacement pattern (see pp. 208-209, Fig. 136). During these molts, replacement of the primaries starts not at p1 but in the center, most commonly among p3-p7, and proceeds distally. After the tertials have been renewed, replacement of the secondaries also begins in the center, commonly among s2-s5, and proceeds proximally to the tertials. In some cases, eccentric replacement can be arrested such that, *e.g.*, just p5-p7, the tertials, and s3-s5 are replaced; but more often, once eccentric replacement begins, it proceeds through the outermost primary and s6. Note that, in this guide, the term "eccentric" refers only to the above-specified pattern of replacement which, contrary to the name, has been found quite regularly in North American passerines (Pyle in press). In Europe, other irregular replacement patterns commencing in the center of the wing may also be termed eccentric (Jenni & Winkler 1994). Although the term "eccentric" implies that the pattern is atypical, when in actuality it appears to be regular among North American birds, it is adopted here, as opposed to a newly defined term. Standard molt terminologies should strive to use fewer rather than more terms than currently exist. It should also be noted that the term "eccentric" describes a replacement pattern rather than a molting period, and can thus be used in conjunction with standard terminology on the molts themselves. Therefore, such expressions as "eccentric replacement patterns" or "eccentric sequences" are used instead of the term "eccentric molt," as employed by Jenni and Winkler (1994).

Occasional birds showing an otherwise partial molt can also replace s6 (occasionally s5-s6 and rarely s4-s6), after all three tertials have been renewed (see Fig. 133E). This replacement of middle secondaries might represent either an extension of the tertial replacement or the tail end of the mechanism resulting in eccentric replacement patterns.

Certain juvenile passerines (notably among swallows) and near-passerines (notably among cuckoos and hummingbirds) normally have a complete first prebasic molt. These, however, often occur during different months or at different localities than the adult prebasic molts of the same species. Complete first prebasic molts generally occur later in the fall or winter than adult prebasic molts and often take place partially or entirely on the winter grounds. This can vary substantially, however, depending on conditions during the breeding season (see Phillips 1951). In only a few North American passerines (e.g., Bushtit and Wrentit) do complete first and adult prebasic molts occur during the same months and in the same general location.

Almost all ageing criteria related to variation in flight-feather color, shape, and wear (see the following sections) are based on differences between the first and adult prebasic molts. Furthermore, species where the first prebasic molt is partial, any bird showing symmetrical and sequential primary, outer secondary, or outer rectrix molt during June to September, or showing evidence of a complete molt, can be reliably aged as an adult. With consideration of the flight feathers being replaced, this often is reliable in species with incomplete first prebasic molts, as well. Late in the molting period, a complete molt can still be detected by the condition of s6, the last flight feather normally replaced. Check for the presence of a sheath or see if this feather is still growing (in most species it should not be shorter than both s7 and s5 when fully grown).

The boundaries between replaced and retained feathers during partial and incomplete molts are termed **molt limits.** Because first and adult prebasic molts usually differ in extent, the presence and/or placement of molt limits are extremely useful for separating first-year birds from adults. See the expanded section on molt limits in this guide (p. 39, p. 67, p. 163, and p. 206, and Figs. 25, 48, 62, 65-66, 71, 121-122, and 133-137), Mulvihill (1993), Jenni and Winkler (1994), Pyle (1995a, 1997b, 1997c, in press), Pyle et al. (1997), and Pyle and Howell (1995) for details on variation in partial and incomplete molts among birds, and for the use of molt limits in ageing.

Presupplemental Molt

In certain passerines an extra molt of some or all body feathers (and occasionally some wing coverts) has been documented in juveniles in summer, prior to the occurrence of the first prebasic molt (which includes some or all of these feathers again) in the fall. First pointed out by Sutton (1935a) in the Northern Cardinal and other sparrows, this molt has been fully documented in certain species only recently, by Rohwer (1986) and Willoughby (1986), and defined as a **presupplemental molt** by Thompson and Leu (1994). Thus far, presupplemental molts have been documented in 16 species of North American passerines, and are to be looked for in many others, as well.

Depending on the species, the presupplemental molt can either overlap with the first prebasic molt or occur during a discrete time period (Thompson & Leu 1994). When occurring in separate time periods, the presupplemental molt often occurs before the fall migration, followed by migration, and then the first prebasic molt on the winter grounds. All presupplemental molts thus far documented are followed by first prebasic molts that are incomplete or complete in most or all individuals. Many species with presupplemental molts show eccentric replacement patterns during the first prebasic molt.

The presupplemental molt results in the **supplemental plumage.** This plumage can resemble that of the juvenile but more often acquires characters of the first-basic plumage. As with juvenal plumage, males and females tend to be similar in supplemental plumage, even in species that acquire sex-specific plumage characters during the first prebasic molt.

Humphrey and Parkes (1959) originally defined presupplemental molts only as extra molts inserted within a two-plumage cycle of adults, referencing in particular the molts of waterfowl. Here, the term is expanded to include these partial molts of juveniles prior to the first prebasic molt, whether or not it occurs within a single-plumage cycle or a two-plumage cycle (see Thompson & Leu 1994).

Prealternate Molt

In many species, including most of the near-passerines treated in this guide, the prebasic molt is the only molt that occurs annually; thus, breeding occurs in basic plumage. In many passerines (approximately 161 of the 303 species treated here), however, there is a second molt of some or all body plumage (and occasionally flight feathers) that occurs prior to the next prebasic molt. This second molt is called the **prealternate molt,** and it occurs in both first-year birds (**first prealternate molt**) and in adults (definitive or **adult prealternate molt**). In north temperate latitudes, the prealternate molt corresponds with the first or adult "prebreeding molt" or "prenuptial molt" of traditional terminology.

In the species treated in this guide, all prealternate molts occur in the winter and spring, typically from January to April, and occasionally as early as November and as late as early June. The timing of prealternate molts on the tropical winter grounds can often include reduced and intensified periods (see Rohwer & Manning 1990, Lefebvre *et al.* 1992, Cramp & Perrins 1994b); more study is needed on this. During prealternate molts, note that at least some feathers are replaced for a second time during the molt cycle, as opposed to protracted and suspended prebasic molts (which can also occur in the winter and spring), in which all feathers are being replaced for the first time since the previous breeding season. Many first-year birds, however, can replace both juvenal and first-basic feathers during the first prealternate molt.

As with prebasic molts, the extent of the prealternate molt varies substantially, both among and within species. In many species, the prealternate molt of first-year males is more extensive than in the other age/sex groups. Some species may replace just a few head or throat feathers during prealternate molts, while others can replace all body plumage, the wing coverts, and some or even all (in one species, the Bobolink) flight feathers during prealternate molts. In migratory species, the prealternate molts take place primarily on the winter grounds, although individuals of certain species may still be molting during spring migration and even after they reach their breeding grounds. For some (possibly many) species, the prealternate molt may be an extended, overwinter process, albeit with concentrated periods of molting in the early spring. In some species, a limited number of head feathers may be replaced almost continually, or at least more than once, following prebasic molts (*e.g.*, see Willoughby 1991). More study is needed on this replacement pattern, and how best to apply molt terminology in such cases.

The most important aspect of the prealternate molt for ageing and sexing is the resulting change in plumage that occurs. The prealternate molts produce the **first-alternate** and definitive- or **adult-alternate** plumages, corresponding to the first- and adult-, "breeding", "summer", or "nuptial" plumages of traditional terminology. Note that, in this guide, birds with several generations of feathers are considered to be in a single "plumage" (Rohwer et al. 1992) rather than several plumages at once (Humphrey & Parks 1959, Palmer 1970, Willoughby 1992); thus, a bird in first-alternate plumage can have up to three genrations of feathers, juvenal, first basic, and first alternate.

In many cases, the alternate plumages of males differ from their basic plumages, whereas in females, both plumages often are similar. In species with more extensive prealternate molts, the timing of plumage-related ageing and sexing criteria can depend on the timing of the prealternate molt, and the molt limits among the wing coverts and flight feathers produced by the first prebasic molt can be affected. In the spring and summer, care must be taken to separate first-year birds (some of which can show three generations of feathers) from adults (some of which can show molt limits) in species with extensive prealternate molts (see p. 208, Fig. 135). Typically, the first-alternate plumage (of males, at least) is duller then the adult-alternate plumage in these species.

Continued Words of Caution and Encouragement

Although we have made some progress since the first edition of this guide was published, when much of the information on molt was based on Dwight (1900a) and the accounts in Bent

(1942-1968), we still have a lot to learn about molt in North American birds. Much of the information presented in the species accounts will probably need to be updated, once thorough studies of the molts in each species are conducted. Even in Europe, where molt studies are comparatively advanced (*e.g.*, see Cramp 1985-1992, Cramp & Perrins 1993-1994b, and Jenni & Winkler 1994), there is still much to learn. The molt-limit surveys for this guide (Pyle 1995, 1997b, 1997c, in press; Pyle *et al.* 1997; Pyle & Howell 1995) concentrated on flight feathers and wing coverts, whereas detailed studies including all feathers (e.g., Rohwer 1986; Willoughby 1986, 1991, unpublished ms.; Rohwer & Manning 1990; Thompson 1991b, Young 1991, Mulvihill & Winstead 1997) are needed to determine molt homologies. Users of this guide are strongly encouraged to pay close attention to all aspects of passerine and near-passerine molt, and to publish any new or conflicting information found.

PLUMAGE

The most apparent method for determining both the age and the sex of many birds is by examining the plumage characters. Among North American near-passerines and passerines, plumage patterns vary widely according to age and sex. In some species the sexes differ markedly but the age classes do not, in others the plumage is similar in the sexes but varies with age. Many species show three or four different plumages, one for each age/sex class, while others have similar plumages regardless of age or sex. Furthermore, plumage patterns may or may not change during any or all of the various molts. One only has to look at the different plumages displayed by one passerine subfamily, the wood-warblers, to realize how complex and varying these patterns and sequences can be.

In this guide, a large part of the age and/or sex portions of the species accounts are comprised of plumage-related characters. Criteria are given only when clearly defined and consistent, age/sex-related plumage patterns occur. However, it is important that users understand the variable nature of plumage (see Fig. 3). Variation occurs both within each defined age/sex plumage association, and among the different age and sex classes, even in species with no clearly defined plumage patterns. These variations can either hinder or assist, respectively, the ageing and sexing process.

In species otherwise showing little plumage variation, males and adults often exhibit slightly brighter and more contrasting plumages than females and first-year birds. The extent to which this plumage variation occurs, itself varies substantially among the species. In many cases, when either the age or the sex is known from other criteria, the relative brightness of the plumage can assist in determining the other class. Bright or well-marked immatures likely are males, for instance, and bright females could likely be adults. The same might work in reverse, for particularly dull or indistinctly marked birds. In many cases, a small to moderate proportion of extremes may be accurately aged or sexed (see Fig. 3), especially if one is familiar with the species. See Heydweiller (1936) for a discussion of this in the American Tree Sparrow (p. 549), a species which shows no definitive age/sex plumage associations.

On the other hand, plumage variation within each age/sex class often is such that intermediates between the classes occur (see Fig. 3). In these cases it is again best to incorporate other ageing and sexing information. When plumage overlap exists, it is most often between young males and adult females, and in many species this is the normal pattern (see Rohwer *et al.* 1980). In these cases, knowing the age can result in accurate sexing, and vice versa. Plumage exceptions can also occur, even in species that normally show no overlap between age/sex classes. In many cases these are senescent females which suddenly may acquire male-like plumage (see Goodpasture 1972, Baumgartner 1986a). Males with plumage typical of females, or even birds with both male and female characters (*e.g.*, see Patten 1993) may also be encountered. When ageing and/or sexing, users are encouraged always to confirm plumage-based determinations with all other available criteria.

Finally, it should be noted that plumages, and thus many plumage-related ageing and sexing criteria, change during periods of molt. These periods can be quite extended, and may vary substantially with different individuals of the same species. Generally, the outgoing plumage will be more instructive for ageing than the incoming plumage. Users should always consider how the molt might affect the reliability of the plumage criteria when ageing and sexing birds in active molt.

Plumage changes may also occur when feathers are replaced adventitiously, especially in brightly-colored males. In tanagers, certain buntings, and certain orioles, for instance, adventitiously replaced feathers during non-molting periods can show color characters of juveniles or females (see accounts for these species), even by males in adult plumage, and this can confuse the age/sex process. This may be the rule in all species; more study is needed on this.

JUVENILES AND SOFT PARTS

The first plumage (subsequent to the natal down) acquired by the nestling and retained by the juvenile is called the **juvenal plumage.** The body feathers of this plumage are replaced during the presupplemental or first prebasic molt, which often occurs within three months of fledging, and usually takes place on the breeding grounds. Because juveniles are aged readily by many criteria and often are indistinguishable to sex, their treatment in the species accounts usually is restricted to a brief description of the differences between juvenal and subsequent plumages, and to the months of the year in which they usually are found.

Ageing Juveniles

In many North American near-passerines and passerines, the juvenal plumage differs quite substantially from subsequent plumages, allowing easy separation of juveniles from adults at the same time of year. In these cases, the juvenal plumage often is more streaked or spotted than that of the adult, will often have wing bars where the adult has none, and is displayed on more loosely textured contour feathers (Fig. 14). In certain owls, the juvenal plumage resembles a second downy stage. In species where the juvenal plumage otherwise resembles that of the adult (e.g., corvids, parids, gnatcatchers, and most mimids), feather structure differences can often (but not always) be used for ageing, and are most evident in the feathers of the nape, back, and undertail coverts.

In addition, many nestling characters are evident in juveniles, and these can be helpful in separating them from adults. Most of these are more apparent through the early stages of juvenal plumage, becoming less so as the juvenile ages. Some of these characters remain useful for separating first-year birds from adults well after the first prebasic molt.

The feathers of the tibiotarsus (leg) and underwing develop later in juveniles than other feathers, hence, these areas often are devoid of feathers for a short time after the bird has fledged. The legs of nestlings and

Juvenal   Non-juvenal

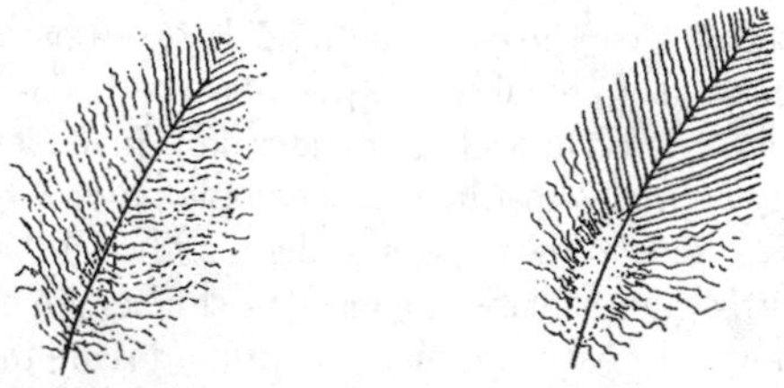

FIGURE 14. Juvenal and non-juvenal body feathers. The differences are most apparent with the undertail coverts and feathers of the nape and back.

recently-fledged juveniles also are more swollen and fleshier than those of adults, and the bill, and sometimes the wing, can take up to a month or more after fledging to reach full size. The gape of nestlings is swollen and more brightly colored than it is in adults, and these traits often carry over in postfledging juveniles. The inside of the mouth, including the "roof" (upper mandible lining) also is brighter in tone and/or paler in hue in juveniles than in adults (Fig. 15). In certain species this latter feature often is useful well after the first prebasic molt, e.g., in corvids (see also Hardy 1973, Heinrich & Marzluff 1992), parids, thrushes, and vireos. In general, more study is needed on changes in the color of the roof of the mouth in these and other species.

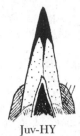  

Juv-HY   HY/SY?   AHY/ASY

FIGURE 15. The roof of the mouth (upper mandible lining) color by age in birds. Differences have been noted in at least some species of corvids (see also Fig. 193), parids, thrushes and vireos. More study is needed.

In turn, several characters useful for separating first-year birds from adults can be applied to juveniles. Molt-related criteria such as the occurrence of molting flight feathers (Fig. 13), the differences in shape and wear of juvenal flight feathers (Figs. 16-18), and the presence of growth bars (Fig. 19) are applicable. In particular, postbreeding adults, especially first-summer birds, show very worn flight feathers while those of juveniles are much fresher. Furthermore, the pneumaticization process is just beginning in juveniles (Fig. 11A) whereas it should be complete (or nearly so) in adults (Fig. 11D-E). Finally, the eye color of juveniles usually is duller, browner, or grayer than is found in adults, especially in those species with brightly-colored eyes. In some species this difference also can be useful for separating first-year birds from adults well into the winter (see Wood & Wood 1973).

In summary, bird handlers should have no trouble with the separation of juveniles from adults during the summer months, when all criteria are used.

Sexing Juveniles

In most of the species treated in this guide, birds in juvenal plumage cannot be reliably sexed by in-hand criteria alone. Although juvenile males often average slightly brighter than juvenile females, only in a few species, where distinctive differences occur in the color pattern of the flight feathers, can juveniles be reliably sexed by plumage. These differences are noted in the species accounts. The only other potential method is by measurements, which (in most species) can probably be used to sex larger males only. Juveniles with measurements indicative of females may actually be males that have not completed growth. When attempting to sex juveniles by wing length note that, in most species, the length will average 1-3 mm shorter than on birds of the same sex with adult primaries. Thus, the wing length of most juveniles should fall in the bottom half of the ranges for each sex, once the primaries are fully grown. The best method for sexing juveniles may entail the use of a combination of characters, accompanied by the realization that only a small proportion of birds can be reliably sexed (cf Borras et al. 1993).

FEATHER SHAPE AND WEAR

In both near-passerines and passerines in which the first prebasic molt is partial or incomplete, the shape and the amount of wear and fadedness of certain flight feathers or primary coverts can serve as very useful clues for ageing. Juvenal feathers typically are thinner and more tapered than adult feathers and may often be of a less durable quality, resulting in their becoming abraded and worn at a quicker pace. These differences are particularly noticeable in first-year birds that have an incomplete first prebasic molt, resulting in the juxtaposition of retained and replaced flight feathers. In using feather shape and wear for ageing, it is important to take into account both the molt sequences and the time of year.

Feather Shape

The shape of the rectrices has long been used as an ageing criterion in both near-passerines and passerines that retain juvenal rectrices during the first prebasic molt. The outer two or three rectrices (r4-r6) usually show the greatest age-specific differences, being narrower and having more tapered inner webs in juvenal feathers, and being broader and more truncate in adults (Fig. 16; see also Fig. 139). Note that the presence (adult) or absence (juvenal) of a corner to the inner web, and the angle at which the outer web descends from the tip often are the most apparent differences (see Meigs *et al.* 1983, Collier & Wallace 1989, Weinberg & Roth

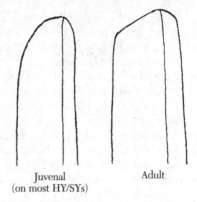

Juvenal
(on most HY/SYs)   Adult

FIGURE 16. An example of the shape of the outer rectrices (r4-r6) by age in birds. See also Figure 139.

1994, Donovan & Stanley 1995). North American families in which outer rectrix shape is particularly useful for ageing include the cuckoos, nightjars, trogons, corvids, chickadees, thrushes, wood-warblers, orioles, and fringillids. It is useful to varying degrees with many other species, as well.

In most of these species, however, a significant percentage of individuals will show intermediate rectrix shapes, and should not be reliably aged, especially without experience with this feature in the species at hand. Caution is advised with late spring and summer birds, as the increasing degrees of wear found in both juvenal and adult feathers can obscure the differences between the two age groups. Reliable ageing also becomes more difficult with birds that have wet or otherwise displaced rectrices, as can often happen during the capture and confinement of birds for banding. In most species, only obvious examples should be reliably aged by rectrix shape alone. Information on rectrix shape is included in most species accounts, and users of this guide are encouraged to become familiar with its usefulness for ageing.

The shape of the outer primaries (Fig. 17; see also Fig. 140) and primary coverts (Fig. 18; see also Fig. 138) also are useful for ageing certain species with partial or incomplete prebasic molts. Like the rectrices, the juvenal primaries and primary coverts tend to be narrower and more tapered than those of adults. These differences are most easily seen in the outermost feathers (p6-p9 or p7-p10 and their corresponding primary coverts).

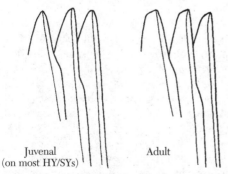

Juvenal
(on most HY/SYs)   Adult

FIGURE 17. An example of the shape of the outer primaries (p6-p9) by age in birds. See also Figure 140.

HY/SY   AHY/ASY

FIGURE 18. Example of the shape of the outer primary coverts by age in birds. See also Figure 138.

Feather Wear

As with feather shape, differences in the amount of wear between juvenal and adult rectrices, primaries, and primary coverts can provide useful clues for ageing. "Wear" can be a function of both abrasion to the feather tips, and general degradation due to, *e.g.*, exposure to solar radiation. These differences are related both to the age of the feathers and to the fact that juvenal feathers wear more quickly than those of adults. However, feather wear also varies with the habits of the species and individuals, the amount of exposure a feather receives, and the extent and timing of molts. All of these factors need to be considered when correlating feather wear with age.

In the early fall, after the prebasic molt, retained juvenal feathers usually are 1-3 months older than corresponding adult feathers, are of a less durable quality than the feathers of adults, and usually show signs of wear. Look for small nicks in the outer webs and less glossiness, especially in the rectrices and outer primaries. Adult feathers at this time should be quite glossy and contain no nicks. On first-year birds that have replaced some but not all flight feathers, contrasts in wear between the old and the new feathers should be visible.

By spring the juvenal feathers are considerably worn and abraded while those of adults usually are only moderately so (see Figs. 138 & 139A), and should still show some glossiness. By mid summer, when birds are well into the breeding season, the feathers of both first-year and adult birds become very abraded, such that it becomes increasingly difficult to distinguish them. This is especially true of breeding females, males that display on open perches, and, in general, all birds that reside in harsh (*e.g.*, xeric or saltmarsh) vegetation. At this time, however, they will be easy to distinguish from the fresh feathers of newly fledged juveniles.

With the primary coverts, it often is useful to compare them with the adjacent, greater (secondary) coverts. First-year birds with partial or incomplete molts will almost always retain the primary coverts and replace some or all of the greater coverts. Next to the slightly fresher and glossier greater coverts, therefore, the primary coverts will appear contrastingly faded and worn, and will usually lack pale edges (see pp. 209-210, Figs. 136-138 for more information). Note, however, that the primary coverts are often duller in coloration than the greater coverts, in both age groups, such that attention must be paid to the degree of wear.

The combination of feather shape and wear has proven quite useful for ageing North American near-passerines and passerines that have a less than complete first prebasic molt, especially in the spring when skulling and other plumage-related criteria usually become less valuable. Unless one is quite experienced with these characters in a particular species or group, however, they should not be relied upon alone. They are best used in combination with all other ageing criteria, and with particular attention given to the timing, sequence, and extent of molts in both first-year and adult birds.

GROWTH BARS

Growth bars (Fig. 19) are caused by small structural differences in the flight feathers, resulting from stress or inconsistencies in a bird's diet when the feathers were growing. Major diet deficiencies, for example, cause actual breaks in the feather vane, referred to as fault bars (Fig. 19). Growth bars are easiest to see on the rectrices and, to a lesser extent, the secondaries, and best are viewed when the feathers are held at an angle and with a strong source of backlighting. Both juvenal and adult feathers can develop growth bars although they probably are more common in juveniles due to diet deficiencies during the nestling period.

Growth bars can be used only in species with partial or incomplete first prebasic molts, and the pattern of the growth bars is the best clue to the age of a bird. A pattern as shown in Figure 18A indicates that the rectrices have grown simultaneously, which always is the case with nestlings. The pattern of Figure 18B is typical of rectrices which did not grow simultaneously, usually the case during the adult prebasic molt. Distinguishing these two pattern types can assist with ageing.

Several problems occur with this ageing technique, however. The growth bars often can be difficult or impossible to see, especially as the feathers become older and more worn. Adults (especially among owls and blackbirds) will sometimes replace rectrices simultaneously during the prebasic molt, resulting in a growth bar pattern typical of juveniles. Birds that have lost their tails accidentally will also replace rectrices simultaneously, and many species may molt some or all of

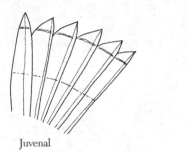
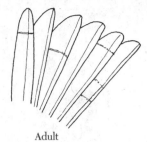

Juvenal   Adult

FIGURE 19. Patterns of growth bars in juvenal and adult rectrices. Breaks in the feather vein, such as the upper bar on the juvenal rectrices, are known as fault bars.

their rectrices during the first prebasic molt, producing an adult-like pattern in first-year birds. Except, perhaps, in owls, where they can be more distinct due to the structure of the feathers, growth bars should be used only to support other ageing criteria. For more information on growth bars see Wood (1950), Grubb (1991), and Svensson (1992).

BREEDING CHARACTERS

The best method for sexing similarly plumaged, adult passerines and some near-passerines during the breeding season is by the presence or absence of the breeding characters (Mason 1938): The cloacal protuberance (**CP**) and the brood patch (**BP**). All North American passerines develop these characters, at least partially, and most are reliably sexed by them during the late spring and summer months. Note that these characters are not developed by juveniles or birds in their first summer. As the user gains experience, cloacal protuberances and brood patches can be detected earlier and later in the season.

Cloacal Protuberance

In order to store sperm and to assist with copulation, external cloacal protuberances are developed by male passerines during the breeding season. They usually begin to develop early in the spring, reaching their peak size 3-5 weeks later, around the time the eggs are laid. Depending on the species and the number of clutches attempted during the breeding season, cloacal protuberances will recede from mid to late summer or later. Although the cloacal region in females will sometimes swell slightly or show a small protuberance, it rarely approaches the size found in males. During the breeding season, the presence of a distinct protuberance can be used to reliably sex males of all North American passerines except one, the Wrentit (p. 407). Among near-passerines, an external cloacal protuberance does not develop nearly as distinctly as in passerines, although it is possible that subtle, sex-specific differences in the shapes of the cloacal regions may occur. More study is needed (see the family accounts for the near-passerines).

To view the cloacal protuberance, simply blow apart the feathers in the region of the vent. Figure 20 shows a cloacal protuberance at the height of its development, as viewed from above. Figure 21 illustrates the sequence with which it develops and recedes, and a typical profile displayed by female birds during the breeding season. The shape of the protuberance, however, can be somewhat variable (see Wolfson 1952, Salt 1954), and non-breeding males may not always develop one. When the female is most swollen in this area, she usually will have a brood patch as well (see below). After a little experience with the shape of the cloacal region during the nesting season, bird handlers should have no problem separating breeding males from females.

In the species accounts, the cloacal protuberance and brood patch often are listed together, followed by the months in which they are most easily used for sexing (see p. 32). In a given population, cloacal protuberances may be developed 10-15 days earlier than brood patches and recede up to a month earlier; this should be considered when using the given month ranges.

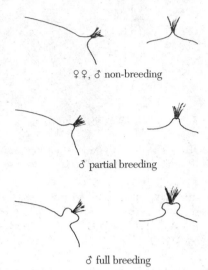

♀♀, ♂ non-breeding

♂ partial breeding

♂ full breeding

FIGURE 20. A cloacal protuberance at its peak in male passerines.

FIGURE 21. Profiles of passerine cloacal protuberances in different breeding conditions.

Males probably should be sexed by cloacal protuberance only during these months, although it is possible that certain individuals can be sexed by the shape of the cloacal region at all times of the year (see Svensson 1992). The lack of a cloacal protuberance, of course, should not necessarily be used to indicate females. Banders are encouraged to routinely examine the cloacal region of both males and females at all times of year, so that the timing and usefulness of sexual differences in cloacal shape in North American species can be more fully understood.

Brood Patch

Incubation patches or brood patches are developed by incubating birds as a means of transferring as much body heat as possible to eggs in the nest. In many near-passerines and almost all North American passerines, females perform all or most of the incubating and develop more complete brood patches than males. The presence of a distinct brood patch thus can be used to reliably sex breeding females of many near-passerine and almost all passerine species.

The development of a brood patch begins with the loss of the feathers of the abdomen, about 3-5 days before the first eggs are laid. Shortly thereafter, the blood vessels of the region begin to increase in size and the skin becomes thicker and more fluid filled. Figure 22 illustrates a full brood patch as viewed by blowing the feathers of the breast and abdomen aside. A few days after the fledglings leave the nest, the swelling and blood vascularization begin to subside. If a second clutch of eggs is laid, the process (except for defeathering) will be repeated. A new set of feathers on the abdomen usually is not grown until the prebasic molt, after completion of breeding.

Between the end of nesting and the onset of molt, the skin of the abdomen will often appear grayish and wrinkled. With experience, the abdomens of adults are distinguished from those of juveniles, which can lack feathers but otherwise are much smoother and pinker than those of the adult females. See Bailey (1952), Lloyd (1965), and Jones (1971) for more information about brood patches.

In many North American near-passerines and most passerines, the male does not develop a brood patch in the breeding season. Slightly fewer feathers may be present on the abdomen than are found in the winter, but the breast basically retains a feathered appearance (Fig. 22**B**). In a few groups, notably the mimids, vireos, *Myiarchus* flycatchers, and a few other species (see accounts), the male may assist with incubation and develop an incomplete brood patch. These will include partial or complete feather loss and slight to moderate vascularization and swelling, which

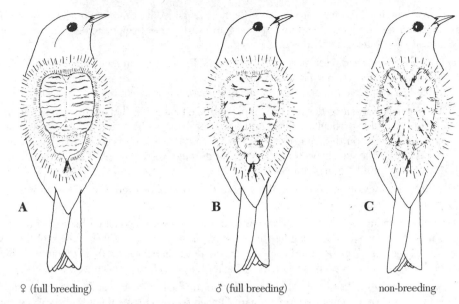

A   B   C

♀ (full breeding)   ♂ (full breeding)   non-breeding

FIGURE 22. Brood patches in different stages of development.

rarely if ever approach the extent of development typically found in females of the same species. With experience, bird handlers should be able to readily distinguish male brood patches in these species, although these may be harder to distinguish from developing female brood patches. In only one North American passerine (again, the Wrentit) do males develop full brood patches that are not reliably separated from those of the female, and this also is true of several near-passerine families, notably among the doves, kingfishers, and woodpeckers. In three passerines (the cowbirds), the female does not develop a brood patch at all.

In most North American species, brood patches should be expected only from April through September, but exceptions are found, especially in southern and California populations (see species accounts) and in year-round breeders such as Barn Owl, Mourning Dove, and Red Crossbill. Finally, non-breeding females may not develop a brood patch or may only develop a partial one. Hence, males should never be reliably sexed solely by the lack of a brood patch during the breeding season.

OTHER TECHNIQUES

Several other surgical or biochemical techniques may be used to age or sex birds in the hand, in given situations. Most of these require special equipment and/or experience, and descriptions of these are beyond the scope of this guide. For sexing, these include direct cloacal examination of larger birds (see Miller & Wagner 1955, Swanson & Rappole 1992), laparotomy (see Bailey 1953, Risser 1971, Wingfield & Farner 1976, Fiala 1979, Ketterson & Nolan 1986, Piper & Wiley 1991) and the less intrusive laparoscopy (see Richner 1989), examination of DNA (see Longmire *et al.* 1993, Tiersch & Mumme 1993, Fleming *et al.* 1996), and examination of steroids (Dieter 1973, Stavy *et al.* 1979). For ageing, examination of the bursa can be used in certain larger birds (see Wight 1956, Keith 1960, Weller 1965).

A SUGGESTED APPROACH TO AGEING AND SEXING

The emphases and format of this guide (see page 3), coupled with the variability and complexity inherent in ageing and sexing criteria, might present an overwhelming scenario at first, especially to those used to dichotomous keys. Do not despair. With time and practice, users will learn this system and find it quite useful for ageing and sexing. For beginners, here are some suggested steps to accurate ageing and sexing:

1) Look for obvious and reliable age or sex indicators. From early summer through winter check the skull. Look for molting flight feathers in late summer. Are there any definitive age- or sex-related plumage characters? Check for breeding characters on adults during the nesting season.

2) Add ageing information derived from more subtle characters. What are the extent and timing of the molts, particularly those of the first prebasic molt? Examine the shape of and amount of wear on the flight feathers. Are these useful with this species? Look for molt limits. Check the skull in winter-spring. Any large windows remaining? Check the plumage for non-definitive, age-related variations.

3) Add similar sexing information. What does the wing chord indicate? Check for subtle plumage indicators.

4) Combine ageing and sexing criteria. Have you reliably determined either the age or the sex? Knowing the age, can the wing length or the plumage assist with determination of the sex? Knowing the sex, can the same be applied to help determine the age? Try to determine which of the age/sex classes fits best when all ageing and sexing information are combined.

5) Based on your experience with the species, what do you think? Can the combination of all criteria lead to reliable determinations? Are you sure of the choices you made? If not, perhaps you should write down what you think on the back of the data sheet, and leave it "unknown" in the data.

6) Is the information presented in these species accounts complete? Is it accurate? Maybe you should publish your data, or notify the author. And, most importantly, is the bird getting tired? Perhaps it should be released.

HYBRIDS

An attempt was made to list all reported hybrids involving the species treated in this guide. References to most of these hybrids can be found in the reference section, although a few reports are based on unpublished information. Good summaries of hybrids in North America are provided by Cockrum (1952) and Gray (1958).

Unless the parental species are known directly, the identity of hybrids is difficult if, not impossible, to confirm (Parkes 1978, 1988a; Sibley 1994). Thus, most of the reports should be considered tentative. Hybrids can take any or all plumage combinations of parental species, and there often is substantial individual variation in the hybrids produced by two species, *e.g.,* Blue-winged and Golden-winged warblers (Parkes 1951, Short 1963; see p. 445). Hybridization also can revive ancestral characters that can sometimes cause a hybrid to resemble an unrelated species. On the other hand, beware of pure individuals showing leucistic, melanistic, or other anomalous plumage coloration, which may coincidentally cause them to resemble a suspected hybrid with another species. Hybrids are of great interest to natural historians and taxonomists (Miller 1949, Sibley 1957a, Short 1969a), and should be documented carefully when encountered. See Sibley (1994) for an excellent treatment of hybrids.

GEOGRAPHIC VARIATION

Geographic variation within species takes many forms among North American birds. Size, plumage, and other phenotypic parameters can vary with latitude, altitude, climate, habitat, migratory strategy, and other factors (Hamilton 1961, James 1970, Selander 1971, Zink & Remsen 1986, Barrowclough 1990, Aldrich & James 1991). Many polytypic species show similar patterns of geographic variation across North America (see Fig. 23), although exceptions to these patterns also are commonplace. Certain species show clinal variation throughout their range, whereas in others, abrupt breaks can occur between adjacent or isolated populations. In many cases, knowledge of geographic variation can assist with ageing and sexing. Age-specific variation in plumage wear (Dwight 1905) and the timing of molt or skull pneumaticization, as well as sex-specific variation in size (*cf.* Aldrich & James 1991) are aspects of ageing and sexing that are particularly affected by geographic variation. Certain species (*e.g.*, see Allen's Hummingbird) may show substantially differing molt strategies by subspecies, and in others (*e.g.*, Bushtit; Yellow-rumped, Palm, and Wilson's warblers; and White-crowned Sparrow), plumage by age and sex varies with subspecies. Thus, geographic variation in a species must be considered when identifying, ageing, and sexing birds.

The most widely used method of representing geographic variation is through the naming of subspecies (Mayr 1954, 1963), as designated by subspecific terms appended to specific names to form trinomens. Despite problems with the subspecies concept (*cf.* Wilson & Brown 1953, Inger 1961, Selander 1971, Barrowclough 1982), it generally is recognized as the only functional means of representing geographic variation in phenotypic parameters (*cf.* Smith & White 1956; Amadon & Short 1976, 1992; Marshall 1967; Mayr 1982; Parkes 1955, 1982a; Phillips 1982, 1986, 1991; Zink & Remsen 1986). In North America, numerous subspecies have been identified, particularly during the latter half of the 1800's and early third of the 1900's. Despite inconsistencies in the degree of differentiation among recognized subspecies, and recent biochemical evidence suggesting that subspecific variation is not always reflected by genetic variation (*e.g.*, Ball & Avise 1992, Gill *et al.* 1993, Zink & Dittmann 1993), these recognized subspecies form the best means of defining geographic variation in North American birds. For details on the definition of subspecies in birds, including various "rules" or statistical methods for their recognition, see Chapman (1924), Relyea (1936), Rand (1948a), Amadon (1949), Rand & Traylor (1950), Mayr (1954, 1963), and Marshall (1997).

All "currently recognized" subspecies are listed in this guide, along with brief descriptive summaries which may assist in their identification (see below). Among species with many subspecies, "**subspecies groups**" are also defined, representing geographically concordant groups of subspecies (occasionally a single subspecies) with shared characters (Amadon & Short 1992; see Fig. 23). The author is not a taxonomist and does not wish for the recognized subspecies or subspecies groups to represent taxonomic opinion. Rather, the most recently recognized subspecies taxonomy is employed uncritically, and subspecies groups are based either on published definition or, in certain cases, are here defined based on shared characters. It should be recognized that subspecies taxonomy is an ever-evolving process, fraught with divergent opinions among taxonomists, and with many species in need of a critical revision. Thus, many future changes to the taxonomy recognized in this guide are anticipated.

Principal sources for the most recently recognized subspecies taxonomy include the AOU (1957) for near-passerines, Phillips (1986, 1991) for swallows through vireos, and references in the "Peters" check-list series (primarily Mayr & Greenway 1960, 1962; Paynter 1968, 1970; and Traylor 1979a) for the remainder of the North American passerines or for those species not covered by the AOU (1957). All subsequent, critical modifications to the subspecies taxonomy of these references and to that of Oberholser (1974), particularly those of Browning (1974, 1978, 1990), have been incorporated. Howard & Moore (1994) was also consulted for subspecies information. Note that the gender of subspecific names corresponds with that of the genus, following the taxonomy of the AOU (1983). Along with specific reference to the sources of the subspecific taxonomy accepted in this guide, an attempt has also been made to list all historical references bearing directly on the identification of subspecies since Ridgway's (1901-1916) classic work. All subspecies synonymized since Ridgway, along with their supposed differentiating characters, also are mentioned.

The purposes of giving descriptive summaries of all subspecies are manyfold. Besides providing information useful in ageing and sexing, it is hoped that some insights might be gained on the recognition of subspecies in the hand. By incorporating age and sex, some knowledge may be gained on geographic variation, particularly in species where females or first-year birds may display more distinctly defined geographic variation than adult males (*e.g.*, see Phillips 1966a, Stutchbury 1991a, and accounts for Northern Wheatear, Varied Thrush, Brewer's Blackbird, and Bronzed Cowbird). Users

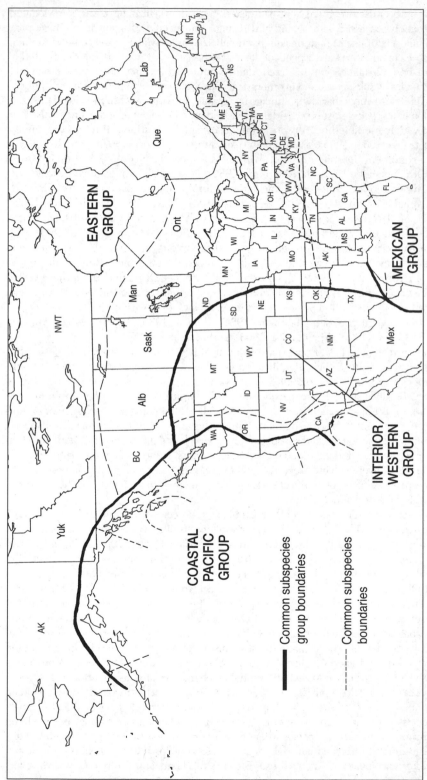

FIGURE 23. Abbreviations for geographical areas used in this guide, and common boundaries between subspecies groups (thick bold lines) and subspecies (thin dashed lines). Continent abbreviations include N.Am (North America), C.Am (Central America), and S.Am (South America). Note that, in general, subspecies of Pacific Coastal Groups are smaller and darker, subspecies of Interior Western Groups are larger and paler, and subspecies of Eastern Groups are medium-sized and more contrasting, in all cases based primarily on plumage adaptions to habitat and climate. Note also, however, that many exceptions occur (see Zink and Remsen 1986).

of this guide should beware, however, that until further insights are gained, most subspecific identifications should only be confirmed with collected individuals and an adequate series of comparative
specimen material (see Monson & Phillips 1981; Phillips 1986, 1991; Knox 1994; Dunn *et al.* 1995).
Nevertheless, it is hoped that the listing of subspecies will encourage banders, birders, and other
ornithologists to start thinking about geographic variation and how it might apply to the birds they
observe (*cf.* Norris & Hight 1957). Locally breeding subspecies can be assumed based on range, and
identifications of other subspecies might then be attempted based on comparative information.
Finally, the listing of references will allow users to gain further information on geographic variation in
species of particular interest.

DIRECTIONS FOR USE

In this section, the abbreviations, definitions, and format used in the species accounts are detailed.

COLORS

Strictly defined and standardized color names are not used in this guide. Rather, the names
used for colors are considered in a relative context when comparing those of different species or
age/sex classes. The geographically and seasonally dependent variation in coloration among individuals of the same species or age/sex class, and the different appearances that colors can assume
under different lighting circumstances, considerably lessen the usefulness of strictly defined color
names (see Burtt 1986). The color names used in this guide follow those of the current ornithological literature, especially of recent field guides and other identification, ageing, and sexing arti-
cles. Modified color names should be interpreted as the second color tinged with the first (*i.e.*,
"grayish-green" is green with a gray tinge). The modifiers "dark", "medium-dark", "medium",
"medium-pale", and "pale" are used to indicate dark to light tints, respectively. The suffix "-ish"
(*e.g.*, "brownish") indicates that more variability can be expected in the nature of the color than
would be indicated by unmodified color names (*e.g.*, "brown"). For the definitions of color names
used and for other information and examples of colors commonly found on birds, readers are
referred to Ridgway (1912), Smithe (1975, 1981), or Wood and Wood (1972).

MONTHS

All months are abbreviated by their first three letters. Parentheses surrounding the months
indicate that the plumage or condition described may be encountered between and/or within the
range of months listed, but usually is not found or can't be reliably used outside of them. Note also
that not all birds will show an indicated plumage or condition for the entire period (especially during the two extreme months), and that exceptions, occurring outside of the given month ranges,
are always possible. As with ranges in measurements, month ranges should be considered in terms
of 95% confidence intervals (see Fig. 3), with the indicated criteria preceding or extending beyond
the given temporal ranges in 5% of individuals.

The species accounts are divided into the following sections:

FORMAT

Heading

For each species, the heading includes the English and scientific names, an alpha (four-let-
ter) code derived from the English name, the AOU or "species" number, and the recommended
band size. The English and scientific names follow those found in the AOU Check-list (1983), as

modified by subsequent supplements (AOU 1985-1997), and the alpha codes, species numbers (for both species and subspecies), and band sizes are those recommended by the CWS and BBL (through BBL MTAB 81, July 1997). When two or more band sizes are given, the first usually indicates the size which best fits a majority of the individuals of the species. With polytypic species, banders should check the section on geographic variation to see if subspecies in their area are large or small, and use the appropriate band size accordingly.

Species

Accounts for identifying birds to species are given only when there exists a potential confusion species which may be difficult to distinguish in the hand. A certain basic knowledge by the user is assumed (the ability to separate a *Myiarchus* flycatcher from a kingbird, for example). The determination of when and when not to use species identifying accounts is based on the author's experience with the identification of North American birds in the hand and field. To assist with identifications, banders and other users of this guide should refer to field guides in conjunction with the use of these accounts.

Within the species identification accounts, potential confusion species are listed along with the age and sex class (if applicable) and a list of characters useful for separating the species at hand. When only one or two characters are given it should be assumed that these will separate all or a vast majority of the potentially confusing species. When many characters are given, the user should combine all of them for accurate determinations; it should be kept in mind that the potential usually exists for one or more characters not to coincide with the other characters, or with what is normal for the species (see page 3). Occasional oddities, hybrids, or intermediates will occur that may not be identifiable to species in the hand, using the characters given.

Geographic Variation

This section begins with an indication of the degree of geographic variation found within the species, the references used for the subspecific taxonomy, other pertinent references, and the number and location of extralimital subspecies. As mentioned above (pp. 26-29), all subspecies are listed based on the most recent taxonomy. English names for subspecies groups are based on the literature or, in some cases, were defined by the author; the scientific names for the subspecies groups are those of the first-named subspecies in that group. Subspecific ranges include resident (**res**), breeding (**br**), wintering (**wint**), and/or vagrant (**vag**), and are defined based on the two-letter postal abbreviations for each state in the United States and standard abbreviations for each province in Canada (see Fig. 23 for these abbreviations). Small-case letters (*e.g.* "e.", "nw.", "sc.", etc.) indicate locations within the state or province based on compass directions ("eastern", "northwestern", "south-central", etc., respectively). Other abbreviations used in these range descriptions include Co (County), Cos (Counties), I (Island), Is (Islands), and Mt (Mountain). It should be noted that the boundaries for ranges of many subspecies may be inexact or temporally unstable, and that not all vagrants may be included in the accounts; thus, the ranges given for each subspecies should be considered only in a general context.

Characters to identify each subspecies are given in the same format as for species and age/sex groups. These were derived from the literature as well as extensive specimen examination (>95% of the subspecies were examined); much new information on appearance and measurements has been incorporated. Generally, however, there is far more overlap in the listed characters between subspecies than between species or age/sex groups; thus, users of the guide should proceed with appropriate caution when considering subspecific differences (see pp. 27-29). By necessity, differentiating characters for subspecies have been exaggerated somewhat. Measurements by sex and subspecies were derived from the literature and elsewhere, augmented by extensive measuring of museum specimens (see below under Age/Sex). An attempt was made to provide wing and tail lengths of at least 10 individuals of each sex for each subspecies.

A three-letter subspecies code system to designate subspecies in data is proposed to users of this guide. For each species, the first three letters of the subspecies name can be used for each subspecies. Under this system, only seven cases of duplication occur (*e.g.*, for Steller's Jay, *C.s. carlottae* and *C.s. carbonacea*). Suggested three-letter codes are listed for the 14 subspecies affected by duplication of subspecies codes.

Molt

A simplified molt terminology, based on Humphrey and Parkes (1959, 1963) with a few modifications (see pp. 12-13), is employed. The extent, timing, location, and sequence of each molt is given for each species. Abbreviations are as follows:

PS—Presupplemental Molt.

PB—Prebasic Molt.

1st PB—First Prebasic Molt.

Adult PB—Adult (Definitive) Prebasic Molt.

PA—Prealternate Molt.

1st PA—First Prealternate Molt

Adult PA—Adult (Definitive) Prealternate Molt.

Five categories define the extent of each molt, as follows:

Absent—No molt or feather replacement occurs.

Limited—Some, but not all, body feathers and no flight feathers are replaced.

Partial—Most or all body feathers and sometimes the tertials and/or central rectrices, but no other flight feathers, are replaced. Note the slight modification to the definition in Pyle *et al.* (1987).

Incomplete—Usually all body feathers and some, but not all, primaries, inner secondaries (excluding the tertials), or outer rectrices (excluding the central pair) are replaced.

Complete—All body and flight feathers are replaced.

For convenience, all abbreviations and these definitions are repeated inside the back cover.

It must be emphasized that the extent of molt always is subject to individual, geographic, and yearly variation. When a single extent is given it is intended to include what is normal for 95% of the population (see Fig. 3); 5% of individuals can be expected with fewer or more feathers replaced. When two molt extents are given it indicates that there is substantial geographic, interannual, and/or individual variation in the extent of that particular molt, usually ranging between the two given extremes. Details on the extent of each molt, to the level of the wing coverts, are given for each species. The following modifiers are used to indicate proportions of the populations which display certain molt conditions: **rarely** (1-4% of the populations), **occasionally** (5-20%), **sometimes** (21-50%), **often** (51-75%), and **usually** (76-95%). No modifier indicates that > 95% of the population can be expected to have the indicated molting condition. Wing-covert and flight-feather replacement sequence is assumed to be **typical** (see p. 14; Figs. 13, 133, & 137) unless it is indicated to be **eccentric** (see p. 15, Fig. 136).

The timing of the molt, as indicated by the range in months, is given after the extent. As with the extent, the timing is subject to much geographic, interannual, and/or individual variation. Here, both the ranges in extent and the month ranges are intended to encompass 95% of the molt over the range of the entire species. For extents, such terminology as, *e.g.*, "0 (~61%) to 7 gr covs replaced," indicates that 61% molt no greater coverts and the remaining 39% replace between one and seven feathers. Note also that individual birds will take less time to molt and, thus, some percentage of individuals will show no molt during most or all times within the given temporal ranges, particularly in species with a wide geographic (especially latitudinal) range.

Localities are expressed by the terms "summer grounds" and "winter grounds". Note that these pertain to the general breeding and wintering areas of the species, respectively, and not necessarily to the actual territory of the molting individual. Some individuals disperse from their breeding or winter territories during part or all of their molts. Unless otherwise stated, prealternate molts in migrant species are assumed to occur on the winter grounds.

Skull

For each species, the seasonal timing of skull pneumaticization is indicated, followed by specific notes (if applicable) on the occurrence of "windows" and/or conditions that may increase the difficulty of skulling (such as the thickness of the skin) for that species. The specific date when the earliest first-year birds usually complete pneumaticization is followed by the month when the last individuals complete or nearly complete the process. The first date is more important to banders because it indicates the onset of the period when completely pneumaticized birds can no longer be assumed to be adults. This date is derived from the timing of both the pneumaticization process and the breeding season of each species, and generally is a conservative estimate. Most first-year birds will show areas without pneumaticization well after the initial dates given in this guide.

Because skulling is possible only on live or freshly dead birds, and potentially is useful for ageing every passerine species, it is afforded its own section. However, banders should always combine skulling information with the characters furnished under **Age** and/or **Sex**.

Age/Sex

In this section, specific plumage and soft-part criteria are given for ageing and sexing each species. Depending on the species and its plumage patterns, age and sex criteria may be given together or separately. A primary emphasis of this guide, however, is that ageing and sexing information should always be combined before either age or sex determinations are made. Even when these criteria are separated, therefore, users are encouraged to consider them at the same time. As with the accounts dealing with species identification, a field guide can provide additional helpful illustrations of the different age/sex classes. Note, however, that some age/sex representations found in field guides are not entirely reliable.

Before these age/sex-specific characters are given, some general characters of the species are provided. These include the timing and a description of juvenal plumage, information on the sexing of juveniles (not possible in most cases), the occurrence and timing of the cloacal protuberance (CP) and brood patch (BP), and a range of wing chord (wg) and tail (tl) lengths for males and females. Unless they are present through the fall migration, juvenal plumages otherwise are not included in the age/sex breakdowns. As with the timing of the molt, month ranges are indicated for both the juvenal plumage and the breeding characters. When the cloacal protuberance and the brood patch are listed together (as CP/BP, in most cases), the month range should be interpreted as the month when the first CP is in evidence to the month when the last BP becomes obscured. When using these month ranges, note that the CP usually develops about two weeks before, and recedes from one to two months earlier than the BP.

Wing and tail length ranges are derived from the literature, from data collected by the MAPS program of The Institute for Bird Populations ("MAPS data"), from data collected at the Palomarin and Farallon Island Field Stations of the Point Reyes Bird Observatory ("PRBO data"), from data collected in New York and New Jersey by Robert P. Yunick, and from extensive measurements by the author of museum skins at almost all museums located in California (see **Acknowledgments;** primarily the California Academy of Sciences, San Francisco, and the Museum of Vertebrate Zoology, Berkeley). If available, a sample of at least 30 wing chords and 20 tail lengths for each sex of each species is listed. Samples of "100" indicate that at least 100 birds are included. Geographic variation in these measurements, if they exist, can be derived from the subspecies accounts. Note that the ranges of measurements under Age/Sex exclude subspecies occurring entirely outside of North America, *e.g.*, those found only in Mexico. **Banders should not use wing chord or tail length data alone to designate sex codes to the CWS and BBL, unless 1) these are given under the individual age/sex groups (*e.g.*, for many icterids), or 2) the bander provides detailed documentation.** See further comments under the Bar Graph section, below.

Age coding used in this guide follows, for the most part, the system used by the CWS and BBL as listed in the Bird Banding Manual (Canadian Wildlife Service & U.S. Fish & Wildlife Service [USFWS] 1991), and is based on the calendar year. The following age codes are used:

Juv—Juvenile. A bird in juvenal plumage, before the first prebasic molt. **Note that the CWS and BBL do not accept this age designation.** Use "L" for "Local" birds that have not fledged, and "HY" for birds in juvenal plumage that have fledged.

HY—A bird in first-basic plumage in its first calendar year (i.e. from the first prebasic molt until 31 December of the year it fledged). Banders may wish to combine this category with juvenile, as is the case in the Bird Banding Manual. Note, however, that the month ranges given in the species accounts assume this distinction.

U—Unknown. This code is only used during the last months of the year, when a bird can be either HY or AHY (see below).

AHY—A bird in *at least* its second calendar year (*i.e.*, After Hatching Year). This code is more significant after the breeding season, when it implies an adult. Before the breeding season, it essentially means "Unknown" (either SY or ASY).

SY—A bird in its second calendar year (i.e. 1 January of the year following fledging through 31 December of the same year).

ASY—An adult in *at least* its third calendar year (*i.e.*, After Second Year).

TY—A bird in its third calendar year.

ATY—An adult in *at least* its fourth calendar year (*i.e.*, After Third Year).

4Y, A4Y, 5Y—Birds in their fourth, after fourth, and fifth calendar years, respectively. At this time, these codes only are suggested as possibilities under the accounts of certain owls and woodpeckers. **Note that the BBL and CWS do not accept these codes; instead, use ATY on schedules and document the age with a note.**

Because molts and plumage sequences do not adhere to the calendar year, most age codes are represented with a slash and the month ranges in which the codes can be assigned. For example, **HY/SY (Aug-Jul)** essentially indicates a bird in first-basic or first-alternate plumage, that can be aged HY in Aug-Dec and SY in Jan-Jul. The code "U/AHY" indicates a bird of unknown age (*i.e.*, U before Jan and AHY after Dec).

The age (or age/sex) code is followed by the range, in months, when the code can be assigned reliably to *at least a portion* of the individuals in the class. Note that not all birds of a specific age (or age/sex) class may be determined during the entire range of months. In most cases, the extreme months roughly indicate the central period of molts. During these months, users should always consider the molt and how it might affect the reliability of the plumage criteria. If the individual has completed the molt, for instance, the criteria may no longer apply. Alternatively, it may be reliable on molting birds a month or so before or after the period given. Both incoming and outgoing plumages should be considered carefully when ageing molting birds. Finally, when a range of months does not span an entire year (most often used with the code, "AHY"), birds found in that category during months outside of the range should be considered "unknown". See the bar graph section (below) for more information.

The age/sex characters given are those that have been found helpful for ageing and sexing each species. They should always be used not only in combination with each other, but also in combination with molt and skull information, measurements, time of year, breeding characters, and the previous experience of the user with the species at hand. Two types of characters often are referred to in these sections, and should be interpreted as follows: **Reliable** characters are those that should, on their own, accurately separate greater than 95% of individuals. **Useful** characters are those that accurately separate between 50% and 95% of individuals (i.e. there is 5-50% overlap), and should either be used only in combination with other ageing or sexing criteria, or used only to separate extremes. Note that the order of characters generally begins with measurements, followed by upperpart, head, and underpart plumage, then soft part color, and thus does not reflect the relative reliability of the listed criteria. The two tenets given on page 3 should always be considered when ageing and sexing birds.

Hybrids Reported

All species known or suspected to have hybridized with the account species are listed. Note that the parentage of hybrids often is difficult or impossible to confirm (see p. 26).

References

References for geographic variation (mostly pertaining to subspecific designations) are listed separately under that section. All other references, including those pertaining to species identification, molt, skull pneumaticization, age/sex, and hybrids, are listed at the end of the account. References used are derived almost entirely from the North American literature. For general and specific references in the European literature (some of which pertain to Holarctic species), see the Birds of the Western Palearctic series (under "Cramp" in **Literature Cited**), Svensson (1992), and Jenni & Winkler (1994). Unpublished manuscripts have only been cited in cases where they are in review or are ready for submission to a scientific journal. There is much other useful information contained in unpublished form (*e.g.*, graduate school theses) which should be published.

A total of 2442 references is listed in the **Literature Cited** section. The author would appreciate receiving reprints of any relevant references that were overlooked.

Also listed under references are unpublished information contained in the files of the Bird Banding Laboratory (indicated by "*in litt.* to the BBL"), data from the MAPS program of The Institute for Bird Populations (IBP), Point Reyes Bird Observatory (PRBO), Powdermill Nature Reserve (PNR), and other sources, and personal communications to the author. Most of the latter include feedback, corrections, or updates to Pyle *et al.* (1987).

BAR GRAPHS

Bar graphs, indicating our ability to age and sex live birds in the hand, have been constructed for each species (Fig. 24). The bar graphs have two primary purposes: 1) To present information (some of which is additional to that of the text) on the degree to which users can reliably age and sex birds throughout the year, and 2) to represent the age and sex codes currently accepted by the Canadian Wildlife Service (CWS) and Bird Banding Laboratory (BBL). They are similar to the graphs previously provided in the Bird Banding Manual (CWS & USFWS 1991), with some modifications resulting in efficiency of presentation and provision of additional information. Referring to Figure 24, the following provides information on how to use the bar graphs.

Ageing and Age Coding Based on the Bar Graphs.

Reliable ageing and age coding is represented by the horizontal bars, as broken down into monthly segments. Solid black segments indicate that > 95% of birds in that age class (essentially all) generally should be aged as indicated, when using all available criteria (primarily information based on skull pneumaticization and plumage); cross-hatched segments indicate that 25-95% of birds in that age class should be aged as indicated; dotted segments indicate that 5-25% of birds in that age class should be aged as indicated; and solid white segments indicate that < 5% of birds in that age class (usually none) should be aged as indicated (or expected, in the case of juvs early in the year). **Note that these proportions indicate the reliability of identifying all birds of the given age class, not the proportion of birds that should be assigned that age code.** For example, only a small proportion of Ruby-throated Hummingbirds will be aged juv-HY in May, but > 95% of birds that have fledged by the end of May should be identifiable as juv-HYs. Question marks indicate the possibility of accurate ageing or age coding during those months, depending on the results of further study.

The proportions indicated by the cross-hatched and dotted segments should be regarded as general, and were assigned based on the experience of the author with live birds in the hand and with specimens. These proportions may vary substantially among users of the accounts, based on their previous experience with the species. An attempt was made to assign proportions representing those of a user with an "average" amount of experience ageing a particular species.

In months when 5-95% of birds can be aged as indicated (dotted and cross-hatched segments), note that the proportion of uncertainty can depend on temporal factors, geographic variation, sex-specific differences, and/or individual variation in reliable ageing. Only about 50% of AHY Northern Cardinals can be aged AHY in October because skulling becomes unreliable for assigning this age class after the 15th of the month. Other examples of temporal factors affecting ageing include the reliable identification of SY Northern Cardinals or SY and ASY White-crowned Sparrows in August, when some birds can be identified at the beginning of the month but few, if any, are identifiable at the end of the month. An example of geographic variation in reliable ageing is that of identifying SY and ASY White-crowned Sparrows in May to July, when the Nuttall's subspecies can be more reliably aged by plumage than the other subspecies. Similarly, in many species, birds of northern populations may show different ageing proportions than birds of southern populations, due to differences in the timing of skull pneumaticization and/or the timing and extent of molts. The proportions indicated by the age-bar patterns attempt to represent the species as a whole. Examples of sex-specific effects on ageing proportions include those of SY/TY and ASY Ruby-throated Hummingbirds after March, and SY Pine Grosbeaks in September and October, when males but not females can be aged as indicated; thus, the proportions during these months are 50%, at best. Finally, much of the variation in the ageing proportions will be based on variation in plumage criteria, as explained in Figure 3.

The bars indicated by "AHY-U" require extra explanation and comparison with the other bars. First, the age code "U" should only be used after the first juveniles have hatched and when < 95% of Juv/HYs can be aged, as represented by a bar segment that is not solid black. Second, the patterning of the monthly segments indicate the proportion of non juv-HYs that should be aged AHY. In Northern Cardinal, for example, only 25-95% of non juv-HYs should be aged AHY in January to August because a portion of those AHYs (5-75%) can be recognized as SYs by

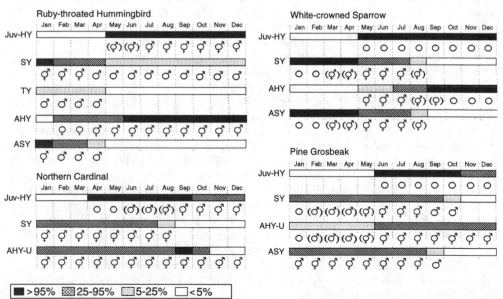

FIGURE 24. Four examples of bar graphs indicating the reliability of ageing, sexing, and age/sex-code assignment. See text for a complete explanation.

plumage. In September, all birds can be aged by skull, and few if any (< 5%) SYs are still identifiable; thus, > 95% of non juv-HYs should be identified as AHY (and > 95% of juv-HYs are also recognizable). In October, as mentioned above, only birds before the 15th can be aged AHY (by skull); the cross-hatching thus indicates approximately 50% during the entire month. In this case, the remaining birds (those after 15 October having finished their molt and with complete pneumaticization) should be aged U. In November and December, < 5% of non juv-HYs (essentially none) are reliably aged AHY; thus, > 95% (essentially all) should be aged U because some juv-HYs can acquire complete adult plumage and pneumaticized skulls by these months. Note that sex designations are given during November and December for unknown-age birds, as opposed to, *e.g.*, AHY White-crowned Sparrows in January to April, where neither AHY nor U should be assigned, and no sex designations are given. In the Pine Grosbeak, 25-95% of non juv-HYs can be aged AHY in June to December, but the reasons differ depending on the month. In June-October, a portion of non juv-HYs can be aged SY or ASY, thus 25-95% should be aged AHY. In November and December, after the skull no longer is reliable for ageing AHYs, 25-95% of non juv-HYs can be recognized as AHY by plumage and the remaining 5-75% of birds should be aged U. Note that the use of U depends on comparison with the "Juv-HY" bar: when < 95% of HYs can be aged, then a proportion of birds should be aged U, as indicated by the proportion noted on the AHY-U bar that can be aged AHY.

Note also that, by comparing bars, the ageing proportions can often be refined further than is indicated by the cross-hatched and dot patterns alone. In White-crowned Sparrow, for example, 75-95% of non juv-HYs should be aged SY or ASY in May and June, 25-75% should be aged SY or ASY in July, and 5-25% should be aged SY or ASY in August, as based on the patterns of all three (SY, AHY, and ASY) bars considered together. When such overall patterns occur, it can essentially be assumed that the proportion of birds that can be aged SY, AHY, and ASY is changing in a clinal manner.

Sexing and Sex Coding Based on the Bar Graphs

Reliable sexing and sex coding is represented by the symbols under the monthly age-bar segments. A female symbol, ♀, a male symbol, ♂, or a "female-male symbol", ⚥, indicate that > 75% of live birds in the hand, of that age-class, and in that month, can be reliably sexed as female, male, or either sex, respectively. Parentheses around these symbols indicate that approximately 5-75% of these groups of birds can be sexed as indicated. A "neither-sex" symbol, ○ indicates that < 5% of birds should be sexed. Sexing proportions are based on the sexing criteria indicated in the text, primarily those of plumage and breeding characters; note that measurement criteria are only included for species in which all or nearly all individuals, within the entire North American range of the species, can be separated based on morphology.

As with the ageing proportions, sexing proportions can reflect individual, geographic, or temporal variation (within the given month) in our ability to reliably sex birds. In the Northern Cardinal, for example, 5-75% of juveniles can be sexed male in June-July by incoming red plumage; < 5% of females can be reliably sexed during this month. In August, 5-75% of birds can be sexed either male or female, and by September > 75% of birds can be sexed. In the White-crowned Sparrow, 5-75% of SYs and ASYs (throughout the entire range of the species) can be sexed in March and April by brood patch or cloacal protuberance. By May to July, > 75% of all birds should be reliably sexed by breeding characters. In September, 5-75% of females may still be recognized by outgoing brood patches, while < 5% of males can still be identified by cloacal protuberance. In the Pine Grosbeak, 5-75% of SY males can be identified in February to April by the presence of a few red feathers in the plumage. By May, breeding characters allow 5-75% of both males and females to be sexed. Many instances of the male-female symbol in parentheses, (⚥), indicate overlap between the plumages of males and females (see Figure 3), which results in 5-75% of extremes being reliably sexed.

Along the "AHY-U" bar (see above), note that the sex codes under cross-hatched or dotted segments indicate the sexing of AHYs, and those under solid white segments (at the end of the year) indicate the sexing of birds aged "U". In the Pine Grosbeak, for example, > 75% (in this case, close to 100%) of AHYs in November and December can be sexed by plumage, as indicated by the symbols, while birds aged U at this time should be left unsexed, as indicated by the symbols under the Juv-HY bar for these months. Notes pointing out these cases are provided under the graphs. In the Northern Cardinal, birds aged U in November and December can still be sexed, as indicated by the male-female symbols under the solid white bar.

CWS and BBL Acceptance Criteria as Reflected in the Bar Graphs

The bar graphs represent what is currently accepted by the CWS and BBL on schedules from banders. For ageing, the CWS and BBL will accept all codes indicated with a solid black bar (> 95% should be aged as indicated) or a cross-hatched bar (25-95% should be aged as indicated). It is up to the bander to be conservative in cases indicated with cross-hatched segments, generally only ageing 25-95% of birds. For segments with the dot pattern (5-25% of birds being reliably aged as indicated), the CWS and BBL will accept these age codes, but may query certain banders that do not have adequate experience, or who are ageing more than 25% of birds without supplying any documentation. **When using the "Juv-HY" bar, note that the CWS and BBL do not accept "Juv" as an age designation. Use "L" for "Local" birds that have not fledged, and "HY" for birds in juvenal plumage that have fledged.** For sexing, all codes indicating that > 75% of birds can be sexed as indicated will be accepted, and banders may be queried if they submit a high proportion of sexed birds where a symbol in parentheses (indicating a 5-75% sexing proportion) is given. Banders may also be queried if they are not ageing or sexing most or all birds, when > 95% ageing or > 75% sexing proportions are indicated. **The CWS and BBL will not accept aged birds during a month-segment indicated by a solid white bar (including those with question marks), or sexed birds during a month indicated by a neither-sex symbol, ○, without accompanying documentation from the bander.** Certain age-sex combinations are also unacceptable to CWS and BBL, such as SY-♀♀ Ruby-throated Hummingbirds in April to December, or AHY-♂♂ White-crowned Sparrows in September, even though a code for the opposite sex may be accepted. If banders feel that they can age or sex birds in situations where the bar graphs indicate otherwise, they are strongly urged to document fully their reasoning when submitting their schedules, and to provide a copy of their documentation to the author of this guide, as well. **This will apply in all cases where banders are sexing birds in their area only by measurements or multiple-variable analyses.** In this way, our knowledge of ageing and sexing, and the bar graphs themselves, can continue to be updated and refined.

NOTES OF INTEREST

A NOTE CONCERNING SPECIMEN COLLECTIONS

The author spent approximately 1000 hours in museum collections (80% at the California Academy of Sciences, San Francisco), and examined over 25,000 specimens in preparation for the second edition of this guide. The value of these specimens (most of which were collected in the 1800's and early 1900's) in providing and checking the information presented here cannot be over-estimated. Currently, however, many ornithologists assume that there is little left to learn from specimens, and funding for museum collections and the staff to run them are steadily decreasing (see Parkes 1963; Phillips 1974a, 1986, 1991; Winker *et al.* 1991; Browning 1995; Remsen 1995). But there are still vast amounts to learn, as exemplified by the expanded sections on molt in this guide (see also Pyle 1995a, 1997b, 1997c, in press; Pyle *et al.* 1997; Pyle & Howell 1995). Although data on specimen tags, especially concerning sex, should be interpreted with some caution (see Clench 1976, Parkes 1989a), users of this guide, including all banders, birders, and other ornithologists, are strongly encouraged to utilize specimen collections in answering questions about identification, molt, and plumage in species of interest, and to support the continued maintenance of museum collections.

Although continued random collecting in North America is no longer necessary, the full utilization of collections will point out areas where judicious collecting to answer specific questions is warranted. Additional specimens can always help with existing questions, however, and banders and birders are strongly encouraged (with the appropriate local permits) to save specimens that perish during banding operations or are found under windows or on the road (see Phillips 1974a, Jett 1991), to carefully note the date, location, and any other pertinent information, and to donate them to the nearest museum collection.

A NOTE TO BANDERS

The information in the accounts, as reflected on the bar graphs under each species, represents the codes accepted by the Canadian Wildlife Service and Bird Banding Laboratory. See the Bar Graph section (above) for details on their interpretation relative to CWS and BBL acceptance. As mentioned in several places in this introduction, banders are in the best position to update information in this guide. Updates to the bar graphs will depend on banders' communicating their information to the author, the CWS, and/or the BBL. The information on molt may especially need to be updated, as molt limits can be easier to discern on live birds than on specimens (see Pyle 1997c). Banders are strongly encouraged to publish updated information, in journals such as *North American Bird Bander* or *Journal of Field Ornithology*.

Species Accounts

NEAR-PASSERINES

Incomplete Molts and Ageing in Near-Passerines

Many "near-passerines" (doves through woodpeckers in the sequence of the AOU [1983] Check-list regularly retain flight feathers during molts, in predictable sequences. Thus, patterns of new and old feathers can result in reliable ageing, in some cases through the third or fourth year of life.

Near-passerines typically have a single, annual, prebasic molt that can occur on the summer grounds, the winter grounds, or both. Individuals of most species follow the same general sequence of flight-feather replacement. Except in cuckoos, owls, hummingbirds, and kingfishers (see family and species accounts), replacement of the primaries starts with the innermost, p1, and continues distally to the outermost, p10. Primary-covert replacement in all families except woodpeckers and kingfishers (see family and species accounts) usually corresponds with that of the primaries. Replacement of the secondaries typically proceeds both distally from the innermost (tertials) and, later, proximally from the outermost (s1), such that the last secondaries replaced often are among s2-s7 (typically, s3-s4). Replacement of the rectrices can be variable and often commences with the innermost (r1), followed by the outermost (r5 or r6), and finishing with feathers among r2-r4. In many species, the sequence of replacement can be protracted and/or suspended during migration or winter, not being completed until spring.

Retention of flight feathers results when the molt sequence does not complete before the next annual cycle, unreplaced feathers being held at least until commencement of the next prebasic molt. Thus, during the first flight-feather molt, retained juvenal feathers often include the outermost primaries, secondaries among s2-s7, and/or rectrices among r2-r4. Secondaries often

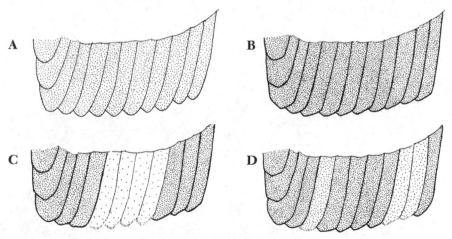

FIGURE 25. Four retention patterns found in the secondaries of near-passerines: uniform juvenal feathers (**A**), uniform adult feathers (**B**), mixed adult and juvenal feathers (**C**), and mixed replaced and retained adult feathers (**D**). Note that juvenal secondaries usually differ from those of adults in being narrower, more tapered at the tip, and contrasting with replaced feathers more markedly in color and wear, whereas retained adult feathers contrast less with replaced feathers. Retained juvenal feathers usually occur among s2-s7 and are often consecutive and symmetrical in both wings, whereas retained adult secondaries can occur throughout the wing, often are not consecutive, and less frequently are symmetrical in both wings. See Pyle (1995a) for more details.

are the last feathers to be replaced, and thus are most frequently retained (Fig. 25C). Juvenal feathers usually are retained symmetrically in both wings and on both sides of the tail, or at most differ by one or two feathers. These juvenal feathers can, or may not, be the first replaced during the next molt; as a consequence, replacement patterns in adults can be irregular, and retained feathers less often are symmetrical. Both juvenal and adult flight feathers can, or may not, be retained, hence four molt-retention pattern categories can be defined: uniformly juvenal feathers, mixed juvenal and adult feathers, uniformly adult feathers, and mixed replaced and retained adult feathers (Fig. 25). Assuming that juvenal and adult feathers can be distinguished, and depending on when replacement of the juvenal flight feathers typically commences (during the first or the second prebasic molt), birds with retained flight feathers can be aged more accurately, or to a later age category, than those with uniformly adult flight feathers (see Fig. 25). See Pyle (1995a) for more information on molt in many near-passerines, and pp. 67 and 163 for details on the complex molts of owls and woodpeckers, respectively.

Reliable ageing of near-passerines, however, frequently requires caution and/or experience. In many birds, replacement patterns may not easily be distinguished without practice, or may conflict with what would be expected given information in the molt sections of the following, individual species accounts. Responsible ageing always includes the willingness to place a bird in a less precise age group should any uncertainty exist, and this especially is true of criteria based on molt-retention patterns. Much of the information presented in the following accounts is based on specimen examination. Further confirmation and/or information is needed based on study of known-age, captive, or marked individuals.

PIGEONS AND DOVES   *COLUMBIDAE*

Nine species. Family characters include small heads, heavy bodies, short wings, short legs, and upper mandibles with convex horny tips and fleshy membranes over the nostrils. North American pigeons and doves have 10 primaries (the 10th full in length), 11 (Inca Dove and ground-doves) to 12 secondaries, and 12 (to 14 in Mourning Dove) rectrices. Juveniles of all species have scalloped wing coverts and average more black checkers on these and on the scapulars (Whitman 1919). Secondaries, and occasionally primaries, can be retained during prebasic molts, which otherwise are complete and can occur year-round in southern populations. Primary coverts are replaced with their corresponding primaries. No prealternate molts apparently occur in North American species. Skull pneumaticization typically does not complete in the larger species but possibly completes in the smaller species (see Parkes 1957a, Johnston 1962, Fig. 88); in either case, the percentage of completion may be useful for age determination (more study is needed). Males average slightly larger than females, but measurements generally are not helpful for sexing. Both sexes incubate and the brood patch is poorly developed, hence it cannot be used to sex pigeons and doves. Cloacal protuberances are not developed by males and thus cannot be used for sexing; however, live adults of the larger species can be sexed by examining the cloaca for the conical papillae of males (the lack of which may not necessarily indicate females), or the oviductal openings of females (Miller & Wagner 1955, Swanson & Rappole 1992). This requires experience and a modified (ground down) nasal speculum (available at medical supply stores), thus cloacal examination may not be an appropriate procedure at all capture stations (Braun *et al.* 1975).

WHITE-CROWNED PIGEON   WCPI
Columba leucocephala   Species # 3140
                                         Band size: 4A

Geographic variation—No subspecies are recognized. Breeding birds of s.FL average slightly larger than those of the W.Indies; see Ridgway (1916).

Molt—Not well known in this species, but apparently as in the other *Columba* pigeons, as follows: PB HY/SY incomplete-complete (Jun-May), AHY incomplete-complete (Jun-Dec); PA absent. The PBs may be suspended over winter. Molting in both age groups may occur year-round, possibly most commonly in Jul-Nov. The outermost 1-2 pp and/or 1-5 ss (usually among s4-s9) often are retained during the 1st PB and sometimes during the adult PB. More study is needed on molt in this species (see p. 39).

Skull—Pneumaticization patterns possibly are useful for ageing (see Family account), but more study is needed.

Age—Juv (May-Nov?) is uniformly dark brown, without head markings, has feathers of the upperparts with pale edging (Fig. 26), ss uniformly juvenal (Figs. 25A & 27), and iris dark brown; juv ♀=♂. The following month ranges may not apply south of FL, where breeding can occur year-round; see Band-tailed Pigeon.

Juv-HY/SY (Jun-2nd Sep): Iris dark brown to dull orange (through Dec?); one or more unreplaced, juvenal wing covs

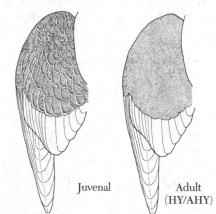

Juvenal   Adult
               (HY/AHY)

FIGURE 26. The wing coverts of juvenal and adult pigeons and doves.

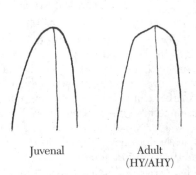

Juvenal   Adult
              (HY/AHY)

FIGURE 27. The shape of the secondaries by age in *Columba* pigeons. The figure shows a typical s6.

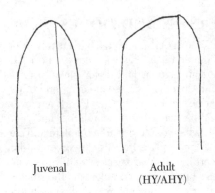

Juvenal   Adult
              (HY/AHY)

FIGURE 28. The shape of the outer rectrices (r4-r6) by age in *Columba* pigeons.

brown with pale or rusty tips; one or more juvenal outer pp tapered and dark brown with pale or rusty edging when fresh; one or more juvenal middle ss (usually among s2-s6) narrow (Fig. 27), sometimes with whitish or rusty edging, and contrastingly worn in spring (Fig. 25C); unreplaced juvenal rects tapered (Fig. 28). **Note: Juv-HYs in Jun-Sep are separated from SYs by much fresher (retained) flight feathers.**

AHY/ASY (Mar-Feb): Iris yellow; adult wing covs, pp, and ss uniformly slate and truncate (Figs. 25B & 27) or, if in molt or retained feathers are present, the old adult feathers are broad (Fig. 27), slate, and not contrasting markedly with the new feathers in shape, color, and/or wear (Fig. 25D); adult rects truncate (Fig. 28). **Note: Some AHY/ASYs can retain adult outer pp, inner ss, and/or rects that contrast minimally with newer feathers; these possibly may be aged ASY through at least Sep, but more study is needed.**

Sex—CP & BP are poorly developed and unreliable for sexing; see Family account regarding cloacal examination. Measurements are useful: ♀ wg(n54) 171-195, tl(n54) 111-134; ♂ wg(n65) 181-204, tl(n65) 113-145.

♀: Crown patch dull whitish; hindneck patch reduced (see Fig. 29) and pinkish-green; breast and back dull blue, slightly tinged brownish. **Note: The above is reliable for all AHY/ASYs and molting HY/SYs with > 3 pp replaced; no reliable means are known to sex HY/SY ♀♀ with < 3 pp replaced. Among all birds, intermediates can occur that cannot be reliably sexed by plumage alone; compare with measurements and age, as these probably are AHY/ASY ♀♀ or HY/SY ♂♂.**

♂: Crown patch bright white; hindneck patch extensive (see Fig. 29) and bright green; breast and back bright blue, without a brownish tinge. **Note: See ♀.**

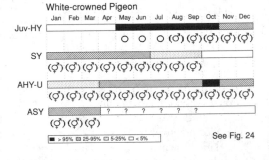

References—Ridgway (1916), Bent (1932), Goodwin (1967), Howell & Webb (1995); S.N.G. Howell, W. Russell (pers. comm.).

RED-BILLED PIGEON
Columba flavirostris

RBPI
Species # 3130
Band size: 5

Geographic variation—Weak to moderate, but ranges fairly well defined. Subspecies taxonomy in N.Am follows the AOU (1957); see Ridgway (1916), van Rossem (1930a), Pitelka (1948). Three other subspecies occur in Mex-C.Am.

C.f. flavirostris (br s.TX): From the subspecies of Mex-C.Am by medium size (see **Sex**, *vs* wg 181-207, tl 111-133 in the other subspecies); coloration darker; pale edging of the gr covs narrower (< 0.5 mm wide, *vs* ≥ 0.5 mm in the other subspecies).

Molt—Not well known in this species, but probably similar to Band-tailed Pigeon, as follows: PB HY/SY incomplete-complete (Jun-May), AHY/ASY incomplete-complete (Jun-Dec); PA absent. The PBs probably occur primarily on the winter grounds and can be suspended. Molting in both age groups can occur year-round, but probably most commonly in Aug-Nov. The outermost 1-2 pp and/or 1-5 ss (usually among s4-s9) can be retained during both the 1st PB and (sometimes) the adult PBs. More study is needed (see p. 39).

Skull—Pneumaticization patterns possibly are useful for ageing (see Family account), but more study is needed.

Age—Juv (May-Sep?) is relatively dull-colored and brownish, with the rust coloration of the head, breast, and lesser covs restricted or absent, gr covs with relatively broad, pale edging, ss uniformly juvenal (Figs. 25A & 27), and iris dark; juv ♀ = ♂. The following month ranges may not apply south of N.Am, where breeding may occur year-round; see Band-tailed Pigeon.

HY/SY (Oct-Sep): Iris dark to dull orange (through Dec?); one or more unreplaced, juvenal wing covs dull brown with buff or whitish tips (Fig. 26); one or more juvenal outer pp tapered and dull brown with pale or rusty edging when fresh; one or more juvenal middle ss (usually among s2-s6) dull brown, narrow (Fig. 27), sometimes with whitish or rusty edging, and contrastingly worn in spring (Fig. 25C); unreplaced juvenal rects tapered (Fig. 28).

AHY/ASY (Mar-Feb): Iris orange; adult wing covs, pp, and ss uniformly slaty brown and truncate (Figs. 25B & 27) or, if in molt or feather retention has occurred, old adult feathers slaty brown and broad (Fig. 27), not contrasting markedly with the replaced feathers in shape, color, and/or wear (Fig. 25D); adult rects truncate (Fig. 28). **Note: Look for some AHYs with retained adult pp, ss, and/or rects, contrasting minimally with the replaced feathers; these probably are reliably aged ASY through at least Sep. More study is needed.**

Sex—CP & BP are poorly developed and unreliable for sexing; see Family account regarding cloacal examination. ♀ wg(n15) 180-199, tl(n15) 105-127; ♂ wg(n10) 185-207, tl(n10) 112-126.

♀: Head, breast and lesser covs brown with a purplish tinge. **Note: This is reliable for all AHY/ASYs, and HY/SYs with ≥ 3 pp replaced; no reliable means are known to sex HY/SY ♀♀ with < 3 pp replaced.**

♂: Head and breast reddish purple to purplish with a brown tinge; lesser covs bright pinkish purple. **Note: See ♀. In addition, some HY/SY ♂♂ in earlier stages of molt (0-2 pp replaced) can be reliably sexed.**

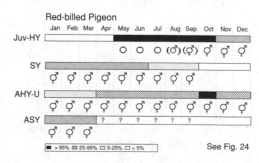

Red-billed Pigeon

See Fig. 24

References—Ridgway (1916), Bent (1932), Dickey & van Rossem (1938), Goodwin (1967), Oberholser (1974), Howell & Webb (1995), Pyle (1995a).

BAND-TAILED PIGEON
Columba fasciata

BTPI
Species # 3120
Band size: 5

Geographic variation—Moderate and ranges fairly well defined. Subspecies taxonomy in N.Am follows the AOU (1957); see Ridgway (1916), Griscom (1935), Brodkorb (1943), Monroe (1968). Six other subspecies occur in Mex-S.Am. The subspecies of N.Am have p10 > p7 (*vs* p7 > p10 in the subspecies of Mex-S.Am). Some differences in wing morphology possibly occur between the two subspecies in N.Am, as well; more study is needed.

    C.f. monilis (br & wint se.AK-CA): Large; plumage (especially breast) averages dark. ♀ wg(n16) 208-224, tl(n11) 126-137; ♂ wg(n22) 218-230, tl(n11) 135-149.

    C.f. fasciata (br UT-CO to s.TX, wint AZ): Small; plumage (especially breast) averages pale. ♀ wg(n35) 198-215, tl(n11) 119-129; ♂ wg(n63) 201-221, tl(n10) 127-139.

Molt—PB: HY/SY incomplete-complete (Jun-May), AHY/ASY incomplete-complete (Jun-May); PA absent. The PBs occur on the summer and/or the winter grounds and often are suspended over winter. Replacement of pp during the 1st PB begins 1-2 months after hatching and can take 10 months to complete. Molting of pp in both age groups occurs year-round, but most commonly in Jul-Nov. The outermost 1-2 pp and/or 1-5 ss (usually among s4-s9) sometimes can be retained during both the 1st and the adult PBs; more study is needed on retained feathers during molt in adults (see p. 39).

Skull—Pneumaticization patterns possibly are useful for ageing (see Family account), but more study is needed.

Age—Juv (Jan-Dec) is uniformly brownish gray, lacking the hindneck markings, has ss uniformly juvenal (Figs. 25A & 27), and feathers of the upperparts with pale edging (Fig. 26); juv ♀ = ♂.

HY/SY (Feb-2nd Aug): One or more unreplaced, juvenal wing covs brownish gray with buff or whitish tips; one or more juvenal outer pp tapered and brownish gray, with pale or rusty edging when fresh; one or more juvenal middle ss (usually among s2-s6) brownish gray, narrow (Fig. 27), sometimes with whitish or rusty edging, and contrastingly worn in spring (Fig. 25C); unreplaced juvenal rects tapered (Fig. 28). **Note: Beware that this species can breed year-round (although primarily in spring), which complicates age-code assignment. The last juvenal wing covs usually dropped are the gr covs above ss 4-7; these can be retained after completion of the primary molt. HYs are distinguished from SYs in Feb-Aug by the progression of the primary molt. Birds hatched around 1 Jan drop successive pp on or around the following dates: P1, 17 Feb; P2, 28 Feb; P3, 19 Mar; P4, 14 Apr; P5, 5 May; P6, 28 May; P7, 14 Jun; P8, 3 Jul; P9, 22 Jul; P10, 10 Aug. If the primary molt is behind this schedule assume HY; if ahead, assume SY.**

AHY/ASY (Mar-Feb): Adult wing covs, pp, and ss uniformly blue and truncate (Figs. 25B & 27) or, if in molt or feather retention has occurred, old adult feathers blue and broad, not contrasting markedly with the replaced feathers in shape, color, and/or wear (Fig. 25D); adult rects truncate (Fig. 28). **Note: See HY/SY. During Oct-May, only birds in the process of molt, with unreplaced pp as described, can be aged AHY/ASY. Birds that have completed molt (showing uniform coloration and wear of pp) should be aged AHY during these months. Look for some AHYs with retained adult pp, ss, and/or rects, contrasting minimally with newer feathers, that probably can be reliably aged ASY through at least Sep. More study is needed.**

Sex—CP & BP are poorly developed and unreliable for sexing; see Family account regarding cloacal examination. Measurements are useful (see **Geographic variation**); however, juvs average substantially smaller than adults. ♀ wg(n51) 198-224, tl(n22) 119-137; ♂ wg(n85) 201-230, tl(n21) 127-149; see **Geographic variation**.

♀: Crown, neck, and head dull brown, gray-brown, or brownish pink; white nape band relatively narrow, and green iridescent patch on the hindneck restricted, usually falling well short of the bends of the wings (Fig. 29). **Note: The above is reliable for all AHY/ASYs and molting HY/SYs with ≥ 3 pp replaced; no reliable means are known to sex HY/SY ♀♀ with < 3 pp replaced. For all birds a percentage (~20%, with experience) of intermediates cannot be reliably sexed by plumage alone; compare with measurements (by subspecies) and age, as these probably are AHY/ASY ♀♀ or HY/SY ♂♂.**

♂: Crown, neck, and head deep pinkish or purple; white nape band relatively broad, and green iridescent patch on the hindneck extensive, usually extending posteriorly to the bends of the wings (Fig. 29). **Note: See ♀. Also, some HY/SY ♂♂ in earlier stages of molt (0-2 pp replaced) can be reliably aged.**

Hybrids reported—Rock Dove (*C. livia*) in a semi-wild state and in captivity.

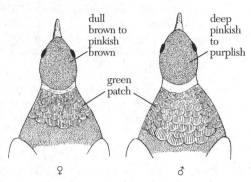

FIGURE 29. Head and back patterns in ♀ and ♂ Band-tailed Pigeons. See text for the timing of the reliability of these criteria. Intermediates likely are AHY/ASY ♀♀ or HY/SY ♂♂. Similar variation in the green feathering (although less pronounced) may be found in White-crowned Pigeon.

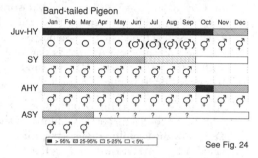

References—Ridgway (1916), Bent (1932), Neff (1947), Morse (1950), Peeters (1962), Goodwin (1967), Silovsky *et al.* (1968), Smith (1968), Braun *et al.* (1971, 1975), Braun (1976a, 1976b), White & Braun (1978), Passmore & Jarvis (1979), Alcocer (1981), Brown (1989), CWS & USFWS (1991), Pyle (1995a); C.E. Braun, R.L. Jarvis (*in litt.* to the BBL); L.F. Baptista (pers. comm.); PRBO data.

WHITE-WINGED DOVE
Zenaida asiatica

WWDO
Species # 3190
Band size: 4-3A

Species—Nestlings and juvs from Mourning Dove (which see for separation from Zenaida and White-tipped doves) by the presence of white tips to both the ss and the gr covs.

Geographic variation—Weak, clinal, and differences are obscured by individual variation. Subspecies taxonomy follows Saunders (1968), as modified by Aldrich (1981) and Browning (1990); see also Ridgway (1916), van Rossem (1947a), Pitelka (1948), Monroe (1968), Hubbard & Crossin (1974), Oberholser (1974). Eight to nine other subspecies occur in Mex-S.Am, depending on the species taxonomy.

Z.a. mearnsi (br & wint s.CA-sw.NM, vag to n.CA & Ont): Large; upperparts pale grayish brown; neck and breast pale brown. ♀ wg(n84) 148-170, tl(n62) 98-120; ♂ wg(n78) 152-175, tl(n77) 102-132. Birds of sw.TX ("*grandis*") may average larger and browner, but differences, if present, are obscured by individual variation.

Z.a. asiatica (br & wint sw.NM-FL, vag to CO & ME): Small; upperparts dark brown with little or no grayish; neck and breast dark brown to fawn. ♀ wg(n85) 144-161, tl(n82) 85-110; ♂ wg(n100) 144-166, tl(n100) 95-115.

Molt—PB: HY/SY incomplete-complete (Jul-Jan), AHY incomplete-complete (Jun-Nov); PA absent. The PBs occur primarily on the summer grounds; the 1st PB can be suspended over migration, completing on the winter grounds. 1-2 juvenal ss (usually among s4-s6) occasionally can be retained during the 1st PB; also, look for occasional retained ss during the adult PB. See p. 39.

Skull—Pneumaticization patterns possibly are useful for ageing (see Family account), but more study is needed.

Age—Juv (Mar-Oct) is grayish brown, with buff to whitish edging to the scapulars and wing covs (Fig. 26), and has uniformly juvenal ss (Fig. 25A), a brown iris, and dull, pinkish-red legs; juv ♀ = ♂.

HY/SY (Jun-2nd Sep): Iris brown, yellowish brown, or dull orange (through Dec?); one or more unreplaced, juvenal outer pp covs with white or buff edging; one or more juvenal middle ss (usually among s4-s6) narrow, old, and worn, contrasting markedly with the adjacent, first-basic (adult) feathers in spring (Fig. 25C); legs and feet dull pinkish red to red (through Dec?). **Note: Only a small percentage of AHYs can be aged SY by retained ss after Jan. Also, beware of some AHY/ASYs that may retain adult ss that do not contrast as much with adjacent feathers. HYs in Jun-Sep are separated from SYs by much fresher (retained) flight feathers.**

U/AHY (Nov-Oct): Iris bright orange or red; legs red to purplish red; adult pp covs without white or buff edging; adult ss uniform in shape, color, and wear (Fig. 25B). **Note: In Oct-Dec, only birds molting pp and ss, with unreplaced, dark-edged, adult feathers, can be reliably aged AHY. Birds during this time that have completed molt, showing uniform adult pp and ss, should be aged U.**

Sex—CP & BP are poorly developed and unreliable for sexing; see Family account regarding cloacal examination. ♀ wg(n100) 144-170, tl(n100) 85-120; ♂ wg(n100) 144-175, tl(n100) 95-132; see **Geographic variation**. The width of the black bar on the neck may be useful for sexing some birds (♀ 1.0-3.5 mm, ♂ 2.5-5.5 mm when the neck is in a relaxed position), but this measure varies with the extension of the neck; more study is needed. Otherwise, ♂♂ average brighter purple on the head and brighter iridescence on the neck than ♀♀, but too much overlap occurs for reliable sexing of single birds.

Hybrids reported—African (Ringed) Collared Dove (*Streptopelia roseogrisea* "*risoria*") in captivity.

White-winged Dove

References—Ridgway (1916), Whitman (1919), Bent (1932), Dickey & van Rossem (1938), Goodwin (1967), Cottam & Trefethen (1968), Oberholser (1974), Aldrich (1981), Acosta & Torres (1984), Brown (1989), CWS & USFWS (1991), Swanson & Rappole (1992), Pyle (1995a); H.T. Harper (*in litt.* to the BBL).

MOURNING DOVE
Zenaida macroura

MODO
Species # 3160
Band size: 3A-3B

Species—Nestlings and juvs from White-winged Dove and Zenaida Dove (*Z. aurita*) by uniformly dark ss and gr covs. Zenaida Dove has broad, white tips to the ss, but not the gr covs, visible before fledging. From juv White-tipped Dove by underwing covs gray and p10 without a notch.

Geographic variation—Weak and broadly clinal in N.Am. Subspecies taxonomy follows Aldrich & Duvall (1958); see also Ridgway (1916), Bailey (1923a), Van Tyne & Sutton (1937), Pitelka (1948), Rand & Traylor (1950), Aldrich (1952), Jewett *et al.* (1953), Monroe (1968), Hubbard & Banks (1970), Oberholser (1974). Two other subspecies occur in Mex.

Z.m. marginella (br BC-MI to CA-c.TX, wint to FL): Large; middle toe medium in size (17.5-22.0); upperparts pale brownish with a gray tinge; breast pale wine to pinkish buff; undertail covs pale to moderately pale buff. ♀ wg(n36) 133-154, tl(n10) 117-144; ♂ wg(n100) 139-159, tl(n29) 129-163. The subspecies name *"caurina"* for birds of coastal OR-WA probably was based on an anomalously dark specimen or a form that is no longer extant.

Z.m. carolinensis (br WI-NS to c.TX-FL; wint to NM): Medium in size; middle toe long (18.0-23.0); upperparts dark brown with a slight or no gray tinge; breast dark brown with a ruddy-pink wash; undertail covs moderately rich to rich buff. ♀ wg(n42) 131-146, tl(n15) 114-137; ♂ wg(n90) 134-152, tl(n24) 120-153.

Z.m. macroura (br s.FL Is): Small; middle toe short (16.0-21.5); breast deep wine to fawn; undertail covs medium-dark pinkish buff. ♀ wg(n31) 128-137, tl(n31) 96-111; ♂ wg(n58) 129-144, tl(n58) 112-133. The subspecies *"peninsulari"* of peninsular FL may have been mistakenly named based upon a vagrant *macroura*.

Molt—PB: HY/SY incomplete-complete (Jun-May), AHY complete (Jun-Nov); PA absent? The 1st PB occurs on the summer and/or the winter grounds; the adult PB occurs primarily on the summer grounds. Replacement of pp during the 1st PB begins 1-2 months after hatching, can take 6 months to complete, and proceeds more rapidly during the summer than during the winter. Molting of pp in HY/SYs occurs year-round, but most frequently in Jul-Oct. 1-2 ss (usually among s4-s6) occasionally can be retained during the 1st PB; also, look for occasional retained ss during the adult PBs. See p. 39. Note that HYs hatched in Jan-Mar could have a 2nd complete body molt during their first fall, which might result in some HYs being incorrectly aged AHYs in southern parts of the range. More study is needed on the timing and sequences of molt (after the 1st PB) in birds fledged during the winter. The adult PB occurs earlier in the year in the southeastern portions of the breeding range, completing after 30 Sep in most of the range but as early as 15 Aug south of NC and east of TX. A limited PA may occur in Feb-Apr; more study is needed.

Skull—Pneumaticization patterns possibly are useful for ageing (see Family account), but more study is needed.

Age—Juv (Jan-Dec) is uniformly brown, with buff to whitish edging on all feathers, creating a scaled appearance (Fig. 26), and has uniformly juvenal ss (Fig. 25A); juv ♀ = ♂.

HY/SY (Feb-2nd Jul): One or more unreplaced, juvenal outer pp covs with white or buff edging; unreplaced, juvenal outer pp with fresh, buff inner edges; one or more juvenal middle ss (usually among s4-s6) narrow and worn, contrasting markedly with the adjacent, first-basic (adult) feathers in spring (Fig. 25C). **Note: Beware that in the southern portions of the range and in CA this species can breed year-round (although primarily in spring), which complicates age-code assignment. Only a small percentage of AHYs can be aged SY by retained ss after Mar. Also, beware of some AHY/ASYs that can retain adult ss; these would not contrast as much with adjacent feathers. The last, white-edged pp covs usually are replaced before replacement of p9-p10. In Feb-May, HYs can be distinguished from SYs in the southern part of the range and in CA by the progression of the primary molt. Birds hatched around**

1 Jan drop successive pp on or around the following dates: P1, 1 Feb; P2, 5 Feb; P3, 14 Feb; P4, 23 Feb; P5, 4 Mar; P6, 13 Mar; P7, 26 Mar; P8, 12 Apr; P9, 7 May; P10, 31 May. If replacement of the pp is behind this schedule assume HY; if ahead, assume SY.

U/AHY (Sep-2nd Nov): Pp covs without white or buff edging; unreplaced, adult outer pp dark, without buff edging; adult ss uniform in shape, color, and wear (Fig. 25B). **Note: See HY/SY. In Oct-Nov, only birds molting pp and ss with unreplaced, adult outer pp and middle ss (dark-edged and/or truncate) can be reliably aged AHY. Birds that have completed the molt, showing uniformly adult pp and ss, cannot be aged after 1 Oct, or 15 Aug south of NC and east of TX. Also, evidence of damage to the feet from frostbite can indicate AHY through Nov.**

Sex—CP & BP are poorly developed and unreliable for sexing; see Family account regarding cloacal examination. Tl is useful for sexing within subspecies (see **Geographic variation**): ♀ wg(n100) 131-154, tl(n100) 114-144; ♂ wg(n100) 134-159, tl(n100) 120-163; excludes *Z.m. macroura* (see **Geographic variation**)

♀: Crown and nape brown to grayish brown, sometimes tinged bluish; throat and breast brown or tan, sometimes tinged rose. **Note: The above is reliable for all AHY/ASYs, and molting HY/SYs with ≥ pp replaced; no reliable means are known to sex HY/SY ♀♀ with < 7 pp replaced. Also, a small percentage of intermediates cannot be reliably sexed by plumage alone.**

♂: Crown and nape bluish; throat and breast washed pink or rose. **Note: See ♀. Also, some HY/SY ♂♂ in earlier stages of molt (4-6 pp replaced) can be reliably sexed.**

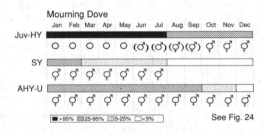

Hybrids reported—At least four other species of doves (including Zenaida Dove) in captivity (see Gray 1958); also, Soccoro Dove (*Z. graysoni*) in captivity.

References—Ridgway (1916), Whitman (1919), Forbush (1927), Bent (1932), Pearson & Moore (1940), Petrides (1950), Thompson (1950), Roberts (1955), Swank (1955), Allen (1963), Hanson & Kossack (1963), Goodwin (1967), Wight *et al.* (1967), Reeves *et al.* (1968), Wood (1969), Sadler *et al.* (1970), Maridon & Holcomb (1971), Zimmerman (1972), Morrison & Lewis (1974), Oberholser (1974), Peterson & Brown (1974), Ault *et al.* (1976), Haas & Amend (1976, 1979), Menasco & Perry (1978), Bivings & Silvey (1981), Armstrong & Noakes (1983), Acosta & Torres (1984), Cannell (1984), Brown (1989), CWS & USFWS (1991), Pyle (1995a), Schulz *et al.* (1995); P.F. Cannell (*in litt.* to the BBL); L.F. Baptista (pers. comm.); IBP (MAPS) data, PRBO data.

INCA DOVE
Columbina inca

INDO
Species # 3210
Band size: 2-3

Species—From Common Ground-Dove by upperparts extensively scalloped; tl long (> 75); outer webs of the outer rects (r6) white.

Geographic variation—No subspecies are recognized, although birds average darker in the southern part of the range (C.Am); see Mueller (1992).

Molt—PB: HY/SY incomplete-complete (Jun-May), AHY/ASY incomplete-complete (Jun-Jan?); PA absent? The 1st PB is protracted, the replacement of the pp, pp covs, and ss typically is not completed until Nov-May; more study is needed on when the earliest HY/SYs can complete the molt. The outermost 1-4 pp and pp covs, and 1-6 ss (among s1-s7) sometimes can be retained during the 1st PB and, occasionally, 1-3 ss (among s1-s7) can be retained during adult PBs. See p. 39. Some birds in Feb-Apr show body molt indicating a possible PA; more study is needed.

Skull—Pneumaticization patterns possibly are useful for ageing (see Family account), but more study is needed.

Age—Juv (Mar-Nov) is uniformly brownish, with pale subterminal spots on the wing covs (Fig. 26), has uniformly juvenal ss (Fig. 25A), and averages less distinct barring to the lower underparts; juv ♀ = ♂. The following month ranges may not apply south of N.Am, where breeding occurs year-round.

HY/SY (May-2nd Aug): Iris grayish or orange (through Nov); unreplaced, juvenal outer pp covs pale rufous with brownish corners (Fig. 30); unreplaced, juvenal inner ss (among s5-s11) with white tips or corners when fresh; outermost 1-4 juvenal pp, and/or 1-6 juvenal ss (usually in a block among s1-s7), retained, contrastingly narrow, pale, and abraded (Fig. 25C). **Note: The emargination on p6-p9 averages shallower on juvenal feathers than on adult feathers, but differences seem slight. Only some AHYs, with retained juvenal feathers, can be aged SY during Mar-Aug.**

U/AHY (Nov-Oct): Iris reddish maroon; adult pp covs uniformly dark rufous with broad, dark brown tips (Fig. 30); inner ss (among s5-s11) uniformly brown; flight-feather molt usually complete by Dec, the adult pp and ss uniform in color and wear (Fig. 25B). **Note: AHYs with uniformly adult flight feathers (Fig. 25B) might be reliably aged ASY through at least Feb, and occasional AHYs with retained adult ss (among s1-s7), perhaps not always in a block, broad, and contrasting with the replaced ss only marginally in wear (Fig. 25D), may be reliably aged ASY through Aug, but more study is needed.**

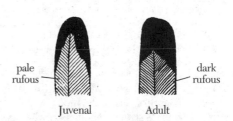

FIGURE 30. The shape and color pattern of the primary coverts by age in *Columbina* doves. Figure from Pyle (1995a)..

Sex—CP & BP are poorly developed and unreliable for sexing. ♀ wg(n29) 88-96, tl(n29) 85-102; ♂ wg(n20) 86-96, tl(n20) 85-103. Examination of the cloaca for conical papillae might be useful in sexing adults (see Family account). Otherwise, no reliable criteria are known for sexing.

Hybrids reported—Scaled Dove (*C. squammata*) in captivity.

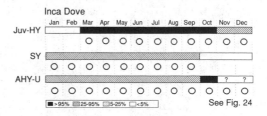

References—Ridgway (1916), Whitman (1919), Bent (1932), Dickey & van Rossem (1938), Goodwin (1967), Oberholser (1974), Tweit (1986a), Mueller (1992), Pyle (1995a); R.S. Crossin (*in litt.* to the BBL); L.F. Baptista, K. Burton (pers. comm.).

COMMON GROUND-DOVE
Columbina passerina

COGD
Species # 3200
Band size: 2

Species—From Inca Dove by upperparts lacking scalloping (adults); tl short (< 75 mm); outer webs of outer rects (r6) primarily brown with white tips. From ♀ Ruddy Ground-Dove by the presence of dark scaling to the head and breast; lesser covs with > 7 dark, copper-colored spots, and scapulars lacking dark spots (Fig. 31); underwing covs chestnut; base of the lower mandible pink or reddish.

Geographic variation—Moderate and ranges in N.Am fairly well defined. Subspecies taxonomy in N.Am follows the AOU (1957); see Ridgway (1916), Schwartz (1970), Oberholser (1974), Buden (1985), Dunn & Garrett (1990). Sixteen other subspecies occur in the W.Indies & Mex-S.Am.

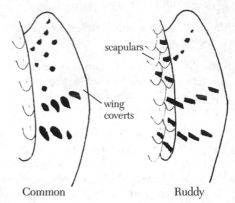

FIGURE 31. Pattern of dark markings on the backs and wing coverts of Common Ground-Dove *vs* ♀ Ruddy Ground-Dove for identification.

C.p. pallescens (br & wint s.CA-c.TX, vag to FL): Plumage medium-pale grayish brown; base of the lower mandible reddish; ♂ with underparts pale pink and nape pale grayish blue; ♀ with scaling of the underparts distinct, but primarily restricted to the throat and head.

C.p. passerina (br & wint e.TX-FL, vag to e.Can): Plumage medium-dark brown; base of the lower mandible yellow, orange-red, or reddish; ♂ with underparts dark pink and nape medium bluish; ♀ with scaling of the underparts indistinct, but extending to the lower breast. Birds of the W.Indies (*bahamensis*), potential vagrants to s.FL, are like *pallescens* in plumage, but average slightly smaller (wg 80-89, tl 53-62) and have the base of the lower mandible dusky reddish to black.

Molt—PB: HY/SY incomplete-complete (Jun-May), AHY/ASY incomplete-complete (Jun-Jan); PA absent. The PBs commence on the summer grounds and complete on the winter grounds. The 1st PB is protracted, the replacement of pp, pp covs, and ss typically is not completed until Nov-May; more study is needed on when the earliest HY/SYs can complete the molt. The outermost 1-4 pp and pp covs, and 1-6 ss (among s1-s7) sometimes can be retained during the 1st PB, and at least 1-3 ss (among s1-s7) occasionally can be retained during adult PBs. See p. 39. Molt can occur year-round in populations south of N.Am.

Skull—Pneumaticization patterns possibly are useful for ageing (see Parkes 1957a, Johnston 1962) but more study is needed.

Age—Juv (Mar-Nov) is uniformly brownish, with the feathers of the upperparts tipped whitish (Fig. 26), gr covs edged cinnamon, and ss uniformly juvenal (Fig. 25A); juv ♂ averages pinker on the breast than juv ♀, but this probably is not reliable for sexing. The following month ranges may not apply south of N.Am, where breeding can occur year-round.

HY/SY (May-2nd Aug): Unreplaced, juvenal outer pp covs pale rufous with brownish corners (Fig. 30); unreplaced, juvenal inner ss (among s5-s11) with white tips or corners when fresh; outermost 1-4 juvenal pp, and/or 1-6 juvenal ss (usually in a block among s1-s7) sometimes retained, contrastingly narrow, pale, and abraded (Fig. 25C). **Note: Only some AHYs, with retained flight feathers, can be aged SY during Mar-Aug. Check also for iris color differences, as in Inca Dove.**

U/AHY (Nov-Oct): Adult pp covs uniformly dark rufous with broad, dark brown tips (Fig. 30); adult inner ss (among s5-s11) uniformly brown; flight-feather molt usually complete by Dec, the adult pp and ss uniform in color and wear (Fig. 25B). **Note: See HY/SY. AHYs with uniformly adult flight feathers (Fig. 25B) might be reliably aged ASY through at least Feb, and some AHYs with retained adult ss (among s1-s7), perhaps not always in a block, broad, and only marginally contrasting with the replaced ss in wear (Fig. 25D), may be reliably aged ASY through Aug, but more study is needed.**

Sex—CP & BP are poorly developed and unreliable for sexing; see Family account regarding cloacal examination. ♀ wg(n35) 82-90, tl(n21) 55-63; ♂ wg(n62) 82-91, tl(n46) 57-66; includes subspecies in N.Am only (see **Geographic variation**).

♀: Hindcrown and nape brown to grayish brown, sometimes tinged bluish; throat and breast brown or tan, sometimes tinged rose; dark spots on the wing covs coppery brown. **Note: In juv-HYs, the above probably is reliable only with HY ♀♀ that have replaced at least p1-p3.**

♂: Hindcrown and nape bluish; throat and breast washed pink or rose; dark spots on wing covs iridescent bluish.

Hybrids reported—Possibly Ruddy Ground-Dove in captivity.

Common Ground-Dove

	Jan	Feb	Mar	Apr	May	Jun	Jul	Aug	Sep	Oct	Nov	Dec
Juv-HY												
				○ ○ ○ (♂)(♂) (♀)(♀) ♀ ♀ ♀								
SY												
	♂ ♂ ♂ ♂ ♂ ♂ ♂ ♂											
AHY-U												
	♂ ♂ ♂ ♂ ♂ ♂ ♂ ♂ ♂ ♂ ♂ ♂											

■ > 95% ▨ 25-95% ▤ 5-25% ☐ < 5%   See Fig. 24

References—Ridgway (1916), Bent (1932), Dickey & van Rossem (1938), Parkes (1957a), Johnston (1962), Goodwin (1967), Oberholser (1974), Foster (1975), Passmore (1984), Dunn & Garrett (1990), Pyle (1995a); D.L. Evans (pers. comm.).

RUDDY GROUND-DOVE
Columbina talpacoti

RUGD
Species # 3201
Band size: 2

Species—♀♀ from Common Ground-Dove by the lack of a scaled appearance to the head and breast; lesser covs with < 7 black spots and scapulars with distinct, black spots (Fig. 31); underwing covs black; lower mandible entirely dark, without pink or reddish color.

Geographic variation—Weak, but ranges fairly well defined. Subspecies taxonomy follows Peters (1937); see Ridgway (1916), Dunn & Garrett (1990). Two other subspecies occur in S.Am. The following distribution in N.Am is presumed, as the identification of few individuals has been confirmed to subspecies.

C.t. eluta (vag/wint to se.CA-sw.NM): Tl possibly shorter; plumage relatively pale; upperparts pale grayish brown (♀) to reddish brown (♂); AHY ♂ with the crown and nape pale grayish and the underparts pinkish with a brown wash; ♀ with a slight or no rufous tinge to the rump. ♀ wg(n8) 80-88, tl(n8) 53-62; ♂ wg(n10) 83-92, tl(n10) 57-67.

C.t. rufipennis (vag/wint to s.TX): Tl possibly longer; plumage relatively dark; upperparts dark brown (♀) to dark rufous (♂); AHY ♂ with the crown and nape pale silvery blue and the underparts deep pinkish to wine-colored; ♀ with the rump sometimes tinged rufous. ♀ wg(n37) 84-92, tl(n37) 55-67; ♂ wg(n53) 84-94, tl(n53) 55-67.

Molt—Apparently follows that of Common Ground-Dove, in general: PB HY/SY incomplete-complete, AHY incomplete-complete, PA absent; but molting occurs year-round, perhaps being suspended only for breeding (which also occurs year-round). Look for retained pp, pp covs, and ss in some AHYs, as in Common Ground-Dove. More study is needed.

Skull—Pneumaticization patterns possibly are useful for ageing (see Johnston 1962) but more study is needed.

Age—Juv (Jan-Dec) is uniformly brownish, with the feathers of the upperparts tipped whitish, gr covs edged pale cinnamon, and ss uniformly juvenal (Fig. 25A); juv ♂ averages ruddier than juv ♀ and the color of the outer web of p9 (see **Sex**) is probably of use in sexing at least some juvs; more study is needed.

HY/SY (May-Apr): Unreplaced, juvenal outer pp covs pale rufous with brownish corners (Fig. 30). **Note: Beware that this species breeds year-round, which complicates age-code assignment. Consider timing of molt when determining age in birds during Jan-Apr. Look also for incomplete ss molt, possibly useful for ageing SYs, as in Common Ground-Dove, through May or later.**

U/AHY (Jul-Jun): Adult outer pp covs uniformly dark rufous with broad, dark brown tips (Fig. 30). **Note: See HY/SY.**

Sex—CP & BP are poorly developed and unreliable for sexing; see Family account regarding cloacal examination. ♀ wg(n45) 80-92, tl(n45) 53-67; ♂ wg(n63) 83-94, tl(n63) 55-67; see **Geographic variation**.

♀: Hindcrown and nape brown to grayish brown; upperparts brown (the rump sometimes tinged rufous); throat and breast grayish brown to brown; webs of the outer pp without rufous. **Note: Beware of juvenile ♂♂ (see above), which can resemble ♀♀. In addition, look for the iris color possibly to be paler in ♀♀ (buff to yellowish) than in ♂♂ (dark reddish to orange), although variation with age also may occur. More study is needed.**

♂: Hindcrown and nape pale blue-gray to silver-gray; upperparts strongly washed rufous; throat and breast strongly washed pinkish brown. **Note: See ♀.**

Hybrids reported—Plain-breasted (*C. minuta*) and Black-winged (*Metriopelia melanoptera*) ground-doves, and possibly Common Ground-Dove, all in captivity.

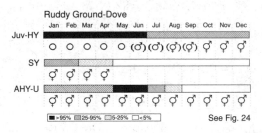

Ruddy Ground-Dove

See Fig. 24

References—Ridgway (1916), Dickey & van Rossem (1938), Snow & Snow (1964), Goodwin (1967), Foster (1975), Cintra (1988), Dunn & Garrett (1990), Patten & Erickson (1994), Howell & Webb (1995).

WHITE-TIPPED DOVE
Leptotila verreauxi

WTDO
Species # 3180
Band size: 3A

Species—Juvs from juv Mourning Dove (which see for separation from Zenaida and White-winged doves) by underwing covs dark rufous; p10 distinctly notched. From Caribbean Dove (*L. jamaicensis*), a possible vagrant to FL, by smaller average wg (133-158, *vs* 146-162 in Caribbean Dove); forehead, throat, and belly darker (less whitish); white tipping to the outer 3-4 rects reduced (*vs* outer 4-5 rects with a greater amount of white in Caribbean Dove).

Geographic variation—Weak to moderate and clinal where ranges meet. Subspecies taxonomy in N.Am follows the AOU (1957); see Ridgway (1916), Bangs & Penard (1922), Dickey & van Rossem (1938), Pitelka (1948). Thirteen other subspecies occur in the W.Indies and Mex-S.Am.

L.v. angelica (res s.TX): From all but two other subspecies (of Mex) by cinnamon on inner webs of ss indistinct and narrow (< 1 mm); from these by smaller size (see **Sex**, *vs* wg 147-153, tl 99-109 in the subspecies of Mex); upperparts paler and grayer; underparts darker pinkish brown and less buffy; undertail covs whitish (*vs* buff in subspecies of Mex).

Molt—Not well known in this species, but probably as in *Columba* pigeons, as follows: PB HY/SY incomplete-complete, AHY incomplete-complete, PA absent; but beware that year-round breeding and molt may occur. Some SYs and probably some ASYs can retain the outermost 1-2 pp and/or 1-5 ss (usually among s4-s9) during the PBs (see p. 39). More study is needed.

Skull—Pneumaticization patterns possibly are useful for ageing (see Family account), but more study is needed.

Age—Juv (May-Oct) averages duller overall, with the ss, scapulars, and wing covs tipped buff to rufous (Fig. 26), pp covs tinged rufous, and ss uniformly juvenal (Fig. 25**A**); juv ♀ = ♂.

HY/SY (Sep-Aug): Unreplaced, juvenal outer pp covs tinged rufous (Sep-Jan?); one or more juvenal outer pp tapered and dull brownish, with pale or rusty edging when fresh; one or more juvenal middle ss (usually among s2-s6) dull brownish and narrow, with whitish or rusty edging when fresh, and contrastingly worn in spring (Fig. 25**C**). **Note: Possible year-round breeding may complicate age-code assignment. HYs in Mar-Jun are separated from SYs by much fresher flight feathers.**

U/AHY (Nov-Oct): Adult outer pp covs uniformly brown; adult pp and ss uniformly grayish and truncate (Fig. 25**B**) or, if in molt, the old adult feathers are grayish and broad, not contrasting markedly with the new feathers in shape, color, and/or wear (Fig. 25**D**). **Note: See HY/SY.**

Sex—CP & BP are poorly developed and unreliable for sexing; see Family account regarding cloacal examination. ♀ wg(n36) 133-153, tl(n27) 95-114; ♂ wg(n41) 140-158, tl(n32) 96-116; includes *L.v. angelica* only (see **Geographic variation**). Otherwise, ♂♂ average brighter purple iridescence on the neck and darker pinkish on the breast than ♀♀, but too much overlap probably occurs for reliable sexing of individuals in the hand.

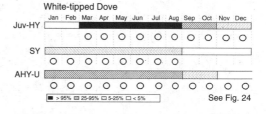

References—Ridgway (1916), Bent (1932), Goodwin (1967), Oberholser (1974), Howell & Webb (1995), Pyle (1995a).

CUCKOOS, ROADRUNNERS, AND ANIS   *CUCULIDAE*

Six species. Family characters include relatively short and broad wings, long tails, and zygodactylous feet (two toes forward and two toes back), with the outer front toe reversed. New World species have 10 primaries (the 10th reduced and the 9th shortened), 10 (to 11 in some roadrunners) secondaries, and 8 (most anis) to 10 rectrices. The first prebasic molt is incomplete to complete, and protracted throughout the winter; a few flight feathers (especially secondaries and rectrices) can occasionally be retained until the second prebasic molt. No prealternate molts occur. Adult molts usually are complete, although some flight feathers can occasionally be retained in cuckoos. Primary coverts are replaced with their corresponding primaries. The sequence of flight-feather replacement is irregular, in cuckoos at least. Primaries are replaced distally from p1 to p4, and proximally from p10 to p5, every other feather often being replaced (*i.e.*, the sequence can be p10-p8-p6-p9-p7-p5). Secondaries are replaced proximally from s6 to s9, and centripetally (inward from the outsides) within s1 to s5. The rectrices also are replaced in an irregular and almost random sequence. Skull pneumaticization probably does not complete; if not, the percentage of completion may be useful for age determination (see Fig. 88; more study is needed). The skin is blackish, however, which makes skulling difficult. Sexes tend to be similar, with measurements showing substantial overlap (averaging larger in females of most species), and brood patches developed by both sexes.

BLACK-BILLED CUCKOO

Coccyzus erythropthalmus

BBCU
Species # 3880
Band size: 2

Species—From Yellow-billed Cuckoo by tl – wg 5-24 mm; inner webs of pp warm brown with little or no rufous; underside of rects primarily gray; outer rects (r2-r5) with black subterminal bands (AHY/ASYs) and small (3-10 mm), relatively indistinct, whitish tips (Fig. 32); orbital ring greenish to dusky (HY), or red (AHY); lower mandible black, sometimes (juvs) with a restricted (< 20%) bluish-gray base; juvs with whitish tipping to the feathers of upperparts; down of nestlings white. Juv from juv Mangrove Cuckoo by the pattern of the rects (Fig. 32); base of bill black or bluish gray.

Geographic variation—No subspecies are recognized.

Molt—PB: HY/SY incomplete-complete (Aug-May), AHY/ASY incomplete-complete (Aug-Mar); PA absent. A presupplemental molt (see p. 16) possibly occurs; otherwise, the 1st PB begins on the summer grounds and resumes on the winter grounds, the replacement of pp, ss, and rects occurring through the winter. Adult PBs occur primarily on the winter grounds. A few ss (often including s3-s4) and rects (rarely 1-2 pp and pp covs) occasionally can be retained during both the 1st and the adult PBs. See p. 39. The sequence of flight-feather replacement is irregular (see Family account).

HY/SY   AHY/ASY

FIGURE 32. The shape and pattern of the outer rectrices (r3-r5) in Black-billed Cuckoo for identification and ageing.

Skull—Pneumaticization patterns possibly are useful for ageing (see Family account), but the skull may be difficult to see through the blackish skin.

Age—Juv (Jun-Sep) has the orbital ring dull greenish and feathers of the upperparts with grayish-white to buff tips; juv ♀ = ♂.

HY/SY (Aug-May): Orbital ring greenish or dusky (through winter); unreplaced juvenal pp covs and ss tipped buff (Fig. 33); unreplaced juvenal rects narrow, tapered, and dull brownish gray, with indistinct or reduced, pale tips on r2-r5 (Fig. 32). **Note: More study is needed on the timing of orbital-ring color changes in winter/spring. Also, on the winter grounds, check for the roof of the mouth (upper mandible lining) color to be gray (possibly with white spots) in HY/SY (through Jan?) and black in AHY/ASY.**

AHY/ASY (Apr-Mar): Orbital ring red; adult pp covs and ss without buff tips (see Fig. 33); adult ss uniform in color and wear (Fig. 25**B**); adult rects uniform in wear, broad, truncate, and dark grayish, with relatively large and distinct, whitish tips on r2-r5 (Fig. 32). **Note: See HY/SY.**

SY/TY (May-Mar): Like AHY/ASY, but 1-5 juvenal ss (among s2-s6) retained, buff-tipped, and contrastingly faded and worn (Fig. 33); and/or 1-3 juvenal rects retained, contrasting with the replaced, first-basic (adult) rects in wear and color (see Fig. 32). **Note: Also, look for some SY/TYs with retained pp and buff-tipped pp covs. Only a small proportion of birds can be aged SY/TY.**

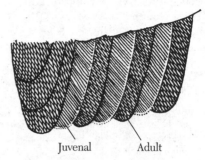

Juvenal   Adult

FIGURE 33. The pattern of retained secondaries in some HY/SY Black-billed and Mangrove cuckoos. Note the buffy tips to the retained juvenal feathers, which can wear off by spring. Similar patterns occur in some AHY/ASYs and in both age groups of Yellow-billed Cuckoos, although the retained feathers lack buffy tips.

ASY/ATY (Apr-Mar): Like AHY/ASY, but 1-3 adult rects retained, contrasting with the replaced, adult rects in wear but not pattern (see Fig. 32). **Note: Beware of birds with adventitiously replaced rects. ASY/ATYs also can retain 1-5 ss (Fig. 25D) that lack buff tips (*cf.* Fig. 33); however, the tips of the juvenal ss on SYs can wear off by Mar, so the presence of older, uniformly brown ss does not necessarily indicate ASY/ATY. The relative wear or position of retained ss may be helpful in ageing some ASY/ATYs (see Yellow-billed Cuckoo).**

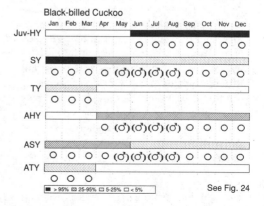

Sex—♀ = ♂ by plumage. The CP is not well developed, but may be useful for sexing some ♂♂ in May-Aug, with experience; the BP, which occurs in both sexes, is unreliable for sexing. ♀ wg(n35) 137-147, tl(n35) 146-167; ♂ wg(n42) 133-144, tl(n42) 142-161.

Hybrids reported—Yellow-billed Cuckoo.

References—Stone (1896), Ridgway (1916), Forbush (1927), Bent (1940), Roberts (1955), Jehl (1959), Wood (1969), Oberholser (1974), Nolan (1975), Parkes (1984), Cramp (1985), Pyle (1995a).

YELLOW-BILLED CUCKOO
Coccyzus americanus

YBCU
Species # 3870
Band size: 2

Species—From Black-billed Cuckoo by tl – wg -5 to 6 mm; inner webs of the pp with substantial rufous; underside of the rects black; outer rects (r2-r5) with wide (14-30 mm) and distinct, white tips (Fig. 34); orbital (eye) ring pale yellow (HY) to gray (AHY); lower mandible bicolored, with > 40% of the base yellow (except some juvs; see **Geographic variation**); juvs without whitish tipping to the feathers of the upperparts; down of nestlings dusky gray. Juv from juv Mangrove Cuckoo by the lack of white tipping to the feathers of the upperparts; pp with extensive rufous; outer rects with distinct and more extensive white to the outer webs (Fig. 34).

Geographic variation—Weak, and clinal in the limited area where the ranges meet. Subspecies taxonomy follows Franzreb & Laymon (1993); see also Ridgway (1916), Todd & Carriker (1922), Swarth (1929), Mees (1970), Oberholser (1974), Banks (1988a, 1990). No other subspecies occur. Note that the following measurement formulae were based upon specimens and may differ, to some extent, on live birds.

> **C.a. occidentalis** (br CA-CO to w.TX): Large; bill averages large (nares to tip 18.1-22.5, upper mandible depth at tip of nares 5.8-7.7); juvs with the lower mandible dark. ♀ wg(n100) 141-159, tl(n53) 137-160; ♂ wg(n100) 136-154, tl(n86) 130-157. The following formulae separate 75-90% of known-sex birds to subspecies: ♀♀, 10.5013 + (wg × -0.0195) + (tl × -0.0268) + (bill nares to tip × -0.1279) + (upper mandible depth at tip of nares × -0.0836) < 0.5; ♂♂, 8.8315 + (wg × -0.0184) + (tl × -0.006) + (bill nares to tip × -0.1606) + (upper mandible depth at tip of nares × 0.2399) < 0.5. In each case *americanus* should be > 0.5.

> **C.a. americanus** (br ND-NB to w.TX-FL): Small; bill averages small (nares to tip 17.3-21.1, upper mandible depth at tip of nares 5.7-7.2); juvs often with a yellow base to the lower mandible. ♀ wg(n100) 135-152, tl(n100) 129-152; ♂ wg(n100) 131-149, tl(n100) 129-148. See *occidentalis* for formulae separating 75-90% of known-sex specimens. Birds of the W.Indies ("*julieni*"), which could occur as vagrants to FL, average smaller and slightly darker, but differences are weak and obscured by individual variation.

Molt—PB: HY/SY incomplete-complete (Aug-May), AHY/ASY incomplete-complete (Sep-Mar); PA absent. A presupplemental molt (see p. 16) possibly occurs; otherwise, the 1st PB begins on the summer grounds and resumes on the winter grounds, the replacement of pp, ss, and rects occurring through winter. Adult PBs occur primarily on the winter grounds. Some ss and rects (and rarely 1-2 pp and pp covs) occasionally can be retained during both the 1st and adult PBs. See p. 39 The sequence of flight-feather replacement is irregular (see Family account).

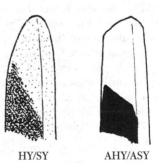

HY/SY   AHY/ASY

FIGURE 34. The shape and pattern of the outer rectrices (r3-r5) in Yellow-billed Cuckoo for identification and ageing.

Skull—Pneumaticization patterns possibly are useful for ageing (see Family account), but the skull may be difficult to see through the blackish skin.

Age—Juv (Jun-Sep) is similar to HY/SY, but has thin, pale tips to the outer gr covs and inner pp, and a duskier (to all dark in *C.a. occidentalis*) base to the lower mandible; juv ♀ = ♂.

HY/SY (Aug-May): Orbital ring pale yellow (through winter); unreplaced juvenal rects tapered and dull blackish to grayish, with the whitish tips to r2-r5 less sharply defined (Fig. 34). **Note:**

On the winter grounds, check for timing of the roof of the mouth (upper mandible lining) and orbital ring color changes (see Species and Black-billed Cuckoo).

AHY/ASY (May-Apr): Orbital ring dusky (sometimes yellow?); adult rects uniform in wear, truncate, and black, with sharply defined white tips on r2-r5 (Fig. 34). **Note: See HY/SY.**

SY/TY (May-Mar): Like AHY/ASY, but 1-3 juvenal rects retained, contrasting with the replaced, first-basic (adult) rects in wear and pattern (see Fig. 34). **Note: See ASY/ATY. Only a small proportion of birds can be aged SY/TY.**

ASY/ATY (Apr-Mar): Like AHY/ASY, but 1-3 adult rects retained, contrasting with the replaced, adult rects in wear but not pattern (see Fig. 34). **Note: Both SY/TYs and ASY/ATYs also can retain 1-5 ss, but distinctions between juvenal and adult feathers are difficult to infer. Relative wear or position of the retained ss may be helpful in ageing some ASY/ATYs. Retained juvenal ss probably average slightly narrower and more tapered than adult ss, and would contrast more markedly with replaced feathers in spring than would retained adult ss (see Fig. 25C–D). More study is needed. Only a small proportion of birds can be aged ASY/ATY.**

Sex—♀=♂ by plumage. The CP is not well developed, but it may be useful for sexing some ♂♂ in Apr-Aug, with experience; the BP, which occurs in both sexes, is unreliable for sexing. ♀ wg(n100) 135-159, tl(n100) 129-160; ♂ wg(n100) 131-154, tl(n100) 129-157; see **Geographic variation**.

Yellow-billed Cuckoo

	Jan Feb Mar Apr May Jun Jul Aug Sep Oct Nov Dec
Juv-HY	
SY	
TY	
AHY	
ASY	
ATY	

■ > 95% ▨ 25-95% ▤ 5-25% ☐ < 5%   See Fig. 24

Hybrids reported—Black-billed Cuckoo.

References—Stone (1896), Ridgway (1916), Forbush (1927), Bent (1940), Roberts (1955), Jehl (1959), Wood (1969), Oberholser (1974), Nolan (1975), Sheppard & Klimkiewicz (1976), Potter (1980), Parkes (1984), Cramp (1985), Banks (1988a, 1988b), Pyle (1995a); E.J. Fisk (*in litt.* to the BBL); IBP (MAPS) data, PRBO data.

MANGROVE CUCKOO
Coccyzus minor

MACU
Species # 3860
Band size: 2

Species—Juv (which lacks the distinct, blackish auricular of adult) from juv Black-billed and Yellow-billed cuckoos by the combination of whitish tipping to the feathers of the upperparts; pp without rufous; pattern of the outer rects (r2-r5) unique (Fig. 35); base of the lower mandible with substantial yellow (> 40%).

Geographic variation—Subspecies taxonomy follows Banks & Hole (1991), who considered the species monotypic (synonymizing up to 13 previously recognized subspecies); see also Ridgway (1916), van Rossem (1934a). Birds from s.FL ("*C.m. maynardi*") may average slightly smaller (see Sex) and paler underparts than other birds, especially "*nesiotes*" and "*continentalis*", which may occur as vagrants to s.FL Is and n.FL-TX, respectively. More study is needed.

Molt—Little known, but molt likely parallels that of Black-billed Cuckoo (which see). In northern, partially migratory birds, the PBs probably commence on the summer grounds and complete on the winter grounds. Molt may occur year-round in resident birds south of N.Am; more study is needed. The sequence of flight-feather replacement is irregular (see Family account).

Skull—Pneumaticization patterns possibly are useful for ageing (see Family account), but the skull may be difficult to see through the blackish skin.

Age—Juv (Jun-Nov?) lacks the distinct, black auricular of non-juvs and has feathers of the upperparts (especially ss and pp covs) tipped buff or cinnamon; juv ♀ = ♂. The following month ranges may not apply south of N.Am, where breeding may occur year-round.

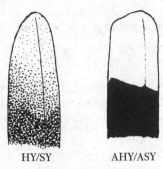

HY/SY   AHY/ASY

FIGURE 35. The shape and pattern of the outer rectrices (r3-r5) in Mangrove Cuckoo for identification and ageing.

HY/SY (Aug-May): Orbital ring dusky (through winter); unreplaced juvenal pp covs and ss tipped buff or cinnamon (see Fig. 33); unreplaced juvenal rects tapered and grayish, with the pale tips of r2-r5 less sharply defined (Fig. 35). **Note: On the winter grounds, check for timing of the roof of the mouth (upper mandible lining) and orbital ring color changes; see Species and Black-billed Cuckoo.**

AHY/ASY (Apr-Mar): Orbital ring yellow; adult ss without buff or cinnamon tips (see Fig. 33) and uniform in color and wear (Fig. 25B); adult rects uniform in wear, truncate, and black, with sharply defined white tips on r2-r5 (Fig. 35). **Note: See HY/SY.**

SY/TY (May-Mar): Like AHY/ASY, but 1-5 juvenal ss (among s2-s6) retained, buff-tipped or cinnamon-tipped, and contrastingly faded and worn (Fig. 33); and/or 1-3 juvenal rects retained, contrasting with the replaced, first-basic (adult) rects in wear and pattern (see Fig. 35). **Note: Also, look for some SY/TYs with retained pp and buff-tipped or cinnamon-tipped pp covs. Only a small proportion of birds can be aged SY/TY.**

ASY/ATY (Apr-Mar): Like AHY/ASY, but 1-3 adult rects retained, contrasting with the replaced, adult rects in wear but not pattern (see Fig. 35). **Note: ASY/ATYs also can retain 1-5 adult ss (Fig. 25D); however, retained ss alone do not necessarily indicate ASY/ATY (see Black-billed Cuckoo).**

Sex—♀ = ♂ by plumage. The CP is not well developed, but it may be useful for sexing some ♂♂ in Apr-Sep, with experience; the BP, which occurs in both sexes, is unreliable for sexing. ♀ wg(n30) 128-145, tl(n30) 147-169; ♂ wg(n30) 127-142, tl(n30) 144-169; measurements are from birds of FL only (see **Geographic variation**).

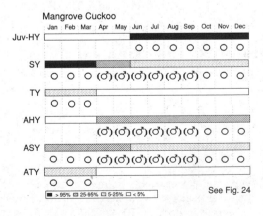

Mangrove Cuckoo

See Fig. 24

References—Ridgway (1916), Bent (1940), Howell & Webb (1995), Pyle (1995a).

GREATER ROADRUNNER
Geococcyx californianus

GRRO
Species # 3850
Band size: 5

Geographic variation—Subspecies taxonomy follows Browning (1990), who considered the species monotypic (synonymizing a previously recognized subspecies); see Oberholser (1974), Browning (1978, 1990), Rea (1983), Hughes (1996). Birds of e.TX-s.AR ("*G.c. dromicus*") may average slightly smaller, darker, and with larger white tips to the outer rects (r3-r5) than western birds, but differences are weak and broadly clinal.

Molt—PB: HY incomplete(?)-complete (Jun-May), AHY incomplete(?)-complete (Jun-May); PA absent(?). Molt in this species is highly irregular and asymmetrical. The PBs possibly suspend over the winter, and body feathers and terts possibly are replaced twice per year (Jun-Oct and Mar-May), in which case a PA would be involved. Juvenal (and probably adult) rects and ss possibly can be retained during the PBs. See p. 39. Adventitious replacement and anomalous retention of flight feathers are common. More study is needed on molts in this species; the sequence of flight-feather replacement possibly follows that of the cuckoos (see Family account).

Skull—Pneumaticization patterns possibly are useful for ageing (see Family account), but the skull may be difficult to see through the blackish skin.

Age—Juv (Apr-Sep) is like HY/SY, but the plumage is loosely textured and white tips of the natal down can be present shortly after fledging; juv ♀ = ♂.

HY/SY (Aug-Jul): Iris brownish to bluish (through Oct?); unreplaced juvenal pp covs dull brownish, with the white tips divided by rounded black shaft streaks (Fig. 36); unreplaced juvenal ss tapered and dull greenish dusky; unreplaced juvenal rects tapered and dull blackish to grayish, with the white tips on r2-r5 indistinctly defined and usually with uneven, straight, or descending borders to the black (Fig. 37). **Note: More study is needed on variation in iris color by age. See also Sex for age-related variation in the color of the orbital apterium.**

AHY/ASY (May-Apr): Iris yellow to orange; unreplaced adult pp covs dark green, with the white tips divided by pointed black shaft streaks (Fig. 36); unreplaced adult ss relatively broad and glossy green; unreplaced adult rects truncate and black, with the white tips on r2-r5 sharply defined, and usually with even and ascending borders to the black (Fig. 37). **Note: See HY/SY. AHYs with uniformly adult flight feathers possibly are reliably aged ASY through**

Juvenal	Adult

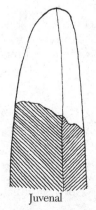 

Juvenal	Adult

FIGURE 36. The shape and color pattern of the outer primary coverts by age in Greater Roadrunner. Figure from Pyle (1995a).

FIGURE 37. The shape and color pattern of the outer rectrices (r3-r5) by age in Greater Roadrunner. Figure from Pyle (1995a).

Apr, but confirmation is needed. Some AHYs appear to retain one or more, very abraded, juvenal ss among two generations of adult ss (see Fig. 121D); these possibly are aged SY/TY through Jul, but more study is needed.

Sex—♀ = ♂ by plumage. The CP is not well developed, but it may be useful for sexing some ♂♂ in Feb-Aug, with experience; the BP, which occurs in both sexes, is unreliable for sexing. ♀ wg(n21) 162-195, tl(n21) 260-305; ♂ wg(n27) 164-196, tl(n27) 268-316.

  ♀: Orbital apterium (Fig. 38) bluish (HY) to bluish white (AHY). **Note: Age birds before sexing. HYs of both sexes can have bluish apteria in Jun-Aug and are not reliably sexed. Also, some intermediate AHYs (~20-25%, with experience) cannot be reliably sexed by apterium color alone (although they may be SY ♂♂).**

  ♂: Orbital apterium (Fig. 38) bluish (juv), bluish white (HY), or white (AHY). **Note: See ♀.**

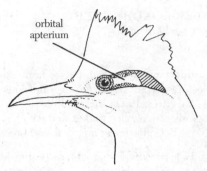

FIGURE 38. The orbital apterium in Greater Roadrunner. The color of the apterium is useful in ageing and sexing (see text).

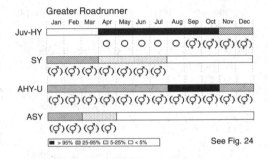

References—Ridgway (1916), G.M. Sutton *in* Bent (1940), Muller (1971), Oberholser (1974), Whitson (1975), Folse & Arnold (1976), Collins (1979), Pyle (1995a), Hughes (1996).

SMOOTH-BILLED ANI
Crotophaga ani

SBAN
Species # 3830
Band size: 3A

Species—From Groove-billed Ani by longer wg (141-161; see **Sex**); culmen of AHY extends above the forehead (Fig. 39); bill depth at the tip of the nares 17-21 (juv) to 20-25 (AHY); upper mandible smooth, occasionally with a few shallow creases on AHYs (Fig. 39; see **Age**); head and nape feathers with brownish-bronze edging, contrasting with the glossy-greenish edging of the back feathers.

Geographic variation—No subspecies are recognized.

Molt—PB: HY incomplete(?)-complete (May-Apr), AHY complete (Jun-Apr); PA absent. The 1st PB can complete by Dec or be protracted and suspended over the winter; in occasional birds, some flight feathers possibly are retained until the 2nd PB. The adult PB usually completes in fall, but replacement of a few flight feathers can be suspended until spring. Molts may vary substantially south of N.Am, where breeding can occur year-round. More study is needed on molts in this species; the sequence of flight-feather replacement possibly follows that of the cuckoos (see Family account).

Skull—Pneumaticization patterns possibly are useful for ageing (see Family account), but the skull may be difficult to see through the blackish skin.

Juvenile   AHY ♀   AHY ♂

FIGURE 39. The shape of the upper mandible by age and sex in Smooth-billed Ani. See text for measurements.

Age—Juv (Apr-Sep) has a small bill (depth at tip of nares 17-21 mm) dull black plumage with little or no glossy coloration, and a relatively flat culmen (Fig. 39); juv ♀ = ♂.

HY/SY (Jun-2nd Aug): Body plumage mixed dull and glossy black (through Nov; occasionally through 2nd Aug); one or more juvenal flight feathers retained and brownish black to brown, contrasting with the glossier black or purplish, replaced first-basic (adult) feathers; unreplaced juvenal rects tapered (Fig. 40). **Note: HYs in Jun-Aug are separated from SYs by much fresher flight feathers. Some SYs in May-Aug should be primarily glossy with a few retained juvenal flight feathers and (occasionally) body feathers; beware of molting adults, which also can show fairly well-marked contrasts between feather generations in summer. HY/SYs also average shallower bills than AHY/ASYs although this varies by sex, as well (see Sex).**

U/AHY (Dec-Nov): Body and flight feathers uniformly adult and glossy black or purplish; flight feathers uniformly glossy in color and wear; rects truncate (Fig. 40). **Note: The second-basic (adult) rects of SY/TYs (Sep-Aug) may average more tapered than those of ASY/ATYs (being intermediate in shape between juvenal and adult; Fig. 40); more study is needed.**

AHY/ASY (May-Apr): Like U/AHY, but one or more (unreplaced) adult pp, ss, and/or rects retained, dull glossy black, and truncate, contrasting with adjacent feathers but not nearly to the extent of the retained, brownish juvenal feathers in HY/SY. **Note: Only a small proportion of adults show this pattern and are reliably aged AHY/ASY.**

Sex—♀ = ♂ by plumage. The CP is not well developed, but it may be useful for sexing some ♂♂ in Feb-Aug, with experience; the BP, which occurs in both sexes, is unreliable for sexing. ♀ wg(n40) 141-156, tl(n25) 166-201; ♂ wg(n44) 142-161, tl(n44) 161-199.

AHY ♀: Bill depth at the tip of the nares 20-23 mm (Fig. 39). **Note: Bill depth is reliable for sexing AHYs only (i.e., HYs in Jun-Dec should not be sexed). Birds with a bill depth of 23 mm can be sexed ♀ if AHY/ASY (Jun-May), or ♂ if SY (Jan-May).**

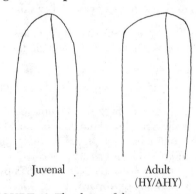

Juvenal   Adult
                          (HY/AHY)

FIGURE 40. The shape of the outer rectrices (r3-r5) by age in Anis.

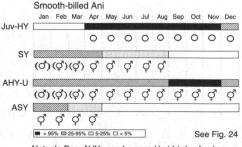

Note: In Dec, AHYs can be sexed but birds of unknown age should be left unsexed.

AHY ♂: Bill depth at the tip of the nares 23-28 mm (Fig. 39). **Note: See AHY ♀.**

References—Ridgway (1916), Bent (1940), Snow & Snow (1964), Balch (1979), Pyle (1995a).

GROOVE-BILLED ANI   GBAN
Crotophaga sulcirostris   Species # 3840
                                                        Band size: 3B

Species—From Smooth-billed Ani by shorter wg (126-157; see **Sex**); culmen not extending above the forehead (Fig. 41); bill depth at the tip of the nares 12-16 (juv) to 16-20 (AHY); upper mandible with grooves (Fig. 41; see **Age**); head and nape feathers with glossy-bluish edging, uniform in color with the edging of the back feathers.

Geographic variation—Weak, but ranges fairly well defined. Subspecies taxonomy follows the AOU (1957); see Bangs & Penard (1921a). No other subspecies occur.

   C.s. pallidula (vag to AZ, probably CA): Glossy green color on edges of feathers pale and dull; feather centers dusky or grayish.
   C.s. sulcirostris (res s.TX, vag to MN-VA): Glossy green color on edges of feathers bright; feather centers black.

Molt—PB: HY incomplete(?)-complete (May-Apr), AHY complete (Jun-Apr); PA absent. The 1st PB can complete by Dec or be protracted and suspended over the winter; some flight feathers possibly are retained until the 2nd PB. The adult PB usually completes in fall, but replacement of a few flight feathers can be suspended until spring. Molts may vary substantially south of N.Am, where breeding may occur year-round. More study is needed; the sequence of flight-feather replacement possibly follows that of the cuckoos (see Family account).

Skull—Pneumaticization patterns possibly are useful for ageing (see Family account), but the skull may be difficult to see through the blackish skin.

Age—Juv (Apr-Sep) has a small bill (depth at tip of nares 12-16), brownish-black plumage with little or no glossy bluish, and a relatively flat and ungrooved culmen (Fig. 41A); juv ♀ = ♂.

   HY/SY (Jun-2nd Aug): Body plumage mixed brownish and bluish black (through Nov; occasionally through 2nd Jun); one or more flight feathers dull black or brownish, contrasting with the bluish-black, replaced feathers; unreplaced juvenal rects tapered (Fig. 40); upper mandible with < 4 shallow grooves, not reaching the cutting edge (Fig. 41A–B). **Note: HYs in Jun-Aug are separated from SYs by much fresher flight feathers. Some SYs in May-Aug should be primarily bluish black, with a few retained and very worn juvenal flight feathers and (occasionally) body feathers; beware of molting adults, which also can show fairly well-marked contrasts between feather generations in summer.**

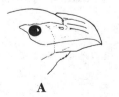   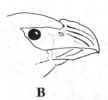   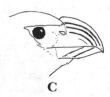

   A   **B**   **C**

FIGURE 41. The shape and grooving pattern of the upper mandible by age and sex in Groove-billed Ani. See text for details and measurements.

AHY/ASY (May-Apr): All feathers and pp black; unreplaced adult rects truncate (Fig. 40); upper mandible with ≥ 4 deep grooves, reaching and forming serrations along the cutting edge (Fig. 41B–C). **Note: Occasional AHY/ASYs can show a few retained adult flight feathers, and the second-basic rects of SY/TYs (Sep-Aug) may average more tapered than those of ASY/ATYs (see Smooth-billed Ani).**

Sex— ♀ = ♂ by plumage. The CP is not well developed, but it may be useful for sexing some ♂♂ in Feb-Aug, with experience; the BP, which occurs in both sexes, is unreliable for sexing. ♀ wg(n45) 126-142, tl(n45) 159-186; ♂ wg(n42) 131-157, tl(n42) 160-197.

AHY ♀: Bill depth at the tip of the nares 16-19 mm (Fig. 41B–C). **Note: Only a proportion of AHYs can be reliably sexed by bill depth; HYs in May-Dec probably are not reliably sexed (without further study). Birds with a bill depth of 18-19 mm can be sexed ♀ if ASY, and ♂ if SY (Jan-May), but are not reliably sexed in most AHYs.**

AHY ♂: Bill depth at the tip of the nares 18-21 mm (Fig. 41C). **Note: See AHY ♀.**

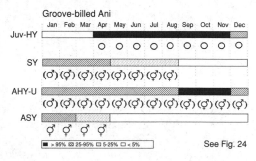

Note: See note under the graph for Smooth-billed Ani

References—Ridgway (1916), Bangs & Penard (1921a), Dickey & van Rossem (1938), Bent (1940), Roberts (1955), Oberholser (1974), Foster (1975), Vehrencamp (1978, 1985), Balch (1979), Vehrencamp *et al.* (1986), Pyle (1995a).

BARN-OWLS   *TYTONIDAE*

One species. Family characters include unique, heart-shaped faces, serrated flanges to the middle toes (AHYs), p10 > p8, and outer > inner rectrices. Barn-owls have 10 primaries (the 10th full in length), 14 secondaries, and 12 rectrices. The "juvenal" body plumage consists of a second downy stage. Adult prebasic molts are incomplete, the juvenal secondaries, primaries, and rectrices being replaced in three to five years. No prealternate molts occur. The replacement of primary coverts, usually occurs with their corresponding primaries. Subspecies and sexes differ by plumage, on average, although there is age-related overlap. An external cloacal protuberance apparently does not develop; however, brood patches are developed by females. Females average larger than males.

BARN OWL
Tyto alba

BNOW
Species # 3650
Band size: 6-7A Lock-on

Geographic variation—Weak to moderate and complicated by sex-specific variation; ranges are poorly to fairly well defined. Subspecies taxonomy in N.Am follows the AOU (1957); see Ridgway (1914), Dickey & van Rossem (1938), Parkes & Phillips (1978), Cramp (1985), Baker (1993). About 33 other subspecies occur worldwide, nine in the New World.

> **T.a. pratincola** (br & wint throughout the range in N.Am): Larger than other New World subspecies (see Sex); ss not whitish or conspicuously lighter than the rest of the wing; plumage medium in coloration (dark *vs* light) by sex (see Sex); dusky spots on the outer pp average larger by age (see **Age**). Pacific coast birds may average smaller and with upperparts darker, but distinction to subspecies has not been documented.

Molt—PB: HY partial (May-Nov), AHY incomplete (Jun-Oct); PA absent. The 1st PB occurs in the nest, the downy juvenal body plumage (but no wing coverts) being replaced. Limited body molt can occur year-round, but replacement of most body feathers and flight feathers occurs primarily on the summer grounds. The 2nd PB usually includes 1-3 pp (p6, p6-p7, or, less commonly, p5-p7), 2-8 ss (s12-s13 or s11-s14, occasionally other ss including s2 and/or s9-s10, and rarely s5), and all (usually), some (occasionally), or no (rarely) rects. The 3rd PB usually includes 2-7 pp around those previously replaced (usually among p4-p8, less commonly among p2-p10), and 6-10 ss among those not previously replaced, often leaving one or more of s1, s3-s4, and/or s7-s8 as juvenal feathers. Subsequent PBs are irregular, resulting in mixed patterns of wing-feather generations (see Fig. 48G-H). Replacement patterns of pp and ss can lack symmetry, especially after the 3rd and subsequent PBs. The PBs after the 2nd usually include all rects. Replacement of pp covs probably coincides with their pp, but contrasts in wear and pattern are difficult to detect. Tropical forms of Barn Owl can replace more flight feathers per year. See p. 67 for more details on molt in owls.

Skull—Pneumaticization patterns possibly are useful for ageing (see *Strigidae* Family account), but more study is needed.

Age—Juv plumage (Jan-Dec) consists of a second grayish white downy stage, ($♀ = ♂$); mesoptile down can remain on HYs (especially on the lower underparts) through Nov. Beware that breeding occurs year-round, complicating age-code assignment. The following talon flange measurements (see Fig. 43) are from European forms of Barn Owl; values for birds in N.Am need confirmation.

HY/SY (Jan-2nd Sep): Juvenal pp, ss, and rects uniform in shape, wear, and pattern, without contrasts between adjacent feathers (see Fig. 48A); numbers of bars on the pp, ss, and rects relatively large, and distances between adjacent bars on these feathers relatively small (Table 1,

Fig. 42; see also Figs. 61-63); outer pp, ss, and rects relatively narrow (Fig. 42; see also Figs. 49 & 61-62); talon flange < 1.5 mm wide and smooth in May-Jan, to 1.5 (♂) or 2 (♀) mm wide and slightly serrated in Nov-Aug (Fig. 43A–B). **Note: HYs in Jan-Sep (more often May-Sep) are separated from SYs by much fresher flight feathers and relative talon flange width and condition. Also, some birds (especially in southern N.Am) can hatch and fledge in Oct-Dec and technically are SY/TYs, but this appears rare (<5% of all birds), so it probably is best to assume birds in this plumage are HY/SYs; the same assumption can be made regarding older age-code assignments.**

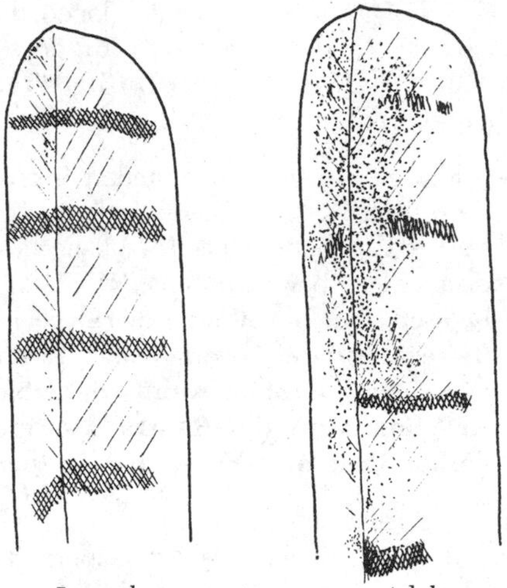

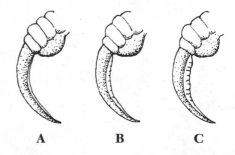

FIGURE 42. The shape and barring pattern of the outer rectrices (r6) by age in Barn Owl. See also Table 1. Substantial variation occurs within both age groups. Figure from Pyle (1997b).

SY/TY (Oct-Sep): P6, p6-p7, or p5-p7 (rarely no pp; see above) **and** 1-7 ss (among s2 and/or s9-s14; rarely s5) adult, glossier, broader, fresher, more mottled, and showing wider bar patterns (Table 1; see also Figs. 61-62), contrasting with all other wing feathers juvenal and uniformly more faded, narrow, worn, less mottled, and showing narrower bar patterns (Table 1, see Fig. 48**B–C**); rects uniformly adult, broad, and fresh, or mixed with some to (rarely) all, more worn and tapered, juvenal rects (Fig. 42); middle talon flange > 2.0 (♀) or > 1.5 (♂) mm, moderately wide, and serrated (Fig. 43**B**). **Note: See HY/SY regarding birds hatched and/or fledged in Oct-Dec. SY/TYs should be aged only if both pp and ss patterns coincide, although birds with all pp juvenal (but ss patterns as above) can be reliably aged. It is possible that second-basic feathers show bar patterns which are intermediate between juvenal and adult feathers, probably closer to adult; more study is needed.**

ASY/ATY (Oct-Sep) Pp and ss with contrasts present but in irregular patterns, including varying numbers and positions of new and old feathers (see Fig. 48**D–H**), and not representing the patterns found in SY/TY; rects uniformly adult, broad, and with few bars (Fig. 42); middle talon flange deeply serrated (Fig. 43**C**). **Note: See SY/TY. Birds with moderately worn, first-basic p6, p6-p7, or p5-p7, surrounded by 2-5 contrastingly fresh, adult pp (among p2-p5 and p7-p10), with the remaining 2-7 pp juvenal and contrastingly narrow, faded, and worn; and the ss also showing three generations, with 2-7 feathers (among s2-s11) contrastingly fresh, and 1-5 ss (among s1, s3-s4, and s7-s8) still juvenal and very worn (see Molt and Fig. 48D–F), probably are reliably aged TY/4Y, with experience. Also, those with irregular patterns (not as above) may be reliably aged ATY/A4Y, but confirmation is needed. It is possible that some ATY/A4Ys may coincidentally show replacement patterns like SY/TYs or TY/4Ys, and are best aged AHY/ASY or ASY/ATY. More study is needed.**

FIGURE 43. The width and degree of serration on the talon flange by age in Barn Owl. See text for details. Figure from Pyle (1997b).

Sex—The CP apparently is not developed; the BP (Mar-Jul, Jan-Dec in southern birds) is reliable for sexing ♀♀, but the lack of a BP does not necessarily indicate ♂♂. ♀ wg(n100) 312-357, tl(n100) 126-157; ♂ wg(n100) 310-345, tl(n100) 123-153; see **Geographic variation.** See Dieter (1973) for sexing using analyses of plasma steroid hormones.

♀: Plumage averages darker; underparts usually > 50% rich buff, with few to many large (> 2 mm) flecks; feathers lateral to the facial ruff pale buff to tawny; face above the eye usually washed dark buff; middle talon flange averages wider by age (Fig. 43; see **Age**); bill pale with dusky edges (beware of some HY/SY ♂♂ with this bill pattern). **Note: The above should not be used alone or without experience, as there is substantial overlap (>20%, with experience); combine with Geographic variation, Age (juv-HY/SYs average darker than AHY/ASYs), and feather wear.**

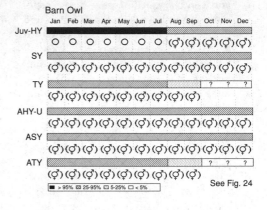

♂: Plumage averages paler; underparts white or with < 50% pale buff, and with few to no large flecks; feathers lateral to the facial ruff white to pale buff; face above the eye usually white; middle talon flange averages narrower by age (see **Age**); bill of AHYs uniformly pale. **Note: See ♀.**

References—Ridgway (1914), Forbush (1927), Sumner (1933), Bent (1938), Dickey & van Rossem (1938), Roberts (1955), Stresemann & Stresemann (1966), Oberholser (1974), Parkes & Phillips (1978), Lenton (1984), Cramp (1985), Marti (1990), Johnson (1991), Baker (1993), Taylor (1993), Pyle (1997b).

Incomplete Molts and Ageing in Owls

Flight-feather molt patterns in owls vary substantially among genera and individuals. Certain species replace all flight feathers during the second prebasic molt, whereas in others, up to five or six years are needed to renew all primaries and secondaries. The extents of the third and subsequent prebasic molts also can vary, from only a few to all primaries and secondaries replaced, depending on the species. Among the 19 North American species, nine have incomplete primary replacement in adults, these and four other species show incomplete secondary replacement, and in six species replacement of primaries and secondaries usually is complete. The rectrices typically are replaced partially or completely during the second prebasic molt and completely during subsequent molts, although in certain species replacement can occur every other year, beginning with the third prebasic molt.

Primary and secondary replacement follows predictable patterns; thus, assuming that juvenal and adult feathers can be distinguished, replacement patterns can be used for precise ageing of owls, in certain species up to SY/TY, and possibly even to TY/4Y (see Figs. 48 & 64-66). In many species the first replacement of primaries is irregular, proceeding centrifugally (in both directions) from p6 or p7, and at the same time or later proceeding distally from p1. Thus the last primaries replaced typically are among p2-p5 (see Fig. 48). Secondaries are replaced in a sequence similar to other near-passerines (see p. 39), except that two or more molt centers may exist among the outer feathers. Thus, secondary replacement commences with the tertials and can conclude with

TABLE 1. Numbers of bars and measurements between bars (see footnotes) on p9, s1, r1, and r6, of juvenal and adult North American owls. Counts and measurements are based on full dark bars in Barn, Great Horned, and Long-eared owls and on pale bars (not including the tip) in Spotted and Barred owls. Sample sizes were 20 for all values. Ranges for measurments indicate 95% confidence intervals (see Fig. 3). See also Figs. 42, 49, 58, and 62-64; Barrows et. al (1982) and Carpenter (1992) provided more on tail barring in *Strix* owls. This table is taken from Pyle (1997b).

Species		Primary 9 number[1]	Primary 9 distance[2]	Secondary 1 distance[3]	Rectrix 1 number[4]	Rectrix 6 distance[5]
Barn Owl	Juvenal	3-5	58-84	42-63	3-4	51-72
	Adult	2-4	72-117	53-95	2-4	67-97
Great Horned Owl	Juvenal	6-8	65-98	61-85	6-8	58-85
	Adult	4-7	78-146	72-103	5-6	79-123
Spotted Owl	Juvenal	5-6	75-122	58-86	5-7	66-83
	Adult	4-6	117-142	75-99	3-6	80-97
Barred Owl	Juvenal	4-5	78-113	88-120	4-6	96-104
	Adult	3-4	108-150	97-150	3-5	110-155
Long-eared Owl	Juvenal	6-8	55-82	26-40	6-8	28-39
	Adult	5-7	70-100	38-55	5-7	37-49

[1] Number of dark or pale (see above) bars between the tips of the pp coverts and the tip of p9.
[2] Distance from the tip of p9 to the proximal (lower) edge of the 4th (Great Horned, Spotted, and Long-eared owl), 3rd (Barred Owl) or 2nd (Barn Owl) dark or pale (see above) bar on the outer web, where the bar meets the feather shaft.
[3] Distance from the tip of s1 to the proximal (lower) edge of the 4th (Great Horned, Spotted, Barred, and Long-eared owl) or 2nd (Barn Owl) dark or pale (see above) bar on the outer web, where the bar meets the feather shaft.
[4] Number of dark or pale (see above) bars between the tips of the uppertail coverts and the tip of r1.
[5] Distance from the tip of r6 to the proximal (lower) edge of the 4th (Great Horned, Spotted, Barred, and Long-eared owl) or 3rd (Barn Owl) dark or pale (see above) bar on the inner web, where the bar meets or comes closest to the feather shaft. Some adult Greated Horned and Barn owl feathers have fewer bars than indicated and this distance thus cannot be measured.

s1, s3-s4, and/or s7-s8 (see Fig. 48), depending, in part, on the number of secondaries present in each species. During subsequent molts the sequence of replacement of both primaries and secondaries can be irregular; in some species replacement is complete or nearly so, whereas in others, individual feathers or pairs from several molt series along the wings are renewed in a given year. As in near-passerines in general (see p. 39) patterns of feather generations more often are symmetrical after the first prebasic molt than after subsequent molts.

Newer primaries and secondaries of owls can be distinguished from older feathers by carefully looking for contrasts in age, wear, and luster. In the Barn and Snowy owls, newer flight feathers tend to be whiter than older ones, whereas in the other species, newer feathers are darker and have a pinkish wash (when fresh) that juvenal feathers lack, except when extremely fresh. In many species of owls, juvenal flight feathers average narrower and more tapered at the tip than adult feathers (see Figs. 42, 49-53 & 60-62). Juvenal feathers, especially outer primaries, tertials, and rectrices, that are retained for more than one year, also tend to be more worn and frayed than adult feathers. In many owl species, juvenal flight feathers have paler and less mottled base coloration (especially at the feather tips), and narrower, more abundant, and more distinct, dark and light barring than adult feathers (Table 1; see also Figs. 42, 47, 49-50, 52-53, 57-58, 60, & 61-63). The light markings on the primary coverts of many species tend to be smaller and rounder on juvenal feathers, vs larger, squarer, or more bar-like on adults (see Fig. 57). Relative differences in each of these criteria vary substantially among owl species, there often is overlap between age groups in flight-feather shape and wear, and distinctions can be difficult to determine, especially when feathers are very fresh or very worn. With practice, however, juvenal and adult feathers often can be distinguished by combining feather shape, wear, and color pattern. See Pyle (1997b) for more details.

Most owls will show patterns of wing-feather replacement that allow confident age-code assignment; however, many individuals can show patterns that are anomalous or ambiguous. Some birds show primary replacement suggesting one age and secondary replacement suggesting another. Individual variation also will be found within age groups, the most advanced individuals of one age group possibly overlapping in patterns with the slowest individuals of another. For these reasons, age codes in owls should be assigned conservatively in ambiguous cases, or when primary and secondary replacement indicate different ages. As with near-passerines in general (see p. 39), much of the information on molts presented in the following accounts on owls is based upon specimen examination, and further confirmation is needed based on study of live, known-age, captive, or marked individuals.

TYPICAL OWLS   *STRIGIDAE*

Eighteen species. Family characteristics include large heads and eyes, soft plumage, strong feet, p8 > p10, and inner > outer rectrices. Owls have 10 primaries (the 10th shortened to full in length), 11-17 secondaries, and 12 rectrices. Juvenal body feathers are downy or down-like in many species. The first prebasic molt is partial, and adult prebasic molts are highly variable, wing-feather replacement fully completing in one to six years or more, depending on the species and individual. Primaries 3-4 and secondaries 1, 3-4, and 7-8 usually are the last juvenal feathers replaced (see p. 67). Primary coverts typically may be replaced with their corresponding primaries, although more study is need to confirm this. Limited prealternate molts possibly occur in two species, but otherwise these are absent. Ageing in many species (up to SY/TY and ASY/ATY in certain cases) can be accomplished through the examination of molt patterns (see p. 67). On species with complete, second prebasic molts, the presence of fault bars (see Fig. 18) can be used, with experience, to age a proportion of HY/SYs. Pneumaticization typically does not complete in the larger species (possibly in the smaller species), but the percentage of completion may be useful for ageing (see Fig. 88); more study is needed. Iris color can be useful in ageing the larger species (and possibly certain of the smaller species), especially females. External cloacal protuberances apparently are not developed; however, brood patches are developed by females. Females are larger than males in most species (see Earhart and Johnson 1970). Females also average darker and redder in coloration than males, although this generally is slight, varies with age and geography, and is unreliable for sexing in most species.

FLAMMULATED OWL   FLOW
Otus flammeolus   Species # 3740
                                                          Band size: 3-3B-2

Species—From the scops-owl complex of Eurasia (*O. scops* & *O. sunia*), individuals of which have occurred as vagrants to AK, by smaller size (wg 124-138, tl 56-67; see **Sex**); shorter ear tufts; different wing morphology (p7 > p9 and p10 ≤ p5, *vs* p7 < p9 and p10 ≥ p5 in scops-owls); outer web of p7-p8 emarginated (*vs* not emarginated); iris brown (*vs* yellow in scops-owls). From the screech-owls of N.Am by smaller wg (122-145; see **Sex**); p10 > ss; toes naked (*cf*. Fig. 47); iris brown. Although dichromatic (or at least highly variable in plumage color) over much of its range, Flammulated Owl lacks a real red plumage, as is present in scops-owls and most screech-owls.

Geographic variation—Weak, clinal where ranges meet, and differences are obscured by individual variation in plumage. Subspecies taxonomy follows Marshall (1997); see also Willett (1912), Ridgway (1914), Griscom (1935), Moore & Peters (1939), Phillips (1942a), Phillips *et al.* (1964), Marshall (1967, 1978), Monson & Phillips (1981), Hekstra (1982), Rea (1983), Browning (1989, 1990). One other subspecies occurs in Mex. In addition to the following, birds in N.Am average larger and less reddish (see **Species**) than birds in Mex.

> *O.f. idahoensis* (br s.BC-w.ID to s.CA): Plumage averages paler brownish; facial discs indistinctly defined and washed reddish or grayish; streaking of the underparts dusky or reddish, and narrow (narrower than the pale basal areas). Birds of interior BC-ne.CA ("*borealis*") may average larger, darker, and duller, but differences are slight and obscured by individual variation.
> *O.f. frontalis* (br s.ID-CO to AZ-w.TX): Plumage averages darker grayish; facial discs well defined and washed dusky; streaking of the underparts blackish and wide (wider than the pale basal areas).

Molt—PB: HY partial (Jul-Oct), AHY incomplete-complete (Jun-Oct); PA absent. The PBs occur on the summer grounds, but look for occasional suspension of molt over fall migration, as in scops-owls. The 1st PB includes all body feathers but no wing covs. The 2nd PB includes most (possibly to all) flight feathers; 0-3 pp (among p2-p5) and 2-5 ss (among s1-s8: often s1, s3-s4, and/or s7) usu-

69

ally, if not always, are retained. Adult PBs vary from incomplete to complete, with 0-2 pp (among p2-p5) and 0-6 ss (among s1-s8) retained. See p. 67 for details on molt in owls, in general.

Skull—Pneumaticization patterns possibly are useful for ageing (see Family account).

Age—Juv (Jun-Sep) has loosely textured or downy feathers, upperparts barred rather than streaked, and the facial pattern of adult lacking (tips of down can remain on HYs after fledging); juv ♀ = ♂.

HY/SY (Sep-Aug): Juvenal flight feathers uniform in coloration and wear; no flight-feather molt occurring in Jul-Oct; outer pp (p7-p10) relatively narrow, tapered at the tips (Fig. 44), and worn; outer web of the outer pp covs usually with small rounded spots (see Fig. 57). **Note: Some birds are intermediate, and best aged U/AHY (with uniform flight feathers) or AHY/ASY (with mixed flight feathers).**

AHY/ASY (Sep-Aug): Adult flight feathers uniform in coloration and wear; flight-feather molt usually occurring in Jul-Oct; outer pp (p7-p10) relatively broad, truncate at the tips (Fig. 44), and fresh; outer webs of outer pp covs usually with relatively large and squared spots (see Fig. 57). **Note: See HY/SY. AHY/ASYs with this pattern possibly are reliably aged ASY/ATY, if the 2nd PB rarely or never is complete; more study is needed.**

SY/TY (Sep-Aug): Like AHY/ASY, but 2-5 juvenal ss (among s1-s8: typically 2 or more of s1, s3-s4, and/or s7-s8) and occasionally some inner pp (among p2-p5 and their corresponding pp covs) retained, contrastingly narrow, faded, and abraded (see Fig. 64).

ASY/ATY (Sep-Aug): Like SY/TY, but retained ss and pp (and probably pp covs) broader, not as contrastingly worn and abraded, more often lacking symmetry between the wings, and usually showing different replacement patterns (see Fig. 64).

Sex— ♀ = ♂ by plumage. The CP apparently is not developed; the BP (Mar-Oct) is reliable for sexing ♀♀. ♀ wg(n48) 124-145, tl(n21) 58-67; ♂ wg(n100) 122-138, tl(n30) 56-64.

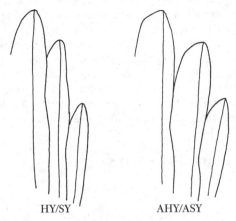

HY/SY   AHY/ASY

FIGURE 44. The shape of the outer primaries (p7-p10) in certain species of owls. Note that many intermediates will be difficult to distinguish. The primary tips on juvs tend to be broad, like those of adults, acquiring the narrower shape of HY/SY through wear. Figure from Pyle (1997b).

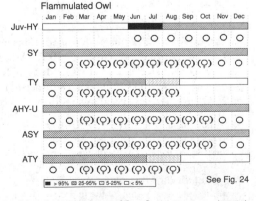

References—Ridgway (1914), Bent (1938), Hubbard (1965a), Hubbard & Crossin (1974), Oberholser (1974), Phillips *et al.* (1964), Marshall (1967, 1978), Richmond *et al.* (1980), Bloom (1983), Reynolds & Linkhart (1984, 1987), Cramp (1985), McCallum (1994), Pyle (1997b); F.R. Gehlbach (*in litt.* to the the BBL).

EASTERN SCREECH-OWL
Otus asio

EASO
Species # 3730
Band size: 5

Species—Polychromatic, with gray, intermediate, and red plumages; but beware that colors can change from gray or red to brown with wear and, for specimens, with time. From Flammulated Owl by larger wg (134-181; see **Geographic variation & Sex**); toes partially feathered (see Fig. 47); p10 < ss; iris yellow. Gray-plumaged birds from brown-plumaged Western Screech-Owl (with caution) by lower flank feathers with narrow central streaks and irregular crossbars (Fig. 45A–B); base of bill greenish. See Western Screech-Owl. From grayer Whiskered Screech-Owl (which has similar plumage patterns but does not overlap geographically) by pattern on the inner web of p10 usually more marked; feet larger (see Fig. 47; middle toe from the outer toe angle > 14 mm).

Geographic variation—Moderate, but somewhat complicated by color polychromatism (with gray, intermediate, and red plumages), and clinal where ranges meet. Subspecies taxonomy follows Marshall (1967); see also Ridgway (1914), Bangs (1930), Bent (1938), Moore & Peters (1939), Sutton & Burleigh (1939), Laskey (1963), Owen (1963a, 1963b), Phillips *et al.* (1964), Oberholser (1974), Hekstra (1982), Fowler (1985), Gehlbach (1995). No other subspecies occur.

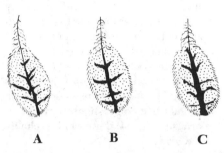

A   B   C

FIGURE 45. Pattern of streaking on the lower flank feathers of Eastern (**A-B**) and Western (**B-C**) screech-owls.

Western (*O.a. mccallii*) Group. Dull; 87-99% gray-plumaged.

O.a. maxwelliae (res Sask-Man to w.OK-ne.CO): Large; upperparts pale and indistinctly marked; underparts with moderately sparse patterning (Fig. 45A) and with substantial white; 7% red-plumaged, 87% gray-plumaged. ♀ wg(n21) 165-181, tl(n21) 80-102; ♂ wg(n21) 157-174, tl(n21) 75-86. Birds of s.Man-w.OK ("*swenki*") average smaller, paler, and with finer black markings, but differences are obscured by individual variation.

O.a. hasbroucki (res KS-OK to n.TX-AR): Medium in size; upperparts moderately dark with coarse and bold patterning; underparts heavily patterned (Fig. 45B) and without visible white; 5% red-plumaged, 94% gray-plumaged. ♀ wg(n10) 153-178, tl(n10) 72-84; ♂ wg(n12) 147-167, tl(n12) 72-82.

O.a. mccallii (res s.TX): Medium-small; upperparts medium in hue with coarse and bold patterning; underparts sparsely patterned (Fig. 45A); 0% red-plumaged and 99% gray-plumaged in N.Am. ♀ wg(n10) 149-165, tl(n10) 74-81; ♂ wg(n14) 145-164, tl(n14) 71-84.

Eastern (*O.a. asio*) Group. Bright; 35-80% red-plumaged.

O.a. asio (res MN-ME to c.MS-GA): Medium in size; upperparts richly colored with somewhat fine and indistinct patterning; underparts sparsely patterned (Fig. 45A); 39-75% red-plumaged, 20-57% gray-plumaged (percent red increases in the southern part of the range); toes feathered. ♀ wg(n50) 153-177, tl(n18) 73-83; ♂ wg(n52) 146-171, tl(n19) 68-83. Birds north of MO-VA ("*naevius*") average larger, but differences are broadly clinal.

O.a. floridanus (res s.AR-LA to FL): Small; upperparts richly colored, with somewhat fine and indistinct patterning; underparts with moderately dense patterning (Fig. 45A–B); 35% red-plumaged, 35% gray-plumaged; toes bristled. ♀ wg(n30) 140-163, tl(n15) 67-76; ♂ wg(n27) 134-152, tl(n12) 63-74.

Molt—PB: HY partial (Jul-Nov), AHY complete (Jun-Nov); PA absent. The 1st PB includes all body feathers but no wing covs. Look for 1-5 ss (among s1, s3-s4, and s7-s8) occasionally to be retained during the 2nd PB. See p. 67 for details on molt in owls, in general.

Skull—Pneumaticization patterns possibly are useful for ageing (see Family account).

Age—Juv (May-Oct) has loosely textured or downy plumage, grayish, olive, or cinnamon, with brownish or reddish barring (tips of down can remain on HYs after fledging); juv ♀ = ♂.

HY/SY (Sep-Aug): No flight-feather molt occurring in Jun-Nov; outer pp (p7-p10) relatively narrow, tapered at the tips (Fig. 44), and worn; outer web of the outer pp covs usually with distinct, notched markings (Fig. 46). **Note: Many intermediates occur that best are aged U/AHY. The shape of the pp tips tends to be very broad in juvs, slowly acquiring the narrower shape of HY/SY through wear. Look also for fault bars (Fig. 18), present on a small proportion of HY/SYs.**

AHY/ASY (Sep-Aug): Flight-feather molt usually occurring in Jun-Oct (to Nov in many); outer pp (p7-p10) relatively broad, truncate at the tips (Fig. 44), and fresh; outer webs of the outer pp covs usually indistinctly patterned (Fig. 46). **Note: See HY/SY. Look for occasional birds to retain one or more juvenal ss (among s1, s3-s4, and/or s7-s8) during the 2nd PB; if contrastingly narrow and worn (see Fig. 64) these can be reliably aged SY/TY.**

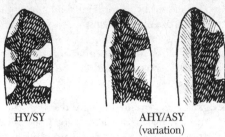

HY/SY   AHY/ASY
                (variation)

FIGURE 46. The pattern of the outer primary coverts by age in the Eastern Screech-Owl. See text for details. Similar (but less distinct) patterns may be found in Elf Owl. Figure from Pyle (1997b).

Sex—♀ = ♂ by plumage. The CP apparently is not developed; the BP (Mar-Sep) is reliable for sexing ♀♀. ♀ wg(n100) 140-181, tl(n74) 67-102; ♂ wg(n100) 134-174, tl(n88) 63-86; see **Geographic variation**. See Smith & Wiemeyer (1992) for a discriminant function analysis, based upon live birds and using weight, wg, and tl, that separated 88% of birds in OH-MD (*O.a. asio*).

Hybrids reported—Western Screech-Owl, at occasional points of contact.

Eastern Screech-Owl

	Jan	Feb	Mar	Apr	May	Jun	Jul	Aug	Sep	Oct	Nov	Dec
Juv-HY						○	○	○	○	○	○	○
SY	○	○	(♀)	(♀)	(♀)	(♀)	(♀)	(♀)	(♀)	○	○	○
TY	○	○	(♀)	(♀)	(♀)	(♀)	(♀)	(♀)				
AHY-U	○	○	(♀)	(♀)	(♀)	(♀)	(♀)	(♀)	(♀)	○	○	○
ASY	○	○	(♀)	(♀)	(♀)	(♀)	(♀)	(♀)				

■ > 95%   ▨ 25-95%   ▥ 5-25%   □ < 5%   See Fig. 24

References—Ridgway (1914), Forbush (1927), Oberholser (1937a, 1974), Bent (1938), Kelso (1950), Roberts (1955), Marshall (1967), Wood (1969), Henny & Van Camp (1979), Kaufman & Bowers (1989), Kaufman (1990a), CWS & USFWS (1991), Smith & Wiemeyer (1992), Dorn & Dorn (1994), Gehlbach (1994, 1995), Pyle (1997b); F.R. Gehlbach, L.F. Van Camp (*in litt.* to the BBL).

WESTERN SCREECH-OWL
Otus kennicottii

WESO
Species # 3732
Band size: 5-4

Species—Essentially monochromatic, with plumage varying clinally between gray and brown (a rare reddish or reddish-brown plumage may occur in coastal AK-BC); beware that colors can change from gray to brown with wear and, for specimens, with time. From Flammulated Owl by larger wg (144-191; see **Geographic variation** & **Sex**); p10 < ss; toes feathered (see Fig. 47); iris yellow. From gray-plumaged Eastern Screech-Owl by lower flank feathers with broad central streaks and regular crossbars (Fig. 45**B–C**); base of the bill dusky or black (except for some birds in the northern parts of the range; see **Geographic variation**). Western Screech-Owls of e.WY (*O.k. bendirei*) approach nearby birds of Eastern Screech-Owl (*O.a. maxwelliae*) in coloration, pattern of the upperparts and bill color, and are best separated by a greater density of barring (less whitish) on the underparts (see Fig. 45). From Whiskered Screech-Owl by feathers of the underparts with broad central shaft streaks and regular crossbars (Fig. 45); base of the bill (except for some birds in the northern parts of the range) dusky or black; inner web of p10 with regular pale markings; feet larger (Fig. 47; middle toe from the outer toe angle > 14 mm); iris of AHY yellow, without an orange cast.

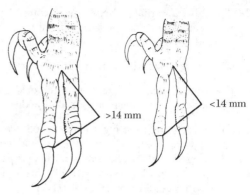

Eastern and Western   Whiskered

FIGURE 47. Feet of Eastern, Western, and Whiskered screech-owls, showing differences in size and a useful measure for identification. Note also the feathering on the toes; Flammulated Owl lacks such feathering.

Geographic variation—Moderate, but clinal where ranges meet. Subspecies taxonomy follows Marshall (1967), as modified by Rea (1983); see also Swarth (1910, 1916a), Ridgway (1914), Grinnell (1915a, 1928a), Grinnell *et al.* (1930), Oberholser (1937a), Bent (1938), Linsdale (1938), Moore & Peters (1939), Moore (1941a), Behle (1948), Miller & Miller (1951), Miller (1955a), Owen (1963a), Phillips *et al.* (1964), Bailey & Niedrach (1965), Browning (1979a), Monson & Phillips (1981), Hekstra (1982) Behle (1985). Two other subspecies occur in Mex.

Northern (*O.k. kennicottii*) Group. Dark; brownish-gray to brownish or red.

O.k. kennicottii (res coastal se.AK-nw.CA): Large; plumage dark brownish gray and coarsely marked (Fig. 45C); bill dark; 7% red-plumaged (AK & BC), 88% gray-plumaged; toes densely feathered. ♀ wg(n11) 170-191, tl(n11) 85-99; ♂ wg(n14) 167-189, tl(n14) 82-96. Birds of s.WA-n.CA ("*brewsteri*") average smaller and more buffy, but differences are broadly clinal and obscured by individual variation. More study is needed on the occurrence and proportion of red-plumaged birds.

O.k. bendirei (res interior BC-WY to coastal s.CA): Variable in size (larger in the north, smaller in the south); plumage plain brown, with moderately fine, black peppering to the upperparts and relatively finely marked underparts (Fig. 45B); bill in northern birds green-based; 0% red-plumaged, 89% grayish-plumaged. ♀ wg(n33) 162-193, tl(n12) 79-99; ♂ wg(n29) 156-188, tl(n16) 75-94. Birds of s.BC-ne.CA ("*macfarlanei*") average larger and birds of s.CA ("*quercinus*") average paler and less reddish, but differences are broadly clinal, obscured by individual variation, and/or due to intergradation with other subspecies. Birds of n.Baja CA (*cardonensis*), possible vagrants to s.CA, are like *bendirei*, but are smaller, darker, and have bristled rather than feathered toes.

Southwestern (*O.k. aikeni*) Group. Pale; gray.

O.k. aikeni (res se.CA-se.CO to c.AZ-s.NM): Medium in size; upperparts pale gray with coarse, blackish streaks; underparts with coarse (Fig. 45C) but sparse, blackish barring; bill dark; 100% gray-plumaged. ♀ wg(n100) 149-180, tl(n28) 74-92; ♂ wg(n100) 147-173, tl(n28) 71-85. Birds of se.CA ("*inyoensis*") average larger and paler, and birds of c.AZ-NM ("*cineraceus*") have markings averaging finer and denser, but differences are broadly clinal and obscured by individual variation.

O.k. yumanensis (res desert s.NV to se.CA-w.AZ): Small; upperparts pale gray (sometimes tinged pinkish) with fine, dusky barring; underparts with relatively narrow (Fig. 45B) and indistinct patterning; bill dark; 100% gray-plumaged. ♀ wg(n15) 148-164, tl(n7) 74-83; ♂ wg(n21) 144-157, tl(n10) 70-79.

O.k. gilmani (res sw-c.AZ): Medium small; upperparts pale grayish-brown with fine, dusky streaks; underparts with coarse (Fig. 45C), but sparse and dusky barring; bill dark; 100% gray-plumaged. ♀ wg(n4) 153-164, tl(n4) 74-79; ♂ wg(n4) 150-160, tl(n4) 72-77.

O.k. suttoni (res sw.NM-sw.TX): Medium small; upperparts pale gray with broad and coarse streaks; underparts with distinct, moderately heavy, black barring (Fig. 45C); bill dark; 100% gray-plumaged. ♀ wg(n10) 154-173, tl(n10) 75-83; ♂ wg(n18) 146-162, tl(n10) 73-81.

Molt—PB: HY partial (Jul-Nov), AHY complete (Jun-Nov); PA absent. The 1st PB includes all body feathers, but no wing covs. Some ss (among s1, s3-s4, and/or s7-s8) occasionally can be retained during the 2nd PB. See p. 67 for details on molt in owls, in general.

Skull—Pneumaticization patterns possibly are useful for ageing (see Family account).

Age—Juv (Apr-Oct) has loosely textured or downy plumage, grayish brown with dusky barring (tips of down can remain on HYs after fledging); juv ♀ = ♂.

HY/SY (Sep-Aug): No flight-feather molt occurring in Jun-Nov; outer pp (p7-p10) relatively narrow, tapered at the tips (Fig. 44), and worn. **Note: Many intermediates occur that are best aged U/AHY. The shape of the pp tips tends to be very broad in juvs, slowly acquiring the narrower shape of HY/SY through wear. Look also for fault bars (Fig. 18), present on a small proportion of HY/SYs.**

AHY/ASY (Sep-Aug): Flight-feather molt usually occurring in Jun-Oct (to Nov in many); outer pp (p7-p10) relatively broad, truncate at the tips (Fig. 44), and fresh. **Note: See HY/SY. Look for occasional birds that have retained one or more juvenal ss (among s1, s3-s4, and/or s7-s8) during the 2nd PB; if contrastingly narrow and worn (see Fig. 64) these can be reliably aged SY/TY.**

Sex—♀ = ♂ by plumage. The CP apparently is not developed; the BP (Mar-Oct) is reliable for sexing ♀♀. ♀ wg(n100) 148-191, tl(n100) 74-99; ♂ wg(n100) 144-189, tl(n100) 70-96; see **Geographic variation**. A combination of measurements possibly are useful for sexing within subspecies (*e.g.*, see Miller & Miller 1951).

Hybrids reported—Eastern Screech-Owl, at occasional points of contact.

Western Screech-Owl

	Jan	Feb	Mar	Apr	May	Jun	Jul	Aug	Sep	Oct	Nov	Dec
Juv-HY				o	o	o	o	o	o	o	o	o
SY	o	o	(♀)	(♀)	(♀)	(♀)	(♀)	(♀)	(♀)	(♀)	o	o
TY	o	o	(♀)	(♀)	(♀)	(♀)	(♀)	(♀)				
AHY-U	o	o	(♀)	(♀)	(♀)	(♀)	(♀)	(♀)	(♀)	(♀)	o	o
ASY	o	o	(♀)	(♀)	(♀)	(♀)	(♀)	(♀)				

■ > 95% ▨ 25-95% ▢ 5-25% □ < 5%   See Fig. 24

References—Ridgway (1914), Bent (1938), Moore & Peters (1939), Miller & Miller (1951), Phillips *et al.* (1964), Marshall (1967), Oberholser (1974), Kaufman & Bowers (1989), Kaufman (1990a), CWS & USFWS (1991), Dorn & Dorn (1994), Pyle (1997b); F.R. Gehlbach, L.F. Van Camp (*in litt.* to the BBL).

WHISKERED SCREECH-OWL
Otus trichopsis

WHSO
Species # 3731
Band size: 3A-4

Species—Essentially monochromatic in N.Am; plumage color grayish, as in Western Screech-Owl (beware that colors can change from gray to brown with wear and, for specimens, with time), but plumage patterns (Fig. 45) as in Eastern Screech-Owl and base of the bill yellowish-green. Additionally from both species by inner web of p10 with few or no pale markings; feet smaller (Fig. 47; middle toe from the outer toe angle < 14 mm); iris of AHY tinged orange. See Eastern and Western screech-owls for separation from other species.

Geographic variation—Weak, clinal, and complicated by color dichromatism (gray and red plumages) south of N.Am. Subspecies taxonomy follows Marshall (1967); see also Griscom (1932), van Rossem (1932a, 1938b, 1945a), Moore & Peters (1939), Hekstra (1982), Browning (1989). Two other subspecies occur in Mex-C.Am.

O.t. aspersus (res s.AZ): From the other subspecies by paler gray plumage, without blackish or brownish tones; crossbars relatively bold and well defined; red plumage absent or rare (up to 33% of birds are red-plumaged in the other subspecies).

Molt—PB: HY partial (Jul-Oct), AHY complete (Jul-Oct); PA absent. The 1st PB includes all body feathers but no wing covs. Look for some ss (likely among s1, s3-s4, and/or s7-s8) occasionally to be retained during the 2nd PB. See p. 67 for details on molt in owls, in general.

Skull—Pneumaticization patterns possibly are useful for ageing (see Family account).

Age—Juv (May-Oct) has loosely textured or downy plumage, brownish gray with dusky and whitish barring (tips of down can remain on HYs after fledging); juv ♀ = ♂.

HY/SY (Sep-Aug): No flight-feather molt occurring in Jul-Oct; outer pp (p7-p10) relatively narrow, tapered at the tips (Fig. 44), and worn. **Note: Many intermediates occur that are best aged U/AHY. The shape of the pp tips tends to be very broad in juvs, slowly acquiring the narrower shape of HY/SY through wear. Look also for fault bars (Fig. 18), present on a small proportion of HY/SYs.**

AHY/ASY (Sep-Aug): Flight-feather molt usually occurring in Jul-Oct; outer pp (p7-p10) relatively broad, truncate at the tips (Fig. 44), and fresh. **Note: See HY/SY. Look for occasional birds in Nov-Jun that can retain a few juvenal ss (among s1, s3-s4, and/or s7-s8); if contrastingly narrow and worn (see Fig. 64) these can be reliably aged SY/TY.**

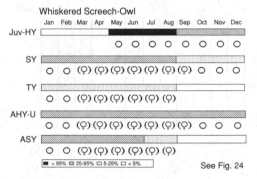

Sex—♀ = ♂ by plumage. The CP apparently is not developed; the BP (Mar-Oct) is reliable for sexing ♀♀. ♀ wg(n20) 141-151, tl(n20) 69-76; ♂ wg(n24) 140-152, tl(n20) 64-76.

References—Ridgway (1914), Bent (1938), Moore & Peters (1939), Phillips *et al.* (1964), Marshall (1967), Kaufman & Bowers (1989), Kaufman (1990a), Pyle (1997b); F.R. Gehlbach (*in litt.* to the BBL).

GREAT HORNED OWL
Bubo virginianus

GHOW
Species # 3750
Band size: 8-9 Lock-on

Species—Juv from other large owls of N.Am by the presence of a whitish throat patch. From Long-eared Owl also by larger size (wg 313-408, tl 187-252; see **Geographic variation**).

Geographic variation—Moderate to marked, although clinal where ranges meet, and variants, exceptions, and migrants are regular, complicating subspecies segregation. Subspecies taxonomy in N.Am follows the AOU (1957), as modified by Snyder (1961), Browning & Banks (1991), and Dickerman (1991b); see also Oberholser (1904, 1914a, 1974), Ridgway (1914), Noble (1919), Bishop (1931a), Swarth (1934a), Griscom (1935), Taverner (1942), Jewett *et al.* (1953), Roberts (1955), Webster & Orr (1958), Todd (1963), Phillips *et al.* (1964), Bailey & Niedrach (1965), Rea (1983), Webster (1984), Behle (1985), McGillivray (1985, 1989), Godfrey (1986), Browning (1990), Browning & Barks (1990), Dickerman (1991a, 1992). Eight other subspecies occur in Mex-S.Am. Some subspecies boundaries (especially those in the Great Plains) are imprecisely known and in need of further study.

Pacific Coastal (*B.v. pacificus*) Group. Small; dark; feet dusky.

B.v. saturatus (res coastal se.AK-nw.CA): Medium small; plumage (especially the face) dark grayish, suffused with dull tawny; feet primarily dusky. ♀ wg(n13) 345-383, tl(n12) 203-242; ♂ wg(n10) 335-358, tl(n10) 194-222.

B.v. pacificus (res nw.CA-w.NV to s.CA): Medium small; plumage gray-brown, the face only tinged tawny; feet whitish with dusky mottling. ♀ wg(n10) 345-371, tl(n10) 208-228; ♂ wg(n10) 328-362, tl(n10) 190-218.

Interior Western (*B.v. subarcticus*) Group. Large; variably pale; feet whitish.

B.v. algistus (res nw.AK): Large; plumage (including the face) pale tawny; feet mottled white and dusky. ♀ wg(n6) 355-408, tl(n6) 225-250; ♂ wg(n4) 354-384, tl(n4) 208-245.

B.v. lagophonus (br c.AK-Yuk to/or ne.OR-nw.MT, wint to UT-NE): Large; plumage (especially the face) grayish suffused with rich tawny; feet whitish with dusky barring. ♀ wg(n10) 352-404, tl(n10) 215-252; ♂ wg(n11) 345-372, tl(n11) 206-235. Birds of c.BC ("*leucomelas*") may average larger and paler, but differences are slight and due to intergradation with *subarcticus*.

B.v. subarcticus (="*wapacuthu*"; br NWT to ne.CA-w.KS, wint to w.WA & IA-NJ): Medium large; plumage whitish buff; face tinged tawny; underparts with indistinct, pale dusky barring; feet buff to white, with little or no dusky mottling. ♀ wg(n100) 353-390, tl(n81) 220-246; ♂ wg(n82) 333-370, tl(n57) 208-232. Birds of c.Alb-ne.CA to w.OK ("*occidentalis*") average smaller but this difference is broadly clinal and due to intergradation with *pallescens*.

B.v. pallescens (res se.CA-s.UT to s.TX): Small; plumage whitish with a variable, grayish-buff to grayish tinge; face lacking tawny; underparts with indistinct or very fine, pale dusky barring; feet whitish. ♀ wg(n22) 331-380, tl(n11) 200-235; ♂ wg(n15) 320-360, tl(n11) 187-225.

Eastern (*B.v. virginianus*) Group. Medium in size; brown; feet medium pale.

B.v. scalariventris (br & wint ne.Man-se.Que): Medium small; plumage grayish with little or no buffy and no rufous; face tinged tawny; underparts with distinct, blackish barring. ♀ wg(n23) 350-380; ♂ wg(n8) 328-355.

B.v. heterocnemis (br & wint n.Que-Nfl): Large; plumage dark grayish-brown; face tinged tawny; underparts (except vent) with heavy, dusky barring; feet pale with light, dusky mottling. ♀ wg(n10) 370-390, tl(n10) 218-250; ♂ wg(n3) 345-365, tl(n3) 219-230. Birds of Nfl ("*neochorus*") average slightly smaller and with less dusky mottling to the feet, but differences are weak and obscured by individual variation.

B.v. virginianus (res MN-NS to e.TX-FL): Medium-large; plumage brownish with a rufous tinge; face dull tawny; underparts with distinct, blackish-brown barring; feet deep tawny to pale buff, often with blackish barring. ♀ wg(n40) 352-395, tl(n37) 200-225; ♂ wg(n46) 320-368, tl(n45) 189-212.

Molt—PB: HY partial (Apr-Dec), AHY incomplete (Jul-Oct); PA absent. The PBs probably occur primarily on the summer grounds, although limited body molt can occur year-round. The 1st PB includes all body feathers but no wing covs. The 2nd PB usually includes 0-3 pp (among p6-p8), 5-12 ss (including at least s13-s17, often s12-s11, occasionally s10-s9 and s1, and rarely s8 and s2; Fig. 48**B–C**), and 6 to (usually) all rects. The 1st replacement of pp usually is in the order p7-p8-p6, such that when one primary is replaced it is p7 and when two are replaced they usually are p7-p8. The 3rd PB usually includes 1-5 pp (among p1-p2 and p4-p10), around those not replaced during the 2nd PB, and 4-8 ss, leaving 2-5 juvenal ss (among s1, s3-4, and s6-s8; Fig. 48**D–F**). Subsequent PBs usually include 3-6 pp and 2-7 ss in an irregular sequence, seldom including three adjacent feathers (Fig. 48**G–H**). Pp and ss replacement patterns can lack symmetry, especially in ASY/ATYs. Adult PBs after the 2nd usually include all rects. Tropical forms of Great Horned Owl appear to have similar replacement patterns. See p. 67 for details on molt in owls, in general.

Skull—Pneumaticization patterns possibly are useful for ageing (see Family account).

Age—Juv (Mar-Oct) has loosely textured or downy plumage, grayish to buff, with dusky barring (tips of down can remain on HYs after fledging), and a brownish to yellow-brown iris; juv ♀ = ♂.

HY/SY (Oct-Sep): Pp, ss, and rects uniform in shape, wear, and pattern, without contrasts between adjacent feathers (Fig. 48**A**); numbers of bars on pp, ss, and rects relatively large and distances between adjacent bars on these feathers relatively small (Table 1, Fig. 49; see also

Figs. 61-62); rects relatively narrow and tapered (Fig. 49); iris brownish yellow to yellow-orange. **Note: In addition to the above, average differences in the pp covs, as in *Strix* owls (see Fig. 57), but less distinct, can be helpful for ageing some birds. Intermediates, birds with anomalous feather replacement patterns, and/or birds with feather ages difficult to detect should be classified AHY/ASY.**

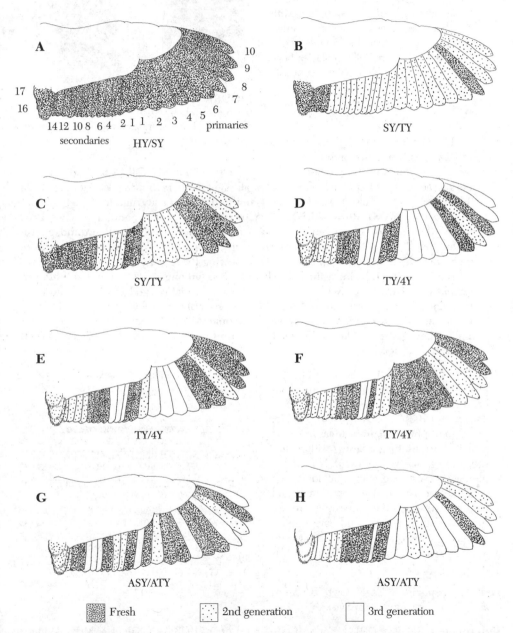

FIGURE 48. Replacement patterns of the secondaries and primaries, by age, in Great Horned Owl. Examples shown are near to the minimum and maximum amount of replacement, within each group. Although TY/4Ys are probably distinguished with experience, more study is needed before this age classification can be reliably assigned. Similar (but not identical) patterns of replacement occur in Barn and Snowy owls (see text). See Pyle (1997b) for more details.

SY/TY (Oct-Sep): P7, p7-p8, or p6-p8 (and corresponding pp covs; occasionally no pp or pp covs) **and** s13-s17, plus some or all of s8-s12 and/or s1-s2, glossier, broader, fresher, more mottled, and showing bar patterns of adult feathers (Table 1, Figs. 48**B–C** & 49; see also Figs. 61-62), contrasting with all other wing feathers uniformly more faded, narrow, worn, less mottled, and showing bar patterns of juvenal feathers; rects sometimes showing contrasts between worn juvenal and fresh adult feathers (see Fig. 49); iris orange-yellow to deep yellow. **Note: See HY/SY.**

HY/SY   AHY/ASY

FIGURE 49. The width and pattern of the central rectrix (r1) by age in Great Horned Owl. See also Table 1. Substantial variation occurs within both age groups.

ASY/ATY (Oct-Sep): Pp, pp covs, and ss with irregular contrasts present, including varying numbers and positions of new and old feathers (Fig. 48D–H), and not representing the patterns found in SY/TY; most or all flight feathers showing bar patterns of adult (Table 1, Fig. 49; see also Figs. 61-62); rects uniformly broad and truncate (Fig. 49); iris yellow. **Note: See HY/SY. Birds with p7, p7-p8, or p6-p8 (and corresponding pp covs) broad and moderately worn, surrounded by 2-5 contrastingly fresh, adult pp and pp covs (among p2-p5 and p7-p10), with the remaining 2-7 pp and pp covs juvenal, contrastingly narrow, faded and worn, and the ss also showing three generations of feathers, with 4-8 ss (among s1-s12) contrastingly fresh and 2-5 ss (among s1, s3-4, and s6-s8) still juvenal and very worn (Fig. 48D–F; see Molt), likely are reliably aged TY/4Y, and those with irregular patterns, not as above (Fig. 48G–H) probably are reliably aged ATY/A4Y, but confirmation is needed. It is possible that some ATY/A4Ys coincidentally may show replacement patterns like SY/TYs or TY/4Ys, and best are aged AHY/ASY or ASY/ATY. More study is needed.**

Sex—The CP apparently is not developed; the BP (Jan-Aug) is reliable for sexing ♀♀, although many birds (especially SY/TYs) may not breed. ♀ wg(n100) 331-408, tl(n100) 200-252; ♂ wg(n100) 313-384, tl(n100) 187-245; see **Geographic variation**. Measurements probably are useful for sexing within subspecies (e.g., see Weller 1965). No reliable plumage criteria are known, although ♀♀ generally are darker, may average more and heavier barring on the underwing covs (vs sparser spotting in ♂♂), and have thinner and more tapered barring to the ss and inner pp than ♂♂, age for age; more study is needed.

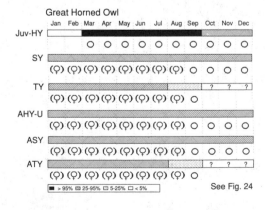

Hybrids reported—Eagle Owl (B. bubo) and Great Gray Owl in captivity.

References—Ridgway (1914), Forbush (1927), Sumner (1933), A.C. Bent & M.P. Skinner in Bent (1938), Roberts (1955), Weller (1965), Stresemann & Stresemann (1966), Oberholser (1974), CWS & USFWS (1991), Dickerman (1992), Pyle (1997b).

SNOWY OWL   SNOW
Nyctea scandiaca   Species # 3760
                                                 Band size: 8-9 Lock-on

Species—Juv from juvs of the other large owls of N.Am by white flight feathers.

Geographic variation—No subspecies are recognized.

Molt—PB: HY partial (Apr-Dec), AHY incomplete (Jul-Oct); PA absent. The PBs probably occur primarily on the summer grounds, although body molt can occur year-round. The 1st PB includes all body feathers but no wing covs. The 2nd PB usually includes no pp or p7 only; the innermost 4-6 ss (among s13-s18), and no to all rects. The 3rd PB usually includes 1-3 pp (among p6-p9) and 4-7 ss (among s9-s14, often s1-s2, and sometimes s6-s7). Subsequent PBs include 1-6 pp and 4-8 ss in irregular patterns, which are similar to those of Great Horned Owl (*cf.* Fig. 48G–H). Pp and ss replacement patterns often lack symmetry, especially in ASY/ATYs. Adult PBs subsequent to the 2nd usually include all rects. See p. 67 for details on molt in owls, in general.

Skull—Pneumaticization patterns possibly are useful for ageing (see Family account).

Age/Sex—Juv (Jul-Oct) has loosely textured or downy plumage, gray-brown with whitish speckling or barring (tips of down can remain on HYs after fledging), and a brownish to yellowish-brown iris; juv ♀ = ♂. The CP apparently is not developed; the BP (May-Aug) is reliable for sexing ♀♀. Measurements are useful: ♀ wg(n100) 406-457, tl(n78) 210-248; ♂ wg(n71) 351-420, tl(n53) 191-230; the formula (2 × wg) + tl, > 1045 mm in ♀ and < 1045 mm in ♂, may separate 95% of birds in N.Am.

HY/SY ♀ (Oct-Sep): Pp, pp covs, and ss uniform in shape and wear, without contrasts between adjacent feathers (see Fig. 48A); plumage grayish white with heavy, black mottling; nape with heavy, black barring (and sometimes with a concealed patch of grayish juvenal down through Jan); scapulars and central rects (r1) with distinct, blackish bars (Fig. 50A), the central rects tapered and with 4-6 bars (including indistinct marks); ventral feathers with 4-7 black bars/feather and a bar width of 3-5 mm; iris brownish to brownish yellow. **Note: In addition, the length of the white bib on the chin may be helpful for ageing and sexing (see Josephson 1980), although this varies with the position of the head.**

SY/TY ♀ (Oct-Sep): Pp and pp covs uniform, as in HY/SY, or with just p7 (and its corresponding p cov) replaced; **and** the innermost 4-6 ss (among s13-s18) newer and fresher than the other, uniformly more faded ss (*cf.* Fig. 48B–C); rects often with mixed juvenal and adult feathers; nape without juvenal down; scapulars and central rects (r1; if second basic) somewhat truncate and with moderately distinct, dusky barring (Fig. 50; intermediate between HY/SY and ASY/ATY ♀♀), the central rects with 3-5 bars (including indistinct marks); ventral feathers with 3-6 black bars/feather and a bar width of 2-4 mm; iris orangish to yellow-orange. **Note: See HY/SY ♀.**

ASY/ATY ♀ (Oct-Sep): Pp, pp-covs, and ss with irregular contrasts present, including varying numbers and positions of new and old feathers, and not representing the patterns found in SY/TY (*cf.* Fig. 48D–H); plumage white with a variable amount of blackish mottling; nape white with little blackish barring; scapulars and central rects (r1) with light to moderate, blackish barring (Fig. 50), the central rects truncate and with 2-5 bars (including indistinct marks); ventral feathers with 2-5 blackish bars/feather and a bar width of 1-3 mm; iris yellow. **Note: See HY/SY ♀. Birds with 1-3 pp and pp covs (among p6-p9) and 4-7 ss (among s9-s14, often s1-s2, occasionally s6-s7) recently replaced, contrasting with the moderately worn, 2nd generation feathers of SY/TY (see above), and with the uniformly and heavily worn, retained juvenal pp, pp covs, and ss (*cf.* Fig. 48D–F), may be reliably aged TY/4Y, and those with irregular patterns, not as above (*cf.* Fig. 48G–H), probably are**

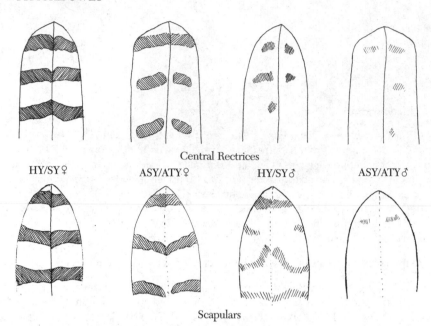

Central Rectrices

HY/SY♀   ASY/ATY♀   HY/SY♂   ASY/ATY♂

Scapulars

FIGURE 50. Typical pattern of the scapulars, and shape and pattern of the central rectrix (r1) by age in Snowy Owl. SY/TYs tend to be intermediate between HY/SYs and ASY/ATYs in both shape and pattern.

reliably aged ATY/A4Y, but confirmation is needed. It also is possible that some birds may be reliably aged 4Y/5Y, with patterns such as p9, p6, s1, and s7-s9 new, or p8 new, p7 2nd generation, and s1-s2 and s8-s10 new. However, some ATY/A4Ys may coincidentally show replacement patterns like SY/TYs or TY/4Ys, and these are best aged AHY/ASY. More study is needed.

HY/SY ♂ (Oct-Sep): Flight-feather replacement patterns as in HY/SY ♀; plumage white with a gray tinge and a variable amount of blackish mottling; nape primarily white; scapulars and central rects (r1) with indistinct, blackish bars (Fig. 50), the central rects tapered and with 2-5 bars (including indistinct marks); ventral feathers with 2-5 blackish bars/feather and a bar width of 1-3 mm; iris yellowish brown to orangish. **Note: See HY/SY ♀.**

SY/TY ♂ (Oct-Sep): Flight-feather replacement patterns as in SY/TY ♀; plumage with light, dusky mottling; scapulars and central rects (r1; if second basic) with light, dusky markings (Fig. 50, intermediate between HY/SY and ASY/ATY ♂♂), the central rects somewhat truncate and with 1-4 bars (including indistinct marks); ventral feathers with 0-2 dusky bars/feather and a bar width of 0-3 mm; iris orange-yellow to yellow. **Note: See HY/SY ♀.**

ASY/ATY ♂ (Oct-Sep): Flight-feather replacement patterns as in ASY/ATY ♀; plumage white, without dusky, or with sparse, dusky markings; nape white; scapulars and central rects with few or no dusky markings (Fig. 50), the central rects truncate and with 0-3 indistinct marks; ventral feathers with 0-2 pale dusky bars/feather and a bar width of 0-3 mm; iris yellow. **Note: Purely white ♂♂ probably are at least ATY/A4Y, but con-**

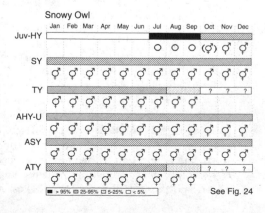

See Fig. 24

firmation is needed. **Also, birds probably are reliably aged TY/4Y, ATY/A4Y, and possibly even 4Y/5Y by flight-feather replacement patterns; see ASY/ATY ♀.**

References—Ridgway (1914), Forbush (1927), Bent (1938), Roberts (1955), Keith (1960), Stresemann & Stresemann (1966), Oberholser (1974), Josephson (1980), Boxall & Lein (1982), Cramp (1985), Kerlinger & Lein (1986), Chevalier (1989), CWS & USFWS (1991), Parmelee (1992), Pyle (1997b); T.C. Erdman, D.L. Evans, F. Hamerstrom, R.D. Weir, J.S. Weske (*in litt.* to the BBL).

NORTHERN HAWK OWL
Surnia ulula

NHOW
Species # 3770
Band size: 7A-7B Short

Geographic variation—Moderate, with well-defined ranges. Subspecies taxonomy follows the AOU (1957); see Ridgway (1914), Bent (1938), Dement'ev & Gladkov (1951), Cramp (1985). Two other subspecies occur in Eurasia.

> ***S.u. caparoch*** (br & wint throughout the range in N.Am): Medium small (see **Sex**); dark; crown feathers dark based, usually with two white bars or spots; nape primarily blackish; white of scapulars broken; dark bars of the underparts ≥ 2.5 mm wide. *S.u. ulula*, a possible vagrant to w.AK, averages larger (♀ wg 230-249, tl 166-191; ♂ wg 224-240, tl 164-192), paler, and has the crown feathers pale based with three or more white bars, the nape primarily white, the white of scapulars unbroken, and the dark bars of the underparts ≤ 2.5 mm wide.

Molt—PB: HY partial (Jun-Sep), AHY incomplete (Apr-Oct); PA absent. The PBs occur on the summer grounds. The 1st PB includes all body feathers but no wing covs. The 2nd and subsequent PBs occasionally may be complete, but typically some ss are retained: usually s3-s4, s6-s8, and sometimes s2 and/or s9 during the 2nd PB, and in irregular patterns (among s1-s15, most often among s1-s10) during subsequent PBs. See p. 67 for details on molt in owls, in general.

Skull—Pneumaticization patterns possibly are useful for ageing (see Family account).

Age—Juv (May-Oct) has loosely textured plumage, dark grayish brown with irregular whitish markings; juv ♀ = ♂.

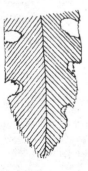
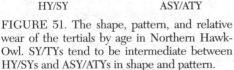
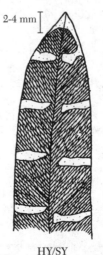
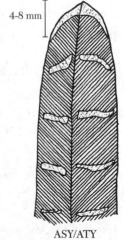

2-4 mm

4-8 mm

HY/SY   ASY/ATY

HY/SY   ASY/ATY

FIGURE 51. The shape, pattern, and relative wear of the tertials by age in Northern Hawk-Owl. SY/TYs tend to be intermediate between HY/SYs and ASY/ATYs in shape and pattern.

FIGURE 52. The shape and pattern of the central rectrix (r1) by age in Northern Hawk-Owl. SY/TYs tend to be intermediate between HY/SYs and ASY/ATYs in both shape and pattern. Figure from Pyle (1997b).

HY/SY (Aug-Jul): Juvenal ss uniform in shape and wear, narrow, tapered, and without contrasts between adjacent feathers (see Fig. 64); outer pp (p7-p10) narrow and tapered (Fig. 44); terts pointed, relatively worn, and with reduced, whitish markings (Fig. 51); central rects (r1) narrow, tapered, with bolder and more complete, white bars, and with the white at the tip restricted (usually 2-4 mm wide; Fig. 52). **Note: Iris color is probably of some use in ageing, as in other medium-large owls, but more study is needed.**

AHY/ASY (Sep-Aug): Adult ss uniform in shape and wear, broad, truncate, and without contrasts between adjacent feathers (*cf.* Fig. 64); outer pp, terts, and central rects as in ASY/ATY (below). **Note: See HY/SY. Most AHYs should have two generations of ss and can be aged SY/TY or ASY/ATY. Retained ss on some birds can be difficult to distinguish as juvenal or adult feathers; these birds also should be aged AHY/ASY.**

SY/TY (Aug-Jul): Ss mixed juvenal and adult, typically with s3-s4, s7, and sometimes with s1, s2, s6, and/or s8 (possibly also s9-s11) narrow, tapered, and worn, contrasting markedly with the other, broader, more truncate, and fresher ss (see Fig. 64); pp uniformly broad, the outer pp (p7-p10) truncate at the tips (Fig. 44); terts and central rects as in ASY/ATY (below), but tending toward HY/SY in pattern (*cf.* Fig. 52). **Note: See HY/SY.**

ASY/ATY (Sep-Aug): Ss mixed, with two generations of adult feathers, showing irregular contrasts in wear, with the older feathers broad, truncate, and only moderately worn in comparison with the newer ss (see Fig. 64); terts truncate, relatively fresh, and with large and bold, whitish markings (Fig. 51); central rects broad, truncate, with indistinct, pale bars, and with the white at the tip expanded (usually 4-8 mm wide; Fig. 52). **Note: See HY/SY.**

Sex—The CP apparently is not developed; the BP (Mar-Jul) is reliable for sexing ♀♀. ♀ wg(n30) 221-253, tl(n20) 171-192; ♂ wg(n30) 218-251, tl(n20) 160-188; includes *S.u. caparoch* of N.Am only. No reliable plumage criteria are known for sexing, although ♀♀ average more rufous brown than ♂♂, when the plumage is fresh.

Northern Hawk Owl

	Jan	Feb	Mar	Apr	May	Jun	Jul	Aug	Sep	Oct	Nov	Dec
Juv-HY								o	o	o	o	o
SY												
	o	o	(♀)	(♀)	(♀)	(♀)	(♀)	o	o	o	o	o
TY												
	o	o	(♀)	(♀)	(♀)	(♀)	(♀)	o				
AHY-U												
	o	o	(♀)	(♀)	(♀)	(♀)	(♀)	o	o	o	o	o
ASY												
	o	o	(♀)	(♀)	(♀)	(♀)	(♀)	o	o	o	o	o
ATY												
	o	o	(♀)	(♀)	(♀)	(♀)	(♀)	o				

■ > 95% ▨ 25-95% ▦ 5-25% □ < 5%   See Fig. 24

References—Ridgway (1914), Forbush (1927), Bent (1938), Roberts (1955), Stresemann & Stresemann (1966), Forsman (1980), Cramp (1985), Kertell (1986), Pyle (1997b); S.L. Loch & A.H. Grewe Jr. (*in litt.* to the BBL).

NORTHERN PYGMY-OWL
Glaucidium gnoma

NOPO
Species # 3790
Band size: 2-3-4

Species—Dichromatic, with gray and rufous plumages, the latter found almost exclusively south of N.Am (beware that coloration can get browner with wear or, on specimens, with time). From Ferruginous Pygmy-Owl by tail brown with white bars; crown and nape with pale spots.

Geographic variation—Weak, complicated by color and sex dichromatism, and (in certain cases) based on voice rather than morphology or plumage; but most ranges are fairly well defined. Subspecies taxonomy in N.Am follows Monson & Phillips (1981); see also Ridgway (1914), Bishop (1931b), van Rossem (1936a), Munro & Cowan (1947), Jewett *et al.* (1953), Oberholser (1974). Two other subspecies occur in Baja CA & Guatemala. Beware that ♀♀ average redder or browner, and ♂♂ average grayer, in all subspecies.

G.g. grinnelli (res coastal se.AK-c.CA): Large; upperparts brown to grayish brown, with distinct, rufous spotting; tail with 3-4 indistinct, pale bars beyond the uppertail covs. ♀ wg(n12) 89-101, tl(n12) 62-73; ♂ wg(n61) 86-96, tl(n61) 60-70.

G.g. swarthi (res Vancouver I, BC): Medium-sized; upperparts chocolate brown with indistinct, pale spotting; tail with 3-4 indistinct, pale bars beyond the uppertail covs. ♀ wg(n10) 88-97, tl(n10) 60-67; ♂ wg(n10) 85-95, tl(n10) 60-66.

G.g. californicum (res interior BC-Alb to s.CA): Large; upperparts gray to brownish gray, with light, pale spotting; streaks on the underparts black; tail with 4-5 distinct, whitish bars beyond the uppertail covs. ♀ wg(n19) 93-105, tl(n19) 64-78; ♂ wg(n22) 90-101, tl(n22) 61-69.

G.g. pinicola (res UT-WY to se.NV-NM): Large; upperparts pale gray with indistinct pale spotting; streaks on the underparts black; tail with 4-5 distinct, white bars beyond the uppertail covs. ♀ wg(n10) 93-103, tl(n10) 63-77; ♂ wg(n10) 90-100, tl(n10) 60-68.

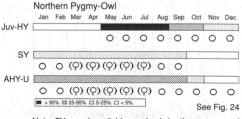

25-30 mm

28-34 mm

HY/SY   AHY/ASY

FIGURE 53. Possible differences in width and pattern of the central rectrix (r1) by age in Northern Pygmy-Owl; birds should not be aged on these criteria alone. Differences in the distance from the tip to the third wide bar between the age groups are tentative, and require confirmation. Similar differences in width by age may be found in other small owls. Figure from Pyle (1997b).

G.g. gnoma (res se.AZ): Small; upperparts dark brownish-gray with moderately heavy, pale spotting; streaks on the underparts dark brown; tail with 4-5 distinct, whitish bars beyond the uppertail covs. ♀ wg(n10) 90-98, tl(n10) 58-64; ♂ wg(n17) 82-92, tl(n17) 57-63.

Molt—PB: HY partial (Jul-Sep), AHY complete (Jun-Sep); PA absent. The 1st PB includes all body feathers but no wing covs. See p. 67 for details on molt in owls, in general.

Skull—Pneumaticization patterns possibly are useful for ageing (see Family account).

Age—Juv (May-Sep) is dark grayish brown, with crown spots indistinct or lacking, and with the other whitish markings indistinct; juv ♀ = ♂. No reliable plumage criteria for ageing are known, although the occurrence of flight-feather molt in Jun-Oct indicates AHY, whereas none in Jul-Aug indicates HY. Markings of HY/SY average less distinct and contrasting than those of AHY/ASY. Also, specimen examination suggests that the width of the central rect (r1) and the distance between the tip of this feather and the third white bar (see Fig. 53) may be useful for separating some HY/SYs from some AHY/ASYs in Aug-Jul, but more study is needed. The presence of fault bars (see Fig. 18) can be used, with experience, to age a proportion of HY/SYs but AHY/ASYs cannot be reliably aged.

Sex—The CP apparently is not developed; the BP (Mar-Jul) is reliable for sexing ♀♀. ♀ wg(n61) 88-105, tl(n61) 58-78; ♂ wg(n100) 82-101, tl(n100) 57-70; see **Geographic variation**. No reliable plumage criteria are known for sexing, although ♀♀ average more rufous brown than ♂♂ when fresh.

Northern Pygmy-Owl

	Jan	Feb	Mar	Apr	May	Jun	Jul	Aug	Sep	Oct	Nov	Dec

Juv-HY

SY

AHY-U

■ > 95%   ▨ 25-95%   ▢ 5-25%   □ < 5%

See Fig. 24

Note: SYs can be reliably aged only by the presence of fault bars.

References—Ridgway (1914), Bishop (1931b), M.P. Skinner *in* Bent (1938), Phillips *et al.* (1964), Oberholser (1974), Cramp (1985), Howell & Webb (1995), Pyle (1997b).

FERRUGINOUS PYGMY-OWL
Glaucidium brasilianum

FEPO
Species # 3800
Band size: 3

Species—Dichromatic, with gray and rufous plumages, the former occurring in two forms (with different tail patterns) and the latter found rarely in N.Am (AZ). Beware that coloration can get browner with wear or, on specimens, with time. From Northern Pygmy-Owl by tail usually rufous with brown barring (birds in N.Am); crown and nape with pale streaks.

Geographic variation—Weak, clinal where ranges meet, and complicated by dichromatism and sexual variation in color. Subspecies taxonomy in N.Am follows the AOU (1957); see Ridgway (1914), van Rossem (1937a). Nine other subspecies occur in S.Am.

G.b. cactorum (res s.AZ & s.TX): Paler and smaller than the subspecies of S.Am (see **Sex** for measurements, *vs* wg 90-108 in S.Am subspecies). Birds of s.TX ("*ridgwayi*") average browner (less grayish) than birds of s.AZ, but differences are weak and obscured by plumage dichromatism.

Molt—PB: HY partial (Jun-Sep), AHY complete (May-Sep); PA absent. The 1st PB includes all body feathers but no wing covs. See p. 67 for details on molt in owls in general.

Skull—Pneumaticization patterns possibly are useful for ageing (see Family account).

Age—Juv (Apr-Sep) has the crown streaking very indistinct or lacking; juv ♀ = ♂. No reliable criteria for ageing are known, although the occurrence of flight-feather molt in May-Oct indicates AHY, whereas none in Jul-Aug indicates HY. Markings of HY/SY may average less distinct and contrasting than those of AHY/ASY, and the central rects (r1) average narrower in HY/SY than in AHY/ASY (see Fig. 53), but ageing based on these criteria probably is not reliable. The presence of fault bars (see Fig. 18) can be used, with experience, to age a proportion of HY/SYs but AHY/ASYs cannot be reliably aged after completion of the molt.

Sex—The CP apparently is not developed; the BP (Feb-Jul) is reliable for sexing ♀♀. ♀ wg(n32) 91-103, tl(n32) 55-70; ♂ wg(n53) 85-97, tl(n50) 53-66. No reliable plumage criteria are known for sexing, although ♀♀ average more rufous brown in plumage color than ♂♂ and, with experience, some AHY/ASYs (Oct-Sep) may be sexed by the relative color of the back and tail: ♀♀ tend to be concolorous and have less distinct bars on the tail, whereas ♂♂ have a darker tail than back and more distinct barring on the tail. More study is needed.

Ferruginous Pygmy-Owl

	Jan	Feb	Mar	Apr	May	Jun	Jul	Aug	Sep	Oct	Nov	Dec
Juv-HY				○	○	○	○	○	○	○	○	○
SY												
	○	(♀)	(♀)	(♀)	(♀)	(♀)	(♀)	○	○			
AHY-U												
	○	(♀)	(♀)	(♀)	(♀)	(♀)	(♀)	○	○	○	○	○

■ > 95% ▨ 25-95% ▨ 5-25% □ < 5%   See Fig. 24

Note: SYs can be reliably aged only by the presence of fault bars.

References—Ridgway (1914), Bent (1938), Phillips *et al.* (1964), Oberholser (1974), Pyle (1997b); G. Proudfoot (pers. comm.).

ELF OWL
Micrathene whitneyi

ELOW
Species # 3810
Band size: 2

Geographic variation—Weak and clinal where ranges meet. Subspecies taxonomy in N.Am follows the AOU (1957); see Ridgway (1914), Oberholser (1974). Two other subspecies occur in Mex.

M.w. whitneyi (br s.CA-sw.TX): Upperparts grayish brown to brown; face and underparts with substantial cinnamon.

M.w. idonea (br s.TX): Upperparts grayish with little if any brownish; face and underparts with little or no cinnamon.

Molt—PB: HY partial (Aug-Oct), AHY complete (Aug-Dec); PA absent. The 1st PB occurs on the summer grounds; adult PBs apparently commence on the summer grounds, suspend for migration, and complete on the winter grounds (more study is needed). The 1st PB includes all body feathers but no wing covs. See p. 67 for details on molt in owls, in general.

Skull—Pneumaticization patterns possibly are useful for ageing (see Family account).

Age—Juv (May-Sep) has loosely textured plumage and slightly less distinct head and back markings than adults (tips of down can remain on HY after fledging); juv ♀ = ♂. Preliminary evidence suggests that the pp covs can differ by age, as in Eastern Screech-Owl (see Fig. 46), and that the central rects of HY/SYs have more distinct, whitish bars than are found on AHY/ASYs, but confirmation of this is needed. Otherwise, no reliable criteria for ageing are known, although replacement of the flight-feathers, or contrasting feathers (due to suspended molt) on migrants, indicates AHY in Aug-Dec. The presence of fault bars (see Fig. 18) can be used, with experience, to age a proportion of HY/SYs but AHY/ASYs cannot be reliably aged after completion of the molt.

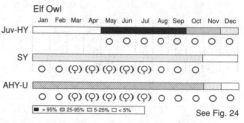

Sex—♂ = ♀ by plumage, although ♀♀ average slightly redder in plumage than ♂♂. The CP apparently not developed; the BP (Mar-Jul) is reliable for sexing ♀♀. ♀ wg(n30) 102-114, tl(n20) 42-52; ♂ wg(n30) 100-113, tl(n20) 41-49.

Note: SYs can be reliably aged only by the presence of fault bars.

References—Ridgway (1914), Bent (1938), Phillips *et al.* (1964), Ligon (1968), Oberholser (1974), Walters (1981, 1983a), Pyle (1997b).

BURROWING OWL
Athene cunicularia

BUOW
Species # 3780
Band size: 4

Geographic variation—Weak to moderate, but N.Am ranges are well defined. Subspecies taxonomy in N.Am follows the AOU (1957); see Ridgway (1914), Stevenson & Anderson (1994). Sixteen other subspecies occur in the W.Indies & S.Am.

A.c. hypugaea (br & wint w.N.Am; vag to NH-FL): Large; plumage pale brown with buff mottling and spotting; underwing covs buff, without spots (sometimes with indistinct streaks); feathering on the outer portion of the tarsus extends > 1/2 the distance to the feet (Fig. 54). ♀ wg(n72) 157-174, tl(n72) 72-85; ♂ wg(n64) 160-178, tl(n64) 75-87. Beware of worn birds (especially ♂♂) in Mar-Jul which can lose the tarsus feathering.

A.c. floridanus (res s.FL; vag to AL): Small; plumage dark brown with whitish mottling and spotting; underwing covs spotted brown; feathering on the outer portion of the tarsus extends < 1/2 the distance to the feet, otherwise the legs are bristled (Fig. 54). ♀ wg(n10) 155-169, tl(n10) 70-79; ♂ wg(n10) 156-170, tl(n10) 73-81.

Molt—PB: HY partial (Jul-Oct), AHY complete (Jul-Oct); PA absent-limited? (Feb-Mar). The PBs occur on the summer grounds. The 1st PB includes all body feathers but no wing covs. The PA, if present, may include just a few breast feathers. See p. 67 for details on molt in owls, in general.

Skull—Pneumaticization patterns possibly are useful for ageing (see Family account).

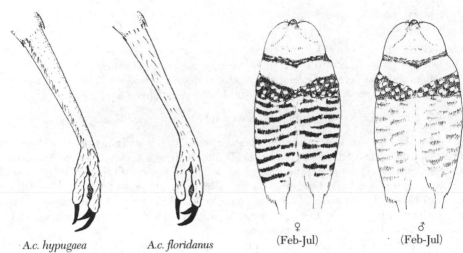

A.c. hypugaea   A.c. floridanus

♀ (Feb-Jul)   ♂ (Feb-Jul)

FIGURE 54. The amount of feathering on the tarsus by subspecies in Burrowing Owl. Note that the feathering of *hypugaea,* especially in ♂♂, can wear off by Feb-Mar.

FIGURE 55. The relative wear and fadedness of body coloration in spring, in ♀ and ♂ Burrowing Owls. These differences result from differences in behavior at the nest site, and should probably only be used to sex individuals of mated pairs.

Age—Juv (Feb-Sep) has loosely textured plumage, pale buff underparts, and plain brown upperparts, with little or no distinct markings (tips of down can remain on HY after fledging); juv ♀ = ♂.

HY/SY (Sep-Aug): No flight-feather molt occurs in Jul-Oct; outer pp (p7-p10) relatively narrow, tapered at the tips (Fig. 44), and worn. **Note: In addition to the above, HY/SYs have slightly narrower terts and rects, with more tapered tips, and slightly more distinct, white barring on the central rects (r1), but much overlap occurs between age groups. Also, many intermediates occur that are best aged U/AHY. The shape of the pp tips tend to be broad in juvs, slowly acquiring the narrower shape of HY/SY through wear. Look also for fault bars (Fig. 18), present on a small proportion of HY/SYs.**

AHY/ASY (Sep-Aug): Flight-feather molt usually occurs in Jul-Sep; outer pp (p7-p10) relatively broad, truncate at the tips (Fig. 44), and fresh. **Note: See HY/SY.**

Sex—The CP apparently is not developed; the BP (Jan-Jul) is reliable for sexing ♀♀. The only owl in N.Am where ♂ ≥ ♀ in average measurements: ♀ wg(n82) 155-174, tl(n82) 70-85; ♂ wg(n74) 156-178, tl(n74) 73-87; see **Geographic variation**. ♀ = ♂ by plumage; however, in Mar-Jul ♂♂ are paler on the underparts than ♀♀ (Fig. 55) due to more wear, the result of differences in behavior at the nest site. Extremes are reliably sexed, with experience or with mated pairs.

Burrowing Owl

	Jan	Feb	Mar	Apr	May	Jun	Jul	Aug	Sep	Oct	Nov	Dec
Juv-HY												
	○	○	○	○	○	○	○	○	○	○	○	○
SY												
	(♀)	(♀)	(♂)	(♂)	(♂)	(♂)	(♂)	○	○			
AHY-U												
	(♀)	(♀)	(♂)	(♂)	(♂)	(♂)	(♂)	○	○	○	○	○
ASY												
	(♀)	(♀)	(♂)	(♂)	(♂)	(♂)	(♂)	○	○			

■ > 95% ▨ 25-95% ▢ 5-25% □ < 5%   See Fig. 24

References—Ridgway (1914), Forbush (1927), Bent (1938), Roberts (1955), Grant (1965), Thomsen (1971), Courser (1972), Martin (1973), Oberholser (1974), CWS & USFWS (1991), Plumpton & Lutz (1994), Pyle (1997b); W.D. Courser (*in litt.* to the BBL); PRBO data.

SPOTTED OWL
Strix occidentalis

SPOW
Species # 3690
Band size: 7B Lock-on

Species—From Barred Owl in all ages by feathers of the lower underparts dark, with subterminal spots or bands. Beware of hybrids.

Geographic variation—Moderate and ranges fairly well defined. Subspecies taxonomy follows Monson & Phillips (1981) and Dickerman (1997); see also Swarth (1910, 1915), Ridgway (1914), Oberholser (1915), Bent (1938), Barrows *et al.* (1982), Barrowclough (1990). Two other subspecies occur in Mex. More study is needed on the number of tail bars (see Table 1) by subspecies, which also varies with age and sex (see **Age** and **Sex**).

> *S.o. caurina* (res coastal BC-c.CA): Plumage medium-dark brown; white spotting on the breast small and indistinct (Fig. 56); wing and tail bars medium-pale brown; number of complete tail bars (see Table 1) may average fewer by age and sex (see **Sex**); leg feathering usually with heavy, brown mottling.
> *S.o. occidentalis* (res e.CA & coastal s.CA): Plumage medium brown; white spotting on the breast medium in size and indistinct (Fig. 56); wing and tail bars pale brown; number of complete tail bars (see Table 1) may average greater by age and sex (see **Sex**); leg feathering buff with a moderate amount of brown mottling.
> *S.o. huachucae* (res UT-AZ to CO-NM): Plumage pale brown; facial discs grayish; white spotting on the breast large and distinct (Fig. 56); wing and tail bars whitish; number of complete tail bars (see Table 1) may average fewer by age and sex (see **Sex**).

Molt—PB: HY partial (May-Oct), AHY incomplete-complete (Apr-Oct); PA absent. The 1st PB includes all body feathers but no wing covs. Flight-feather replacement is irregular during the adult PBs. The 2nd PB probably is incomplete in most cases; it often includes at least p2-p3, the outermost 1-6 pp (among p4-p10), and some or all of s1-s3, s5, and s10-s13, and it occasionally includes more feathers. The 3rd PB usually includes those feathers not replaced during the 2nd PB, often more and occasionally fewer. Subsequent PBs are irregular and sometimes complete, but sometimes with some pp and ss retained for three or more years. Complete replacement of rects usually occurs every other year, beginning with the 3rd PB, although it can rarely occur during the 2nd PB. See p. 67 for details on molt in owls, in general.

Skull—Pneumaticization patterns possibly are useful for ageing (see Family account).

Age—Juv (May-Oct) has loosely textured or downy feathers, and plumage like HY/AHY but paler and with markings (especially around the head) less distinct (tips of down can remain on HY after fledging); juv ♀ = ♂.

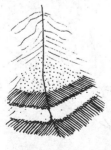   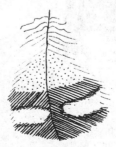   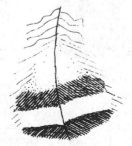

S.o. caurina   *S.o. occidentalis*   *S.o. huachucae*

FIGURE 56. The pattern on the central, upper breast feathers in Spotted Owl by subspecies. Note especially the width and distinctness of the white bars.

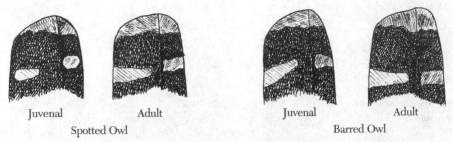

Juvenal   Adult   Juvenal   Adult

Spotted Owl   Barred Owl

FIGURE 57. The pattern on the primary coverts by age in Spotted and Barred owls. Similar differences (although less pronounced) are found in Flammulated, Great Horned, Great Gray, and Long-eared owls. Figure from Pyle (1997b).

HY/SY (Sep-Aug): Juvenal flight feathers retained; pp, pp covs, and ss uniform in wear (see Fig. 48A), narrow, and tapered; juvenal pp covs with small and rounded, pale markings (Fig. 57); numbers of bars on the pp, ss, and rects relatively large and distances between adjacent bars on these feathers relatively small (Table 1, Fig. 58; see also Figs. 61-62); rects narrow and tapered, with the terminal band pure whitish (Fig. 58). **Note: In addition, the shape of the outer pp may show average differences, as in the screech-owls (Fig. 44), but differences are subtle and can be difficult to assess. See also Geographic variation and Sex regarding the width of the bars on the rects.**

AHY/ASY (Sep-Aug): Pp, pp covs, and ss uniformly adult, broad, truncate, and with fewer bars (Table 1, Fig. 57; see also Figs. 61-62); pale markings of pp covs uniformly large and squared (Fig. 57); adult rects uniformly broad and fresh (Fig. 58), as in ASY/ATY. **Note: See HY/SY and SY/TY. AHY/ASYs showing this pattern may be rare or are ASY/ATYs with undetectable differences among feather generations.**

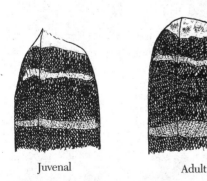

Juvenal   Adult

FIGURE 58. The width and pattern of the central rectrix (r1) by age in Spotted and Barred owls. See also Table 1. Substantial variation occurs within both age groups. A similar (but less pronounced) difference is found in Great Gray Owl. Note that juvenal feathers are often retained for two years in these species, resulting in the rectrices becoming substantially abraded in SY/TYs.

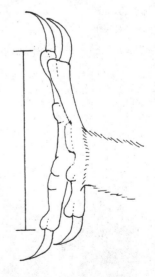

FIGURE 59. Example of a footpad measurement useful for sexing Spotted Owls. Sex-specific differences in this measurement should be looked for in other species of owls.

SY/TY (Sep-Aug): Pp, pp covs, and ss usually showing contrasts between juvenal and adult feathers (*cf.* Fig. 48**B–C**), often with 3-9 pp (and corresponding pp covs) and 4-10 ss (see **Molt**) fresher, broader, more truncate, and having bar patterns of adults (Table 1, Fig. 57; see also Figs. 61-62), contrasting with the other, replaced pp, pp covs, and ss, which are narrower, more faded and abraded, and show bar patterns of juvenal feathers; retained juvenal pp covs showing small rounded spots, in contrast to renewed pp covs with larger and squarer bars (Fig. 57); rects usually juvenal (occasionally adult) but very abraded, with whitish tips nearly worn off (see Fig. 58). **Note: See HY/SY. Occasional SY/TYs may be found with uniformly adult pp and ss, but with juvenal rects as above. Exceptions and intermediates occur that are not reliably aged; caution is advised, especially in separating SY/TY from ASY/ATY.**

ASY/ATY (Sep-Aug): Pp, pp covs, and ss showing slight contrasts between new and old, adult feathers, with the new and old feathers interspersed along the wing (*cf.* Fig. 48**D–H**), all feathers being broad, truncate and showing bar patterns of adult (Table 1, Fig. 57; see also Figs. 61-62); all pp covs showing the square bars of adult feathers (Fig. 57); rects broad and rounded, with the terminal band mixed pale gray and brown (Fig. 58). **Note: See SY/TY and AHY/ASY. Intermediates between this and SY/TY can occur; these should be aged AHY/ASY. Look also for some ASY/ATYs with two generations of adult feathers and a few worn juvenal feathers retained, that probably are reliably aged TY/4Y.**

Sex—The CP apparently is not developed; the BP (Feb-Jun) is reliable for sexing ♀♀. ♀ wg(n100) 300-349, tl(n100) 176-228; ♂ wg(n100) 293-339, tl(n100) 169-221. See Blakesley *et al.* (1990) for discriminant function analyses, based on live birds, including weight, wg, tl, bill length from the forehead, bill depth at the tip of the nares, and tarsus, that reliably separated ~80% of individuals of *S.o. caurina* by sex.

♀: Head and face relatively dark; footpad length (Fig. 59) in *S.o. caurina* 69-74 mm. **Note: Footpad lengths in the other subspecies (see Geographic variation) probably are similar, but measurement ranges need to be determined. In addition, the number of tail bars averages fewer in ♂♂ than in ♀♀ (see Table 1), but this also varies with subspecies (see Geographic variation) and age. Reliable sexing only should be performed with experience or on mated pairs; many intermediates occur which cannot be determined reliably by plumage alone.**

♂: Head and face relatively pale; footpad length (Fig. 59) in *S.o. caurina* 64-70 mm. **Note: See ♀.**

Hybrids reported—Barred Owl. The alpha code for a hybrid is **SBOH** and the **Species #** is **3686.**

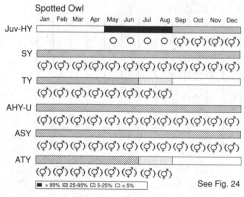

Note: Other than ♀♀ with brood patches, reliable sexing is currently only possible by footpad length in the northern subspecies, *S.o. caurina.*

References—Swarth (1910), Ridgway (1914), Oberholser (1915, 1974), Bent (1938), Forsman (1981), Barrows *et al.* (1982), Miller *et al.* (1985), Kaufman (1987a), Blakesley *et al.* (1990), CWS & USFWS (1991), Fleming *et al.* (1991, 1996), Moen *et al.* (1991), Hamer *et al.* (1994), Gutierrez *et al.* (1995), Pyle (1997b); E.D. Forsman (*in litt.* to the BBL).

BARRED OWL

Strix varia

BDOW
Species # 3680
Band size: 7B Lock-on

Species—All ages from Spotted Owl by feathers of the lower underparts light, with prominent, brown central streaks. Beware of hybrids.

Geographic variation—Weak to moderate and clinal where ranges meet. Subspecies taxonomy in N.Am follows the AOU (1957); see Ridgway (1914), Bishop (1931a), Nicholson (1938), Oberholser (1974), Stevenson & Anderson (1994). One other subspecies occurs in Mex.

S.v. varia (br & wint BC-n.CA to NB-nc.GA, wint to LA): Plumage dark brown; upperparts with dark and light brown barring; bill and feet small (measurements are needed); toes densely feathered at the base and bristled in the center. Birds of n.MN (*"brunnescens"*) may average darker and more contrasting, and birds of Que (*"albescens"*) may average paler, but differences are slight and obscured by individual variation.

S.v. helveola (res s.TX): Plumage pale brown; upperparts with brown and whitish barring; bill and feet large (measurements are needed); toes naked (except sides of the middle toe bristled).

S.v. georgica (res e.TX to coastal NC-FL): Plumage dark brown; upperparts with dark and light brown barring; bill and feet small (measurements are needed); toes naked, as in *helveola*. The description of a subspecies from Cape Sable, FL (*"sablei"*) was probably based on an anomalous individual.

Molt—PB: HY partial (May-Oct), AHY incomplete-complete (Apr-Oct); PA absent. The 1st PB includes all body feathers but no wing covs. The 2nd and subsequent PBs probably are similar to those of Spotted Owl, although the proportion of birds with complete molts may be higher; more study is needed. The 2nd PB usually includes at least p2-p3, 1-6 sequential pp (among p4-p10), and some or all of s1-s3, s5, and s10-s13; often more feathers may be replaced. The 3rd PB usually includes those feathers not replaced during the 2nd PB, often more, and occasionally less. Subsequent PBs are irregular and sometimes(?) complete, but sometimes with some pp and ss retained for three or more years. Complete replacement of rects apparently occurs every other year in most cases, beginning with the 3rd PB, as in Spotted Owl. See p. 67 for details on molt in owls, in general.

Skull—Pneumaticization patterns possibly are useful for ageing (see Family account).

Age—Juv (May-Sep) has loosely textured or downy feathers, and plumage like HY/AHY but paler and with markings (especially around the head) less distinct (tips of down can remain on HY after fledging); juv ♀ = ♂. Ageing criteria otherwise parallels those of Spotted Owl (which see), although contrasts between feathers are more difficult to detect, and many birds may have to be aged AHY/ASY, or even U/AHY.

Sex—The CP apparently is not developed; the BP (Jan-Jun) is reliable for sexing ♀♀. ♀ wg(n51) 330-357, tl(n51) 207-257; ♂ wg(n51) 308-340, tl(n51) 192-231. See Carpenter (1992) for a discriminant function analysis, based on specimens and using wg and tl, that separated 74% of MN-MI individuals by sex. Otherwise, no reliable sexing criteria are known; the number of bars on the tail (see Spotted Owl) appears to be unhelpful for sexing. Footpad length (Fig. 59) may be helpful, as in Spotted Owl, but more study is needed.

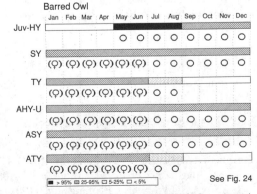

Barred Owl

See Fig. 24

Hybrids reported—Spotted Owl. The alpha code for a hybrid is **SBOH** and the **Species #** is **3686**.

References—Ridgway (1914), Forbush (1927), Bent (1938), Roberts (1955), Oberholser (1974), Kaufman (1987a), CWS & USFWS (1991), Carpenter (1992), Hamer *et al.* (1994), Pyle (1997b).

GREAT GRAY OWL
Strix nebulosa

GGOW
Species # 3700
Band size: 8 Lock-on

Geographic variation—Moderate, with well-defined ranges. Subspecies taxonomy in N.Am follows the AOU (1957); see Ridgway (1914), Oberholser (1922), Dement'ev & Gladkov (1951), Cramp (1985). Two other subspecies occur in Eurasia.

S.n. nebulosa (br & wint throughout the range in N.Am): From *lapponica* of Eurasia (a potential vagrant to N.Am) by plumage darker with few or no distinct bars; underparts with heavy, dusky mottling (*vs* dusky streaking in *lapponica*).

Molt—Not well studied in this species; it probably parallels that of the other *Strix* owls, but could take more years to complete: PB HY partial (Jul-Sep), AHY incomplete (Jul-Dec); PA absent. The 1st PB includes all body feathers but no wing covs. The 2nd PB probably includes p5-p6, perhaps some or all of p7-p9, possibly other pp (as in Spotted Owl), and up to 8 ss (among s1-s3 and the innermost, s11-s15). The 3rd PB could include all or some of the remaining juvenal pp, and subsequent PBs probably are irregular. More study is needed, especially regarding the replacement of the ss. See p. 67 for details on molt in owls, in general.

Skull—Pneumaticization patterns possibly are useful for ageing (see Family account).

Age—Juv (May-Sep) has loosely textured or downy feathers, and plumage like HY/AHY, but with the upperparts and head brown, lacking the facial pattern (tips of down can remain on HYs after fledging); juv ♀ = ♂.

HY/SY (Aug-Jul): Juvenal pp, pp covs, and ss uniform in wear, showing no contrasts (*cf.* Fig. 48**A**); terts narrow and tapered, with dusky barring, and without a dark shaft streak (Fig. 60); central rects(r1) relatively abraded, and narrow (45-60 mm wide in *lapponica*), with the terminal band (when present) whitish (see Fig. 58). **Note: Ageing criteria in this species are untested and caution is advised; intermediates and exceptions can occur that are not reliably aged. In addition, differences occur in the pattern of the pp covs and the number of bars on the flight feathers, as in Spotted, Barred, and other owls (see Table 1 & Figs. 57 & 61-62), but distinctions between juvenal and adult feathers are not as clear. Iris color is probably also of some use in ageing, as in other large owls, but more study is needed.**

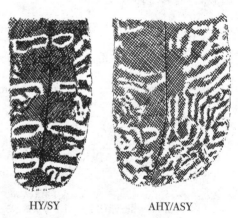

HY/SY   AHY/ASY

FIGURE 60. The width and pattern of the tertials by age in Great Gray Owl. Wide variation in this feature is shown in both age groups.

SY/TY (Aug-Jul): Pp, pp covs, and ss showing distinct contrasts in wear between juvenal and adult feathers (*cf.* Fig. 48**B–C**), p5-p6, sometimes p7-p9, occasionally other pp, the corresponding pp covs, and some ss (among s1-s3 and s11-s15, possibly more) fresh and broad, contrasting with the more tapered, abraded, and worn, retained juvenal pp, pp covs, and ss; terts broad, rounded, irregularly vermiculated, and with dark shaft streaks (Fig. 60); central rects as in HY/SY, as in ASY/ATY, or showing contrasts between two or more generations. **Note: See HY/SY.**

ASY/ATY (Aug-Jul): Pp, pp covs, and ss showing slight contrasts between new and old, adult feathers, with the new and the old feathers interspersed along the wing (*cf.* Fig. 48D–H); terts as in SY/TY (Fig. 60); central rects relatively fresh, broad (55-70 mm wide in *lapponica*), and with the terminal band pale dusky (see Fig. 58). **Note: See HY/SY. Occasional intermediates between SY/TY and ASY/ATY occur that should be aged AHY/ASY.**

Sex—The CP apparently is not developed; the BP (Feb-Jul) is reliable for sexing ♀♀. ♀ wg(n28) 419-465, tl(n20) 285-347; ♂ wg(n30) 402-447, tl(n20) 270-323; see **Geographic variation**. Otherwise, no reliable criteria for sexing are known, although ♀♀ may average slightly buffier and have a longer and darker throat patch than ♂♂; more study is needed.

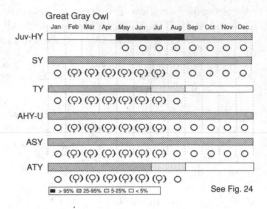

References—Ridgway (1914), Forbush (1927), Bent (1938), Roberts (1955), Brunton & Pittaway (1971), Oberholser (1974), Cramp (1985), Pyle (1997b).

LONG-EARED OWL
Asio otus

LEOW
Species # 3660
Band size: 5-6 Lock-on

Species—From Great Horned Owl by smaller size (wg 265-308, tl 133-163; see **Sex**) and lack of a white throat patch. From Short-eared Owl by the presence of long ear tufts (> 30 mm); iris yellowish orange; outer pp of adults with brownish barring, but not a distinct black tip (see Fig. 61); inner pp and ss lacking a pale trailing edge (see Fig. 64). The last feature should separate juvs, as well.

Geographic variation—Weak and clinal where the ranges in N.Am meet. Subspecies taxonomy in N.Am follows the AOU (1957); see Oberholser (1922, 1974), Godfrey (1947), Rea (1983), Unitt (1984), Cramp (1985). Two other subspecies occur in Eurasia.

    A.o. tuftsi (br & wint s.NWT-Sask to s.CA-w.TX): Small; overall plumage pale brownish with a grayish wash; tail bars distinct. ♀ wg(n17) 272-295, tl(n10) 138-157; ♂ wg(n20) 265-293, tl(n16) 133-145. Nominate *otus* of Eurasia, a possible vagrant to N.Am, is paler, has 1-3 fewer bars on the flight feathers (*cf.* Table 1), and has a larger pale base to the outer pp (*cf.* Fig. 61).

    A.o. wilsonianus (br & wint s.Man-NS to s.TX-FL): Large; overall plumage dark brownish with a dusky wash; tail bars indistinct. ♀ wg(n10) 288-308, tl(n15) 144-163; ♂ wg(n20) 275-302, tl(n16) 139-158.

Molt—PB: HY partial (Jul-Oct), AHY incomplete-complete (Jul-Oct); PA absent. The PBs occur primarily on the summer grounds, completing during migration in some individuals. The 1st PB includes all body feathers but no wing covs. The 2nd PB can be complete; when incomplete, up to 8 ss (among s1-s9; typically including s4, often s3 and s7, and sometimes others; Fig. 64) and rarely p10 or p9-p10 can be retained, the patterns of retained feathers often (but not always) being symmetrical. Subsequent PBs also can be incomplete or complete; when incomplete, up to 6 ss can be retained, usually not involving the same positions as are found on HY/SYs (Fig. 64) and less often being symmetrical; the outermost 1-2 pp and pp covs rarely if ever are retained. Replacement of the rects typically is complete during the adult PBs. See p. 67 for details on molt in owls, in general.

Skull—Pneumaticization patterns possibly are useful for ageing (see Family account).

Age—Juv (Apr-Sep) has loosely textured or downy plumage, the feathers of the upperparts dusky with white tips, the facial pattern of adult lacking (tips of down can remain on HYs after fledging), and the iris brownish; juv ♀ = ♂.

HY/SY (Sep-Aug): Juvenal flight feathers retained, the ss and pp uniform in wear, showing no contrasts (see Fig. 48A; *cf.* Fig. 64), tapered, and with little or no pinkish tinge to the undersurfaces; numbers of bars on the pp, ss, and rects relatively large and distances between adjacent bars on these feathers relatively small (Table 1, Figs. 61-64); tips of the outer webs of r4-r6 uniformly whitish; iris brownish yellow to orangish. **Note: In addition, average differences in the shape of the buff markings on the pp covs, as in *Strix* owls (Fig. 57), may be helpful for ageing some birds. Some intermediates with uniform flight feathers can occur (~20%, with experience) that are not reliably aged.**

AHY/ASY (Sep-Aug): All ss and pp adult, uniformly broad (*cf.* Fig. 64), with a moderate to strong pinkish wash to the under-

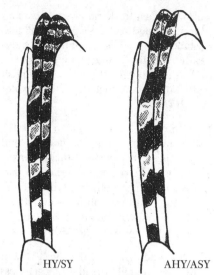

HY/SY   AHY/ASY

FIGURE 61. The shape and pattern of barring on the outer primaries (most distinct on p8-p9) by age in Long-eared Owl. See also Table 1. Similar differences in pattern, with juvenal feathers showing narrower and more distinct bars, can be found in many other species of owls. Figure from Pyle (1997b).

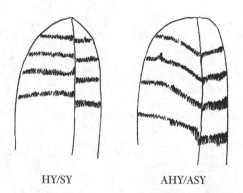

HY/SY   AHY/ASY

FIGURE 62. The shape and pattern of barring on the outermost secondary (s1) by age in Long-eared Owl. See also Table 1. Similar differences in pattern, with the juvenal feathers showing narrower and more distinct bars, can be found in many other species of owls. Figure from Pyle (1997b).

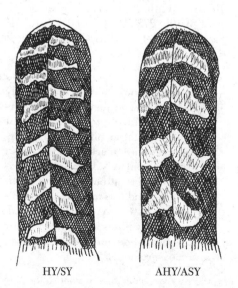

HY/SY   AHY/ASY

FIGURE 63. The shape and pattern of barring on the central rectrix (r1) by age in Long-eared Owl. See also Table 1. Similar differences in pattern, with the juvenal feathers showing narrower and more distinct bars, can be found in many other species of owls (see also Figs. 49, 52, & 58). Figure from Pyle (1997b).

surfaces when fresh; numbers of bars on the pp, ss, and rects relatively small and distances between adjacent bars on these feathers relatively large (Table 1, Figs. 61-64); tips of outer webs of r4-r6 whitish with dusky speckling; iris yellow. **Note: See HY/SY.**

SY/TY (Sep-Aug): Like AHY/ASY, but 1-8 ss, including s4, often s3 and s7, and sometimes others, contrastingly narrow and worn (Fig. 64) and showing bar patterns of juvenal feathers (Table 1, Fig. 62), the patterns often symmetrical between wings, or nearly so; iris orange-yellow to yellow. **Note: See HY/SY.**

ASY/ATY (Sep-Aug): Like SY/TY, but retained ss adult, broad, truncate, less distinctly worn in comparison with the newer ss, and usually not with the same patterns of replacement as are found in SY/TYs (Fig. 64), the patterns less often symmetrical between the wings; iris yellow. **Note: See HY/SY.**

Sex—The CP apparently is not developed; the BP (Feb-Jun) is reliable for sexing ♀♀. ♀ wg(n100) 272-308, tl(n100) 138-163; ♂ wg(n100) 265-302, tl(n100) 133-158; see **Geographic variation**.

♀: Underwing covs rich buff to tawny. **Note: In addition, ♀♀ may average darker overall, with richer buff and more heavily streaked plumage than ♂♂, but differences are difficult to assess without comparison (these differences apparently are more marked in Eurasian subspecies than in N.Am). Reliable sexing should be attempted only with experience and, even then, intermediates (up to 50%) are not reliably sexed. In sexing, synthesize plumage color with information on subspecies, age, and measurements.**

♂: Underwing covs silvery, whitish, or pale buff. **Note: See ♀.**

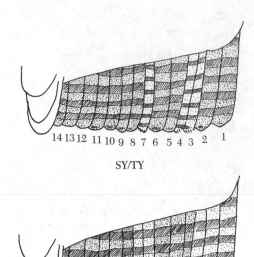

14 13 12 11 10 9 8 7 6 5 4 3 2 1

SY/TY

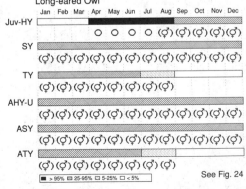

ASY/ATY

FIGURE 64. Patterns of retained secondaries in SY/TY and ASY/ATY Long-eared Owls. See also Figure 25. Note the narrower barring on the juvenal secondaries in SY/TYs. Similar retention patterns can be found in Flammulated Owl, Northern Hawk-Owl, some Short-eared Owls, and occasional screech-owls. Figure from Pyle (1997b).

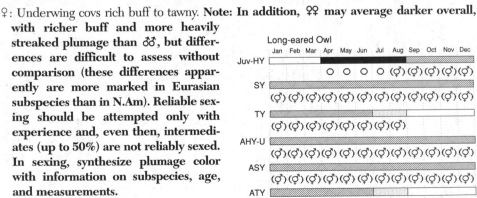

See Fig. 24

References—Ridgway (1914), Forbush (1927), Bent (1938), Roberts (1955), Stresemann & Stresemann (1966), Oberholser (1974), Wijnandts (1984), Cramp (1985), Marks (1985), Evans & Rosenfield (1987), CWS & USFWS (1991), Baker (1993), Marks *et al.* (1994), Pyle (1997b); D.L. Evans, R.D. Weir (*in litt.* to the BBL); PRBO data.

SHORT-EARED OWL
Asio flammeus

SEOW
Species # 3670
Band size: 6 Lock-on

Species—From Long-eared Owl by ear tufts lacking or rudimentary (<25 mm); iris pale yellow; tips of adult outer pp black (*cf.* Fig. 61); inner pp and ss with a distinct, pale trailing edge (*cf.* Fig. 64). The last feature should separate juvs, as well.

Geographic variation—Weak and complicated by substantial individual variation. Subspecies taxonomy in N.Am follows the AOU (1957); see Ridgway (1914), Cramp (1985). Eight other subspecies occur in Africa, S.Am, and on isolated oceanic islands.

   A.f. flammeus (br & wint throughout N.Am & Eurasia): Averages paler (by sex; see **Sex**) and longer-winged than most other subspecies (although darker than some and shorter-winged than some); wg/tl (see **Sex**) probably larger than most other subspecies, which are resident or less migratory.

Molt—PB: HY partial (Jul-Oct), AHY incomplete-complete (May-Oct); PA absent-limited(?). The 1st PB includes all body feathers but no wing covs. Adult PBs primarily are complete; when incomplete (~20% of birds in N.A), 1-6 ss (among s1-s8) are retained, most likely the same feathers (but averaging fewer) that are retained during the 2nd and subsequent PBs in Long-eared Owl (which see); more study is needed. The PBs occur primarily on the summer grounds, completing during migration in some individuals. A limited PA (Mar-May) may occur in some birds. See p. 67 for details on molt in owls, in general.

Skull—Pneumaticization patterns possibly are useful for ageing (see Family account).

Age—Juv (May-Sep) has loosely textured or downy plumage, with the upperparts and head dusky with buff tips, the facial pattern of adult lacking (tips of down can remain on HYs after fledging), and the iris brownish to brownish yellow; juv ♀ = ♂.

   U/AHY (Sep-Aug): All ss uniform in wear. **Note: No other reliable means are known to age this species after the 1st PB. Juvenal and adult pp, pp covs, ss, and rects show average differences in shape, pattern and wear, as in Long-eared Owl, but these differences are greatly obscured by substantial individual variation within both age groups (perhaps more so than in Europe; see Baker 1993). Look also for a pink bloom to the undersurface of the wings on AHY/ASYs that may not be found in HY/SYs (see Long-eared Owl), for average differences in the pattern to the tips of the rects, and for differences in iris color (as in Long-eared Owl), that may be helpful in ageing some birds; more study is needed.**

   AHY/ASY (Sep-Aug): 1-6 ss (among s1-s8; check both wings) retained, more faded and worn than the other ss (see Fig. 64), with the patterns often symmetrical between the wings. **Note: See U/AHY. Only ~20% of birds show contrasts in the ss and can be aged AHY/ASY. With experience, some AHY/ASYs may be separated into SY/TY or ASY/ATY by the condition, relative shape and wear, and the pattern of retention of older ss, as in Long-eared Owl (Fig. 64), although differences in color pattern appear to be slight at best.**

Sex—The CP apparently is not developed; the BP (Feb-Jun) is reliable for sexing ♀♀. ♀ wg(n45) 305-331, tl(n43) 138-162; ♂ wg(n56) 298-326, tl(n51) 135-157.

   ♀: Plumage (in consideration of wear) relatively rich and dark; underparts dark buff with heavy, dark brown streaking; undertail covs buff, usually with narrow, brown streaks; underwing covs cream to pale buff, usually with large brown spots on the covs. **Note: Reliable sexing only should be attempted with experience and, even then, intermediates (up to 50%) are not reliably sexed; synthesize the above information with measurements and plumage wear.**

♂: Plumage (in consideration of wear) relatively pale and gray; underparts whitish with relatively sparse, brownish streaking; undertail covs whitish, usually with indistinct or no streaks; underwing covs white to pale creamy white, without spots or with small spots on the covs. **Note: See ♀.**

References—Ridgway (1914), Forbush (1927), Bent (1938), Roberts (1955), Stresemann & Stresemann (1966), Oberholser (1974), Austin & Rea (1976), Cramp (1985), CWS & USFWS (1991), Baker (1993), Pyle (1997b).

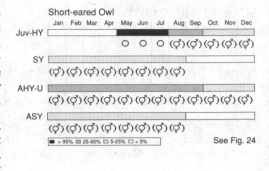

BOREAL OWL
Aegolius funereus

BOOW
Species # 3710
Band size: 5-6 Lock-on

Species—From Northern Saw-whet Owl by larger size (wg 163-198, tl 91-117; see **Sex**); crown spotted whitish; bill pale horn; juv chocolate-colored.

Geographic variation—Moderate and ranges well defined. Subspecies taxonomy in N.Am follows the AOU (1957); see Ridgway (1914), Cramp (1985). Six other subspecies occur in Eurasia.

> *A.f. magnus* (vag to w.AK Is): Plumage pale grayish; whitest scapulars with small (<5 mm) or no brown tips; underparts primarily white with pale brown streaking.
>
> *A.f. richardsoni* (br & wint throughout the range in N.Am): Plumage dark brownish; whitest scapulars with brown tips > 5 mm; underparts primarily brown with whitish streaking.

Molt—PB: HY partial (Jul-Dec), AHY incomplete-complete (May-Nov); PA absent. The PBs occur primarily on the summer grounds. The 1st PB includes all body feathers but no wing covs. The 2nd PB usually includes the outermost 3-6 (rarely up to 9 or 10) pp, and the innermost 3-9 (of 13) ss (rarely more), perhaps occasionally some isolated outer ss, as well. The 3rd PB usually includes 2-6 sequential central pp (among p3-p8), adjacent to the pp replaced during the 2nd PB, and leaving the innermost 3-6 ss (among s1-s6) as juvenal feathers, and probably often a block of central ss (among s3-s10) leaving a block of outer ss (among s1-s6) as juvenal feathers (Fig. 65); more study on the replacement of ss is needed. Subsequent PBs are irregular, the outer pp usually being replaced for the 2nd time, at the same time or before the juvenal p1 & p2, which can be retained for 4-5 yrs before being replaced. Replacement of the rects usually is complete during adult PBs, but it occasionally can be incomplete (perhaps most often during the 2nd PB). Complete adult PBs in this species are reported to occur, but this should be confirmed. Reported differences in the 3rd PB between Boreal and Northern Saw-whet owls are interesting, and should be studied further. See p. 67 for details on molt in owls, in general.

Skull—Pneumaticization patterns possibly are useful for ageing (see Family account).

Age—Juv (Jun-Sep) has loosely textured or downy plumage, with the upperparts and head uniformly chocolate in coloration (tips of down can remain on HYs after fledging); juv ♀ = ♂.

HY/SY (Sep-Aug): Juvenal ss and pp uniform in wear, showing no contrasts (*cf.* Fig. 65); pp sometimes with narrow, white tips when fresh; outer pp (p7-p10) somewhat narrow and tapered at the tips (see Fig. 44); central rects (r1) relatively narrow (see Fig. 53). **Note: In addition, HY/SYs average slightly redder in the browns of the coloration, average slightly smaller spots on the upperparts, have white bars on the rects that tend to be shaped** more like chevrons, and average narrower and more pointed terts than adult age groups; with experience these criteria can be helpful for ageing some birds. Exceptions and intermediates occur that are not reliably aged; thus, caution is advised, especially in separating SY/TY from ASY/ATY.

SY/TY (Sep-Aug): Sequential blocks of 3-9 outer pp (among p3-p10) and 3-9 inner ss (among s5-s13; perhaps also isolated outer ss among s1-s3) molting or fresh, contrasting with the uniformly older and faded, inner pp and outer ss (*cf.* Fig. 65); pp without white edges; replaced, outer pp (p7-p10) somewhat broad and truncate (see Fig. 44); adult central rects (r1) relatively broad (see Fig. 53), the rects occasionally mixed juvenal and adult. **Note: See HY/SY.**

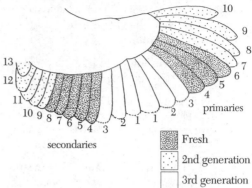

FIGURE 65. A replacement pattern of the secondaries and primaries in Boreal Owl, perhaps suggesting TY/4Y. More study is needed before this age classification can be reliably assigned (see text). The replacement of the outer primaries and inner secondaries (2nd-generation feathers in this illustration) is typical of SY/TYs. Note the difference in replacement during the third prebasic molt between this and Northern Saw-whet Owl (see Figure 66).

ASY/ATY (Sep-Aug): Pp and ss showing at least three generations of feathers, or showing irregular contrasts in freshness, unlike the patterns of SY/TYs (*cf.* Fig. 65), with new and old feathers interspersed along the wing (*cf.* Fig. 48G–H). **Note: See HY/SY. Occasional birds with uniformly adult-like feathers may be encountered and should be aged U/AHY or AHY/ASY, although these likely are ASY/ATYs. Birds with blocks of sequential pp and ss, including some or all of p3-p8 and s4-s7, fresh and new, contrasting with the slightly older, sequential pp to the outside and ss to the inside (among p5-p10 and s5-s13), and the much older, sequential juvenal pp to the inside and ss to the outside (among p1-p5 and s1-s5), each of the blocks uniform in wear and without gaps of 1-2 feathers (Fig. 65), may be reliably aged TY/4Y, and those with irregular patterns (*e.g.*, Fig. 48G–H) might be aged ATY/A4Y, but confirmation is needed. Difficulty in separating feather generations may preclude precise ageing beyond ASY/ATY.**

Sex—The CP apparently is not developed; the BP (Feb-Jul) is reliable for sexing ♀♀. Measurements are useful: ♀ wg(n54) 173-198, tl(n50) 95-117; ♂ wg(n48) 163-179, tl(n51) 91-107; see Hayward & Hayward (1991) for discriminant function analyses, based on live birds, including weight, wg, and tl (or wg, tl, bill from nares, and length of alula), that separated sexes of mated pairs in ID with 100% reliability. No reliable plumage criteria are known for sexing, although, age for age, ♀♀ average tawnier in the face than ♂♂.

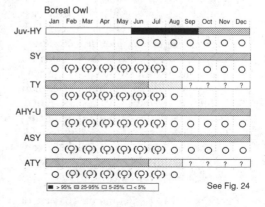

References—Ridgway (1914), Forbush (1927), Bent (1938), Roberts (1955), Phillips et al. (1984), Cramp (1985), Korpimäki (1987, 1990), Hörnfeldt *et al.* (1988), CWS & USFWS (1991), Hayward & Hayward (1991), Pyle (1997b).

NORTHERN SAW-WHET OWL
Aegolius acadicus

NSWO
Species # 3720
Band size: 4-3A Lock-on

Species—From Boreal Owl by smaller size (wg 125-147, tl 61-73; see **Sex**); crown and nape streaked white; bill dark with a pale tip; juv reddish brown (sooty in *A.a. brooksi*; see **Geographic variation**).

Geographic variation—Moderate and ranges well defined. Subspecies taxonomy follows the AOU (1957); see Ridgway (1914), Fleming (1916). No other subspecies occur.

> ***A.a. acadicus*** (br & wint throughout the range in N.Am, except for the Queen Charlotte Is, where found only in migration or wint): Plumage reddish or brown, with heavy, pale streaking; juv dark brown.
> ***A.a. brooksi*** (res Queen Charlotte Is, BC): Plumage dark sooty brown with light, pale streaking; juv sooty blackish.

Molt—PB: HY partial (Jul-Dec), AHY incomplete-complete (May-Nov); PA absent. The PBs occur primarily on the summer grounds. The 1st PB includes all body feathers but no wing covs. The 2nd PB usually includes the outermost 1-7 pp and the innermost 3-9 (of 13) ss. The 3rd PB usually includes the innermost 2-4 pp (among p1-p4), usually leaving 2-4 central pp (among p3-p7) as juvenal feathers, and the outermost 2-6 ss (among s1-s6), often leaving 1-6 central ss (among s4-s9) as juvenal feathers (Fig. 66). Subsequent PBs are irregular, resulting in mixed wing-feather generations. Occasional complete adult PBs have been suspected, but this requires confirmation; see Boreal Owl. Replacement of the rects typically is complete during adult PBs. See p. 67 for details on molt in owls, in general.

Skull—Pneumaticization patterns possibly are useful for ageing (see Family account).

Age—Juv (May-Sep) has loosely textured or downy plumage, with the upperparts and head uniformly dark reddish brown or sooty in coloration (tips of down can remain on HYs after fledging); juv ♀=♂.

HY/SY (Sep-Aug): Juvenal flight feathers retained, the ss and pp uniform in wear, and showing no contrasts (*cf.* Fig. 66); pp often with narrow, white edges when fresh; outer pp (p7-p10) somewhat narrow and tapered at the tips (see Fig. 44); central rects (r1) relatively narrow (see Fig. 53). **Note: In addition, HY/SYs may average slightly redder in coloration, may average slightly smaller spots on the upperparts, and may average narrower and more pointed terts than adult age groups; with experience, these criteria may be helpful for ageing some birds. Exceptions and intermediates occur that are not reliably aged; caution is advised, especially in separating SY/TY from ASY/ATY.**

SY/TY (Sep-Aug): Sequential blocks of outer pp and inner ss, including at least p8-p10 and s9-s12 (sometimes some or all of p4-p7 and/or s5-s8) molting or

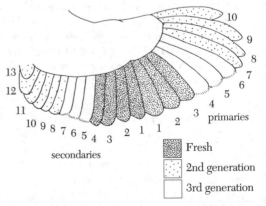

FIGURE 66. A replacement pattern of the secondaries and primaries in Northern Saw-whet Owl, perhaps suggesting TY/4Y. More study is needed before this age classification can be reliably assigned (see text). The replacement of the outer primaries and inner secondaries (2nd-generation feathers in this illustration) is typical of SY/TYs. Note the difference in replacement during the third prebasic molt between this and Boreal Owl (see Figure 65).

fresh, contrasting with the uniformly older and faded, sequential inner pp (*cf.* Fig. 66); replaced outer pp (p7-p10) somewhat broad and truncate (see Fig. 44); central rects relatively broad (see Fig. 53). **Note: See HY/SY.**

ASY/ATY (Sep-Aug): Pp and ss showing at least three generations of feathers, or showing irregular contrasts in freshness, unlike the patterns of SY/TYs (*cf.* Fig. 66), with new and old feathers interspersed along the wing (*cf.* Fig. 48G–H). **Note: See HY/SY. Occasional birds with uniformly adult feathers may be encountered and should be aged U/AHY or AHY/ASY, although these likely are ASY/ATYs. Birds with a block of sequential inner pp and outer ss, including some or all of p1-p4 and s1-s4, fresh and new, contrasting with the slightly older sequential pp to the outside and ss to the inside (among p5-p10 and s5-s13) and the much older, sequential juvenal pp and ss in the center (among p3-p7 and s5-s9), each of the blocks uniform in wear and without gaps of 1-2 feathers (Fig. 66), may be reliably aged TY/4Y, and those with irregular patterns (*e.g.*, Fig. 48G–H) may be reliably aged ATY/A4Y, but confirmation is needed. Difficulty in separating feather generations may preclude precise ageing beyond ASY/ATY.**

Sex—The CP apparently is not developed; the BP (Feb-Jul) is reliable for sexing ♀♀. ♀ wg(n100) 129-147, tl(n20) 65-73; ♂ wg(n100) 125-142, tl(n20) 61-69. Buckholtz *et al.* (1984) analyzed wg by sex in s.Ont fall migrants, and came up with reliable sexing of both HY (≥ 139.3 = ♀; ≤ 131.8 = ♂) and AHY (≥ 140.8 = ♀; ≤ 133.1 = ♂); however, this is likely not valid throughout the range of the species (see Mueller 1990). Otherwise, no reliable plumage criteria are known for sexing, although, age for age, ♀♀ may average richer tawny in the face than ♂♂.

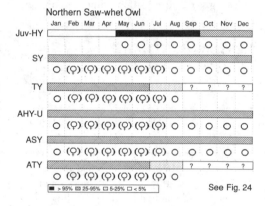

Northern Saw-whet Owl

See Fig. 24

References—Ridgway (1914), Forbush (1927), Bent (1938), Roberts (1955), Collins (1961), Mueller & Berger (1967), Wood (1969), Sheppard & Klimkiewicz (1976), Weir *et al.* (1980), Edwards *et al.* (1982), Mueller (1982, 1990), Buckholtz *et al.* (1984), Phillips *et al.* (1984), Evans & Rosenfield (1987), CWS & USFWS (1991), Slack (1992a, 1992b), Carpenter & Carpenter (1993), Pyle (1997b); D.F. Brinker, P.M. Catling, D.L. Evans, W.A. Lamb, K. McKeever (*in litt.* to the BBL); PRBO data.

NIGHTJARS

CAPRIMULGIDAE

Eight species. Large-headed, large-eyed, and large-mouthed nocturnal birds with pectinate combs on the middle claws, prominent rictal bristles, soft body plumage, and small, semipalmated feet. Nightjars have 10 primaries (the 10th full in length), 12 (sometimes 13) secondaries, and 10 (occasionally 12 in Pauraque) rectrices. The first prebasic molt is partial, the juvenal flight feathers and some (but not all) wing coverts being retained though the second summer; in most species, some body feathers, wing coverts, and/or secondaries can be retained during prebasic molts. Primary coverts usually are replaced with their corresponding primaries. No prealternate molts apparently occur in North American species. Pneumaticization typically does not complete, but the percentage of completion may be useful for ageing (see Fig. 88); more study is needed. Also, check for variation in the width of the middle toe comb with age, as in Barn Owl (see Fig. 43). Adult males have white in the tail whereas females usually are buffier here; certain species show similar characters in juveniles and HYs, whereas others do not. Cloacal protuberances apparently are not developed, but brood patches are reliable for sexing females. Males average larger than females; however, HY/SYs average much smaller wing lengths than AHY/ASYs, complicating sex determination using measurements.

LESSER NIGHTHAWK
Chordeiles acutipennis

LENI
Species # 4210
Band size: 1A-2

Species—From Common and Antillean nighthawks by smaller size (wg 158-196, tl 92-118; see **Sex**); p10 usually ≤ p9 (Fig. 67); pale patch on the pp buff (♀) or white (♂), on p7-p10 at most, opposite the tip of p5, distal to the tip of p4, and tapered toward the trailing edge (Fig. 67); tip of the pp covs to the base of the white patch 18-35 mm (Fig. 67); inner pp, ss, and pp covs distinctly spotted or mottled buff; underwing covs with buff and narrower dusky bars (Fig. 68); juv without heavy, black markings on the dorsum (see Fig. 73); downy young relatively uniform in color, without blotchy black and white mottling. In contrast to Common Nighthawk, Lesser Nighthawk replaces flight feathers on the summer grounds, so relative wear of AHY/ASYs (fresh in fall, worn in spring), especially of the outer pp, also can be helpful for identifications. From the other nightjars of N.Am by the combination of rictal bristles absent or greatly reduced; white or buff patches present in both the wings and the tail; tail notched (r5 > r1); throat white to buff.

Geographic variation—Moderate, but clinal where ranges meet. Subspecies taxon-

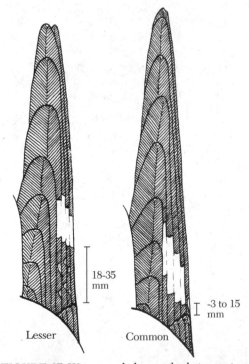

18-35 mm

-3 to 15 mm

Lesser   Common

FIGURE 67. Wing morphology and relative position of the white wing patch in Lesser and Common nighthawks. The figures show ♂♂; ♀♀ have smaller and less distinct patches (see Figures 70 and 74), but the locations of the patches are similar.

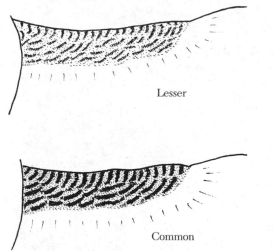

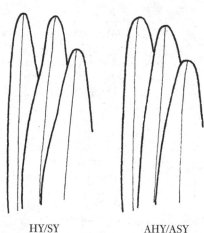

HY/SY   AHY/ASY

FIGURE 68. The pattern of the underwing coverts in Lesser and Common nighthawks.

FIGURE 69. The shape of the outer primaries (p7-p10) by age in nightjars.

omy follows Dickerman (1985); see also Oberholser (1914b), Ridgway (1914), van Rossem (1942a), Wetmore (1968), Dickerman (1981, 1982). Six other subspecies occur in Mex-S.Am.

C.a. texensis (br throughout the range in N.Am): Larger (see **Sex**, *vs* wg 158-184, tl 90-115), browner, and paler than the other subspecies; pale bars on the central rect (r1) broader (4-8 mm, *vs* 2-5 mm) and dark bars more distinct; juv plumage paler gray, the feathers edged cinnamon with finer, dusky vermiculations. Birds of c-n.Baja CA (*"inferior"*) average smaller, but differences are broadly clinal. Birds of Sonora and s.Baja CA (*micromeris*), which may occur in CA-NM as vagrants, are smaller (wg 166-185), grayer, and average more black in the upperparts and underparts.

Molt—PB: HY partial (Aug-Sep), AHY incomplete-complete (Jun-Sep); PA absent. The PBs occur primarily on the summer grounds. The 2nd and subsequent PBs often (in ~76% of birds) are incomplete. During the 2nd PB, a consecutive block of 1-4 ss (among s2-s7) often are retained (see Fig. 71); perhaps occasionally some pp and pp covs also can be retained. During subsequent PBs, 1-5 ss (among s1-s8) often are retained, usually in irregular patterns (see Fig. 71), not including consecutive blocks, as during the 2nd PB. All rects usually are replaced during the 2nd and subsequent PBs.

Skull—Pneumaticization patterns possibly are useful for ageing (see Family account).

Age—Juv (Jun-Sep) is mottled pale gray and cinnamon and has brown scapulars without a bold, black and buff pattern (Fig. 73); juvs can be sexed by the p7 and rect criteria, as in HY/SYs (see Figs. 70 & 72).

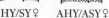

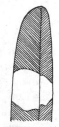

HY/SY♀   AHY/ASY♀   HY/SY♂   AHY/ASY♂

FIGURE 70. The typical pattern of white on p7 by age and sex in Lesser Nighthawk.

HY/SY (Sep-Aug): Pp covs and retained juvenal outer gr covs with full buff or cinnamon tips (see Fig. 77); outer pp narrow and tapered (Fig. 69); pale patch on p7 averages buffier and reduced by sex (Fig. 70); juvenal ss uniform in wear (Fig. 25A), the outer ss and inner pp tipped buffy white or pale cinnamon with dusky mottling (Fig. 71); rects with narrower bars by sex (Fig. 72).

AHY/ASY (Sep-Aug): Pp covs and outer gr covs with few or no, buff to cinnamon tips (see Fig. 77); outer pp broad and truncate (Fig. 69); pale patch on p7 averages whiter and larger by sex (Fig. 70); adult ss uniform in wear (Fig. 25B), the outer ss and inner pp tipped grayish with relatively little mottling (Fig. 71); rects with broader bars by sex (Fig. 72). **Note: Only ~24% of birds show this pattern (uniform adult ss); the remainder should be separated reliably into SY/TY or ASY/ATY.**

SY/TY (Sep-Aug): Like AHY/ASY, but 1-4 juvenal ss (often in a block among s2-s7) narrow, worn, and buff-tipped, contrasting markedly with the broader, fresher, and grayish-tipped, replaced ss (Fig. 71; see also Fig. 25C); **Note: See AHY/ASY. Look also for one or more juvenal, outermost pp and pp covs to occasionally be retained.**

ASY/ATY (Sep-Aug): Like AHY/ASY, but 1-5 adult ss (among s1-s8, usually not in a block) retained, faded, and worn, contrasting moderately with the fresher, replaced ss (Fig. 71; see also Fig. 25D). **Note: See AHY/ASY.**

Sex—The CP apparently is not developed; the BP (May-Aug) is reliable for sexing ♀♀. ♀ wg(n76) 168-185, tl(n59) 92-112; ♂ wg(n100) 173-196, tl(n71) 94-118; HY/SYs average 10 mm shorter wg than AHY/ASYs; measurements exclude the smaller populations of *C.a. texensis* from Baja CA (see **Geographic variation**).

♀: Throat patch washed buff; patch on p7 tawny (HY/SY) to buff (AHY/ASY) and reduced by age (Fig. 70); rects with an

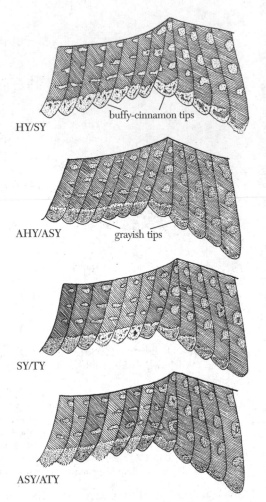

buffy-cinnamon tips

HY/SY

AHY/ASY   grayish tips

SY/TY

ASY/ATY

FIGURE 71. Replacement patterns in the secondaries by age in Lesser Nighthawk. See also Figure 25. The same patterns of replacement are found in most other nightjars, but the contrasts between the cinnamon and grayish tips of these feathers are not as pronounced in the other species (see Fig. 78). Figure from Pyle (1995a).

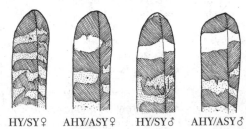

HY/SY ♀   AHY/ASY ♀   HY/SY ♂   AHY/ASY ♂

FIGURE 72. The shape and typical patterns of buff and white on the outer rectrix (r5), by age and sex, in Lesser Nighthawk.

indistinct or no, buffy-white subterminal band (Fig. 72).

♂: Throat patch white; patch on p7 white (tinged buff in HY/SY) and larger by age (Fig. 70); rects with a white subterminal band (Fig. 72).

References—Oberholser (1914b, 1974), Ridgway (1914), Bent (1940), Selander (1954), Dickerman (1981, 1982, 1985), Stevenson *et al.* (1983), Cavanagh (1985), Wilds (1985a), Czaplak & Wilds (1986), Langridge (1986), Janos & Prather (1989), Stevenson & Anderson (1994), Howell & Webb (1995), Pyle (1995a).

Lesser Nighthawk

See Fig. 24

COMMON NIGHTHAWK
Chordeiles minor

CONI
Species # 4200
Band size: 2-1A

Species—From Lesser Nighthawk by larger size of most subspecies (wg 163-210, tl 95-123; see **Geographic variation** & **Sex**); p10 usually ≥ p9 (Fig. 67); patch on the pp white, on p6-p10 at least, opposite the tip of p4, curved, and widening toward the trailing edge (Fig. 67); tip of the pp covs to the base of the white patch -3 to 15 mm (Fig. 67); inner pp, ss, and pp covs usually with few or no buff spots (except in *C.m. henryi*; see **Geographic variation**); underwing covs with dusky and narrower whitish bars (Fig. 68); juv with heavy, black markings on the dorsum (Fig. 73); downy young with blotchy black and white mottling. Common Nighthawk replaces flight feathers on the winter grounds (*vs* the summer grounds in Lesser Nighthawk) so relative wear of AHY/ASYs (worn in fall, fresh in spring), especially of the outer pp, also can be helpful in identification.

From Antillean Nighthawk by larger size; distance between the white on the outer web of p9 and the tip of the wing 89-115 mm; eastern subspecies (*chapmani* and *minor*; see **Geographic variation**) with upperparts and underwing covs (see Fig. 68) darker and blacker; white patch in the pp averages larger and less mottled in ♀♀; black bars on the underparts average wider (1.0-4.0 mm; see **Geographic variation**); undertail covs creamy whitish, not contrasting with the color of the underparts; juvs lack strong, warm or buff tones and have wing covs and terts with little or no contrast in color. From the other nightjars of N.Am by the combination of rictal bristles absent or greatly reduced; white patches present in both the wings and the tail; throat white; tail notched (r5 > r1).

Geographic variation—Moderate, but broadly clinal where most ranges meet, and differences are complicated by individual variation. Subspecies taxonomy in N.Am follows the AOU (1957); see Oberholser (1914b, 1974), Ridgway (1914), Hawkins (1948), Selander (1954), Roberts (1955), Selander & Alvarez de Toro (1955), Eisenmann (1962a), Bailey & Niedrach (1965), Browning (1978, 1990), Behle (1985), Goossen (1986), Dickerman (1990). One other subspecies occurs in C.Am-S.Am. Combine subspecies identification with the information under **Age/Sex**; ♀♀ and immatures average buffier than adult ♂♂ in all subspecies, and HY/SYs average 10 mm shorter wgs than AHY/ASYs. Juvs generally parallel adults in plumage differences. Beware of possible dichromatism (gray and brown plumages) in juvs (and possibly also adults) that can confuse subspecies separation. More study is needed.

Western (*C.m. hesperis*) Group. Medium-dark; grayish.

C.m. hesperis (br e.WA-s.CA to c.MT-c.UT; vag to FL): Large; upperparts medium-dark grayish dusky with numerous, fine, whitish markings; basal portion of pp and ss with few or no indistinct spots; underparts whitish with moderately wide, dusky bars (1.5-2.0 mm wide at the center of the breast). ♀ wg(n10) 187-203, tl(n10) 105-119; ♂ wg(n100) 184-210, tl(n100) 100-119. Birds of s.ID-c.UT ("*twomeyi*") may average paler, but differences are due to slight intergradation toward other subspecies.

Southwestern/Great Basin (*C.m. henryi*) Group. Pale; buffy.

C.m. henryi (br se.UT-se.CO to s.AZ-w.TX; vag to FL): Medium large; upperparts brownish with coarse, buff or tawny mottling, giving an overall cinnamon appearance; ♀ (and to a lesser extent ♂) with distinct, buff to cinnamon spots on the basal portion of the pp and ss (as in Lesser Nighthawk); underparts buffy with moderately narrow, dusky bars (1.0-1.5 mm wide at the center of the breast). ♀ wg(n12) 182-198, tl(n12) 103-116; ♂ wg(n73) 185-209, tl(n74) 100-117.

C.m. howelli (br WY to ne.NM-c.TX): Large; upperparts pale brownish with light buff mottling; basal portion of the pp and ss with indistinct or no spots; underparts whitish buff with moderately wide, dusky bars (1.0-2.0 mm wide at the center of the breast). ♀ wg(n10) 184-204, tl(n10) 104-123; ♂ wg(n52) 185-209, tl(n51) 102-119. Birds of w.CO ("*divisus*") may average paler and buffier, but differences are obscured by individual variation or due to intergradation with other subspecies.

C.m. sennetti (br s.Sask-ND to n.CO-sw.MN; vag to FL): Large; upperparts medium-pale grayish, without buff tones, and with numerous fine, whitish markings; basal portion of the pp and ss with indistinct or no spots; underparts whitish with narrow, dusky bars (~1 mm wide at the center of the breast). ♀ wg(n10) 179-201, tl(n10) 103-115; ♂ wg(n41) 183-208, tl(n43) 100-114.

C.m. aserriensis (br s.TX): Small; upperparts medium-pale grayish, with a buff tinge, and with numerous, fine, whitish markings; basal portion of the pp and ss with few or no indistinct spots; underparts whitish with narrow, dusky bars (~1 mm wide at the center of the breast). ♀ wg(n10) 175-186, tl(n10) 95-105; ♂ wg(n10) 179-189, tl(n10) 95-105.

Eastern (*C.m. minor*) Group. Dark; blackish.

C.m. minor (br AK-w.WA to Que-VA): Large; upperparts primarily blackish with light, whitish or buffy mottling; underparts washed buff, with wide, dusky bars (1.5-4.0 mm wide at the center of the breast); white of the outer rect (r5) in ♂♂ often reaches the outer web. Birds of w.BC (including juvs) are blacker and may be distinct at the subspecies level, but documentation is needed. ♀ wg(n10) 187-203, tl(n10) 105-119; ♂ wg(n25) 184-209, tl(n25) 106-119.

C.m. chapmani (br s.IL-e.TX to NC-FL): Small; upperparts primarily blackish brown, with moderately heavy, whitish or buffy mottling; underparts washed buff with wide, dusky bars (1.5-3.5 mm wide at the center of the breast); white of the outer rect (r5) in ♂♂ only occasionally reaches the outer web. ♀ wg(n10) 173-185, tl(n10) 99-109; ♂ wg(n42) 178-195, tl(n42) 98-111.

Molt—PB: HY incomplete (Jul-Mar), AHY incomplete-complete (Sep-Jan); PA absent. The PBs can begin on the summer grounds but take place primarily on the winter grounds; juvenal body plumage is replaced in Jul-Oct on the summer grounds; more study is needed on the timing of flight-feather replacement on the winter grounds (it is possible that the juvenal rects are not replaced until March, but verification is needed). The 1st PB includes the rects, apparently a variable number of wing covs (from none to most or all), and possibly 1-3 terts; more study is needed. The 2nd and subsequent PBs often (in ~54% of birds) are incomplete. During the 2nd PB, up to 4 juvenal ss (often in a block, as in Lesser Nighthawk; see Figs. 25C & 71) and sometimes other feathers (including pp and gr covs) can be retained. During subsequent PBs, up to 5 adult ss (usually not in a central block; see Figs. 25D & 71) and/or wing covs can be retained.

Juvenile
Lesser

Juvenile
Common

Adult
Common

FIGURE 73. The patterns on the juvenal and adult scapulars of nighthawks for ageing and identification of juveniles. Adult Lesser Nighthawks have a bold pattern, similar to that of adult Common Nighthawks, but somewhat less pronounced.

Skull—Pneumaticization patterns possibly are useful for ageing (see Family account).

Age—Juv (Jul-Sep) is paler in plumage due to heavy, whitish to tawny spotting, has the throat patch absent or obscured, and has brown scapulars with only a moderately bold, black and buff pattern (Fig. 73); juv ♀=♂ although some birds may be sexed by the p10 characters, as in HY/SYs (see Fig. 74). The timing of flight-feather replacement on the winter grounds, hence the timing of the following age-code assignments, is in need of further study.

HY/SY (Sep-2nd Nov): Pp covs and retained, juvenal outer gr covs usually with complete, whitish or buff tips (see Fig. 77); outer pp narrow, tapered (Fig. 69), relatively fresh in the 1st fall, and heavily abraded in the 1st spring to 2nd fall; patch on p10 buff (♀) or whitish to pale buff (♂), reduced in size by sex (Fig. 74); juvenal ss uniform in wear (Fig. 25A, except 1-3 terts possibly replaced in some birds), the outer ss and inner pp distinctly tipped with whitish or buff (see Fig. 71); ♂ without a white subterminal band to the rects (Fig. 75) through 1st Dec-Mar. **Note: HYs in Sep-Dec are separated from SYs by much fresher flight feathers.**

AHY/ASY (Dec-Nov): Pp covs and outer gr covs without complete whitish or buff tips (see Fig. 77); outer pp broad, truncate (Fig. 69), relatively abraded in fall, and fresh in spring; patch on p10 creamy (♀) or white (♂), larger in size by sex (Fig. 74); adult ss uniform in wear (Fig. 25B), the inner pp and outer ss without whitish or buff tips (see Fig. 71); ♂ with a white subterminal band to the rects (Fig. 75). **Note: This pattern, with uniformly adult ss, occurs in ~46% of AHY/ASYs; see SY/TY.**

SY/TY (Dec-Nov): Like AHY/ASY, but 1-4 juvenal ss (often in a block among s2-s5) retained, tipped whitish (if not worn off), narrow, faded, and worn, contrasting markedly with the darker, broader, and fresher, replaced ss (Fig. 25C; see also Fig. 71). **Note: See AHY/ASY. Many intermediates between this and ASY/ATY (with two generations of ss) occur that should be aged AHY/ASY. Occasional birds that have also retained one or more juvenal, outermost pp and pp covs can be reliably aged SY/TY.**

ASY/ATY (Dec-Nov): Like AHY/ASY, but 1-5 adult ss (among s1-s8, usually not in a block) retained, not tipped whitish, and slightly worn, contrasting slightly to moderately with the

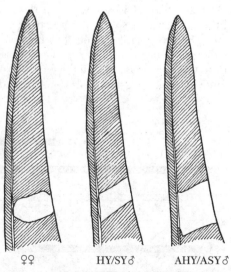

♀♀   HY/SY♂   AHY/ASY♂

FIGURE 74. The typical pattern of white on the outer primary (p10) by age and sex in Common Nighthawk. AHY/ASY ♀♀ average larger spots than HY/SY ♀♀ but there is some overlap.

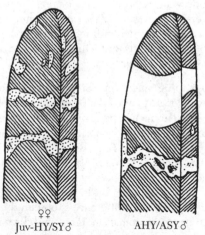

♀♀

Juv-HY/SY♂   AHY/ASY♂

FIGURE 75. The pattern of the outer rectrix (r5) by age and sex in Common Nighthawk.

fresher, replaced ss (Fig. 25D; see also Fig. 71). **Note: Many intermediates occur with SY/TY (which see).**

Sex—The CP apparently is not developed; the BP (May-Sep) is reliable for sexing ♀♀. ♀ wg(n72) 173-203, tl(n72) 95-123; ♂ wg(n100) 178-210, tl(n100) 97-119; HY/SYs average 10 mm shorter wg than AHY/ASYs; see **Geographic variation**.

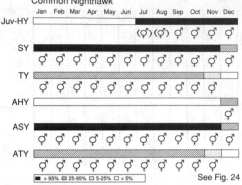

Common Nighthawk

♀: Throat patch indistinct, with extensive brownish mottling; patch on p10 creamy or tinged buff and reduced in size (Fig. 74); rects without a white subterminal band (Fig. 75).

♂: Throat patch white, without extensive brownish mottling; patch on p10 white or whitish and distinct (Fig. 74); rects without (HY/SYs, Sep-Mar) or with (AHYs) a white subterminal band (Fig. 75).

References—Stone (1896), Oberholser (1914b, 1974), Ridgway (1914), Forbush (1927), A.M. Gross & A.C. Bent *in* Bent (1940), Selander (1954), Roberts (1955), Eisenmann (1962a), Wood (1969), Stevenson *et al.* (1983), Cavanagh (1985), Cramp (1985), Wilds (1985a), Czaplak & Wilds (1986), Goossen (1986), Langridge (1986), Dickerman (1990), Lewington *et al.* (1991), Stevenson & Anderson (1994), Howell & Webb (1995), Pyle (1995a), Poulin *et al.* (1996).

ANTILLEAN NIGHTHAWK
Chordeiles gundlachii

ANNI
Species # 4201
Band size: 2-1A

Species—From Common Nighthawk (which see for separation from Lesser Nighthawk and the other nightjars of N.Am) by smaller size (wg 150-183, tl 89-103; see **Age/Sex**); distance between the white on the outer web of p9 and the tip of wing 73-93 mm; upperparts and underwing covs paler gray or more clay-colored (*cf.* Fig. 68); black bars on the underparts average narrower (1.0-2.5 mm); white patch in the pp averages smaller and more heavily washed or mottled buff in ♀♀; undertail covs buff to tawny, contrasting with the grayer color of the underparts; juv with strong, warm or buff tones and pale wing covs contrasting markedly with the darker terts.

Geographic variation—Subspecies taxonomy follows Monroe (1968), who considered the species monotypic (synonymizing a previously recognized subspecies); see also Oberholser (1914b), Ridgway (1914), Eisenmann (1962a). Birds of FL and the Bahamas ("*C.g. vicinus*") may average grayer than nominate birds of the Greater Antilles, but this difference is obscured by plumage dichromatism (gray and brown plumages).

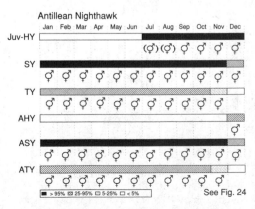

Antillean Nighthawk

Molt—Unknown, but probably parallels that of Common Nighthawk, which see.

Skull—Pneumaticization patterns possibly are useful for ageing (see Family account).

Age/Sex—See Common Nighthawk. Plumage in Antillean Nighthawk differs from that of Common only in that the throat and wing patch of ♀ averages buffier or tawnier, and the patch on p10 may average smaller by age and sex (*cf.* Fig. 74). ♀ wg(n23) 160-185, tl(n20) 90-103; ♂ wg(n26) 158-183, tl(n20) 89-103; HY/SYs average 10 mm shorter wg than AHY/ASYs.

References—Oberholser (1914b), Ridgway (1914), Nicholson (1957), Eisenmann (1962a), Stevenson *et al.* (1983), Czaplak & Wilds (1986), Stevenson & Anderson (1994), Howell & Webb (1995); S.N.G. Howell, W. Russell (pers. comm.).

COMMON PAURAQUE
Nyctidromus albicollis

COPA
Species # 4190
Band size: 2

Species—Dichromatic (with gray and rufous plumages), although only gray-plumaged birds typically are found in N.Am. From the other nightjars of N.Am by the combination of tl long (128-180; see **Sex**) and graduated (r1 – outer rect 15-40 mm); pp with a white or buff patch; r3-r4 with a variable amount of white, the proximal edge of the white not evenly distributed across the feather webs (see Fig. 79); tarsus naked; rictal bristles present.

Geographic variation—Weak, complicated by individual variation, and clinal where ranges meet. Subspecies taxonomy in N.Am follows the AOU (1957); see Ridgway (1914), Griscom (1929a), Bent (1940). Five other subspecies occur in Mex-S.Am.

  N.a. merrilli (res s.TX): Larger than all other subspecies (see **Sex**, *vs* wg 141-178, tl 112-167 in the other subspecies); plumage pale grayish (*vs* brownish or cinnamon); rufous plumage absent or rare (*vs* regular in the other subspecies).

Molt—PB: HY partial (Jul-Dec), AHY incomplete-complete (Jul-Sep); PA absent. The 1st PB includes a variable number of wing covs, from none to most or all; more study is needed. The 2nd and subsequent PBs sometimes (in ~35% of birds) are incomplete. During the 2nd PB, 1-4 ss (usually among s2-s7) can be retained (Figs. 25C & 71); perhaps occasionally some pp and pp covs also can be retained. During subsequent PBs, 1-3 or more ss (among s1-s8) can be retained, usually in irregular patterns (Figs. 25D & 71). Replacement of rects usually is complete during the 2nd and subsequent PBs.

Skull—Pneumaticization patterns possibly are useful for ageing (see Family account).

Age—Juv (May-Sep) has the upperparts spotted rather than streaked, brown scapulars, without a bold, black and buff pattern (Fig. 76),

Juvenal   Basic
(HY/AHY)

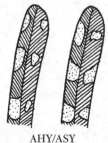

HY/SY   AHY/ASY
(variation)   (variation)

FIGURE 76. The patterns on the juvenal and adult scapulars of nightjars for ageing juveniles. These figures are based on Poorwill; patterns in most of the other species are similar.

FIGURE 77. The pattern of the primary coverts by age in nightjars. Figure from Pyle (1995a)

and an indistinct throat patch; juvs can be sexed by tl (if full grown; see **Sex**) and the amount of white in the rects, as in HY/SYs (see Fig. 79).

HY/SY (Sep-Aug): Pp covs and retained, juvenal outer gr covs with complete buff tips (Fig. 77); outer pp narrow and tapered (Fig. 69); juvenal ss uniform in wear (Fig. 25A), the outer ss and inner pp (when fresh) distinctly tipped with buff or cinnamon (Fig. 78; see also Fig. 71); rects narrow and tapered, the amount of white on the 3rd rect from the outside reduced by sex (Fig. 79; note that Pauraques can have either 10 or 12 rects).

AHY/ASY (Sep-Aug): Pp covs and outer gr covs without complete buff tips (Fig. 77); outer pp broad and truncate (Fig. 69); adult ss uniform in wear (Fig. 25B), the outer ss and inner pp without distinct, buff or cinnamon tips (Fig. 78; see also Fig. 71); rects broad and truncate, the amount of white on the 3rd rect from the outside reduced by sex (Fig. 79). **Note: This pattern, with uniform adult ss, occurs in ~65% of AHY/ASYs; see SY/TY.**

SY/TY (Sep-Aug): Like AHY/ASY, but 1-4 juvenal ss, (often in a block among s2-s7) narrow, tipped buff or cinnamon (Fig. 78), and worn, contrasting markedly with the broader, fresher, and grayish-tipped, replaced ss (Fig. 25C; see also Fig. 71). **Note: See AHY/ASY. Some intermediates between this and ASY/ATY (with two generations of ss) occur that should be aged AHY/ASY. Occasional birds that may retain one or more juvenal, outermost pp and pp covs, can be reliably aged SY/TY.**

ASY/ATY (Sep-Aug): Like AHY/ASY, but 1-3 or more adult ss (among s1-s8, usually not in a block) retained, faded, and worn, contrasting moderately with the fresher, replaced ss (Fig. 25D; see also Fig. 71). **Note: Some intermediates occur with SY/TY (which see).**

Sex—The CP apparently is not developed; the BP (Mar-Jul) is reliable for sexing ♀♀. Tl is useful for sexing: ♀ wg(n30) 165-181, tl(n20) 128-160; ♂ wg(n30) 173-188, tl(n20) 147-180.

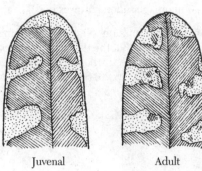

Juvenal   Adult

FIGURE 78. The pattern of the outer secondaries (s1-s5) by age in Pauraque and Chuck-wills-widow. Similar (but less pronounced) patterns can be found in Buff-collared Nightjar, Whip-poor-will, and, to a lesser extent, in Poorwill. See also Figure 71.

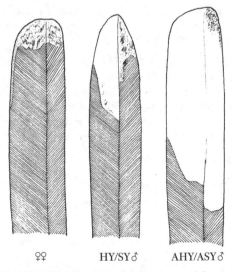

♀♀   HY/SY♂   AHY/ASY♂

FIGURE 79. The shape and pattern of the 3rd rectrix from the outside by age and sex in Pauraque. HY/SY ♀ has a shape similar to that of HY/SY ♂. Note that Pauraques can have either 10 or 12 rectrices; thus, this feather can be either r3 or r4. The amount of white on this feather in ♂♂ can show much variation, within both age groups.

♀: White of the 3rd rect from the outside absent or reduced (Fig. 79); pale patch in the pp buff or tawny; throat patch indistinct, tinged buff, and mottled brown.

♂: White of the 3rd rect from the outside large (Fig. 79); patch in the pp white; throat patch distinct and uniformly white.

References—Ridgway (1914), Dickey & van Rossem (1938), Bent (1940), Oberholser (1974), Foster (1975), Pyle (1995a).

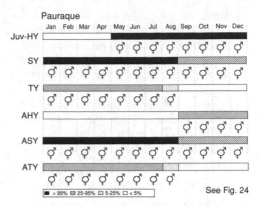

See Fig. 24

COMMON POORWILL
Phalaenoptilus nuttallii

COPO
Species # 4180
Band size: 1A

Species—From the other nightjars of N.Am by the combination of small size, especially tl (75-96; see **Geographic variation** & **Sex**); pp without a white or buff patch; tail rounded (r5 < r1); outer three rects (r2-r5) tipped white, the proximal edges evenly distributed across the feather webs (Fig. 80); tarsus naked; rictal bristles present.

Geographic variation—Weak and complicated by dichromatism (gray and brown plumages) and substantial individual variation. Subspecies taxonomy in N.Am follows Rea (1983); see also Ridgway (1914), Grinnell (1914a, 1928b), Dickey (1928), Oberholser (1932, 1974), van Rossem (1936a, 1941a), Bent (1940), Miller (1941a), Phillips (1959a), Monson & Phillips (1981), Unitt (1984). One other subspecies occurs in Mex.

    P.n. californicus (br & wint coastal s.OR-sw.CA): Large; upperparts dark brown with gray and tawny streaks; underparts dusky gray with distinct, heavy, blackish bars. ♀♂ wg(n20) 137-153, tl(n20) 82-96. Birds of coastal cw-sw.CA may average paler, but subspecies distinctions are undocumented.

    P.n. hueyi (br & wint desert se.CA-sw.AZ): Small; upperparts pale gray (sometimes tinged pinkish) with fine, dusky barring; underparts pale pinkish gray and indistinctly patterned. ♀♂ wg(n17) 129-140, tl(n10) 75-84.

    P.n. adustus (br & wint montane s.AZ): Medium large; upperparts pale grayish brown with fine, dusky streaks; underparts pale whitish with distinct but sparse, dusky bars. ♀♂ wg(n15) 134-145, tl(n10) 77-85.

    P.n. nuttallii (br & wint s.BC-ec.CA to w.ND-s.TX): Large; upperparts dark grayish with dusky streaks; underparts gray with distinct but sparse, blackish bars. ♀♂ wg(n72) 135-152, tl(n72) 78-94. Birds of e.OR to e.CA-w.NV ("*nyctophilus*") may average brighter and with more white in the rects, and birds of c.KS-sw.MO to s.TX ("*nitidus*") may average smaller and more frosty gray, but differences are weak and obscured by individual variation.

Molt—PB: HY partial (Jul-Dec), AHY incomplete-complete (Jul-Sep); PA absent. The PBs occur on the summer grounds. The 1st PB includes a variable number of wing covs, from none to most or all; more study is needed. The 2nd and subsequent PBs occasionally (in ~7% of birds) are incomplete, with 1-4 ss (among s2-s7) retained (Figs. 25C-D & 71); rarely some pp and pp covs also can also be retained.

Skull—Pneumaticization patterns possibly are useful for ageing (see Family account).

Age—Juv (Apr-Sep) has less distinct markings, scapulars without a bold, black and buff pattern (Fig. 76), and an indistinct throat patch; juv ♀ = ♂.

HY/SY (Sep-Aug): Pp covs and retained juvenal outer gr covs with complete buff tips (Fig. 77); outer pp narrow and tapered (Fig. 69); juvenal ss uniform in wear (Fig. 25A); rects narrow, the white on the outer rects averaging slightly reduced and buffier by sex (Fig. 80; see **Sex**); **Note: In addition, HY/SYs average slightly buffier tips to the outer ss than AHY/ASYs, but these distinctions are very difficult to assess.**

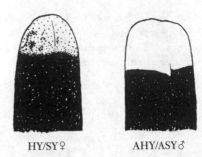

HY/SY♀   AHY/ASY♂

FIGURE 80. The shape and pattern of the outer rectrix (r5) by age and sex in Poorwill. These illustrations represent extremes; most birds will show intermediate shapes and patterns. These criteria alone should not be relied upon for ageing or (especially) sexing, but may be of assistance when combined with other criteria.

AHY/ASY (Sep-Aug): Pp covs and outer gr covs without complete buff tips (Fig. 77); outer pp broad and truncate (Fig. 69); adult ss uniform in wear (Fig. 25B); rects broad, the tips of the outer rects averaging slightly whiter by sex (Fig. 80; see **Sex**). **Note: See HY/SY. Occasional AHY/ASYs retain ss, as in other nightjars (Figs. 25C–D & 71), but distinctions between juvenal and adult feathers are difficult to assess; ageing to SY/TY or ASY/ATY thus is unlikely, although rarely some AHY/ASYs also can retain pp or pp covs and can be aged SY/TY or ASY/ATY by the pattern on the retained pp covs (Fig. 77).**

Sex—The CP apparently is not developed; the BP (Mar-Aug) probably is reliable for sexing ♀♀; Aldrich (1935) presumably was unaware of the similarity of the sexes when concluding that ♂♂ do most of the incubation. ♀ wg(n63) 132-153, tl(n44) 79-96; ♂ wg(n63) 129-152, tl(n58) 75-96. The white tips of the outer rects average buffier and, perhaps, less extensive in ♀♀ than in ♂♂, age for age (Fig. 80); but sexing by this alone is not recommended (except, perhaps, with extremes), and no other plumage criteria are known.

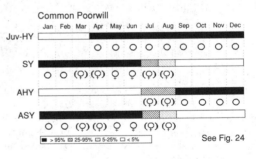

References—Ridgway (1914), Aldrich (1935), Van Tyne & Sutton (1937), Bent (1940), Oberholser (1974), Csada & Brigham (1992), Pyle (1995a); PRBO data.

CHUCK-WILL'S-WIDOW
Caprimulgus carolinensis

CWWI
Species # 4160
Band size: 3

Species—From the other nightjars of N.Am by the combination of large size (wg 200-225, tl 128-151; see **Age/Sex**); pp without a white or buffy patch; tail graduated (r5 < r1); r3-r5 of ♂♂ with extensive white to the inner webs (Fig. 81); rictal bristles present and with lateral filaments on the basal half; throat without white.

Geographic variation—No subspecies are recognized.

Molt—PB: HY partial (Jun-Sep), AHY incomplete-complete (May-Sep); PA absent. The PBs occur primarily on the summer grounds. The 1st PB includes a variable number of wing covs, from none to most or all; more study is needed. The 2nd and subsequent PBs sometimes (in ~48% of birds) are incomplete, typically with 1-4 ss (among s2-s7) retained (Figs. 25C–D & 71); rarely some pp and pp covs also are retained.

Skull—Pneumaticization patterns possibly are useful for ageing (see Family account).

Age/Sex—Juv (Apr-Sep) averages lighter buff to clay-colored, and has brown scapulars without a bold, black and buff pattern (Fig. 76); juv ♀ = ♂, although perhaps occasional juvs with some pale buffy-cinnamon at the tips of r4-r5 are reliably sexed ♂♂ (see HY/SY ♀♂). The CP apparently is not developed; the BP (Mar-Aug) is reliable for sexing ♀♀. ♀ wg(n30) 200-219, tl(n20) 128-144; ♂ wg(n27) 205-225, tl(n20) 134-151.

HY/SY ♀♂ (Sep-Aug): Pp covs and retained, juvenal outer gr covs with narrow but complete buff or tawny tips when fresh (Fig. 77); outer pp narrow and tapered (Fig. 69); juvenal ss uniform in wear (Fig. 25C; see also Fig. 71), the outer portions washed with little to substantial cinnamon (Fig. 78); body feathers uniform in wear; outer rects (r3-r5) narrow, tapered, and without white but with indistinct, dark buff to tawny tips (Fig. 81). **Note: The tips to the pp covs can wear off by late spring. The pp and rect shape criteria are reliable (but can be difficult) through the replacement of p7 during the 2nd PB. In addition to the above, the terts average paler and grayer (relative to the rest of the ss) on HY/SYs than on AHY/ASYs. Occasional HY/SY ♂♂ may have reduced pale buffy-orange in the rects (Fig. 81) and are reliably sexed; otherwise, ♀ = ♂.**

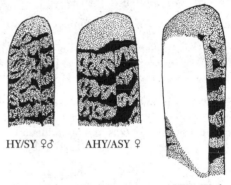

HY/SY ♀♂   AHY/ASY ♀

AHY/ASY ♂

FIGURE 81. The shape and pattern of the outer rectrix (r5) by age and sex in Chuck-wills-widow. Occasional HY/SY ♂♂ may show a small whitish or buffy patch in the outer web; more study is needed.

AHY/ASY ♀ (Sep-Aug): Pp covs and outer gr covs without complete buff or tawny tips (Fig. 76); outer pp broad and truncate (Fig. 69); adult ss uniform in wear (Fig. 25B), the outer portions with a slight or no cinnamon wash (Fig. 78); body feathers sometimes showing contrasts between two generations of plumage; outer rects (r3-r5) broad, truncate, and without white but often with broad, buff tips (Fig. 81). **Note: See HY/SY ♀♂. Many AHY/ASYs retain ss, as in other nightjars, but distinctions between juvenal and adult feathers can be difficult to assess (see Fig. 78); ageing to SY/TY or ASY/ATY thus is difficult, although rarely some birds also can retain pp or pp covs, and can be aged SY/TY or ASY/ATY by the pattern on the pp covs (Fig. 77).**

AHY/ASY ♂: Like AHY/ASY ♀, but r3-r5 with extensive white (Fig. 81). **Note: AHY/ASY ♀.**

Chuck-will's-widow

	Jan	Feb	Mar	Apr	May	Jun	Jul	Aug	Sep	Oct	Nov	Dec
Juv-HY												
SY												
AHY												
ASY												

Juv-HY: ○ ○ ○ ○ ○ ○ ○ ○ ○ (Apr-Dec)
SY: ○ ○ (♀) (♀) (♀) (♀) (♀) (♂)
AHY: (♀) (♂) ♂ ♂ ♂ ♂
ASY: ♂ ♂ ♂ ♂ ♂ ♂ ♂ ♂

■ > 95%   ▨ 25-95%   ▥ 5-25%   □ < 5%   See Fig. 24

References—Ridgway (1914), Forbush (1927), Bent (1940), Rohwer (1971), Oberholser (1974), Mengel (1976), Rohwer & Butler (1977), Pyle (1995a).

BUFF-COLLARED NIGHTJAR
Caprimulgus ridgwayi

BCNI
Species # 4161
Band size: 2

Species—From the other nightjars of N.Am, including Whip-poor-will, by the combination of small size (wg 146-164, tl 109-125; see **Sex**); nape with a distinct, unbroken, tawny collar; pp with large buff or tawny spots; tail graduated (r5 < r1); r3 of ♂♂ with the white tip < 30 mm (Fig. 82); rictal bristles present.

Geographic variation—Weak and probably clinal. Subspecies taxonomy follows Peters (1940); see Ridgway (1914), Griscom (1929), van Rossem (1931a). One other subspecies occurs in C.Am.

> **C.r. ridgwayi** (br se.AZ-sw.NM): From C.Am subspecies by larger size (see **Sex**). Birds of N.Am-cw.Mex ("*goldmani*") may average larger and paler than birds of s.Mex, but differences, if present, are obscured by individual variation.

Molt—Poorly known, but presumably similar to other *Caprimulgus* species: PB HY partial (Jun-Sep), AHY incomplete-complete (May-Sep); PA absent. The 1st PB probably includes a variable number of wing covs, from none to most or all; more study is needed. The 2nd and subsequent PBs can be incomplete, perhaps typically with 1-4 ss (among s2-s7) retained (Figs. 25C–D & 71); rarely some pp and pp covs also may be retained.

Skull—Pneumaticization patterns possibly are useful for ageing (see Family account).

Age—Juv (Apr-Sep) has a pale gray crown with black spotting, buff to tawny wing covs with pale buff tips forming wing bars, and brown scapulars, without a bold, black and buff pattern (Fig. 76); juv ♀ and ♂ are separated reliably by the pattern of the rects (Fig. 83).

HY/SY (Sep-Aug): Pp covs and retained, juvenal outer gr covs with complete buff to cinnamon tips (Fig. 77); outer pp narrow and tapered (Fig. 69); juvenal ss uniform in wear (Fig. 25A), the tips to the outer ss mottled with buff or cinnamon (see Fig. 78); r3-r5 narrow and tapered, the ♂♂ without white in r3 and with reduced white patches in r4-r5 (Figs. 82-83).

AHY/ASY (Sep-Aug): Pp covs and outer gr covs without full, buff to cinnamon tips (Fig. 77); outer pp broad and truncate (Fig. 69); adult ss uniform in wear (Fig. 25B), the brown tipping of the outer ss with little or no mottling (see Fig. 78); r3-r5 broad and truncate, the ♂♂ with an indistinct to distinct white patch in r3 (Fig. 82) and extensive and distinct white patches in r4-r5 (*cf.* Fig. 83). **Note: This**

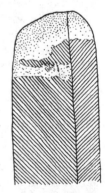

HY/SY ♂   AHY/ASY ♀

FIGURE 83. The shape and pattern of the outer rectrix (r5) by age and sex in Buff-collared Nightjars. Whip-poor-will shows a similar pattern (but with more white in HY/SY ♂). HY/SY ♀ has a shape similar to HY/SY ♂ and a pattern similar to AHY/ASY ♀, whereas AHY/ASY ♂ has a shape similar to AHY/ASY ♀ and a substantial amount of white.

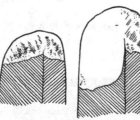

HY/SY ♂   AHY/ASY ♂♂
                   (variation)

FIGURE 82. The shape and pattern of r3 by age in ♂ Buff-collared Nightjars.

pattern, with uniform adult ss, probably occurs in a majority of AHY/ASYs; see SY/TY.

SY/TY (Sep-Aug): Like AHY/ASY, but 1-4 juvenal ss (often in a block among s2-s7) narrow and worn, with buff or cinnamon mottling to the tips, contrasting markedly with the broader, fresher, and brownish-tipped, replaced ss (Fig. 25C; see also Fig. 71). **Note: See AHY/ASY. Many intermediates between this and ASY/ATY (with two generations of ss) can occur that should be aged AHY/ASY, although occasional birds that may retain one or more juvenal, outermost pp and pp covs, can be reliably aged SY/TY.**

ASY/ATY (Sep-Aug): Like AHY/ASY, but 1-5 adult ss (among s1-s8, usually not in a block) faded and worn, contrasting moderately with the fresher, replaced ss (Fig. 25D; see also Fig. 71). **Note: Many intermediates can occur with SY/TY (see above).**

Sex—The CP apparently is not developed; the BP (Mar-Aug) probably is reliable for sexing ♀♀, although incubation by ♂♂ has been documented; more study is needed. ♀ wg(n17) 146-162, tl(n16) 110-121; ♂ wg(n32) 147-164, tl(24) 109-125; pertains to the subspecies in N.Am only (see **Geographic variation**).

♀: Tips to r4-r5 buff, without whitish patches (Fig. 83).

♂: Tips to r4-r5 with whitish patches (Fig. 83).

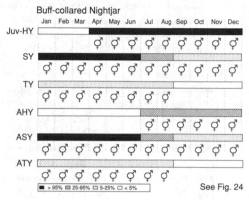

References—Ridgway (1914), Howell & Webb (1995), Pyle (1995a), Bowers & Dunning (1997).

WHIP-POOR-WILL
Caprimulgus vociferus

WPWI
Species # 4170
Band size: 1A-2

Species—From the other nightjars of N.Am, including Buff-collared Nightjar, by the combination of medium size (wg 147-179, tl 105-135; see **Sex**); nape without a distinct, tawny collar; pp without a white or buffy patch; tail graduated (r5 < r1); white on r3 of ♂♂ > 30 mm from the tip (Fig. 84); rictal bristles present but without lateral filaments on the basal half.

Geographic variation—Moderate, but complicated by some plumage dichromatism (gray and brown plumages); the ranges in N.Am are well defined. Subspecies taxonomy in N.Am follows the AOU (1957); see Ridgway (1914), Bent (1940), Craig (1971), Hubbard & Crossin (1974), Oberholser (1974), Howell & Webb (1995). Four other extant subspecies occur in Mex-C.Am.

C.v. vociferus (br Sask-NS to n.TX-VA): Small; central rects (r1) pale gray or brown, contrasting with the darker back; white on r3-r5 of AHY/ASY ♂♂ extensive (43-65 mm from tip; Fig. 84); rictal bristles short (longest 25-45 mm). ♀ wg(n15) 147-163, tl(n15) 105-124; ♂ wg(n15) 149-169, tl(n15) 114-128.

C.v. arizonae (br c.AZ-sw.TX): Large; central rects (r1) pale buff, contrasting only moderately with the back color; white on r3-r5 of AHY/ASY ♂♂ reduced (37-55 mm from tip; Fig. 84); rictal bristles long (longest 35-60 mm). ♀ wg(n13) 157-167, tl(n13) 114-128; ♂ wg(n23) 162-179, tl(n23) 114-135.

Molt—PB: HY partial (Jul-Sep), AHY incomplete-complete (Jul-Sep); PA absent. The PBs occur primarily on the summer grounds. The 1st PB includes a variable number of wing covs, from none to most or all; more study is needed. The 2nd and subsequent PBs sometimes (in ~28% of birds) are incomplete, with 1-4 ss (among s2-s7) retained (Fig. 25C-D & 71); rarely some pp and pp covs also are retained.

Skull—Pneumaticization patterns possibly are useful for ageing (see Family account).

Age—Juv (Apr-Sep) has a pale gray crown with black spotting, buff to tawny wing covs with pale buff tips forming wing bars, and brown scapulars, without a bold, black and buff pattern (Fig. 76); juv ♀♀ and ♂♂ are separated reliably by the absence or presence of white in the rects (see Figs. 83-84).

HY/SY (Sep-Aug): Pp covs and retained, juvenal outer gr covs with complete buff to cinnamon tips (Fig. 77); outer pp narrow and tapered (Fig. 69); juvenal ss uniform in wear (Fig. 25**A**), the tips to the outer ss mottled with whitish or buff (see Fig. 78); r3-r5 narrow and tapered, the ♂♂ with a reduced white patch in r3 by subspecies (Fig. 84).

AHY/ASY (Sep-Aug): Pp covs and outer gr covs without full buff to cinnamon tips (Fig. 76); outer pp broad and truncate (Fig. 69); adult ss uniform in wear (Fig. 25**B**), the brown tipping to the inner pp and outer ss with little or no mottling (see Fig. 78); r3-r5 broad and truncate, the ♂♂ with a more extensive white patch in r3 by subspecies (Fig. 84). **Note: This pattern, with uniform adult ss, occurs in ~72% of AHY/ASYs; see SY/TY.**

SY/TY (Sep-Aug): Like AHY/ASY, but 1-4 juvenal ss (often in a block among s2-s7) narrow, worn, and mottled buff to cinnamon at the tips (see Fig. 78), contrasting markedly with the broader, fresher, and brownish-tipped, replaced ss (Fig. 25**C**; see also Fig. 71). **Note: See AHY/ASY. Many intermediates between this and ASY/ATY (with two generations of ss) may occur that should be aged AHY/ASY. Occasional birds that may retain one or more juvenal, outermost pp and pp covs, can be reliably aged SY/TY.**

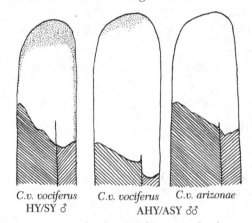

C.v. vociferus   *C.v. vociferus*   *C.v. arizonae*
HY/SY ♂   AHY/ASY ♂♂

FIGURE 84. The shape and pattern of r3 by age and subspecies in ♂♂ Whip-poor-wills.

ASY/ATY (Sep-Aug): Like AHY/ASY, but 1-5 adult ss (among s1-s8, usually not in a block) faded and worn, contrasting moderately with the fresher, replaced ss (Fig. 25**D**; see also Fig. 71). **Note: Many intermediates can occur with SY/TY (which see).**

Sex—The CP apparently is not developed; the BP (Mar-Aug) probably is reliable for sexing ♀♀, although incubation by ♂♂ has been documented; more study is needed. ♀ wg(n28) 147-167, tl(n28) 105-128; ♂ wg(n38) 149-179, tl(n38) 114-135; see **Geographic variation**.

♀: Tips to outer 3 rects (r2-r5) buff, < 18 mm (see Fig. 83; *cf.* Fig. 84).

♂: Outer 3 rects (r2-r5) with large white patches, usually > 20 mm (Fig. 84; see also Fig. 83).

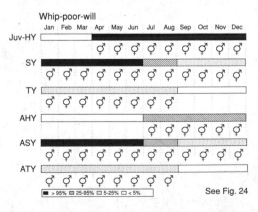

References—Stone (1896), Ridgway (1914), Forbush (1927), Bent (1940), Sutton (1941a), Roberts (1955), Wood (1969), Oberholser (1974), Babcock (1975), Pyle (1995a).

SWIFTS   *APODIDAE*

Four species. Family characters include large heads, long wings, short tails, small beaks, and relatively large but weak feet. Swifts have 10 primaries (the 10th full in length), 7-9 secondaries, and 10 rectrices. The first prebasic molt is partial in three of the four species, juvenal wing coverts and flight feathers appear to be retained through the second summer. The adult prebasic molts are complete, without retained secondaries, as in other near-passerines, and the primary coverts are replaced with their corresponding primaries. Prealternate molts do not occur. Skulling appears to be useful for ageing certain species (see Fig. 88, Johnston 1958) but requires further study. Sexes are similar in size and plumage; more study is needed on the reliability of sexing females by brood patch. Two species show sexual dimorphism in the shape of the rectrices and degree of the fork in the tail.

BLACK SWIFT   BLSW
Cypseloides niger   Species # 4220
                                                            Band size: 1A

Species—From the other species of *Cypseloides*, possible vagrants to N.Am, by p1 > p2; chin and hind neck without distinct, white spots or patches; rects without spiny tips when fresh (*vs* with small, soft tips in the other *Cypseloides* swifts). From Chimney and Vaux's swifts by much larger size (wg 152-171, tl 45-66; see **Age/Sex**); hind toe > 1/2 the length of the middle toe; rects without spiny tips when fresh.

Geographic variation—Weak and poorly known; ranges are variably defined. Subspecies taxonomy in N.Am follows the AOU (1957); see Ridgway (1911), Zimmer (1945), Webster (1958a). Two other subspecies occur in the W.Indies & Mex-C.Am.

  C.n. borealis (br throughout the range in N.Am): From the other subspecies by larger size (see **Age/Sex** and below); upperparts uniformly colored (*vs* head and nape slightly frostier or grayer than the back in *costaricensis* of Mex-C.Am); body feathers with broader white edging; tail fork relatively shallow by age/sex (see Fig. 85). Birds of the W.Indies (*niger*), potential vagrants to s.FL or elsewhere, are smaller (wg 148-161, tl 53-69), have tail forks relatively deep (r5 – r1 ♀ 0-8 mm; ♂ 8-16 mm in AHY/ASYs; see **Age/Sex** for *borealis*), are darker in the head, and have body feathers with narrower white edging by age/sex.

Molt—PB: HY complete (Nov-Apr?), AHY complete (Sep-Mar?); PA absent. The PBs apparently occur on the winter grounds and are protracted, with most body feather replacement occurring by Jan and flight-feather replacement occurring throughout the winter and early spring. Watch for incomplete PBs, with some feathers retained, especially p10, and possibly one or more inner ss or gr covs. More study is needed.

Skull—Pneumaticization probably does not fully complete; however, birds with larger windows (see Fig. 88) probably are reliably aged HY/SY and those with smaller windows (see Fig. 88) probably are reliably aged AHY through Nov. More study is needed.

Age/Sex—Juv (Jul-Nov) has white tips to most or all of the body and flight feathers; juv ♀ = ♂. The CP apparently is not developed; the BP (Jun-Jul) probably is reliable for sexing ♀♀. ♀ wg(n30) 152-171, tl(n20) 45-62; ♂ wg(n30) 154-170, tl(n20) 49-66. The following pertains only to birds of N.Am (*C.n. borealis*; see **Geographic variation**).

Juv-HY/SY ♀♂ (Jul-Apr): Tail squared (r5 – r1 < 2 mm; Fig. 85); flight feathers relatively fresh in Jul-Feb; pp covs, outer ss (also inner ss and pp when fresh), and many body feathers with broad, whitish tipping; outer rects relatively broad and rounded at the tip (Fig. 86). **Note: Juv-HY/SY ♀♀ may average slightly broader outer rects (Fig. 86) and broader**

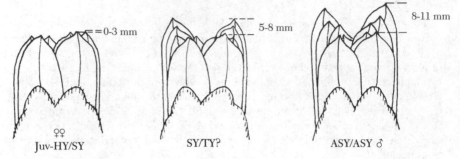

FIGURE 85. Tail fork by age and sex in Black Swifts. The potential difference between SY/TY ♂♂ and ASY/ATY ♂♂ requires confirmation. Also, the measurements pertain to North American *C.n. borealis* and likely are greater by age and sex in other subspecies (see **Geographic variation**).

white tipping to the body feathers than juv HY/SY ♂♂, but these distinctions probably are too slight to sex individuals.

AHY/ASY ♀ (Apr-Mar): Tail squared (r5 – r1 < 3 mm; Fig. 85); flight feathers relatively worn in Jul-Feb; pp covs, pp, and ss not tipped whitish; feathers of the abdomen sometimes with narrow, whitish tipping; head usually without frosty coloration; outer rects moderately narrow and pointed on the outer web at the tip (Fig. 86). **Note: There are reports that the amount of pale edging on the abdomen may be more prominent in SY/TY ♀♀ than in ASY/ATY ♀♀, but more study is needed; see also AHY/ASY ♂.**

AHY/ASY ♂ (Apr-Mar): Tail notched (r5 – r1 > 4 mm; Fig. 85); plumage like AHY/ASY ♀, but feathers of the abdomen with little or no pale edging; head often with frosty coloration; outer rects narrow and thinly pointed on the outer web at the tip (Fig. 86). **Note: The tail notch may be useful for separating SY/TY ♂♂ (5-8 mm) from ASY/ATY ♂♂ (8-11 mm; Fig. 85), but more study is needed. Also, see AHY/ASY ♀ regarding the feathers of the abdomen; some SY/TY ♂♂ may have thin, whitish tips.**

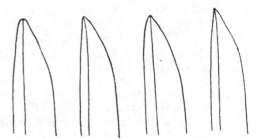

Juv-HY/SY ♀   AHY/ASY ♀   Juv-HY/SY ♂   AHY/ASY ♂

FIGURE 86. The width and shape of the outer rectrix (r5) by age and sex in Black Swift. These criteria alone should not be relied upon for ageing and sexing.

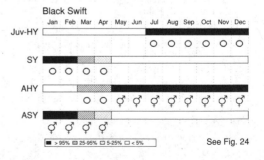

References—Drew (1882), Ridgway (1911), Swarth (1911, 1912a, 1922), Rathbun (1925), Bailey (1931, 1932), Bent (1940), Zimmer (1945), Lack (1956, 1957), Marin & Stiles (1992), Pyle (1995a).

CHIMNEY SWIFT
Chaetura pelagica

CHSW
Species # 4230
Band size: 1B

Species—From Black Swift by much smaller size (wg 122-136, tl 40-48; see **Sex**); hind toe < 1/2 the length of the middle toe; rects with spiny tips. From Vaux's Swift by larger size (see above); bill thicker and culmen angled (Fig. 87; depth at tip of nares 2.3-2.8); rump and throat usually dark, not contrasting markedly with the cap and back (see Fig. 87; the rump/back contrast is indistinct and clinal); tip of the longest uppertail cov often extends to the base of the spiny portion of the rects.

Geographic variation—No subspecies are recognized.

Molt—PB: HY partial (Sep-Nov), AHY complete (May-Nov); PA absent. The PBs occur primarily on the summer grounds, but can complete (Sep-Nov or later?) during fall migration or on the winter grounds; the outer pp are the last feathers replaced in AHYs. The juvenal wing covs apparently are retained during the 1st PB. The 2nd PB (SYs) may commence earlier (May-Jun) than subsequent PBs (ASYs; Jul-Aug); this may reflect deferred breeding until at least the 2nd year. Extent of molt on the winter grounds (if any) requires further study.

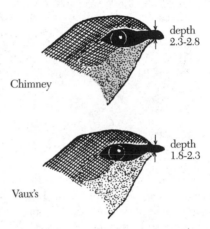

Skull—Pneumaticization does not fully complete; however, birds with larger windows (Fig. 88) are reliably aged HY/SY and those with small windows (Fig. 88) are reliably aged AHY through Nov.

FIGURE 87. The bill shape and depth, and relative throat color in Chimney and Vaux's swifts.

Age—Juv (Jul-Oct) has thin, whitish edging to the pp and outer ss that wears off very quickly; juv ♀=♂.

HY/SY (Aug-Jul): Flight feathers relatively fresh and not actively molting in Aug-Oct; outer pp and outer ss with thin, white edging when fresh; outer pp worn and brown in Mar-Jul, contrasting with the body plumage; rects narrow, tapered, and relatively abraded in Mar-Jul (Fig. 89). **Note: Some intermediates occur that are not reliably aged after completion of the PB. See AHY/ASY.**

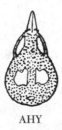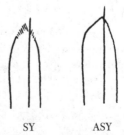

FIGURE 88. Pneumaticization patterns by age in Chimney and Vaux's swifts. Similar degrees of pneumaticization should be looked for in other swifts and near-passerines.

FIGURE 89. The shape and degree of wear on the outer rectrix (r5) by age in spring Chimney and Vaux's swifts. Figure from Pyle (1995a).

AHY/ASY (Aug-Jul): Unreplaced flight feathers (*e.g.*, the outer pp) relatively worn and/or being replaced in Aug-Nov or later; outer pp and outer ss without thin, white edging; outer pp relatively fresh and blackish in Mar-Jul, contrasting little with the body plumage; rects broad and relatively fresh in Mar-Jul (Fig. 89). **Note: See HY/SY. AHYs molting flight feathers in May-Jun may be SYs (see Molt), but more study is needed.**

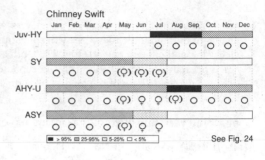

Sex—♀ = ♂ by plumage. The CP apparently is not developed; the BP (May-Aug) probably is reliable for sexing ♀♀. ♀ wg(n100) 123-136, tl(n20) 40-48; ♂ wg(n100) 122-134, tl(n20) 41-48.

References—Ridgway (1911), Forbush (1927), Coffey (1937), Bent (1940), Roberts (1955), Lack (1956), Wetmore (1957), Fischer (1958), Johnston (1958), Brooke (1969), Wood (1969), Devillers (1970a), Oberholser (1974), Zammuto & Franks (1979), Pyle (1995a); P.E. Downing (*in litt.* to the BBL).

VAUX'S SWIFT
Chaetura vauxi

VASW
Species # 4240
Band size: 1C

Species—From Black Swift by smaller size (wg 106-118, tl 32-40; see **Sex**); hind toe < 1/2 the length of the middle toe; rects with spiny tips. From Chimney Swift by smaller size (see above); bill thinner and culmen gradually decurved (Fig. 87; depth at tip of nares 1.8-2.3); rump and throat usually pale, contrasting distinctly with the darker cap and back (see Fig. 87; the rump/back contrast is horizontal and sharp); tip of the longest uppertail cov usually falls 2-4 mm < the bases of the spiny tips to the rects.

Geographic variation—Moderate, but clinal where ranges meet. Subspecies taxonomy in N.Am follows the AOU (1957); see Ridgway (1911), Griscom (1932), Sutton (1941b), Phillips (1954, 1961a, 1966a), Phillips & Webster (1957), Devillers (1970a). Five other subspecies occur in Mex-S.Am.

> **C.v. vauxi** (br throughout range in N.Am; wint s.FL): Crown and back brownish or dusky, without a glossy sheen; thin, white supercilium usually distinct; underparts medium-pale gray.
>
> **C.v. tamaulipensis** (br ne.Mex; vag to s.AZ): Crown and back blackish with a slight, glossy greenish sheen; pale supercilium absent or indistinct; underparts medium-dark gray.

Molt—PB: HY partial (Aug-Oct), AHY complete (Apr-Oct); PA absent. The PBs occur primarily on the summer grounds, but complete (Sep-Nov or later?) during fall migration or on the winter grounds; the outer pp are the last feathers replaced in AHYs. The juvenal wing covs apparently are retained during the 1st PB. The 2nd PB (SYs) may commence earlier (Apr-May) than subsequent PBs (ASYs; Jun-Jul); see Chimney Swift.

Skull—Pneumaticization probably does not fully complete; however, birds with larger windows are reliably aged HY/SY and those with small windows are reliably aged AHY through Nov (Fig. 88). More study is needed.

Age—Juv (Jun-Oct) has thin, whitish edging to the pp and outer ss that wears off very quickly; juv ♀ = ♂.

HY/SY (Aug-Jul): Flight feathers relatively fresh and not actively molting in Aug-Oct; outer pp and outer ss with thin, white edging when fresh; outer pp worn and brown in Mar-Jul, contrasting with the body plumage; rects narrow, tapered, and relatively abraded in Mar-Jul (Fig. 89). **Note: Some intermediates occur that are not reliably aged after completion of the PB. See AHY/ASY.**

AHY/ASY (Aug-Jul): Unreplaced flight feathers (*e.g.*, the outer pp) relatively worn and/or being replaced in Aug-Nov or later; outer pp and outer ss without thin, white edging; outer pp relatively fresh and blackish in Mar-Jul, contrasting little with the body plumage; rects broad and relatively fresh in Mar-Jul (Fig. 89). **Note: See HY/SY. AHYs molting flight feathers in Apr-May may be SYs (see Molt), but more study is needed.**

Vaux's Swift

	Jan	Feb	Mar	Apr	May	Jun	Jul	Aug	Sep	Oct	Nov	Dec
Juv-HY							O	O	O	O	O	O
SY												
	O	O	O	(♀)	(♀)	(♀)	(♀)					
AHY-U												
	O	O	O	(♀)	(♀)	♀	♀	(♀)	O	O	O	O
ASY												
	O	O	O	(♀)	(♀)	♀	♀					

■ > 95%   ▨ 25-95%   ▥ 5-25%   □ < 5%   See Fig. 24

Sex—♀ = ♂ by plumage. The CP apparently is not developed; the BP (Apr-Aug) probably is reliable for sexing ♀♀. ♀ wg(n37) 106-118, tl(n37) 33-40; ♂ wg(n36) 107-116, tl(n36) 32-39.

References—Ridgway (1911), Bent (1940), Phillips (1954), Lack (1956), Wetmore (1957), Baldwin & Hunter (1963), Baldwin & Zaczkowski (1963), Brooke (1969), Devillers (1970a), Bull & Collins (1993a, 1993b), Pyle (1995a); D.E. Payne (*in litt.* to the BBL).

WHITE-THROATED SWIFT
Aeronautes saxatalis

WTSW
Species # 4250
Band size: 2

Geographic variation—Subspecies taxonomy follows Behle (1973a), who synonymized a previously recognized subspecies in N.Am. See also Dickey & van Rossem (1928), Rogers (1939), Oberholser (1974). One other subspecies occurs in Mex-C.Am.

A.s. saxatalis (br & wint throughout range in N.Am): From *nigrior* of Mex-C.Am by upperparts lighter; forehead, lores, and auricular paler than (*vs* uniform in color with) the rest of the upperparts; pale supercilium more distinct; white areas of the underparts and flanks larger. Birds of MT-UT to SD-NE ("*sclateri*") average longer-winged and slightly longer-tailed, but differences are slight and broadly clinal. Birds of CA also may average darker (less white) than other birds in N.Am.

Molt—PB: HY partial (Jul-Oct), AHY complete (Jul-Oct); PA absent. The PBs occur primarily on the summer grounds, but can complete (Sep-Nov or later?) during fall migration or on the winter grounds, as in *Chaetura* swifts; more study is needed. The juvenal wing covs apparently are retained during the 1st PB.

Skull—Pneumaticization probably does not fully complete; however, birds with larger windows (see Fig. 88) probably are reliably aged HY/SY and those with small windows (see Fig. 88) probably are reliably aged AHY through Nov, as in Chimney Swift; more study is needed.

Age/Sex—Juv (Jul-Oct) has the upperparts tinged brownish, the crown and nape tinged pale, and the pp, pp covs, outer ss, and undertail covs edged whitish; juv ♀ = ♂, although the depth of the tail fork, pattern on the terts, and shape of the outer pp may be useful for sexing some juvs, as in HY/SYs (see below). The CP apparently is not developed; the BP (Jun-Jul) probably is reliable for sexing ♀♀. ♀ wg(n93) 129-149, tl(n90) 50-65; ♂ wg(n95) 131-149, tl(n77) 51-64; see **Geographic variation.**

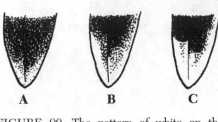

FIGURE 90. The pattern of white on the largest tertials (s5-s6) by age and sex in White-throated Swift. See text for details.

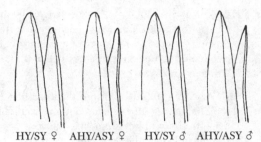

FIGURE 91. The shape and width of the outer primaries (p9-p10) by age and sex in White-throated Swift. These criteria alone should not be relied upon for ageing or sexing.

HY/SY ♀ (Aug-Jul): Tail fork averages shallow (r5 – r1 8-12 mm); flight feathers relatively abraded in Feb-Jul; largest terts (s5-s6) dull grayish with indistinct paling at tip (Fig. 90A); outer pp bluntly rounded (Fig. 91). **Note: In addition, the pale tips to the undertail covs may average broader on HY/SYs than on AHY/ASYs. Some intermediates cannot be reliably aged and/or sexed by plumage and measurements alone.**

AHY/ASY ♀ (Aug-Jul): Tail fork shallow to moderately deep (r5 – r1 9-14 mm); flight feathers relatively fresh in Feb-Jul; largest terts (s5-s6) grayish with little to a moderate amount of white at the tip (Fig. 90A–B); outer pp moderately broad and rounded (Fig. 91). **Note: See HY/SY ♀.**

HY/SY ♂ (Aug-Jul): Tail fork moderately deep (r5 – r1 10-15 mm); flight feathers relatively abraded in Feb-Jul; largest terts (s5-s6) grayish with a moderate amount of white at the tip (Fig. 90B–C); outer pp moderately narrow and pointed (Fig. 91). **Note: See HY/SY ♀.**

AHY/ASY ♂ (Aug-Jul): Tail fork deep (r5 – r1 13-17 mm); flight feathers relatively fresh in Feb-Jul; largest terts (s5-s6) blackish with substantial and distinct white at the tip (Fig. 90C); outer pp narrow and pointed (Fig. 91). **Note: See HY/SY ♀.**

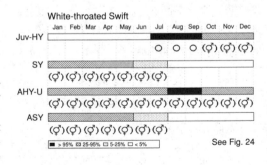

References—Ridgway (1911), Rogers (1939), Behle (1973a), Oberholser (1974), Chantler & Driessens (1995), Pyle (1995a).

HUMMINGBIRDS   *TROCHILIDAE*

Sixteen species. The smallest of birds, with brilliant metallic plumage in the males of many species, slender bills, double-tubular and brush-tipped tongues, and tiny feet. North American hummingbirds have 10 primaries (the 10th full in length), 6 secondaries, and 10 rectrices. Protracted prebasic molts usually are complete in both HY/SYs and AHY/ASYs and typically take place on the non-breeding grounds; occasionally rectrices or other flight feathers can be retained during the first prebasic molt. First-year males can acquire a few iridescent gorget feathers prior to the prebasic molt, perhaps part of a presupplemental molt (see p. 16). The sequence of flight-feather replacement is typical of near-passerines for the most part (see p. 39), although the outer primaries are replaced in order p7-p8-p10-p9. The iridescent gorget feathers of males are the last feathers to be replaced, just prior to the northbound migration or breeding. Some birds retain juvenal feathers or characters, in the flight feathers and/or the gorgets of males. More study is needed on the timing of molt in southern species. True prealternate molts do not occur in hummingbirds. The skull does not attain the normal double-layering of other landbirds; rather, it becomes thicker and less transparent with age (Stiles 1972). The condition of the skull may be useful to age certain species, with experience; however the occurrence and extent of corrugations on the culmen (Ortiz-Crespo 1972, Yanega *et al.* 1997; Fig. 92) provides a much easier and more reliable ageing method. Breeding seasons are extended in some species and may occur year-round south of North America, complicating age-code assignment. Cloacal protuberances and brood patches apparently are not developed sufficiently to be useful in sexing. In most species, individuals are reliably aged and sexed by the combination of measurements, extent of the bill corrugation, occurrence or extent of the gorget, and/or characters of the rectrices. Females average longer wings than males in the smaller, "gorgetted" species (see Table 2).

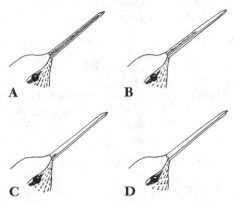

FIGURE 92. Variation in the extent of bill corrugation in hummingbirds. In all species, the bills of nestlings are soft and deeply corrugated along the ramphotheca, lateral to the culmen (**A**). In the first 5-9 months after fledging the bill hardens and the corrugations are lost due to the hardening process and wear (**B-D**). Some older birds can retain a small proportion (≤ 10%) of these corrugations (**C**), or other similar markings, for perhaps as long as they live. Birds with > 10% of the bill corrugated (**A-B**), however, can be aged HY/SYs during their first 5-9 months of life. Figure from Yanega *et al.* (1997).

BROAD-BILLED HUMMINGBIRD
Cynanthus latirostris

BBLH
Species # 4410
Band size: XB

Species—From most hummingbirds of N.Am by measurements (wg 46.8-54.8, tl 26.5-33.1, see **Age/Sex**); bill red or reddish at the base; underparts of ♀ primarily grayish; underparts of ♂ dark except for white undertail covs. ♀ and juv ♂ from White-eared Hummingbird by bill longer (exp culmen 18.7-24.7) and more decurved; supercilium absent, or reduced and pale grayish to whitish; broad stripe behind eye dark gray; throat and underparts gray with sparse or no green flecking; central rect (r1) dull greenish to bluish green with a dusky tip (♀♀), or black with a gray tip (juv ♂); white of the outer rects centrally pointed (see Fig. 93).

Geographic variation—Moderate, but clinal where ranges meet. Subspecies taxonomy in N.Am follows the AOU (1957); see Ridgway (1911), Berlioz (1937), Moore (1939a, 1939b), Binford (1985), Howell & Webb (1995). Six other subspecies occur in Mex.

 C.l. magicus (br se.AZ-sw.TX; vag to n.CA & Ont): From subspecies of Mex by larger size (see **Age/Sex**, *vs* wg 44-53 in the other subspecies); bill averages long (exp culmen 18.7-24.7 *vs* 16.5-23.2) ♀ with little or no green mottling to the underparts (confined to the sides of the breast), basal part of the rects brighter green, and central rect (r1) without or with a reduced, bluish subterminal band; AHY/ASY ♂ with tail fork averaging deeper (r5 – r1 5.3-10.7 mm *vs* 4.0-8.3 in subspecies of Mex) and with the belly paler green; undertail covs whiter.

Molt—PB: HY/SY complete (Nov-May), AHY/ASY complete (Oct-Apr); PA absent. PBs occur on the non-breeding grounds. Flight-feather replacement is usually completed by Apr in SYs; the feathers of the throat and head of SY ♂♂ usually are the last feathers replaced. The timing of molt could differ or be year-round in populations of Mex. Look for SY/TYs rarely to retain a few flight feathers until the 2nd PB, as in other hummingbirds.

Skull—Experience by species is required for the use of pneumaticization in ageing (see Family account).

Age/Sex—Juv (Mar-Aug) has a soft and corrugated bill (Fig. 92**A**), feathers of the upperparts distinctly edged buff, underparts tinged buffy (yellowish in some ♀♀), and base of the mandible dark reddish; nestlings and juvs can be reliably sexed by the pattern of the central (r1) and outer rects (Fig. 93), as in HY/SYs (see below). CP and BP apparently are not well developed. ♀ wg(n26) 46.8-52.1, tl(n20) 26.5-30.1; ♂ wg(n30) 47.7-54.8, tl(n28) 26.9-33.1.

Juv-HY/SY ♀ (Apr-Mar): Bill soft (through Jul-Sep) with deep to shallow corrugations covering > 10% of the culmen (Fig. 92**A-B**; through Nov-Mar); upper mandible black; base of the lower mandible dull reddish, blending indistinctly with the dark tip (through Dec?); central rect (r1) primarily greenish; outer rects with broad, white or grayish tips (Fig. 93); underparts gray, without iridescent blue or green feathers. **Note: See U/AHY ♀.**

U/AHY ♀ (Dec-Nov): Like HY/SY ♀, but bill hard with shallow to no corrugations covering < 10% of the culmen (Fig. 92**C-D**); lower mandible with a brighter red base, more distinctly cut off from the black tip. **Note: A few iridescent bluish feathers can occur in the throats of occasional AHY ♀♀; confirm age (hence sex) with the bill corrugations (Fig. 92) and pattern of the outer rects (Fig. 93).**

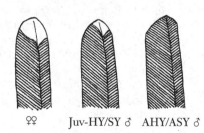

  ♀♀ Juv-HY/SY ♂ AHY/ASY ♂

FIGURE 93. The amount of white in the outer rectrix (r5), by age and sex, in Broad-billed Hummingbirds. Similar (although not identical) patterns can be found in White-eared Hummingbird.

Juv-HY/SY ♂ (Apr-2nd May): Bill corrugations as in juv-HY/SY ♀; upper mandible becoming bright red by Sep-Dec; central rects bluish green to dusky, with grayish-brown tips (Fig. 93; through Feb-May); outer rects with reduced pale tips (Fig. 93); chin, throat, and underparts gray, with a few (May-Aug) to many (Nov-Apr) iridescent blue or dark green feathers, becoming uniformly blue and green by May. **Note: Juv-HYs are separated from SYs in Apr-May by corrugated bills and much less green and blue feathering to the underparts. Beware of possible AHY ♀♀ with a few bluish feathers in the throat; see U/AHY ♀.**

AHY/ASY ♂ (May-Apr): Bill corrugations as in U/AHY ♀; bill (both mandibles) bright red at the base, contrasting distinctly with the black tip; central and outer rects blackish blue without pale tips, or sometimes with very indistinct pale tips (Fig. 93); chin and throat uniformly dark, iridescent blue; rest of the underparts (except undertail covs) dark green. **Note: Look for occasional ♂♂ that may have a few grayish body feathers among the green and blue plumage and/or one or two juvenal, white-tipped rects (Fig. 93); these probably are reliably aged SY/TY through Apr or later. More study is needed in the variation of the white in the adult rects of AHY/ASYs; it is possible that birds with indistinct pale tips may be reliably aged SY/TY.**

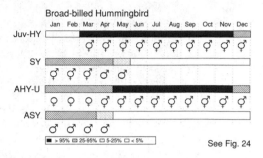

Broad-billed Hummingbird

See Fig. 24

Hybrids reported—Violet-crowned Hummingbird, Magnificent Hummingbird. Hybridization with Dusky Hummingbird (*C. sordidus*) has been reported but is questionable.

References—Ridgway (1911), Moore (1939b), Bent (1940), Wagner (1955, 1957), Phillips *et al.* (1964), Short & Phillips (1966), Oberholser (1974), Binford (1985), Kaufman (1990a), Howell & Webb (1995).

WHITE-EARED HUMMINGBIRD
Hylocharis leucotis

WEHU
Species # 4401
Band size: XA

Species—From most hummingbirds of N.Am by measurements (wg 50.6-57.9, tl 29.0-36.1; see **Age/Sex**); bill red or reddish at the base; underparts of ♀ white with heavy, green spotting; ♂ with a prominent white supercilium. ♀♀ and juv ♂ from Broad-billed Hummingbird by bill shorter (exp culmen 14.5-18.5) and staighter; whitish to white supercilium prominent; broad stripe behind eye black; throat and underparts white with distinct, green spotting; central rects uniformly bright green; white of the outer rects laterally extended or irregular (*cf.* Fig. 93).

Geographic variation—Weak and clinal where ranges meet. Subspecies taxonomy in N.Am follows the AOU (1957); see Ridgway (1911), Griscom (1929a), Dickey & van Rossem (1938). Two other subspecies occur in Mex-C.Am.

H.l. borealis (br/vag to se.AZ-sw.TX): Larger than other subspecies (see **Age/Sex**, *vs* wg 46-53, tl 27-34 in the other subspecies); underparts of ♀♀ whiter, with sparser green spotting.

Molt—PB: HY/SY complete (Jul-Feb), AHY/ASY complete (Jun-Jan); PA absent. PBs commence on the breeding grounds but can complete on the winter grounds. Flight-feather replacement is usually completed by Dec in HYs; the crown feathers of SY ♂♂ usually are the last feathers to be replaced. The timing of the molt could differ in populations of Mex. Look for SY/TYs rarely to retain a few flight feathers until the 2nd PB, and for differences in the timing of the molt between sexes (*e.g.*, earlier in ♂♂, during breeding season, *vs* after breeding in ♀♀, as reported for populations near Mexico City).

Skull—Experience by species is required for the use of pneumaticization in ageing (see Family account).

Age/Sex—Juv (May-Aug) has a soft and corrugated bill (Fig. 92**A**), feathers of the upperparts (especially crown and nape) distinctly edged cinnamon, and underparts buff; some nestling and juv ♂♂ can be reliably sexed by the pattern of the outer rects (see Fig. 93), but juv ♀♀ probably are not reliably sexed. CP and BP apparently are not well developed. ♀ wg(n21) 50.6-55.1, tl(n20) 29.0-32.5; ♂ wg(n30) 51.6-57.9, tl(n20) 31.0-36.1. Month ranges for the following need further study in consideration of possible year-round breeding.

Juv-HY/SY ♀ (May-Apr): Bill soft (through Jul-Oct) with deep to shallow corrugations covering > 10% of the culmen (Fig. 92**A-B**; through Oct-Apr); upper mandible blackish; base of the lower mandible dull reddish, blending indistinctly with the dark tip (through Dec?); crown dull olive-brown (through Feb); forehead and chin without iridescent violet feathers; r2-r5 dusky and narrow, the outer pair with broad, whitish tips (Fig. 93; through Dec); underparts white with green spotting on the throat and sides.

AHY ♀ (Jan-Dec): Like HY/SY ♀, but bill hard with shallow to no corrugations covering < 10% of the culmen (Fig. 92**C-D**); lower mandible with a brighter red base, distinctly cut off from the black tip; crown green with a bronze tinge; r2-r5 black and broad, the outer pair with broad, grayish tips (Fig. 93). **Note: A few iridescent violet or green feathers may occur in the crown, chin, and/or throat of occasional ♀♀ (see Juv-HY/SY ♂); if so these birds probably can be aged ASY. Also, some SY ♀♀ may be reliably aged through Oct or later by duller hindcrown feathers or retained flight feathers; see AHY/ASY ♂.**

Juv-HY/SY ♂ (May-Apr): Bill corrugations as in Juv-HY/SY ♀; bill (including the upper mandible) dull reddish blending indistinctly with the dusky tip (through Dec?); head with one (by Jun) to many iridescent violet (forehead and chin), bronze (hindcrown), or green (throat) feathers, seldom becoming fully colored (especially hindcrown) until Mar or later; outer rect blackish with whitish tips averaging narrower than in ♀♀ (Fig. 93; through Dec), or black, often with indistinct, grayish tipping (Nov-Apr). **Note: Beware of possible AHY/ASY ♀♀ with a few violet feathers in the crown and/or green feathers in the throat; confirm age (hence sex) with the bill corrugations (see p. 121). See AHY/ASY ♂ concerning birds that acquire full plumage early or birds with incomplete iridescent feathering.**

AHY/ASY ♂ (Mar-Feb): Bill corrugations as in AHY ♀; bill bright red at the base, contrasting distinctly with the black tip; crown uniformly iridescent violet (forehead) and bronzy green (hindcrown); chin uniformly iridescent violet; throat uniformly iridescent green; outer rect blackish, often without pale tipping. **Note: HY/SY ♂♂ of some populations may acquire full plumage by Dec and should be aged by bill only. Occasional ♂♂ can have incomplete gorgets or (especially) a few dull olive or dusky hindcrown feathers (see Figs. 99F-G & 104); and/or one or two juvenal rects (♀♀ also?), and are reliably aged SY/TY through Feb. Full iridescent crowns (see Fig. 104) also may indicate ASY/ATY ♂, but more study is needed. More study also is needed on the usefulness of grayish tips to the adult outer rects (cf. Fig. 93), possibly reliable for SY ♂ through Nov or later.**

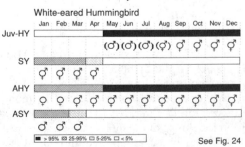

White-eared Hummingbird

See Fig. 24

References—Swarth (1904a), Ridgway (1911), Dickey & van Rossem (1938), A.F. Skutch *in* Bent (1940), Wagner (1955, 1957), Phillips *et al.* (1964), Oberholser (1974), Kaufman (1990a), Howell & Webb (1995).

BERYLLINE HUMMINGBIRD
Amazilia beryllina

BEHU
Species # 4381
Band size: X

Species—From most hummingbirds of N.Am by measurements (wg 49.4-57.7, tl 27.5-32.6; see **Sex**); upper mandible black; lower mandible red at the base; ss, bases of the pp, and rects with rufous; breast largely iridescent green. From Buff-bellied (which see) and Rufous-tailed (*A. tzacatl*) hummingbirds (the latter a possible vagrant to TX), by the combination of shorter tl (see above); lores green; rump, uppertail covs, central rects (r1), and underwing covs uniformly bluish to bronzy violet, with little or no green; lateral rects coppery to rufous.

Geographic variation—Moderate to well marked, but somewhat clinal where ranges meet. Subspecies taxonomy follows Peters (1945); see Ridgway (1911), Griscom (1934a). Three other subspecies occur in Mex-C.Am.

> **A.b. viola** (res se.AZ): From the subspecies of Mex by slightly larger exp culmen (18.4-21.1, *vs* 16.8-19.8); outer pp darker rufous; uppertail covs and central rects (r1) bluish (*vs* bronzy violet in the other subspecies); cinnamon of the lower underparts duller and more grayish.

Molt—PB: HY complete (Apr-Sep), AHY complete (Mar-Sep); PA absent. PBs probably occur primarily on the breeding grounds. Flight-feather replacement may be completed by Aug in most HYs. Year-round breeding and molting possibly occurs and the timing of molt also may vary geographically. Look for HY/SYs rarely to retain a few flight feathers until the 2nd PB, as in other hummingbirds.

Skull—Experience by species is required for the use of pneumaticization in ageing (see Family account).

Age—Juv (Mar-Jul) has a soft and corrugated bill (Fig. 92**A**) and underparts buff with little or no green; juv ♀=♂. Timing for the following ageing criteria requires more study in consideration of possible year-round breeding in this species.

> HY/SY (Jun-Mar): Bill soft (through Jul-Nov) with deep to shallow corrugations covering > 10% of the culmen (Fig. 92**A-B**; through Sep-Mar); breast and belly mixed buffy and green (through Aug or later?). **Note: Some HY/SYs may retain buffy feathers in belly through May or later; more study is needed.**

> U/AHY (Oct-Sep): Bill hard with shallow to no corrugations covering < 10% of the culmen (Fig. 92**C-D**); breast and belly uniformly green, without buffy feathers. **Note: See HY/SY. Look for occasional AHYs with retained flight feathers (especially rects) that probably are reliably aged SY through Aug or later.**

Sex—CP and BP apparently are not well developed. ♀ wg(n22) 49.4-55.6, tl(n20) 26.3-31.5; ♂ wg(n30) 50.8-57.7, tl(n20) 27.5-32.6.

> ♀: Tail notch absent or shallow (r5 – r1 0-3 mm); feathers of the chin whitish or green with broad, whitish edging (Fig. 94); belly grayish.

> ♂: Tail notch deep (r5 – r1 3-6 mm); feathers of the chin uniformly iridescent green (Fig. 94); belly grayish-cinnamon.

Hybrids reported—Blue-tailed Hummingbird (*A. cyanura*), Azure-crowned Hummingbird (*A. cyanocephala*).

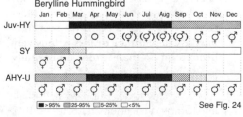

Berylline Hummingbird

See Fig. 24

References—Ridgway (1911), Griscom (1934a), Wagner (1957), Howell & Webb (1995).

BUFF-BELLIED HUMMINGBIRD
Amazilia yucatanensis

BUFH
Species # 4390
Band size: XA

Species—From most hummingbirds of N.Am by measurements (wg 51.6-58.9, tl 29.9-37.6; see **Sex**); bill red or reddish at the base; rects largely rufous; underparts green and buff. From Berylline Hummingbird by longer tl (see above); lores bronze; pp and ss dusky (without rufous), contrasting with the rufous tail; rump, uppertail covs, and underwing covs primarily green with some rufous. From Rufous-tailed Hummingbird, a possible vagrant to TX, by shorter wg but longer tl (see above, *vs* wg 56-61, tl 29-35 in Rufous-tailed Hummingbird); longest uppertail covs primarily green (*vs* entirely rufous); underwing covs with buff (*vs* uniformly green); belly and undertail covs uniformly buffy (*vs* undertail covs grayish, contrasting with the buffy belly in Rufous-tailed Hummingbird).

Geographic variation—Moderate, but clinal where ranges meet. Subspecies taxonomy in N.Am follows the AOU (1957); see Ridgway (1911), Traylor (1949). Two other subspecies occur in Mex-C.Am.

  A.y. chalconota (br s.TX, wint to LA): From the other subspecies by upperparts bronzier; buff of the underparts duller and paler, with less cinnamon; flanks with more distinct, green spotting.

Molt—PB: HY complete (Apr-Nov), AHY complete (Apr-Oct); PA absent. PBs occur primarily on the breeding grounds. Flight-feather replacement probably is completed by Oct in most HYs. The timing of the molt could differ in populations of Mex & C.Am. Look for HY/SYs rarely to retain a few flight feathers until the 2nd PB, as in other hummingbirds.

Skull—Experience by species is required for the use of pneumaticization in ageing (see Family account).

Age/Sex—Juv (May-Sep) has a soft and corrugated bill (Fig. 92**A**), the feathers of the upperparts distinctly edged buff or cinnamon, and the throat and breast grayish buff; juv ♀ = ♂. CP and BP apparently are not well developed. ♀ wg(n19) 51.6-55.6, tl(n19) 29.9-35.1; ♂ wg(n26) 52.8-58.9, tl(n20) 32.0-37.6.

Juv-HY/SY ♀ (May-Mar): Bill soft (through Aug-Oct) with deep to shallow corrugations covering > 10% of the culmen (Fig. 92**A-B**; through Oct-Mar), dull reddish at the base, blending indistinctly with the dusky tip (*cf.* Fig. 94; through Dec?); tail fork absent or shallow (longest r – r1 0-3 mm); feathers of the chin white or green with broad, white edging (Fig. 94); throat and breast buff or mixed grayish buff and green (May-Oct). **Note: Also, the central rects (r1) may average duller or less extensively bronze in ♀♀ than in ♂♂; more study is needed.**

U/AHY ♀ (Nov-Oct): Bill hard with shallow to no corrugations covering < 10% of the culmen (Fig. 92**C-D**), bright red at the base, contrasting distinctly with

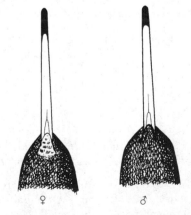

FIGURE 94. The chin of ♀ and ♂ Berylline and Buff-bellied hummingbirds.

the blackish tip (see Fig. 94); tail fork moderate (longest r – rl 3-5 mm); feathers of the chin white or green with broad, white edging (Fig. 94); throat and breast green, without grayish-buff feathers. **Note: See Juv-HY/SY ♀. Look also for occasional AHYs with retained flight feathers (especially rects) that probably are reliably aged SY through Sep or later.**

Juv-HY/SY ♂ (May-Apr): Bill corrugations and color as in juv-HY/SY ♀ (perhaps averaging slightly brighter red); tail fork moderate (longest r – rl 3-5 mm) through Oct; feathers of the chin (if replaced adult) uniformly iridescent green (Fig. 94); throat and breast buff or buff mixed grayish buff and green (May-Oct). **Note: See Juv-HY/SY ♀.**

U/AHY ♂ (Nov-Oct): Bill corrugations and color as in U/AHY ♀ (perhaps averaging slightly brighter red); tail fork deep (longest r – rl 5-7 mm); feathers of the chin uniformly iridescent green (Fig. 94); throat and breast green, without grayish-buff feathers. **Note: See Juv-HY/SY ♀ and U/AHY ♀.**

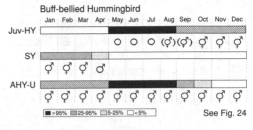

Buff-bellied Hummingbird

See Fig. 24

References—Ridgway (1911), Bent (1940), Oberholser (1974), Howell & Webb (1995).

VIOLET-CROWNED HUMMINGBIRD
Amazilia violiceps

VCHU
Species # 4391
Band size: XA

Species—From all hummingbirds of N.Am by bill red or reddish at the base; crown usually with iridescent bluish or violet feathers; throat and underparts white with little or no mottling or spotting.

Geographic variation—Fairly well marked, but clinal where ranges meet. Subspecies taxonomy in N.Am follows the AOU (1957); see Griscom (1934a), Wetmore (1947), Phillips (1964). One other subspecies occurs in Mex.

A.v. ellioti (res se.AZ-sw.NM; vag to CA): From *violiceps* of Mex by smaller size (see **Sex**, *vs* wg 55-60, tl 30-33 in *violiceps*); crown averages more violet by sex (see **Sex**); tail dull greenish bronze (*vs* coppery bronze in *violiceps*).

Molt—PB: HY complete (Jun-Sep), AHY complete (Jun-Sep); PA absent. PBs may occur on either the non-breeding or the breeding grounds; more study needed. Flight-feather replacement usually is completed by Aug in HYs; the crown feathers may be the last to be replaced. The timing of the molt may differ in populations of Mex. Look for HY/SYs rarely to retain a few flight feathers until the 2nd PB, as in other hummingbirds.

Skull—Experience by species is required for the use of pneumaticization in ageing (see Family account).

Age—Juv (Feb-Aug) has a soft and corrugated bill (Fig. 92A), the base of the upper mandible blackish, the crown primarily brown or dull bluish green, and the rects and feathers of the upperparts distinctly edged buff or cinnamon; juv ♀ = ♂.

HY/SY (Apr-Mar): Bill soft (through Jun-Sep) with deep to shallow corrugations covering > 10% of the culmen (Fig. 92**A-B**; through Dec-Mar), dull reddish at the base, blending indistinctly with the dusky tip (through Oct?); crown dull brown to greenish, with one or more iridescent blue or violet feathers, becoming fully blue or violet by Sep (or later in some birds?).

AHY (Jan-Dec): Bill hard with shallow to no corrugations covering < 10% of the culmen (Fig. 92**C-D**), bright red at the base, contrasting distinctly with the blackish tip; crown uniformly iridescent blue or violet. **Note: Look for occasional AHYs with retained flight feathers (especially rects) that probably are reliably aged SY through Sep or later.**

Sex—CP and BP apparently are not well developed. ♀ wg(n17) 48.0-54.9, tl(n17) 26.4-30.1; ♂ wg(n30) 48.6-56.5, tl(n20) 28.7-32.3; measurements pertain to *A.v. ellioti* of N.Am only (see **Geographic variation**). No reliable plumage criteria are known, although ♀♀ average duller violet or blue crowns than ♂♂; this also varies geographically (see **Geographic variation**).

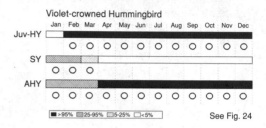

Hybrids reported—Broad-billed Hummingbird.

References—Ridgway (1911), Wetmore (1947), Wagner (1955), Howell & Webb (1995).

BLUE-THROATED HUMMINGBIRD
Lampornis clemenciae

BLUH
Species # 4270
Band size: X-0A

Species—From most hummingbirds of N.Am by large size (wg 67.1-78.5, tl 40.4-51.1; see **Age/Sex**); bill black without red; throat of ♂ with iridescent blue feathers. ♀ from ♀ Magnificent Hummingbird by shorter bill (exp culmen 20.2-24.3; see **Geographic variation**); forehead feathers not covering nares; supercilium white and well defined; central rects (r1) black; outer rects with distinct and extensive white patches (> 13 mm from the tip; Fig. 95); throat gray, without dusky mottling.

Geographic variation—Weak and clinal where ranges meet. Subspecies taxonomy follows Browning (1990); see Oberholser (1918a, 1974), Van Tyne (1929, 1953), Browning (1978), Baldridge *et al.* (1983). One other subspecies occurs in Mex.

L.c. bessophilus (br se.AZ-sw.NM): Bill medium in length and relatively slender (exp culmen 21.8-23.2, width at tip of nares 2.0-3.0); rump green with a bronze tinge, contrasting with the bronze back; underparts (including the throat in ♀♀) uniformly medium-pale gray.

L.c. phasmorus (br w.TX): Bill short and relatively broad (exp culmen 20.2-22.2, width at tip of nares 2.4-3.1); rump and back uniformly dull green with a bronze tinge; underparts (including the throat in ♀♀) uniformly dark gray. Birds of nc.Mex (*clemenciae*), potential vagrants to TX, have larger bills (exp culmen 22.1-24.3, width at tip of nares 2.8-3.1), rump and back uniformly bright green, and underparts dark gray, the throat of ♀♀ dusky, contrasting with the paler breast.

Molt—PB: HY/SY complete (Oct-May), AHY/ASY complete (Oct-Jan); PA absent. PBs occur primarily on the winter grounds. Flight-feather replacement usually is completed by Apr in

HY/SYs; the gorget feathers of SY ♂♂ probably are the last feathers to be replaced. The timing of breeding and molt may differ in populations of Mex. Look for SY/TYs rarely to retain a few flight feathers until the 2nd PB, as in other hummingbirds.

Skull—Experience by species is required for the use of pneumaticization in ageing (see Family account).

Age/Sex—Juv (May-Nov) has a soft and corrugated bill (Fig. 92**A**), feathers of the upperparts tinged golden and distinctly edged pale gray, and mandible flesh-colored or pink at the base; sexes are readily distinguished by lack (♀♀) or presence (♂♂) of blue in the throat. CP and BP apparently are not well developed. Measurements (especially tl) are useful: ♀ wg(n21) 67.1-74.1, tl(n20) 40.4-45.5; ♂ wg(n30) 71.9-78.5, tl(n30) 43.5-51.1.

Juv-HY/SY ♀ (Jun-Mar): Bill soft (through Jul-Sep) with deep to shallow corrugations covering > 10% of culmen (Fig. 92**A-B**; through Dec-Mar); throat brownish-gray without iridescent blue feathers (Fig. 99**A**); mandible pinkish at base (through Nov?).

AHY/ASY ♀ (Feb-Jan): Bill hard with shallow to no corrugations covering < 10% of culmen (Fig. 92**C-D**); throat gray, without iridescent blue (Fig 99**A**) or (occasionally) with 1-2 blue feathers; mandible dark at base. **Note: Look for retained flight feathers on occasional SY/TYs (see AHY/ASY ♂).**

Juv-HY/SY ♂ (Jun-Mar): Bill as in Juv-Hy/SY ♀; throat with blue feathers but gorget incomplete (Fig. 99**F-G**), 43-73 blue-tipped feathers and distance between the closest blue-tipped feather and the auricular usually > 2 mm; r3 with broad, triangular, white terminal patch (Fig. 94.5**A-B**); mandible pinkish at base (through Nov?). **Note: Beware of occasional AHY/ASY ♀♀ with a few blue feathers (but not a complete patch) in the throat.**

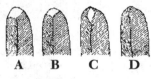

AHY/ASY ♂ (Mar-Feb): Bill as in AHY/ASY ♀; throat uniformly iridescent blue (*cf.* Fig. 99**H**), with 70-122 blue-tipped feathers and distance between the closest blue-tipped feather and the auricular usually < 2 mm; r3 with a small irregular or diamond-shaped patch along the shaft (Fig. 94.5**C-D**); mandible dark at base. **Note: Occasional ♂♂ with intermediate gorget or r3 characteristics, or with retained flight feathers, may be reliably aged SY/TY; more study is needed.**

A   B   C   D

FIGURE 94.5.

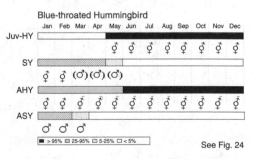

Blue-throated Hummingbird

See Fig. 24

Hybrids reported—Probably with Anna's Hummingbird. Possibly with Black-chinned Hummingbird.

References—Ridgway (1911), Bent (1940), Wagner (1957), Phillips *et al.* (1964, 1984), Oberholser (1974), Phillips & Chase (1982), Baldridge *et al.* (1983).

MAGNIFICENT HUMMINGBIRD
Eugenes fulgens

MAHU
Species # 4260
Band size: X-0A

Species—From most hummingbirds of N.Am by large size (wg 66.1-77.5, tl 37.4-51.1; see **Age/Sex**); bill black without red. ♀ from ♀ Blue-throated Hummingbird by nares covered by forehead feathers; supercilium whitish and indistinct; central rects (r1) green; outer rects with indistinct and reduced whitish patches (< 10 mm from the tip; Fig. 95); throat gray with dusky mottling.

Geographic variation—Well marked and ranges well defined. Subspecies taxonomy follows Monson & Phillips (1981), who considered recognition of two subspecies in N.Am to be unwarranted; see also Ridgway (1911), van Rossem (1939a), Phillips *et al.* (1964), Short & Phillips (1966). One other subspecies occurs in C.Am.

> ***E.f. fulgens*** (br throughout range in N.Am): From *spectabilis* of C.Am by AHY/ASY ♂ with the chest black (*vs* bronzy green in *spectabilis*); undertail covs not washed bronzy greenish; ♀ and HY/SY ♂ with the gray tips of the outer rects broader (see Fig. 95). Birds of AZ ("*aureoviridis*") may average slightly duller and paler than birds of TX, with the green throat of ♂♂ tinged yellowish rather than bluish, but differences are slight and obscured by individual variation.

Molt—PB: HY complete (Jul-Apr), AHY complete (Jun-Nov); PA absent. PBs commence on the breeding grounds or during migration and complete on the winter grounds. More study is needed on the protracted molt in this species: it is possible that HY/SY ♂♂ (at least) replace some body feathers twice in their first year, in Jun-Dec and again in Jan-Apr (with the flight feathers), in which case a presupplemental molt (see p. 16) would be involved. Flight-feather replacement is usually completed by Mar in HY/SYs; the throat feathers in SY ♂♂ probably are the last feathers to be replaced and possibly may be retained in some birds until the 2nd PB. The timing of the molts could differ in populations of Mex & C.Am. Look for SY/TYs rarely to retain a few flight feathers until the 2nd PB, as in other hummingbirds.

Skull—Experience by species is required for the use of pneumaticization in ageing (see Family account).

Age/Sex—Juv (Jun-Sep) has a soft and corrugated bill (Fig. 92A), feathers of the upperparts (especially the crown and rump) narrowly edged buffy gray; juvs are reliably sexed by the throat and tail criteria, as in HY/SYs (see below). CP and BP apparently are not well developed. Measurements (especially tl) are useful: ♀ wg(n30) 66.1-72.1, tl(n30) 37.4-43.9; ♂ wg(n41) 69.8-77.5, tl(n39) 43.5-51.1.

Juv-HY/SY ♀ (Jun-May): Bill soft (through Sep-Nov) with deep to shallow corrugations covering > 10% of the culmen (Fig. 92A-B; through Dec-Mar); tail squared (longest – shortest rect < 2 mm); crown green and gray, without iridescent violet feathers; outer rects green and dusky with distinct, white tips (Fig. 95); throat grayish, without iridescent green or greenish spots (Fig. 99A); underparts gray.

AHY ♀ (Jan-Dec): Like HY/SY ♀, but bill hard with shallow to no corrugations covering < 10% of the culmen (Fig. 92C-D).

Juv-HY/SY ♂ (Jun-May): Bill corrugations as in juv-HY/SY ♀; tail notched (r5 – r1 2-5 mm); crown and throat grayish, with a few (Jul) to many (Nov) iridescent violet (crown) or green (throat) feathers (*e.g.*, Fig. 99C-G), sometimes(?) becoming fully violet and

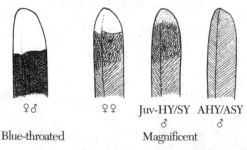

♀♂   ♀♀   Juv-HY/SY AHY/ASY
                        ♂   ♂
Blue-throated   Magnificent

FIGURE 95. The amount of white in the outer rectrix (r5) in Blue-throated Hummingbird and in Magnificent Hummingbird by age and sex. All age/sex groups show a similar pattern in Blue-throated Hummingbird.

green by Apr; outer rects dusky with moderately large but indistinct, grayish tips (Fig. 95; through Jan); breast and belly gray, mottled dusky or black, sometimes(?) becoming fully black by Mar.

AHY/ASY ♂ (Mar-Feb): Bill corrugations as in AHY ♀; tail forked (r5 – r1 7-10 mm); crown uniformly iridescent violet; outer rects uniformly dark green, sometimes with small and indistinct, gray tips (Fig. 95); throat uniformly iridescent green (see Fig. 99**H**); breast and belly black. **Note: Beware of AHY/ASY ♂♂ molting the crown or throat feathers, that may resemble HY/SY ♂♂. It is possible that ♂♂ with complete, iridescent coloration may be aged ASY/ATY, but more study is needed.**

SY/TY ♂ (Jun-Feb): Like AHY/ASY ♂, but iridescent coloration of the crown and underparts incomplete, with a few or more brownish feathers (e.g., Fig. 99**G**); outer rects average more gray in tips or (if retained) are contrastingly worn and have large white tips as in juv-HY/SY ♂ (Fig. 95). **Note: This age classification may be rare; more study is needed.**

Magnificent Hummingbird

See Fig. 24

Hybrids reported—Broad-billed Hummingbird.

References—Ridgway (1911), Dickey & van Rossem (1938), Bent (1940), Wagner (1955, 1957), Phillips et al. (1964, 1984), Short & Phillips (1966), Oberholser (1974), Phillips & Chase (1982), Howell & Webb (1995), Powers (1996).

LUCIFER HUMMINGBIRD
Calothorax lucifer

LUHU
Species # 4370
Band size: XB

Species—From most hummingbirds of N.Am by the combination of measurements (wg 36.3-43.9, tl 21.7-31.3; see **Age/Sex**); bill black, strongly decurved, and without red. ♀♀ and juv-HY/SYs from the other small species in N.Am (especially Costa's Hummingbird) by bill more decurved, and longer (exp culmen 19.4-23.3, > 1/2 wg); juv-HY/SY ♂ with the tail fork greater (see **Age/Sex**); ♀♀ and juv-HY/SY ♂♂ with rufous in the base of the outer rects (r5); gorget feathers iridescent purplish, restricted to the throat in ♂♂; underwing covs cinnamon; underparts including the undertail covs washed buff to cinnamon.

Geographic variation—No subspecies are recognized.

Molt—PB: HY/SY incomplete(?)-complete (Sep-Mar), AHY/ASY complete (Aug-Jan); PA absent. PBs occur primarily on the winter grounds. Gradual replacement of some gorget feathers in HY/SY ♂♂, before the 1st PB, might be considered a partial presupplemental molt (see p. 16), as many of these feathers are replaced for a second time during the 1st PB. Flight-feather replacement usually is completed by Mar in HY/SYs. Many gorget feathers of the throat in SY ♂♂ apparently may not be replaced until the 2nd PB; more study needed.

The timing of the molt could differ in populations of Mex. Look for SY/TYs rarely to retain a few flight feathers until the 2nd PB, as in other hummingbirds.

Skull—Experience by species is required for the use of pneumaticization in ageing (see Family account).

Age/Sex—Juv (May-Oct) has a soft and corrugated bill (Fig. 92**A**), feathers of the upperparts distinctly edged buffy gray, and underparts averaging richer cinnamon; juv ♀ and ♂ can be separated by the depth of the tail fork and width of the outer rect, as in HY/SYs (see below). CP and BP apparently are not well developed. ♀ wg(n18) 39.1-43.9, tl(n18) 21.7-26.9; ♂ wg(n30) 36.3-41.1, tl(n25) 27.9-31.3 (AHY/ASY), tl(n5) 20.4-25.5 (HY/SY).

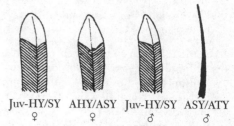

Juv-HY/SY ♀   AHY/ASY ♀   Juv-HY/SY ♂   ASY/ATY ♂

FIGURE 96. The shape and pattern of the outer rectrix (r5), by age and sex, in Lucifer Hummingbird. Look for this feather in SY/TY ♂♂ to be intermediate in shape and pattern between that of juv-HY/SY ♂ and that of ASY/ATY ♂ (see text).

Juv-HY/SY ♀ (May-Mar): Bill soft (through Aug-Oct) with deep to shallow corrugations covering > 10% of the culmen (Fig. 92**A-B**; through Dec-Mar); throat without iridescent purplish feathers (Fig. 99**A-B**); underparts buffy cinnamon; p10 averages broader and blunter (Fig. 97**B-C**); tail squared (longest – shortest rect 0-4 mm; see Fig. 102); outer rects broad (usually > 4 mm at widest point), rounded, and rufous and dusky with white tips (Fig. 96).

AHY/ASY ♀ (Feb-Jan): Like juv-HY/SY ♀, but bill hard with shallow to no corrugations covering < 10% of the culmen (Fig. 92**C-D**) and rects more spatulate in shape (Fig. 96). **Note: A few iridescent purplish feathers occur in the throats of occasional ♀♀ (Fig. 99C-E; see Juv-HY/SY ♂); these are reliably aged ASY through Sep or perhaps ATY through Feb; more study is needed. Look also for retained flight feathers on occasional SY/TYs; see SY/TY ♂.**

Juv-HY/SY ♂ (Jun-May): Bill and underparts as in juv-HY/SY ♀; throat without (May-Aug), or with some (Feb-Apr), iridescent purplish feathers (Fig. 99**A-E**); p10 averages narrower and more curved (Fig. 97**A-B**); tail notched (r5 – r1 usually 4-7 mm; see Fig. 102); outer rects narrow (usually < 4 mm at widest point) and rufous and dusky with white tips (Fig. 96). **Note: Beware of possible ASY ♀♀ with a few purplish feathers in the throat; confirm age and sex with the bill corrugations and the depth of the tail fork.**

AHY/ASY ♂ (May-Apr): Bill corrugations as in AHY/ASY ♀; gorget completely iridescent purplish, with fully elongated "tails" (Fig. 99**H**); tail moderately to deeply forked (r5 – r1 12-17 mm; see Fig. 102); outer rects narrow, tapered, blackish, and usually without pale coloration in the outer portions (Fig. 96). **Note: AHY/ASYs with complete iridescent gorgets with long tails, tail forks averaging deeper (> 10 mm), and entirely black outer rects may be reliably aged ASY/ATY through Mar, but more study is needed.**

SY/TY ♂ (Jun-Apr): Like AHY/ASY ♂, but gorget mixed iridescent purplish and dusky, or incomplete, with the "tails" less elongated (Fig. 99**F-G**); tail fork averages shallower (r5 – r1 7-10 mm); outer rect usually (if not always) with pale coloration (cf. Fig. 96). **Note: This plumage is found only in some SY/TYs. Look also for some SY/TYs with one or** two retained juvenal rects. **More study is needed on ageing AHY ♂♂ of this species.**

References—Ridgway (1911), Bent (1940), Wagner (1946, 1955, 1957), Fox (1954), Phillips *et al.* (1964), Oberholser (1974), Phillips & Chase (1982), Kaufman (1990a, 1992a), Russell *et al.* (1994), Scott (1994), Howell & Webb (1995), Pyle *et al.* (in press).

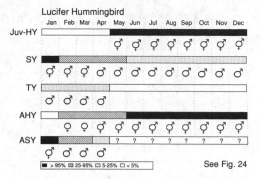

See Fig. 24

Identifying, Ageing, and Sexing Small Hummingbirds

There are eight species of small, "gorgetted" hummingbirds in North America, those species which predominantly are migratory and extend their breeding ranges to the north. AHY/ASY males of these species are separated readily by the color and placement of their striking iridescent gorgets. Females and juv-HY/SY males, however, are predominantly greenish above, whitish or buffy below, and resemble each other quite closely. In the field they can present quite an identification challenge due to their small size and quick behavior. In the hand they are more easily identified, aged, and sexed by the combination of measurements and the other characters listed in Table 2.

When identifying one of these hummingbirds, it is best to age and sex the bird first. Ageing and sexing are similar among species (see species accounts) and thus can be accomplished before the identification process is concluded. All species can be aged for at least 5-9 months after fledging by the extent of the corrugations along the lateral portions of the upper mandible (Ortiz-Crespo 1972, Yanega *et al.* 1997; Fig. 92). Once a bird has been aged, the combination of other characters, including the shape and width of the outer primaries (Fig. 97), the shape and amount of white on the outer rectrix (Fig. 98), and the plumage of the throat (Fig. 99) can be used to distinguish the sexes. Beware that some AHY/ASY ♀♀ of almost all species can obtain iridescent feathers on the throat (in some species this is regular), which can cause them to be misclassified as HY/SY males. It is best to age hummingbirds first, by their bill corrugations, and then to sex them.

Once a hummingbird is aged and sexed, measurement data (especially that of the bill, the tail fork, and the width of r5) then are of greater use in identification. Every species has at least one character that should allow it to be separated from each of the other species, especially when the age/sex class is known. The more important of these are listed in Table 2, and many are illustrated further in Figures 97-111. These should be consulted for initial identifications, which then should be confirmed with the information provided in the species accounts. As with any identification challenge, it is best to synthesize as much information as possible, and to realize that not every character on an individual may concur exactly with the identified species. Anomalous individuals (with one or more characters falling beyond the ranges of 95% of the population; see page 3) can be expected. Occasional hummingbirds not identified to species (**UNHU, Species # 4409**) also may be encountered. These could be hybrids. To date, many AHY/ASY ♂ hybrids between members of these eight species have been documented (see species accounts), but few such juv-HY/SY ♂♂ and ♀♀ have been identified. It is hoped that more of the latter will be documented, in consultation with the information presented here.

It is probable that a small proportion of hummingbirds, especially ♂♂, can be age SY/TY by the combination of retained flight feathers and incomplete iridescent feathering. Occasional AHY/ASY hummingbirds can retain flight feathers, especially rectrices. Most of these are SY/TYs, but more study is needed to confirm this as a reliable ageing criterion, especially in species where flight-feather retention is more common (see Calder & Calder 1992, Pyle *et al.* 1997). In ♂♂, the

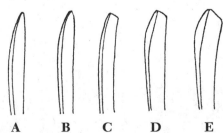

FIGURE 97. Variation in the width and shape of the outer primary, by species, age, and sex, in the small "gorgetted" hummingbirds. See text and Table 2 for details.

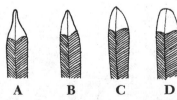

FIGURE 98. Variation in the width and shape of the outer rectrix (r5), by species, age, and sex, in ♀ and juv-HY/SY ♂, small "gorgetted" hummingbirds. AHY/ASY ♂♂ have narrower outer rectrices and usually lack white in the feather tips (*e.g.*, See Fig. 96). See text and Table 2 for details.

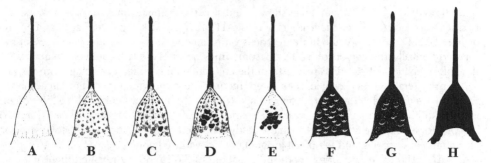

FIGURE 99. Variation in the throat patterns, by species, age, and sex, of small "gorgetted" hummingbirds. See text for details.

TABLE 2. Information for separating ♀♀ and juv-HY/SY ♂♂ hummingbirds in North America. Measurement information is based on references (especially Ridgway 1911; Stiles 1971, 1972; and Baltosser 1987) supplemented by specimen data. Ranges as based on mean ± 2 × S.D. (see page 3) are presented. Sample size is at least 20 for all measurements, substantially more in most cases. The top (**bold**) row includes all age/sex groups listed except AHY/ASY ♂♂.

	Ruby-throated	Black-chinned	Anna's	Costa's	Calliope	Broad-tailed	Rufous	Allen's[1]
Wing chord	**38.1-47.3**	**40.0-48.7**	**46.2-51.5**	**42.3-46.5**	**37.2-44.0**	**46.3-52.1**	**38.1-46.6**	**36.2-43.3**
♀♀	43.4-47.3	43.5-48.7	46.4-51.5	42.9-46.5	40.1-44.0	47.9-52.1	42.6-46.6	39.5-43.3
♂♂	38.1-44.2	40.0-44.8	46.2-51.3	42.3-45.7	37.2-41.3	46.3-51.0	38.1-42.5	36.2-39.9
Tail length	**22.8-28.9**	**22.4-28.3**	**24.9-30.1**	**20.9-25.3**	**17.9-23.3**	**25.7-32.6**	**22.5-28.3**	**21.9-25.9**
♀♀	23.7-28.9	24.6-28.3	24.9-29.3	21.3-25.3	19.7-23.3	26.8-32.6	23.9-28.3	21.9-25.9
Juv-HY/SY ♂♂	22.8-26.1	22.4-27.3	25.2-30.1	20.9-24.2	17.9-21.4	25.7-31.0	22.5-26.9	22.3-24.9
(AHY/ASY ♂)	(25.9-31.0)	(23.7-28.3)	(29.1-33.9)	(21.0-24.7)	(19.6-22.1)	(28.7-35.4)	(25.6-29.5)	(22.8-26.1)
Exp culmen[2]	**13.4-19.0**	**16.0-22.9**	**16.1-20.6**	**15.5-18.8**	**12.8-16.5**	**16.0-20.3**	**14.4-19.0**	**14.0-18.8**
♀♀	15.2-19.0	17.9-22.9	15.4-19.6	16.3-18.8	14.3-16.5	17.4-20.3	16.4-19.0	15.8-18.8
♂♂	13.4-17.2	16.0-20.5	15.3-19.5	15.5-18.1	12.8-15.7	16.0-19.0	14.4-18.0	14.0-17.0
Tail fork[3]	**0-5**	**-2 to 2**	**0-4**	**-4 to 1**	**-4 to 3**	**-5 to 0**	**-7 to -4**	**-7 to -3**
♀♀	0-3	-2 to 2	0-2	-4 to -2	-4 to -2	-5 to -2	-7 to -5	-7 to -4
Juv-HY/SY ♂	2-5	-2 to 2	2-4	-2 to 1	-1 to 3	-4 to 0	-6 to -4	-6 to -3
Width of r5	**4.2-5.5**	**4.0-5.3**	**5.0-6.3**	**2.8-4.2**	**3.1-4.5**	**3.1-5.6**	**2.7-4.7**	**1.6-3.3**
Juv-HY/SY ♀	4.9-5.5	4.6-5.3	5.3-6.3	3.2-4.2	3.5-4.5	4.5-5.6	3.3-4.7	2.4-3.3
AHY/ASY ♀	4.8-5.3	4.5-5.1	5.0-6.0	3.1-4.1	3.4-4.3	4.3-5.4	2.7-4.0	2.0-2.8
Juv-HY/SY ♂	4.2-5.0	4.0-4.7	5.2-6.2	2.8-3.8	3.1-4.0	3.1-4.1	2.7-3.7	1.6-2.5
Outer primary shape[4]	**A-C**	**C-E**	**A-C**	**A-C**	**A-C**	**A-D**	**A-C**	**A-C**
Juv-HY/SY ♀	B-C	E	C	C	B-C	C-D	B-C	B-C
AHY/ASY ♀	B	D-E	B	B	B	B-C	B	B
Juv-HY/SY ♂	A-B	C-D	A-B	A-B	A-B	A-B	A-B	A-B
P1-p6 *vs* p7-p10	narrower	narrower	equal	equal	equal	equal	equal	equal
Rufous in tail?	no	no	no	no	yes	yes	yes	yes
Flank color	green & cinnamon	grayish-buff	green & gray	whitish buffy	deep buffy	pale rufous	buffy rufous	buffy rufous

[1] Includes the migratory *S.s. sasin* only. See text for differences in measurements of the local resident *sedentarius*.
[2] Beware of juvs with less than full-grown bills.
[3] Tail fork is the distance between the tips of the outermost (r5) and innermost (r1) rectrices (see Figure 102). Negative values indicate that r1 > r5.
[4] Letters refer to Figure 97.

replaced rectrices of SY/TYs sometimes show an indistinct to distinct whitish or pale area near the tip, a juvenal character which the feathers of most AHY/ASY ♂♂ lack (*e.g.*, see Fig. 108). The proportion of SY/TY ♂♂ with white in the rectrices varies among the species, and is in need of further study. Finally, the gorgets of SY/TY ♂♂ sometimes or often are less complete than those of full adults (see Fig. 99**F-G**). This results from the coloration on each feather being more restricted, and the lateral feathers being less elongated. Incomplete gorgets are more common in the two species of *Calypte*, which molt at a younger age (during the first summer) and have iridescent feathers on the crown. ♂♂ with incomplete iridescent feathering are reliably aged HY/SY (*Calypte*), or SY/TY (the other species); more study is needed on the incidence of incomplete gorgets within each species, and the possible ageing of ♂♂ with full gorgets as AHY/ASY (*Calypte*), or ASY/ATY. Until further study is performed, ageing of SY/TY ♂♂ by retained flight feathers, white in the rectrices, and/or incomplete gorgets only should be attempted with caution and experience, and perhaps only when at least two of these three criteria coincide.

RUBY-THROATED HUMMINGBIRD
Archilochus colubris

RTHU
Species # 4280
Band size: XB

Species—From the other small hummingbirds of N.Am by the combination of measurements (Table 2); gorget feathers (when present) iridescent red, only slightly laterally elongated, and not extending to the crown in AHY/ASY ♂♂; upperparts bright to golden green, without rufous; rects of ♀♀ and juv-HY/SY ♂♂ without rufous; undertail covs with little or no buff or rufous.

♀♀ and juv-HY/SY ♂♂ should be separated with caution from the other small hummingbirds of corresponding age/sex classes (see p. 134 and **Age/Sex**). From Anna's and Costa's hummingbirds by p1-p6 narrower than p7-p10 (Fig. 100) and p6 attenuate (see Fig. 101). From Anna's Hummingbird further by shorter measurements, especially wg (Table 2); outer rect narrower (Table 2, Fig. 98**B-D**); sides of the underparts without heavy, green mottling. From Costa's Hummingbird further by longer average tl (Table 2); outer rect broader (Table 2, Fig. 98**B-D**); tail forked (see Fig. 102; Table 2); throat usually with dusky markings (Fig. 99**B-D**). From Black-chinned Hummingbird (with caution) by shorter bill by sex (Table 2; beware of juv Black-

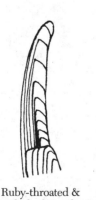
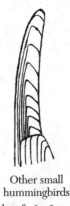
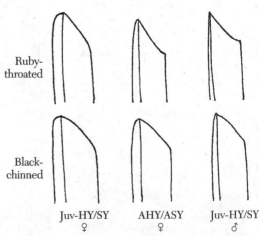

Ruby-throated

Black-chinned

Ruby-throated &   Other small
Black-chinned   hummingbirds

Juv-HY/SY   AHY/ASY   Juv-HY/SY
♀   ♀   ♂

FIGURE 100. Relative widths of p1-p6 *vs* p7-p10 in hummingbirds as an aid to identification. This difference is most useful in separating Ruby-throated and Black-chinned hummingbirds from Costa's Hummingbird in ♀ and juv-HY/SY ♂ plumages.

FIGURE 101. Variation in the shape of p6, by species, age, and sex, in ♀ and juv-HY/SY ♂ Ruby-throated and Black-chinned hummingbirds. The shape of this feather in AHY/ASY ♂♂ is more attenuate than that of juv-HY/SY ♂♂, in each species.

chinned Hummingbirds without fully grown bills); upperparts (especially forehead) brighter green; inner pp (*e.g.*, p6) with more attenuate inner webs (Fig. 101); p10 narrower and less curved by age and sex (Fig. 97**A-C**); tail fork deeper, especially in juv-HY/SY ♂♂ (Table 2, see Fig. 102); outer rects average broader and usually without a nipple (Table 2, Fig. 98**B-D**); flanks often mixed greenish and buff or cinnamon. Any HY/SY or ♀ *Archilochus* with a green forehead should be Ruby-throated, whereas some Ruby-throateds may have duller foreheads. See also differences in timing of the molt for further identification clues.

Geographic variation—No subspecies are recognized.

Molt—PB: HY/SY complete (Nov-Apr), AHY/ASY complete (Oct-Mar); PA absent. PBs occur on the winter grounds. Gradual replacement of some gorget feathers in HY/SY ♂♂, before the 1st PB, might be considered a partial presupplemental molt (see p. 16), as these feathers are replaced for a second time in Mar-Apr. Flight-feather replacement usually is completed by mid Mar in HY/SYs; the gorget feathers of SY ♂♂ are the last feathers to be replaced. Also, SY/TYs rarely retain a few flight feathers (especially rects) until the 2nd PB.

Skull—Experience by species is required for the use of pneumaticization in ageing (see Family account).

Age/Sex—Juv (May-Dec) has a soft and corrugated bill (Fig. 92**A**), feathers of the upperparts with distinct, grayish-brown edging, and sides of the underparts buffy; nestlings and juvs can be reliably sexed by the combination of wg, p10, tail fork, and throat criteria as in juv-HY/SYs (see below). CP and BP apparently are not well developed. Measurements are useful for sexing (see Table 2).

Juv-HY/SY ♀ (May-Mar): Wg 43.4-47.3 (Table 2); bill soft (through Jul-Sep) with deep to shallow corrugations covering > 10% of the culmen (Fig. 92**A-B**; through Nov-Mar); throat whitish, without iridescent red feathers and with no to a few dusky markings (Fig. 99**A-B**); p6 relatively broad and less attenuate at tip (Fig. 101; through Feb); p10 averages broader and blunter (Fig. 97**B-C**; through Mar); tail double-rounded, with a shallow notch (Fig. 102, see Table 2); outer rects broad (Table 2, Fig. 98**D**; through Feb).

AHY/ASY ♀ (Feb-Jan): Like juv-HY/SY ♀, but bill hard with shallow to no corrugations covering < 10% of the culmen (Fig. 92**C-D**); throat whitish, usually without iridescent red feathers, and with few to a moderate amount of dusky markings (Fig. 99**B**); p6 with the inner web indistinctly attenuate (Fig. 101); p10 averages slightly narrower and more curved (Fig. 97**B**); outer rects narrower and more tapered at the tip (Table 2, Fig. 98**C**). **Note: Occasional ♀♀ can have one to a few iridescent red feathers in the throat (Fig. 99C; see Juv-HY/SY ♂); these probably are reliably aged AHY/ASY through Sep or later but more study is needed. Also, ♀♀ rarely may retain flight feathers (especially rects) and may be reliably aged SY/TY through Jan or later.**

Juv-HY/SY ♂ (May-Apr): Wg 38.1-44.2 (Table 2); bill corrugations as in juv-HY/SY ♀; throat usually with heavy, dusky markings (juv; Fig. 99**B**), or with one (often by Aug) to many iridescent red feathers (Fig. 99**C-D**), becoming fully red by Apr-May; p6 with the inner web distinctly attenuate at the tip (Fig. 101; through Feb); p10 narrow and curved (Fig. 97**A-B**; through Mar); tail fork moderately deep (Fig. 102, see Table 2; through Feb); outer rects nar-

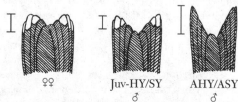

♀♀   Juv-HY/SY   AHY/ASY
                  ♂   ♂

FIGURE 102. The extent of the tail fork (when rectrices are fresh) by age and sex in Buff-bellied, Lucifer, Ruby-throated, and Anna's hummingbirds. Similar (although less-pronounced) differences can be found in the other "gorgetted" species. See Table 2 for measurements.

row and tapered, with white at the tip (Table 2, Fig. 98**B**; through Feb). **Note: Beware of occasional AHY/ASY ♀♀ that can have a few red feathers in the throat; confirm age (hence sex) with the bill corrugations (see p. 121).**

AHY/ASY ♂ (Apr-Mar): Bill corrugations as in AHY/ASY ♀; gorget completely iridescent red, without partially dusky feathers, and with the "tails" partially elongated (Fig. 99**H**); inner pp relatively attenuate (*cf.* Fig. 101); p10 very narrow and curved (*cf.* Fig. 97); tail deeply forked (r5 – r1 6-9 mm) and outer rects very narrow, attenuate, and black without white tips (Fig. 102).

SY/TY ♂ (Apr-Mar): Like AHY/ASY ♂, but gorget incomplete, some feathers partially dusky, and with the "tails" less elongated (Fig. 99**G**). **Note: Occasional SY/TYs also can have one or two retained juvenal flight feathers (especially rects) or pale areas in the distal portion of the outer rects (see Fig. 108). Most SY/TY ♂♂ cannot be reliably aged (see p. 134).**

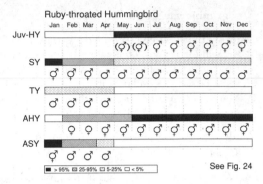

Ruby-throated Hummingbird

See Fig. 24

References—Stone (1896), Ridgway (1911), Forbush (1927), Dickey & van Rossem (1938), Bent (1940), Roberts (1955), Norris *et al.* (1957), Phillips *et al.* (1964), Wood (1969), Johnson (1972), Leberman (1972), Oberholser (1974), Phillips (1975a), Sheppard & Klimkiewicz (1976), Sorrie (1980), Phillips & Chase (1982), Mulvihill & Leberman (1985), Baltosser (1987, 1995), Baumgartner (1989), Bevier (1990), Kaufman (1990a), Backstrom (1995), Robinson *et al.* (1996), Howell & Pyle (1997), Pyle *et al.* (1997); R. Bertin, R.R. Sargent (*in litt.* to the BBL).

BLACK-CHINNED HUMMINGBIRD
Archilochus alexandri

BCHU
Species # 4290
Band size: XB

Species—From the other small hummingbirds of N.Am by the combination of measurements (Table 2); gorget feathers (when present) black and iridescent violet, only slightly laterally elongated, and not extending to the crown in AHY/ASY ♂♂; upperparts bronzy green without rufous; rects of ♀♀ and juv-HY/SY ♂♂ without rufous; undertail covs white with little or no buff or rufous.

♀♀ and juv-HY/SY ♂♂ should be separated with caution from the other small hummingbirds of corresponding age/sex classes (see p. 134 and **Age/Sex**). From Anna's and Costa's hummingbirds by p1-p6 narrower than p7-p10 (Fig. 100); p10 broader and more truncate (Fig. 97**C-E**); outer rects narrower and often with a nipple (Fig. 98**A-C**). From Anna's Hummingbird further by shorter wg and tl (Table 2); tail fork shallower in juv-HY/SY ♂ (*cf.* Fig. 102); sides of the underparts without heavy, green mottling. From Costa's Hummingbird further (with caution) by tl and bill average longer (Table 2); tail slightly more forked (Table 2); throat often with dusky markings (Fig. 99**A-D**). From Ruby-throated Hummingbird (with caution; see **Geographic variation**) by longer bill by sex (Table 2; beware of juvs without fully grown bills); forehead dusky or brownish, without green (see Ruby-throated Hummingbird); upperparts bronzy or grayish green; inner pp (*e.g.*, p6) with a less attenuated inner web by age/sex (Fig. 101); p10 broader and more truncate (Fig. 97**C-E**); tail fork (especially of juv-HY/SY ♂) shallower (Table 2, *cf.* Fig. 102); outer rects narrower and often with a nipple (Table 2, Fig. 98**A-C**); flanks usually grayish with a buff tinge. See also differences in the timing of molt for further identification clues.

Geographic variation—No subspecies are recognized; however, a smaller race may occur in n.Mex & sw.N.Am (see Phillips & Chase 1982, Baltosser 1987), which also may be paler and have a more distinctly defined postocular stripe than populations to the north (Stiles 1971). More study is needed.

Molt—PB: HY/SY complete (Sep-Mar), AHY/ASY complete (Aug-Feb); PA absent. PBs occur on the winter grounds. Gradual replacement of some gorget feathers in HY/SY ♂♂, before the 1st PB, might be considered a partial presupplemental molt (see p. 16), as these feathers are replaced for a second time in Feb-Mar. Flight-feather replacement usually is completed by Mar in HY/SYs; the gorget feathers in SY ♂♂ are the last feathers to be replaced. Also, SY/TYs rarely retain a few flight feathers (especially rects) until the 2nd PB.

Skull—Experience by species is required for the use of pneumaticization in ageing (see Family account).

Age/Sex—Juv (May-Oct) has a soft and corrugated bill (Fig. 92**A**), feathers of the upperparts with distinct, brownish-gray edging, and sides of the underparts buff; nestlings and juvs can be reliably sexed by the combination of the wg, p10, rect, and throat criteria, as in juv-HY/SYs (see below). CP and BP apparently are not well developed. Measurements are useful for sexing (see Table 2), although they do not include certain southern populations which average smaller (see **Geographic variation** and Baltosser 1987).

Juv-HY/SY ♀ (May-Mar): Wg 43.5-48.7 (Table 2); bill soft (through Aug-Oct) with deep to shallow corrugations covering > 10% of the culmen (Fig. 92**A-B**; through Nov-Mar); throat whitish, without black or iridescent violet feathers and usually with few dusky markings (Fig. 99**A-B**); p6 relatively broad at the tip (Fig. 101; through Jan); p10 averages broader and blunter (Fig. 97**E**; through Feb); r2 often with a white tip; outer rects relatively broad (Table 2, Fig. 98**B-C**; through Jan).

U/AHY ♀ (Dec-Nov): Like juv-HY/SY ♀, but bill hard with shallow to no corrugations covering < 10% of the culmen (Fig. 92**C-D**); throat whitish, usually without black or iridescent violet feathers and with few to a moderate amount of dusky markings (Fig. 99**B**); p6 more attenuate (Fig. 101); p10 averages slightly narrower (Fig. 97**D-E**); outer rects narrower and more tapered at the tip (Table 2, Fig. 98**A-B**). **Note: Look for occasional ♀♀ with one to a few black and/or iridescent violet feathers in the throat (Fig. 99C-D), which probably can be reliably aged AHY/ASY through Sep or later; more study is needed. Also, look for ♀♀ rarely to retain flight feathers (especially rects) that may be reliably aged SY/TY through Dec or later.**

Juv-HY/SY ♂ (May-Mar): Wg 40.0-44.8 (Table 2); bill corrugations as in juv-HY/SY ♀; throat whitish, usually with heavy, dusky markings (juv; Fig. 99**B**), and with one (usually by Aug) to many distinct, black and/or iridescent violet feathers (Fig. 99**C-D**), usually becoming fully violet by Mar; p6 with inner web indistinctly attenuate at the tip (Fig. 101); p10 relatively narrow and curved (Fig. 97**C-D**; through Feb); outer rects narrow and tapered, with white at the tip (Table 2, Fig. 98**A-B**; through Jan). **Note: Beware of occasional AHY/ASY ♀♀ that may have a few black and/or violet feathers in the throat; confirm age (hence sex) with the bill corrugations (see p. 121).**

AHY/ASY ♂ (Mar-Feb): Bill corrugations as in U/AHY ♀; chin completely black and throat completely iridescent violet, without partially dusky feathers, and with the "tails" partially elongated (Fig. 99**H**); inner pp relatively attenuate (*cf.* Fig. 101); p10 moderately narrow and curved (Fig. 97**B-C**); tail forked or deeply notched (r5 – r1 2-5 mm); outer rects narrow, tapered, and black, without white tips (*cf.* Fig. 98).

SY/TY ♂ (Mar-Feb): Like AHY/ASY ♂, but gorget incomplete, some feathers partially dusky, and with the "tails" less elongated (Fig. 99G). **Note: Occasional SY/TYs also may have one or two retained juvenal flight feathers (especially rects) or pale areas in the distal portion of the outer rects (see Fig. 108). Most SY/TY ♂♂ cannot be reliably aged (see p. 134).**

Hybrids reported—Anna's Hummingbird, Costa's Hummingbird, Broad-tailed Hummingbird, Allen's Hummingbird. Possibly Blue-throated Hummingbird.

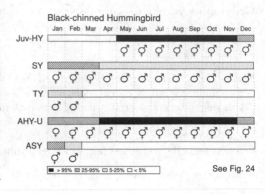

References—Ridgway (1911), Bent (1940), Banks & Johnson (1961), Phillips *et al.* (1964), Short & Phillips (1966), Lynch & Ames (1970), Stiles (1971), Oberholser (1974), Phillips (1975a), Ewald & Rohwer (1980), Sorrie (1980), Phillips & Chase (1982), Baldridge (1983), Baldridge *et al.* (1983), Collins (1983), Baltosser (1987, 1994, 1995), Kaufman (1990a), Elliston & Baltosser (1995), Howell & Pyle (1997), Pyle *et al.* (1997); IBP (MAPS) data.

ANNA'S HUMMINGBIRD
Calypte anna

ANHU
Species # 4310
Band size: XA

Species—From the other small hummingbirds of N.Am by the combination of measurements (Table 2); gorget feathers (when present) iridescent pinkish red, showing moderate lateral elongation, and extending to the crown in ♂♂; upperparts green or golden-green, without rufous; rects of ♀♀ and juv-HY/SY ♂♂ without extensive rufous; underparts gray with extensive green mottling on the sides; undertail covs with little or no buff or rufous.

♀♀ and juv-HY/SY ♂♂ should be separated with caution from the other small hummingbirds of corresponding age/sex classes (see p. 134 and **Age/Sex**). From Ruby-throated and Black-chinned hummingbirds by longer wg and tl (Table 2); p1-p6 not distinctly narrower than p7-p10 (Fig. 100); p6 not attenuate (*cf.* Fig. 101); outer rects broader (Table 2, Fig. 98C-E). From Black-chinned Hummingbird further by p10 narrower and more curved (Fig. 97A-D) and tail notch deeper in juv HY/SY ♂♂ (Table 2, Fig. 102). From Costa's Hummingbird by longer wg and tl (Table 2); throat more heavily marked by age/sex (Fig. 99B-D); gorget feathers (if present) redder; tail fork more defined (Fig. 102; Table 2); outer rect broader (Table 2, Fig. 98C-E); underparts gray with heavy, greenish mottling. Beware of hybrids, especially with Costa's Hummingbird. See also differences in timing of the molt for further identification clues.

Geographic variation—No subspecies are recognized, although birds of BC-c.CA may average pinker gorget feathers (less red) than birds of s.CA.

Molt—PB: HY/SY complete (May-Feb), AHY/ASY complete (May-Jan); PA absent. Gradual replacement of some to many gorget feathers in HY/SY ♂♂, before the 1st PB, might be considered a partial presupplemental molt (see p. 16), as these feathers are replaced for a second time in Jul-Feb. Flight-feather replacement usually is completed by Oct (but as late as Dec) in HYs; the gorget feathers of HY/SY ♂♂ are the last feathers to be replaced. Also, HY/SYs rarely can retain one or more juvenal flight feathers (especially rects) until the 2nd PB.

Skull—Experience by species is required for the use of pneumaticization in ageing (see Family account).

Age/Sex—Juv (Feb-Sep) has a soft and corrugated bill (Fig. 92**A**) and feathers of the upperparts with distinct, brownish-buff edging; nestlings and juvs can be reliably sexed by the combination of the throat, p10, tail fork, and rect criteria, as in juv-HY/SY (see below). CP and BP apparently are not well developed. See Table 2 for measurements.

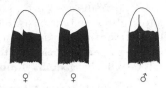

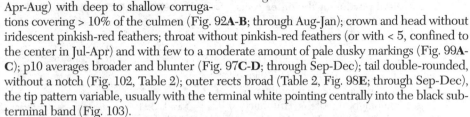

FIGURE 103. Variation in the shape of white at the tip of the outer rectrix (r5) in ♀ and juv-HY/SY ♂ Anna's and Costa's hummingbirds. This difference is especially useful in sexing juvs and nestlings.

Juv-HY/SY ♀ (Feb-Jan): Bill soft (through Apr-Aug) with deep to shallow corrugations covering > 10% of the culmen (Fig. 92**A-B**; through Aug-Jan); crown and head without iridescent pinkish-red feathers; throat without pinkish-red feathers (or with < 5, confined to the center in Jul-Apr) and with few to a moderate amount of pale dusky markings (Fig. 99**A-C**); p10 averages broader and blunter (Fig. 97**C-D**; through Sep-Dec); tail double-rounded, without a notch (Fig. 102, Table 2); outer rects broad (Table 2, Fig. 98**E**; through Sep-Dec), the tip pattern variable, usually with the terminal white pointing centrally into the black sub-terminal band (Fig. 103).

U/AHY ♀ (Oct-Sep): Like juv-HY/SY ♀, but bill hard with shallow to no corrugations covering < 10% of the culmen (Fig. 92**C-D**); throat with moderately heavy to heavy, dusky-greenish markings, and usually 10-20 iridescent pinkish-red feathers confined to the center (Fig. 99**D-E**); p10 averages slightly narrower (Fig. 97**C**); outer rects slightly narrower and more tapered at the tip (Table 2, Fig. 98**D-E**). **Note: Occasional ♀♀ have a few iridescent pinkish-red feathers in the head (including the crown); these probably can be aged AHY/ASY through Aug, but more study is needed. Also, ♀♀ rarely can retain flight feathers (especially rects), and these may be reliably aged SY through Sep or later.**

Juv-HY/SY ♂ (Mar-Feb): Bill corrugations as in HY/SY ♀; throat with moderately heavy to heavy, dusky-greenish markings (juv; Fig. 99**B**; Feb-Jul), or crown, head and throat with one (on throat by Mar-Aug; on the crown/head by Jun-Sep) to many iridescent pinkish-red feathers (Fig. 99**C-D**), not confined to the center of the throat, the gorget usually becoming fully pinkish red in Nov-Feb; p10 narrow and curved (Fig. 97**A-B**; through Sep-Dec); tail notched (Table 2, see Fig. 102; through Sep-Dec); outer rects relatively narrow and tapered (Table 2, Fig. 98**C-D**; through Sep-Dec), the white tip usually with a point of black extending distally from the subterminal band (Fig. 103). **Note: Beware of occasional AHY ♀♀ with a few red feathers in the lateral portions of the throat, head and/or crown; confirm age (hence sex) with the bill corrugations (see p. 121).**

AHY ♂ (Jan-Dec): Bill corrugations as in U/AHY ♀; gorget and crown completely iridescent pinkish red, without dusky or green feathers (especially in the hind-

FIGURE 104. Variation in the completeness of iridescent feathering on the crowns of AHY ♂ Anna's and Costa's hummingbirds. It is possible that birds with complete crowns ("AHY" above) can be aged ASY, especially in Costa's Hummingbird, but more study is needed to determine this. Figure from Pyle *et al.* (1997).

crown or above the eyes), and with the "tails" moderately extended (Figs. 99**H** & 104); p10 relatively narrow and curved (*cf.* Fig. 97); tail forked or deeply notched (r5 – r1 7-9 mm) and outer rects very narrow, tapered, and black, without white tips (Fig. 102). **Note: AHYs with complete gorgets, especially in the hindcrown, along with completely dark outer rects might be reliably aged ASY through Nov or later, but more study is needed.**

SY ♂ (Jan-Jun): Like AHY ♂, but gorget and iridescent crown plumage incomplete, some feathers (especially in the hindcrown or above the eyes) partially dusky or greenish, and with the "tails" of the throat less-elongated (Figs. 99**F-G** & 104). **Note: Also, SY/TYs rarely can have one or two retained juvenal flight feathers (especially rects) or pale areas in the distal portion of the outer rects (see Fig. 108). Many SY ♂♂ probably cannot be reliably aged (see p. 134).**

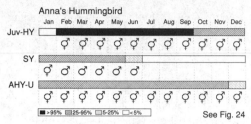

Anna's Hummingbird

Note: In Oct-Dec, ♀♀ should be aged U whereas ♂♂ can be aged AHY.

Hybrids reported—Black-chinned Hummingbird, Costa's Hummingbird, Calliope Hummingbird, Broad-tailed Hummingbird, Rufous Hummingbird, Allen's Hummingbird. Probably Blue-tailed Hummingbird.

References—Ridgway (1911), R.S. Woods *in* Bent (1940), Pitelka (1951a), F.S.L. Williamson (1956, 1957), Banks & Johnson (1961), Phillips *et al.* (1964), Stiles (1971, 1973, 1982), Ortiz-Crespo (1972), Oberholser (1974), Wells *et al.* (1978, 1996), Wells & Baptista (1979a), Ewald & Rohwer (1980), Stiles (1982), Baldridge *et al.* (1983), Baltosser (1987), Kaufman (1990a), Russell (1996), Pyle *et al.* (1997), Yanega *et al.* (1997); J.R. King, G. Yanega (pers. comm.); PRBO data.

COSTA'S HUMMINGBIRD
Calypte costae

COHU
Species # 4300
Band size: XB

Species—From the other small hummingbirds of N.Am by the combination of measurements (Table 2); gorget feathers (when present) iridescent violet, showing extensive lateral elongation, and extending to the crown in ♂♂; upperparts grayish (less green or bronzy), without rufous; rects of ♀♀ and juv-HY/SY ♂♂ without rufous; underparts (including the undertail covs) whitish with little or no buff or rufous. From Lucifer Hummingbird further by bill straighter and shorter; exp culmen < 1/2 wg (see Table 2).

♀♀ and juv-HY/SY ♂♂ should be separated with caution from the other small hummingbirds of corresponding age/sex classes (see p. 134 and **Age/Sex**). From Ruby-throated and Black-chinned hummingbirds by tl averages shorter (Table 2); p1-p6 not distinctly narrower than p7-p10 (Fig. 100); p6 not attenuate (*cf.* Fig. 101); throat less heavily marked by age/sex (Fig. 99**A** & **E**). From Ruby-throated Hummingbird further by outer rect slightly narrower (Fig. 98**B-C**; Table 2); tail rounded (Table 2). From Black-chinned Hummingbird further (with caution) by bill averages shorter (Table 2); p10 narrower and more curved (Fig. 97**A-C**); outer rects slightly broader (Table 2, Fig. 98**B-C**). From Anna's Hummingbird by shorter wg and tl (Table 2); throat less heavily marked by age/sex (Fig. 99**A** & **E**); gorget feathers (if present) violet without a reddish tinge; tail rounded (Table 2); outer rect narrower (Table 2, Fig. 98**B-C**); underparts and flanks whitish, without heavy, green mottling. Beware of hybrids, especially with Anna's Hummingbird. See also differences in the timing of the molt for further identification clues.

Geographic variation—No subspecies are recognized.

Molt—PB: HY complete (Jun-Nov), AHY complete (May-Oct); PA absent. PBs probably occur primarily on the non-breeding grounds. Gradual replacement of some gorget feathers in HY/SY ♂♂, before the 1st PB, might be considered a partial presupplemental molt (see p. 16), as these feathers are replaced for a second time in Oct-Nov. Flight-feather replacement usually is completed by Nov in HYs; the gorget feathers of HY ♂♂ are the last feathers to be replaced. Also, HY/SYs rarely can retain one or more juvenal flight feathers (especially rects) until the 2nd PB.

Skull—Experience by species is required for the use of pneumaticization in ageing (see Family account).

Age/Sex—Juv (Mar-Sep) has a soft and corrugated bill (Fig. 92**A**) and feathers of the upperparts with distinct, grayish-buff edging (which can wear off quickly); nestlings and juvs can be reliably sexed by the combination of the throat, p10, tail fork, and rect criteria, as in juv-HY/SYs (see below). CP and BP apparently are not well developed. See Table 2 for measurements by sex.

Juv-HY/SY ♀ (Mar-Feb): Bill soft (through Jul-Oct) with deep to shallow corrugations covering > 10% of the culmen (Fig. 92**A-B**; through Sep-Feb); crown and head without iridescent violet feathers; throat without violet feathers and usually without dusky markings (Fig. 99**A**); p10 averages broader and blunter (Fig. 97**C**; through Oct); tail graduated (Table 2); r2 often tipped white; outer rects relatively broad (Table 2, Fig. 98**C**; through Sep), the tip pattern variable, usually with an extensive terminal white patch pointing centrally into the black subterminal band (Fig. 103).

U/AHY ♀ (Dec-Nov): Like juv-HY/SY ♀, but bill hard with shallow to no corrugations covering < 10% of the culmen (Fig. 92**C-D**); throat without dusky markings and no to a few (< 20) iridescent violet feathers, the latter usually confined to the center (Fig. 99**E**); p10 averages narrower and more curved (Fig. 97**B**); outer rects average slightly narrower and more tapered at the tip (Table 2, Fig. 98**B-C**). **Note: Occasional ♀♀ have a few iridescent violet feathers in the head and/or crown; these probably can be aged AHY/ASY through Aug, but more study is needed. Also, look for rare ♀♀ with retained flight feathers (especially rects) that may be reliably aged SY through Sep or later.**

Juv-HY/SY ♂ (Mar-Feb): Bill corrugations as in HY/SY ♀; throat usually with moderately heavy, dusky-greenish markings (juv; Fig. 99**A-B**; Feb-Jul), or crown, head and throat with one (on throat by May-Jul; on the crown/head by Jul-Aug) to many iridescent violet feathers (Fig. 99**C-F**), not necessarily confined to the center of the throat, and sometimes(?) becoming fully violet by Nov; p10 narrow and curved (Fig. 97**A-B**; through Sep); tail squared (Table 2); outer rects narrow and tapered (Table 2, Fig. 98**B**; through Sep), the white tip usually with a point of black extending distally from the subterminal band (Fig. 103). **Note: Beware of occasional AHY ♀♀ with a few iridescent violet feathers in the lateral portions of the throat, head and/or crown; confirm age (hence sex) with the bill corrugations (see p. 121).**

U/AHY ♂ (Dec-Nov): Bill corrugations as in U/AHY ♀; gorget and iridescent crown completely violet, without partially dusky or greenish feathers (especially in the hindcrown), and with the "tails" extensively elongated (Figs. 99**H** & 104); p10 relatively narrow and curved (*cf.* Fig. 97); tail forked or deeply notched (r5 > r1 by 3-5 mm); outer rects (r5) very narrow, sickle-shaped, black, and usually without white tips. **Note: U/AHY ♂♂ with complete gorgets, including the hindcrown (Fig. 104), and fully dark outer rects (see Fig. 108) likely are reliably aged AHY/ASY through Nov, but more study is needed.**

SY ♂ (Apr-Oct): Like U/AHY ♂, but gorget and/or iridescent feathering of crown incomplete, especially in the hindcrown (Fig. 104), some feathers partially dusky or greenish, and with the "tails" of the throat less elongated (Fig. 99**G**). **Note: Look for occasional SY ♂♂ also to** have one or two retained juvenal flight feathers (especially rects) or pale areas in the distal portion of the outer rects (see Fig. 108). Some SY ♂♂ probably cannot be reliably aged beyond Feb, when bill corrugations are no longer reliable (see p. 134).

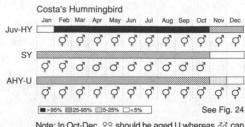

Costa's Hummingbird

Note: In Oct-Dec, ♀♀ should be aged U whereas ♂♂ can be aged AHY.

Hybrids reported—Black-chinned Hummingbird, Anna's Hummingbird, Broad-tailed Hummingbird, Calliope Hummingbird.

References—Ridgway (1911), Bent (1940), Huey (1944), Banks & Johnson (1961), Phillips *et al.* (1964), Short & Phillips (1966), Stiles (1971), Wells *et al.*(1978, 1996), Baltosser (1987), Kaufman (1990a), Baltosser & Scott (1996), Pyle *et al.* (1997); PRBO data.

CALLIOPE HUMMINGBIRD
Stellula calliope

CAHU
Species # 4360
Band size: XB

Species—From the other small hummingbirds of N.Am by the combination of smaller measurements (especially bill and tl; Table 2); gorget feathers (when present) iridescent violet or purplish red, elongated, not extending to the crown, and incompletely (as opposed to uniformly) colored in AHY/ASY ♂♂ (see Fig. 107); upperparts bronzy green without rufous; ♀♀ and juv-HY/SY ♂♂ with the central rect uniquely wedge-shaped and usually dusky at the tip (Fig. 105); bases of most rects (especially r3-r5) with a limited amount of rufous in most birds; outer rect relatively broad (Table 2; Fig. 98C); underparts and undertail covs strongly washed buff.

♀♀ and juv-HY/SY ♂♂ from Bumblebee Hummingbird (*Atthis heloisa*), a possible vagrant to AZ, by longer wg (Table 2, *vs* 32-38 in Bumblebee Hummingbird); upperparts bronzy green (*vs* more emerald); central rect wedge-shaped (Fig. 105) and with extensive (*vs* narrow), blackish tips; r2 without (*vs* with) extensive rufous at the base. See also differences in the timing of the molt for further identification clues.

Geographic variation—No subspecies are recognized. One named from sw.Mex (*S.c. "lowei"*) was almost certainly based on northern migrants; see Griscom (1934a), Oberholser (1974), Binford (1985), Howell & Webb (1995).

Molt—PB: HY/SY complete (Sep-Apr), AHY/ASY complete (Aug-Mar); PA absent. PBs occur on the winter grounds. Gradual replacement of some gorget feathers in HY/SY ♂♂, before the 1st PB, might be considered a partial presupplemental molt (see p. 16), as these feathers are replaced for a second time in Mar-Apr. Flight-feather replacement usually is completed by Apr in HY/SYs; the throat feathers in SY ♂♂ are the last feathers to be replaced. Look also for SY/TYs rarely to retain a few flight feathers until the 2nd PB, as in other hummingbirds.

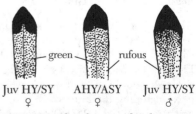

Juv HY/SY   AHY/ASY   Juv HY/SY
♀   ♀   ♂

FIGURE 105. The shape and color pattern of the central rectrix (r1) in ♀ and juv-HY/SY ♂ Calliope Hummingbirds. Note especially the amount of rufous coloration (shown with light stippling) at the bases.

Skull—Experience by species is required for the use of pneumaticization in ageing (see Family account).

Age/Sex—Juv (Jun-Oct) has a soft and corrugated bill (Fig. 92**A**), feathers of the upperparts with distinct, buff edging, and center of the underparts more buffy; nestlings and juvs can be reliably sexed by differences in wg, p10 shape, degree of the tail fork, and pattern of the central rect, as in juv-HY/SYs (see below). CP and BP apparently are not well developed. Measurements are useful (see Table 2).

Juv-HY/SY ♀ (Jul-Mar): Wg 40.1-44.0 (Table 2); bill soft (through Jul-Oct) with deep to shallow corrugations covering > 10% of the culmen (Fig. 92**A-B**; through Dec-Mar); throat without iridescent reddish or violet feathers and with a moderate amount of dull bronze markings (Fig. 99**B**); p10 averages broader and blunter (Fig. 97**B-C**; through Mar); r5 usually < r1 (Table 2); central rect with green and with little or no rufous on the sides at the base (Fig. 105; through Feb-Mar); r3-r5 with white, the white tip to r5 averaging larger (Fig. 106; through Feb-Mar).

AHY/ASY ♀ (Feb-Jan): Like juv-HY/SY ♀, but bill hard with shallow to no corrugations covering < 10% of the culmen (Fig. 92**C-D**); throat with few to a moderate amount of dull bronze markings and occasionally with one to a few iridescent reddish or violet feathers (Fig. 99**B-C**); p10 averages slightly narrower and more curved (Fig. 97**B**); central rects with green and without rufous, or with some rufous on the sides at the base (Fig. 105); r3-r5 with white, the white tip to r5 averaging slightly smaller (*cf.* Fig. 106). **Note: ♀♀ with one to a few iridescent reddish or violet feathers in the throat probably can be aged ASY through Nov, but more study is needed. Also, rare ♀♀ retain flight feathers (especially rects) and may be reliably aged SY/TY through Jan or later.**

Juv-HY/SY ♂ (Jul-Apr): Wg 37.2-41.3 (Table 2); bill corrugations as in juv-HY/SY ♀; throat usually with moderately heavy to heavy, bronze-green markings (juv; Fig. 99**C**; Jul-Oct), and with one (by Sep-Nov) to many iridescent reddish or violet feathers, the gorget often becoming "fully" reddish or violet in Apr; p10 narrow and curved (Fig. 97**A-B**; through Mar); r5 often > r1 (Table 2; through Feb); central rect with green and with rufous on the sides at the base (Fig. 105; through Feb-Mar); r3-r5 with white, the white tip to r5 averaging smaller (Fig. 106; through Feb-Mar). **Note: Beware of occasional AHY ♀♀ with a few reddish or violet feathers in the throat; confirm age (hence sex) with the bill corrugations (see p. 121).**

AHY/ASY ♂ (Apr-Mar): Bill corrugations as in AHY/ASY ♀; gorget with full iridescent violet streaking, without partially dusky feathers, and with iridescent feathers, especially those of the "tails", elongated (Fig. 107); central rects primarily blackish, without green, but with rufous on the sides at the base; r5 > r1 by 0-3 mm; r3-r5 blackish, usually without white, the outer rect sometimes with a pale spot in the distal portion.

Juv HY/SY ♀   Juv HY/SY ♂

FIGURE 106. The amount of white at the tip of r5 by sex in juv-HY/SY Calliope and Broad-tailed hummingbirds. AHY/ASY ♀♀ have an amount of white intermediate between juv-HY/SY ♀ and juv-HY/SY ♂.

SY/TY ♂   AHY/ASY ♂

FIGURE 107. Variation in the throat patterns in AHY ♂♂ Calliope Hummingbirds. This should not be used alone for reliable ageing.

SY/TY ♂ (Apr-Mar): Like AHY/ASY ♂, but gorget incomplete, some feathers partially dusky, and iridescent feathers, especially those of the "tails", less elongated (Fig. 107). **Note: Occasional SY/TY ♂♂ also can have one or two retained juvenal flight feathers (especially rects) or pale areas in the distal portions of the outer rects (see Fig. 108). Most SY/TY ♂♂ cannot be reliably aged (see p. 134), especially without experience.**

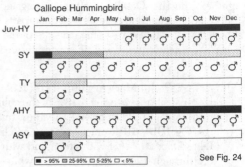

Calliope Hummingbird

See Fig. 24

Hybrids reported—Anna's Hummingbird, Costa's Hummingbird, Broad-tailed Hummingbird, Rufous Hummingbird.

References—Ridgway (1911), Bent (1940), Wagner (1955), Banks & Johnson (1961), Phillips *et al.* (1964), Stiles (1971), Oberholser (1974), Kaufman (1990a), Baltosser (1994), Calder & Calder (1994), Pyle *et al.* (1997).

BROAD-TAILED HUMMINGBIRD
Selasphorus platycercus

BTLH
Species # 4320
Band size: XA

Species—From the other small hummingbirds of N.Am by the combination of larger measurements (especially wg and tl; Table 2); gorget feathers (when present) iridescent reddish, only showing slight lateral elongation, and not extending to the crown in AHY/ASY ♂♂; central rects (r1) broadly pointed; outer rect very broad (Table 2; Fig. 98E). ♀♀ and juv-HY/SY ♂♂ also separated by upperparts green with a limited amount of rufous in the rump and lower back; r2-r5 with the basal portions (< 1/2 feathers) rufous; underparts and undertail covs washed buff. See also differences in the timing of the molt for further identification clues.

Geographic variation—Moderately weak but ranges fairly well defined. Subspecies taxonomy in N.Am follows the AOU (1957); see Griscom (1930a, 1932). One other subspecies occurs in Mex-C.Am.

   S.p. platycercus (br throughout range in N.Am): From *guatemalae* of C.Am by larger size (see Table 2); ♂ with more cinnamon edging, especially in the axillars and lower underparts; ♀ (and juvs?) with heavier dusky-bronze spotting on the throat.

Molt—PB: HY/SY incomplete-complete (Nov-Apr), AHY/ASY complete (Oct-Mar); PA absent. PBs occur on the winter grounds. Gradual replacement of some gorget feathers in HY/SY ♂♂, before the 1st PB, might be considered a partial presupplemental molt (see p. 16), as these feathers are replaced for a second time in Mar-Apr. Flight-feather replacement usually is completed by Apr in HY/SYs; the gorget feathers of SY ♂♂ are the last feathers to be replaced. Also, SY/TYs occasionally can retain one or more juvenal flight feathers (especially rects) until the 2nd PB.

Skull—Experience by species is required for the use of pneumaticization in ageing (see Family account).

Age/Sex—Juv (Jun-Nov) has a soft and corrugated bill (Fig. 92A), feathers of the upperparts with distinct, cinnamon edging, and sides of the underparts more pinkish cinnamon; nestlings and juvs can be reliably sexed by differences in the shape of p10 and the pattern of the central rects, as in juv-HY/SYs (see below). CP and BP apparently are not well developed. See Table 2 for measurements by sex.

Juv-HY/SY ♀ (Jul-Mar): Bill soft (through Jul-Oct) with deep to shallow corrugations covering > 10% of the culmen (Fig. 92**A-B**; through Dec-Mar); throat without iridescent reddish feathers and with a few to a moderate amount of dull greenish markings (Fig. 99**A-B**); p10 averages broader and blunter (Fig. 97**C-D**); central rect (r1) with a black tip and without rufous on the sides at the base; r3-r5 with white, the white tip to r5 averaging large (Fig. 106; through Feb).

AHY/ASY ♀ (Mar-Feb): Like juv-HY/SY ♀, but bill hard with shallow to no corrugations covering < 10% of the culmen (Fig. 92**C-D**); throat with few to a moderate amount of greenish-bronze markings, and no to a few (< 5) iridescent reddish feathers, usually confined to the center (Fig. 99**A-E**); p10 averages slightly narrower and more curved (Fig. 97**B-C**); central rect (r1) green, usually without a black tip, and with rufous on the sides at the base; r3-r5 with white, the white tip to r5 averaging moderately large (Fig. 106). **Note: ♀♀ with substantial numbers of iridescent feathers in the throat, not necessarily confined to the center, probably can be aged ASY through Dec, but more study is needed. Also, look for occasional ♀♀ with retained flight feathers (especially rects) that may be reliably aged SY/TY through Jan or later.**

Juv-HY/SY ♂ (Jul-Apr): Bill corrugations as in juv-HY/SY ♀; throat usually with heavy, dull greenish markings (juv; Fig. 99**C**; Jul-Oct), and with one (by Nov) to many iridescent reddish feathers (Fig. 99**C-F**), not necessarily confined to the center, and usually becoming fully reddish in Apr; p10 narrow and curved (Fig. 97**A-B**; through Mar); central rect (r1) green, without a black tip, and with rufous confined to the sides at the base (through Feb); r3-r5 with a small to moderate amount of white at the tips, the white tip to r5 averaging small (Fig. 106; through Feb). **Note: Beware of occasional AHY/ASY ♀♀ (which see) with a few to many reddish feathers in the throat; confirm age (hence sex) with the bill corrugations (see p. 121).**

AHY/ASY ♂ (Apr-Mar): Bill corrugations as in AHY/ASY ♀; throat completely iridescent reddish, without partially dusky feathers, and with the "tails" partially elongated (Fig. 99**H**); p10 with a unique, outwardly curved tip; central rect (r1) primarily blackish or steely bluish, without green or rufous; r3-r5 blackish, the outer rects often with a small amount of white in the distal portion (Fig. 108). **Note: AHY/ASYs with a full gorget and no pale coloration in outer rects probably are reliably aged ASY/ATY through Feb, but more study is needed.**

SY/TY ♂ (Mar-Feb): Like AHY/ASY ♂, but gorget incomplete, some feathers partially dusky, and with the "tails" less elongated (Fig. 99**G**). **Note: Occasional SY/TY ♂♂ also can have one or two retained juvenal flight feathers (especially rects) and the amount of pale in the distal portion of the outer rects probably is age related (Fig. 108). Most SY/TY ♂♂ probably cannot be reliably aged (see p. 134).**

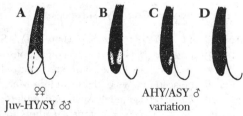

♀♀
Juv-HY/SY ♂♂

AHY/ASY ♂
variation

FIGURE 108. Variation in the amount of white in the outer rectrix (r5), by age, in ♂ Broad-tailed Hummingbirds. ♂♂ of the other "gorgeted" species show similar patterns, with all juv-HY/SYs having distinct tips (**A**) and most AHY/ASYs having entirely black feathers (**D**). More study is needed on birds with pale spots in this feather (**B-C**). In most species, pale spots may indicate SY (*Calypte*) or SY/TY individuals. In Broad-tailed Hummingbird pale spots are more regular, although large spots (**B**) possibly may indicate SY/TYs. See the species accounts. Figure from Pyle *et al.* (1997).

Hybrids reported—Black-chinned Humming-bird, Anna's Hummingbird, Costa's Hum-mingbird, Calliope Hummingbird, Rufous Hummingbird, Allen's Hummingbird.

References—Ridgway (1911), Bent (1940), Huey (1944), Wagner (1948, 1957); Banks & Johnson (1961), Phillips *et al.* (1964), Stiles (1971), Oberholser (1974), Sorrie (1980), Phillips & Chase (1982), Goetz (1987), Kaufman (1990a), Calder & Calder (1992), Pyle *et al.* (1997).

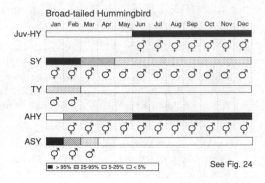

See Fig. 24

RUFOUS HUMMINGBIRD
Selasphorus rufus

RUHU
Species # 4330
Band size: XB

Species—From the other small hummingbirds of N.Am by the combination of measurements, especially the thinness of the outer rects (r5; Table 2); gorget feathers (when present) iridescent orange-red and showing slight lateral elongation, but not extending to the crown in AHY/ASY ♂♂; upperparts with at least a moderate amount of distinct rufous; rects with the basal portions rufous (usually > 50% of feathers in r2-r5); flanks and undertail covs strongly washed buff or rufous.

♀♀ and juv-HY/SY ♂♂ from Allen's Hummingbird (with caution) by wg averages longer by sex (Table 2); r2 slightly to moderately notched by age/sex (Fig. 109); outer rects broader by age/sex (Table 2; Fig. 110). AHY/ASY ♂♂ from Allen's Hummingbird by longer wg (Table 2); upperparts (especially rump) primarily or entirely rufous including some to most feathers fully rufous (beware of some SY ♂♂ with up to 50% green on the upper back); r2 distinctly notched (see Fig. 109); outer rect (r5) relatively broad (width 1.8-2.6 mm). See also differences in the timing of the molt for further identification clues.

Geographic variation—No subspecies are recognized.

Molt—PB: HY/SY complete (Sep-Mar), AHY/ASY complete (Aug-Feb); PA absent. PBs occur on the winter grounds. Gradual replacement of some gorget feathers in HY/SY ♂♂ (and some ♀♀), before the 1st PB, might be considered a partial presupplemental molt (see p. 16), as these feathers are replaced for a second time in Feb-Mar.

Flight-feather replacement usually is completed by Mar in HY/SYs; the gorget feathers in

♀   ♂
Juv-HY/SY
Rufous

♀   ♂
Juv-HY/SY
Allen's

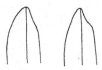

minimum   typical
Rufous

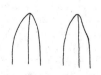

typical   maximum
Allen's

FIGURE 109. Variation in the shape of r2 in ♀ and juv-HY/SY ♂ Rufous and Allen's humming-birds. In each species, ♀♀ average less of a notch than juv-HY/SY ♂♂. AHY/ASY ♂♂ have a greater notch than is shown, in each species.

FIGURE 110. Variation in the shape and width of the outer rectrix (r5), by sex, in juv-HY/SY Rufous and Allen's hummingbirds. In each species AHY/ASY ♀♀ average feather widths in between those of juv-HY/SY ♀♀ and ♂♂ (see Table 2). AHY/ASY ♂♂ have extremely narrow feathers (see text), without white tips.

SY ♂♂ are the last feathers to be replaced. Also, SY/TYs of both sexes rarely can retain some juvenal flight feathers (especially rects) until the 2nd PB.

Skull—Experience by species is required for the use of pneumaticization in ageing (see Family account).

Age/Sex—Juv (Jun-Nov) has a soft and corrugated bill (Fig. 92**A**), crown with distinct, cinnamon edging, and throat with greenish-bronze spots; nestlings and juvs can be reliably sexed by differences in wg, p10 shape, and pattern of the central rects, as in juv-HY/SYs (see below). CP and BP apparently are not well developed. Measurements are useful (see Table 2).

Juv-HY/SY ♀ (Jun-Mar): Wg 42.6-46.6 (Table 2); bill soft (through Aug-Dec) with deep to shallow corrugations covering > 10% of the culmen (Fig. 92**A-B**; through Nov-Mar); throat with moderately heavy, dull bronze markings (Fig. 99**B**), occasionally with a few iridescent orange-red feathers confined to the center (Fig. 99**C-D**); p10 averages broader and blunter (Fig. 97**B-C**; through Feb); central rects broader and primarily green, without rufous or with some rufous at the base (Fig. 111; through Feb); r3-r5 tipped white, the outer rect relatively broad (Table 2, Fig. 110; through Feb).

AHY/ASY ♀ (Feb-Jan): Like juv-HY/SY ♀, but bill hard with shallow to no corrugations covering < 10% of the culmen (Fig. 92**C-D**); throat with few bronze markings and scattered iridescent orange-red feathers (usually < 20), often confined to the center, and not elongated at the sides (Fig. 99**E**); p10 averages slightly narrower and more curved (Fig. 97**B**); central rects average narrower and with greater amounts of rufous, but less than in ♂♂ (Fig. 111); outer rect slightly narrower (Table 2; *cf.* Fig. 110). **Note: Look for occasional ♀♀ with substantial numbers of iridescent orange-red feathers in the throat, possibly showing some elongation at the sides, or showing an almost-complete gorget (Fig. 99E-F), that probably can be aged ASY/ATY through Feb, but more study is needed. Also, look for rare ♀♀ with retained flight feathers (especially rects) that may be reliably aged SY/TY through Jan or later.**

Juv-HY/SY ♂ (Jun-May): Wg 38.1-42.5 (Table 2); bill corrugations as in juv-HY/SY ♀; throat heavily marked with greenish dusky (juv; Fig. 99**C**) and with several to many iridescent orange-red feathers (Fig. 99**C-F**), not necessarily confined to the center, and usually becoming fully orange-red in Mar-Apr; p10 narrow and curved (Fig. 97**A-B**; through Feb-Mar); central rect narrower and with substantial rufous at the base (Fig. 111; through Feb); r3-r5 with white at the tips (through Feb); outer rect relatively narrow (Table 2, Fig. 110; through Feb). **Note: Beware of occasional AHY ♀♀ (which see) with many orange-red feathers in the throat; confirm age (hence sex) with the bill corrugations (see p. 121).**

AHY/ASY ♂ (Feb-Jan): Bill corrugations as in AHY/ASY ♀; gorget completely orange-red, without partially dusky feathers, and with the "tails" partially elongated (Fig. 99**H**); p10 very thin and curved at the tip (*cf.* Fig. 97); central rects primarily rufous with small greenish tips

Juv-HY/SY ♀   AHY/ASY ♀   Juv-HY/SY ♂   AHY/ASY ♂

FIGURE 111. Shape and pattern of the central rectrix (r1) in ♀ and juv-HY/SY ♂ Rufous and Allen's hummingbirds. The light stippling indicates rufous coloration and the dark stippling indicates green.

(Fig. 111); r3-r5 very narrow and pointed (width of r5 1.8-2.6 mm), usually without white.

SY/TY ♂ (Feb-Jan): Like AHY/ASY ♂, but gorget incomplete, some feathers partially dusky, and with the "tails" less elongated (Fig. 99G). **Note: Some SY/TYs have been recorded with adult flight feathers but throats as in HY/SY. Occasional SY/TY ♂♂ also can have one or two retained juvenal flight feathers (especially rects) or, possibly, pale areas in the distal portions of the outer rects (see Fig. 108). SY ♂♂ also average more green in the back than ASY ♂♂, but more study is needed on the reliability of this feature for ageing. Most SY/TY ♂♂ cannot be reliably aged (see p. 134).**

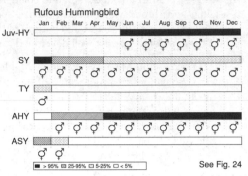

Rufous Hummingbird

Hybrids reported—Anna's Hummingbird, Calliope Hummingbird, Broad-tailed Hummingbird. Hybrids with Allen's Hummingbird have been suspected but have not been fully documented.

See Fig. 24

References—Ridgway (1911), Bent (1940), Aldrich (1956), Banks & Johnson (1961), Phillips *et al.* (1964), Ortiz-Crespo (1971, 1972), Stiles (1971, 1972), Oberholser (1974), Phillips (1975b), Sorrie (1980), Phillips & Chase (1982), Newfield (1983), Goetz (1987), Patterson (1988, 1990), Andrews & Baltosser (1989), Kaufman (1990a), Jones (1992, 1993), Calder (1993), Carpenter *et al.* (1993), Pyle *et al.* (1997), Yanega *et al.* (1997); J.M. Patterson (*in litt.* to the BBL); J.R. King, D.A. Sibley (pers. comm.); PRBO data.

ALLEN'S HUMMINGBIRD

Selasphorus sasin

ALHU
Species # 4340
Band size: XB

Species—See Rufous Hummingbird for separation from the other small hummingbirds of N.Am. ♀♀ and juv-HY/SY ♂♂ from Rufous Hummingbird (with caution) by wg averages shorter by sex (Table 2); r2 not notched to slightly notched by age/sex (Fig. 109); outer rects narrower by age/sex (Table 2, Fig. 110). AHY/ASY ♂ from Rufous Hummingbird by shorter wg (Table 2); upperparts (including the rump) primarily or entirely green (although beware of some ASY ♂♂ with up to 40% rufous) and without fully rufous feathers; r2 usually without a distinct notch (see Fig. 109); outer rect (r5) narrow (width 1.2-1.9 mm). See also differences in the timing of the molt for further identification clues.

Geographic variation—Moderate, but intermediates likely occur in coastal CA. Subspecies taxonomy follows the AOU (1957); see Grinnell (1929), Stiles (1972), Wells & Baptista (1979b). No other subspecies occur.

S.s. sasin (br OR-s.CA, vag to WA, MA & LA): Small (Table 2); outer rect narrow by age/sex (see Table 2). In addition, the rects can average more black in the tips in AHY/ASY ♂♂ and more orange and less green and white in ♀♀ and juvs of *sasin* than of *sedentarius*, but differences are slight.

S.s. sedentarius (res Channel Is & Los Angeles Co, CA): Large (especially exp culmen and wg); width of the outer rect larger by age/sex (see **Age/Sex**). ♀ wg(n40) 41.0-45.4, tl(n40) 22.9-27.4, exp culmen(n40) 17.9-22.1; ♂ wg(n40) 36.4-40.5, tl(n40) 22.7-26.6, exp culmen(n40) 16.7-19.7. Note that *sedentarius* can breed year round; differences in the timing of breeding condition, molt, and plumages may be helpful in subspecies separation.

Molt—PB: HY/SY complete (Aug-Feb), AHY/ASY complete (Jul-Jan); PA absent. Dates apply to *sasin*; molts of *sedentarius* may occur year-round. In *sasin*, PBs occur on the non-breeding grounds. Gradual replacement of some gorget feathers in HY/SY ♂♂ (and some HY/SY ♀♀), before the 1st PB, might be considered a partial presupplemental molt (see p. 16), as these feathers are replaced for a second time in Dec-Feb. Flight-feather replacement usually is completed by Jan in HY/SYs; the throat feathers in SY ♂♂ are the last feathers to be replaced. Look also for SYs rarely to retain some juvenal flight feathers (especially rects) until the 2nd PB.

Skull—Experience by species is required for the use of pneumaticization in ageing (see Family account).

Age/Sex—Juv (Mar-Aug in *S.s. sasin*; all year possible in *sedentarius*) has a soft and corrugated bill (Fig. 92**A**), crown with distinct, cinnamon edging, and throat with greenish-bronze spots; nestlings and juvs can be reliably sexed by differences in wg, p10 shape, and pattern of the central rects, as in juv-HY/SYs (see below). CP and BP apparently are not well developed. Measurements are useful for sexing (Table 2 and see **Geographic variation**).

Juv-HY/SY ♀ (Mar-Jan): Bill soft (through May-Jul) with deep to shallow corrugations covering > 10% of the culmen (Fig. 92**A-B**; through Sep-Jan); throat with moderately heavy, dull bronze markings (Fig. 99**B**), occasionally with a few iridescent orange-red feathers confined to center (Fig. 99**C-D**) in Jul-Feb; p10 averages broader and blunter (Fig. 97**B-C**; through Dec); central rects primarily green with no rufous or some rufous at the base (Fig. 111; through Nov-Dec); r3-r5 tipped white; outer rect broad (Fig. 110; see Table 2 for *S.s. sasin*, in *sedentarius* 2.54-3.46 mm). **Note: Date ranges pertain to the relatively widespread *sasin* (see Geographic variation). The sequences and criteria are the same for both subspecies; the timing can occur year-round in *sedentarius*, although most birds of this subspecies probably follow the timing of *sasin*.**

U/AHY ♀ (Dec-Nov): Like juv-HY/SY ♀, but bill hard with shallow to no corrugations covering < 10% of the culmen (Fig. 92**C-D**); throat with few bronze markings and scattered iridescent orange-red feathers (usually < 20), often confined to the center, and not elongated at sides (Fig. 99**E**); p10 averages slightly narrower and more curved (Fig. 97**B**); central rects average greater amounts of rufous, but less than in ♂♂ (Fig. 111); outer rect moderate in width (see Table 2 for *sasin*, in *sedentarius* 2.24-2.96 mm). **Note: See Juv-HY/SY ♀. Look for rare ♀♀ with substantial numbers of orange-red feathers in the throat, possibly showing some elongation at sides, or showing an almost-complete gorget (Fig. 99F), that probably can be aged ASY through Oct, but more study is needed. Also, look for occasional ♀♀ with retained flight feathers (especially rects) that can be reliably aged SY through Nov or later.**

Juv-HY/SY ♂ (Mar-Feb): Bill corrugations as in juv-HY/SY ♀; throat heavily marked with greenish dusky (juv; Fig. 99**C**), and with one (by Jun) to many iridescent orange-red feathers (Fig. 99**C-F**), not necessarily confined to the center, and usually becoming fully orange-red in Feb; p10 narrow and curved (Fig. 97**A-B**; through Dec); central rect with substantial rufous at the base (Fig. 111; through Nov-Dec); r3-r5 with white at the tips (through Nov-Dec); outer rect narrow (Fig. 110; see Table 2 for *sasin*, in *sedentarius* 1.73-2.61 mm; through Nov-Dec). **Note: See Juv-HY/SY ♀. Beware of occasional AHY ♀♀ with many orange-red feathers in the throat (see above); confirm age (hence sex) with the bill corrugations (see p. 121).**

AHY ♂ (Jan-Dec): Bill corrugations as in U/AHY ♀; gorget completely iridescent orange-red, without partially dusky feathers, and with the "tails" partially elongated (Fig. 99**H**); p10 very thin and curved at the tip (*cf.* Fig. 97); central rects primarily rufous with small greenish tips (Fig. 111); r3-r5 very narrow and pointed (width of r5 1.2-1.9 mm), usually without white. **Note: See Juv-HY/SY ♀.**

SY ♂ (Jan-Dec): Like AHY ♂, but gorget incomplete, some feathers partially dusky, and with

the "tails" less elongated (Fig. 99**F-G**).
**Note: See Juv-HY/SY ♀. Occasional SY
♂♂ also may have one or two retained
juvenal flight feathers (especially rects)
or, possibly, pale areas in the distal portions of the outer rects (see Fig. 108).
ASY ♂♂ also may average more rufous
in the back than SY ♂♂, but more study
is needed on the reliability of this feature for ageing. Most SY ♂♂ cannot be
reliably aged (see p. 134).**

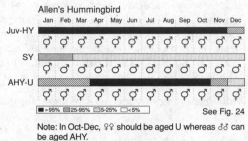

Note: In Oct-Dec, ♀♀ should be aged U whereas ♂♂ can be aged AHY.

Hybrids reported—Black-chinned Hummingbird, Anna's Hummingbird, Broad-tailed Hummingbird. Hybrids with Rufous Hummingbird have been suspected but have not been fully documented.

References—Ridgway (1911), Bent (1940), Pitelka (1951a), Aldrich (1956), F.S.L. Williamson (1957), Banks & Johnson (1961), Phillips *et al.* (1964), Lynch & Ames (1970), Stiles (1971, 1972), Phillips (1975b), Wells & Baptista (1979a, 1979b), Sorrie (1980), Phillips & Chase (1982), Newfield (1983), Patterson (1988, 1990), Andrews & Baltosser (1989), Kaufman (1990a), Pyle *et al.* (1997); M. Patterson (*in litt.* to the BBL); D.A. Sibley (pers. comm.); PRBO data.

TROGONS   *TROGONIDAE*

Two species. Family characters include round heads, short bills, soft plumage, large eyes, and zygodactylous feet (two toes back and two toes forward) with the inner front toe reversed. Trogons have 10 primaries (the 10th shortened), 9 secondaries, and 12 rectrices. The first prebasic molt is partial to incomplete (most or all wing coverts and occasionally a few tertials are replaced), and is protracted through the winter. Subsequent prebasic molts occur in the summer and usually are complete; one or more secondaries occasionally can be retained. The primary coverts typically are replaced with their corresponding primaries. Prealternate molts do not occur. Pneumaticization probably does not complete, but the percentage of completion may be useful for ageing (see Fig. 88); more study is needed. Plumage differs by age through AHY/ASY. Sexes are similar in size, but easily distinguished by plumage; the presence of a brood patch also is reliable for sexing females.

ELEGANT TROGON   ELTR
Trogon elegans   Species # 3890
                                                             Band size: 1A-2

Geographic variation—Moderate and ranges fairly well defined. Subspecies taxonomy in N.Am follows the AOU (1957), as modified by Webster (1984); see also Ridgway (1911), Griscom (1930a), van Rossem (1934a), Dickey & van Rossem (1938), Oberholser (1974). Two other subspecies occur in Mex-C.Am.

T.e. goldmani (= "*canescens*"; br s.AZ; vag to NM): Medium large; red of the underparts relatively pale, scarlet, and less extensive on the flanks; upperparts and underparts of ♀ tinged gray. ♀ wg(n17) 127-138, tl(n17) 171-186; ♂ wg(n17) 130-139, tl(n17) 158-177.

T.e. ambiguus (vag to s.TX): Medium small; red of the underparts relatively deep, bright, and more extensive on the flanks; upperparts and underparts of ♀ tinged brown. ♀ wg(n13) 123-134, tl(n13) 165-175; ♂ wg(n34) 127-136, tl(n34) 154-167.

Molt—PB: HY/SY partial (Aug-Jun), AHY incomplete-complete (Aug-Oct); PA absent. The 1st PB can be partly suspended over the winter, with peak molting in Aug-Nov and Feb-Jun. The 1st PB usually includes all wing covs and sometimes the terts, but no other flight feathers. One or more ss (usually among s4-s7) occasionally can be retained during adult PBs.

Skull—Pneumaticization patterns possibly are useful for ageing (see Family account), but more study is needed.

Age/Sex—Juv (Jun-Nov) has the belly grayish with indistinct, dusky barring, and tips of the wing covs and terts with large buff or white patches (Fig. 112); most juv ♂♂ are separated reliably from juv ♀♀ by the presence of some green feathers in the upperparts and the presence of a bronze iridescence to the central rects (r1). CPs apparently do not develop, but BPs (Jun-Jul) are reliable for

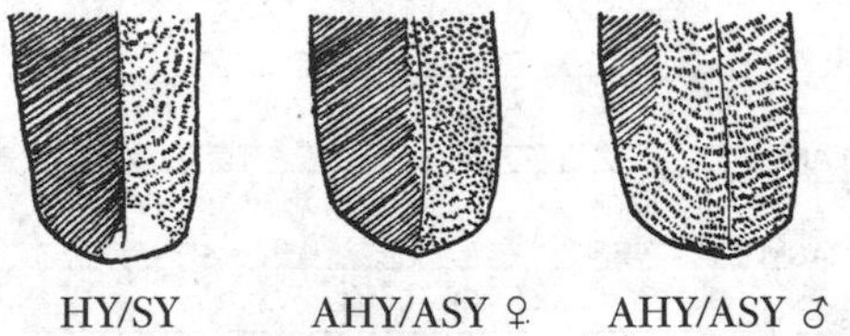

HY/SY   AHY/ASY ♀   AHY/ASY ♂   HY/SY   AHY/ASY

FIGURE 112. The pattern of the tertials by age and sex in Elegant Trogon.

FIGURE 113. The pattern of s1-s6 by age in Elegant Trogon. The color of the edging is whitish in HY/SYs, olive in AHY/ASY ♀♀, and gray in AHY/ASY ♂♂.

sexing ♀♀. ♀ wg(n30) 123-138, tl(n30) 165-
186; ♂ wg(n51) 127-139, tl(n51) 154-177.

HY/SY ♀ (Oct-Sep): Upperparts and breast
brown without green feathers; central
belly (just below breast band) without red
feathers; inner web of juvenal terts with
black and olive mottling and a white spot
at the tip (Fig. 112; one or more terts
sometimes are replaced); outer webs of
s1-s6 thinly edged white with coarse, black
flecking (Fig. 113); outer rects narrow,
tapered, with black on the outer web, and

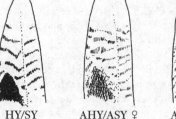

HY/SY   AHY/ASY ♀   AHY/ASY ♂

FIGURE 114. Typical shape and pattern of the
outer rectrix (r6) by age and sex in Elegant Trogon.

with distinct black bars on the inner web (Fig. 114); central rects without bronze iridescence
and with the black tips absent or very narrow (0-2 mm); r4 with black bars to the outer web.

AHY/ASY ♀ (Oct-Sep): Like HY/SY ♀, but inner web of the terts speckled olive, without a
white spot at the tip (Fig. 112); outer webs of s1-s6 broadly edged olive-gray (Fig. 113); outer
rects broad, truncate, with dusky on the inner web, and indistinct barring on the outer web
(Fig. 114); black tips of the central rects (r1) broader (3-10 mm); r4 without black bars to the
outer web. **Note: Occasional SY/TYs and ASY/ATYs can be separated; see below.**

HY/SY ♂ (Oct-Sep): Variably plumaged; upperparts and breast with a few (Aug) to many (Dec)
green feathers, usually becoming extensively green by Jun; central belly (just below breast
band) brown with one to many red feathers; inner web of the terts with black and olive mottling and a white spot at the tip (Fig. 112); outer webs of s1-s6 thinly edged white with coarse,
black flecking (Fig. 113); outer rects as in HY/SY ♀ (Fig. 114); central rects (r1) with bronze
iridescence and narrow, black tips (0-4 mm); r4 with black bars to the outer web.

AHY/ASY ♂ (Oct-Sep): Upperparts and breast completely iridescent green; central belly (just
below breast band) uniformly red; inner web of the terts speckled gray, without a white spot
at the tip (Fig. 112); outer webs of s1-s6 broadly edged gray (Fig. 113); outer rects broad,
truncate, finely marked on the inner and outer webs (Fig. 114); central rects (r1) coppery
with broad, black tips (13-20 mm); r4 without black bars to the outer web. **Note: Occasional
SY/TYs and ASY/ATYs can be separated; see below.**

SY/TY ♀ & ♂ (Sep-Aug): Like AHY/ASY ♀ & ♂, but one or more juvenal ss (usually among
s4-s7) retained, abraded and edged white with coarse, black flecking (Fig. 113; if edging
not worn off), contrasting with the
fresher, replaced ss (Fig. 25C), broadly
edged olive (♀) or gray (♂). **Note: This
age class only occasionally can be
distinguished.**

ASY/ATY ♀ & ♂ (Sep-Aug): Like AHY/ASY
♀ & ♂, but one or more adult ss (usually
among s4-s7), retained, abraded and
broadly edged olive (♀) or gray (♂; Fig
114), contrasting moderately and in wear
only with the replaced outer ss (Fig.
25D). **Note: This age class only rarely
can be distinguished.**

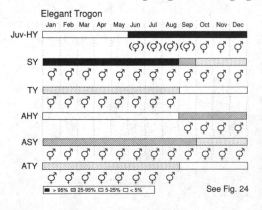

See Fig. 24

References—Ridgway (1911), Dickey & van Rossem (1938), Bent (1940), Oberholser (1974),
Pyle (1995a).

EARED TROGON
Euptilotus neoxenus

EATR
Species # 3891
Band size: 2

Geographic variation—No subspecies are recognized.

Molt—PB: HY/SY partial (Aug-Jun), AHY incomplete-complete (Jun-Sep); PA absent. The 1st PB can include the terts, and may be partly suspended over the winter, with peak molting in Aug-Nov and Feb-Jun. One or more ss (usually among s4-s7) and/or rects sometimes can be retained during adult PBs.

Skull—Pneumaticization patterns possibly are useful for ageing (see Family account), but more study is needed.

Age—Juv (Jun-Sep) is not well known, but has brownish and somewhat loosely textured breast feathers; ♀ = ♂, although some ♂♂ may possibly be sexed by the presence of some green in the head and/or upper breast, or some bright red in the central breast (see **Sex**); more study is needed.

HY/SY (Sep-Aug): Ss brown with a slight green tinge, sometimes contrasting with the bright green and fresher terts; outer rects relatively narrow and tapered (Fig. 115); r3 tipped white; central rects (r1) dusky with a blue tinge; ♂ with the head and/or upper breast brown mixed with no (Aug) to a few (Jun) green feathers.

AHY/ASY (Sep-Aug): Ss (including the terts) uniformly bright green; outer rects relatively broad and truncate (Fig. 115); r3 without a white tip; central rects steely blue; ♂ with the head and upper breast uniformly bright green.

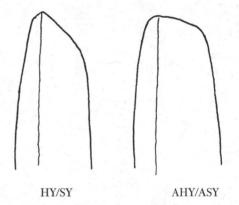

HY/SY   AHY/ASY

FIGURE 115. The shape of the outer rectrices (r4-r6) by age in Eared Trogon. SY/TYs possibly have an intermediate shape.

SY/TY (Aug-Jul): Like AHY/ASY, but one or more juvenal ss (usually among s4-s7) retained and brown, contrasting markedly with the fresher and brighter green, replaced ss (Fig. 25**C**); and/or one or more juvenal rects retained and relatively narrow (Fig. 115), contrasting markedly in wear with the more truncate, adult rects. **Note: Also, check for the rect shape to intermediate between HY/SY and AHY/ASY (*cf.* Fig. 115). This age class only sometimes can be distinguished.**

ASY/ATY (Aug-Jul): Like AHY/ASY, but one or more adult ss (usually among s4-s7) retained, faded green and abraded, contrasting only moderately in wear with the replaced ss (Fig. 25**D**); and/or one or more adult rects retained and truncate (Fig. 115), contrasting only moderately with the replaced adult rects. **Note: See SY/TY. This age class only occasionally can be distinguished.**

Sex—CPs apparently do not develop, but BPs (Jun-Jul) are reliable for sexing ♀♀. ♀ wg(n15) 183-200, tl(n15) 185-197; ♂ wg(n15) 181-205, tl(n15) 189-201.

♀: Head, upper breast, and central breast (to a point adjacent to the tips of the pp covs) slate grayish.

♂: Head and upper breast brown (juv-HY/SYs) to completely iridescent green (AHY/ASYs); central breast partially reddish to completely red.

References—Ridgway (1911), Pyle (1995a); M. Gustafson (pers. comm.).

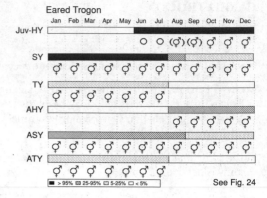

KINGFISHERS   *ALCEDINIDAE*

Three species. Family characters include large heads and bills, zygodactylous feet (two toes back and two toes forward) with the outer front toe reversed, and partially fused middle toes. Kingfishers have 10 primaries (the 10th full in length), 13-15 secondaries, and 12 rectrices. Prebasic molts are variable, the first being protracted and including a variable number of flight feathers, and subsequent molts often being incomplete (some secondaries and primary coverts retained) and occurring in the early fall. The sequence of primary replacement occurs from two centers, distally from p1 and centrifugally (outwards in both directions) from p7. The primary coverts appear not to be replaced with their corresponding primaries, perhaps being replaced in a similar pattern to those of woodpeckers (see p. 165, Fig. 122). Prealternate molts do not occur. Pneumaticization typically does not complete but the percentage of completion may be useful for ageing (see Fig. 88); more study is needed. Both sexes are similar in size and males incubate, so brood patch may be unreliable for sexing; however, females and males are easily distinguished by plumage.

RINGED KINGFISHER   RIKI
Ceryle torquata   Species # 3901
                                                           Band size: 4

Geographic variation—Weak to moderate, but ranges fairly well defined. Subspecies taxonomy in N.Am follows the AOU (1957); see Ridgway (1914), Fry *et al.* (1992). Two other subspecies occur in the W.Indies & S.Am.

> ***C.t. torquata*** (res. s.TX): From the other subspecies by outer webs of the ss with indistinct or no white spots (*vs* with distinct, white spots); undertail covs with light, gray barring (*vs* unbarred white in the other subspecies).

Molt—Largely unknown, but could be as follows; PB: HY/SY partial-incomplete (Jul-Jun), AHY/ASY incomplete-complete (Jun-Apr); PA absent. The 1st PB may include few or no pp, pp covs, or ss, but possibly some to all rects. Retention of pp, pp covs, and ss during adult PBs appears to parallel that of Belted Kingfisher (which see), although more feathers on average might be retained. Year-round breeding is possible in this species, which may complicate the timing and extent of molts, although most molting probably occurs in Aug-Oct. More study is needed.

Skull—Pneumaticization patterns possibly are useful for ageing (see Family account).

Age—Juv (Jun-Dec) has the crown more heavily streaked dusky, upperparts with white subterminal spotting on the feathers, throat and breast washed rufous, and belly and undertail covs cinnamon (*vs* dark rufous after the 1st PB); juv ♀ = ♂, although the sexes possibly can be separated by the color of the underwing covs (see **Sex**); more study is needed.

Juv-HY/SY (Aug-Jul): Feathers of the upperparts heavily streaked dusky and with white spots (spotting can wear off by Dec); juvenal pp and ss uniform in wear (Fig. 25A); outer pp and juvenal rects narrow and tapered (Fig. 116);

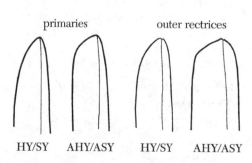

primaries   outer rectrices

HY/SY   AHY/ASY   HY/SY   AHY/ASY

FIGURE 116. The shape of the outer primaries (p7-p10) and outer rectrices (r4-r6) by age in kingfishers.

blue edging to the outer web of s6 thin (usually < 5 mm), not reaching or approaching the shaft at the tip (see Fig. 118); pp covs uniform in wear, dull black in fall to brown and abraded in spring (see Fig. 122**A-B**); black shaft streaks of the central rects may average broader by sex (through Jan-Jul; see Fig. 119); breast dusky blue with a rufous tinge.

AHY/ASY (Aug-Jul): Feathers of the upperparts lightly streaked dusky and without white spotting; adult pp and ss uniform in wear (Fig. 25**B**); outer pp and rects broad and truncate (Fig. 116); blue edging to the outer web of s6 broad (usually > 5 mm) and reaching or approaching the shaft near the tip (see Fig. 118); pp covs uniformly black to dull black (see Fig. 122**B**), or irregularly mixed with two or more generations of feathers (see Fig. 122**D**); black shaft streaks of the central rects may average narrower by sex (see Fig. 119); breast blue and white, without rufous (♀), or uniformly dark rufous (♂).

SY/TY (Aug-Jul): Like AHY/ASY, but 1-6 juvenal ss (see Fig. 118; among s2-s6) retained, often symmetrically in both wings, faded, and abraded, contrasting markedly with the replaced adult feathers (Fig. 25**C**); outer 1-3 pp covs possibly dark and fresh, contrasting with the brownish and worn, consecutive, retained inner pp covs (see Fig. 122**C**). **Note: Look for some SY/TYs possibly to retain all juvenal pp covs; more study is needed on pp-cov replacement patterns by age. Also, some SY/TYs probably retain 1-4 pp (among p2-p6), as well, but this needs confirmation.**

ASY/ATY (Aug-Jul): Like AHY/ASY, but 1-6 adult ss (see Fig. 118; among s1-s8) retained, often not symmetrically in both wings, and worn, contrasting only moderately with the replaced feathers (Fig. 25**D**). **Note: Some ASY/ATYs with three generations of ss; and/or pp covs, as shown in Figure 122F, may be reliably aged TY/4Y, but more study is needed.**

Sex—CPs apparently do not develop and BPs (Mar-Jun) may be found in both sexes; more study is needed. ♀ wg(n46) 185-210, tl(n46) 112-132; ♂ wg(n53) 183-211, tl(n53) 110-129.

♀: Breast blue with a white chest band; underwing covs rufous; black shaft streaks of the central rects may average broader by age (see Fig. 119); undertail covs rufous. **Note: Juv-HYs may be separable only by the underwing color and, perhaps, the pattern on the rects; more study is needed on plumages at this time.**

♂: Breast and chest primarily to completely rufous; underwing covs white; black shaft streaks of the central rects may average narrower by age (see Fig. 119); undertail covs white. **Note: See ♀.**

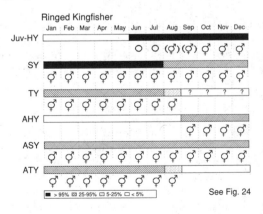

References—Ridgway (1914), Dickey & van Rossem (1938), Bent (1940), Oberholser (1974), Pyle (1995a).

BELTED KINGFISHER
Ceryle alcyon

BEKI
Species # 3900
Band size: 3B-3A

Geographic variation—Subspecies taxonomy follows Phillips (1962), who considered the species monotypic (synonymizing a previously recognized subspecies); see also Ridgway (1914), Rand (1948a, 1948b), Rand & Traylor (1950), Dickinson (1953), Todd (1963), Monroe (1968), Wetmore (1968), Oberholser (1974). Western birds ("*C.a. caurina*") may average slightly larger and with a shorter wing tip (longest p – longest s) than nominate eastern birds, but differences, if present, are slight and broadly clinal.

Molt—HY/SY limited-incomplete (Aug-May), AHY/ASY incomplete-complete (Jul-Jan); PA absent. The 1st PB occurs on the winter grounds and can include some or all body plumage, sometimes some or all rects, but few if any wing covs. Some pp (usually among p7-p10) and some ss may be replaced during the 1st PB in some migratory eastern birds, but more study is needed. The juvenal pp covs are retained. Adult PBs usually commence on the breeding grounds and complete on the winter grounds. From 1-3 juvenal pp (among p2-p6), all but 1-4 outer pp covs, and 1-6 juvenal ss (among s2-s6), usually in a block, and often symmetrical in both wings, can be retained during the 2nd PB; 1-6 adult ss (among s1-s8), seldom in a block, and not symmetrical in both wings, and an irregular number of pp covs can be retained during subsequent PBs. More study is needed on molt in Belted and the other kingfishers of N.Am.

Skull—Pneumaticization patterns possibly are useful for ageing (see Family account).

Age—Juv (Jun-Dec) has more rufous feathering in the breast bands than adults; juv ♀ and ♂ are separated reliably by the extent of rufous in the lower breast band (Fig. 117), and by the color of the longest underwing axillar (see **Sex**).

Juv-HY/SY (Sep-Aug): No active pp or ss molt in evidence during the 1st Aug-Dec; blue breast band heavily (Aug-Dec) to lightly (Jan-2nd Oct) smattered with relatively worn, rufous-tinged feathers (through at least Jan, usually through Jun, often through 2nd Oct); juvenal pp and ss usually uniform in wear (Fig. 25A); outer pp and juvenal rects narrow and tapered (Fig. 116); blue edging to the outer web of s6 thin (usually < 4 mm) and not reaching or approaching the shaft at the tip (Fig. 118); pp covs uniform in wear, dull black in fall to brown and abraded in spring (see Fig. 122A-B); black shaft streaks of the central rects average broader by sex (through Jan-Jul; Fig. 119). **Note: Some SYs can lose all rufous feathering in the breast band by Jan.**

Juv-HY

FIGURE 117. The breast band in Belted Kingfisher. The illustration depicts an intermediate lower (rufous) band. Birds with more rufous can be sexed ♀ while those with less or no rufous are ♂♂. This is especially helpful in sexing juv-HY/SYs, in which ♂♂ can have partial, rufous bands.

AHY/ASY (Sep-Aug): Active replacement of the pp and ss usually in evidence in Sep-Dec; breast band uniformly blue, without rufous-tinged feathers; adult pp and ss uniform in wear (Fig. 25**B**); outer pp and rects broad and truncate (Fig. 116); blue edging to the outer web of s6 broad (usually > 4 mm) and reaching or approaching the shaft near the tip (Fig. 118); pp covs uniformly black to dull black (see Fig. 122**A**) or irregularly mixed with two or more generations of feathers (see Fig. 122**D**); black shaft streaks of the central rects average narrower by sex (Fig. 119). **Note: See SY/TY and ASY/ATY.**

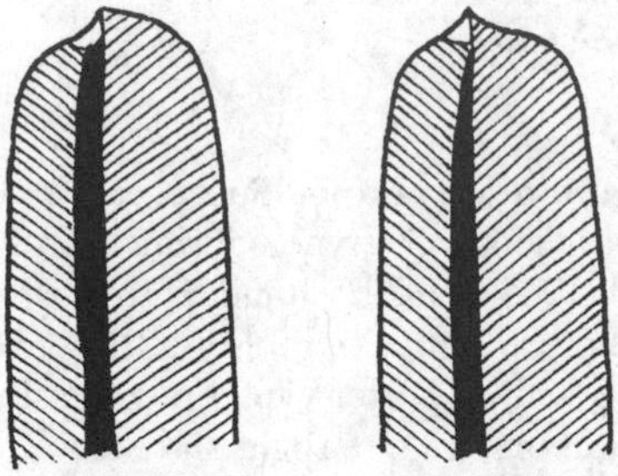

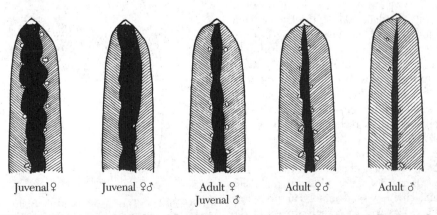

FIGURE 118. The color pattern of s6 by age in Belted Kingfisher. Note the width of the shaft streak near the tip. The patterns of s1-s5 show similar variation, although the widths of the streaks may differ. Similar patterns also are found in Ringed Kingfisher. Figure from Pyle (1995a).

SY/TY (Sep-Aug): Like AHY/ASY, but 1-6 juvenal ss (Fig. 118; among s2-s6) and/or 1-3 juvenal pp (among p2-p6) retained, often symmetrically in both wings, faded, and abraded, contrasting markedly with the replaced adult feathers (Fig. 25**C**); outermost 1-4 pp covs possibly dark and fresh, contrasting with the brownish and worn, consecutive, retained inner pp covs (see Fig. 122**C**). **Note: More study is needed to confirm pp-cov replacement patterns during adult PBs in kingfishers; see also ASY/ATY.**

ASY/ATY (Sep-Aug): Like AHY/ASY, but pp usually uniformly adult after completion of the molt; 1-6 adult ss (Fig. 118; among s1-s8) retained, often not symmetrically in both wings, worn, and contrasting only moderately with the replaced feathers (Fig. 25**D**). **Note: See SY/TY. Some ASY/ATYs, with three generations of ss and/or pp covs as shown in Fig. 122F, may possibly be reliably aged TY/4Y, but more study is needed.**

Sex—CPs apparently do not develop and BPs (Apr-Jul) may be found in both sexes; more study is needed. ♀ wg(n100) 149-171, tl(n50) 81-101; ♂ wg(n75) 145-169, tl(n55) 82-97; see **Geographic variation**.

FIGURE 119. Variation in the width of the shaft streak on the central rectrix (r1), by age and sex, in Belted Kingfisher. Note that some or most HY/SYs may replace the rectrices during the first prebasic molt, showing patterns of adults. Similar patterns also are found in Ringed Kingfisher.

♀: Belly with a complete or nearly complete, rufous band (*cf.* Fig. 117); longest underwing axillar cinnamon.

♂: Belly white, without rufous or (juvs) with an incomplete, rufous band (*cf.* Fig. 117); longest underwing axillar white.

References—Stone (1896), Ridgway (1914), Forbush (1927), Dickey & van Rossem (1938), Bent (1940), Roberts (1955), Stresemann & Stresemann (1961, 1966), Wood (1969), Oberholser (1974), Cramp (1985), Hamas (1994), Pyle (1995a); IBP (MAPS) data.

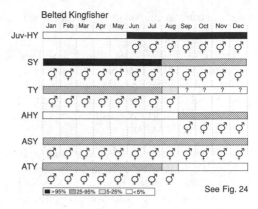

Belted Kingfisher

See Fig. 24

GREEN KINGFISHER
Chloroceryle americana

GKIN
Species # 3910
Band size: 2, filed down

Geographic variation—Weak to moderate and clinal where ranges meet. Subspecies taxonomy in N.Am follows the AOU (1957); see Ridgway (1914), van Rossem & Hachisuka (1938a), Brodkorb (1940), Wetmore (1968), Oberholser (1974), Fry *et al.* (1992). Three other subspecies occur in the W.Indies & C.Am-S.Am.

C.a. hachisukai (res c-sw.TX; vag to AZ): Upperparts green with a bronze tinge; all lesser covs usually with small white spots; white of the forehead often extends to the area above the eyes.
C.a. septentrionalis (res s.TX): Upperparts green with a slight or no bronze tinge; lesser covs with white spots absent or restricted to some but not all feathers; white of the forehead with green mottling and less extensive, usually not extending to the area above the eyes.

Molt—PB: HY/SY partial-incomplete (Sep-May), AHY incomplete(?)-complete (Aug-Nov); PA absent. The 1st PB is protracted and eccentric (see p. 208, Fig. 136), including up to 5 outermost pp, 3-5 inner ss, and some to all rects, but apparently no pp covs. A few pp, pp covs, and ss may be retained during the 2nd and subsequent PBs, but this needs confirmation. Year-round breeding is possible in this species, which may complicate the timing and extents of the molts. More study is needed.

Skull—Pneumaticization patterns possibly are useful for ageing (see Family account).

Age/Sex—Juv (Jun-Apr) differs in plumage by sex (see Juv-HY/SYs, below). CPs apparently do not develop and BPs (Apr-Jul) may be found in both sexes; more study is needed. ♀ wg(n31) 82-90, tl(n31) 55-63; ♂ wg(n47) 80-88, tl(n33) 55-62.

Juv-HY/SY ♀ (Sep-Aug): Breast brownish or tinged buff, sometimes with elongated green streaks, gradually becoming white with mottled green bands by May; outermost 0-5 pp (among p6-p10) and 3-5 ss (among s6-s13, often the innermost) molting or contrastingly fresh in Nov-Aug; pp covs narrow, relatively abraded, and brown with a green tinge (see Fig. 122**A-B**).

AHY/ASY ♀ (Sep-Aug): Breast without buff or rufous, but with two bands of round, dark, iridescent green spotting; pp and ss in complete molt during Sep-Nov and not molting or showing contrasts in Nov-Aug; pp covs broad, relatively fresh, and dark iridescent green (see Fig. 122**A**).

Juv-HY/SY ♂ (Sep-Aug): Breast mixed green, white, and rufous, gradually becoming entirely rufous by May; outermost 0-5 pp (among p6-p10) and 3-5 ss (among s6-s13, often the innermost) molting or contrastingly fresh in Nov-Aug; pp covs narrow, relatively abraded, and brown with a green tinge (see Fig. 122**A-B**).

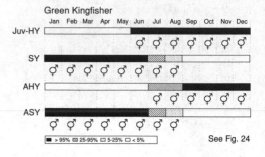

Green Kingfisher

AHY/ASY ♂ (Sep-Aug): Breast uniformly rich rufous, without white or green; pp and ss in complete molt during Sep-Nov and not molting or showing contrasts in Nov-Aug; pp covs broad, relatively fresh, and dark iridescent green (see Fig. 122**A**).

See Fig. 24

References—Ridgway (1914), Dickey & van Rossem (1938), Bent (1940), Snow & Snow (1964), Oberholser (1974), Foster (1975), Pyle (1995a).

Twenty-two species. Family characters include strong and sharp beaks, short and stiff tails with pointed rectrices, long and barbed tongues, and zygodactylous feet (two toes back and two toes forward), with the outer front toe reversed. Woodpeckers have 10 primaries (the 10th reduced), 10-12 secondaries, and 12 rectrices, the outer rectrices (r6) being vestigial or minute, such that there are only 10 visible feathers. Juveniles of many species begin flight-feather replacement before leaving the nest, initially replacing the innermost rudimentary juvenal primaries which are only one tenth the length of fully grown feathers (see Chapin 1922, Sibley 1957). The first prebasic molt is variable among the species, including no to all primaries and rectrices, no to a few secondaries, and usually no primary coverts. Incomplete replacement of the secondaries and primary coverts during adult prebasic molts allows ageing of many individuals to their third or fourth year of life (Pyle and Howell 1995; see below). Prealternate molts do not occur. Skulling live birds is thought unhelpful for ageing because the cranium is difficult to see through the tongue musculature, and the skull remains largely apneumatic through life; differences in the sizes of apneumaticized areas may exist among the age groups (see Fig. 88), but more study is needed. Eye color is useful for ageing certain species and should be examined in others. Juveniles of both sexes often show red in the crown,

a trait of adult males but not of adult females in most species; the amount of red usually is greater in juvenile males than in juvenile females (more study is needed on accurately sexed specimens). Both sexes incubate and the cloacal protuberance apparently is not developed by males; thus, breeding condition criteria are unreliable for sexing. Sexes are similar in wing and tail lengths, but males have larger bills than females in some species. Sexual dimorphism in the length and width of the tongue and its barbed, horny tip has also been found in Golden-fronted, Red-bellied and Downy woodpeckers (Selander 1966, Wallace 1974, Williams 1980; Fig. 120) and should be looked for in other woodpeckers, especially those showing no sex-specific differences in plumage.

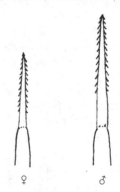

FIGURE 120. Variation in the length of the tongue barb by sex in certain woodpeckers. More study is needed on this, especially in sexually monochromatic species such as Lewis' and Red-headed woodpeckers and Red-breasted Sapsucker.

Incomplete Molts and Ageing in Woodpeckers

As with other near-passerines (see p. 39) and owls (see p. 67), flight-feather molt in woodpeckers is complex, but follows predictable patterns that can result in reliable ageing through at least the third year of life. Both juvenile and adult woodpeckers have a single annual molt that usually occurs in the late summer and fall. In migratory species this molt can be suspended or protracted, active replacement continuing until the following winter, spring, or summer. In all but four North American species, the primaries and rectrices typically are fully replaced during the first prebasic molt. In contrast, all species but one typically retain most or all secondaries, and all species typically retain all primary coverts during the first prebasic molt. The regular retention of some secondaries during adult prebasic molts is found in at least some individuals of most species, and replacement of the primary coverts during the second prebasic molt is incomplete. Reliable ageing through at least ATY involves inspection of the primaries, secondaries, and primary coverts for differences in shape, color pattern, and extent of wear, identifying retained juvenal feathers, retained adult feathers, and replaced adult feathers.

Juveniles of all species have primaries and rectrices that are tapered and pointed in comparison with those of adults (see Figs. 123 & 124). In two species (Lewis' and Acorn woodpeckers) these feathers are fully retained, differences in shape being reliable indicators of age through the second prebasic molt. In the other twenty North American species, the first molt of the primaries begins in the nest with the replacement of the minute juvenal p1-p2 (Chapin 1921, Sibley 1957b, Cramp 1985), and proceeds distally until all primaries are replaced, usually within 3-4 months after fledging. Some birds of at least two species (Red-headed and Red-bellied woodpeckers) can arrest this molt before it is completed, retaining up to five juvenal outer primaries until the second prebasic molt. In 19 of these species (all but Lewis', Acorn, and Red-headed woodpeckers), the juvenal outermost primary (p10) is larger and broader than it is in adults (see Fig. 127 and George 1972, Jackson 1979). This difference provides a method for separating HY from AHY birds until this feather is dropped in the fall. Replacement of the primaries and rectrices during the adult prebasic molts typically is complete.

Replacement of the secondaries usually proceeds both distally and proximally from s8. In many individuals a second series of replacement proceeds proximally from the outermost secondary, s1, such that the last secondaries replaced often are s3 and s4; however, just as regularly, this second sequence seems not to occur and the outermost feather (s1) is the last replaced. Except in one species (Red-headed Woodpecker), most individuals retain most or all secondaries during the first prebasic molt (Fig. 121A). A variable (by species) proportion can replace one to four (rarely to seven) inner secondaries among s7-s10 (rarely s5-s11), following the sequence noted above, *i.e.*, s8 only, or s8-s9, s7-s9, etc., if more than one secondary is replaced (Fig. 121B). Species of more open, drier habitats (*e.g.*, Gila and Ladder-backed woodpeckers) replace larger numbers of ss, on average, than birds of forested habitats (*e.g.*, White-headed and Three-toed woodpeckers).

At least a small proportion of woodpeckers in most North American species also retain some secondaries during adult prebasic molts. Juvenal secondaries retained by SY/TYs during the second prebasic molt are very abraded, often with the white areas (if present in a given species) worn

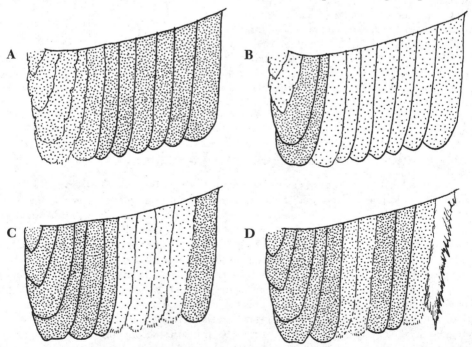

FIGURE 121. Replacement patterns among the secondaries of woodpeckers as an aid to ageing; see text and Figure 25. A single retained juvenal secondary (as shown in illustration **D**) can be found in occasional ASY/ATYs, and may indicate TY/4Y, but more study is needed. Many ASY/ATYs have a pattern similar to that in illustration **D** but without the juvenal feather. Figure from Pyle & Howell (1995).

away, contrasting greatly with the replaced, second-basic secondaries (Fig. 121**C**). Retained adult secondaries of ASY/ATYs, although more worn than newly replaced adult secondaries, contrast less with these newer feathers in color, wear, and shape (Fig. 121**D**). In addition, retained juvenal secondaries in SY/TYs often are s3 and/or s4, s2-s5, s1-s6 or a series of consecutive feathers within these blocks (*e.g.*, Fig. 121**C**), and retention patterns often are symmetrical in both wings, or nearly so. ASY/ATYs average fewer adult secondaries retained. These not always are in the same patterns noted above for SY/TYs (*e.g.*, Fig. 121**D**), and the patterns less frequently are symmetrical. With practice, most SY/TYs can readily be separated from ASY/ATYs by the relative contrasts between retained and replaced secondaries, the positions of the retained secondaries, and the relative symmetry in the wings of replacement patterns. Occasionally, one or more juvenal secondaries apparently can be retained during the third prebasic molt, at this time becoming extremely abraded (Fig. 121**D**). Along with an appropriate primary covert replacement pattern (see below), the presence of such feathers may reliably indicate TY/4Y, but more study is needed to confirm this.

The extent of primary covert replacement during the first and subsequent prebasic molts appears to be similar in all species of North American woodpeckers. Like the secondaries, the retained juvenal primary coverts of HY/SYs become faded and abraded relative to adult coverts, especially in spring (Fig. 122**B**), although fresh juvenal coverts in fall can closely resemble those of adults (Fig. 122**A**). During the second prebasic molt, only 0-5 consecutive outer primary coverts typically are replaced, the contrast between these and adjacent juvenal inner primary coverts (Fig. 122**C**) being a reliable indicator of SY/TY. A small percentage of SY/TY Lewis', Red-headed, and Acorn woodpeckers, and many sapsuckers apparently retain all primary coverts during the second prebasic molt, having uniformly very abraded and brown coverts and mixed adult and juvenal secondaries as SY/TYs. ASY/ATY woodpeckers replace either all or most primary coverts, resulting in retention patterns that differ from those of SY/TYs (Fig. 122**D**), less frequently being symmetrical. In occasional ASY/ATYs, one or two isolated juvenal coverts, usually among the second to the fifth from the outside, can be found among one or more generations of definitive feathers (Fig. 122**E**). As with the retained juvenal secondaries, it is possible that this only occurs during the third prebasic molt, thus indicating a TY/4Y individual. Finally, in some birds, three generations of coverts can be present, the outer 1-3 appearing to be first-basic feathers, the adjacent 1-2 coverts being newly replaced, second-basic feathers, and subsequent inner coverts appearing to be juve-

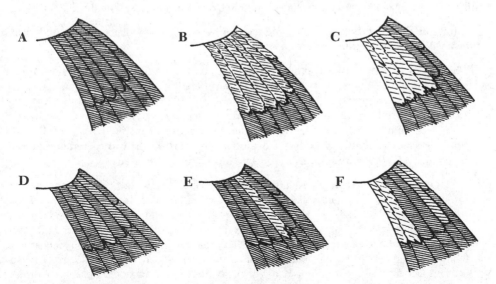

FIGURE 122. Replacement patterns among the primary coverts of woodpeckers as an aid to ageing; see text for details. Figure from Pyle & Howell (1995).

nal (Fig. 122**F**). Along with indicative replacement patterns among the secondaries (see above) this pattern also may indicate TY/4Y, but again, more study on known-age birds is needed.

Most woodpeckers will show patterns of wing-feather replacement that allow confident age-code assignment; however, many individuals can show patterns that are anomalous or ambiguous. Some birds show secondary replacement indicating one age and primary covert replacement indicating another. Individual variation also will be found within age groups, the most advanced individuals of one age group possibly overlapping in patterns with the slowest individuals of another. For these reasons age codes in woodpeckers should be assigned conservatively in ambiguous cases, or when the replacement patterns of the secondaries and primary coverts indicate different ages. In all cases, birds in active molt, usually in July-October (but in some species through winter or spring), should be carefully assessed, older flight-feather generations usually providing more clues to precise aging than do newly replaced feathers. As with near-passerines and owls, much of the information on molts presented in the following accounts on woodpeckers is based on specimen examination, and further confirmation is needed based on study of known-age, captive, or marked individuals.

LEWIS' WOODPECKER
Melanerpes lewis

LEWO
Species # 4080
Band size: 3-2

Geographic variation—No subspecies are recognized.

Molt—PB: HY/SY partial (Sep-Feb), AHY incomplete-complete (Aug-Dec); PA absent. PBs can be suspended over migration, completing on the winter grounds. The 1st PB includes few if any wing covs. The 2nd PB usually includes all pp and all or most rects, but just 0-3 outer pp covs (see Fig. 122**C**); 2-6 ss are retained during this molt, usually in a block among s1-s6 (see Figs. 25**C** & 121**C**), and often symmetrically in both wings. During subsequent PBs, from 1-5 ss often (in ~51% of birds) can be retained, among s1-s8, seldom in a block (see Figs. 25**D** & 121**D**), and less often symmetrically in both wings. A variable number of pp covs can be retained during the 3rd and subsequent PBs; these molts rarely are complete. See p. 163 for details.

Skull—Pneumaticization patterns probably are unhelpful for ageing; see Family account.

Age—Juv (Jun-Oct) has the entire head and nape brownish, breast and sides of the underparts brown with blackish mottling, and iris brown; juv ♀ = ♂.

HY/SY (Oct-Sep): Head, nape, and upper breast with brown juvenal feathers mixed with adult plumage (see SY/TY), becoming fully adult by Sep-Feb; flight feathers lacking in green luster, especially in spring/summer; p6-p10 tapered (Fig. 123); pp covs uniformly fresh (Fig. 122**A**) to uniformly worn (Fig. 122**B**); ss uniformly juvenal (Fig. 122**A**), relatively narrow and worn; rects pointed at the tip (Fig. 124), becoming worn by spring (Fig. 124). **Note: In addition, iris color probably is useful in distinguishing HY/SYs (brown to reddish brown) from most AHY/ASYs (reddish) through Jan; more study is needed.**

SY/TY (Oct-Sep): Head dark green and red, and breast and nape silvery gray, each without brown feathers; adult pp and rects uniformly dark green, relatively fresh, lustrous, blunt, and truncate (Figs. 123 & 124); pp covs either uniformly juvenal and very brownish and abraded (Fig. 122**B**), or outer 1-3 pp covs dark and fresh, contrasting with the brownish and worn, consecutive, retained inner pp covs (Fig. 122**C**); **and** ss mixed, with 2-6 retained juvenal feathers (among s1-s6), usually in a block, often symmetrically in both wings, narrow, abraded, and lacking luster, contrasting markedly with the fresher, broader, and more lustrous, replaced adult feathers (Fig. 121**C**). **Note: Intermediates, birds with anomalous feather**

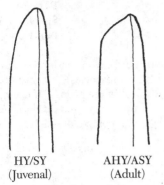

HY/SY   AHY/ASY
(Juvenal)   (Adult)

FIGURE 123. The shape of the outer primaries in Lewis' and Acorn woodpeckers. Many HY/SY Red-headed and some HY/SY Red-bellied woodpeckers also can retain juvenal outer primaries during the first prebasic molt.

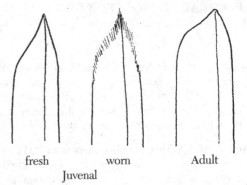

fresh   worn   Adult
Juvenal

FIGURE 124. Shape of the outer rectrices (r3-r5) by age in woodpeckers. Only Lewis' and Acorn woodpeckers regularly retain all juvenal rectrices during the first prebasic molt, showing worn feathers in the first spring and summer. In other species the shape can be used to separate juveniles from older birds. See also Figure 132.

replacement patterns, and/or birds with feather ages that are difficult to infer may not be separated reliably from ASY/ATY and should be classified AHY/ASY. Occasional SY/TYs also can show mixed juvenal and adult rects.

ASY/ATY (Oct-Sep): Body plumage, pp, and rects as in SY/TY; pp covs either uniformly dark and fresh (Fig. 122A), or pp covs irregularly mixed with fresh and moderately worn, retained adult feathers (Fig. 122D); ss either uniformly adult, or ss with 1-5 older adult feathers (among s1-s8) retained, often not symmetrically in both wings, and moderately worn, contrasting only slightly with the replaced feathers (Fig. 121D). **Note: See SY/TY. ASY/ATYs with uniformly adult flight feathers possibly are reliably aged ATY/A4Y, and birds with isolated, retained juvenal ss (Fig. 121D) and/or pp covs (Fig. 122E), or pp covs with three generations, consecutively replaced from the outside as shown in Figure 122F, might be reliably aged TY/4Y or even 4Y/5Y (see p. 165), but more study is needed. Also, look for occasional ASY/ATYs with mixed, old and new, adult rects.**

Sex— ♀ = ♂ by plumage. CP & BP are unreliable for sexing. ♀ wg(n45) 153-175, tl(n44) 86-104; ♂ wg(n63) 159-180, tl(n55) 88-106. The length of the tongue and its barbed, horny tip (see Fig. 120) should be examined for possible sex-specific differences.

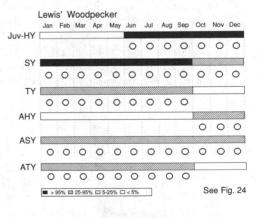

References—Ridgway (1914), Forbush (1929), Bent (1939), Bock (1970), Oberholser (1974), Short (1982), Pyle & Howell (1995), Tobalske (1997).

RED-HEADED WOODPECKER
Melanerpes erythrocephalus

RHWO
Species # 4060
Band size: 2

Geographic variation—Subspecies taxonomy follows Short (1982), who considered the species monotypic (synonymizing up to two previously recognized subspecies); see also Ridgway (1914), Oberholser (1919a, 1974), Brodkorb (1935a). Birds west of the plains ("*M.e. eryphthalmus*" and/or "*caurinus*") average slightly larger and have a more extensive reddish or yellowish tinge to underparts than eastern birds, but variation is slight and completely clinal.

Molt—PB: HY/SY incomplete (Sep-Mar), AHY incomplete-complete (Aug-Dec); PA absent. PBs can be suspended over migration, completing on the winter grounds. The 1st PB is extremely variable in this species. Juvenal feathers retained during the 1st PB can include 1-5 outer pp (in ~50% of birds), 1-8 ss (in ~90% of birds; usually the innermost, among s1-s6, and occasionally one or more of s9-s11), rarely some body feathers, and no, some, or all gr covs. All juvenal pp covs usually are retained, as well (occasionally the outermost is replaced). None, some, or all rects can be replaced. The 2nd PB usually includes all pp and most if not all ss and rects, but just 0-3 outer pp covs (see Fig. 122**C**); 1-5 inner ss and 1-4 rects (including both juvenal and/or 1st basic feathers) can occasionally be retained. Subsequent PBs usually are complete, except that some pp covs can be retained in some ASY/ATYs. See p. 163 for details on woodpecker molt.

Skull—Pneumaticization patterns probably are unhelpful for ageing; see Family account.

Age—Juv (Jun-Oct) has the head, upperparts and breast brown with pale mottling, all ss with a distinct, subterminal, blackish bar (see Fig. 125), rects uniformly pointed (Fig. 124), and iris grayish or grayish brown; juv ♀ = ♂.

Juv-HY/SY (Oct-Sep): Head, upperparts and/or breast with one or more brown feathers (through Jan in most HY/SYs, Sep in some SYs); flight feathers in symmetrical molt through winter or spring; one to all juvenal gr covs often retained, brownish with whitish tips; 1-8 juvenal ss (often among s1-s6 and sometimes including one or more of s9-s11) usually retained, with a full subterminal blackish band (Fig. 125); the outermost 1-5 juvenal pp sometimes retained through the 2nd Sep and relatively tapered (Fig. 123), contrasting with the fresher and more truncate, replaced inner pp; pp covs uniformly juvenal, black in fall (Fig. 122**A**) to brownish and worn in spring/summer (Fig. 122**B**), or occasionally with the outermost replaced, contrastingly black and fresh (see Fig. 122**C**); some or all juvenal rects usually retained, pointed, and relatively abraded in spring (Fig. 124). **Note: Both HY/SYs and SY/TYs (which see) can show uniformly adult pp and ss and uniformly juvenal pp covs (or with**

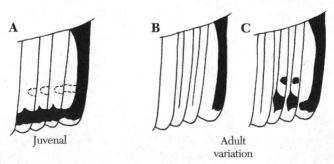

A   B   C

Juvenal   Adult
variation

FIGURE 125. Color patterns on the outer secondaries (s1-s3) by age in Red-headed Woodpecker. All juvenal secondaries show a full bar and in some birds a second black area occurs (indicated by dashed lines in illustration **A**). Typical adult secondaries lack black on s2-s11 (**B**). Some adults (perhaps SY/TYs) show some black on s2-s3 (**C**), although note that the black does not form a full bar. Figure from Pyle & Howell (1995).

the outermost, reduced pp cov replaced). On birds with this pattern look for some retained juvenal body feathers or gr covs, retained juvenal rects, and, perhaps, a grayer iris in HY/SYs (*vs* rects primarily or completely adult and a dark red iris in SY/TYs). Also, the condition of the juvenal pp covs should be relatively fresher on HY/SYs than on SY/TYs. Some of these should be aged AHY/ASY. In Aug-Sep, HYs are separated from SYs by having fresher flight feathers and substantial, fresh (as opposed to very worn) juvenal body plumage remaining.

SY/TY (Oct-Sep): Head and breast uniformly red; back uniformly blue-black; flight feathers usually not in molt beyond Dec; gr covs uniformly adult and blue-black; ss usually uniformly adult (Figs. 25**B** & 125), or ss occasionally with retained, adult or juvenal feathers (Figs. 121**C-D** & 125), contrastingly worn and faded; pp uniformly adult, truncate, and relatively fresh (Fig. 123); pp covs with 0-3 outer feathers replaced, black, and fresh, contrasting with the brown and abraded, retained inner juvenal pp covs (Fig. 122**B-C**); rects uniformly adult and truncate (Fig. 124), sometimes with a few old adult and/or very old juvenal feathers (Fig. 124) retained. **Note: Some overlap may occur with HY/SYs (which see). It is possible that SY/TYs may average more black on the replaced adult outer ss (s1-s3; see Fig. 125) than ASY/ATYs; more study is needed.**

ASY/ATY (Oct-Sep): Head, breast, back, gr covs, and pp as in SY/TY; ss uniformly adult (Figs. 25**B** & 125), perhaps rarely with one or more retained adult feathers, contrasting moderately in wear with the replaced ss (Fig. 25**D**; see also Fig. 121**D**); pp covs either uniformly black and fresh (Fig. 122**A**), or (occasionally) pp covs irregularly mixed with fresh and moderately worn, retained adult feathers (see Fig. 122**D**); rects usually uniformly adult and truncate (Fig. 124), occasionally with one or two retained adult feathers, contrasting only moderately in wear. **Note: See SY/TY. ASY/ATYs with isolated, retained juvenal pp covs (Fig. 122E) or with three generations of pp covs, consecutively replaced from the outside as shown in Figure 122F, might be reliably aged TY/4Y (see p. 165) but more study is needed.**

Sex—♀ = ♂ by plumage. CP & BP are unreliable for sexing. ♀ wg(n66) 125-148, tl(n66) 63-85; ♂ wg(n100) 125-150, tl(n100) 63-82. The length of the tongue and its barbed, horny tip (see Family account and Fig. 120) should be examined for possible sex-specific differences.

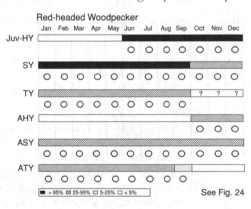

References—Stone (1896), Ridgway (1914), Forbush (1927), Bent (1939), Roberts (1955), Wood (1969), Hoover (1973), Oberholser (1974), Sheppard & Klimkiewicz (1976), Short (1982), Pyle & Howell (1995); W. Lueshen, L.L. Hood (*in litt.* to the BBL).

ACORN WOODPECKER
Melanerpes formicivorus

ACWO
Species # 4070
Band size: 2-3

Geographic variation—Fairly well marked and ranges moderately well defined. Subspecies taxonomy follows Benitez-Diaz (1993); see also Ridgway (1914), Grinnell & Swarth (1926a), Griscom (1932), van Rossem (1934a, 1945a), Phillips *et al.* (1964), Oberholser (1974), Troetschler (1974), Browning (1978), Short (1982). Five other subspecies occur in Mex-S.Am.

Sexes are similar in wg and tl measurements (see **Sex**) and thus are combined for each sub-species.

M.f. bairdi (br & wint sw.WA-s.CA): Large; bill long and stout; black chest band broad (solid black portion 25-40 mm wide) with sparse, pale streaking or mottling; belly and flanks with sparse, black streaking. ♀♂ wg(n100) 135-154, tl(n100) 72-88; exp culmen ♀(n100) 26.6-32.6, ♂(n100) 28.3-35.4; bill width at tip of nares ♀(n13) 7.3-8.3, ♂(n15) 7.3-8.9; note that bills of HYs (Aug-Dec) are shorter and possibly thinner than bills of AHYs. Birds of n.Baja CA to the border with N.Am (*"martirensis"*) average smaller and with less black on the breast than birds of N.Am, but variation is slight.

M.f. formicivorus (br & wint AZ-sw.TX): Small; bill short and thin; black chest band narrow (solid black portion 20-30 mm wide) with dense, pale streaking; belly and flanks with dense, black streaking. ♀♂ wg(n100) 131-151, tl(n100) 63-85; exp culmen ♀(n77) 22.1-28.4, ♂(n73) 23.4-29.4; bill width at tip of nares ♀(n29) 6.2-8.0, ♂(n28) 6.3-7.6; see *bairdi* regarding bill size by age. Birds of N.Am (*"aculeatus"*, including *"phasmus"* of sw.TX) average shorter wg, shorter and more slender bill, and paler yellow on the throat than nominate birds of nc.Mex, but variation is broadly clinal.

Molt—PB: HY partial (Jul-Sep), AHY incomplete-complete (Jul-Sep); PA absent. PBs occur primarily on the summer grounds. The 1st PB includes some but usually not all wing covs, 0-6 inner gr covs usually being replaced. The crown feathers often are the last replaced during the 1st PB. The 2nd PB usually includes all pp and all or most rects, but just 0-3 outer pp covs (see Fig. 122C); 1-6 ss are retained during this molt, usually in a block among s1-s6 (see Figs. 25C & 121C), and often symmetrically in both wings. During subsequent PBs, from 1-6 ss sometimes (in ~42% of birds) can be retained, among s1-s8, seldom in a block (see Figs. 25D & 121D), and less often symmetrically in both wings. A variable number of pp covs can be retained during the 3rd and subsequent PBs; these molts usually are not complete. See p. 163 for details on woodpecker molt.

Skull—Pneumaticization patterns probably are unhelpful for ageing; see Family account.

Age—Juv (May-Oct) is duller, has upperparts and breast band brownish, red of the head tinged orange and dusky, throat feathers sometimes tipped pinkish, and iris dark. Juv ♀ = ♂, with head plumage resembling adult ♂, although juv ♀ may average more dusky in the crown than juv ♂. Sexing of juvs is not recommended without further study.

HY/SY (Sep-Aug): All juvenal flight feathers retained, uniform in color, shape, and wear (Figs. 25A & 121A), relatively worn, and lacking in luster (especially in spring/summer), contrasting with the blacker back and replaced wing covs; p6-p10 tapered (Fig. 123); pp covs uniformly fresh (Fig. 122A) to worn in spring (Fig. 122B); rects pointed at the tip (Fig. 124), becoming worn by May-Aug (Fig. 124); outer rects (r5) average more pale spots (usually 2-4 rows). **Note: In addition, iris color may be useful in distinguishing some HY/SYs (brown to grayish) from most AHY/ASYs (white to pinkish) through May. Measurements (particularly wg and bill) also are smaller in HY/SYs than in AHY/ASYs and this can be useful within each population (see Geographic variation and Sex).**

SY/TY (Sep-Aug): Adult pp and rects uniformly black, relatively fresh, lustrous, blunt, and truncate (Figs. 123 & 124), the outer rects (r5) averaging fewer pale spots (usually 0-2 rows); pp covs either uniformly juvenal, very brownish, and abraded (Fig. 122B), or outer 1-3 pp covs dark and fresh, contrasting with the brownish and worn, consecutive, retained, inner pp covs (Fig. 122C); **and** ss mixed, with 1-6 juvenal feathers (among s1-s6) retained, usually in a block, often symmetrically in both wings, faded, abraded (sometimes tinged chestnut), and contrasting markedly with the fresher and more lustrous, replaced adult feathers (Figs. 25C & 121C). **Note: See HY/SY. Intermediates, birds with anomalous feather replacement patterns, and/or birds with feather ages that are difficult to infer cannot be separated reliably from ASY/ATY, and should be classified AHY/ASY. Also, look for occasional SY/TYs with mixed juvenal and adult rects.**

ASY/ATY (Oct-Sep): Pp and rects as in SY/TY; pp covs either uniformly dark and fresh (Fig. 122**A**), or pp covs irregularly mixed with fresh and moderately worn, retained adult feathers (Fig. 121**D**); ss either uniformly adult (Fig. 25**B**), or ss with 1-6 older adult feathers (among s1-s8) retained, often not symmetrically in both wings, moderately worn, and contrasting only slightly with the replaced feathers (Figs. 25**D** & 121**D**). **Note: See SY/TY. ASY/ATYs with uniformly adult flight feathers possibly can be aged ATY/A4Y. Look for ASY/ATYs with isolated, retained juvenal ss (Fig. 121D) and/or pp covs (Fig. 122E), or birds with three generations of pp covs, consecutively replaced from the outside as shown in Figure 122F, that might be reliably aged TY/4Y (see p. 165), but more study is needed. Also, look for occasional ASY/ATYs with mixed old and new adult rects.**

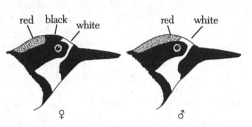

Sex—CP & BP are unreliable for sexing. ♀ wg(n100) 131-154, tl(n100) 67-88, exp culmen (n100) 22.1-32.6; ♂ wg(n100) 132-153, tl(n100) 63-88, exp culmen (n100) 23.4-35.4; see **Geographic variation**.

FIGURE 126. The head pattern by sex in Acorn Woodpecker.

♀: Red of the crown restricted to the nape and separated from the white forehead by a black bar (Fig. 126). **Note: Juvs cannot be sexed; See ♂.**

♂: Red of the central crown extending from the nape to the white forehead, without an intervening black bar (Fig. 126). **Note: Beware that juv ♀♀ (see Age) can retain this pattern through Aug and thus are inseparable from juv ♂♂ before commencement of the crown molt.**

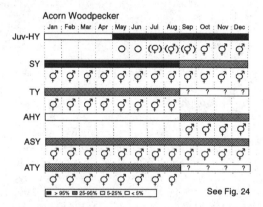

References—Swarth (1904a), Ridgway (1914), Dickey & van Rossem (1938), Bent (1939), Oberholser (1974), Troetschler (1974), Spray & MacRoberts (1975), Sanders (1979), Koenig (1980), Short (1982), Koenig *et al.* (1995), Pyle & Howell (1995).

GILA WOODPECKER
Melanerpes uropygialis

GIWO
Species # 4110
Band size: 2-3

Species—From Golden-fronted and Red-bellied woodpeckers by smaller bill by sex (23.3-32.2; see **Sex**); head usually without yellow; red or yellow on the nape absent; central belly yellow; uppertail covs white with distinct, black chevrons; inner web of the central rects (r1) barred black and white. Beware of ♀♀ showing intermediate characters; on these the most reliable criterion for separation from Golden-fronted Woodpecker appears to be the pattern of the central rects. Also, beware of hybrids with Golden-fronted Woodpecker.

Geographic variation—Moderately weak and clinal where ranges meet. Subspecies taxonomy follows Short (1982); see also Ridgway (1914), van Rossem (1931a, 1934a, 1942b), Selander &

Giller (1963), Phillips *et al.* (1964), Monson & Phillips (1981), Rea (1983). Three other sub-species occur in Mex.

M.u. uropygialis (res throughout range in N.Am): Larger (see **Sex**) or paler than subspecies of Mex; white bars on the back broader (2.0-2.5, *vs* 1.0-2.0 mm). Birds of AZ-sw.NM (*"albescens"*) average slightly larger and paler (upperparts with the white bars usually broader than the black bars) than nominate birds of se.CA (black bars usually broader than the white bars), but variation is broadly clinal, especially in n.Mex.

Molt—PB: HY incomplete (Aug-Oct), AHY incomplete-complete (Jul-Oct); PA absent. The 1st PB includes some to all inner lesser and med covs, usually 1-8 inner gr covs, all pp and rects, and the innermost 0-6 ss (among s5-s11; replacement of ss occurs in ~71% of HY/SYs, usually 1-5 feathers among s6-s10; see Fig. 121**B**), but usually no pp covs. The 2nd PB includes all wing covs, pp, rects, and ss (rarely 1-2 ss may be retained), but just 1-5 outer pp covs (see Fig. 121**C**). Subsequent PBs usually are complete, except that some pp covs and, rarely (~2% of birds), 1-2 ss (among s1-s8) can be retained. See p. 163 for details on woodpecker molt.

Skull—Pneumaticization patterns probably are unhelpful for ageing; see Family account.

Age—Juv (Apr-Sep) has the crown and breast with fine, black streaks, the red crown patch of ♂ averaging smaller and darker, black and white barring of the back indistinct, p10 rounded and large (tip > 10 mm from the pp covs, *vs* < 10 mm in adults; see Fig. 127), rects pointed (Fig. 124), and iris brown. Juv ♀♀ usually lack red but can have 1-2 red feathers (Fig. 130**A-B**) whereas juv ♂♂ usually have a mottled red patch (> 2 feathers) in the crown (Fig. 130**C-E**); thus, sexes are separated reliably.

HY/SY (Oct-Sep): Pp covs uniform (Fig. 122**A**; rarely the small outermost feather can be contrastingly fresh), quickly becoming brown and worn (Fig. 122**B**); **and** ss either uniform in color and wear, the terts becoming extremely worn by spring (Fig. 121**A**), or (often) ss uniform except for 1-5 feathers among s7-s11 (rarely to 6 among s5-s11) contrastingly fresh (Fig. 121**B**). **Note: Fresh fall HY/SYs can resemble ASY/ATYs with uniform ss and pp covs; see Red-bellied Woodpecker. Iris color also may be helpful in distinguishing some HY/SYs (brown to reddish brown) from most AHY/ASYs (reddish) through Jan. Look also for occasional HY/SYs to retain a few outer pp during the 1st PB, as in Red-bellied Woodpecker.**

SY/TY (Oct-Sep): Consecutive, replaced outer 1-5 pp covs black and fresh, contrasting with the brown and abraded, consecutive, retained inner pp covs (Fig. 122**C**); **and** ss either uniformly adult (Fig. 25**B**), the terts usually only moderately worn by spring, or (rarely) ss with 1-2 juvenal feathers (among s1-s5) retained, usually symmetrically in both wings, very faded and abraded, and contrasting

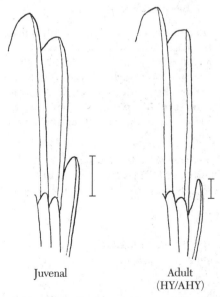

Juvenal   Adult
(HY/AHY)

FIGURE 127. The shape and size of p10 relative to the primary coverts, by age, in most woodpeckers. See species accounts for measurement information. The features of this feather may be most helpful in separating molting HYs (in Sep-Oct) from ASYs, as the primary coverts in these two groups can appear similar (Fig. 122**A**). Look for SY/TYs possibly to have the p10 intermediate in shape and size between the juvenal feather and that of AHY/ASY.

markedly with the fresher, replaced adult feathers (Figs. 25C & 121C). **Note: See HY/SY. Some intermediates can be difficult to separate reliably from ASY/ATY and should be aged AHY/ASY.**

ASY/ATY (Oct-Sep): Pp covs either uniformly black and fresh (Fig. 122**A**), or pp covs irregularly mixed with fresh and moderately worn, retained adult feathers (Fig. 122**D**); **and** ss either uniformly adult (Fig. 25**B**), the terts usually fresh or only slightly worn, or (rarely) ss with 1-2 older, adult feathers (among s1-s8) retained, often not symmetrically in both wings, moderately worn, and contrasting only slightly with the replaced feathers (Figs. 25**D** & 121**D**). **Note: See HY/SY and SY/TY. ASY/ATYs with isolated, retained juvenal pp covs (Fig. 122E), or with three generations of pp covs, sequentially replaced as in Figure 122F, might be reliably aged TY/4Y (see p. 165), but more study is needed.**

Sex—CP & BP are unreliable for sexing. Bill length useful; ♀ wg(n100) 122-133, tl(n100) 74-88; exp culmen(n100) 23.3-27.7; ♂ wg(n100) 127-138, tl(n100) 77-93, exp culmen(n100) 27.4-32.2.

♀: Crown without a red patch (Fig. 130**A**) or occasionally with up to a few red feathers (Fig 130**B**; probably in juvs and ASY/ATYs only).

♂: Crown with a red patch (Fig. 130**E**) consisting of > 2 red feathers.

Hybrids reported—Golden-fronted Woodpecker.

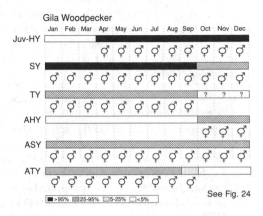

References—Ridgway (1914), Bent (1939), Selander & Giller (1963), Short (1982), Martindale & Lamm (1984), Pyle & Howell (1995).

GOLDEN-FRONTED WOODPECKER
Melanerpes aurifrons

GFWO
Species # 4100
Band size: 2

Species—From Gila and Red-bellied woodpeckers by larger bill by sex (27.9-35.7; see **Sex**); presence of yellow or orange on the nape; nasal tufts and belly with yellow; uppertail covs white with few or no black marks; inner web of the central rects (r1) black or black with a few white marks (see **Geographic variation**). Beware of ♀♀ showing intermediate characters; the most reliable criterion on these appears to be the pattern of the central rects. Also, beware of hybrids.

Geographic variation—Fairly well marked, with moderately well-defined ranges, although fairly substantial individual variation (especially regarding red and yellow colors of the head) obscure certain subspecies boundaries. Subspecies taxonomy follows Short (1982); see also Ridgway (1914), Griscom (1932), Wetmore (1943, 1948), Todd (1946), Selander & Giller (1959, 1963), Oberholser (1974). Nine other subspecies occur in Mex-C.Am.

M. a. aurifrons (res s.OK-TX): From the other subspecies of Mex-C.Am by larger size (see **Sex**, *vs* wg 125-137, tl 67-79 in the other subspecies); white bars of the upperparts wider (> 3.0 mm), roughly equal to the black bars (*vs* white bars narrower than the black bars); nape, nasal tufts, and belly yellow (*vs* orange or red in subspecies of Mex-C.Am); inner web of the central rects (r1) without or with fewer white marks. Birds of s.OK-sw.TX ("*incanescens*") may average slightly paler overall than birds of s.TX, and have no (*vs* few) black marks on the inner web of the uppertail covs, but differences are broadly clinal and obscured by individual variation.

Molt—PB: HY incomplete (Aug-Oct), AHY incomplete-complete (Jul-Oct); PA absent. The 1st PB includes some to most inner lesser and med covs, often 1-6 inner gr covs, all pp and rects, and the innermost 0-6 ss (among s5-s11; replacement of ss occurs in ~30% of HY/SYs, usually 1-4 feathers among s7-s10; see Fig. 121**B**), but usually no pp covs. The 2nd PB usually includes all wing covs, pp, and rects, but just 1-5 outer pp covs (see Fig. 121**C**). Subsequent PBs usually are complete, except that some pp covs and, rarely (~2% of birds), 1-2 ss (among s1-s8) can be retained. See p. 163 for details on woodpecker molt.

Skull—Pneumaticization patterns probably are unhelpful for ageing; see Family account.

Age—Juv (Apr-Sep) has the crown and breast with fine, black streaks, nasal tufts and nape without distinct yellow or orange, black and white barring of the back indistinct, p10 rounded and large (tip > 10 mm from the pp covs, *vs* < 12 mm in adults; see Fig. 127), rects pointed (Fig. 124), and iris brown. Juv ♀♀ usually lack red but possibly can have 1-2 red feathers (Fig. 130**A-B**) whereas juv ♂♂ usually have a small red patch (> 2 feathers) in the crown (Fig. 130**C-E**); thus, sexes are separated reliably.

HY/SY (Oct-Sep): Yellow of the nape averages paler by sex; pp covs uniform in color and wear (Fig. 122**A**; rarely the small outermost cov can be contrastingly fresh), quickly becoming brown and worn (Fig. 122**B**); **and** ss either uniform in color and wear, the terts becoming extremely worn by spring (Fig. 121**A**), or (sometimes) ss uniform except for 1-4 feathers (among s7-s10, rarely to 6 among s5-s11) contrastingly fresh (Fig. 121**B**). **Note: Fresh fall HY/SYs can resemble ASY/ATYs with uniform ss and pp covs; see Red-bellied Woodpecker. In addition, iris color probably is helpful in distinguishing some HY/SYs (brown to reddish brown) from most AHY/ASYs (reddish) through Jan. Look also for occasional HY/SYs to retain a few outer pp during the 1st PB, as in Red-bellied Woodpecker.**

SY/TY (Oct-Sep): Yellow of the nape averages deeper by sex; consecutive, replaced outer 1-5 pp covs black and fresh, contrasting cov with the brown and abraded, consecutive, retained inner pp covs (Fig. 122**C**); **and** ss either uniformly adult (Fig. 25**B**), the terts usually only moderately worn by spring, or (sometimes) ss with 1-2 juvenal feathers (among s1-s5) retained, often symmetrically in both wings, faded, abraded, and contrasting markedly with the fresher, replaced adult feathers (Figs. 25**C** & 121**C**). **Note: See HY/SY. Some intermediates can be difficult to separate reliably from ASY/ATY and should be aged AHY/ASY.**

ASY/ATY (Oct-Sep): Nape as in SY/TY; pp covs either uniformly black and fresh (Fig. 122**A**), or pp covs irregularly mixed with fresh and moderately worn, retained adult feathers (Fig. 122**D**); **and** ss either uniformly adult (Fig. 25**B**), the terts usually fresh or only slightly worn, or (rarely) ss with 1-2 older adult feathers (among s1-s8) retained, often not symmetrically in both wings, moderately worn, and contrasting only slightly with the replaced feathers (Figs. 25**D** & 121**D**). **Note: See HY/SY and SY/TY. ASY/ATYs with isolated, retained juvenal pp covs (Fig. 122E), or with three generations of pp covs, sequentially replaced as in Figure 122F, might be reliably aged TY/4Y (see p. 165), but more study is needed.**

Sex—CP & BP are unreliable for sexing. Bill size is useful: ♀ wg(n30) 130-141, tl(n20) 72-83, exp culmen(n23) 27.9-32.0; ♂ wg(n46) 131-144, tl(n42) 75-85, exp culmen(n25) 30.2-35.7; see **Geographic variation**. The horny tip of the tongue varies in size (especially width) by sex (Fig. 120; see Wallace 1974) and this also may be helpful in sexing juvs or anomalous birds; more study is needed.

♀: Crown without a red patch (Fig 130**A**), or at most with 2-3 red feathers (Fig. 130**B**; probably in juvs and ASY/ATYs only).

♂: Crown with a red patch of > 3 feathers (Fig. 130C-E). **Note: Some extralimital races have red through the nape (*e.g.*, Fig. 130H), as well.**

Hybrids reported—Gila Woodpecker, Red-bellied Woodpecker, Hoffmann's Woodpecker (*M. hoffmannii*).

References—Ridgway (1914), Dickey & van Rossem (1938), Bent (1939), Selander & Giller (1959, 1963), Selander (1966), Oberholser (1974), Wallace (1974), Short (1982), Gerber (1986), Smith (1987), Pyle & Howell (1995).

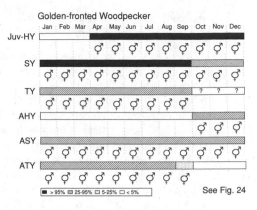

Golden-fronted Woodpecker

See Fig. 24

RED-BELLIED WOODPECKER
Melanerpes carolinus

RBWO
Species # 4090
Band size: 2

Species—From Gila and Golden-fronted woodpeckers by smaller bill by sex (25.4-33.0; see **Sex**): nape and nasal tufts without yellow; belly with red (rarely yellow); uppertail covs white, often with distinct, blackish spotting; inner web of the central rects (r1) barred black and white. Beware of ♀♀ showing intermediate characters; the most reliable criterion on these appears to be the pattern of the central rects. Also, beware of hybrids with Golden-fronted Woodpecker.

Geographic variation—Subspecies taxonomy follows Short (1982), who considered the species monotypic (synonymizing three previously recognized subspecies); see also Ridgway (1914), Burleigh & Lowery (1944), Todd (1946), Koelz (1954), Mengel (1965), Oberholser (1974). Nominate forms of PA-MS to n.FL average longer bills, darker upperparts (black bars wider than white bars) and grayer and less yellow-tinged underparts than birds of MN to NY-c.TX ("*M.c. zebra*") and s.FL ("*perplexus*", which also averages smaller and with less white in the central rects), but variation is broadly clinal and obscured by individual variation. Birds of se.TX ("*harpaceus*") may average slightly paler than other birds, but this is completely obscured by individual variation. Also, birds of the FL Keys may average smaller and darker, but more study is needed on the possible distinction of this form to subspecies.

Molt—PB: HY incomplete (Aug-Oct), AHY incomplete-complete (Jul-Oct); PA absent. The 1st PB includes no to most inner lesser and med covs, sometimes 1-6 inner gr covs, all pp and rects, and 0-6 inner ss among s5-s11 (replacement of ss occurs in ~26% of HYs, usually 1-4 feathers among s7-s10; see Fig. 121**B**), but usually no pp covs. Occasional HY/SYs (~10% of birds) can retain 1-4 or more outer pp during the 1st PB. The 2nd PB usually includes all wing covs, pp, rects, and ss (rarely 1-2 ss may be retained), but just 1-5 outer pp covs (see Fig. 121**C**). Subsequent PBs usually are complete, except that some pp covs and, rarely (~2% of birds), 1-2 ss (among s1-s8) can be retained. See p. 163 for details on woodpecker molt.

Skull—Pneumaticization patterns probably are unhelpful for ageing; see Family account.

Age—Juv (May-Sep) has the crown dusky, nasal tufts and nape without red, black and white barring of the back indistinct, p10 rounded and large (tip > 7 mm from the pp covs, *vs* < 9 mm in adults; see Fig. 127), rects pointed (Fig. 124), breast with fine, dusky streaks, and iris brown. Juv ♀♀ usually lack red but can have up to a few pale red feathers in the crown (Fig. 130**A-B**) and have no or a slight yellow-orange tinge to the belly, whereas juv ♂♂ usually have a small dark red patch (> 2 feathers) in the crown (Fig. 130C-E) and a moderate yellow-orange wash to the belly; thus, most juvs are reliably sexed.

HY/SY (Oct-Sep): Outer 1-4 juvenal pp occasionally retained, more worn, and tapered at the tip (Fig. 123) than the inner pp; pp covs uniform (Fig. 122A; rarely the small outermost can be contrastingly fresh), quickly becoming brown and worn by winter/spring (Fig. 122B); **and** ss either uniform in color and wear, the terts becoming very worn by spring (Fig. 121A), or (sometimes) ss uniform except for 1-4 feathers (among s7-s10, rarely to 6 among s5-s11) contrastingly fresh (Fig. 121B). **Note: Fresh fall HY/SYs can resemble fresh ASY/ATYs (which see) with uniform ss and pp covs. On these look for retention of juvenal characters on HY/SYs (through Oct), especially a larger p10 (the last primary replaced, in Sep-Nov or later), juvenal pointed rects, and/or iris color browner (vs redder in ASY/ATYs) through Jan. Look also for the p10 of HY/SYs to average intermediate in size and shape between those of juvs and AHY/ASYs (see Fig. 127); more study is needed.**

SY/TY (Oct-Sep): Outer pp uniformly adult and truncate at the tip (Fig. 123); consecutive, replaced outer 1-5 pp covs black and fresh, contrasting with the brown and abraded, consecutive, retained inner pp covs (Fig. 122C); **and** ss either uniformly adult (Fig. 25B), the terts usually only moderately worn by spring, or (rarely) ss with 1-2 juvenal feathers (among s1-s6) retained, often symmetrically on both wings, faded, and abraded, contrasting markedly with the fresher, replaced adult feathers (Figs. 25C & 121C). **Note: See HY/SY. Some intermediates can be difficult to separate reliably from ASY/ATY and should be aged AHY/ASY.**

ASY/ATY (Oct-Sep): Pp as in SY/TY; pp covs either uniformly black and fresh (Fig. 122A), or pp covs irregularly mixed with fresh and moderately worn, retained adult feathers (Fig. 122D); **and** ss either uniformly adult (Fig. 25B), the terts usually fresh or only slightly worn, or (rarely) ss with 1-2 older adult feathers (among s1-s8) retained, often not symmetrically in both wings, moderately worn, and contrasting only slightly with the replaced feathers (Figs. 25D & 121D). **Note: See HY/SY and SY/TY. ASY/ATYs with isolated, retained juvenal pp covs (Fig. 122E), or with three generations of pp covs, sequentially replaced as in Figure 122F, might be reliably aged TY/4Y (see p. 165), but more study is needed.**

Sex—CP & BP are unreliable for sexing. Bill size is useful: ♀ wg(n71) 118-133, tl(n40) 68-84, exp culmen(n40) 25.4-29.9; ♂ wg(n100) 122-139, tl(n41) 72-85, exp culmen(n41) 28.1-33.0. The horny tip of the tongue varies by sex in size (Fig. 120; see Wallace 1974) and this also may be useful for sexing juvs; more study is needed.

♀: Nasal tufts dull red; crown grayish brown, with the red of the head usually restricted to the hindcrown and nape (see Fig. 130G). **Note: occasional ♀♀ (probably AHY/ASYs) have 1-2 red feathers on the central crown.**

♂: Crown from the nasal tufts to the nape entirely bright red, or (in some ♂♂) red with a small brown band across the central forehead, < 5 mm wide. **Note: See ♀.**

Hybrids reported—Golden-fronted Woodpecker.

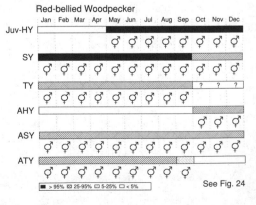

References—Ridgway (1914), Forbush (1927), Bent (1939), Roberts (1955), Selander & Giller (1959, 1963), Wood (1969), Oberholser (1974), Wallace (1974), Short (1982), Gerber (1986), Smith (1987), CWS & USFWS (1991), Pyle & Howell (1995); C.H. Blake, J.S. Weske (*in litt.* to the BBL); D.A. Sibley (pers. comm.); IBP (MAPS) data.

YELLOW-BELLIED SAPSUCKER
Sphyrapicus varius

YBSA
Species # 4020
Band size: 1B-1A

Species—From Red-naped Sapsucker by nape white, usually without red (Fig. 128); ♀ with the crown red or largely to completely black, and the throat white, usually without red (Fig. 128); ♂ with the chin and throat completely red, this separated from the white of the cheek by a broad, black bar (Fig. 128); upperparts with extensive pale mottling and without well-defined streaks; underparts more strongly washed yellow; outer rects average more white by sex (*cf.* Fig. 129). Juvs can be difficult to separate from juv Red-naped Sapsuckers, by the plumage of the upperparts, underparts, and outer rects (as above); crown brown with light, yellow scalloping; overall coloration paler. The 1st PB (see **Molt**) also is more protracted such that Yellow-bellied Sapsuckers retain more juvenal body plumage later into the fall and winter, *e.g.*, HY/SYs after Sep with largely juvenal head plumage most likely are Yellow-bellied Sapsuckers. Use care in the separation of ♂ Yellow-bellied from ♀ Red-naped sapsuckers, and beware of hybrids and occasional birds showing some (but unlikely all) intermediate characters. From Red-breasted Sapsucker in all plumages (including juvs) by the lack of red in the face or breast (Fig. 128).

Geographic variation—Subspecies taxonomy follows Short (1982), who considered the species monotypic (synonymizing two previously recognized subspecies); see also Oberholser (1938, 1974), Wetmore (1939), Burleigh & Peters (1948), Ganier (1954). Northern birds (*"S.v. atrothorax"*) may average slightly larger and with more white on the upperparts than southern birds, and breeding birds of sw.VA-nw.GA (*"appalachiensis"*) average slightly smaller and darker, but in both cases there is almost complete overlap in characters.

Molt—PB: HY/SY incomplete (Jun-May), AHY incomplete-complete (Jun-Oct); PA absent. The 1st PB includes no to a few inner lesser and med covs and all pp and rects, which usually are completely replaced by Aug; the 1st body and wing cov molt is usually suspended over migration, completing on the winter grounds. Adult PBs occur on the summer grounds. The 2nd PB usually includes all wing covs and pp, and all or most rects, but often no pp covs, or only the outermost 1-2 pp covs (in ~42% of birds); 1-6 ss are retained during this molt (usually in a block among s1-s6; see Figs. 25C & 121C), and often symmetrically in both wings. During subsequent PBs, from 1-5 ss often (in ~68% of birds) can be retained, among s1-s8, seldom in a block (see Figs. 25D & 121D), and less often symmetrically in both wings. A variable number of pp covs also can be retained during the 3rd and subsequent PBs; adult molts seldom (if ever) are complete. See p. 163 for details on woodpecker molt.

Skull—Pneumaticization patterns probably are unhelpful for ageing; see Family account.

Age—Juv (Jun-Aug; some to Dec) has the head, back, and breast largely mottled brown and yellowish, p10 rounded and large (tip 1-8 mm > pp covs, *vs* 2-7 mm < pp covs in adults; see Fig. 127), rects pointed (Fig. 124), and iris gray-brown. Some juv ♂♂ can be identified by a slight red tint to the crown and throat; generally, however, juv ♀ = ♂, although sexing is possible after a few throat feathers have been replaced (see **Sex**).

HY/SY (Oct-Sep): Head, back, and/or upper breast with brown juvenal feathers mixed with adult plumage (see SY/TY), becoming fully adult by Dec-May, occasionally as late as the 2nd PB; pp covs uniform (Fig. 122A), quickly becoming brown and worn by winter/spring (Fig. 122B); ss uniform in color and wear, the terts becoming relatively worn by spring (Fig. 121A). **Note: In addition, iris color probably is helpful in distinguishing HY/SYs (grayish brown to brown) from most AHY/ASYs (reddish brown) through Jan. Look also for occasional HY/SYs with mixed juvenal and adult rects.**

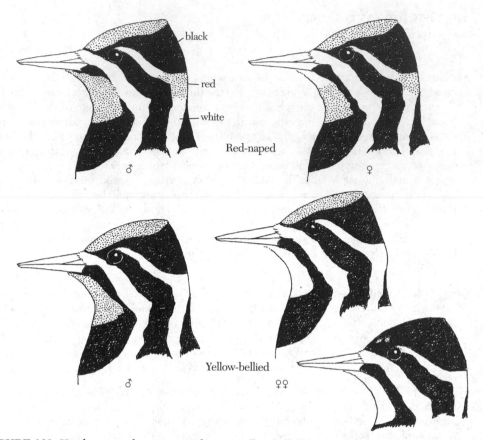

FIGURE 128. Head patterns by species and sex in Yellow-bellied and Red-naped sapsuckers. Note that some ♀ Red-naped Sapsuckers can lack red on the throat.

SY/TY (Oct-Sep): Head, back, and breast black, white, and/or red (see Fig. 128), without brown juvenal feathers (adult feathers can be tipped brown); pp covs either uniformly juvenal and very brownish and abraded (Fig. 122**B**), or the outermost 1-2 pp covs contrastingly dark and fresh; **and** ss mixed, with 1-6 juvenal feathers (among s1-s6) retained, usually in a block, often symmetrically in both wings, abraded, and contrasting markedly with the fresher, replaced adult feathers (Figs. 25**C** & 121**C**). **Note: See HY/SY. Look for occasional AHY/ASYs with mixed old and new adult rects. Intermediates, birds with anomalous feather replacement patterns, and/or birds with indeterminate feather ages occur that are difficult to separate reliably from ASY/ATY, and should be aged AHY/ASY.**

ASY/ATY (Oct-Sep): Body plumage as in SY/TY; pp covs either uniformly dark and fresh (Fig. 122**A**), or pp covs irregularly mixed with fresh and moderately worn, retained adult feathers (Fig. 122**D**); ss either uniformly adult (Fig. 25**B**), or (often) ss with 1-6 older adult feathers (among s1-s8) retained, often not symmetrically in both wings, moderately worn, and contrasting only slightly with the replaced feathers (Figs. 25**D** & 121**D**). **Note: See SY/TY. ASY/ATYs with uniformly adult flight feathers possibly can be reliably aged ATY/A4Y, and ASY/ATYs with isolated, retained juvenal pp covs (Fig. 122E), or with three generations of pp covs consecutively replaced from the outside (Fig. 122F), might be reliably aged TY/4Y or even 4Y/5Y (see p. 165), but more study is needed.**

Sex—CP & BP are unreliable for sexing. ♀ wg(n77) 110-129, tl(n57) 62-76, exp culmen(n26) 19.3-23.9; ♂ wg(n73) 111-130, tl(n54) 64-77, exp culmen(n26) 19.6-25.2.

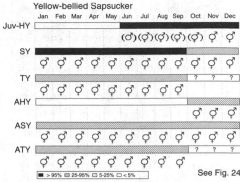

♀: Crown completely black to primarily red, usually less extensively red than in ♂, and throat and chin white with no to a few red feathers (Fig. 128).

♂: Crown primarily red and throat and chin red (Fig. 128).

Hybrids reported—Red-naped Sapsucker, Red-breasted Sapsucker. Hybrid sapsuckers (HYSA) are given species # 4023.

References—Stone (1896), Ridgway (1914), Swarth (1922), Forbush (1927), Bent (1939), Rand (1948a), Howell (1952, 1953), Roberts (1955), Phillips *et al.* (1964), Lawrence (1967), Goodwin (1968), Rea (1968), Wood (1969), Devillers (1970b), Oberholser (1974), Wolcott (1975), Scott *et al.* (1976), Sheppard & Klimkiewicz (1976), Dunn (1978), DeBenedictis (1979), Short (1982), Johnson & Zink (1983), Cramp (1985), Kaufman (1988a, 1990a), Landing (1991), Lehman (1991), Pyle & Howell (1995); IBP (MAPS) data.

RED-NAPED SAPSUCKER
Sphyrapicus nuchalis

RNSA
Species # 4021
Band size: 1A-1B

Species—From Yellow-bellied Sapsucker by nape red (Fig. 128); ♀ with the crown largely red and throat primarily red, but chin white (Fig. 128); ♂ with little or no black separating the red chin and throat from the white of the cheek (Fig. 128); upperparts primarily black, with little pale mottling and two, well-defined, white streaks; yellow on the underparts paler and less extensive; outer rects average less white by sex (see Fig. 129 and **Sex**). Juvs separated from Yellow-bellied Sapsucker, with caution, by the coloration to the upperparts and underparts and the amount of white in the outer rects (as above); crown dark brown to slate, with little or no yellow scalloping; overall coloration darker. The 1st PB (see **Molt**) is completed primarily on the summer grounds (in contrast to Yellow-bellied Sapsucker, which see), juvenal body feathers usually fully replaced by Oct-Nov. From Red-breasted Sapsucker in all plumages (including juvs) by the lack of red on the face and breast. Beware of hybrids and birds showing intermediate characters; see Yellow-bellied and Red-breasted sapsuckers. See also Williamson's Sapsucker.

Geographic variation—No subspecies are recognized.

Molt—PB: HY incomplete (Jun-Oct), AHY incomplete-complete (Jun-Oct); PA absent. The 1st PB occurs primarily on the summer grounds; occasional HY/SYs (hybrids with Yellow-bellied Sapsucker?) can retain a few juvenal body feathers through Jan, but most birds complete this replacement by Nov. Otherwise, molt is very similar to that of Yellow-bellied Sapsucker, which see.

Skull—Pneumaticization patterns probably are unhelpful for ageing; see Family account.

Age—Juv (Jun-Sep) has the head, back, and breast largely mottled brown and yellowish, p10 rounded and large (tip 1-8 mm > pp covs, *vs* 2-7 mm < pp covs in adults; see Fig. 127), rects pointed (Fig. 124), and iris gray-brown. Juv ♀ = ♂ although sexing is possible with some juvs shortly after fledging by white (♀) vs red (♂) feathers in the chin (see **Sex**); more study is needed on the outer rect pattern by sex in juvs (see **Sex** and Fig. 129). Juvenal body plumage usually is lost by Nov in this species (see **Molt**). Otherwise, reliable ageing through ASY/ATY, by flight-feather criteria, follows that of Yellow-bellied Sapsucker (which see).

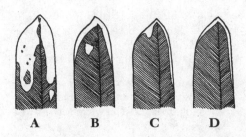

A   B   C   D

FIGURE 129. Variation in the amount of white in the outer rectrix (r5), by age and sex, in Red-naped and Red-breasted sapsuckers. See species accounts for details.

Sex—CP & BP are unreliable for sexing. ♀ wg(n81) 117-131, tl(n23) 71-83, exp culmen(n12) 20.1-24.4; ♂ wg(n100) 118-132, tl(n44) 68-79, exp culmen(n20) 20.6-25.6.

♀: Chin usually white, sometimes with red mottling, throat white to red with white mottling, and malar region with little or no red (Fig. 128); outer rect black with a pale tip and (usually) some pale mottling (Fig. 129A-C).

♂: Throat and chin uniformly red, without pale mottling (can be mottled in juvs) and malar region (adjacent to the throat) more extensively red (Fig. 128); outer rects black with pale edging, but usually without a white tip or mottling (Fig. 129C-D).

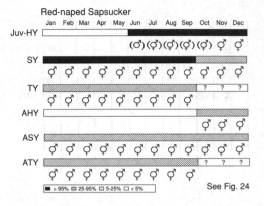

Hybrids reported—Yellow-bellied Sapsucker, Red-breasted Sapsucker, Williamson's Sapsucker.

References—Ridgway (1914), Bent (1939), Rand (1948a), Howell (1952, 1953), Phillips *et al.* (1964), Rea (1968), Devillers (1970b), Short & Morony (1970), Oberholser (1974), Scott *et al.* (1976), Browning (1977a), Dunn (1978), DeBenedictis (1979), Short (1982), Johnson & Zink (1983), Behle (1985), Johnson & Johnson (1985), Kaufman (1988a, 1990a), Landing (1991), Lehman (1991), Pyle & Howell (1995); IBP (MAPS) data.

RED-BREASTED SAPSUCKER
Sphyrapicus ruber

RBSA
Species # 4030
Band size: 1A-1B

Species—From Yellow-bellied and Red-naped sapsuckers in all plumages (including juvs and nestlings) by face and breast with red. *S.r. daggetti* (see **Geographic variation**) can show the black and white head pattern of Red-naped Sapsucker, but most feathers are red-tipped. Beware of hybrids and intermediates with Red-naped Sapsucker; birds that show patches of feathers in the head that are not red-tipped likely are hybrids. The 1st PB (see **Molt**) also is more rapid than in the other sapsuckers, all juvenal feathers typically being replaced by Oct.

Geographic variation—Moderately well marked, but intermediates occur where ranges meet. Subspecies taxonomy follows Short (1982); see also Swarth (1912b), Grinnell (1937) and references listed below. No other subspecies occur. Sexes are similar in all measurements (see **Sex**) and thus are combined for each subspecies.

S.r. ruber (br se.AK-s.OR, wint to c.CA-c.AZ): Large; red of the head and breast deep and tinged violet; black and white head markings of the other sapsuckers absent to very indistinct; back largely black, with sparse white or yellowish-white spotting; outer rects of both sexes usually black, with thin, pale edging when fresh (Fig. 129**C-D**); red of the breast sharply separated from the bright yellow belly; upperparts of juvs primarily or entirely black. ♀♂ wg(n35) 122-134, tl(n20) 72-85, exp culmen(n20) 23.5-27.0.

S.r. daggetti (br s.OR-c.CA to e.NV, wint to s.CA-s.AZ): Small; red of the head and breast medium in hue and tinged with scarlet; black and white head markings of the other sapsuckers indistinct to moderately distinct; black back with dense, white (without yellow) spotting; outer rects of ♀♀ often with some white mottling in the center (Fig. 129**A-B**); red of the breast separated indistinctly from the pale yellow belly; upperparts of juvs with a moderate amount of pale barring or mottling. ♀♂ wg(n33) 114-128, tl(n20) 71-79, exp culmen(n20) 22.0-25.5.

Molt—PB: HY incomplete (Jun-Sep), AHY incomplete-complete (Jun-Sep); PA absent. The 1st PB occurs on the summer grounds; occasional HYs (hybrids?) can retain a few juvenal body feathers through Dec, but most have completed the molt by Oct. Otherwise, molt is very similar to that of Yellow-bellied Sapsucker, which see.

Skull—Pneumaticization patterns probably are unhelpful for ageing; see Family account.

Age—Juv (May-Aug) has the head, back and breast largely mottled brown and yellowish, p10 rounded and large (tip 1-8 mm > pp covs, *vs* 2-7 mm < pp covs in adults; see Fig. 127), rects pointed (Fig. 124), and iris gray-brown; juv ♀ = ♂. More study is needed on the outer rect pattern by sex in juvs (see **Sex** and Fig. 129). Juvenal body plumage usually is lost by Oct in this species. Otherwise reliable ageing through ASY/ATY by flight-feather criteria follows that of Yellow-bellied Sapsucker (which see).

Sex—CP & BP are unreliable for sexing. ♀ wg(n36) 114-133, tl(n20) 71-85, exp culmen(n20) 22.4-27.0; ♂ wg(n32) 114-134, tl(n20) 71-84, exp culmen(n20) 22.8-27.3; see **Geographic variation**. Some ♀♀ of *S.r. daggetti* (and perhaps occasional ♀♀ of *S.r. ruber*) with some white mottling to the center of the outer rects (Fig. 129**A-B**) may be reliably sexed; however, ♂♂ cannot be reliably sexed, as some ♀♀ (possibly AHY/ASYs only) show entirely black-centered outer rects. Otherwise, ♀ = ♂ by plumage. The length of the tongue and its barbed, horny tip (see Fig. 120) should be examined for possible sex-specific differences.

Red-breasted Sapsucker

	Jan	Feb	Mar	Apr	May	Jun	Jul	Aug	Sep	Oct	Nov	Dec
Juv-HY							○	○	○	○	(♀) (♀)	(♀) (♀)
SY												
	(♀)	(♀)	(♀)	(♀)	(♀)	(♀)	(♀)	(♀)	(♀)	(♀)	(♀)	(♀)
TY										?	?	?
	(♀)	(♀)	(♀)	(♀)	(♀)	(♀)	(♀)	(♀)	(♀)			
AHY										(♀) (♀)	(♀)	
ASY												
	(♀)	(♀)	(♀)	(♀)	(♀)	(♀)	(♀)	(♀)	(♀)	(♀)	(♀)	(♀)
ATY										?	?	?
	(♀)	(♀)	(♀)	(♀)	(♀)	(♀)	(♀)	(♀)	(♀)			

■ > 95% ▨ 25-95% ▧ 5-25% ☐ < 5%   See Fig. 24

Hybrids reported—Yellow-bellied Sapsucker, Red-naped Sapsucker.

References—Ridgway (1914), Swarth (1922), Bent (1939), Howell (1952, 1953), Phillips *et al.* (1964), Rea (1968), Devillers (1970b), Scott *et al.* (1976), Browning (1977a), Dunn (1978), DeBenedictis (1979), Short (1982), Johnson & Zink (1983), Behle (1985), Johnson & Johnson (1985), Kaufman (1988a, 1990a), Pyle & Howell (1995); IBP (MAPS) data, PRBO data.

WILLIAMSON'S SAPSUCKER
Sphyrapicus thyroideus

WISA
Species # 4040
Band size: 1A

Species—Juv ♀ from juvs of the other sapsuckers by larger size (wg 128-143, tl 72-89; see **Sex**); head plain brown without red feathering; upperparts and underparts with distinct, black barring.

Geographic variation—Subspecies taxonomy follows Browning (pers. comm.) who considered the species monotypic (synonymizing a previously recognized subspecies); see also Ridgway (1914), Swarth (1917a), Cowan (1938), Todd (1946), Short (1982). Birds of interior s.BC to s.AZ-sw.TX ("*S.t. nataliae*") average smaller bills and slightly greener (*vs* lemon-yellow) bellies than coastal BC-CA birds, but differences are too slight for subspecies recognition.

Molt—PB: HY incomplete (Aug-Oct), AHY incomplete-complete (Jul-Oct); PA absent. PBs occur on the summer grounds. The 1st PB includes no to some inner, lesser and med covs, sometimes 1-6 inner gr covs, all pp and rects, and 0-6 inner ss among s5-s11 (replacement of ss occurs in ~27% of HYs, usually 1-4 feathers among s7-s10; see Fig. 121**B**), but usually no pp covs. The 2nd PB usually includes all wing covs, pp, and rects, but only 1-4 outer pp covs (see Fig. 122**C**); 1-5 ss often (in ~80% of birds) can be retained during this molt, usually in a block among s1-s6 (see Figs. 25**C** & 121**C**), and often symmetrically in both wings. During subsequent PBs, from 1-4 ss also sometimes (in ~20% of birds) can be retained, among s1-s8, seldom in a block (see Figs. 25**D** & 121**D**), and less often symmetrically in both wings. A variable number of pp covs can be retained during the 3rd and subsequent PBs, although these molts often are complete. See p. 163 for details on woodpecker molt.

Skull—Pneumaticization patterns probably are unhelpful for ageing; see Family account.

Age—Juv (Jun-Sep) resembles adults of each sex (juvs are easily sexed by the same criteria; see **Sex**), but the central breast of juv ♀ without a distinct, black patch or mottling, the throat of juv ♂ white, p10 rounded and large (tip 1-8 mm > pp covs, *vs* 2-7 mm < pp covs in adults; see Fig. 127), rects pointed (Fig. 124), belly primarily whitish, and iris probably brown.

HY/SY (Oct-Sep): Pp covs uniform (Fig. 122**A**), quickly becoming brown and worn by winter/spring (Fig. 122**B**); **and** ss either uniform in color and wear, the terts becoming relatively worn by spring (Fig. 121**A**), or (sometimes) ss uniform except for 1-4 feathers (among s7-s10, rarely to 6 among s5-s11) contrastingly fresh (Fig. 121**B**). **Note: Fresh fall HY/SYs can closely resemble ASY/ATYs with uniform ss and pp covs. On these look for retention of juvenal characters on HY/SYs (through Oct), especially a larger p10 (the last primary replaced, in Sep-Oct), juvenal pointed rects, and/or iris color browner (*vs* redder in ASY/ATYs). Iris color also may be helpful in distinguishing some HY/SYs (brown to reddish brown) from most AHY/ASYs (reddish) through Jan. See Sex for possible additional plumage clues in ♀♀. Also, look for the p10 of HY/SYs to average intermediate in size and shape between those of juvs and AHY/ASYs (see Fig. 127); more study is needed.**

SY/TY (Oct-Sep): Consecutive outer 1-4 pp covs black and fresh, contrasting with the brown and abraded, consecutive, retained inner pp covs (Fig. 122**C**); **and** ss either uniformly adult (Fig. 25**B**), the terts usually only moderately worn by spring, or (often) ss with 1-5 juvenal feathers (among s1-s6) retained, usually symmetrically in both wings, faded, abraded, and contrasting markedly with the fresher, replaced adult feathers (Figs. 25**C** & 121**C**). **Note: See HY/SY. Some intermediates can be difficult to separate reliably from ASY/ATY and should be aged AHY/ASY.**

ASY/ATY (Oct-Sep): Pp covs either uniformly black and fresh (Fig. 122**A**), or pp covs irregularly mixed with fresh and moderately worn, retained adult feathers (Fig. 122**D**); **and** ss either uniformly adult (Fig. 25**B**), the terts usually fresh or only slightly worn, or (sometimes) ss with 1-4 older adult feathers (among s1-s8) retained, often not symmetrically in both wings, moderately worn, and contrasting only slightly with the replaced feathers (Figs. 25**D** & 121**D**). **Note: See HY/SY. ASY/ATYs with isolated, retained juvenal pp covs (Fig. 122E), or with three generations of pp covs, sequentially replaced as in Figure 122F, might be reliably aged TY/4Y (see p. 165), but more study is needed.**

Sex—CP & BP are unreliable for sexing. ♀ wg(n50) 129-143, tl(n26) 74-89, exp culmen(n17) 21.5-28.5; ♂ wg(n63) 128-142, tl(n37) 72-89, exp culmen(n20) 23.1-28.0; see **Geographic variation**.

♀: Head and throat completely or primarily brown; wing covs without white; upperparts barred black and buff; belly pale yellow. **Note: Some ♀♀ can show ♂ characters such as red in the throat, black in the head, and brighter yellow in the belly, but still show primarily ♀-like plumage; these may be reliably aged ASY/ATY, but more study is needed.**

♂: Crown, nape and back glossy black; wing covs with a bold white patch; throat red; belly bright yellow. **Note: See ♀.**

Williamson's Sapsucker

See Fig. 24

Hybrids reported—Red-naped Sapsucker.

References—Ridgway (1914), Swarth (1917a), Bent (1939), Short & Morony (1970), Oberholser (1974), Crockett & Hansley (1977), Short (1982), Johnson & Zink (1983), Pyle & Howell (1995), Dobbs *et al.* (1997); IBP (MAPS) data.

LADDER-BACKED WOODPECKER
Picoides scalaris

LBWO
Species # 3960
Band size: 1A-1B

Species—From other small woodpeckers, particularly Nuttall's Woodpecker, by red patch of non-juv ♂ extends proximal to the eyes (Fig. 130**H**); auricular buffy white, bordered by black; back barred black and white, this pattern extending to the nape; outer rects (r5) with 3-4 full black bars beyond the undertail covs. See also Downy Woodpecker. Beware of hybrids.

Geographic variation—Moderate and most ranges are fairly well defined. Subspecies taxonomy follows Short (1982), who synonymized up to three other subspecies in N.Am; see also Oberholser (1911a, 1974), Ridgway (1914), van Rossem (1942b), Todd (1946), Sutton (1967), Short (1968a), Monson & Phillips (1981), Rea (1983). Six other subspecies occur in Mex-C.Am.

P.s. cactophilus (res throughout range in N.Am): From subspecies of Mex-C.Am by relatively short tail (see **Sex**; tl/wg 0.54-0.63, *vs* usually > 0.60 in subspecies of Mex); black barring on the upperparts narrower (1.9-4.7 mm, *vs* usually > 3 mm in subspecies of Mex-C.Am) outer rects (r5) with wider black bars (2.4-3.3 mm, *vs* 1.5-2.8 mm in subspecies of Mex-C.Am). Birds of sc.CA (*"mojavensis"*) average larger and with broader black bars in the outer rects, and those from the Colorado River Valley (desert s.NV-se.CA-sw.AZ; *"yumanensis"*), and from se.CO-s.TX (*"symplectus"*) average paler on the upperparts and with narrower black bars in the outer rects than the other populations of *cactophilus*, but in all cases variation is slight and broadly clinal. Birds of n.Baja CA (*eremicus*), potential vagrants to s.CA, are like *cactophilus*, but have the tl relatively longer (tl/wg 0.63-0.69), the black barring on the upperparts wider (3.5-6.0 mm), and the outer rects (r5) with thinner black bars (1.5-2.5 mm).

Molt—PB: HY incomplete (May-Oct), AHY incomplete-complete (Jun-Oct); PA absent. The 1st PB includes no to some, inner lesser and med covs, often 1-6 inner gr covs, all pp and rects, and 0-5 inner ss among s6-s11 (replacement of ss occurs in ~31% of HYs, usually 1-4 feathers among s7-s10; see Fig. 121**B**), but usually no pp covs. The 2nd PB usually includes all wing covs, pp, and rects, but only 1-5 outer pp covs (see Fig. 121**C**); 1-4 ss occasionally (in ~17% of birds) can be retained during this molt, usually in a block among s1-s5 (see Figs. 25**C** & 121**C**), and often symmetrically in both wings. During subsequent PBs, from 1-5 ss also occasionally (in ~15% of birds) can be retained, among s1-s8, seldom in a block (see Figs. 25**D** & 121**D**), and less often symmetrically in both wings. A variable number of pp covs can be retained during the 3rd and subsequent PBs, although these molts often are complete. See p. 163 for details on woodpecker molt.

Skull—Pneumaticization patterns probably are unhelpful for ageing; see Family account.

Age—Juv (May-Sep) averages duller than adults and has the crown dull black with sparse white fleck-ing and red confined to the center (Fig. 130**B-E**), p10 rounded and large (tip > 10 mm from the pp covs, *vs* < 10 mm in adults; see Fig. 127), rects pointed (Fig. 124), and iris grayish brown. Juv ♀ has red tipping to a few central crown feathers, usually not extending forward of the eyes (Fig. 130**B-C**), whereas juv ♂ has more extensive and more fully red feathers, usually extending forward of the eyes (Fig. 130**C-F**); most (but possibly not all) juvs may be reliably sexed; more study is needed.

HY/SY (Oct-Sep): Pp covs uniform (Fig. 122**A**), quickly becoming brown and worn by win-ter/spring (Fig. 122**B**); back feathers and replaced inner wing covs (see **Molt**) black, con-

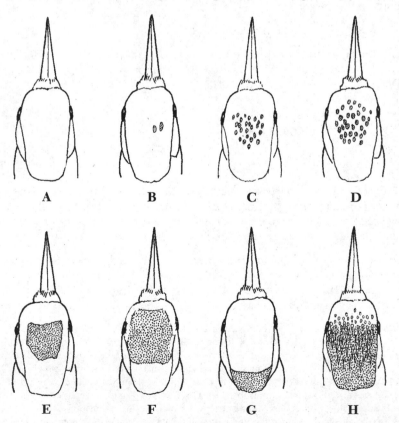

FIGURE 130. Variation in the amount of red in the crown, by age and sex, in woodpeckers. Note that juveniles of both sexes often have red feathers in the crown (**B-F**), although the amount of red is usu-ally greater in ♂♂ than in ♀♀. See text for details within each species.

trasting with the browner, retained outer wing covs; **and** ss either uniform in color and wear, the terts becoming extremely worn by spring (Fig. 121**A**), or (sometimes) ss uniform except for 1-5 feathers (among s7-s10) contrastingly fresh (Fig. 121**B**). **Note: Fresh fall HY/SYs can closely resemble ASY/ATYs with uniform ss and pp covs, and the p10 of HY/SYs can be intermediate in size and shape between those of juvs and those of AHY/ASYs; see Downy Woodpecker. Iris color also may be helpful in distinguishing some HY/SYs (grayish brown to brown) from most AHY/ASYs (deep reddish) through Jan.**

SY/TY (Oct-Sep): Consecutive outer 1-5 pp covs black and fresh, contrasting with the brown and abraded, consecutive, retained inner pp covs (Fig. 122**C**); back feathers and wing covs uniformly black; **and** ss either uniformly adult (Fig. 25**B**), the terts only moderately worn by spring, or (occasionally) ss with 1-4 juvenal feathers (among s1-s5) retained, often symmetrically in both wings, very faded and abraded, and contrasting markedly with the fresher, replaced adult feathers (Figs. 25**C** & 121**C**). **Note: See HY/SY. Some intermediates can be difficult to reliably separate from ASY/ATY and should be aged AHY/ASY.**

ASY/ATY (Oct-Sep): Pp covs either uniformly black and fresh (Fig. 122**A**), or pp covs irregularly mixed with fresh and moderately worn, retained adult feathers (Fig. 122**D**); **and** ss either uniformly adult (Fig. 25**B**), the terts only slightly worn, or (occasionally) ss with 1-5 older adult feathers (among s1-s8) retained, often not symmetrically in both wings, moderately worn, and contrasting only slightly with the replaced feathers (Figs. 25**D** & 121**D**). **Note: See HY/SY and SY/TY. ASY/ATYs with isolated, retained juvenal pp covs (Fig. 122E), or with three generations of pp covs, sequentially replaced as in Figure 122F, might be reliably aged TY/4Y (see p. 165), but more study is needed.**

Sex—CP & BP are unreliable for sexing. ♀ wg(n100) 95-106, tl(n94) 53-66, exp culmen(n30) 17.5-22.1; ♂ wg(n100) 96-110, tl(n100) 54-69, exp culmen(n30) 20.1-24.4.

♀: Crown and nape without red (Fig 130**A**), or (perhaps rarely, in ASY/ATYs only?) with 1-2 red feathers (Fig. 130**B**). **Note: See ♂.**

♂: Crown and nape extensively red (Fig. 130**H**). **Note: Beware of juvenal ♀♀ with red-tipped feathers in the crown (Fig. 130B-C; see Age).**

Hybrids reported—Nuttall's Woodpecker, Hairy Woodpecker.

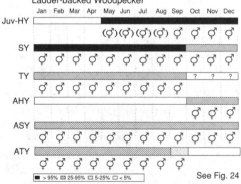

Ladder-backed Woodpecker

References—Ridgway (1914), Bent (1939), Miller (1955b), Short (1971a, 1982), Oberholser (1974), Pyle & Howell (1995); IBP (MAPS) data.

NUTTALL'S WOODPECKER
Picoides nuttallii

NUWO
Species # 3970
Band size: 1A-1B

Species—From other small woodpeckers, especially Ladder-backed, by the red patch of non-juv ♂ extending to the central crown but not proximal to the eyes; auricular black; back barred black and white, this pattern not extending to the nape; outer rects (r5) with 1-2 full bars (across both webs) beyond the tip of the undertail covs. See Downy Woodpecker. Beware of hybrids.

Geographic variation—No subspecies are recognized.

Molt—PB: HY incomplete (Jun-Oct), AHY incomplete-complete (Jun-Oct); PA absent. The 1st PB includes no to some inner, lesser and med covs, occasionally 1-6 inner gr covs, all pp and rects, and sometimes 1-4 inner ss among s7-s11 (replacement of ss occurs in ~17% of HYs, usually 1-3 feathers among s7-s9; see Fig. 121**B**), but usually no pp covs. The 2nd PB usually includes all wing covs, pp, and rects, but only 1-5 outer pp covs (see Fig. 121**C**); 1-5 ss sometimes (in ~23% of birds) can be retained during this molt, usually in a block among s1-s6 (see Figs. 25**C** & 121**C**), and often symmetrically in both wings. During subsequent PBs, from 1-5 ss occasionally (in ~19% of birds) can be retained, among s1-s8, seldom in a block (see Figs. 25**D** & 121**D**), and less often symmetrically in both wings. A variable number of pp covs can be retained during the 3rd and subsequent PBs, although these molts often are complete. See p. 163 for details on woodpecker molt.

Skull—Pneumaticization patterns probably are unhelpful for ageing; see Family account.

Age—Juv (May-Sep) averages duller than adults and has the crown dull black, flecked white, and with red confined to the center (Fig. 130**B-F**), p10 rounded and large (tip > 10 mm from the pp covs, *vs* < 10 mm in adults; see Fig. 127), rects pointed (Fig. 124), and iris grayish brown. Juv ♀ has red tipping to a few central crown feathers, often not extending forward of the eyes (Fig. 130**B-D**) whereas juv ♂ has more extensive and more fully red feathers, often extending forward of the eyes (Fig. 130**D-F**); thus, most (but possibly not all) juvs can be reliably sexed; more study is needed.

HY/SY (Oct-Sep): Pp covs uniform (Fig. 122**A**), quickly becoming brown and worn by winter/spring (Fig. 122**B**); back feathers and replaced inner wing covs (see **Molt**) black, contrasting with the browner, retained outer wing covs; **and** ss either uniform in color and wear, the terts becoming very worn by spring (Fig. 121**A**), or (occasionally) ss uniform except for 1-4 feathers (among s7-s11) contrastingly fresh (Fig. 121**B**). **Note: Fresh fall HY/SYs can closely resemble ASY/ATYs with uniform ss and pp covs, and the p10 of HY/SYs can be intermediate in size and shape between those of juvs and those of AHY/ASYs; see Downy Woodpecker. Iris color also may be helpful in distinguishing some HY/SYs (grayish brown to brown) from most AHY/ASYs (deep reddish) through Jan.**

SY/TY (Oct-Sep): Consecutive outer 1-5 pp covs black and fresh, contrasting with the brown and abraded, consecutive, retained inner pp covs (Fig. 122**C**); back feathers and wing covs uniformly black; **and** ss either uniformly adult (Fig. 25**B**), the terts only moderately worn by spring, or (sometimes) ss with 1-5 juvenal feathers (among s1-s6) retained, often symmetrically in both wings, very faded and abraded, and contrasting markedly with the fresher, replaced adult feathers (Figs. 25**C** & 121**C**). **Note: See HY/SY. Some intermediates can be difficult to separate reliably from ASY/ATY and should be aged AHY/ASY.**

ASY/ATY (Oct-Sep): Pp covs either uniformly black and fresh (Fig. 122**A**), or pp covs irregularly mixed with fresh and moderately worn, retained adult feathers (Fig. 122**D**); **and** ss either uniformly adult (Fig. 25**B**), the terts fresh or only slightly worn, or (occasionally) ss with 1-5 older adult feathers (among s1-s8) retained, often not symmetrically in both wings, moderately worn, and contrasting only slightly with the replaced feathers (Figs. 25**D** & 121**D**). **Note: See HY/SY and SY/TY. ASY/ATYs with isolated, retained juvenal pp covs (Fig. 122E), or with three generations of pp covs, sequentially replaced as in Figure 122F, might be reliably aged TY/4Y (see p. 165), but more study is needed.**

Sex—CP & BP are unreliable for sexing. ♀ wg(n30) 96-107, tl(n20) 59-67, exp culmen(n10) 18.0-21.0; ♂ wg(n43) 97-108, tl(n20) 61-68, exp culmen(n10) 19.5-22.0.

♀: Central crown to hindcrown without red (Fig. 130**A**) or (perhaps rarely, in ASY/ATYs only?)

with 1-2 red feathers (Fig. 130**B**). **Note: See ♂.**

♂: Central crown to the hindcrown with a red patch **Note: Beware of juvenal ♀♀ with red-tipped feathers in the crown (Fig. 130B-D; see Age).**

Hybrids reported—Ladder-backed Woodpecker, Downy Woodpecker.

References—Ridgway (1914), Bent (1939), Short (1971a, 1982), Oberholser (1974), Unitt (1986), Manolis (1987), Pyle & Howell (1995); IBP (MAPS) data, PRBO data.

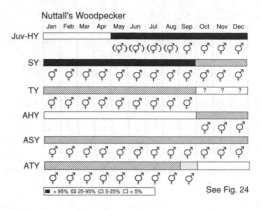

Nuttall's Woodpecker

See Fig. 24

DOWNY WOODPECKER
Picoides pubescens

DOWO
Species # 3940
Band size: 1B

Species—From other small woodpeckers by shorter bill (exp culmen 14.2-18.8; see **Sex**); red patch of non-juv ♂ restricted to the hindcrown (Fig. 130**G**); auricular black; back black with a single, broad, white streak; outer rects (r5) with 0-2 full bars beyond the tip of the undertail covs (Fig. 131). From Hairy Woodpecker by wg usually < 110 and exposed culmen < 20 (see **Geographic variation** & **Sex**); outer rects usually with 0-2 full black bars present beyond the longest undertail covs (Fig. 131; see **Geographic variation**).

Geographic variation—Moderate to well marked, but individual variation is fairly substantial, and intergradation occurs between most adjacent forms. Subspecies taxonomy follows Short (1982) as modified by Browning (1997); see also Oberholser (1914a, 1974), Ridgway (1914), Noble (1919), Burleigh & Peters (1948), Rand (1948a, 1948b), Burleigh (1960a), Todd (1963), Bailey & Niedrach (1965), Mengel (1965), James (1970), Blake (1981), Browning (1990). No other subspecies occur. Sexes are similar in measurements (see **Sex**) and thus are combined for each subspecies.

Coastal Pacific (*P.p. gairdnerii*) Group. Small; underparts dark.
P.p. fumidus (res coastal sw.BC-w.WA): Medium small; terts with medium-large white spots on 85% of birds; wing covs often without white spots; outer rects with heavy, black barring (often 2 full bars beyond the tip of the undertail covs; Fig. 131); underparts washed gray. ♀♂ wg(n100) 91-99, tl(n10) 54-63.
P.p. gairdnerii (res coastal w.OR-nw.CA): Medium small; terts with small white spots on 50% of birds; wing covs without (most) or with a few (1-8) small to medium white spots; outer rects with heavy, black barring (1-2 full broad bars beyond the tip of the undertail covs; Fig. 131); underparts washed brown. ♀♂ wg(n100) 89-103, tl(n40) 53-62.
P.p. turati (res nc.WA-s.CA): Small; terts with medium-sized spots on 70% of birds; wing covs usually with 1-10 medium to large white spots; outer rects with a moderate amount of black barring (1-2 full narrow bars beyond the tip of the undertail covs; Fig. 131); underparts tinged brown. ♀♂ wg(n100) 85-96, tl(n34) 51-63.

Interior Western (*P.p. leucurus*) Group. Large; underparts pale or white.
P.p. glacialis (res sc.AK): Medium large; wing covs black with no or few (1-8) small white spots; outer rects with heavy, black barring (1-2 full broad bars beyond the tip of the undertail covs; Fig. 131); underparts washed gray. ♀♂ wg(n10) 94-102, tl(n10) 54-64.
P.p. leucurus (res se.AK-n.AZ to w.NE-n.NM): Large; tertials with large white spots on all birds; wing covs black with few (2-10) small to medium white spots; outer rects with a variable amount of black bar-

ring (0-2 full bars beyond the tip of the undertail covs; Fig. 131); underparts white. ♀♂ wg(n88) 91-115, tl(n60) 58-73. Birds of s.BC-ne.OR ("*parvirostris*") may average smaller and darker dorsally, but differences are obscured by individual variation and are due to intergradation toward *gairdnerii*.

Eastern (*P.p. pubescens*) Group. Medium small; upperparts with substantial white spotting.

P.p. medianus (br & wint nc.AK-ce.KS to Nfl-s.VA): Medium in size; most or all wing covs blackish with large white spots; outer rects with light, black barring (0-1 full narrow bars beyond the tip of the undertail covs; Fig. 131); underparts washed lightly with gray. ♀♂ wg(n100) 86-101, tl(n76) 51-72. Breeding birds of nc.AK-BC to w.Ont ("*nelsoni*") average larger and whiter, and have less barring on the outer rects, and birds of Nfl ("*microleucus*") may average longer tailed and darker underparts than the other populations, but size variation is broadly clinal and individual variation obscures plumage differences.

P.p. pubescens (res se.KS-se.TX to se.VA-s.FL): Small; tl relatively short; wing covs brownish black, most with medium to large white spots; outer rects with a moderate amount of black barring (1-2 full narrow bars beyond the tip of the undertail covs; Fig. 131); underparts washed brownish. ♀♂ wg(n100) 84-96, tl(n27) 48-55.

Molt—PB: HY incomplete (Jun-Oct), AHY incomplete-complete (Jun-Oct); PA absent. The 1st PB includes no to some inner, lesser and med covs, occasionally 1-6 inner gr covs, all pp and rects, and 0-5 inner ss among s6-s11 (replacement of ss occurs in ~13% of HYs, usually 1-3 feathers among s7-s9; see Fig. 121**B**), but usually no pp covs. The 2nd PB usually includes all wing covs, pp, and rects, but only 1-5 outer pp covs (see Fig. 121**C**); 1-4 ss sometimes (in ~24% of birds) can be retained during this molt, usually in a block among s1-s5 (see Figs. 25**C** & 121**C**), and often symmetrically in both wings. During subsequent PBs, from 1-5 ss occasionally (in ~24% of birds) can be retained, among s1-s8, seldom in a block (see Figs. 25**D** & 121**D**), and less often symmetrically in both wings. A variable number of pp covs can be retained during the 3rd and subsequent PBs, although these molts often are complete. See p. 163 for details on woodpecker molt.

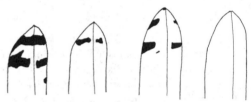

typical   minimum   maximum (rare)   typical
   Downy   Hairy

FIGURE 131. Variation in the amount of black in the outer rectrix, by species and subspecies, in Downy and Hairy woodpeckers.

Skull—Pneumaticization patterns probably are unhelpful for ageing; see Family account.

Age—Juv (May-Sep) averages duller than adults and has the crown dull black, often flecked white, and with red (if present) confined to the center (Fig. 130**B-E**), p10 rounded and large (tip usually > 7 mm from the pp covs, *vs* usually < 6 mm in adults; see Fig. 127), flanks washed buff and with dusky spots, rects pointed (Fig. 124), and iris gray-brown. Juv ♀ often has no red or up to a few red-tipped feathers to the central crown, usually not extending forward of the eyes (Fig. 130**A-B**), whereas juv ♂ has more extensive and more fully red feathers, often extending forward of the eyes (Fig. 130**C-E**); thus, juvs can be reliably sexed.

HY/SY (Oct-Sep): Pp covs uniform (Fig. 122**A**), quickly becoming brown and worn by winter/spring (Fig. 122**B**); back feathers and replaced inner wing covs (see **Molt**) black, contrasting with the browner, retained outer wing covs; **and** ss either uniform in color and wear, the terts becoming worn to very worn by spring (Fig. 121**A**), or (occasionally) ss uniform except for 1-4 feathers (among s7-s11) contrastingly fresh (Fig. 121**B**). **Note: Fresh fall HY/SYs can closely resemble ASY/ATYs with uniform ss and pp covs. On these look for retention of juvenal characters on HY/SYs (through Oct), especially a larger p10 (the last primary replaced, in Sep-Oct), juvenal pointed rects, and/or iris color grayer or browner (*vs* deep red in ASY/ATYs). Look also for the p10 of HY/SYs to average intermediate in size and shape between those of juvs and AHY/ASYs (see Fig. 127); more study is needed.**

SY/TY (Oct-Sep): Consecutive outer 1-5 pp covs black and fresh, contrasting with the brown and abraded, consecutive, retained inner pp covs (Fig. 122**C**); back feathers and wing covs uniformly black; **and** ss either uniformly adult (Fig. 25**B**), the terts fresh or slightly worn by spring, or ss (occasionally) with 1-4 juvenal feathers (among s1-s5) retained, often symmetrically in both wings, faded, abraded, and contrasting markedly with the fresher, replaced adult feathers (Figs. 25**C** & 121**C**). **Note: See HY/SY. Some intermediates can be difficult to separate reliably from ASY/ATY and should be aged AHY/ASY.**

ASY/ATY (Oct-Sep): Pp covs either uniformly black and fresh (Fig. 122**A**), or pp covs irregularly mixed with fresh and moderately worn, retained adult feathers (Fig. 122**D**); **and** ss either uniformly adult (Fig. 25**B**), the terts relatively fresh, or (occasionally) ss with 1-5 older adult feathers (among s1-s8) retained, often not symmetrically in both wings, moderately worn, and contrasting only slightly with the replaced feathers (Figs. 25**D** & 121**D**). **Note: See HY/SY and SY/TY. ASY/ATYs with isolated, retained juvenal pp covs (Fig. 122E), or with three generations of pp covs, sequentially replaced as in Figure 122F, might be reliably aged TY/4Y (see p. 165), but more study is needed.**

Sex—CP & BP are unreliable for sexing. ♀ wg(n100) 84-113, tl(n100) 48-73, exp culmen(n100) 14.2-17.9; ♂ wg(n100) 86-115, tl(n100) 48-72, exp culmen(n100) 15.4-18.8; see **Geographic variation**.

♀: Hindcrown without red (Fig. 130**A**) or (perhaps rarely, in ASY/ATYs only?) with 1-2 red feathers (Fig. 130**B**). **Note: See ♂.**

♂: Hindcrown with a distinct, red patch (Fig. 130**G**). **Note: Beware of occasional juvenal ♀♀ with a few red-tipped feathers in the crown (Fig. 130B); see Age.**

Downy Woodpecker

Hybrids reported—Nuttall's Woodpecker.

References—Stone (1896), Ridgway (1914), Snyder (1923), Forbush (1927), Bent (1939), Roberts (1955), Lawrence (1967), Wood (1969), Short (1971a, 1982), George (1972), Wood & Wood (1973), Oberholser (1974), Sheppard & Klimkiewicz (1976), Williams (1980), Short (1982), Baumgartner (1986b), Unitt (1986), James (1987), Manolis (1987), Parkes (1987a), CWS & USFWS (1991), Kaufman (1993a), Pyle & Howell (1995); C.H. Blake, E.J. Fisk, J.A. Jackson, C.S. Robbins, K.E. Bartlet (*in litt.* to the BBL); IBP (MAPS) data, PRBO data.

HAIRY WOODPECKER
Picoides villosus

HAWO
Species # 3930
Band size: 1A-2

Species—From Downy Woodpecker by wg usually > 110 and exposed culmen > 24 (see **Geographic variation** & **Sex**); outer rects (r5) usually without bars (Fig. 131; see **Geographic variation**). From Strickland's Woodpecker by back usually blacker and with white; underparts without dusky spots; outer rects with no or few black marks and no full black bars (Fig. 131). Occasional juvs with yellow crowns from Three-toed Woodpecker (especially white-backed *P.t. dorsalis*) by wider supercilium (2-5 mm); nasal tufts white to brownish; feet with four toes.

Geographic variation—Moderate to well marked, but individual variation is fairly substantial and intergradation occurs between most adjacent forms. Subspecies taxonomy follows Short (1982); see also Oberholser (1911b, 1974), Swarth (1911, 1912b, 1922), Ridgway (1914), Rand

(1948a, 1948c), Parkes (1954), Phillips *et al.* (1964), Bailey & Niedrach (1965), Mengel (1965), James (1970), Blake (1981), Behle (1985), Godfrey (1986). Four other subspecies occur in the W.Indies & Mex-C.Am. Although primarily resident, watch for southward wandering in the winter by northern subspecies into the ranges of other subspecies. Juvs can show more variation toward other races. Sexes are similar in measurements (see **Sex**) and thus are combined for each subspecies.

Pacific Coastal *(P.v. harrisi)* Group. White of the back usually with dusky or black; wing covs with little white spotting; underparts washed brown.

P.v. sitkensis (br coastal se.AK-cw.BC, wint to sw.BC): Medium in size; bill medium long; upperparts black; white of the back tinged buff and usually without black marks; wing covs with 0-8 small to medium white spots; outer rect white (Fig. 131); underparts tinged brownish. ♀♂ wg(n10) 122-129, tl(n10) 74-83, exp culmen(n10) 26.3-30.2.

P.v. harrisi (res coastal cw.BC-nw.CA): Medium in size; bill medium long; white of the back washed brown and with a moderate amount of black markings; wing covs usually without white spots or with a few (1-5) small white spots; outer rect sometimes marked blackish (Fig. 131); underparts moderately dark gray-brown. ♀♂ wg(n30) 116-128, tl(n12) 74-83, exp culmen(n12) 26.0-31.0.

P.v. picoideus (res Queen Charlotte Is, BC): Medium large; bill short; white of the back washed brown and heavily marked black; wing covs without white spots; outer rect often marked blackish (Fig. 131); underparts smoky brown. ♀♂ wg(n10) 121-128, tl(n10) 74-83, exp culmen(n10) 25.4-28.7.

P.v. hyloscopus (res nc.CA-coastal s.CA): Medium small; bill medium long (exp culmen/wg 0.21-0.24); white of the back variably marked black; wing covs with a variable number (0-15) of small to large white spots; outer rect white (Fig. 131); underparts brownish. ♀♂ wg(n44) 112-129, tl(n17) 67-82, exp culmen(n16) 26.7-28.8.

Interior Western *(P.v. septentrionalis)* Group. White of the back usually unmarked; wing covs with heavy, white spotting; underparts tinged brown.

P.v. orius (br & wint interior s.BC-se.CA to sw.UT-sw.TX): Medium large; white of the back unmarked or with light dusky markings; wing covs without white or with a few (1-5) small white streaks; outer rect white (Fig. 131); underparts lightly washed brown. ♀♂ wg(n100) 114-133, tl(n14) 73-83, exp culmen(n14) 24.0-27.5. Birds of se.CA to sw.UT-sw.TX *("leucothorectis")* may average slightly smaller and whiter below than northern birds, but individual variation obscures subspecies differences.

P.v. septentrionalis (br sc.AK-n.AZ to Que, wint to NE-ME): Large; white stripe on the back without black marks; most to all wing covs with medium to large white spots in most birds (see below); underparts white. ♀♂ wg(n100) 121-138, tl(n18) 74-91, exp culmen(n18) 28.0-33.5. Birds of the Rocky Mts *("monticola")* may average slightly shorter bill and fewer white spots in the wing covs (0-20) but differences are obscured by individual variation.

Mexican *(P.v. jardinii)* Group. Small; brownish.

P.v. icastus (res se.AZ-sw.NM): Medium small; bill medium short (exp culmen/wg 0.19-0.21); white of the back lightly to heavily marked brownish; wing covs with no or few (0-3) white spots or streaks; underparts washed brown. ♀♂ wg(n12) 119-129, tl(n12) 70-83, exp culmen(n12) 23.0-26.5.

Eastern *(P.v. villosus)* Group. White of the back variably marked with black; wing covs with a variable amount of white spotting; underparts white.

P.v. terraenovae (res Nfl): Medium in size; tl medium long; white stripe on the back with heavy, black mottling or barring; wing covs without white or with a few (1-5) white spots; outer rects usually with black marks (Fig. 131); underparts white; juvs very dark. ♀♂ wg(n20) 119-130, tl(n20) 75-86, exp culmen(n20) 25.3-29.1.

P.v. villosus (res c.ND-n.TX to NS-w.VA, wint to s.TX-NC): Medium in size; tl medium short; white stripe on the back without black marks; all wing covs with large white spots; underparts white. ♀♂ wg(n100) 110-128, tl(n41) 69-82, exp culmen(n41) 25.5-30.0.

P.v. audubonii (res s.IL-e.TX to se.VA-FL): Small; white of the back usually without marks; most or all wing covs with small to medium white spots; underparts grayish. ♀♂ wg(n20) 107-120, tl(n20) 58-70, exp culmen(n20) 24.6-28.9.

Molt—PB: HY incomplete (Jun-Oct), AHY incomplete-complete (Jun-Oct); PA absent. The 1st PB includes no to a few inner lesser and med covs, and all pp and rects, but usually no pp covs, gr covs, or ss; look for occasional HYs to replace one or more inner gr covs or ss (among s7-s9). The 2nd PB usually includes all wing covs, pp, and rects, but only 1-5 outer pp covs (see Fig. 122**C**); 1-6 ss sometimes (in ~33% of birds) can be retained during this molt, usually in a block among s1-s6 (see Figs. 25**C** & 121**C**), and often symmetrically in both wings. During subsequent PBs, from 1-5 ss also sometimes (in ~30% of birds) can be retained, among s1-s8, seldom in a block (see Figs. 25**D** & 121**D**), and less often symmetrically in both wings. A variable number of pp covs can be retained during the 3rd and subsequent PBs, although these molts often are complete. See p. 163 for details on woodpecker molt.

Skull—Pneumaticization patterns probably are unhelpful for ageing; see Family account.

Age—Juv (Apr-Sep) averages duller than adults and has the crown dull black, often flecked white, and with red, pink, or yellow coloration (if present) confined to the center (Fig. 130**B-E**); white eye ring absent; p10 rounded and large (tip usually > 9 mm from the pp covs, *vs* usually < 7 mm in adults; see Fig. 127); flanks washed buff and with dusky spots; rects pointed (Fig. 124); and iris gray-brown. Juv ♀ often lacks red in the crown, but can have up to a few red-tipped feathers to the central crown, usually not extending forward of the eyes (Fig. 130**A-C**), and juv ♂ rarely lacks red, but usually has more extensive and more fully red feathers often extending forward of the eyes (Fig. 130**B-E**); juvs without red (Fig. 130**A**) probably are reliably sexed ♀♀ whereas those with more extensive red (Fig. 130**D-E**) can be reliably sexed ♂♂; more study is needed.

HY/SY (Oct-Sep): Pp covs uniform (Fig. 122**A**), quickly becoming brown and worn by winter/spring (Fig. 122**B**); back feathers black, contrasting with the browner, retained outer wing covs; **and** ss (usually) uniform in color and wear, the terts becoming worn to very worn by spring (Fig. 121**A**), or (perhaps rarely) ss uniform except for 1-2 feathers (among s7-s9) contrastingly fresh (Fig. 121**B**). **Note: Fresh fall HY/SYs can closely resemble ASY/ATYs with uniform ss and pp covs, and the p10 of HY/SYs can be intermediate in size and shape between those of juvs and those of AHY/ASYs; see Downy Woodpecker. Iris color also may be helpful in distinguishing some HY/SYs (grayish brown to brown) from most AHY/ASYs (deep reddish) through Jan.**

SY/TY (Oct-Sep): Consecutive outer 1-5 pp covs black and fresh, contrasting with the brown and abraded, consecutive, retained inner pp covs (Fig. 122**C**); back feathers and wing covs uniformly black; **and** ss either uniformly adult (Fig. 25**B**), the terts fresh or slightly worn by spring, or (sometimes) ss with 1-6 juvenal feathers (among s1-s6) retained, often symmetrically in both wings, faded, abraded, and contrasting markedly with the fresher, replaced adult feathers (Figs. 25**C** & 121**C**). **Note: See HY/SY. Some intermediates can be difficult to separate reliably from ASY/ATY and should be aged AHY/ASY.**

ASY/ATY (Oct-Sep): Pp covs either uniformly black and fresh (Fig. 122**A**), or pp covs irregularly mixed with fresh and moderately worn, retained adult feathers (Fig. 122**D**); **and** ss either uniformly adult (Fig. 25**B**), the terts relatively fresh, or (sometimes) ss with 1-5 older adult feathers (among s1-s8) retained, often not symmetrically in both wings, moderately worn, and contrasting only slightly with the replaced feathers (Figs. 25**D** & 121**D**). **Note: See HY/SY and SY/TY. ASY/ATYs with isolated, retained juvenal pp covs (Fig. 122E), or with three generations of pp covs, sequentially replaced as in Figure 122F, might be reliably aged TY/4Y (see p. 165), but more study is needed.**

Sex—CP & BP are unreliable for sexing. ♀ wg(n100) 107-137, tl(n100) 59-91, exp culmen(n100) 23.0-33.5; ♂ wg(n100) 110-138, tl(n100) 58-90, exp culmen(n100) 24.6-33.5; see **Geographic variation**.

♀: Hindcrown without red (Fig. 130**A**) or (perhaps rarely, in ASY/ATYs only?) with 1-2 red feathers (Fig. 130**B**). **Note: See ♂.**

♂: Hindcrown with a distinct, red patch (Fig. 130G). **Note: Beware of occasional juvenal ♀♀ with a few red-tipped feathers in the crown (Fig. 130B-C);** see Age.

Hybrids reported—Ladder-backed Woodpecker.

References—Stone (1896), Ridgway (1914), Snyder (1923), Forbush (1927), Bent (1939), Miller (1955b), Roberts (1955), Lawrence (1967), Wood (1969), George (1972), Oberholser (1974), Sheppard & Klimkiewicz (1976), Short (1982), Manolis (1987), CWS & USFWS (1991), Kaufman (1993a), Pyle & Howell (1995); E.J. Fisk, J.A. Jackson, C.S. Robbins, K.E. Bartlet (*in litt.* to the BBL); IBP (MAPS) data, PRBO data.

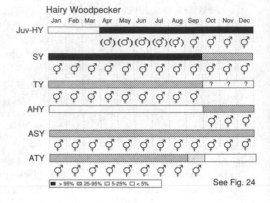

STRICKLAND'S WOODPECKER
Picoides stricklandi

STWO
Species # 3980
Band size: 1A

Species—From the other *Picoides* woodpeckers by back brown, usually without white markings (*P.s. arizonae* only; see **Geographic variation**); underparts with dusky spots; outer rects (r5) with many (4-5) black bars.

Geographic variation—Fairly well marked, but somewhat clinal where ranges meet. Subspecies taxonomy follows Short (1982); see also Ridgway (1914), Moore (1946a), Davis (1953, 1965), Phillips (1961a). Two other subspecies occur in Mex.

   P.s. arizonae (res se.AZ-sw.NM): From subspecies of Mex by larger average size (see **Sex**, *vs* wg 103-114, tl 56-70 in subspecies of Mex); upperparts paler brown (*vs* smoky brown), without white or (rarely) with one to a few white spots in the scapulars or indistinct white bars on the rump (*vs* back with moderate to heavy white barring in subspecies of Mex).

Molt—PB: HY incomplete (Jun-Oct), AHY incomplete-complete (Jun-Oct); PA absent. The 1st PB includes no to some inner, lesser and med covs, occasionally 1-4 inner gr covs, all pp and rects, and 0-5 inner ss among s6-s11 (replacement of ss occurs in ~10% of HYs, usually 1-4 feathers among s7-s10; see Fig. 121B), but usually no pp covs. The 2nd PB usually includes all wing covs, pp, and rects, but only 1-5 outer pp covs (see Fig. 121C); 1-6 ss sometimes (in ~32% of birds) can be retained during this molt, usually in a block among s1-s6 (see Figs. 25C & 121C), and often symmetrically in both wings. During subsequent PBs, from 1-5 ss also sometimes (in ~30% of birds) can be retained, among s1-s8, seldom in a block (see Figs. 25D & 121D), and less often symmetrically in both wings. A variable number of pp covs can be retained during the 3rd and subsequent PBs, although these molts often are complete. See p. 163 for details on woodpecker molt.

Skull—Pneumaticization patterns probably are unhelpful for ageing; see Family account.

Age—Juv (May-Sep) averages duller than adults and has the crown dull brownish, flecked white, and with red confined to the center (Fig. 130B-F), p10 rounded and large (tip usually > 4 mm from the pp covs, *vs* usually < 5 mm in adults; see Fig. 127), rects pointed (Fig. 124), and iris probably grayish brown. Juv ♀ has red tipping to a few central crown feathers, usually not extending forward of the eyes (Fig. 130**B-D**) whereas juv ♂ has more extensive and more fully red feathers, usually extending forward of the eyes (Fig. 130**C-F**); most (but possibly not all) juvs can be reliably sexed; more study is needed.

HY/SY (Oct-Sep): Pp covs uniform (Fig. 122**A**), quickly becoming worn by winter/spring (Fig. 122**B**); back feathers and replaced inner wing covs (see **Molt**) dark brown, contrasting with the paler brown, retained outer wing covs; **and** ss either uniform in wear, the terts becoming very worn by spring (Fig. 121**A**), or (occasionally) ss uniform except for 1-4 feathers (among s7-s10, rarely to 5 among s6-s11) contrastingly fresh (Fig. 121**B**). **Note: Fresh fall HY/SYs can closely resemble ASY/ATYs with uniform ss and pp covs, and the p10 of HY/SYs can be intermediate in size and shape between those of juvs and those of AHY/ASYs; see Downy Woodpecker. Iris color also may be helpful in distinguishing some HY/SYs (grayish brown to brown) from most AHY/ASYs (deep reddish) through Jan.**

SY/TY (Oct-Sep): Consecutive outer 1-5 pp covs fresh, contrasting with the abraded, consecutive, retained inner pp covs (Fig. 122**C**); back feathers and wing covs uniformly dark brown; **and** ss either uniformly adult (Fig. 25**B**), the terts only moderately worn by spring, or (sometimes) ss with 1-5 juvenal feathers (among s1-s6) retained, often symmetrically in both wings, faded, abraded, and contrasting markedly in wear with the fresher, replaced adult feathers (Figs. 25**C** & 121**C**). **Note: See HY/SY. Some intermediates can be difficult to separate from ASY/ATY and should be aged AHY/ASY; contrasts in wear among the different generations of ss and pp covs are more difficult to detect than in other *Picoides* species due to the browner color of fresh feathers.**

ASY/ATY (Oct-Sep): Pp covs either uniformly fresh (Fig. 122**A**), or pp covs irregularly mixed with fresh and moderately worn, retained adult feathers (Fig. 122**D**); **and** ss either uniformly adult (Fig. 25**B**), the terts fresh or only slightly worn, or ss (sometimes) with 1-5 older adult feathers (among s1-s8) retained, often not symmetrically in both wings, moderately worn, and contrasting only slightly with the replaced feathers (Figs. 25**D** & 121**D**). **Note: See HY/SY and SY/TY. ASY/ATYs with isolated, retained juvenal pp covs (Fig. 122E), or with three generations of covs, sequentially replaced as in Figure 122F, might be reliably aged TY/4Y (see p. 165), but more study is needed.**

Sex—CP & BP are unreliable for sexing. ♀ wg(n77) 107-116, tl(88) 63-73, bill nares to tip(n79) 17.5-21.0; ♂ wg(n100) 111-119, tl(n58) 62-72, bill nares to tip(n100) 20.1-24.8; measurements from subspecies of N.Am only; see **Geographic variation**.

♀: Hindcrown without red (Fig. 130**A**) or (perhaps rarely, in ASY/ATYs only?) with 1-2 red feathers (Fig. 130**B**). **Note: See ♂.**

♂: Hindcrown with a distinct, red patch (Fig. 130**G**). **Note: Beware of juvenal ♀♀ with red-tipped feathers in the crown (Fig. 130B-D; see Age).**

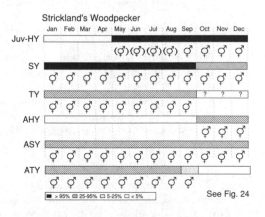

References—Swarth (1904a), Ridgway (1914), Bent (1939), Davis (1965), Short (1982), Manolis (1987), Pyle & Howell (1995).

RED-COCKADED WOODPECKER
Picoides borealis

RCWO
Species # 3950
Band size: 1A

Species—From the other *Picoides* woodpeckers by cap entirely black (Fig 130**A**; both non-juv ♂ & ♀); auricular entirely white; back black with white barring; outer rects (r5) white, usually with 2-3 partial bars but no full bars.

Geographic variation—Subspecies taxonomy follows Short (1982), who considered the species mono-typic (synonymizing a previously recognized subspecies); see also Ridgway (1914), Wetmore (1941), Todd (1946), Jackson (1971, 1994), Mengel & Jackson (1977). Birds of coastal SC-s.FL (including "*P.b. hylonomus*") average shorter-winged than other forms, but variation is broadly clinal.

Molt—PB: HY incomplete (May-Oct), AHY incomplete-complete (Jun-Oct); PA absent. The 1st PB includes no to some inner, lesser and med covs, occasionally 1-4 inner gr covs, all pp and rects, and 0-4 inner ss among s7-s10 (replacement of ss occurs in ~8% of HYs, usually 1-3 feath-ers among s7-s9; see Fig. 121**B**), but usually no pp covs. The 2nd PB usually includes all wing covs, pp, and rects, but only 1-5 outer pp covs (see Fig. 121**C**); 1-5 ss sometimes (in ~29% of birds) can be retained during this molt, usually in a block among s1-s6 (see Figs. 25**C** & 121**C**), and often symmetrically in both wings. During subsequent PBs, from 1-5 ss also sometimes (in ~25% of birds) can be retained, among s1-s8, seldom in a block (see Figs. 25**D** & 121**D**), and less often symmetrically in both wings. A variable number of pp covs can be retained during the 3rd and subsequent PBs, although these molts often are complete. See p. 163 for details on woodpecker molt.

Skull—Pneumaticization patterns probably are unhelpful for ageing; see Family account.

Age—Juv (Apr-Sep) averages duller than adults and has the crown dull black, flecked white, and with red (if present) confined to the center (Fig. 130**B-E**), white supercilium abbreviated and not connecting with the white of the auricular, p10 rounded and large (tip 3-12 mm > pp covs, *vs* < 2 mm in adults; see Fig. 127), rects pointed (Fig. 124), and iris grayish yellow to grayish. Juv ♀ has no red in the crown (Fig. 130**A**) or (perhaps rarely) red tipping to one or a few cen-tral crown feathers, usually not extending forward of the eyes (Fig. 130**B-C**), whereas juv ♂ has slightly more extensive and more fully red feathers, usually extending forward of the eyes (Fig. 130**C-E**); most (but possibly not all) juvs can be reliably sexed; more study is needed.

HY/SY (Oct-Sep): Pp covs uniform (Fig. 122**A**), quickly becoming brown and worn by win-ter/spring (Fig. 122**B**); back feathers and replaced inner wing covs (see **Molt**) black, con-trasting with the browner, retained outer wing covs; **and** ss either uniform in color and wear, the terts becoming very worn by spring (Fig. 121**A**), or (occasionally) ss uniform except for 1-4 feathers (among s7-s10, rarely 5 among s6-s11) contrastingly fresh (Fig. 121**B**). **Note: Fresh fall HY/SYs can closely resemble ASY/ATYs with uniform ss and pp covs, and the p10 of HY/SYs can be intermediate in size and shape between those of juvs and those of AHY/ASYs; see Downy Woodpecker. Iris color also may be helpful in distinguishing some HY/SYs (grayish brown to brown) from most AHY/ASYs (deep reddish) through Jan.**

SY/TY (Oct-Sep): Consecutive outer 1-5 pp covs black and fresh, contrasting with the brown and abraded, consecutive, retained inner pp covs (Fig. 122**C**); back feathers and wing covs uniformly black; **and** ss either uniformly adult (Fig. 25**B**), the terts only moderately worn by spring, or (sometimes) ss with 1-5 juvenal feathers (among s1-s6) retained, often symmetri-cally in both wings, very faded and abraded, and contrasting markedly with the fresher, replaced adult feathers (Figs. 25**C** & 121**C**). **Note: See HY/SY. Some intermediates can be difficult to separate reliably from ASY/ATY and should be aged AHY/ASY.**

ASY/ATY (Oct-Sep): Pp covs either uniformly black and fresh (Fig. 122**A**), or pp covs irregularly mixed with fresh and moderately worn, retained adult feathers (Fig. 122**D**); **and** ss either uniformly adult (Fig. 25**B**), the terts fresh or only slightly worn, or (sometimes) ss with 1-5 older adult feathers (among s1-s8) retained, often not symmetrically in both wings, moderately worn, and contrasting only slightly with the replaced feathers (Figs. 25**D** & 121**D**). **Note: See HY/SY and SY/TY. ASY/ATYs with isolated, retained juvenal pp covs (Fig. 122E), or with three generations of pp covs, sequentially replaced as in Figure 122F, might be reliably aged TY/4Y (see p. 165), but more study is needed.**

Sex—CP & BP are unreliable for sexing. ♀ wg(n67) 111-123, tl(n67) 69-81, exp culmen(n67) 19.1-22.6; ♂ wg(n81) 110-124, tl(n81) 65-81, exp culmen(n81) 20.7-24.0; see **Geographic variation**.

♀: Side of the head above the auricular without red. **Note: See ♂.**

♂: Side of the head above the auricular with a small red patch. **Note: Beware that the patch can be concealed by overlying black feathers. Also, beware of juv ♀♀ that may have one to a few red-tipped feathers in the center of the crown (Fig. 130B-C).**

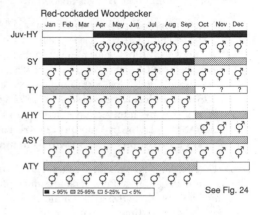

References—Ridgway (1914), E.E. Murphey *in* Bent (1939), Goodwin (1968), Ligon (1970), Oberholser (1974), Mengel & Jackson (1977), Jackson (1979, 1994), Short (1982), Gowaty & Lennartz (1985), Pyle & Howell (1995); J.A. Jackson (*in litt.* to the BBL).

WHITE-HEADED WOODPECKER
Picoides albolarvatus

WHWO
Species # 3990
Band size: 1A-2

Geographic variation—Weak, but ranges allopatric. Subspecies taxonomy follows Short (1982); see also Ridgway (1914) Garrett *et.al* (1996) . No other subspecies occur.

P.a. albolarvatus (res sc.BC-c.CA): Bill small. ♀ exp culmen(n84) 23.1-27.5, exp culmen ÷ wg 0.192-0.219; ♂ exp culmen(n100) 25.1-30.5, exp culmen ÷ wg 0.210-0.240.

P.a. gravirostris (res s.CA): Bill large. ♀ exp culmen(n61) 24.2-29.2, exp culmen ÷ wg 0.203-0.233; ♂ exp culmen(n56) 27.8-32.5, exp culmen ÷ wg 0.226-0.252.

Molt—PB: HY incomplete (Jun-Oct), AHY incomplete-complete (Jun-Oct); PA absent. The 1st PB includes no to a few inner lesser and med covs, occasionally 1-2 inner gr covs, and all pp and rects, but usually no pp covs or ss; look for occasional HYs to replace one or more of s7-s9. The 2nd PB usually includes all wing covs, pp, and rects, but only 1-5 outer pp covs (see Fig. 122**C**); 1-6 ss sometimes (in ~41% of birds) can be retained during this molt, usually in a block among s1-s6 (see Figs. 25**C** & 121**C**), and often symmetrically in both wings. During subsequent PBs, from 1-5 ss also sometimes (in ~38% of birds) can be retained, among s1-s8, seldom in a block (see Figs. 25**D** & 121**D**), and less often symmetrically in both wings. A variable number of pp covs can be retained during the 3rd and subsequent PBs, although these molts often are complete. See p. 163 for details on woodpecker molt.

Skull—Pneumaticization patterns probably are unhelpful for ageing; see Family account.

Age—Juv (Jun-Sep) averages browner than adults and has a dull, dusky crown with red confined to the center (Fig. 130**B-F**), p10 rounded and large (tip usually > 8 mm from the pp covs, *vs* usually < 7 mm in adults; see Fig. 127), white of the outer web of p6-p7 often broken by black marks (*vs* continuously white in adult), rects pointed (Fig. 124), and iris probably grayish or gray-brown. Juv ♀ usually has up to a few red-tipped feathers to the central crown, usually not extending forward of the eyes (Fig. 130**B-D**), whereas juv ♂ has more extensive and more fully red feathers extending forward of the eyes (Fig. 130**D-F**); most (but possibly not all) juvs can be reliably sexed; more study is needed.

HY/SY (Oct-Sep): Pp covs uniform (Fig. 122**A**), quickly becoming brown and worn by winter/spring (Fig. 122**B**); back feathers and replaced inner wing covs (see **Molt**) black, contrasting with the browner, retained outer wing covs; **and** ss (usually) uniform in color and wear, the terts becoming worn to very worn by spring (Fig. 121**A**), or (perhaps rarely) ss uniform except for 1-3 feathers (among s7-s9) contrastingly fresh (Fig. 121**B**). **Note: Fresh fall HY/SYs can closely resemble ASY/ATYs with uniform ss and pp covs, and the p10 of HY/SYs can be intermediate in size and shape between those of juvs and those of AHY/ASYs; see Downy Woodpecker. Iris color also may be helpful in distinguishing some HY/SYs (grayish brown to brown) from most AHY/ASYs (deep reddish) through Jan.**

SY/TY (Oct-Sep): Consecutive outer 1-5 pp covs black and fresh, contrasting with the brown and abraded, consecutive, retained inner pp covs (Fig. 122**C**); back feathers and wing covs uniformly black; **and** ss either uniformly adult (Fig. 25**B**), the terts fresh or slightly worn by spring, or (sometimes) ss with 1-6 juvenal feathers (among s1-s6) retained, often symmetrically in both wings, faded, abraded, and contrasting markedly with the fresher, replaced adult feathers (Figs. 25**C** & 121**C**). **Note: See HY/SY. Some intermediates can be difficult to separate reliably from ASY/ATY and should be aged AHY/ASY.**

ASY/ATY (Oct-Sep): Pp covs either uniformly black and fresh (Fig. 122**A**), or pp covs irregularly mixed with fresh and moderately worn, retained adult feathers (Fig. 122**D**); **and** ss either uniformly adult (Fig. 25**B**), the terts relatively fresh, or (sometimes) ss with 1-5 older adult feathers (among s1-s8) retained, often not symmetrically in both wings, moderately worn, and contrasting only slightly with the replaced feathers (Figs. 25**D** & 121**D**). **Note: See HY/SY and SY/TY. ASY/ATYs with isolated, retained juvenal pp covs (Fig. 122E), or with three generations of pp covs, sequentially replaced as in Figure 122F, might be reliably aged TY/4Y (see p. 165), but more study is needed.**

Sex—CP & BP are unreliable for sexing. ♀ wg(n63) 118-130, tl(n52) 76-90; ♂ wg(n56) 120-131, tl(n49) 76-89. See **Geographic variation** for bill measurement.

   ♀: Hindcrown without red (Fig 130**A**) or (perhaps rarely, in ASY/ATYs only?) with 1-2 red feathers (Fig. 130**B**). **Note: See ♂.**

   ♂: Hindcrown with a distinct, red patch (Fig. 130**G**). **Note: Beware of juvenal ♀♀ with red-tipped feathers in the crown (Fig. 130B-D); see Age.**

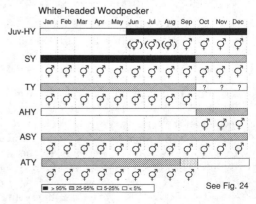

White-headed Woodpecker

See Fig. 24

References—Ridgway (1914), Bent (1939), Short (1982), Manolis (1987), Pyle & Howell (1995), Garrett *et.al.* (1996); IBP (MAPS) data.

THREE-TOED WOODPECKER
Picoides tridactylus

TTWO
Species # 4010
Band size: 2

Species—From juv Hairy Woodpeckers with yellow crowns by back black with white barring (except occasional *P.t. dorsalis;* see **Geographic variation**); supercilium narrower (0-2 mm wide); nasal tufts black; feet with three toes. From Black-backed Woodpecker by smaller size (wg 108-129, tl 68-83, exp culmen 22.0-30.5; see **Geographic variation & Sex**); supercilium usually distinct; yellow crown patch usually with white streaks; back usually with some white or grayish; r4 usually with black barring. *P.t. bacatus* (see **Geographic variation**), which rarely can lack white in the back, also should show black barring on the outer rects.

Geographic variation—Moderate, with fairly well-defined ranges, although individual variation and intermediates occur. Subspecies taxonomy follows Short (1982); see also Bangs (1900), Ridgway (1914), Rand (1948a), Dement'ev and Gladkov (1951), Todd (1963), Cramp (1985). Five other subspecies occur in Eurasia; the subspecies group of N.Am is separated from these by narrower white streaks on the forehead, white distal portions of r3-r5 without black markings, and iris of AHYs reddish brown (*vs* whitish in the Eurasian Subspecies Group). Sexes are similar in wg and tl measurements (see **Sex**) and thus are combined for each subspecies.

> *P.t. fasciatus* (res AK-s.OR to Sask-nw.MT): Small; forehead with numerous white spots; back primarily white with narrow black barring (1-4 mm wide); outer rects (r5) with little or no black. ♀♂ wg(n73) 108-122, tl(n63) 68-81; exp culmen ♀(n33) 22.0-26.0, ♂(n30) 24.0-29.5. Birds of s.BC average darker and can overlap with *bacatus* in plumage (but not range).
>
> *P.t. dorsalis* (res nc.MT to c.AZ-c.NM, vag to NE): Large; forehead with few to a moderate number of white spots; white of the back without black or with few, very narrow (1 mm) black markings; outer rects (r5) with little or no black. ♀♂ wg(n20) 118-129, tl(n20) 70-82; exp culmen ♀(n10) 25.0-28.0, ♂(n10) 26.0-30.5.
>
> *P.t. bacatus* (res n.Man-n.MN to Nfl-n.ME, wint to IA-DE): Small; forehead with few or no white spots; back dark, primarily (rarely entirely) blackish with narrow (0-4 mm), white, gray, or brown barring; outer rects (r5) sometimes with black bars. ♀♂ wg(n39) 109-119, tl(n39) 68-83; exp culmen ♀(n18) 22.5-26.5, ♂(n21) 24.0-28.0. See *P.t. fasciatus*.

Molt—PB: HY incomplete (Jun-Oct), AHY incomplete-complete (Jun-Oct); PA absent. The 1st PB includes no to a few inner lesser and med covs, and all pp and rects, but usually no pp covs, gr covs, or ss; look for occasional HYs to replace one or more inner gr covs or ss (among s7-s9). The 2nd PB usually includes all wing covs, pp, and rects, but only 1-5 outer pp covs (see Fig. 122C); 1-6 ss sometimes (in ~47% of birds) can be retained during this molt, usually in a block among s1-s6 (see Figs. 25C & 121C), and often symmetrically in both wings. During subsequent PBs, from 1-5 ss also sometimes (in ~44% of birds) can be retained, among s1-s8, seldom in a block (see Figs. 25D & 121D), and less often symmetrically in both wings. A variable number of pp covs can be retained during the 3rd and subsequent PBs, although these molts often are complete. See p. 163 for details on woodpecker molt.

Skull—Pneumaticization patterns probably are unhelpful for ageing; see Family account.

Age—Juv (Jun-Sep) averages duller than adults and has the crown dull black with the yellow patch (if present) reduced (Fig. 130**B-F**), p10 rounded and large (tip usually > 7 mm from the pp covs, *vs* usually < 6 mm in adults; see Fig. 127), underparts washed buff, flanks with brownish spots, rects pointed (Fig. 124), and iris gray-brown. Juv ♀ can have no (rarely) to a moderate number of yellow-tipped feathers to the central crown, usually not extending forward of the eyes (Fig. 130**A-D**), whereas juv ♂ usually has more extensive and more fully yellow feathers extending forward of the eyes (Fig. 130**D-F**); most (but possibly not all) juvs can be reliably sexed; more study is needed.

HY/SY (Oct-Sep): Pp covs uniform (Fig. 122**A**), quickly becoming brown and worn by winter/spring (Fig. 122**B**); back feathers and replaced inner wing covs (see **Molt**) black, contrasting with the browner, retained outer wing covs; **and** ss (usually) uniform in color and wear, the terts becoming worn to very worn by spring (Fig. 121**A**), or (perhaps rarely) ss uniform except for 1-3 feathers (among s7-s9) contrastingly fresh (Fig. 121**B**). **Note: Fresh fall HY/SYs can closely resemble ASY/ATYs with uniform ss and pp covs, and the p10 of HY/SYs can be intermediate in size and shape between those of juvs and those of AHY/ASYs; see Downy Woodpecker. Iris color also may be helpful in distinguishing some HY/SYs (grayish brown to brown) from most AHY/ASYs (deep reddish) through Jan.**

SY/TY (Oct-Sep): Consecutive outer 1-5 pp covs black and fresh, contrasting with the brown and abraded, consecutive, retained inner pp covs (Fig. 122**C**); back feathers and wing covs uniformly black; **and** ss either uniformly adult (Fig. 25**B**), the terts fresh or slightly worn by spring, or (sometimes) ss with 1-6 juvenal feathers (among s1-s6) retained, often symmetrically in both wings, faded, abraded, and contrasting markedly with the fresher, replaced adult feathers (Figs. 25**C** & 121**C**). **Note: See HY/SY. Some intermediates can be difficult to separate reliably from ASY/ATY and should be aged AHY/ASY.**

ASY/ATY (Oct-Sep): Pp covs either uniformly black and fresh (Fig. 122**A**), or pp covs irregularly mixed with fresh and moderately worn, retained adult feathers (Fig. 122**D**); **and** ss either uniformly adult (Fig. 25**B**), the terts relatively fresh, or (sometimes) ss with 1-5 older adult feathers (among s1-s8) retained, often not symmetrically in both wings, moderately worn, and contrasting only slightly with the replaced feathers (Figs. 25**D** & 121**D**). **Note: See HY/SY and SY/TY. ASY/ATYs with isolated, retained juvenal pp covs (Fig. 122E), or with three generations of pp covs, sequentially replaced as in Figure 122F, might be reliably aged TY/4Y (see p. 165), but more study is needed.**

Sex—CP & BP are unreliable for sexing. ♀ wg(n64) 108-129, tl(n61) 68-82, exp culmen(n61) 22.0-28.0; ♂ wg(n68) 110-128, tl(n61) 68-83, exp culmen(n61) 24.0-30.5; see **Geographic variation**.

♀: Crown without yellow (Fig. 130**A**) or (perhaps rarely, in ASY/ATYs only?) with 1-2 yellow feathers (Fig. 130**B**). **Note: See ♂.**

♂: Crown with a distinct, yellow patch (Fig. 130**F**). **Note: Beware of juvenal ♀♀ with yellow-tipped feathers in the crown (Fig. 130B-D); see Age.**

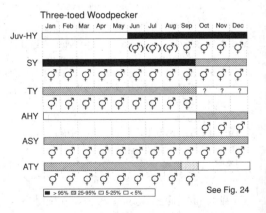

References—Ridgway (1914), Forbush (1927), Bent (1939), Roberts (1955), Stresemann & Stresemann (1966), Wood (1969), Short (1982), LaFrance (1983), Cramp (1985), Kaufman (1993a), Pyle & Howell (1995); W. Taber (*in litt.* to the BBL); IBP (MAPS) data.

BLACK-BACKED WOODPECKER

Picoides arcticus

BBWO
Species # 4000
Band size: 2

Species—From darker Three-toed Woodpeckers (*e.g.*, *P.t. bacatus*) by larger size (wg 123-134, tl 73-85, exp culmen 28.5-35.0; see **Sex**); supercilium indistinct to absent; yellow crown patch of adults more distinct and without white streaking; back uniformly black; r4 primarily to entirely white.

Geographic variation—No subspecies currently recognized, although see Bangs (1900), Grinnell *et al.* (1930), Todd (1963), and Short (1982).

Molt—PB: HY incomplete (Jun-Oct), AHY incomplete-complete (Jun-Oct); PA absent. The 1st PB includes no to a few inner lesser and med covs, and all pp and rects, but usually no pp covs, gr covs, or ss; look for occasional HYs to replace one or more inner gr covs or ss (among s7-s9). The 2nd PB usually includes all wing covs, pp, and rects, but only 1-5 outer pp covs (see Fig. 122C); 1-6 ss often (in ~60% of birds) are retained during this molt, usually in a block among s1-s7 (see Figs. 25C & 121C), and often symmetrically in both wings. During subsequent PBs, from 1-5 ss sometimes (in ~50% of birds) can be retained, among s1-s8, seldom in a block (see Figs. 25D & 121D), and less often symmetrically in both wings. A variable number of pp covs can be retained during the 3rd and subsequent PBs, although these molts sometimes are complete. See p. 163 for details on woodpecker molt.

Skull—Pneumaticization patterns probably are unhelpful for ageing; see Family account.

Age—Juv (Jun-Sep) averages duller than adults and has the crown dull black with the yellow patch absent or reduced (Fig. 130A-E), p10 rounded and large (tip usually > 8 mm from the pp covs, *vs* usually < 7 mm in adults; see Fig. 127), underparts washed buff, flank spotting brownish, rects pointed (Fig. 124), and iris gray-brown. Juv ♀ can have no to a few yellow-tipped feathers to the central crown, not extending forward of the eyes (Fig. 130A-C), where-as juv ♂ usually has more extensive and more fully yellow feathers, usually extending forward of the eyes (Fig. 123C-E); most (but possibly not all) juvs can be reliably sexed; more study is needed.

HY/SY (Oct-Sep): Pp covs uniform (Fig. 122A), quickly becoming brown and worn by winter/spring (Fig. 122B); back feathers and replaced inner wing covs (see **Molt**) black, contrasting with the browner, retained outer wing covs; **and** ss (usually) uniform in color and wear, the terts becoming worn to very worn by spring (Fig. 121A), or (perhaps rarely) ss uniform except for 1-3 feathers (among s7-s9) contrastingly fresh (Fig. 121B). **Note: Fresh fall HY/SYs can closely resemble ASY/ATYs with uniform ss and pp covs, and the p10 of HY/SYs can be intermediate in size and shape between those of juvs and those of AHY/ASYs; see Downy Woodpecker. Iris color also may be helpful in distinguishing some HY/SYs (grayish brown to brown) from most AHY/ASYs (deep reddish) through Jan.**

SY/TY (Oct-Sep): Consecutive outer 1-5 pp covs black and fresh, contrasting with the brown and abraded, consecutive, retained inner pp covs (Fig. 122C); back feathers and wing covs uniformly black; **and** ss either uniformly adult (Fig. 25B), the terts fresh or slightly worn by spring, or (often) ss with 1-6 juvenal feathers (among s1-s7) retained, often symmetrically in both wings, faded, abraded, and contrasting markedly with the fresher, replaced adult feathers (Figs. 25C & 121C). **Note: See HY/SY. Some intermediates can be difficult to separate reliably from ASY/ATY and should be aged AHY/ASY.**

ASY/ATY (Oct-Sep): Pp covs either uniformly black and fresh (Fig. 122**A**), or pp covs irregularly mixed with fresh and moderately worn, retained adult feathers (Fig. 122**D**); **and** ss either uniformly adult (Fig. 25**B**), the terts relatively fresh, or (sometimes) ss with 1-5 older adult feathers (among s1-s8) retained, often not symmetrically in both wings, moderately worn, and contrasting only slightly with the replaced feathers (Figs. 25**D** & 121**D**). **Note: See HY/SY and SY/TY. ASY/ATYs with isolated, retained juvenal pp covs (Fig. 122E), or with three generations of covs, sequentially replaced as in Figure 122F, might be reliably aged TY/4Y (see p. 165), but more study is needed.**

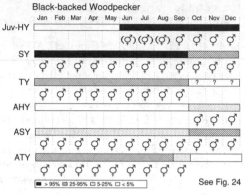

Sex—CP & BP are unreliable for sexing. ♀ wg(n34) 123-133, tl(n34) 73-85, exp culmen(n34) 28.5-34.5; ♂ wg(n39) 125-134, tl(n39) 74-85, exp culmen(n39) 31.0-35.0.

♀: Crown without yellow (Fig. 130**A**) or (perhaps rarely, in ASY/ATYs only?) with 1-2 yellow feathers (Fig. 130**B**). **Note: See ♂.**

♂: Crown with a distinct, yellow patch (Fig. 130**E-F**). **Note: Beware of juvenal ♀♀ with a few yellow-tipped feathers in the crown (Fig. 130B-C); see Age.**

References—Ridgway (1914), Forbush (1927), Bent (1939), Wood (1969), Short (1982), Pyle & Howell (1995); W. Taber (*in litt.* to the BBL).

NORTHERN FLICKER
Colaptes auratus

See below
Band size: 3

      Red-shafted Flicker (RSFL)   Species # 4130
      Yellow-shafted × Red-shafted Flicker (FLIN)   Species # 4123
      Yellow-shafted Flicker (YSFL)   Species # 4120

Species—Yellow-shafted Group from Gilded Flicker by larger average size (wg 137-171, tl 88-124; see **Geographic variation**); crown and nape bluish gray with a red nape patch; face tan; moustache of ♂ black; black tips to the outer rects (r5) relatively small (< 20 mm from the tip in adult). Beware of hybrids and intergrades with Red-shafted forms.

Geographic variation—Moderate (within subspecies groups) to well marked (between groups), with substantial intergradation. Subspecies taxonomy follows Short (1982); see also Grinnell (1927a), Ridgway (1914), Griscom (1934a), Taverner (1934), Brodkorb (1935b), Deakin (1936), van Rossem (1936b, 1944, 1947a), Rand (1944a, 1948b), Jewett *et al.* (1953), Miller (1955a), Phillips (1961a), Phillips *et al.* (1964), Short (1965, 1971b), Short & Banks (1965), Sutton (1967), James (1970), Oberholser (1974), Kaufman (1979a, 1991a), D.M. Power (1980), Rea (1983), Unitt (1984), Behle (1985), Moore & Buchanan (1985), Godfrey (1986), McGillivray & Biermann (1987), Moore (1987, 1995). Four other subspecies occur in Mex-C.Am & the W.Indies. Sexes are similar in wg and tl measurements (see **Sex**) and thus are combined in each subspecies.

Red-shafted (*C.a. cafer*) Group. Crown brown; face gray; nape without red; moustache of ♂ red.

C.a. cafer (br & wint coastal s.AK-n.CA): **Red-shafted Flicker.** Large; upperparts rich brown; underparts dark brown with a heavy, pinkish-brown wash. ♀♂ wg(n51) 153-177, tl(n38) 104-124; exp culmen ♀(n10) 36.0-40.0, ♂(n10) 37.0-42.5.

C.a. collaris (br & wint se.BC-s.CA to sw.Sask-TX, vag to AR): **Red-shafted Flicker.** Medium large; upperparts pale, grayish brown; underparts pale brown with a light, pinkish-tan wash. ♀♂ wg(n100) 150-174, tl(n100) 100-121; exp culmen ♀(n26) 35.3-39.1, ♂(n35) 36.2-40.9. Birds in the western part of the range (*"canescens"*) can average grayer upperparts and pinker underparts than eastern forms, and birds of Santa Cruz I, CA (*"sedentarius"*), can average slightly smaller and richer in coloration but distinctions are slight. Breeding birds of OK may average smaller and deserve further study.

C.a. nanus (br & wint sw.TX): **Red-shafted Flicker.** Small; upperparts pale grayish brown; underparts pale brown with a light, pinkish-tan wash. ♀♂ wg(n20) 138-155, tl(n20) 90-106; exp culmen ♀(n36) 34.0-36.1, ♂(n10) 34.5-36.9.

Yellow-shafted (*C.a. auratus*) Group. Crown bluish gray; face tan; nape with red; moustache of ♂ black.

C.a. luteus (br c.AK-n.TX to Nfl-w.NC, wint to s.CA-n.FL): **Yellow-shafted Flicker.** Large. ♀♂ wg(n100) 148-171, tl(n100) 97-124; exp culmen ♀(n49) 31.3-38.6, ♂(n58) 32.6-39.9. Birds of the northern and western parts of the range (*"borealis"*) average longer winged, but variation is broadly clinal.

C.a. auratus (res e.TX to se.VA-s.FL): **Yellow-shafted Flicker.** Small. ♀♂ wg(n44) 137-155, tl(n44) 88-109; exp culmen ♀(n22) 27.9-34.7, ♂(n22) 30.6-35.8.

Molt—PB: HY incomplete (Jun-Oct), AHY incomplete-complete (Jun-Oct); PA absent. The 1st PB includes no to a few inner lesser and med covs, occasionally 1-3 inner gr covs, all pp and rects, and occasionally 1-3 inner ss (among s7-s11; replacement of ss occurs in ~8% of HYs; see Fig 121**B**), but usually no pp covs. The 2nd PB usually includes all wing covs, pp, and rects, but only 1-5 outer pp covs (see Fig. 121**C**); 1-4 ss sometimes (in ~24% of birds) can be retained during this molt, usually in a block among s1-s5 (see Figs. 25**C** & 121**C**), and often symmetrically in both wings. During subsequent PBs, from 1-4 ss occasionally (in ~18% of birds) can be retained, among s1-s8, seldom in a block (see Figs. 25**D** & 121**D**), and less often symmetrically in both wings. A variable number of pp covs can be retained during the 3rd and subsequent PBs, although these molts often are complete. See p. 163 for details on woodpecker molt.

Skull—Pneumaticization patterns probably are unhelpful for ageing; see Family account.

Age—Juv (May-Sep) is like HY/SY but averages duller and has the central crown rarely (Red-shafted Group) to often (Yellow-shafted Group) washed with red, p10 rounded and large (tip usually > 17 mm from the pp covs, *vs* usually < 16 mm in adults; see Fig. 127), rects narrow and pointed with the contrast between the red/yellow and the black tip less pronounced (Fig. 132), and iris gray-brown. Juv ♀♀ usually have no red wash to the crown (possibly a tint of red in ♀♀ of the Yellow-shafted Group) whereas juv ♂♂ sometimes (Red-shafted Group) to usually (Yellow-shafted Group) have a slight to

Juvenal   Adult
(HY/AHY)

FIGURE 132. Shape and color pattern of juvenal and adult rectrices (r2-r5) in Northern and Gilded flickers. Note that the juvenal rectrices are replaced during the first prebasic molt, and do not indicate HY/SY birds, as has been reported previously. See also Figure 124.

moderate red wash to the crown, and juv ♀♀ of both subspecies groups lack the reddish moustache whereas juv ♂♂ have a pale orange moustache (even in the Yellow-shafted Group, where the adult ♂♂ have black moustaches). Thus, juvs can be reliably sexed by reddish-tinged moustaches and crowns (Yellow-shafted Group having a stronger reddish wash to the crown than Red-shafted Group, sex for sex); more study is needed.

HY/SY (Oct-Sep): Pp covs uniform (Fig. 122A), quickly becoming faded brown and worn by winter/spring (Fig. 122B); **and** ss either uniform in color and wear, the terts becoming worn to very worn by spring (Fig. 121A), or (occasionally) ss uniform except for 1-4 feathers (among s7-s11) contrastingly fresh (Fig. 121B). **Note: Fresh fall HY/SYs can closely resemble ASY/ATYs with uniform ss and pp covs. On these look for retention of juvenal characters on HY/SYs (through Oct), especially a larger p10 (the last primary replaced, in Sep-Oct), juvenal pointed rects (Fig. 132), and/or iris color grayer or browner (vs deep red in ASY/ATYs) through Jan. Look also for the p10 of HY/SYs to average intermediate in size and shape between juvs and AHY/ASYs (see Fig. 127); more study is needed.**

SY/TY (Oct-Sep): Consecutive outer 1-5 pp covs dark brown and fresh, contrasting with the faded brown and abraded, consecutive, retained inner pp covs (Fig. 122C); **and** ss either uniformly adult (Fig. 25B), the terts fresh or slightly worn by spring, or (sometimes) ss with 1-4 juvenal feathers (among s1-s5) retained, often symmetrically in both wings, faded, abraded, and contrasting markedly with the fresher, replaced adult feathers (Figs. 25C & 121C). **Note: See HY/SY. Some intermediates can be difficult to separate reliably from ASY/ATY and should be aged AHY/ASY.**

ASY/ATY (Oct-Sep): Pp covs either uniformly dark brown and fresh (Fig. 122A), or pp covs irregularly mixed with fresh and moderately worn, retained adult feathers (Fig. 122D); **and** ss either uniformly adult (Fig. 25B), the terts relatively fresh, or (occasionally) ss with 1-4 older adult feathers (among s1-s8) retained, often not symmetrically in both wings, moderately worn, and contrasting only slightly with the replaced feathers (Figs. 25D & 121D). **Note: See HY/SY and SY/TY. ASY/ATYs with isolated, retained juvenal pp covs (Fig. 122E), or with three generations of pp covs, sequentially replaced as in Figure 122F, might be reliably aged TY/4Y (see p. 165), but more study is needed.**

Sex—CP & BP are unreliable for sexing. ♀ wg(n100) 138-175, tl(n100) 88-123, exp culmen(n100) 27.9-40.0; ♂ wg(n100) 140-177, tl(n100) 86-124, exp culmen(n100) 30.6-42.5; see **Geographic variation**.

♀: Moustachial region uniform in color with the rest of the face. **Note: The amount of red in the hindcrown varies more by subspecies group than it does by sex (present on both sexes in the Yellow-shafted Group and usually absent in both sexes of the Red-shafted Group) and thus should not be used in sexing. Also, see Age regarding the red wash to the crown in juvs.**

♂: Red, black, or mixed red-and-black moustache present. **Note: See ♀.**

Northern Flicker

See Fig. 24

Hybrids reported—Gilded Flicker.

References—Stone (1896), Ridgway (1914), Forbush (1927), Bent (1939), Test (1945), Roberts (1955), Wood (1969), Rea (1970a), Oberholser (1974), Sheppard & Klimkiewicz (1976), Short

(1982), CWS & USFWS (1991), Moore (1995), Pyle & Howell (1995); C.S. Robbins (*in litt.* to the BBL); IBP (MAPS) data, PRBO data.

GILDED FLICKER
Colaptes chrysoides

GIFL
Species # 4140
Band size: 3-2

Species—From yellow-shafted forms of Northern Flicker by smaller average size (wg 140-153, tl 86-101; see **Sex**); crown and nape pale cinnamon, without red; face pale bluish gray; moustache of ♂ red; black tips of the outer rects (r5) large (> 20 mm from tip in adult). Beware of hybrids.

Geographic variation—Weak and clinal where ranges meet. Subspecies taxonomy follows Short (1982); see also Grinnell (1914a), Ridgway (1914), van Rossem (1930b), Phillips (1961a), Phillips *et al.* (1964), Short (1965), Kaufman (1979a, 1991a), Rea (1983), Behle (1985), Moore (1995). Three other subspecies occur in Mex.

    C.c. mearnsi (res desert se.CA-sw.AZ): From the other subspecies of Mex by larger size (see **Sex**, *vs* wg 135-147, tl 88-97 in the other subspecies); upperparts paler and grayer with the dusky barring less distinct.

Molt—PB: HY incomplete (Jun-Oct), AHY incomplete-complete (Jun-Oct); PA absent. The 1st PB may include more wing covs and inner ss, on average, than in Northern Flicker: 1-4 inner ss (among s7-s11) may be replaced in ~22% of HYs. Otherwise, replacement patterns are similar to those of Northern Flicker (which see).

Skull—Pneumaticization patterns probably are unhelpful for ageing; see Family account.

Age—Juv (Apr-Sep) is like HY/SY, but averages duller and has the central crown rarely washed with red, p10 rounded and large (tip usually > 16 mm from the pp covs, *vs* usually < 15 mm in adults; see Fig. 127), rects narrow and pointed with the contrast between the yellow and the black tip less pronounced (Fig. 132), and iris gray-brown. Juv ♀♀ usually have no red wash to the crown and lack the reddish moustache whereas juv ♂♂ sometimes have a slight to moderate red wash to the crown and have a pale orange moustache; thus, juvs can be reliably sexed by reddish-tinged crowns and/or moustaches. Otherwise, ageing through TY or ATY closely follows that of Northern Flicker (which see).

Sex—CP & BP are unreliable for sexing. ♀ wg(n23) 140-153, tl(n28) 86-100, exp culmen(n18) 29.6-35.5; ♂ wg(n30) 141-153, tl(n20) 86-101, exp culmen(n11) 34.2-40.1; see **Geographic variation**.

♀: Moustachial region uniform in color with the rest of the face. **Note: See Northern Flicker regarding red in the hindcrown, which Gilded Flicker usually lacks. Occasional ♂♂ (non-juvs) can show a few red feathers in the hindcrown.**

♂: Red moustache present. **Note: See ♀.**

Hybrids reported—Northern Flicker.

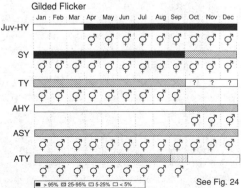

Gilded Flicker

See Fig. 24

References—Ridgway (1914), Bent (1939), Test (1945), Rea (1970a), Short (1982), CWS & USFWS (1991), Moore (1995), Pyle & Howell (1995).

PILEATED WOODPECKER
Dryocopus pileatus

PIWO
Species # 4050
Band size: 4-3A

Geographic variation—Moderate, but clinal where ranges meet. Subspecies taxonomy follows Short (1982); see also Ridgway (1914), Howell (1932), Rand (1948a), Mengel (1965). No other subspecies occur.

> ***D.p. abieticola*** (br & wint Alb-c.CA to NS-MD): Large; bill long. ♀ wg(n38) 220-243, tl(n25) 146-180, exp culmen(n19) 47.0-53.0; ♂ wg(n50) 228-255, tl(n33) 147-188, exp culmen(n27) 52.5-59.7. Birds of BC-CA *("picinus")* may average slightly darker upperparts, grayer throats, and less white in the wing than eastern birds,but differences are weak and obscured by individual variation.

> ***D.p. pileatus*** (br & wint sc.TX-s.IL to s.PA-FL): Small; bill short. ♀ wg(n32) 210-233, tl(n32) 136-158, exp culmen(n32) 41.4-49.0; ♂ wg(n28) 220-235, tl(n28) 142-161, exp culmen(n28) 45.0-52.5. Birds of FL *("floridanus")* average smaller, with blacker upperparts, and with less white in the pp but variation is broadly clinal; supposed distinction also may have been based on foxed specimens.

Molt—PB: HY incomplete (Jun-Oct), AHY incomplete-complete (Jun-Oct); PA absent. The 1st PB includes no to a few inner lesser and med covs, occasionally 1-4 inner gr covs, all pp and rects, and occasionally 1-3 inner ss (among s7-s10; replacement of ss occurs in ~17% of HYs; see Fig 121**B**), but usually no pp covs. The 2nd PB usually includes all wing covs, pp, and rects, but only 1-4 outer pp covs (see Fig. 121**C**); 1-4 ss sometimes (in ~40% of birds) can be retained during this molt, usually in a block among s1-s6 (see Figs. 25**C** & 121**C**), and often symmetrically in both wings. During subsequent PBs, from 1-4 ss also sometimes (in ~38% of birds) can be retained, among s1-s8, seldom in a block (see Figs. 25**D** & 121**D**), and less often symmetrically in both wings. A variable number of pp covs can be retained during the 3rd and subsequent PBs, although these molts often are complete. See p. 163 for details on woodpecker molt.

Skull—Pneumaticization patterns probably are unhelpful for ageing; see Family account.

Age—Juv (May-Sep) averages duller than adults and has the p10 rounded and large (tip usually > 24 mm from the pp covs, *vs* usually < 21 mm in adults; see Fig. 127), rects narrow and pointed (Fig. 124), and iris probably gray-brown or brownish. Juv ♀ and ♂ resemble adults in the color pattern of the head (although the red color averages pinker; see **Sex**) and can be reliably sexed, even as nestlings.

HY/SY (Oct-Sep): Pp covs uniform (Fig. 122**A**), quickly becoming faded brown and worn by winter/spring (Fig. 122**B**); back feathers and replaced inner wing covs (see **Molt**) black, contrasting with the browner, retained outer wing covs; **and** ss either uniform in color and wear, the terts becoming worn to very worn by spring (Fig. 121**A**), or (occasionally) ss uniform except for 1-3 feathers (among s7-s10) contrastingly fresh (Fig. 121**B**). **Note: Fresh fall HY/SYs can closely resemble ASY/ATYs with uniform ss and pp covs. On these look for retention of juvenal characters on HY/SYs (through Oct), especially a larger p10 (the last primary replaced, in Sep-Oct), juvenal pointed rects, and/or iris color probably grayer or browner (*vs* deep red in ASY/ATYs) through Jan. Look also for the p10 of HY/SYs to average intermediate in size and shape between those of juvs and AHY/ASYs (see Fig. 127); more study is needed.**

SY/TY (Oct-Sep): Consecutive outer 1-5 pp covs blackish and fresh, contrasting with the brown and abraded, consecutive, retained inner pp covs (Fig. 122**C**); back feathers and wing covs uniformly black; **and** ss either uniformly adult (Fig. 25**B**), the terts fresh or slightly worn by spring, or (sometimes) ss with 1-4 juvenal feathers (among s1-s5) retained, often symmetrically in both wings, faded, abraded, and contrasting markedly with the fresher, replaced adult feathers (Figs. 25**C** & 121**C**). **Note: See HY/SY. Some intermediates can be difficult to separate reliably from ASY/ATY and should be aged AHY/ASY.**

ASY/ATY (Oct-Sep): Pp covs either uniformly blackish and fresh (Fig. 122**A**), or pp covs irregularly mixed with fresh and moderately worn, retained adult feathers (Fig. 122**D**); **and** ss either uniformly adult (Fig. 25**B**), the terts relatively fresh, or (sometimes) ss with 1-4 older adult feathers (among s1-s8) retained, often not symmetrically in both wings, moderately worn, and contrasting only slightly with the replaced feathers (Figs. 25**D** & 121**D**). **Note: See HY/SY and SY/TY. ASY/ATYs with isolated, retained juvenal pp covs (Fig. 122E), or with three generations of pp covs, sequentially replaced as in Figure 122F, might be reliably aged TY/4Y (see p. 165), but more study is needed.**

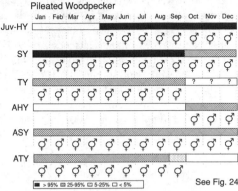

Pileated Woodpecker

Sex—CP & BP are unreliable for sexing. ♀ wg(n70) 210-243, tl(n57) 136-180, exp culmen(n51) 41.4-53.0; ♂ wg(n78) 220-255, tl(n61) 142-188, exp culmen(n55) 45.0-59.7; see **Geographic variation**.

♀: Forehead blackish to olive-brown, contrasting with the red crest; malar region without red.

♂: Forehead (from lores) and crest uniformly red; malar region with a distinct, red stripe.

References—Ridgway (1914), Forbush (1927), Bent (1939), J.S.Y. Hoyt (1944), S.F. Hoyt (1953), Roberts (1955), Wood (1969), Short (1982), Bull & Jackson (1995), Pyle & Howell (1995).

PASSERINES

Molt Limits in North American Passerines

"Molt limits" refer to the boundaries between replaced and retained feathers, resulting from partial or incomplete molts. Recently, Jenni and Winkler (1994) have demonstrated the utility of molt limits, particularly among the wing coverts, tertials, and rectrices, in ageing European passerines. Juvenal wing coverts and flight feathers are relatively worn and often show more subdued color patterns, contrasting noticeably with the fresher and brighter feathers replaced during the first prebasic molt (Fig. 133). Because adult prebasic molts in North American passerines usually are complete, the presence of molt limits indicates an HY/SY bird, at least until the prealternate molt, and often until the second prebasic molt (Mulvihill 1993). Thus, molt limits can be especially useful for ageing in the winter and spring, after HY/SY birds typically have completed skull pneumaticization. To effectively use molt limits, however, variation in the extent of replacement during the first prebasic molt, and the occurrence and extent of prealternate molts (especially in ASYs), must be known. For this guide, over 16,000 specimens of 288 species of North American passerines were examined, to help determine the occurrence and locality of molt limits (Pyle 1997c).

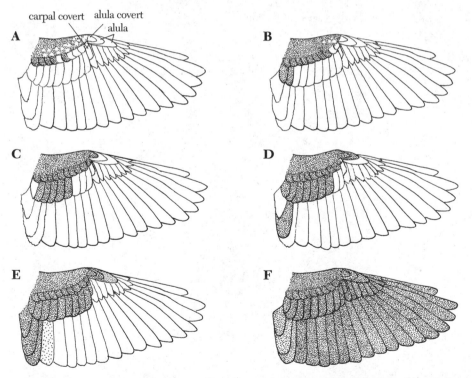

FIGURE 133. Variation in the extent of wing-covert and tertial replacement during partial molts. HY/SYs of many North American passerines will show molt limits similar to those in illustrations **A** to **E**, although exceptions to this pattern of replacement are to be expected; *e.g.*, many species typically replace all greater coverts but no tertials (Figure 134). Most AHY/ASY passerines show uniform replacement (**F**), at least until the prealternate molt, when some AHY/ASYs undergo a partial molt resulting in molt limits as in **A-E**. Note in illustration **F** that the more exposed feathers (such as the tertials) may appear slightly more worn than the less exposed feathers, but that the amount of wear is clinal rather than abrupt. Also beware that many species have "pseudolimits" (see text), comprised of darker feathers that appear to be fresher when they are not. See the accounts for details on each species. Figure from Pyle (1997c)

Molt limits resulting from partial or incomplete, first prebasic molts

The sequence and extent of wing-covert and tertial replacement generally follow similar patterns among North American passerines, although numerous exceptions, both among individuals and among species, can be expected. Molt of the wing coverts typically begins with the proximal lesser coverts, and proceeds distally and toward the greater coverts (Jenni and Winkler 1994, Fig. 133). Thus, it usually commences with the inner lesser and median coverts (Fig. 133A). Often, when about half of the lesser coverts have been replaced, molt of the median coverts commences (Fig. 133A); when about half of the median coverts have been replaced, molt of the greater coverts commences (Fig. 133B); and when about half of the greater coverts have been replaced, molt of the tertials commences (Fig. 133D). Replacement of the greater coverts usually proceeds proximally (Fig. 133B-E), although irregular sequences and skipped feathers, particularly involving the innermost covert (Fig. 133C) often are encountered (Jenni and Winkler 1994). The alula covert is often replaced when molt of the median coverts has been completed, and the carpal covert and alula feathers often are not replaced until molt of the greater coverts has been completed (Fig. 133C-E). Although the alula and carpal coverts are not specifically mentioned in the following species accounts, and the greater and lesser alula feathers are only occasionally mentioned, the age-specific properties of these feathers parallel those of the median, greater and primary coverts, and they should be considered when examining a wing for molt limits or juvenal characters. Partial molts can suspend at any point during this replacement process, and variation in the point of suspension, sometimes substantial, occurs within each species.

In a few birds of some species, s6 and occasionally s5 can be replaced after all three tertials have been renewed (Fig. 133E). It is possible that the same mechanism resulting in "eccentric" replacement patterns of the primaries and secondaries (see below), is responsible for the occasional replacement of s5 and/or s6.

In many species, the central rectrices (r1) can be replaced if and when the tertials are replaced. In a few species, the central rectrices are replaced but the tertials are retained. In some species, some or all other rectrices can be renewed during incomplete molts. These often are replaced from the central pair outwards, although in many individuals the outermost pair may be replaced immediately following the central pair. In many species of passerines, particularly among the vireos, warblers, and sparrows, all wing coverts but no tertials or rectrices are replaced (Fig. 134).

By comparing the typical replacement sequences of Figures 133 & 134 with information presented in the species accounts, on variation in the extent of the first prebasic molts and the differences in appearance between juvenal and first-basic feathers, molt limits can be used to age many HY/SY birds through at least the prealternate molt. Individuals of almost all North American passerines in fall and winter, not in active molt, that show molt limits (Figs. 133A-E & 134) are HY/SYs. Sometimes, the retained juvenal greater coverts also are shorter than the replaced adult coverts, resulting in a "step". AHY/ASYs typically show wing coverts which are uniform in color, size, and wear (Fig. 133F), at least until the prealternate molt.

Accidental or adventitious loss can often result in assymetrically replaced feathers, that should not be considered part of a molt limit. In some species **"pseudolimits"** also occur. These are natural contrasts in color pattern between adjacent feathers, that can simulate

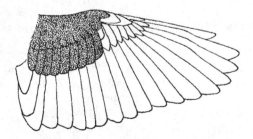

FIGURE 134. Many vireos, warblers, and sparrows show a slight variation to the general pattern of replacement shown in Figure 133, replacing all wing coverts but no alula feathers or flight feathers (see species accounts). In these look for slight contrasts between the fresher greater coverts and the more worn primary coverts. Figure from Pyle (1997c).

molt limits. In *Zonotrichia* sparrows, for instance, the innermost two or three greater coverts and the tertials are a darker or richer brown than adjacent, distal feathers, in both HY/SYs and AHY/ASYs. With these species, care must be taken to distinguish between pseudolimits and true molt limits; it is best to carefully examine the extent of wear to the tips of these feathers to determine if one or more generations of feathers is involved. Jenni and Winkler (1994) provide more information, accompanied by numerous illustrations, on pseudolimits and the process of ageing passerines using molt limits.

Molt limits resulting from partial or incomplete, prealternate molts

Most North American passerines do not have prealternate molts that include greater coverts or tertials, but in those that do, the sequence often is similar to that of prebasic molts, as illustrated in Figure 133. Partial prealternate molts usually are fairly similar in both SYs and ASYs, although the extent of this molt in ASYs usually averages less than that of SYs. In some species, the tertials and/or central rectrices can be replaced during prealternate molts that otherwise include few if any wing coverts.

Care must be taken when ageing these species in spring and summer, as both SYs and ASYs can show molt limits (Mulvihill 1993). Many SYs of certain species (those with more extensive first prebasic than first prealternate molts) can show three generations of feathers in the wing or tail: juvenal feathers, first-basic feathers, and first-alternate feathers (Fig. 135). These individuals can be aged SY. Otherwise, the relative contrast between retained and replaced feathers is the best means of distinguishing the age groups, this contrast being much greater between juvenal and first-alternate feathers than between adult-basic and adult-alternate feathers (see Jenni and Winkler 1994). Contrasts involving the juvenal primary coverts, which are completely or partially retained by most HY/SY North American passerines, often provide the best means of distinguishing SYs and ASYs in the spring and summer.

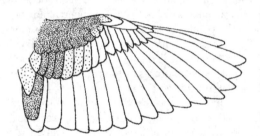

FIGURE 135. An example of molt limits in SY passerines that have partial first prebasic and first prealternate molts, and thus can show three generations of feathers (juvenal, first basic, and first alternate). Most ASYs of these species show only two generations of feathers after the adult prealternate molt, with limits similar to those shown in Figure 133. Figure from Pyle (1997c).

Species that replace at least some primaries during incomplete molts

In at least 54 species of North American passerines, a variable proportion of individuals replace some but not all primaries during incomplete molts. Several replacement strategies occur. The majority of these species (n=46) show **"eccentric"** replacement patterns (see p. 208, Fig. 136), in which the outer primaries, inner secondaries, and (sometimes) the outermost primary coverts are replaced (Jenni and Winkler 1994, Pyle in press). In most of these species, eccentric patterns are found during the first prebasic molt only; however, in several species they can occur during the first and/or adult prealternate molts, at least in some birds. In species showing eccentric replacement of the primaries, the largest distance between adjacent primaries among p2-p7 may assist with ageing, as has been documented in Yellow-breasted Chat (see Fig. 282). Such distances should be analyzed in other species with eccentric molt patterns.

At least eight species of North American passerines show incomplete (arrested) primary and secondary replacement in typical sequence (Fig. 137), the primaries commencing from the innermost and proceeding distally, and the secondaries (after replacement of the tertials) commencing

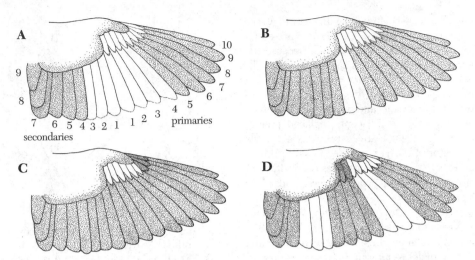

FIGURE 136. Eccentric replacement patterns in North American passerines. Most species show a pattern similar to that of illustration **A**, although some species can show more extensive eccentric replacement, as in illustrations **B** and **C**. A few species can show both an eccentric and a typical pattern, as in illustration **D**. The replacement sequence proceeds distally among the primaries, and proximally among the secondaries, after the tertials have been renewed. Note that many if not all primary coverts are retained during these molts. This figure is typical of eccentric patterns in flycatchers; note that many other species showing these patterns have the p10 abbreviated or lacking. Figure from Pyle (in press).

with the outermost and proceeding proximally (see Fig. 13). In these cases, primary coverts typically are replaced with their corresponding primaries, although one or two coverts often can be retained, despite the replacement of the adjacent primaries (*e.g.*, Fig. 137**B**). At least six species that showed eccentric molt patterns also replaced up to three inner primaries and three outer secondaries, in typical sequence (Fig. 136**D**). In these species, only small proportions of birds (5-16%) showing eccentric replacement also had replaced feathers in typical sequence.

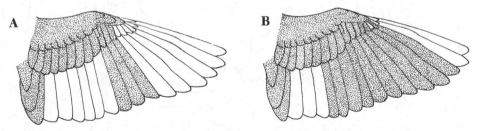

FIGURE 137. Replacement patterns based on incomplete (arrested) flight feather molts in typical sequence (as in complete, adult molts), found during the first prebasic molt in some species of North American passerines. Note that the primary coverts are usually replaced with their corresponding primaries, although one or more coverts can occasionally be retained, otherwise, as in illustration **B**. Figure from Pyle (in press).

Differences between juvenal and adult primary coverts

As can be seen in Figures 133-137, at least some and usually all primary coverts are retained during partial and incomplete first prebasic molts. The shape and the condition of juvenal primary coverts differ from those of adults, being narrower, more tapered, and having thinner edging (if present), matching the color of the upperparts (Fig. 138). Differences are easier to detect in spring than in fall, because the juvenal coverts are less durable and usually wear at a quicker rate than do the adult coverts (Fig. 138C). In all cases, limits between the duller and more worn primary coverts and the adjacent, replaced greater coverts or flight feathers provides a reliable indicator of HY/SYs. AHY/ASYs have primary coverts that do not contrast as markedly (if at all) with adjacent wing coverts and flight feathers, as they all are of the same feather generation. During summer, in species exposed to lots of sunlight (*e.g.*, males that sing on open perches) or to harsh vegetation (*e.g.*, females nesting in thorn scrub or reeds) the primary coverts and other wing feathers of both age groups can become quite worn, making it impossible to age many birds by molt limits involving these feathers. On these, the shape and condition of the rectrices (Fig. 139) and (sometimes) the primaries (Fig. 140) can still be useful in ageing.

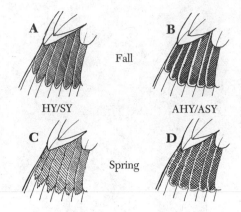

FIGURE 138. The shape and relative condition of the primary coverts in HY/SY (**A** & **C**) and AHY/ASY (**B** & **D**) passerines, in fresh (fall) and worn (spring) condition. The contrast between these feathers and replaced greater coverts often is very useful in ageing (Figure 134). Note that the edging on these feathers, if present in a given species, is thinner in HY birds than in AHY birds in the fall, and it is often absent in SY birds but still present in ASY birds in the spring. Figure from Pyle (1997c).

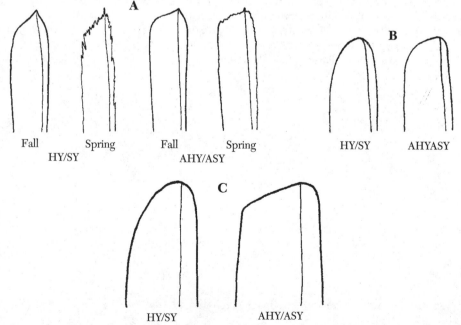

FIGURE 139. The shape of the outer rectrices (r4-r6) by age, as found in many passerines of different sizes. Note the "corner" effect on the inner webs of AHY/ASY feathers, absent or reduced in HY/SY feathers. Also note that the juvenal feathers of SY typically become more abraded by spring than the adult feathers of ASY (as shown in illustration **A**), although many adults, especially nesting ♀♀ of arid habitats, can also show extremely abraded rectrices.

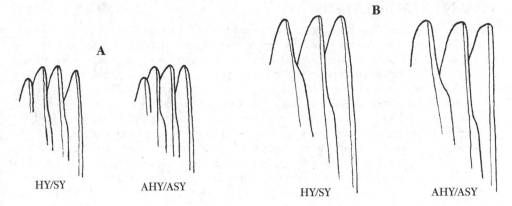

FIGURE 140. The shape of the outer primaries (p7-p10) as is found in passerines of different sizes.

A call to banders: More study is needed

The information presented in the species accounts should be used as a starting point toward a more complete understanding of molt limits and their use in ageing North American passerines. Detection of molt limits on specimens is often difficult, in part because the wings cannot be freely examined without risking damage to specimens that were not prepared with open wings. In the species accounts, errors likely exist on molt limits which will need to be corrected, see Pyle (1997c). In addition, the usefulness of molt limits involving the carpal covert, alula covert, and greater and lesser alula feathers, not covered in detail by most of the accounts, should be examined more fully (see Mulvihill & Leberman 1988).

Molt limits are much easier to detect on live birds in the hand than they are on specimens. The ability to open a bird's wing to examine the feathers, and the fact that the feathers are in better relative shape on live birds than on specimens, should allow banders to detect molt limits in most species (a few species such as House Wren, Cedar Waxwing, and Common Yellowthroat will always present difficulties, even on live birds in the hand). Beware, however, that the detection of molt limits usually requires experience with a given species; to gain this experience it is best to carefully examine the wing coverts in a series of birds in the fall, in which ages have been determined through skull pneumaticization. Banders are strongly urged to start looking for molt limits in North American passerines and to publish their information, whether it substantiates or contradicts to that of the species accounts in this guide.

TYRANT FLYCATCHERS   *TYRANNIDAE*

Thirty-six species. Family characters include wide and flat bills, pointed wings, and prominent whiskers on most species. Tyrant flycatchers have 10 primaries (the 10th full in length), 9 secondaries, and 12 rectrices. The first prebasic molt, quite variable in extent and location (even within genera), is partial to complete, with no, some, or all primaries, secondaries and rectrices replaced, but most or all primary coverts usually retained. Prealternate molts also are variable, partial in many SY birds and adults, to nearly complete in SY birds of some species. Windows in the pneumaticization of the skull often are present through spring and should be looked for, although birds with windows may not necessarily be in their first year; more study is needed. In most species plumages are similar by age and sex, with molt limits and the characters of the primary coverts being the best means of ageing. Sexual characters are fairly reliable in the breeding season, although males generally have reduced cloacal protuberances and males of some species develop partial brood patches. Males average slightly larger than females; in two species tail length is sex-specific.

NORTHERN BEARDLESS-TYRANNULET
Camptostoma imberbe

NBTY
Species # 4720
Band size: 0A-0

Species—From other flycatchers by small size (wg 46-59, tl 33-49; see **Geographic variation** & **Sex**); bill narrow and vireo-like; prominent whiskers lacking. From juvenile Verdin and Bushtit by much shorter tl (see above); p10 full in length; p9 ≈ p7; indistinct eye line and supercilium present; bill vireo-like (*cf.* Fig. 214). From Hutton's and Bell's vireos and Ruby-crowned Kinglet by tarsus short (<16 mm); p10 full in length; p9 > p6; presence of a small but distinct crest; wing bars less distinct and buffier; basal half of the lower mandible bright yellow to orange.

Geographic variation—Weak and clinal where ranges meet. Subspecies taxonomy follows Traylor (1979a); see Ridgway (1907), van Rossem (1930c, 1934a), Griscom (1934a). No other subspecies occur.

> *C.i. ridgwayi* (br & wint s.AZ): Large; bill long (exp culmen 8.2-9.6); upperparts olive with little or no grayish; belly washed lemon. ♀ wg(n16) 52-57, tl(n16) 40-46; ♂ wg(n16) 54-59, tl(n16) 42-49.
> *C.i. imberbe* (br s.TX): Small; bill short (exp culmen 7.0-8.7); upperparts olive with a gray wash; belly whitish with a lemon tinge. ♀ wg(n25) 46-54, tl(n25) 33-41; ♂ wg(n32) 50-59, tl(n24) 37-44.

Molt—PB: HY complete (Aug-Nov), AHY complete (Jul-Oct); PA absent-partial (Feb-Mar). The PBs probably occur on the winter grounds. More study is needed on the PAs.

Skull—Pneumaticization completes in HY from 15 Sep through Dec, possibly later.

Age—Juv (May-Sep) has the upperparts washed brownish and the wing edging and tips to rects cinnamon-buff; juv ♀ = ♂. Otherwise, no plumage or flight-feather criteria for ageing are known after the 1st PB (see **Skull**).

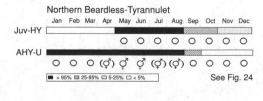

Sex—♀ = ♂ by plumage. CP/BP (Apr-Aug). ♀ wg(n41) 46-57, tl(n41) 33-46; ♂ wg(n48) 50-59, tl(n40) 37-49; see **Geographic variation**.

References—Ridgway (1907), Dickey & van Rossem (1938), Bent (1942), Oberholser (1974), Kaufman (1990a), Pyle (1997c).

OLIVE-SIDED FLYCATCHER
Contopus cooperi

OSFL
Species # 4590
Band size: 1-1B

Species—From Greater Pewee by shorter tl (61-79; see **Sex**); p10 > p7 by 4-6 mm; tarsus < middle toe with claw; sides of the rump with white patches; sides of the underparts with heavy and dusky streaks or mottling, contrasting markedly with the white underparts; lower mandible horn-colored to blackish. From the wood-pewees by most of the above, plus much longer wg (96-117; see **Sex**).

Geographic variation—Weak and complicated by possible dichromatism (grayish and olive plumages), but ranges moderately well defined. Subspecies taxonomy follows Rea (1983); see also Bangs & Penard (1921b), Grinnell (1928c), Wetmore (1939), Zimmer (1939), van Rossem (1945a), Todd (1963), Sutton (1967), Oberholser (1974), Austin & Rea (1976). No other subspecies occur.

C.c. marjorinus (br s.CA): Large, especially bill (exp culmen 16.6-20.9); underparts with extensive gray or dusky olive, the pale central stripe narrow and indistinct. ♀ wg(n40) 103-110, tl(n40) 66-74; ♂ wg(n46) 110-117, tl(n46) 69-79.

C.c. cooperi (br AK-c.CA to Nfl-w.NC): Small, especially bill (exp culmen 15.0-18.8); underparts with reduced, gray or dusky olive, the pale central stripe wide and distinct. ♀ wg(n40) 96-105, tl(n40) 61-70; ♂ wg(n53) 103-112, tl(n53) 64-73.

Molt—PB HY incomplete (Sep-Mar), AHY/ASY complete (Sep-Feb); PA absent. All molting occurs on the winter grounds. The 1st PB is eccentric (see p. 208, Fig. 136), with 7 to 10 (~88%) inner gr covs, the outermost 5-9 pp, the innermost 3-9 ss, the outermost 0 (~72%) to 3 pp covs, and the rects replaced. All pp and ss are replaced in ~21% of HY/SYs. The adult PB is protracted, with the replacement of some flight feathers (usually s5-s6 and p7-p10) often being suspended over the winter. More study is needed on the timing of molt; it is possible that HY/SYs have a protracted overwinter molt whereas AHY/ASYs replace most if not all feathers in Sep-Nov.

Skull—Pneumaticization completes in HY/SY from 15 Oct. Some SYs (and ASYs?) can retain windows (> 3 mm; see Figs. 11**D** & 204) at the rear of the skull through Jun.

Age—Juv (Jun-Nov) has a brownish wash to the upperparts and buff wing bars; juv ♀ = ♂.

Juv-HY/SY (Aug-2nd Nov): Wing bars distinct and brownish buffy or brownish white (through 1st Nov?); most or all outer pp covs narrow and relatively abraded (Fig. 138), the outermost 1-4 pp covs sometimes contrastingly fresher and broader (Fig. 136**C**) in Mar-2nd Nov, contrasting with the slightly fresher gr covs (Fig. 134); the outermost 3-6 ss (among s1-s6), the innermost 1-5 pp (among p1-p5) and sometimes 1-3 outer gr covs juvenal, contrasting with the fresher, replaced gr covs, inner ss, and outer pp (Fig. 136**A-C**) in Mar-2nd Nov; rects narrow and tapered (Fig. 139**A-B**) in Aug-Mar. **Note: Juvs on fall migration are easily separated from SY/ASYs by skull condition (see Skull), wing bar color, and much fresher flight feathers. More study is needed on HY/SYs in Dec-Mar, which may be molting at this time and/or showing contrasting flight-feather generations. Also, HY/SYs in active molt should not be renewing most or all pp covs with their corresponding pp, in contrast to AHY/ASYs which should have pp covs and corresponding pp being replaced simultaneously. Some intermediates may not be reliably aged after Nov.**

AHY/ASY (Aug-2nd Nov): Wing bars indistinct and pale grayish olive; outer pp covs uniformly broad, truncate, relatively dark, and unworn (Fig. 138), not contrasting in wear with the gr covs (Fig. 133**F**); ss and pp uniformly adult (Fig. 133**F**; s5 and/or s6 sometimes contrastingly fresh in Mar-2nd Nov; see Fig. 161); rects truncate (Fig. 139**A-B**). **Note: See Juv-HY/SY.**

Sex—♀ = ♂ by plumage. CP/BP (Apr-Aug). ♀ wg(n100) 96-110, tl(n80) 61-74; ♂ wg(n100) 103-117, tl(n69) 64-79; see **Geographic variation**.

References—Stone (1896), Dwight (1900a), Ridgway (1907), Todd & Carriker (1922), Forbush (1927), Bent (1942), Roberts (1955), Todd (1963), Wood (1969), Oberholser (1974), Pyle (1997c, in press); PNR data, PRBO data.

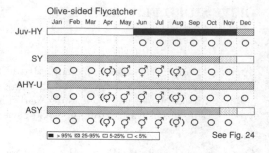

Olive-sided Flycatcher

See Fig. 24

GREATER PEWEE
Contopus pertinax

GRPE
Species # 4600
Band size: 1B

Species—From Olive-sided Flycatcher by longer tl (75-92; see **Sex**); p10 <p7; tarsus – middle toe with claw; sides of the rump without white patches; sides of underparts without streaks and not contrasting markedly with the central belly; lower mandible bright orange-yellow, sometimes tinged pinkish. From wood-pewees by much larger size (wg 95-114; see **Sex**).

Geographic variation—Weak and clinal where ranges meet. Subspecies taxonomy follows Traylor (1979a), as modified by Monson & Phillips (1981); see also Ridgway (1907), Miller & Griscom (1925a), Monroe (1968). One other subspecies occurs in C.Am.

   C.p. pertinax (br & wint s.AZ): From *minor* of C.Am by larger size (see **Sex**; *vs* wg 92-106, tl 72-81 in *minor*). Birds of s.AZ (*"pallidiventris"*) average paler and grayer than birds of s.Mex, but differences are slight and broadly clinal.

Molt—PB: HY partial (Aug-Oct), AHY complete (Jul-Sep); PA absent. The PBs occur primarily or entirely on the summer grounds, although the 1st PB can complete on the winter grounds. The 1st PB includes some or most med covs and 0 (~56%) to 7 inner gr covs, but no terts or rects.

Skull—Pneumaticization completes in HY/SY from 15 Oct. Some SYs (and ASYs?) can retain windows (> 3 mm; see Figs. 11**D** & 204) through spring.

Age—Juv (Jun-Sep) has a cinnamon wash to the upperparts and buffy-cinnamon wing bars; juv ♀ = ♂.

   HY/SY (Sep-Aug): Molt limits occur among the med and gr covs (Fig. 133**A-C**; see **Molt**), the retained outer covs brown with buffy-cinnamon tipping, contrasting with darker and dusky-olive, replaced inner covs; outer pp covs narrow and relatively abraded (Fig. 138); rects narrow, tapered (Fig. 139**A-B**), and tipped buffy cinnamon when fresh (Sep-Dec).

   AHY/ASY (Sep-Aug): Wing covs uniformly adult (Fig. 133**F**) and dusky olive; outer gr covs without buffy-cinnamon tips (sometimes thinly edged yellowish when fresh); outer pp covs broad and relatively fresh (Fig. 138); rects broad, truncate (Fig. 139**A-B**), and not tipped buffy cinnamon.

Sex—♀ = ♂ by plumage. CP/BP (Apr-Aug). ♀ wg(n33) 95-111, tl(n20) 75-86; ♂ wg(n36) 101-114, tl(n20) 82-92.

Hybrids reported—Western Wood-Pewee.

References—Swarth (1904a), Ridgway (1907), Bent (1942), Phillips & Short (1968), Pyle (1997c, in press).

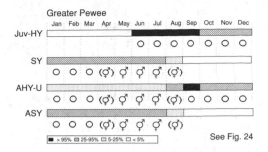

Greater Pewee

See Fig. 24

WESTERN WOOD-PEWEE
Contopus sordidulus

WEWP
Species # 4620
Band size: 0-1C

Species—From Olive-sided Flycatcher by smaller wg (77-92; see **Sex**); p7 > p10 (Fig. 141); tarsus – middle toe with claw; sides of the rump without white patches; underparts fairly uniform, the sides without streaks. From Greater Pewee by much shorter wg (77-92); underside of the lower mandible usually primarily dark (Fig. 142**A-C**). From *Empidonax* flycatchers (especially "Traill's Flycatcher", which see) by much longer wg (77-92); p10 > p6 by 3-8 mm (Fig. 141); eye ring lacking; wing bars less contrasting; lower mandible mostly dusky (Fig. 142**A-C**).

From Eastern Wood-Pewee with extreme caution. The best means of identification of specimens involves the following measurements and formula: tip of the tail to the tip of the longest uppertail cov (**A**) 24.9-33.9 mm (Fig. 143), longest p – longest s (**B**) 22.3-29.7 mm; thus, **A** – **B** = -1.2 to 7.0 mm. A cutoff of 6.5 mm for this formula (**A** – **B**, with Western Wood-Pewee <6.5) identifies ~97.5% of specimens regardless of age, sex or season. **More study is needed on this formula in live birds; it appears as though a cutoff of 8-10 mm may apply.** Plumage and bill characters can provide secondary assistance, but age, plumage wear, and geographic variation must be considered. AHY Western Wood-Pewees have upperparts (including the crown, nape, rump, and uppertail covs) uniformly brown to brown with a slight, dark olive tinge, usually lacking greenish or grayish tones; edging to the underwing covs and bend of the wing usually buff to mustard (occasionally the feathers are entirely dusky); chest band smoky brown, broad, and seldom distinctly interrupted by a pale stripe down the center; sides of the underparts usually without indistinct streaks; centers to the undertail covs average slightly darker; underside of the lower

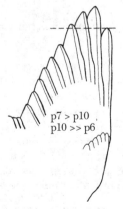

p7 > p10
p10 >> p6

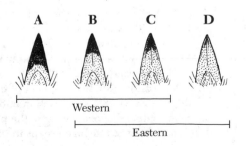

A   B   C   D

Western

Eastern

FIGURE 141. The wing morphology of wood-pewees to separate them from Olive-sided and *Empidonax* flycatchers.

FIGURE 142. Variation in the color of the lower mandible in Western and Eastern wood-pewees.

mandible usually primarily dark (blackish tip usually > 3.5 mm; Fig. 142**A–C**). Juv-HYs are more difficult to separate on plumage and bill color, although most of the above criteria (including the formula **A – B**) apply.

Geographic variation—Weak and clinal where ranges meet. Subspecies taxonomy follows Traylor (1979a); see Ridgway (1907), van Rossem (1940), Phillips & Parkes (1955), Webster (1957), Burleigh (1960b), Behle (1967, 1985), Mayr & Short (1970), Wetmore (1972), Browning (1977b, 1990), Rea (1983). Three other subspecies occur in Mex-C.Am.

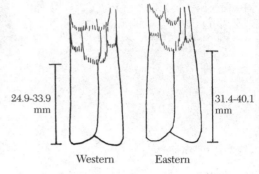

FIGURE 143. The distance between the longest uppertail covert and the tip of the tail in specimens of Western and Eastern wood-pewees. More study is needed on live birds.

C.s. veliei (br interior c.AK-Man to coastal s.CA-w.TX): Upperparts (including the crown) medium-pale grayish with an olive tinge; breast dusky with a pale gray wash; flanks with little or no yellow wash. Birds in the northeastern part of the range may average slightly more olive (hence, closer to Eastern Wood-Pewee) than birds to the southwest. Other described subspecies, larger and darker birds from c.AK-NWT to MT-SD ("*amplus*"), paler and grayer birds from interior s.BC to e.OR-w.MT ("*siccicola*"), and smaller and paler birds from sc.AZ ("*placens*"), were probably based on relative variation in specimen foxing and/or measurement error. Most other subspecies of Mex-C.Am (which could occur as vagrants to N.Am) average darker and slightly smaller by sex; birds from s.Baja CA (*peninsulae*) are paler and have larger bills.

C.s. saturatus (br coastal se.AK-c.OR): Crown dusky, contrasting with the medium-dark brownish or olive back; breast dusky brownish; flanks often washed yellow.

Molt—PB: HY/SY incomplete (Oct-Apr), AHY/ASY complete (Aug-Mar); PA absent. The PBs occur primarily or entirely on the winter grounds, although the adult PB can commence on the summer grounds. Most flight feathers are replaced in Dec-Feb. The 1st PB probably is later than the adult PB. The 1st PB includes all feathers except the pp covs, which apparently are retained. More study is needed, especially on the extent and timing of the 1st PB.

Skull—Pneumaticization completes in HY/SY from 1 Oct through Jan. Look for some SYs (and ASYs?) to retain windows (> 2 mm; see Figs. 11**D** & 204) at the rear of the skull through summer and even fall.

Age—Juv (Jun-Nov) has a brownish to cinnamon wash to the upperparts and buff or cinnamon wing bars; juv ♀ = ♂.

Juv-HY/SY (Aug-Mar): Wing covs with cinnamon or buff edging; outer pp covs narrow and tapered (Fig. 138**A**); unreplaced outer rects and pp tapered (Figs. 139**A** & 140**B**) and relatively fresh. **Note: Some intermediates or birds with early molt of the rects, especially in Jan-Mar, may not be separated reliably from AHY/ASY. The juvenal pp covs apparently are retained through the 2nd PB, although in this species, juvenal and adult feathers are difficult to distinguish. Replacement of the pp without the pp covs in Dec-Apr, however, should indicate HY/SY. With caution and experience, some SYs and ASYs may be separated by relative shape and wear of the pp covs (see Fig. 158) through Oct. Also, look for differences between the age groups in the timing of flight-feather molt (see Molt).**

AHY/ASY (Apr-Mar): Lesser covs uniform in coloration (possibly with narrow, pale grayish edging when fresh); med and gr covs tipped pale grayish or olive; outer pp covs broad and truncate (Fig. 138**B**); unreplaced outer pp and rects truncate (Figs. 139**A** & 140**B**) and relatively abraded in Aug-Feb. **Note: See HY/SY.**

Sex—♀ = ♂ by plumage. CP/BP (Apr-Aug); the CP is poorly developed. ♀ wg(n100) 77-88, tl(n100) 55-69; ♂ wg(n100) 82-92, tl(n100) 61-73.

Hybrids reported—Greater Pewee, Willow Flycatcher.

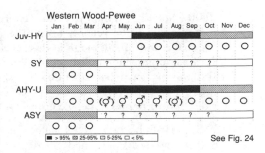

Western Wood-Pewee

See Fig. 24

References—Ridgway (1907), Grinnell (1928c), Bent (1942), Phillips & Parkes (1955), Phillips *et al.* (1964, 1966), Barlow & Rising (1965), Short & Burleigh (1965), Phillips & Short (1968), Wetmore (1972), Oberholser (1974), Phillips (1975a), Browning (1977b), Rising & Schueler (1980), Kaufman (1990a), Pyle & McCaskie (1992), Pyle (1997a, 1997c, in press); S.F. Bailey, J.D. Rising, G.E. Wallace (pers. comm.); IBP (MAPS) data, PRBO data.

EASTERN WOOD-PEWEE
Contopus virens

EAWP
Species # 4610
Band size: 0-1C

Species—See Western Wood-Pewee for separation from Olive-sided Flycatcher, Greater Pewee, and *Empidonax* flycatchers; except for the color of the lower mandible (Fig. 142**B-D**), the same criteria apply. From Western Wood-Pewee with extreme caution. The best means of identification of specimens involves the following measurements and formula: tip of the tail to the tip of the longest uppertail cov (**A**) 31.4-40.1 mm (Fig. 143), longest p – longest s (**B**) 17.3-26.4 mm; thus, **A – B** = 7.0-19.9 mm; a cutoff of 6.5 mm for this formula (**A – B**, with Eastern Wood-Pewee > 6.5) identifies ~97.5% of specimens regardless of age, sex or season. **More study is needed on this formula in live birds; it appears as though a cutoff of 8-10 mm may apply.** Plumage and bill characters can provide secondary assistance, but age, plumage wear, and geographic variation must be considered. AHY Eastern Wood-Pewees have crown dark olive to brownish-olive, usually contrasting slightly with the paler olive or grayish back, the rump and uppertail covs sometimes also being contrastingly grayer; edging to the underwing covs and the bend of the wing feathers often pale yellow; chest band dusky, narrow, and often interrupted by a distinct, pale break down the center; sides of underparts sometimes with indistinct, dusky or olive streaks; centers to undertail covs average paler; lower mandible usually completely or primarily yellow, with the dusky tip usually measuring <3.5 mm (Fig. 142**B-D**). Juv-HYs are more difficult to separate by plumage and bill features, although most of the above criteria (including the formula **A – B**) apply.

Geographic variation—No subspecies are recognized.

Molt—PB: HY/SY incomplete or complete (Oct-Apr), AHY/ASY complete (Aug-Mar); PA absent. The PBs occur primarily or entirely on the winter grounds, although the adult PB can commence on the summer grounds. Flight-feather replacement occurs primarily in Dec-Mar. The 1st PB probably is later than the adult PB and may include all feathers except the pp covs, which may be retained. More study is needed.

Skull—Pneumaticization completes in HY/SY from 15 Oct. Some SYs (and ASYs?) can retain windows (> 2 mm; see Figs. 11**D** & 204) at the rear of the skull through summer and even fall.

Age—Juv (Jul-Nov) has a brownish wash to the upperparts and buff wing bars; juv ♀ = ♂.

Juv-HY/SY (Aug-Mar): Wing covs with cinnamon or buff edging; outer pp covs narrow and tapered (Fig. 138**A**); unreplaced outer pp and rects tapered and relatively fresh (Figs. 139**A**

& 140**B**). **Note: Some intermediates or birds with early molt of the rects, especially in Jan-Mar, may not be reliably aged. The juvenal pp covs apparently(?) are retained through the 2nd PB, although in this species juvenal and adult feathers are very difficult (if not impossible) to distinguish. With caution and experience, occasional SYs and ASYs possibly may be separated by this criterion (see Fig. 158) through Oct. Replacement of the pp without the pp covs in Dec-Apr should indicate HY/SY. Also, look for differences between the age groups in the timing of flight-feather molt (see Molt).**

AHY/ASY (Mar-Feb): Lesser covs uniform in coloration (possibly with narrow, pale grayish edging when fresh); med and gr covs tipped pale grayish or olive; outer pp covs broad and truncate (Fig. 138**B**); unreplaced outer pp and rects truncate (Figs. 139**A** & 140**B**) and relatively abraded in Aug-Feb. **Note: See HY/SY.**

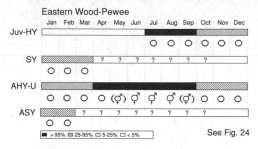

Sex— ♀ = ♂ by plumage. CP/BP (May-Sep); the CP is poorly developed. ♀ wg(n100) 75-86, tl(n50) 55-69; ♂ wg(n100) 78-90, tl(n53) 61-71.

References—Stone (1896), Dwight (1900a), Ridgway (1907), Forbush (1927), Grinnell (1928c), Bent (1942), Roberts (1955), Phillips *et al.* (1964, 1966), Barlow & Rising (1965), Wood (1969), Wetmore (1972), Oberholser (1974), Phillips (1975a), Browning (1977b), Rising & Schueler (1980), Kaufman (1990a), Pyle & McCaskie (1992), McCarty (1996); Pyle (1997a, 1997c, in press); S.F. Bailey, J.D. Rising, G.E. Wallace (pers. comm.); IBP (MAPS) data, PNR data.

Identifying *Empidonax* Flycatchers

We have come a long way since the 1960s, when many, if not all *Empidonax* flycatchers were considered impossible to identify in the hand, unless compared with a series of skins. We also are making progress in identifying vagrants (see Wander & Brady 1984, Keith 1986, DeSante *et al.* 1985, Gibson 1987, Winkler 1988, Haas 1990, Witmer 1991); yet there are still birds that seem to defy certain identification, and separation cannot always be secured without considerable effort (see Winker 1991). The following accounts should enable users to distinguish almost all *Empidonax* flycatchers in the hand (excepting birds of the "Traill's" and "Western" complexes), and especially will emphasize the separation of similar eastern and western species.

A couple of general points should be mentioned. First, when using the finer details of the wing morphology, note that ♂♂ have wings averaging slightly more pointed than ♀♀, generally resulting in primaries 7-10 being slightly longer in comparison with primaries 4-6. Knowing or surmising the sex of the bird (by breeding condition or wing length), therefore, can help in identifying it. Second, as with ageing and sexing, all criteria should be considered before confirming the identification. Many features are given, and reliable identifications are made when almost all (or if lucky, all) features coincide to one species. This usually should be the case, but note that occasional individuals will not be identifiable by in-hand criteria alone. Table 3 summarizes the more important identifying features and Figure 144 depicts the size, shape, and typical color pattern of the lower mandible of each species. These should be consulted for preliminary identifications, which then should be confirmed with the species accounts. As a final clue to identification, check the pattern and extent of molt, as these generally vary substantially by species. Molt is very complicated and variable in *Empidonax*, (see Dickey & van Rossem 1938, Moore 1940a, Mengel 1952, Johnson 1963b, Pyle 1997c, in press), so caution also should be applied when considering molt-related clues.

TABLE 3. Some key characters for the separation of *Empidonax* flycatchers. Measurements are in mm. See the species accounts for more information. Ranges in measurements are based on 95% confidence intervals (see Figure 3) as determined from measurements on at least 40 of each species (see Pyle 1997a). See text for further details, including those on separating Willow from Alder and Pacific-slope from Cordilleran flycatchers.

	Yellow-bellied	Acadian	"Western"	"Traill's"	Least	Hammond's	Dusky	Gray
Upperparts	green	olive	olive	brownish olive to green	grayish olive	grayish olive to grayish	grayish olive to brownish	pale gray or tinged olive
Wg	60-72	65-80	56-72	61-77	56-67	62-75	61-73	63-76
Tl	46-55	52-62	50-63	48-61	49-61	52-62	57-68	55-66
Wg – tl	12-19	12-21	6-15	7-20	6-13	11-19	3-12	8-16
Bill from nares	7.0-9.4	9.2-10.1	7.7-9.2	7.6-10.3	6.3-8.4	6.0-8.0	6.5-8.9	7.6-10.4
Bill width	4.8-5.6	5.3-6.3	5.0-5.8	5.0-6.1	4.4-5.1	4.0-4.6	4.2-5.3	4.4-5.8
Wing Morphology								
Longest p – longest s	10.3-17.5	13.3-23.5	8.6-17.1	10.2-17.4	9.0-15.7	13.3-20.6	9.2-15.2	9.0-16.9
Longest p – p6	2.2-6.7	5.2-9.3	0.2-4.4	1.7-7.4	0.8-3.7	1.8-5.5	0.0-3.0	0.9-4.6
P6 – p10	1.9-6.3	-2.9-1.7	4.7-9.8	-1.4-7.0	2.7-7.0	2.8-8.0	6.0-10.8	4.1-8.1
P9 – p5	5.8-11.5	8.6-14.4	2.8-9.8	4.7-11.6	3.4-7.8	5.6-11.6	2.2-5.5	3.5-8.8
P6 emarginated?	variable	no	yes	no	yes	yes	yes	yes

The inexperienced also should beware of Hutton's and HY White-eyed vireos (which see), surprisingly often mistaken in the hand for *Empidonax* flycatchers (and vice versa), both in banding labs and museum skin trays.

Good summaries or information on general *Empidonax* identification have been compiled by Snyder (1953), Phillips *et al.* (1964, 1966), McBriar (1968), Phillips & Lanyon (1970), Robbins (1972), Phillips (1979), Whitney & Kaufman (1985-1987), McKinney (1988), and Kaufman (1990a). Also, see Benson & Benson (1988) for discriminant function analyses useful in separating eastern *Empidonax* flycatchers, and Pyle (1997a) for 95% confidence intervals of the wing and tail morphology in all species. Note, however, that most of these treatments were based on specimens, and criteria can differ, to some extent, on live birds in the hand. Finally, beware of hybrids (which hopefully will be left unidentified if encountered!); fortunately, hybrids appear to be rare between species of *Empidonax* (see Johnson 1963a, Phillips 1966b).

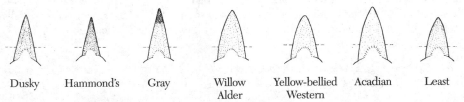

Dusky   Hammond's   Gray   Willow Alder   Yellow-bellied Western   Acadian   Least

FIGURE 144. The relative sizes and shapes of the bills, and the color of the lower mandibles in *Empidonax* flycatchers. See Table 3 for ranges of bill widths at the tip of the nares.

YELLOW-BELLIED FLYCATCHER
Empidonax flaviventris

YBFL
Species # 4630
Band size: 0-0A

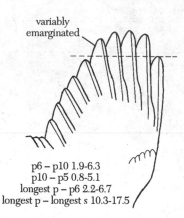

variably
emarginated

p6 – p10 1.9-6.3
p10 – p5 0.8-5.1
longest p – p6 2.2-6.7
longest p – longest s 10.3-17.5

FIGURE 145. The wing morphology of Yellow-bellied Flycatcher. See Figure 10 for measurement techniques.

Species—Separated from the other species of *Empidonax* with caution (Table 3). Medium in size with a relatively short tl (hence, long wg – tl) and moderately long wing morphology (Table 3, Fig. 145); upperparts green; complete eye ring narrow, yellowish and rounded or slightly almond shaped; pp and ss blackish to dark brown, contrasting distinctly with the broad, lemon or whitish wing edging; p6 often (but not always) emarginated; underparts (including the throat) usually strongly washed yellow, the breast band and (sometimes) the flanks dusky greenish; lower mandible usually completely pinkish or pinkish-yellow (Fig. 144); mouth lining orangish; legs dark grayish to brownish.

The uniformly greenish upperparts, complete eye ring, yellow lower mandible, and gray or brownish leg coloration eliminate all other species of *Empidonax* except for Acadian and "Western" flycatchers. From Acadian Flycatcher by smaller size (wg, tl, and bill) and wing morphology, (Table 3, Fig. 145), especially, p10 > p5 by 0.8-5.1 mm, yellower coloration of the underparts (especially the chin and throat), and brighter mouth coloration. From Western Flycatcher by wing morphology, especially the longer longest p – p6, shorter p6 – p10, and longer wg – tl (Table 3, Fig. 145), pp and ss darker (blackish) and with bolder edging, upperparts brighter green, eye ring more rounded, greenish breast band present, and color of the underwing paler. Also, see differences in molt strategies and limits for further identification clues.

Geographic variation—No subspecies are recognized.

Molt—PB: HY partial (Jul-Sep), AHY incomplete-complete (Aug-Oct); PA: SY incomplete (Mar-May), ASY partial-incomplete (Mar-Apr). The 1st PB occurs primarily on the summer grounds, but can be suspended until after migration(?); it can include most to all med covs, 0 (~22%) to 7 inner gr covs and usually (in ~89% of birds) 1-3 terts, but no rects. The 1st PA occurs rapidly and is eccentric (see p. 208 and Fig. 136), with the outermost 5-10 pp and the innermost 3-9 ss, but no pp covs replaced; the gr covs and rects are renewed. The adult PB occurs on the winter grounds, the body plumage and all or most flight feathers being replaced; 1-6 ss (among s1-s7) and the outermost 1-5 pp (among p6-p10) sometimes can be retained. The adult PA includes the body feathers, those flight feathers not replaced during the adult PB, 2-7 inner gr covs, and 1-3 terts.

Skull— Completes in HY/SY from 15 Oct. Some SYs (and ASYs?) can retain windows (> 2 mm; see Figs. 11**D** & 204) at the rear of the skull through summer and even fall.

Age—Juv (Jun-Aug) has brownish upperparts and buff wing bars; juv ♀ = ♂.

Juvenal (Aug-Oct) and Basic (Oct-Apr) plumages

Juv-HY/SY (Aug-Apr): Most juvenal flight feathers retained, not in molt (except sometimes the terts) in Aug-Oct, and relatively abraded in Nov-Apr; molt limits occur among the lesser, med, and gr covs (Fig. 146A; see also Fig. 133A-D and **Molt**), the retained outer covs with buffy-brownish tipping, contrasting with the fresher, duskier, and whitish-tipped or lemon-tipped, replaced inner covs; 1-3 terts usually contrastingly fresh (Fig. 146A); outer pp covs narrow and relatively abraded, with reduced, greenish edging (Fig. 138A); pp and outer ss uniform in wear (Fig. 146A); rects narrow and tapered (Fig. 139A). **Note: Juvs on fall migration are easily separated from SY/ASYs (which see) by skull condition (see Skull), plumage characters (see above) and much fresher flight feathers.**

AHY/ASY (Aug-Apr): Flight feathers molting in Aug-Oct and relatively fresh in Nov-Apr; wing covs and terts uniform in wear (Fig. 146B) and abraded, with the tipping or edging worn off (Aug-Sep), to fresh, with whitish to lemon tipping or edging (Oct-Apr); outer pp covs broad with substantial green edging when fresh (Oct-Apr; Fig. 138B); pp and ss uniformly adult and fresh, or 1-6 ss (among s1-s7) and (occasionally) the outermost 1-5 pp contrastingly worn in Oct-Apr (Fig. 146B); rects broad and truncate (Fig. 139A). **Note: See Juv-HY/SY.**

Alternate Plumage (Apr-Sep)

SY (Apr-Sep): The outermost 5-10 pp and the innermost 3-9 ss often replaced at the PA, contrasting markedly with the retained, juvenal innermost 1-5 pp and middle 1-4 ss (Fig. 146C; see also Fig. 136A); gr covs and terts usually uniformly fresh (Fig. 146C); outer pp covs uniformly narrow, abraded, and brown with little or no green edging (Figs. 146C & 138C); rects fresh. **Note: The separation of SY from ASY in alternate plumage is accomplished readily in this species, although criteria are complex (see Molt) and some relative experience may be required.**

ASY (Apr-Sep): The outermost 1-5 pp, and 1-6 ss (among s1-s7) often replaced at the PA, contrasting slightly with the innermost, adult-basic 5-9 pp and inner and/or outer 2-6 ss (Fig. 146D); 2-7 inner gr covs and 1-3 terts contrastingly fresh (Fig. 146D); outer pp covs broad, fresh, and dusky with green edging (Figs. 139B & 146D); rects relatively worn. **Note: See SY.**

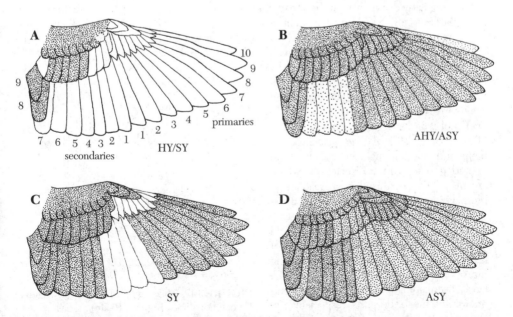

FIGURE 146. Typical molt limits in Yellow-bellied Flycatchers of different age/season groups. Note that the molt strategies differ quite substantially between the ages. See text for details.

Sex—♀ = ♂ by plumage. CP/BP (May-Aug); the CP is poorly developed. ♀ wg(n50) 60-69, tl(n20) 46-53; ♂ wg(n84) 62-72, tl(n20) 48-55. Also, the formula 63.4 + (0.42 × [p10 − p6]) mm, with ♀♀ have wg(flat) less and ♂♂ having wg(flat) more than this value, correctly sexed 97% of specimens (Phillips *et al.* 1966).

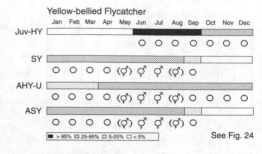

References—Dwight (1900a), Ridgway (1907), Forbush (1927), Dickey & van Rossem (1938), Bent (1942), Mengel (1952), Roberts (1955), Johnson (1963a), Phillips *et al.* (1966), McBriar (1968), Wood (1969), Phillips & Lanyon (1970), Robbins (1972), Oberholser (1974), Sheppard & Klimkiewicz (1976), Phillips (1979), Hussell (1982a, 1982b), DeSante *et al.* (1985), Whitney & Kaufman (1985a, 1986a), McKinney (1988), Kaufman (1990a), CWS & USFWS (1991), Pyle & McCaskie (1992), Pyle (1997a, 1997c, in press); C.S. Robbins (*in litt.* to the BBL); L. Bevier, J. Dierschke, A.R. Phillips (pers. comm.); IBP (MAPS) data, PNR data, PRBO data.

ACADIAN FLYCATCHER
Empidonax virescens

ACFL
Species # 4650
Band size: 0-0A

Species—From the wood-pewees by greenish coloration to the upperparts; p10 < p6, or p10 > p6 by up to 3 mm (Fig. 147); eye ring usually distinct and complete. Separated from the other species of *Empidonax* with caution (Table 3). This is the largest species, with a long wing morphology (Table 3, Fig. 147); upperparts green to greenish olive; eye ring complete, narrow, whitish and rounded, sometimes indistinct or nearly lacking; pp and ss dark and dusky brown, contrasting fairly distinctly with the broad, lemon or whitish wing edging; p6 not emarginated; underparts variably washed yellow; chin usually white; throat white (AHY) to yellowish (juv-HY); breast band dusky olive with a yellow tinge; lower mandible usually almost entirely yellowish-pink (Fig. 144); mouth lining usually flesh to pale yellowish; legs gray.

From most species of *Empidonax* by large size, uniformly green upperparts, yellow lower mandible, and gray legs. From Traill's Flycatchers by bill longer and broader (Table 3), wing morphology longer (Table 3, Fig. 147), eye ring usually complete, and mouth lining usually duller; larger and greener Alder Flycatchers, which are most likely confused with Acadian by plumage and measurements, should be separated readily by their shorter bills (see Tables 3 & 4). From Yellow-bellied and Western flycatchers by the combination of larger size (wg, tl and bill), longer wing morphology and wg − tl (Table 3, Fig. 147), lack of emargination on p6, whiter coloration of the underparts (especially the chin and throat), and pinker mouth col-

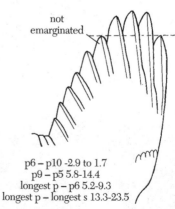

FIGURE 147. The wing morphology of Acadian Flycatcher. See Figure 10 for measurement techniques.

oration. From Western Flycatchers further by eye ring rounded or indistinct. Juvs (see **Age**) have buff edging to the body feathers, creating a scalloped plumage unique among *Empidonax*. Also, see differences in molt strategies and limits for further identification clues.

Geographic variation—No subspecies are recognized.

Molt—PB: HY partial (Jul-Sep), AHY complete (Jul-Sep); PA SY partial-incomplete (Feb-May), ASY partial (Feb-Apr). The PBs occur on the summer grounds. The 1st PB includes few if any lesser and med covs and no gr covs or flight feathers. The 1st PA includes some to all med covs, 0 (~22%) to 7 inner gr covs and usually (in ~83% of birds) 1-3 terts (occasionally s6, as well), but no rects. The adult PA includes fewer feathers: 0 (~73%) to 2 inner gr covs and sometimes (in ~28% of birds) 1-3 terts, but no rects.

Skull—Pneumaticization completes in HY/SY from 15 Nov (as early as 15 Oct in southeastern populations). Some SYs (and ASYs?) can retain windows (> 2 mm; see Figs. 11**D** & 204) at the rear of the skull through summer and even fall.

Age—Juv (May-Aug) has the feathers of the upperparts edged buff, wing bars wide and deep buff, and underparts dull white or faintly suffused with yellowish or brownish; juv ♀ = ♂.

Basic Plumage (Aug-Mar)

HY/SY (Aug-Mar): Underparts (often including the throat) strongly washed yellow; med and gr covs uniformly juvenal, with broad, dark buff tips; outer pp covs narrow and relatively brown with reduced, green edging (Fig. 138**A**); rects tapered (Fig. 139**A**) and tipped buff when fresh (Aug-Oct).

AHY/ASY (Aug-Mar): Throat usually whitish, contrasting with the yellowish breast and belly; med and gr covs uniformly adult, with broad and yellowish tipping; outer pp covs broad and relatively dusky with substantial green edging (Fig. 138**B**); rects truncate (Fig. 139**A**) and without buff tips.

Alternate Plumage (Mar-Aug)

SY (Mar-Aug): Molt limits usually occur among the med and/or gr covs (Fig. 133**A-E**; see **Molt**), the retained, juvenal outer covs brown and tipped buff (when fresh), contrasting markedly with the fresher, dusky and whitish-tipped or lemon-tipped, replaced inner covs; 1-3 terts (and occasionally s6) usually contrastingly fresh (Fig. 133**D-E**; occasionally uniformly juvenal and worn); outer pp covs narrow, brown, abraded, and lacking green edging (Fig. 138**C**); outer pp and rects relatively worn and brownish; rects tapered (Fig. 139**A**). **Note: Intermediates with ASYs can occur that are not reliably aged.**

ASY (Mar-Aug): Molt limits sometimes occur among the wing covs and terts (Fig. 133**A-D**), retained, adult outer covs and terts contrasting slightly with the fresher, replaced inner covs and adjacent ss; outer pp covs broad, relatively fresh, and dusky with green edging (Fig. 138**D**); outer pp and rects relatively fresh; rects truncate (Fig. 139**A**). **Note: See SY.**

Sex—♀ = ♂ by plumage. CP/BP (Apr-Aug); the CP is poorly developed. ♀ wg(n100) 65-75, tl(n22) 52-59; ♂ wg(n100) 69-80, tl(n40) 55-62. The longest p – longest s varies substantially by sex in specimens of this species, being 13.2-18.8 in ♀♀ and 16.9-24.1 in ♂♂. Also, the formula (longest p – longest s) ÷ ([p6 – p10] + 5) with ♀♀ < 32.5 mm and ♂♂ > 32.5 mm correctly sexed 82.5% of specimens (Pyle in press1). More study is needed on the reliability of such formulae for sexing live *Empidonax* flycatchers and other species in the hand.

References—Dwight (1900a), Ridgway (1907), Forbush (1927), Bent (1942), Phillips (1948, 1979), Mengel (1952), Snyder (1953), Roberts (1955), Mumford (1964), Phillips *et al.* (1966), McBriar (1968), Traylor (1968), Wood (1969), Phillips & Lanyon (1970), Robbins (1972), Oberholser (1974), Sheppard & Klimkiewicz (1976), Whitney & Kaufman (1985a, 1986a), Cramp (1988), McKinney (1988), Kaufman (1990a), CWS & USFWS (1991), Winker (1991, 1993), Pyle (1997a, 1997c); C.S. Robbins (*in litt.* to the BBL); A.R. Phillips, C.A. Renk (pers. comm.); IBP (MAPS) data, PNR data.

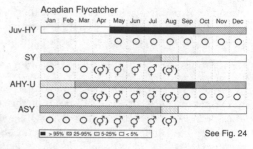

Acadian Flycatcher

See Fig. 24

TRAILL'S FLYCATCHER

TRFL
Species # 4669
Band size: 0

ALDER FLYCATCHER
Empidonax alnorum

ALFL
Species # 4661

WILLOW FLYCATCHER
Empidonax traillii

WIFL
Species # 4660

Southwestern Willow Flycatcher (SWFL)

Species # 4664

Species—"Traill's" Flycatchers (in the broad sense) from wood-pewees by wing shorter (61-77; see Table 3) and less pointed (p10 < p6 or p10 > p6 by up to 1.5 mm; see Fig. 148); partial eye ring and/or pale lores usually present (but sometimes lacking entirely in western forms of Willow Flycatcher; see **Geographic variation**); wing bars boldly contrasting; lower mandible entirely or primarily yellowish or pinkish (Fig. 144). From the other species of *Empidonax* (especially Acadian Flycatcher, which see) by large bill (Table 3); wg and wing morphology generally long (Table 3, Fig. 148); upperparts brownish to olive, with the crown often darker than the back; eye ring absent or incomplete, sometimes with distinctly paler lores; p6 not (occasionally slightly) emarginated; throat usually white; lower mandible entirely or primarily yellowish or pinkish (Fig. 144); mouth lining usually bright orange-yellow; legs blackish.

Alder Flycatchers should be separated from most Willow Flycatchers with great caution, and only with extreme individuals. Alders average slightly longer and more pointed wings (Fig. 148), and smaller bills, such that a scatter diagram involving these characters provides the best clue to their separation from Willows. Following Hussell (1990; but see Seutin 1991) a buffer zone of 15% around the best equations for separation is recommended, within which birds should be left unidentified (Fig. 149). Other measurements and wing-morphology differences

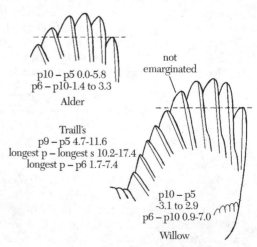

not emarginated

p10 – p5 0.0-5.8
p6 – p10-1.4 to 3.3
Alder

Traill's
p9 – p5 4.7-11.6
longest p – longest s 10.2-17.4
longest p – p6 1.7-7.4

p10 – p5
-3.1 to 2.9
p6 – p10 0.9-7.0

Willow

FIGURE 148. The wing morphology of Alder and Willow flycatchers. See Figure 10 for measurement techniques, and Table 4 for more details.

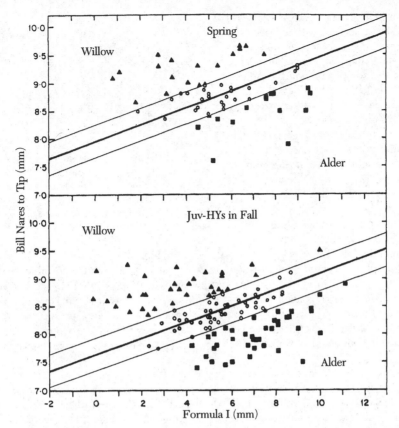

FIGURE 149. A scatter diagram of the bill length (nares to tip) *vs* a wing formula equation in Willow and Alder flycatchers, following Hussell (1990). Formula I is (longest p – p6) – (p5 – p10), the latter value (p5 – p10) being positive if p5 > p10 or negative if p10 > p5. The thin lines represent a buffer zone of 30% around the optimal equation (thick line). Birds with measurements falling within the two thin lines should not be identified.

TABLE 4. 95% confidence intervals (see Figure 3), in mm, useful for identifying "Traill's" Flycatchers. Eastern and western Willow Flycatchers refer roughly to *E.t. campestris* and *trailli vs* the other subspecies, respectively.

Measure	Alder	Eastern Willow	Western Willow
Wg	**66-77**	**63-74**	**61-72**
♀	66-74	63-71	61-69
♂	68-77	67-74	64-72
Tl	**50-61**	**48-59**	**49-60**
♀	50-58	48-56	49-58
♂	52-61	50-59	51-60
Wg – tl	**12.4-20.3**	**11.2-20.1**	**7.1-14.6**
Bill from nares	**7.64-9.24**	**8.06-9.96**	**8.41-10.33**
Wing Morphology			
Longest p – p6	4.0-7.4	3.1-5.9	1.7-4.8
P10 – p5	0.0-5.8	-1.9-2.9	-3.1-1.7
P6 – p10	-1.4-3.3	0.9-4.5	2.0-7.0
P9 – p5	7.2-11.6	6.3-10.2	4.7-9.1
Formula R[1]	2.41-4.68	1.77-2.91	0.98-2.16

[1]Formula R = [(longest p – p6) + (p9 – p5) + (wg – tl)] ÷ [(p6 – p10) + bill from tip of nares].

which can help separate the two species are found in Table 4. As with all species of *Empidonax*, ♂♂ have longer and more pointed wings than ♀♀, hence knowing or surmising the sex (by breeding condition or wg) can be of use. ♀ Alders will most closely approach ♂ Willows in structure and possibly plumage, as well.

Overall, the best plumage features to separate the two species are color of the upperparts (brightish olive in Alder, brown to olive in Willow), size of the crown spots by age (larger in Alder than Willow, by age; Fig. 150), and boldness of the wing bars and edging to the terts (averaging brighter and more contrasting in Alder than in Willow).

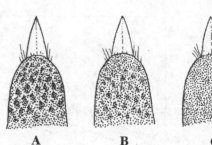

A   **B**   **C**

FIGURE 150. Variation of the distinctness of the crown spots by age (and perhaps by species; see text) in Alder and Willow flycatchers. AHYs, Alder flycatchers, and eastern Willow Flycatchers (*E.t. traillii*) tend to show more distinct spots than HYs and western Willow Flycatchers (see text).

Look also for the lores possibly to average paler and brighter in Alder than in Willow. Western Willow Flycatchers (including *E.t. brewsteri*, *adastus*, and *extimus;* see **Geographic variation**) are decidedly browner or grayer, with less distinct, wing-feather edging than the midwestern and eastern subspecies (*E.t. campestris* and *traillii*; see **Geographic variation**), and western birds average shorter and slightly less pointed wings than eastern birds (See Table 4). Western Willows therefore are identified readily whereas eastern Willows are closer to Alders in plumage and structure and are more difficult (if not impossible) to separate by in-hand criteria alone.

Thus, successful identification of Alder and Willow flycatchers in the hand involves a synthesis of plumage characters, measurements, and wing morphology by age, sex, and geographic variation, and the use of a buffer zone in which birds should be left unidentified. Brown or grayish birds with indicative measurements (Table 4, Fig. 149) are identified reliably as Willow Flycatchers, whereas uniformly greenish birds with relatively bold wing-feather edging only should be identified (by in-hand criteria alone) if their measurements fall outside the buffer zone (Fig. 149, Table 4).

Geographic variation—Alder Flycatcher is here considered monotypic due to confusion related to the species taxonomy; see Phillips (1948). Birds breeding in AK-NWT (*"E.a. alascens"*) average larger than other birds, but variation may be broadly clinal. Variation is moderate to relatively well marked in Willow Flycatcher, although intermediates occur where ranges meet. Subspecies taxonomy follows Browning (1993a); see also Oberholser (1918b, 1932, 1947, 1974), Ridgway (1907), Moore (1940a), Miller (1941a), Twomey (1942), Behle (1948, 1985), Phillips (1948), Aldrich (1951), Jewett *et al.* (1953), Snyder (1953), Stein (1963), Bailey & Niedrach (1965), Wetmore (1972), Unitt (1984, 1987), Pyle (1997a, in press). No other subspecies occur.

Willow Flycatcher

E.t. brewsteri (br se.BC-sw.CA): Wg – tl variably short (4-13 mm); p10 usually ≤ p5; crown and back uniformly dark brown to brownish olive; wing-feather edging indistinct, dull buff or whitish; underparts white with a brown breast band and a pale lemon wash to the vent.

E.t. adastus (br s.BC-sw.Alb to e.CA-c.CO): Wg – tl medium in length (8-13 mm); p10 often ≤ p5; crown and back uniformly medium-dark, brownish olive to grayish olive; wing-feather edging medium buff to whitish; underparts white with a brownish-olive breast band and a moderate lemon wash to the vent. Birds of coastal sw.BC-CA (*"zopholegus"*) may average smaller and darker, but differences, if present, are weak and broadly clinal.

E.t. extimus (br s.NV-c.CO to s.CA-sw.TX): **Southwestern Willow Flycatcher.** Wg – tl short (5-12 mm); p10 usually ≤ p5; crown medium-pale grayish; back medium-pale brownish gray, slightly tinged olive; wing-feather edging pale buff to white; underparts whitish with an indistinct breast band and a slight or no pale lemon wash to the vent.

E.t. campestris (br s.Alb-s.Que to c.CO-c.AR): Wg – tl long (10-15 mm); p10 usually ≥ p5; crown grayish, contrasting with the moderately pale, olive to green back; wing feather edging whitish with a lemon wash; underparts white with a brownish-olive breast band and a moderate lemon wash to the vent. See *E.t. traillii.*

E.t. traillii (br IL-ME to c.AR-c.NC): Wg – tl long (9-15 mm); p10 usually > p5; crown and back uniformly dark to bright olive; wing-feather edging bright, whitish to lemon-yellow; underparts white with a brownish-olive breast band and a moderate to substantial lemon wash to the vent. A recent examination by P. Unitt (pers. comm.) suggests that *traillii* and *campestris* possibly should be synonymized, and that all eastern birds may resemble *campestris,* as described above.

Molt—Exact sequences and extents in all populations are not known, but all molts occur on the winter grounds and strategies appear to differ among populations. In western Willow Flycatchers (*E.t. brewsteri*, at least) it apparently is as follows: PB HY partial (Sep-Nov), AHY incomplete-complete (Aug-Nov); PA SY incomplete (Mar-May), ASY partial-incomplete (Mar-Apr). The 1st PB apparently includes the body plumage but few if any wing covs. The 1st PA is eccentric (see p. 208 and Fig. 136), with the outermost 5-10 pp, the innermost 3-9 ss, and the rects, but no pp covs replaced (~30% replace all pp and ss). A few middle ss (among s2-s6) sometimes can be retained during the adult PB, which are replaced during the adult PA. Alders and eastern Willows (*E.t. traillii*, at least) show flight-feather replacement in Jan-Mar (the timing can be quite variable among individuals), and both SYs and ASYs appear to replace most if not all flight feathers (including the pp covs in SYs?). Whether this occurs during a protracted PB or includes a PA as well (i.e., whether body feathers are replaced once or twice in Aug-Apr), and how this might differ between the age groups is not known. More study obviously is needed on the molting patterns, based on individuals of known species, subspecies, and age.

Skull—Pneumaticization completes in HY/SY from 15 Oct (as early as 15 Sep in populations of Willow in CA). Small proportions (2.6% of 76 birds in Ont) of SYs can retain small windows (> 2 mm; see Figs. 11**D** & 204) at the rear of the skull through May.

Age—Juv (Jun-Oct or Jun-Jan?) has brownish-washed upperparts and buff wing bars; juv ♀ = ♂. Ageing differs among the populations (see **Molt**). For Alder and eastern Willow flycatchers no molt limits or plumage criteria are apparent in spring specimens. Juvenal characters plus relatively fresh flight feathers are reliable for separating HYs through at least Oct and probably HY/SYs through Feb or later. Look also for juv-HY/SYs to have smaller spots in the crown than AHY/ASYs, by species and subspecies (Fig. 150). More study is needed. For western Willow Flycatcher the following appears reliable through the 2nd PB.

Juvenal (Jun-Oct) and Basic (Oct-Apr) plumages (western Willow only?)

Juv-HY/SY (Jun-Apr): Most or all juvenal flight feathers retained, relatively abraded in Dec-Mar, and molting extensively in Mar-May; wing bars buffy brownish; outer pp covs narrow, relatively abraded, and brownish with reduced, olive or brownish edging (Fig. 138A); pp and ss uniform in wear; rects narrow and tapered (Fig. 139A). **Note: Juvs on fall migration are easily separated from SY/ASYs by skull condition (see Skull), wing bar color (see above) and much fresher flight feathers. See above regarding ageing of Alder and eastern Willow flycatchers, and regarding the spots in the crown (Fig. 150).**

AHY/ASY (Aug-Apr): Flight feathers relatively fresh, not molting extensively in Mar-May; wing bars buffy-whitish to lemon; outer pp covs broad and dusky, substantially edged brownish or olive (Fig. 138B); pp and ss uniformly adult and fresh, or up to 5 middle ss (among s2-s6) contrastingly worn (see Fig. 146B); rects broad and truncate (Fig. 139A). **Note: See above regarding ageing of Alder and eastern Willow flycatchers.**

Alternate Plumage (Apr-Sep; western Willow only?)

SY (Apr-Sep): The innermost 1-5 pp and the outermost 1-6 ss often retained juvenal feathers, contrasting markedly with the fresher, outermost 5-9 pp and the innermost 3-9 ss, replaced at the 1st PB (Fig. 136**A-C**); outer pp covs narrow, abraded, and brown with little or no green edging (Fig. 138**C**), contrasting with the slightly fresher gr covs (Fig. 134); rects relatively fresh. **Note: AHYs in Apr-May on the winter grounds, showing extensive replacement of flight feathers, should be SYs. See above regarding ageing of Alder and eastern Willow flycatchers.**

ASY (Apr-Sep): Flight feathers uniformly adult (Fig. 133**F**) or, at most, 1-5 middle ss (among s2-s6) replaced at the PA, slightly fresher than the pp and terts (see Fig. 146**D**); outer pp covs broad, fresh, and dusky with green edging (Fig. 138**B**), not contrasting in wear with the gr covs (Fig. 133**F**); rects relatively worn. **Note: See SY. Also, see above regarding ageing of Alder and eastern Willow flycatchers.**

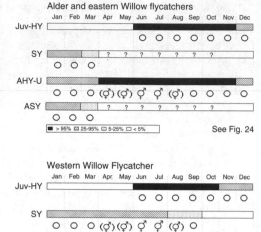

Sex— ♀ = ♂ by plumage. CP/BP (Apr-Aug); the CP is poorly developed. See Table 4 for measurements of each species by sex. Also, the formula $70.9 - (0.27 \times (\text{longest p} - \text{p6}) - (\text{p10} - \text{p5})])$ mm, with ♀♀ have wg(flat) less and ♂♂ having wg(flat) more than this value, correctly sexed 90% of Alder Flycatcher specimens (Phillips *et al.* 1966).

Hybrids reported—Western Wood-Pewee (with Willow Flycatcher).

References—Dwight (1900a), Ridgway (1907), Todd & Carriker (1922), Forbush (1927), Dickey & van Rossem (1938), Bent (1942), Twomey (1942), Phillips (1944a, 1948, 1979), Snyder (1953), Roberts (1955), Stein (1963), Phillips et al. (1964, 1966, 1984), Short & Burleigh (1965), Wood (1969), Phillips & Lanyon (1970), Robbins (1972), Oberholser (1974), Sheppard & Klimkiewicz (1976), Whitney & Kaufman (1985a, 1986a), McKinney (1988), Hussell (1990, 1991a, 1991b), Kaufman (1990a), CWS & USFWS (1991), Winker (1991), Browning (1993a), Pyle (1997a, 1997c, in press); A.B. Flanigan, M.K. Klimkiewicz, C.S. Robbins, K. Winker (*in litt.* to the BBL); D.J.T. Hussell, A.R. Phillips, P. Unitt (pers. comm.); IBP (MAPS) data, PNR data, PRBO data.

LEAST FLYCATCHER
Empidonax minimus

LEFL
Species # 4670
Band size: 0-0A

Species—Separated from the other species of *Empidonax* with caution (Table 3). Small, variable in plumage, with a short wing morphology (Table 3, Fig. 151); upperparts variably brownish olive, grayish, or olive, often with a moderately distinct contrast between the crown and the back; complete eye ring whitish and slightly almond shaped; pp and ss black to dusky brown, contrasting moderately distinctly with the broad, lemon or whitish wing edging; p6 emarginated; throat whitish; underparts pale olive dusky to white with varying amounts of yellow; tail slightly notched (r6 – r1 1-4 mm); outer web of the outer rect (r6) usually slightly and indistinctly paler than the rest of the tail; bill convex in shape and lower mandible variable, often dusky and with a yellow-orange base (Fig. 144); legs blackish. From eastern species of *Empidonax* by the combination of the smaller measurements and shorter wing morphology (Table 3, Fig. 151); the variable and often contrasting plumage of the upperparts and underparts; and the blackish legs. Among western species, Least is most similar to Hammond's and Dusky flycatchers (which see for separation from Gray Flycatcher). From Hammond's Flycatcher by shorter wg, wg – tl, and (especially) longest p – longest s (Table 3, Fig. 151); pp and ss darker, with bolder and whiter edging; tail notch shallower; bill

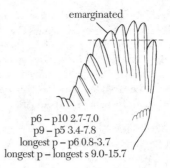

emarginated

p6 – p10 2.7-7.0
p9 – p5 3.4-7.8
longest p – p6 0.8-3.7
longest p – longest s 9.0-15.7

FIGURE 151. The wing morphology of Least Flycatcher. See Figure 10 for measurement techniques.

wider (Table 3) and convex, with the lower mandible usually paler (Fig. 144). From Dusky Flycatcher by shorter tl and wing morphology (especially p6 – p10; Table 3, Fig. 151), bolder wing edging, duller and less contrasting outer web to the outer rect (r6), and wider, more convex bill (Table 3, Fig. 144). Look also for larger and more contrasting dark centers to the crown feathers than in the other *Empidonax* (except Alder Flycatcher; *cf.* Fig. 150). Also, see differences in molt strategies and limits for further identification clues.

Geographic variation—No subspecies are recognized.

Molt—PB: HY partial (Jul-Oct), AHY complete (Jul-Nov); PA: SY partial-incomplete (Jan-May), ASY partial (Feb-Apr). The 1st PB occurs primarily on the summer grounds and includes few if any wing covs and no flight feathers; look for some molting (including terts and rects?) possibly to occur in Oct-Dec on the winter grounds. The 1st PA usually includes most or all med covs, 3-9 gr covs, usually (in ~93% of birds) 1-3 terts (occasionally s6 and rarely s5, as well), and 0 (~44%) to all 12 (~11%) rects; those that replace all rects invariably replace all three terts, as well. Both the 1st PB and the 1st PA can be extended into migration. The adult PB can commence on the summer grounds, but most replacement (including all flight feathers) occurs on the winter grounds. The adult PA includes 2-10 inner gr covs, 1-3 terts, and sometimes (in ~22% of birds) 1-2 central rects (r1).

Skull—Pneumaticization completes in HY/SY from 15 Oct. Some SYs (and ASYs?) retain windows (> 2 mm; see Figs. 11**D** & 204) through spring.

Age—Juv (Jun-Sep) is washed brownish and has buff wing bars; juv ♀ = ♂.

Basic Plumage (Aug-Apr)

HY/SY (Aug-Apr): Flight feathers not molting in Aug-Nov and relatively worn in Oct-Apr; gr and med covs with broad, buff tips; outer pp covs narrow and relatively brown with reduced, green edging (Fig. 138**A**); rects tapered (Fig. 139**A**) and tipped buff when fresh (Aug-Oct).

AHY/ASY (Aug-Apr): Flight feathers molting in Aug-Nov and relatively fresh in Oct-Apr; gr and med covs with fresh, lemon to whitish tips; outer pp covs broad and relatively dusky with substantial green edging (Fig. 138**B**); flight feathers relatively fresh after completion of molt (in Oct-Nov); rects truncate (Fig. 139**A**) and not tipped buff.

Alternate Plumage (Apr-Sep)

SY (Apr-Sep): Molt limits occur among the gr covs and terts (Fig. 133**B-E**; see **Molt**), the retained, outer covs brown and abraded, contrasting markedly with the duskier and lemon-tipped or whitish-tipped, replaced inner covs; outer pp covs narrow, abraded, and brown with little or no green edging (Fig. 138C); 1-3 replaced terts (and occasionally s6) usually contrasting markedly with the adjacent ss (133D-E); outer pp and often at least some rects relatively worn and brownish; rects tapered (Fig. 139A), mixed tapered and truncate, or (occasionally) uniformly truncate. **Note: Those SYs (~11% of birds) that replace all rects during the first PA also will show contrastingly fresh terts. Worn birds in Jul-Sep may be difficult to separate from ASY.**

ASY (Apr-Sep): Molt limits as in SY (see **Molt**) but retained outer gr covs brownish-dusky with lemon tips, contrasting slightly with the duskier and lemon-tipped or whitish-tipped inner covs; outer pp covs broad, relatively fresh, and dusky with broader green edging (Fig. 138D); replaced terts contrasting slightly with the adjacent ss; outer pp and rects relatively fresh; rects uniformly truncate (Fig. 139A). **Note: See SY.**

Sex— ♀ = ♂ by plumage. CP/BP (May-Aug); the CP is poorly developed. ♀ wg(n100) 56-63, tl(n40) 49-56; ♂ wg(n100) 60-67, tl(n48) 51-59. Also, the formula 61.8 + (0.13 × [p10 − p5]) mm, with ♀♀ have wg(flat) less and ♂♂ having wg(flat) more than this value, correctly sexed 93% of specimens (Phillips *et al.* 1966).

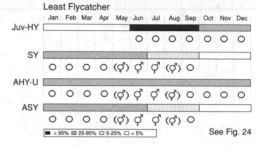

References—Dwight (1900a), Ridgway (1907), Forbush (1927), Dickey & van Rossem (1938), Moore (1940a), Bent (1942), Snyder (1953), Roberts (1955), Johnson (1963a, 1963b), Phillips *et al.* (1964, 1966), Phillips (1966b, 1979), Wood (1969), Phillips & Lanyon (1970), Robbins (1972), Oberholser (1974), Sheppard & Klimkiewicz (1976), Hussell (1980), Sealy & Biermann (1983), Whitney & Kaufman (1985a, 1985b), Kaufman (1990a), McKinney (1988), CWS & USFWS (1991), Briskie (1994), Pyle (1997a, 1997c); C.S. Robbins (*in litt.* to the BBL); I. Hannay, A.R. Phillips, C. Roberts, K.P. Winkler (pers. comm.); IBP (MAPS) data, PNR data, PRBO data.

HAMMOND'S FLYCATCHER
Empidonax hammondii

HAFL
Species # 4680
Band size: 0-0A

Species—Separated from the other species of *Empidonax* with caution (Table 3). Small with a short wg and tl and a short and fine bill, but a long wing morphology (Table 3, Fig. 152); crown olive (fall) or gray, contrasting with the olive upperparts (spring); complete eye ring white and slightly almond shaped; lores uniform in color with the face or only indistinctly paler; pp and ss dusky, contrasting slightly to moderately with the grayish or lemon-washed (fall) to whitish (spring) wing edging; p6 emarginated; throat gray to grayish white; underparts dark olive and yellow (fall) to grayish olive with a yellow wash (spring); outer web of the outer rects (r6) indistinctly paler than the rest of the tail; tail strongly notched (r6 − r1 4-6 mm); bill small, thin (Table 3), and straight; lower mandible dusky with a slightly paler base (AHY) to primarily orange (juv-HY; Fig. 144); legs blackish.

From most other species of *Empidonax* by the combination of smaller measurements and longer wing morphology (Table 3, Fig. 152), darker underparts, and blackish legs. From Least Flycatcher by longer wg, wg − tl and (especially) longest p − longest s (Table 3, Fig. 152); pp and ss duskier and with less distinct edging; tail notch deeper; bill narrower (Table 3) and straighter, with the lower mandible usually darker (Fig. 144). From Dusky and Gray flycatchers by smaller bill, larger wg − tl and p9 − p5 (Table 3, Fig. 152), and outer web to the outer rect (r6) usually less contrasting. Also, see differences in molt strategies and limits for further identification clues: fall adult Hammond's are fresh, with bright lemon underparts, and spring adults are very worn; whereas in Least, Dusky, and Gray flycatchers (which see) adults are worn in the fall and relatively fresh in the spring.

Geographic variation—No subspecies are recognized. See Johnson (1966a), Pyle (1997a).

Molt—PB: HY partial (Jul-Oct), AHY complete (Jul-Sep); PA partial (Feb-Apr). The PBs occur on the summer grounds. The 1st PB includes few if any wing covs and no flight feathers. The 1st PA includes some med covs, 0 (~23%) to 5 inner gr covs, and occasionally (in ~19% of birds) 1-2 terts,

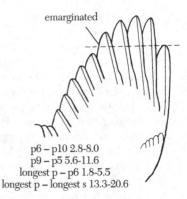

emarginated

p6 – p10 2.8-8.0
p9 – p5 5.6-11.6
longest p – p6 1.8-5.5
longest p – longest s 13.3-20.6

FIGURE 152. The wing morphology of Ham_mond's Flycatcher. See Figure 10 for measurement techniques.

but usually no other flight feathers. The adult PA usually includes 0 (~7%) to 7 inner gr covs and often (in ~73% of birds) 1-3 terts, but no rects.

Skull—Pneumaticization completes in HY/SY from 15 Oct. Some SYs (and ASYs?) retain windows (> 2 mm; see Figs. 11**D** & 204) through summer.

Age—Juv (May-Sep) has brownish-washed upperparts and buff wing bars; juv ♀ = ♂.

HY/SY (Sep-Aug): Wing bars and edging washed buff in Sep-Mar; molt limits occur among the med and gr covs in Mar-Aug (Fig. 133**A-D**; see **Molt**), the retained, outer covs brownish, contrasting markedly with the lemon to grayish-olive, replaced inner covs; 1-2 terts occasionally fresh and contrasting markedly with the adjacent ss in Mar-Jul (Fig. 133**D**), but terts usually (in ~79% of birds) retained and relatively abraded; outer pp covs narrow, brownish, and abraded (Fig. 138); rects narrow and tapered (Fig. 139**A**); underparts dingy olive in Sep-Mar; lower mandible averages more orange (through Nov, possibly later).

AHY/ASY (Sep-Aug): Wing bars and edging lemon to grayish olive in Sep-Mar; molt limits occur among the med and gr covs in Mar-Aug (Fig. 133**A-D**; see **Molt**), the retained, outer wing covs lemon to grayish olive, contrasting only slightly with the replaced inner covs; 1-3 terts often fresh and contrasting slightly with the adjacent ss in Mar-Aug (Fig. 133**D-E**) or (in ~27% of birds) retained but relatively fresh; outer pp covs broad, relatively dusky, and fresh (Fig. 138); rects broad and truncate (Fig. 139**A**); underparts bright yellowish in Sep-Mar; lower mandible averages duskier.

Sex—♀ = ♂ by plumage. CP/BP (Apr-Aug); the CP is poorly developed. ♀ wg(n100) 62-72, tl(n100) 52-59; ♂ wg(n62) 65-75, tl(n100) 55-62. ♂♂ have much more pointed wings than ♀♀ and probably can be distinguished reliably using a wing-morphology formula, as in other species of *Empidonax*.

Hammond's Flycatcher

	Jan	Feb	Mar	Apr	May	Jun	Jul	Aug	Sep	Oct	Nov	Dec
Juv-HY						○	○	○	○	○	○	○
SY				○	○	○	(♀)	♂	♂	♂	(♀)	
AHY						○	(♀)	♂	♂	♂	(♀) ○	○ ○ ○
ASY				○	○	○	(♀)	♂	♂	♂	(♀)	

■ > 95% ▨ 25-95% ▢ 5-25% ☐ < 5%

See Fig. 24

Hybrids reported—Dusky Flycatcher.

References—Ridgway (1907), Swarth (1922), Dickey & van Rossem (1938), Moore (1940a), Bent (1942), Johnson (1963a, 1963b, 1966a), Phillips *et al.* (1964), Phillips (1966b, 1979), Phillips & Lanyon (1970), Oberholser (1974), Whitney & Kaufman (1985a, 1985b), Kaufman (1990a), Sedgwick (1994), Pyle (1997a, 1997c); I. Hannay, A.R. Phillips, K.P. Winkler (pers. comm.); IBP (MAPS) data, PRBO data.

DUSKY FLYCATCHER
Empidonax oberholseri

DUFL
Species # 4690
Band size: 0-0A

Species—Separated from the other species of *Empidonax* with caution (Table 3). Medium wg and moderately long tl (thus short wg – tl), fairly short and fine bill and short wing morphology (Table 3, Fig. 153; p10 often < p4, unique among the *Empidonax* of N.Am); head usually grayish, contrasting with the grayish-olive or grayish-brown back; complete eye ring white and rounded; lores usually distinctly pale; pp and ss dusky, contrasting slightly with the buff-washed (fall juv-HY) to olive (AHY) wing edging; p6 emarginated; throat dingy whitish; underparts primarily grayish olive with a varying amount of yellow wash (greater in the spring than in the fall, unlike Hammond's); outer edge of the outer rects (r6) whitish, contrasting fairly distinctly with the rest of the tail; tail slightly notched (r6 – r1 1-5 mm); bill thin (Table 3) and straight, the lower mandible varying from primarily dusky (AHY/ASY) to dull horn (juv-HY) or (often) horn, with an indistinctly defined dusky tip (Fig. 144); legs blackish.

From most other species of *Empidonax* by the combination of short wg – tl and medium wing morphology (Table 3, Fig. 153), grayish and contrasting upperparts, dingy grayish-olive and yellow underparts, and blackish legs. From Least Flycatcher by longer tl and wing morphology (especially p6 – p10; Table 3, Fig. 153), wing edging duller, outer web to the outer rect (r6) brighter and more contrasting, and bill narrower and less convex (Table 3, Fig. 144). From Hammond's Flycatcher by larger bill, smaller wg – tl difference and shorter p9 – p5 (Table 3, Fig. 153); lores often contrastingly pale, and outer web to the outer rect (r6) usually more contrastingly whitish. From Gray Flycatcher with caution, especially with HYs in autumn: useful criteria include shorter bill, wg – tl and p9 – p5, and longer p6 – p10 (Table 3, Fig. 153), slightly darker and more contrasting upperparts, and indis-

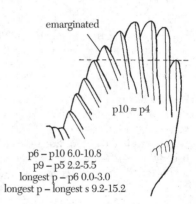

FIGURE 153. The wing morphology of Dusky Flycatcher. See Figure 10 for measurement techniques.

tinctly defined color pattern to the lower mandible (Fig. 144). Also, see differences in molt strategies and limits for further identification clues; fall adults are worn and spring adults are fresh, in contrast to Hammond's Flycatcher (which see).

Geographic variation—Subspecies taxonomy follows Traylor (1979a), who considered the species monotypic (synonymizing a previously recognized subspecies); see also Johnson (1963a, 1966b), Browning (1974, 1978, 1990), Oberholser (1974), Pyle (1997a). Birds of BC-Sask to OR (*"E.o. spodius"*) may average grayer and longer-winged, but variation, if present, is slight and broadly clinal. Birds of coastal BC-CA also average shorter wg – tl (3.2-9.6 mm) than birds of interior BC-AZ (4.5-12.8 mm).

Molt—PB: HY partial (Sep-Nov), AHY complete (Sep-Nov); PA: SY partial (Feb-May), ASY limited-partial (Feb-Apr). The PBs can commence on the summer grounds, but most or all molts usually occur on the winter grounds. The 1st PB includes 0 (~15%) to 5 inner gr covs and often (in ~77% of birds) 1-3 terts, but no rects. The 1st PA includes 0 (~10%) to 6 inner gr covs, usually (in ~83% of birds) 1-3 terts, and occasionally (in ~7% of birds) 1-2 central rects. The adult PA usually includes no gr covs or flight feathers.

Skull—Pneumaticization completes in HY/SY from 15 Oct. Some SYs (and ASYs?) occasionally retain windows (> 2 mm; see Figs. 11**D** & 204) through summer/fall.

Age—Juv (May-Sep) has buff wing bars; juv ♀ = ♂.

> Juv-HY/SY (Aug-2nd Oct): Wing bars and edging washed buff (especially in Aug-Dec); molt limits occur among the wing covs and terts (Fig. 133**A-D**; see **Molt**), with three generations of feathers often present in Mar-2nd Oct (see Fig. 135); the retained outer covs brown with buff to whitish tips, contrasting with the duskier and olive-tipped or lemon-tipped, replaced inner covs; 1-3 terts usually contrastingly fresh (Fig. 133**D-E**), occasionally uniformly juvenal and relatively abraded; outer pp covs narrow, brownish, and relatively abraded (Fig. 138); pp and rects relatively fresh in the 1st Aug-Sep, not molting in Sep-Nov, and relatively worn in Nov-2nd Oct; rects narrow and somewhat tapered (Fig. 139**A**), r1 occasionally contrastingly fresh in Mar-2nd Oct. **Note: HYs are separated from SYs in Aug-Oct by incompletely pneumaticized skulls (see Skull), uniformly buff wing bars, and much fresher flight feathers, which are very abraded on SYs at this time. Intermediates will occur which are not separated reliably from AHY/ASY by plumage alone, especially without experience.**

> AHY/ASY (Nov-Oct): Wing bars and edging lemon to pale olive (Oct-May), or whitish to worn off (Jun-Sep); wing covs and terts uniformly adult (Fig. 133**F**); outer pp covs broad, dusky, and relatively fresh (Fig. 138); pp and rects relatively worn in Aug-Sep, molting in Sep-Oct, and relatively fresh in Nov-Jul; rects uniformly adult, broad, and somewhat truncate (Fig. 139**A**). **Note: See Juv-HY/SY.**

Sex—♀ = ♂ by plumage. CP/BP (Apr-Aug); the CP is poorly developed. ♀ wg(n100) 61-70, tl(n86) 57-64; ♂ wg(n100) 63-73, tl(n100) 59-68. A wing-morphology formula probably can be used to sex some birds, as in other *Empidonax* flycatchers; more study is needed.

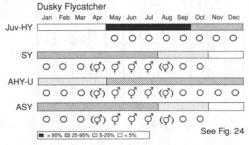

Hybrids reported—Hammond's Flycatcher, Gray Flycatcher.

See Fig. 24

References—Ridgway (1907), Phillips (1939, 1944b, 1959b, 1966b, 1979), Moore (1940a), Bent (1942), Johnson (1963a, 1963b, 1966b), Phillips *et al.* (1964, 1966), Phillips & Lanyon (1970), Oberholser (1974), Whitney & Kaufman (1985a, 1985b), Kaufman (1990a), Sedgwick (1993), Pyle (1997a, 1997c); K. Burton, A.R. Phillips, E. Ruhlen (pers. comm.); IBP (MAPS) data, PRBO data.

GRAY FLYCATCHER
Empidonax wrightii

GRFL
Species # 4691
Band size: 0-0A

Species—Separated from the other species of *Empidonax* with caution (Table 3). Large, with a long bill and a medium wing morphology (Table 3, Fig. 154); upperparts uniformly pale grayish or brownish gray (adult) to grayish olive (juv-HY); complete eye ring white and rounded; pp and ss dusky or brownish gray, contrasting moderately with the pale lemon or buff-washed (fall) to whitish (spring) wing edging; p6 emarginated; throat whitish; underparts olive-dusky with a slight (AHY) to a moderate (juv-HY), yellow wash; outer web of the outer rect (r6) white,

contrasting markedly with the rest of the
tail; tail slightly notched (r6 – r1 1-4 mm);
bill long (Table 3) and straight, the lower
mandible pale pinkish to yellowish, with a
distinctly defined dark tip (Fig. 154); legs
blackish.

From most other species of *Empidonax*
by the combination of the long wg and bill
(Table 3), uniformly pale and grayishwashed upperparts, relatively pale underparts, blackish legs, and lower mandible pattern (Fig. 144). From Dusky Flycatcher
(which see for separation from Least and
Hammond's flycatchers) with caution, especially with HYs in autumn: useful criteria
include longer bill, wg – tl and p9 – p5, and
shorter p6 – p10 (Table 3, Fig. 154), slightly
paler upperparts, and distinctly defined color pattern of the lower mandible (Fig. 144). Also, see
differences in molt strategies and limits for further identification clues.

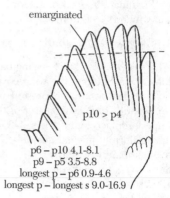

FIGURE 154. The wing morphology of Gray
Flycatcher. See Figure 10 for measurement
techniques.

Geographic variation—No subspecies are recognized. See Johnson (1966b).

Molt—PB: HY partial (Aug-Nov), AHY complete (Jul-Nov); PA: SY partial-incomplete (Mar-
May), ASY limited-partial (Mar-May). All molts occur on the winter grounds. The 1st PB
includes 3-7 inner gr covs, usually (in ~92% of birds) 1-3 terts, and occasionally (in ~17%
of birds) 1-2 central rects (r1). The 1st PA includes some or all med covs, 0 (9%) to 6 inner
gr covs, usually (in ~95% of birds) 1-3 terts (occasionally s6 as well), and sometimes (in
~36% of birds) 1-2 central rects (r1). The adult PA includes 0 (63%) to 5 inner gr covs and
sometimes (in ~50% of birds) 1-3 terts, but no rects; occasional replacement of s6 during
the adult PA might indicate retention of this feather during the adult PB; more study is
needed.

Skull—Pneumaticization completes in HY/SY from 15 Oct. Some SYs (and ASYs?) can retain
windows (> 2 mm; see Figs. 11**D** & 204) through spring.

Age—Juv (May-Sep) has olive-washed upperparts, buff-washed wing bars, and a stronger lemon
wash to the underparts; juv ♀ = ♂.

Juv-HY/SY (Aug-2nd Oct): Wing bars and edging washed buff; molt limits occur among the
wing covs and terts (Fig. 133**B-E**; see **Molt**), with three generations of feathers often present
in Apr-2nd Oct (see Fig. 135); retained outer covs brown with buff to whitish tips, contrasting markedly with the duskier and olive-tipped to lemon-tipped, replaced inner covs; 1-3
terts usually contrastingly fresh (Fig. 133**D-E**), rarely retained (juvenal) and relatively abraded; outer pp covs narrow, brownish, and relatively abraded (Fig. 138); pp and rects relatively fresh in the 1st Aug-Sep, not molting in Sep-Nov (except occasionally 1-2 central rects),
and relatively worn in Nov-2nd Oct; rects narrow and somewhat tapered (Fig. 139**A**), the central rects (r1) occasionally (Aug-Mar) to sometimes (Mar-2nd Oct) contrastingly fresh. Note: HYs
are separated from SYs in Aug-Oct by incompletely pneumaticized skulls (see Skull), more green
in the coloration of the upperparts, uniformly buff wing bars, more yellow in the underparts and
(especially) much fresher flight feathers, which are very abraded on SYs at this time.

AHY/ASY (Nov-Oct): Wing bars and edging lemon to whitish (Nov-May), or whitish to worn off
(Jun-Oct); wing covs and terts uniformly adult (Fig. 133**F**; Nov-Mar), or molt limits sometimes
present among the med and gr covs in Apr-Oct (Fig. 133**A-D**; see **Molt**), but at most only two

generations of feathers present, and the replaced, adult terts and inner covs contrast only slightly with the adjacent ss and outer covs; outer pp covs broad, dusky, and relatively fresh (Fig. 138); pp and rects relatively worn in Aug-Sep, molting in Sep-Oct, and relatively fresh in Nov-Jul; rects uniformly adult, broad, and somewhat truncate (Fig. 139**A**).

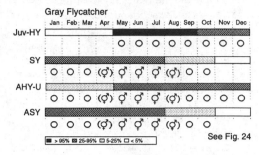

Gray Flycatcher

See Fig. 24

Sex—♀=♂ by plumage. CP/BP (May-Jul); the CP is poorly developed. ♀ wg(n55) 63-73, tl(n20) 55-63; ♂ wg(n61) 66-76, tl(n20) 57-66. A wing-morphology formula probably can be used to sex some birds, as in other *Empidonax* flycatchers; more study is needed.

Hybrids reported—Dusky Flycatcher.

References—Ridgway (1907), Phillips (1939, 1944b, 1959b, 1966b, 1979), Moore (1940a), Bent (1942), Johnson (1963a, 1963b, 1966b), Phillips *et al.* (1964, 1966), Phillips & Lanyon (1970), Oberholser (1974), Whitney & Kaufman (1985a, 1985b), Kaufman (1990a), Pyle (1997a, 1997c); A.R. Phillips (pers. comm.); IBP (MAPS) data, PRBO data.

WESTERN FLYCATCHER

WEFL
Species # 4649
Band size: 0-0A

PACIFIC-SLOPE FLYCATCHER
Empidonax difficilis

PSFL
Species # 4641

CORDILLERAN FLYCATCHER
Empidonax occidentalis

COFL
Species # 4640

Species—"Western" Flycatcher (in the broad sense) separated from the other species of *Empidonax* with caution (Table 3). Medium in size with a relatively long tl (hence, short wg – tl) and a moderately short wing morphology (Table 3, Fig. 155); upperparts greenish olive (brownish olive in some juvs); complete eye ring wide, whitish or yellowish, and almond shaped; pp and ss brownish, contrasting relatively indistinctly with the dull whitish, brownish-white, or buff wing edging; p6 emarginated; underparts (including the throat) variably washed yellow, with the breast band and flanks sometimes washed brownish to brownish olive but not contrastingly greenish; lower mandible usually entirely yellow or flesh-colored (Fig. 144); mouth lining orangish; legs gray.

The greenish-olive upperparts, the presence of a complete, almond-shaped eye ring, the yellow or flesh lower mandible, and the gray leg coloration eliminates the other *Empidonax* of N.Am except for Yellow-bellied and Acadian flycatchers. From Acadian Flycatcher by smaller size (wg, tl, and bill) and much shorter wing morphology (Table 3, Fig. 155), emargination of p6, and mouth coloration brighter. From Yellow-bellied Flycatcher by wing morphology (Table 3, Fig. 155), especially, p10 usually < p5 (by -0.3 to 4.4 mm), upperparts duller green or olive, eye ring almond shaped, indistinct breast band brownish or olive, and pp and ss browner with duller edging. Also, see differences in molt strategies and limits for further identification clues. Pine Flycatcher (*E. affinis*), a potential vagrant to se.AZ, can be separated from Western by having bill width at tip of nares ≤ 4.5 mm (< 5/8 bill nares to tip, *vs* > 5/8 in Western); p6 – p10 9-14 mm (*vs* 5-10 in Western; see Table 3); p5 > p10 by 3-8 mm (*vs* p5 < p10 or p5 > p10 by 0-2 mm in Western Flycatcher); wing edging bolder and yellower; underparts darker olive.

The separation of Pacific-slope from Cordilleran flycatchers by in-hand criteria alone should be performed with extreme caution and the realization that many individuals cannot be identified. In addition to subtle (and overlapping) plumage features and differences in bill size (see Geographic variation), Pacific-slope Flycatchers average slightly smaller and shorter wing morphology (see Pyle 1997a), especially p9 – p5. The best formula known using a combination of measurements is: ([p6 – p10] + [longest p – longest s] + [wg – tl]) × (p9 – p5) = 61.7-283.5 mm in Pacific-slope and 157.8-331.0 mm in Cordilleran, allowing separation of about 60% of individuals. Within each sex, this formula results in 75-216 mm for ♀ and 88-299 mm for ♂ Pacific-slope Flycatchers, and 156-279 mm for ♀ and 191-346 mm for ♂ Cordilleran Flycatchers, allowing separation of about 70% of individuals of known sex. This formula is based on specimens and the values may differ somewhat on live birds; more study is needed. There likely are other formulas (e.g., including bill measurements; see **Geographic variation**) that can help distinguish even larger proportions of individuals. Also, see differences in the average placement of molt limits.

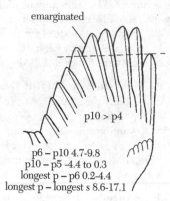

FIGURE 155. The wing morphology of "Western" Flycatcher. See Figure 10 for measurement techniques. See text for formulas useful in separating Pacific-slope and Cordilleran flycatchers.

Geographic variation—Generally weak, although most ranges are well defined. Subspecies taxonomy (of both species) follows Traylor (1979a); see Ridgway (1907), Brodkorb (1935c, 1949), Moore (1940a, 1940b), Behle (1948), Phillips *et al.* (1964), Phillips (1966b, 1966c, 1994a), Hubbard & Crossin (1974), Weske (1976), Johnson (1980, 1994), Whitney & Kaufman (1986b). No other subspecies of *E. difficilis* occur, and one other subspecies of *E. occidentalis* occurs in Mex.

Pacific-slope Flycatcher

E.d. difficilis (br coastal se.AK-s.CA): Medium in size; bill small (exp culmen 9.5-12.2, bill width at tip of nares 4.7-5.7); exp culmen ÷ wg small (0.14-0.19 mm); plumage medium pale, dull, olive and yellow; wing bars dark ochre-buff (juv-HY) to pale lemon (basic). ♀ wg(n100) 59-68, tl(n74) 51-58; ♂ wg(n100) 61-70, tl(n100) 54-61.

E.d. insulicola (br Channel Is, CA): Wg medium in length but tl and bill long (exp culmen 10.7-11.3); exp culmen ÷ wg small (0.15-0.18 mm); wing bars buffy (juv-HY) to white (basic). ♀ wg(n9) 62-67, tl(n9) 54-61; ♂ wg(n10) 64-70, tl(n10) 57-63.

E.d. cineritius (br s.Baja CA; vag to AZ): Small but bill long (exp culmen 10.6-13.2); exp culmen ÷ wg large (0.18-0.24 mm); wing bars dingy buff (juv-HY) or dingy whitish with a lemon tinge (basic). ♀ wg(n11) 59-67, tl(n11) 52-57; ♂ wg(n16) 62-69, tl(n16) 55-61.

Cordilleran Flycatcher

E.o. helmayri (br s.BC-s.Alb to ne.CA-w.TX): Large; bill large (exp culmen 11.2-13.5, bill width at tip of nares 5.4-6.2); plumage medium dark, brightish olive and yellow; wing bars dark buffy (juv-HY) to buffy lemon (basic); ♀ wg(n60) 62-71, tl(n20) 54-62; ♂ wg(n62) 65-75, tl(n32) 57-65.

Molt—PB: HY partial (Sep-Dec), AHY complete (Aug-Nov); PA: SY partial-incomplete (Mar-May), ASY partial (Feb-Apr). Most molting occurs on the winter grounds. The 1st PB varies in extent between Pacific-slope and Cordilleran flycatchers. In Pacific-slope it often (in ~60% of birds) includes 1-5 inner gr covs and sometimes (in ~28% of birds) includes 1-3 terts (rarely s6 as well), but no rects. In Cordilleran it usually (in ~93% of birds) includes 1-8 inner gr covs and includes 1-3 terts (sometimes s6 and rarely s5), but no rects. The 1st PAs include 0 (~40%) to 5 inner gr covs, often (in ~70% of birds) 1-3 terts, and rarely (in ~5% of birds) 1-2 central rects (r1). The adult PAs include 0 (~70%) to 3 inner gr covs, sometimes (in ~29% of birds) 1-3 terts, and occasionally (in ~6% of birds) 1-2 central rects (r1). The PAs also average more extensive in Cordilleran than in Pacific-slope Flycatcher.

Skull—Pneumaticization completes in HY/SY from 15 Oct (as early as 15 Sep in birds of s.CA). Some SYs (and ASYs?) can retain windows (> 2 mm; see Figs. 11**D** & 204) through spring.

Age—Juv (May-Oct) has dull, brownish-washed upperparts and underparts, and buffy wing bars; juv ♀ = ♂.

Juv-HY/SY (Aug-2nd Oct): Wing bars and edging washed buff; molt limits occur among the wing covs and terts (Fig. 133**A-D** in Pacific-slope, Fig. 133**B-D** in Cordilleran; see **Molt**), with three generations of feathers often present in Mar-2nd Oct (see Fig. 135); retained outer covs brown with buff to whitish tips, contrasting with the duskier and olive-tipped to lemon-tipped, replaced inner covs; 1-3 terts sometimes (Pacific-slope) or usually (Cordilleran) contrastingly fresh in Nov-Mar (Fig. 133**D-E**) or very worn and abraded (see **Molt**); outer pp covs narrow, relatively abraded, and brownish with reduced or no olive edging (Fig. 138); pp and rects relatively fresh in Aug-Oct, not molting in Sep-Nov, and relatively worn in Nov-2nd Oct; rects narrow and tapered (Fig. 139A). **Note: HYs are separated from SYs in Aug-Oct by incompletely pneumaticized skulls (see Skull), uniformly buff wing bars, and much fresher flight feathers, which are very abraded on SYs at this time.**

AHY/ASY (Nov-Oct): Wing bars and edging lemon to whitish (Oct-May), or whitish to worn off (Jun-Sep); wing covs and terts uniformly adult (Fig. 133**F**) or with some replaced, adult feathers in Mar-Oct (see **Molt**; at most only two generations of feathers are present); outer pp covs broad, relatively fresh, and dusky with broader olive edging (Fig. 138); pp and rects relatively worn in Aug-Sep, molting in Sep-Oct, and relatively fresh in Nov-Aug; rects broad and truncate (Fig. 139A).

Sex—♀ = ♂ by plumage. CP/BP (Mar-Aug); the CP is poorly developed. Pacific-slope ♀ wg(n100) 59-68, tl(n100) 51-61; ♂ wg(n100) 61-70, tl(n100) 54-63; see **Geographic variation.** Cordilleran ♀ wg(n60) 62-71, tl(n20) 54-62; ♂ wg(n62) 65-75, tl(n32) 57-65. Wing-morphology formulas for each species probably can be used to sex some birds, as in other *Empidonax* flycatchers; more study is needed.

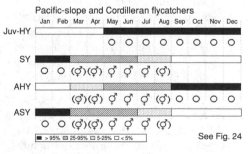

Pacific-slope and Cordilleran flycatchers

References—Ridgway (1907), Bent (1942), Miller (1955a), Phillips & Lanyon (1970), Johnson (1974, 1980), Oberholser (1974), DeSante *et al.* (1985), Whitney & Kaufman (1985a, 1987), Kaufman (1990a), Pyle (1997a, 1997c); I. Hannay, A.R. Phillips (pers. comm.); IBP (MAPS) data, PRBO data.

BUFF-BREASTED FLYCATCHER
Empidonax fulvifrons

BBFL
Species # 4700
Band size: 0-0A

Species—Juvs and worn adults in spring/summer may resemble other species of *Empidonax*, especially Least Flycatcher. From these by smaller size (wg 55-64, tl 43-50; see **Geographic variation** & **Sex**); wg – tl long (12-19 mm); bill small (exp culmen < 11.0, width at tip of nares < 5.0); upperparts brownish; wing edging dull grayish.

Geographic variation—Moderate, with the ranges of the northern subspecies well defined. Subspecies taxonomy follows Traylor (1979a); see Ridgway (1907), Lowery & Dalquest (1951), Phillips (1959a, 1966c). Five other subspecies occur in Mex-C.Am.

> **E.f. pygmaeus** (br s.AZ-s.NM; possible vag to sw.TX): From subspecies of Mex-C.Am by smaller size (wg 55-64, tl 43-50; see **Sex**); upperparts relatively dark brownish and/or tinged grayish. Nominate birds of ne.Mex, potential vagrants to s.TX, are larger (wg 59-67, tl 47-57) and have upperparts relatively pale brownish and/or washed olive.

Molt—PB: HY partial (Aug-Sep), AHY complete (Aug-Sep); PA limited (Mar-Apr). The PBs occur primarily on the summer grounds. The 1st PB includes some to most med covs and often (in ~56% of birds) 1-3 inner gr covs, but no flight feathers.

Skull—Pneumaticization completes in HY from 1 Oct through Dec.

Age—Juv (Jun-Sep) has duller brown upperparts and distinct, buff wing bars; juv ♀ = ♂.

> HY/SY (Sep-Aug): Breast relatively rich buff (Sep-Mar); molt limits occur among the med and (often) the gr covs (Fig. 133**A-B**; see **Molt**), the replaced inner covs fresher, with pale lemon tips, contrasting with the browner and buff-tipped to whitish-tipped, retained outer covs; outer pp covs narrow, relatively abraded, and brownish with reduced or no brownish-olive edging (Fig. 138); terts, outer pp, and rects relatively worn; rects tapered (Fig. 139A). **Note: Intermediates can be difficult to separate from AHY/ASYs.**

> AHY/ASY (Sep-Aug): Breast relatively pale buff (Sep-Mar); wing covs uniformly adult (Fig. 133**F**), tipped pale lemon or buffy lemon; outer pp covs broad, relatively fresh, and dusky with broader brownish-olive edging (Fig. 138); terts, outer pp, and rects relatively fresh; rects truncate (Fig. 139A). **Note: See HY/SY.**

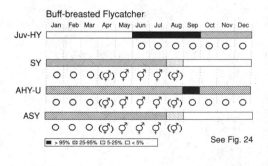

Sex—♀ = ♂ by plumage. CP/BP (Apr-Aug); the CP is poorly developed. ♀ wg(n37) 55-61, tl(n20) 43-48; ♂ wg(n40) 57-64, tl(n23) 44-50; measurements include *E.f. pygmaeus* only (see **Geographic variation**).

References—Swarth (1904a), Ridgway (1907), Bent (1942), Phillips *et al.* (1964), Phillips & Lanyon (1970), Whitney & Kaufman (1987), Bowers & Dunning (1994), Pyle (1997c); R.K. Bowers (pers. comm.).

BLACK PHOEBE
Sayornis nigricans

BLPH
Species # 4580
Band size: 1C

Geographic variation—Moderate, but broadly clinal where ranges meet. Subspecies taxonomy follows Traylor (1979a); see Ridgway (1907), Grinnell (1927a), Swarth (1929), van Rossem (1931a), Dickey & van Rossem (1938), Hubbard & Crossin (1974). Five other subspecies occur in Mex-S.Am.

> ***S.n. semiatra*** (br & wint throughout range in N.Am): From other subspecies by head plumage dull dusky black (*vs* sooty black); white wing bars absent; undertail covs white (CA-AZ), sometimes tinged grayish (NM-TX; *vs* dusky or streaked grayish in the other subspecies). Birds of n.Baja CA & s.AZ (*"salictaria"*) may average slightly smaller and darker, but variation is weak and broadly clinal.

Molt—PB: HY partial-incomplete (Jul-Oct), AHY complete (Jun-Sep); PA absent. The PBs occur primarily on the summer grounds, although post-breeding dispersal is possible before molting completes. The 1st PB includes most to all med covs, 4 to 10 (~14%) inner gr covs, usually (in ~86% of birds) 1-3 terts, and often (in ~54% of birds) 1-2 central rects (r1; occasionally other rects).

Skull—Pneumaticization completes in HY/SY from 15 Jul. Some SYs (and ASYs?) can retain windows (> 2 mm; see Figs. 11**D** & 204) through spring.

Age—Juv (Apr-Sep) has cinnamon tipping to the feathers of the upperparts and cinnamon wing bars; juv ♀ = ♂.

> HY/SY (Aug-Jul): Molt limits usually occur among the med and/or gr covs (Fig. 133**C-E**; see **Molt**), the retained outer covs brown with buff or cinnamon tips when fresh, contrasting with the blackish and gray-tipped, replaced inner covs (all covs occasionally are uniformly blackish); 1-3 terts contrastingly fresh (Fig. 133**D-E**), or occasionally (in ~14% of birds) uniformly juvenal and relatively abraded; outer pp covs narrow and brownish with broad, rusty tips (Aug-Feb) to very abraded and brownish (Jan-Jul; Fig. 138**C**); pp and rects brownish black to brownish and relatively worn; rects tapered (Fig. 139**B**) and tipped buff when fresh (Aug-Oct); central rects (r1; occasionally others) often contrastingly fresh.

> AHY/ASY (Aug-Jul): Wing covs uniformly adult (Fig. 133**F**), the gr covs tipped grayish to grayish white (sometimes tinged buff when fresh); terts and middle ss uniform in color and wear and relatively fresh; outer pp covs broad and blackish with little or no rusty tipping (Fig. 138; they can be edged narrowly with rusty when fresh); pp and rects blackish to grayish black and relatively fresh; rects uniformly adult, truncate (Fig. 139**B**), and tipped whitish when fresh.

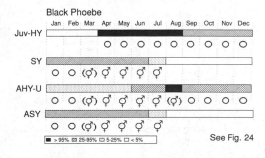

Sex—♀ = ♂ by plumage. CP/BP (Mar-Aug); CP may be poorly developed. ♀ wg(n100) 79-92, tl(n44) 69-83; ♂ wg(n100) 82-96, tl(n43) 72-87; see **Geographic variation.**

References—Ridgway (1907), Dickey & van Rossem (1938), Bent (1942), Oberholser (1974), Shields (1993), Pyle (1997c), Wolf (1997); R. Colwell, K. Shields (pers. comm.); IBP (MAPS) data, PRBO data.

EASTERN PHOEBE
Sayornis phoebe

EAPH
Species # 4560
Band size: 0-1C-1

Species—From *Empidonax* flycatchers and wood-pewees by the combination of large size (wg 76-91, tl 63-78; see **Sex**); p10 < p5; wing bars lacking or indistinct; lower mandible entirely black.

Geographic variation—No subspecies are recognized.

Molt—PB: HY partial (Aug-Nov), AHY complete (Jul-Oct); PA absent. The PBs occur on the summer grounds. The 1st PB includes most to all med covs, 4 to 10 (~18%) inner gr covs, usually (in ~82% of birds) 1-3 terts, and often (in ~64% of birds) 1-2 central rects (r1).

Skull—Pneumaticization completes in HY/SY from 15 Sep. Some SYs (and ASYs?) can retain windows (> 2 mm; see Figs. 11**D** & 204) at the rear of the skull through spring or summer.

Age—Juv (Jun-Aug) has a brownish-cinnamon wash to the upperparts and indistinct, buff wing bars; juv ♀ = ♂.

HY/SY (Aug-Jul): Molt limits usually occur among the med and/or gr covs (Fig. 133**C-E**), the retained outer covs brownish olive with dark buff tips when fresh, contrasting with the olive and grayish-tipped, replaced inner covs (all covs are occasionally uniformly olive); 1-3 terts usually contrastingly fresh (Fig. 133**D-E**) or occasionally (in ~18% of birds) uniformly juvenal and relatively abraded; outer pp covs narrow and tipped rusty (Aug-Feb), or brownish and relatively abraded (Jan-Jul; Fig. 138**C**); pp and rects relatively worn; rects tapered (Fig. 139**B**) and tipped buff when fresh (Aug-Oct); central rects often contrastingly fresh; white area of the breast averages smaller and grayer. Note: Some intermediates can be difficult or impossible to separate from AHY/ASY.

AHY/ASY (Aug-Jul): Wing covs uniformly adult (Fig. 133**F**), the gr covs tipped grayish to grayish white (sometimes tinged buff when fresh); terts and middle ss uniformly adult and relatively fresh; outer pp covs broad, blackish, without buff tips, and relatively fresh (Fig. 138); pp and rects blackish to grayish black and relatively fresh; rects uniformly truncate (Fig. 138) and tipped whitish when fresh; white area of the breast averages larger. **Note: See HY/SY.**

Sex—♀ = ♂ by plumage. CP/BP (Apr-Aug); CP may be poorly developed. ♀ wg(n100) 76-89, tl(n20) 63-75; ♂ wg(n72) 79-91, tl(n20) 67-78; see Conrad & Robertson (1993) for a discriminant function analysis, based on live birds, using wg and tarsus, that correctly sexed 79-95% of birds in Ont.

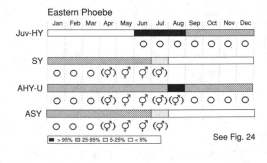

References—Stone (1896), Dwight (1900a), Ridgway (1907), Forbush (1927), Bent (1942), Roberts (1955), Wood (1969), Oberholser (1974), Yunick (1984), Conrad & Robertson (1993), Weeks (1994), Pyle (1997c); D. Cimprich (pers. comm.); IBP (MAPS) data, PNR data.

SAY'S PHOEBE
Sayornis saya

SAPH
Species # 4570
Band size: 1C

Geographic variation—Weak to moderate and confused by rapid feather wear and individual variation; note that specimen foxing has also complicated the subspecies designations. Subspecies taxonomy follows Traylor (1979a), as modified by Rea (1983); see also Bishop (1900), Grinnell (1926a), Swarth (1926a, 1926b), Rand (1948b), Phillips *et al.* (1964), Oberholser (1974), Browning (1976). One other subspecies occurs in Mex.

S.s. yukonensis (br AK-NWT to coastal OR, wint s.CA-sw.TX): Bill averages small (nares to tip 9.4-11.7, width at tip of nares 4.3-5.7); upperparts medium-dark gray; underparts deep orangish.

S.s. saya (br BC-Man to interior s.CA-w.TX, wint c.CA-w.TX): Bill medium in size (nares to tip 9.8-12.2, width at tip of nares 4.6-5.9); upperparts medium gray; underparts medium tan.

S.s. quiescens (br & wint desert se.CA-sw.AZ): Bill averages large (nares to tip 10.5-12.4, width at tip of nares 5.1-6.1); upperparts pale brownish gray; underparts pale tan to buffy white.

Molt—PB: HY partial (Jul-Sep), AHY complete (Jul-Sep); PA absent-partial (Feb-Apr). The PBs occur on the summer grounds. The 1st PB apparently includes 5 to 10 (~4%) inner gr covs and often (in ~67% of birds) 1-3 terts, but no rects. The 1st PA possibly may include terts in occasional birds. More study is needed; molt limits are difficult to detect due to rapid plumage wear and fading.

Skull—Pneumaticization completes in HY/SY from 1 Sep. Some SYs (and ASYs?) can retain windows (> 2 mm; see Figs. 11**D** & 204) through spring.

Age—Juv (Apr-Aug) has wide, buff wing bars; juv ♀ = ♂.

HY/SY (Aug-May): Molt limits usually occur among the gr covs (Fig. 133**C-E**), the retained outer covs pale brown with buff tips (when fresh), contrasting with the darker brown and whitish-tipped, replaced inner covs; 1-3 terts often contrastingly fresh (Fig. 133**D-E**), but sometimes (in ~33% of birds) uniformly juvenal and relatively abraded; outer pp covs narrow and tipped rusty (Aug-Nov), or relatively brownish and abraded (Dec-May; Fig. 138); pp and rects brownish and relatively worn; rects tapered (Fig. 139**B**) and tipped buff when fresh (Aug-Oct). **Note: Many intermediates cannot be separated reliably from AHY/ASY, especially later in spring when birds of both age groups become very abraded.**

AHY/ASY (Jun-May): Wing covs uniformly adult (Fig. 133**F**), the gr covs tipped pale grayish (sometimes tinged buff when fresh); terts and middle ss (s4-s6) uniformly adult and relatively fresh; outer pp covs broad, dark brown, without buff tips, and relatively fresh (Fig. 138); pp and rects blackish to brownish black and relatively fresh; rects truncate (Fig. 139**B**).

Sex—♀ = ♂ by plumage. CP/BP (Feb-Aug); CP may be poorly developed. ♀ wg(n78) 92-105, tl(n68) 74-86; ♂ wg(n84) 98-109, tl(n74) 77-88.

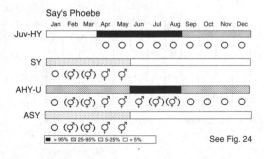

Say's Phoebe

References—Ridgway (1907), Forbush (1927), Bent (1942), Oberholser (1974), Browning (1976), Pyle (1997c); PRBO data.

VERMILION FLYCATCHER
Pyrocephalus rubinus

VEFL
Species # 4710
Band size: 0-0A

Geographic variation—Moderately weak between subspecies of N.Am, and clinal where ranges meet; more marked among the subspecies of Mex-S.Am. Subspecies taxonomy follows Traylor (1979a); see Ridgway (1907), van Rossem (1933, 1934b), Oberholser (1974), Webster (1984). Eleven other subspecies occur in Mex-S.Am.

P.r. flammeus (br & wint s.CA-s.NV to sw.TX; vag to n.CA-NE): Back medium-pale brown with a grayish tinge; head and breast of ASY ♂ red to orange-red, often with pale mottling.

P.r. mexicanus (br & wint TX, wint TX-n.FL; vag to CO-VA): Back medium-dark brown, without grayish; head and breast of ASY ♂ deep red, without orange or pale mottling.

Molt—PB: HY incomplete (Aug-Oct), AHY complete (Jul-Sep); PA absent-limited (Feb-Apr). The PBs occur on the breeding grounds. The 1st PB is eccentric (see p. 208 and Fig. 136), with all gr covs, the outermost 5-10 pp, the innermost 3-9 ss (all pp and ss being replaced in ~54% of birds), the outermost 0 (~30%) to 5 (most often 0-3) pp covs, and the rects replaced. The PA includes few if any wing covs and may be more extensive in SY ♂ than in the other age/sex classes, but more study is needed; most SY ♂♂ seem to retain first-basic plumage through summer.

Skull—Pneumaticization completes in HY/SY from 1 Aug. Some SYs (and ASYs?) can retain windows (> 2 mm; see Figs. 11**D** & 204) through spring.

Age/Sex—Juv (Apr-Sep) has scaly brown upperparts and white underparts with dusky oval spotting; juv ♀=♂, although some juv ♂♂ are tinged pink or have one or more pink or red feathers in the breast, and can be reliably sexed. CP/BP (Feb-Aug); CP may be poorly developed. ♀ wg(n40) 73-84, tl(n20) 55-63; ♂ wg(n100) 76-87, tl(n20) 56-65.

HY/SY ♀ (Aug-Jul): Crown and breast without red feathers; most or all pp covs retained, the inner feathers (at least) narrow, faded, abraded, and brown with buff tips when fresh (Fig. 138), contrasting with the slightly fresher gr covs (Fig. 134), and often contrasting with the darker brown, replaced outer pp (Fig. 136**C**); the innermost 1-5 pp and the outermost 1-6 ss often contrastingly faded (Fig. 136**A-B**), or uniformly first basic in ~54% of HY/SYs (Fig. 136**C**); lower belly and vent washed pale yellow.

AHY/ASY ♀ (Aug-Jul): Crown and breast without red feathers; pp covs uniformly broad, truncate, (Fig. 138), dark brown, and without buff tips, not contrasting in wear with the gr covs (Fig. 133**F**); pp and ss uniformly adult (Fig. 133**F**); lower belly and vent pale salmon-pink. **Note: Some AHY/ASY ♀♀ can show a few pinkish-red feathers on the crown and breast.**

HY/SY ♂ (Sep-Aug): Crown and/or breast with varying amounts of bright red, from a few feathers on a brown-streaked background, to almost entirely dull red with some paler (whitish, yellow, or orange) mottling; pp covs, pp, and ss as in HY/SY ♀; lower belly and vent strongly washed salmon-pink to orangish red. **Note: See AHY/ASY ♀.**

AHY/ASY ♂ (Aug-Jul): Crown and breast uniformly bright red; pp covs, pp, and ss as in AHY/ASY ♀. **Note: Some AHY/ASY**

Vermilion Flycatcher

See Fig. 24

♂♂ of *P.r. flammeus* (see Geographic variation) can be slightly mottled whitish or orange, overlapping with the brightest HY/SY ♂♂; confirm age with the wing-feather criteria. Mottled AHY/ASYs with adult wing feathers might be SY/TYs, but more study is needed.

References—Swarth (1904a), Ridgway (1907), Oberholser (1930a, 1974), Bent (1942), Webster (1984), Pyle (1997c, in press).

DUSKY-CAPPED FLYCATCHER
Myiarchus tuberculifer

DCFL
Species # 4550
Band size: 1B-1

Species—From the other *Myiarchus* flycatchers of N.Am (especially Ash-throated Flycatcher), with caution, by the combination of small size (wg 72-86, tl 68-80; see **Sex**); bill small (nares to tip 11.0-13.5, width at tip of nares 5.9-6.9; Fig. 156); p10 < p4 by 2-9 mm; upperparts brownish olive; wing bars dull grayish; tert edging narrow and cinnamon (juvenal, 1.0-1.5 mm wide when fresh), or pale grayish (basic, 0.5-1.0 mm wide when fresh), contrasting moderately indistinctly with the brownish wings (Fig. 157); outer rects (r6) with a moderate amount (juvenal) to little or no (basic) rufous, confined to narrow edging if present (Fig. 156; *M.t. olivascens* only; see

Geographic variation); breast gray; belly and vent brightish lemon yellow; lower mandible blackish brown with a slightly paler base (Fig. 156). La Sagra's Flycatcher (*M. sagrae*; **LASF, Species # 4551**), a vagrant to FL, is similar in size, but has a longer bill (nares to tip 13.1-15.8), outer rect (r6) with < half of the inner web rufous, and abdomen whitish to white. The above measurements and plumage pertain to the subspecies *M.t. olivascens* (see **Geographic variation**), although most of these separating characters also are reliable with the other subspecies of Mex-C.Am.

Geographic variation—Moderate to well marked, but variable and often clinal. Subspecies taxonomy follows Traylor (1979a); see also Nelson (1904), Ridgway

bill width 5.9-6.9

Juvenal   Adult

FIGURE 156. Bill shape and size, color of the lower mandible, and outer rectrix (r6) pattern by age in Dusky-capped Flycatcher. Note that the underside of the tail reflects the color of r6, in this case brown with little or no rufous. The illustrations of the rectrices are typical of the northern subspecies *M.t. olivascens*. Other subspecies show more rufous to the rectrices, in both age groups.

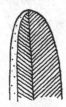
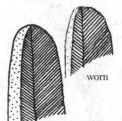
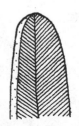

worn

Dusky-capped   Ash-throated   Great-crested   Brown-crested

FIGURE 157. The width and distinctness of the edging to the tertials for identifying *Myiarchus* flycatchers. Note that the edging becomes less extensive with wear, but that many individuals of these species (see text) replace the tertials during the prealternate molts.

(1907), Miller & Griscom (1925a), Parkes (1982b), Phillips *et al.* (1984), Howell & Webb (1994). Ten other subspecies occur in Mex-S.Am.

M.t. olivascens (br throughout the range in N.Am): Smaller (see **Sex**); crown and upperparts uniformly dull olive, without dusky or blackish; rufous wing edging indistinct; rects with reduced (juvenal) or no (basic) rufous edging (Fig. 156); lower underparts dull yellow.

M.t. lawrenceii (br e.Mex; vag to sw.TX): Large; crown dark brown, contrasting with the olive back; rufous wing edging brighter and more distinct; rects with substantial (juvenal) to a moderate amount (basic) of rufous edging (*cf.* Fig. 156); lower underparts bright yellow. ♀ wg(n18) 77-88, tl(n14) 71-83; ♂ wg(n33) 80-90, tl(n15) 74-87.

Molt—PB: HY/SY incomplete (Aug-Jan), AHY complete (Jul-Oct); PA limited-partial (Mar-Apr). The PBs usually commence on the summer grounds and complete on the winter grounds, where most flight feathers are replaced. The 1st PB usually includes all feathers except the pp covs and (sometimes) one or more alula feathers; occasionally (~15%?) the innermost 1-3 pp and the outermost 1-3 ss can be retained until the 2nd PB. Look also for some middle ss (among s2-s6) to be retained until the 1st PA, as in Ash-throated Flycatcher (see Fig. 161). The 1st PA sometimes (in ~33% of birds) includes 1-2 terts and the adult PA occasionally (in ~6% of birds) includes s8; the PAs otherwise include no gr covs or flight feathers.

Skull—Pneumaticization completes in HY from 15 Oct through Dec. Look for windows (> 2 mm; see Figs. 11**D** & 204) in some birds through spring or summer.

Age—Juv (Jun-Nov) has cinnamon wing-feather edging and more rufous in the rects (Fig. 156); juv ♀ = ♂.

Juv-HY/SY (Sep-Aug): Unreplaced, wing covs, ss, uppertail covs, and central rects broadly edged rufous in Sep-Dec; unreplaced flight feathers relatively fresh in Sep-Nov; outer pp covs narrow, faded brown or tinged rufous, and paler than the gr covs and bases of the pp (Fig. 158; especially in Jan-Aug); 1-2 terts sometimes contrastingly fresh in Apr-Aug (Fig. 133**D**); the innermost 1-3 pp and the outermost 1-2 ss occasionally (in ~15% of birds) contrastingly worn (Fig. 136**B**). **Note: Intermediates can occur that cannot be separated from AHY/ASY, especially in May-Aug when feathers of both age groups become quite abrad-**

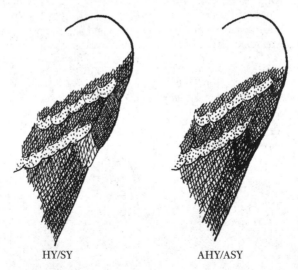

HY/SY   AHY/ASY

FIGURE 158. Relative wear of the primary coverts by age in *Myiarchus* flycatchers. The primary coverts (and perhaps the alula), are the only feathers typically retained during the first prebasic molts of these species. Similar (although less pronounced) contrasts are found in the wood-pewees and, perhaps, in Eastern Kingbird.

ed. With experience, however, some SYs also may be reliably aged through the adult PB in Oct-Nov. The shape and condition of the pp covs is the most reliable criterion.

AHY/ASY (Sep-Aug): Wing covs, ss, uppertail covs, and central rects (r1) with little or no rufous edging; unreplaced flight feathers relatively abraded in Aug-Nov; outer pp covs broad, dark brown or dusky, without a rufous tinge, and as dark as or darker than the gr covs and bases of the pp (Fig. 158); s8 occasionally contrastingly fresh in Mar-Sep; pp and ss uniformly adult. **Note: See Juv-HY/SY.**

Sex— ♀ = ♂ by plumage. CP (Apr-Jul) may be poorly developed; the BP (May-Aug) can occur in both sexes, but probably is more extensive in ♀♀ (see Fig. 22**B-C**). ♀ wg(n30) 72-82, tl(n20) 68-76; ♂ wg(n30) 76-86, tl(n30) 70-80; measurements include *M.t. olivascens* only (see **Geographic variation**).

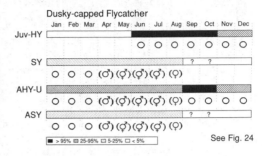

References—Swarth (1904a), Ridgway (1907), Dickey & van Rossem (1938), Bent (1942), Oberholser (1974), Lanyon (1975), Phillips *et al.* (1984), Howell & Webb (1994, 1995), Pyle (1997c).

ASH-THROATED FLYCATCHER
Myiarchus cinerascens

ATFL
Species # 4540
Band size: 1B-1

Species—From the other *Myiarchus* flycatchers of N.Am, with caution, by the combination of medium size (wg 88-105, tl 81-97; see **Sex**); bill medium-small (Fig. 159; nares to tip 12.6-17.1, width at tip of nares 5.9-8.3; see **Geographic variation**); p10 – p4 -4 to 3 mm; upperparts pale grayish brown; wing bars dingy whitish; tert edging moderately wide and buff (juvenal, 1.5-2.0 mm wide when fresh) to dingy whitish (basic, 1.0-1.5 mm wide when fresh), contrasting indistinctly with the pale grayish-brown wings (Fig. 157); outer rects with broad, rufous edges to the inner webs (the brown median stripe extending < 1 mm from the shaft) but tipped brown (Fig. 159; see **Age**); throat whitish; face gray; breast pale gray; belly and vent pale yellow; lower mandible dark brown, sometimes slightly paler at the base in juv-HYs (Fig. 159); mouth lining flesh-colored.

Nutting's Flycatcher *(M. nuttingi)*, a vagrant to AZ, is separated, with caution, by the slightly smaller wg (83-99); shorter average wg – tl (0-9 mm, *vs* 4-13 mm in Ash-throated Flycatcher); p9 – p5 -1 to 3 mm, *vs* 3-7 mm in Ash-throated Flycatcher; face brownish; pp edging rufous, not contrasting distinctly with the buffy edging to the outer ss *(vs* pp edging contrastingly whitish); outer rects (r6) with brown less distinct and expanding less abruptly at the tip than in Ash-throated Flycatcher (Fig. 160); mouth lining brighter, orange-yellow. See Dickerman & Phillips (1953), Phillips (1959b), Lanyon (1961), Bowers & Dunning (1987), Howell & Webb (1994, 1995), and Pyle (1997a) for more information on separating

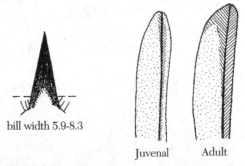

bill width 5.9-8.3

Juvenal   Adult

FIGURE 159. Bill shape and size, color of the lower mandible, and outer rectrix (r6) pattern by age in Ash-throated Flycatcher. Note that the underside of the tail reflects the color of r6, in this case largely rufous.

Ash-throated from Nutting's flycatchers.

Geographic variation—Moderately weak and clinal where ranges meet. Subspecies taxonomy follows Traylor (1979a); see Nelson (1904), Ridgway (1907), Griscom (1934a), van Rossem (1931a, 1945a), Lanyon (1961, 1963). One other subspecies occurs in Baja CA.

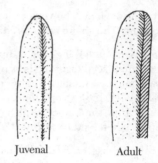

Juvenal   Adult

FIGURE 160. The outer rectrix (r6) pattern by age in Nutting's Flycatcher, for use in separation from Ash-throated Flycatcher (Fig. 159).

M.c. cinerascens (br throughout the range in N.Am): Large (see **Sex** and below); bill averages small (nares to tip 12.6-17.1; see below); upperparts pale grayish brown; underparts pale lemon yellow. Birds of nc.Mex *("mexicanus")* average slightly smaller in size and have slightly more rounded wings than birds of N.Am, but variation is slight and broadly clinal. Within *cinerascens*, birds of the eastern part of the range average larger bills than those in the western part of the range; more study is needed. Birds breeding in c-s.Baja CA *(pertinax),* possible vagrants to N.Am, are smaller (wg 84-99, tl 79-94) and have longer bills (nares to tip 13.3-17.8), upperparts darker brown, and underparts deeper yellow.

Molt—PB: HY incomplete (Aug-Dec), AHY complete (Jul-Oct); PA: SY limited-incomplete (Mar-May), ASY limited-partial (Feb-Apr). The PBs commence on the summer grounds and complete on the summer or the winter grounds. The 1st PB usually includes all feathers except most or all pp covs and one or more alula feathers, although sometimes (in ~33% of birds) up to two outer pp covs can be replaced. Sometimes (in ~30% of birds) 1-4 middle ss (among s2-s6) can be retained until the 1st PA, and rarely (in ~5% of birds) the innermost 1-3 pp and/or the outermost 1-3 ss can be retained until the 2nd PB. The 1st PA usually includes those middle ss not replaced at the PA, sometimes (in ~33% of birds) 1-3 inner gr covs, and often (in ~58% of birds) 1-3 terts, but no rects. The adult PA also can include 1-3 gr covs and 1-2 terts but less frequently (~23% in both cases) than in SYs.

Skull—Pneumaticization completes in HY from 1 Sep through Dec. Look for windows (> 3 mm; see Figs. 11**D** & 204) in some birds through spring or summer.

Age—Juv (Jun-Nov) has pale buff wing-feather edging and more rufous in the rects (Fig. 159); juv ♀ = ♂.

Juv-HY/SY (Oct-Sep): Unreplaced wing covs, ss, uppertail covs, and central rects broadly edged rufous in Aug-Dec; unreplaced flight feathers relatively fresh in Aug-Nov; outer pp covs narrow, faded brown or tinged rufous, and paler than the gr covs and bases of the pp (Fig. 158; especially in Dec-Jul), outer 1-2 pp covs sometimes contrasting fresh (see Fig. 136**C**); 1-3 middle ss

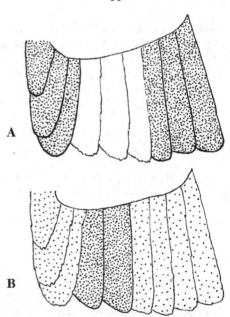

A

B

FIGURE 161. Molt limits among the secondaries in small proportions of HY/SY *Myiarchus* and Sulphur-bellied flycatchers. These patterns reflect the retention of secondaries during the first prebasic molt (**A**), which are then replaced during the first prealternate molt (**B**). See also Figures 146 and 172.

(among s3-s6) sometimes retained until the 1st PA (rarely until the 2nd PB?), contrast-ingly worn in Oct-Apr and contrastingly fresh in Apr-Jul (Fig. 161); 1-3 inner gr covs and 1-3 terts more often contrastingly fresh in Apr-Jul (see **Molt**). **Note: Some HY/SYs also retain up to six (contrastingly worn) inner pp and outer ss (see Molt and Fig. 136) until the 2nd PB. Some SYs can be reliably aged through the adult PB in Sep-Oct, with experience.**

AHY/ASY (Oct-Sep): Wing covs, ss, uppertail covs, and central rects (r1) with little or no rufous edging; unreplaced flight feathers relatively abraded in Aug-Oct; outer pp covs broad, dark brown or dusky, without a rufous tinge, and as dark or darker than the gr covs and bases of the pp (Fig. 158); gr covs and ss uni-formly adult (Fig. 133**F**), except that 1-2 terts only occasionally are contrastingly fresh in Apr-Jul (see **Molt**). **Note: See Juv-HY/SY.**

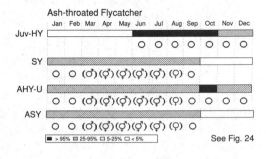

Sex—♀ = ♂ by plumage. CP (Mar-Jul) may be poorly developed; the BP (Apr-Aug) can occur in both sexes, but is more extensive in ♀♀ (see Fig. 22**B-C**). Measurements are useful: ♀ wg(n100) 88-99, tl(n100) 81-92; ♂ wg(n100) 95-105, tl(n100) 86-97; mea-surements pertain to the nominate sub-species only (see **Geographic variation**).

References—Ridgway (1907), Bent (1942), Dickerman & Phillips (1953), Phillips (1959b), Lanyon (1961), Phillips *et al.* (1966), Phillips & Lanyon (1970), Oberholser (1974), Bowers & Dunning (1987), Svingen & Risen (1991), Howell & Webb (1994, 1995), Pyle (1997c); K. Burk (pers. comm.); IBP (MAPS) data, PRBO data.

GREAT CRESTED FLYCATCHER
Myiarchus crinitus

GCFL
Species # 4520
Band size: 1A-1B

Species—From the other *Myiarchus* flycatchers of N.Am, with caution, by the combination of medium-large size (wg 91-109, tl 81-95; see **Sex**); bill medium large (Fig. 162; nares to tip 14.2-16.7, width at tip of nares 7.4-9.2); p10 > p4 by 2-9 mm; upperparts olive; wing bars white; tert edging substantial and buffy lemon (juvenal, 2.0-3.0 mm wide when fresh) to lemon (basic, 1.5-2.5 mm wide when fresh), contrasting distinctly with the dusky wings (Fig. 157); inner web of the rects primarily rufous, the brown color extending < 2 mm from the shaft, and the rufous extending all the way to the tip (Fig. 162); face, throat, and breast dark gray; belly and vent bright yellow; lower mandible brownish with a horn-colored to yellow-orange base (Fig. 162); mouth lining yellow-orange.

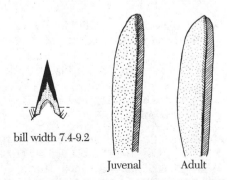

FIGURE 162. Bill shape and size, color of the lower mandible, and outer rectrix (r6) pattern by age in Great-crested Flycatcher.

Geographic variation—Subspecies taxonomy follows Traylor (1979a), who considered the species monotypic (synonymizing two previously recognized subspecies); see Nelson (1904), Ridgway (1907), Oberholser (1917a, 1974), Bent (1942), Todd (1963), Phillips *et al.* (1964), Monroe (1968), Mayr & Short (1970), Wetmore (1972), Stevenson & Anderson (1994). Northwestern birds *("M.c. boreus")* average larger and paler than southeastern birds, but variation is completely clinal throughout the range. Birds of FL ("residuus"), especially s.FL, also average shorter-billed and paler, but differences probably are too slight for subspecies recognition.

Molt—PB: HY/SY incomplete (Aug-Jan), AHY complete (Jul-Aug); PA: SY partial-incomplete (Mar-May), ASY partial (Feb-Apr). The 1st PB commences on the summer grounds (body plumage and some wing covs) and completes on the winter grounds (some wing covs and all flight feathers), whereas the adult PB is completed on the summer grounds. The 1st PB usually includes all feathers except the pp covs, one or more alula feathers, and often (in ~70% of birds) 1-3 middle ss (among s3-s6). The 1st PA usually includes those middle ss not replaced during the 1st PB, often (in ~65% of birds) 1-3 inner gr covs, and 2-3 terts, but no rects. The adult PA sometimes (in ~45% of birds) includes 1-4 inner gr covs and includes 1-3 terts, but the average number of feathers replaced is less than in SY.

Skull—Pneumaticization completes in HY from 15 Oct (possibly as early as 15 Sep in southern birds) through Dec. Look for windows (> 3 mm; see Figs. 11**D** & 204) in some birds through spring or summer.

Age—Juv (May-Nov) has cinnamon wing-feather edging and slightly more rufous in the rects (Fig. 162); juv ♀ = ♂.

HY/SY (Aug-Jul): Outer pp covs narrow, faded brown, and slightly paler than the gr covs and bases of the pp (Fig. 158); 1-3 middle ss (among s3-s6) usually retained until the 1st PA (rarely until the 2nd PB?), contrastingly worn in Oct-Apr and contrastingly fresh in Apr-Jul (Fig. 161); 2-3 terts more often contrastingly fresh in Apr-Jul (see **Molt**). **Note: Many intermediates may occur that cannot be aged, especially without previous experience.**

AHY/ASY (Aug-Jul): Outer pp covs broad, dark brown or dusky, and as dark or darker than the gr covs and bases of the pp (Fig. 158); ss uniformly adult (*cf.* Fig. 161), except that 1-3 terts usually are contrastingly fresh in Apr-Jul (see **Molt**). **Note: See HY/SY.**

Sex—♀ = ♂ by plumage. CP (Mar-Jul) may be poorly developed; the BP (Mar-Aug) is acquired by both sexes, but usually is more extensive in ♀♀ (see Fig. 22**B-C**). ♀ wg(n100) 91-104, tl(n30) 81-90; ♂ wg(n100) 97-109, tl(n44) 86-95; see **Geographic variation**.

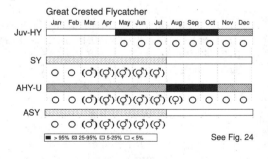

Great Crested Flycatcher

See Fig. 24

References—Stone (1896), Dwight (1900a), Ridgway (1907), Forbush (1927), Dickey & van Rossem (1938), Bent (1942), Parkes (1953a), Roberts (1955), Phillips *et al.* (1966, 1984), Wood (1969), Phillips & Lanyon (1970), Oberholser (1974), Lanyon (1975), Howell & Webb (1994, 1995), Pyle (1997c); D. Cimprich, J.L. Dunn, B. Walker (pers. comm.); IBP (MAPS) data.

BROWN-CRESTED FLYCATCHER
Myiarchus tyrannulus

BCFL
Species # 4530
Band size: 1A

Species—From the other *Myiarchus* flycatchers of N.Am, with caution, by the combination of large size (wg 92-115, tl 83-107; see **Geographic variation**); bill large (Fig. 163; nares to tip 15.0-20.6, width at tip of nares 7.7-10.1; see **Geographic variation**); p10 ≤ p4 by 0-8 mm; upperparts grayish brown to olive-brown; wing bars white; tert edging narrow and buffy-lemon (juvenal, 1.0-1.5 mm wide when fresh), or pale lemon to grayish (basic, 0.5-1.0 mm wide when fresh), contrasting moderately to distinctly with the brownish wings (Fig. 157); inner web of the rects with substantial (juvenal) to a moderate amount (basic) of rufous, the brown color extending 2-6 mm from the shaft (basic) and the rufous extending to the feather tip (Fig. 163); face, throat and breast pale gray; belly and vent pale yellow; lower mandible black, sometimes slightly paler at the base (Fig. 163); mouth lining flesh to buffy yellowish.

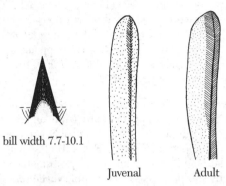

bill width 7.7-10.1

Juvenal   Adult

FIGURE 163. Bill shape and size, color of the lower mandible, and outer rectrix (r6) pattern by age in Brown-crested Flycatcher.

Geographic variation—Moderately well marked (although based on size only) and ranges are well defined. Subspecies taxonomy follows Traylor (1979a); see Nelson (1904), Ridgway (1907), Lanyon (1960a), Monroe (1968), Howell & Webb (1994). Four other subspecies occur in C.Am-S.Am.

> **M.t. magister** (br se.CA-sw.NM; vag to n.CA): Large, especially bill (nares to tip 16.4-20.6, width at tip of nares 8.6-10.1). ♀ wg(n48) 97-105, tl(n48) 88-100; ♂ wg(n63) 101-115, tl(n63) 92-107.
>
> **M.t. cooperi** (br s.TX; vag to FL): Small, especially bill (nares to tip 15.0-18.3, width at tip of nares 7.7-9.2). ♀ wg(n50) 92-99, tl(n50) 82-92; ♂ wg(n100) 96-104, tl(n100) 87-97.

Molt—PB: HY/SY incomplete (Aug-Jan), AHY complete (Jul-Oct); PA: SY limited-incomplete (Mar-Apr), ASY limited-partial (Feb-Apr). The PBs usually commence on the summer grounds and complete on the winter grounds, where most flight feathers are replaced. The 1st PB usually includes all feathers except the pp covs and one or more alula feathers; often (in ~65% of birds) 1-4 middle ss (among s2-s6) can be retained until the 1st PA, and occasionally (in ~11% of birds) the innermost 1-2 pp and/or the outermost 1-2 ss can be retained until the 2nd PB. The 1st PA includes 0 (~82%) to 4 inner gr covs, those middle ss not replaced during the 1st PB, and occasionally (in ~6% of birds) s8 (possibly rarely 1-2 other terts), but no rects. The adult PA includes 0 (~33%) to 5 inner gr covs, but no terts or rects.

Skull—Pneumaticization completes in HY from 15 Sep through Dec. Look for windows (> 3 mm; see Figs. 11**D** & 204) in some birds through spring or summer.

Age—Juv (Jun-Nov) has pale buff wing-feather edging and more rufous in the rects (Fig. 163); juv ♀ = ♂.

> Juv-HY/SY (Sep-Aug): Unreplaced wing covs, ss, uppertail covs, and central rects broadly edged rufous in Sep-Nov; unreplaced flight feathers relatively fresh in Aug-Oct; outer pp covs narrow, faded brown or tinged rufous, and paler than the gr covs and bases of the pp (Fig. 158; especially in Dec-Aug); the innermost 1-2 pp and the outermost 1-2 ss occa-

sionally (in ~11% of birds) contrastingly worn (Fig. 136**B**); 1-4 middle ss (among s2-s6) sometimes retained until the 1st PA, contrastingly worn in Nov-Apr, and contrastingly fresh in Apr-Aug (Fig. 161); 1-2 terts (including s8) occasionally contrastingly fresh in Apr-Aug (Fig. 133**D**). **Note: Intermediates can occur that cannot be separated from AHY/ASY, especially in May-Aug when feathers of both age groups become quite abraded.**

AHY/ASY (Sep-Aug): Wing covs, ss, uppertail covs, and central rects (r1) with little or no rufous edging; unreplaced flight feathers relatively abraded in Aug-Oct; outer pp covs broad, dark brown or dusky, without a rufous tinge, and as dark or darker than the gr covs and bases of the pp (Fig. 158); pp and ss uniformly adult (Fig. 133**F**, *cf.* Fig. 161). **Note: See Juv-HY/SY.**

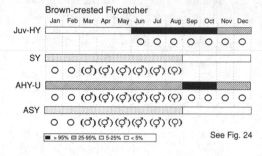

Sex— ♀ = ♂ by plumage. CP (Mar-Jul) may be poorly developed; the BP (Apr-Aug) can occur in both sexes, but probably is more developed in ♀♀ (see Fig. 22**B-C**). Measurements are useful, but vary substantially by subspecies; see **Geographic variation.**

References—Ridgway (1907), Bent (1942), Lanyon (1960a), Phillips & Lanyon (1970), Oberholser (1974), Phillips *et al.* (1984), Howell & Webb (1994, 1995), Pyle (1997c); J.L. Dunn, J. Mueller (pers. comm.).

GREAT KISKADEE
Pitangus sulphuratus

GKIS
Species # 4490
Band size: 2

Geographic variation—Generally weak to moderate, and clinal where ranges meet. Subspecies taxonomy follows Traylor (1979a); see Ridgway (1907), Griscom (1930b), van Rossem (1937b, 1940), Zimmer (1937a), Webster (1984). Nine other subspecies occur in Mex-S.Am.

  P.s. derbianus (vag to s.AZ-s.NM): Tl short; back medium to pale olive-brown; outer rects (r6) with more rufous (*cf.* Fig. 164); underparts pale yellow. Tl ♀ (n10) 82-91, ♂ (n35) 86-96. Birds of nw.Mex (*"palliatus"*) average smaller, paler, and grayer, with a shallower bill than birds of c-sw.Mex, but differences are weak and broadly clinal.

  P.s. texanus (res s.TX, vag to LA): Tl long (see **Sex**); back medium olive with a brownish tinge; outer rects (r6) with less rufous (Fig. 164); underparts deep yellow.

Molt—PB: HY partial (Jul-Oct), AHY complete (Jul-Nov); PA absent-limited? (Feb-Mar). The 1st PB includes some to most med covs and 0 (~61%) to 3 inner gr covs, but no flight feathers. The PAs include no gr covs or flight feathers.

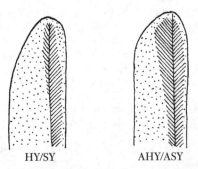

HY/SY   AHY/ASY

FIGURE 164. The shape and pattern of the outer rectrix (r6) in Great Kiskadee. The illustrations depict what is typical in the subspecies *P.s. texanus* of Texas. Other subspecies (including *derbianus*) average less brown in this feather by age.

Skull—Pneumaticization completes in HY from 1 Oct through Dec. Look for windows (> 3 mm; see Figs. 11**D** & 204) in some birds through spring or summer.

Age—Juv (May-Sep) has no yellow in the crown and has plumage generally washed brownish; juv ♀ = ♂.

HY/SY (Sep-Aug): Molt limits occur among the med and (sometimes) the gr covs (Fig. 133**A**-**B**); retained outer covs edged pale cinnamon, contrasting with the deeper, rufous-edged, replaced inner covs; outer pp covs narrow and primarily rufous with a narrow, brown shaft streak; rufous of the outer webs of the central rects (r1) 1-3 mm wide; outer rects (r6) tapered and with little or no dusky on the inner web (Fig. 164).

AHY/ASY (Sep-Aug): Wing covs uniformly adult (Fig. 133**F**); outer pp covs broad and primarily brown with thin, rufous edging; rufous of the outer webs of the central rects (r1) 0-2 mm wide; outer rects (r6) truncate, with extensive dusky on the inner web (Fig. 164).

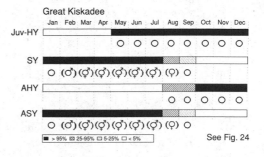

Sex—♀ = ♂ by plumage. CP/BP (Feb-Aug); CP may be poorly developed. ♀ wg(n30) 113-123, tl(n20) 89-97; ♂ wg(n30) 117-128, tl(n20) 91-101; measurements include *P.s. texanus* only (see **Geographic variation**).

References—Ridgway (1907), Dickey & van Rossem (1938), Bent (1942), Foster (1975), Oberholser (1974), Pyle (1997c).

SULPHUR-BELLIED FLYCATCHER
Myiodynastes luteiventris

SBFL
Species # 4510
Band size: 1B

Species—From Streaked Flycatcher *(M. maculatus)*, a possible vagrant to N.Am, by smaller bill (nares to tip 17-19, *vs* 19-22 in Streaked Flycatcher); outer rects with narrow streaks < 3 mm wide (Fig. 165, *vs* > 3 mm); malar stripe extensively black and chin and throat heavily streaked black *(vs* malar stripe indistinct and dusky, and chin and throat whitish); lower mandible with an indistinct or no pale base *(vs* base of the lower mandible extensively pale pinkish in Streaked Flycatcher).

Geographic variation—Subspecies taxonomy follows Traylor (1979a), who considered the species monotypic (synonymizing a previously recognized subspecies); see also Ridgway (1907), van Rossem (1927a, 1940), Zimmer (1937a), Dickey & van Rossem (1938), Monroe (1968), Wetmore (1972). Birds breeding in AZ-nw.Mex *("M.l. swarthi")* average slightly larger, with paler upperparts, whiter wing edging, and sparser streaking to the underparts than birds breeding in e.Mex-C.Am (which may occur as vagrants to e.N.Am), but differences are broadly clinal and obscured by individual variation.

Molt—PB: HY/SY incomplete (Jul-Feb), AHY/ASY complete (Jul-Feb); PA: SY limited-incomplete (Mar-May), ASY limited (Feb-Apr). Replacement of body feathers during the PBs occurs on the summer grounds whereas flight-feather replacement occurs on the winter grounds. The 1st PB usually includes all feathers except the pp covs and sometimes (in ~50% of birds) 1-3 middle ss (among s4-s6). The 1st PA includes those ss not replaced during the PA; no gr covs or flight feathers otherwise are replaced during the first or adult PAs.

Skull—Pneumaticization completes in HY/SY from 1 Nov through at least Jan. Look for windows (> 3 mm; see Figs. 11**D** & 204) in some birds through spring or summer.

Age—Juv (Jun-Nov) has little or no yellow in the crown, upperparts washed brownish, wing feathers edged cinnamon, and outer rect (r6) with a reduced, black streak (Fig. 165); juv ♀ = ♂.

HY/SY (Oct-Sep): Unreplaced flight feathers relatively fresh in Aug-Jan; outer pp covs narrow, faded brown, and paler than the gr covs and bases of the pp (Fig. 158; especially in Dec-Aug); 1-3 middle ss (among s3-s6) sometimes retained until the 1st PA, contrastingly worn in Nov-Apr and contrastingly fresh in Apr-Aug (Fig. 161); outer rect (r6) with a reduced black streak (Fig. 165; through Nov-Feb).

AHY/ASY (Oct-Sep): Unreplaced flight feathers relatively abraded in Aug-Jan; outer pp covs broad, dark brown or dusky, and as dark or darker than the gr covs and bases of the pp (Fig. 158); pp and ss uniformly adult (*cf.* Fig. 161); outer rect (r6) with a broad black streak (Fig. 165).

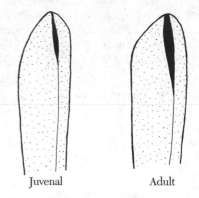

Juvenal   Adult

FIGURE 165. The shape and pattern of the outer rectrix (r6) by age in Sulphur-bellied Flycatcher.

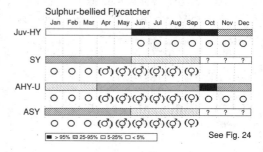

Sex—♀ = ♂ by plumage. CP/BP (Apr-Sep); CP may be poorly developed. ♀ wg(n30) 107-116, tl(n22) 77-82; ♂ wg(n30) 111-120, tl(n28) 78-89.

References—Swarth (1904a), Ridgway (1907), Zimmer (1937a), Dickey & van Rossem (1938), van Rossem (1940), Bent (1942), Pyle (1997c).

TROPICAL KINGBIRD
Tyrannus melancholicus

TRKI
Species # 4460
Band size: 1A

Species—From Western and Cassin's kingbirds by the combination of shorter wg (108-122) and longer tl (84-105; see **Sex**); bill wide (width at tip of nares 9.1-11.0 mm); head grayish; back grayish green; tail brownish black; outer rects unicolored (basic), or with thin, buff outer edges (juvenal; see Fig. 169); breast yellow or greenish yellow; tail notched (r6 – r1 ≥ 4 mm; see Fig. 167).
    Tropical and Couch's kingbirds should be separated with care, especially regarding sympatric *T.m. satrapa* (see **Geographic variation**). Tropical Kingbird is a slightly smaller bird, but with a relatively longer, thinner bill, such that the ratios of (bill nares to tip) ÷ wg, and (bill nares to tip) ÷ (bill depth at tip of nares) provide good identification guides (Table 5). Tropical Kingbird also has a slightly less pointed wing than Couch's Kingbird (Fig. 166) and, in *satrapa*, a deeper notch to the tail (Fig. 167; see **Geographic variation**). A scatter diagram plotting (bill

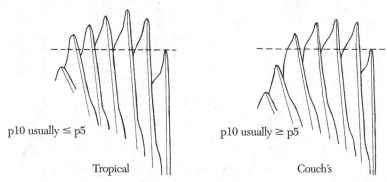

FIGURE 166. Wing morphology differences for the separation of Tropical and Couch's kingbirds.

nares to tip) ÷ wg against a wing morphology formula (Fig. 168) perhaps provides the best means for separating the two species. As with the *Empidonax* flycatchers, determination of sex and subspecies can assist with species separation (see Traylor 1979b and **Geographic variation**). Also, see differences in molt strategies and limits for further identification clues. The following measurements, separating characters, and scatter diagram are derived from Traylor (1979b), Phillips (1994b), and specimen data.

   Geographic variation—Moderately weak in N.Am-Mex, although ranges are well defined; more marked between subspecies of Mex & S.Am. Subspecies taxonomy follows Phillips (1994b); see also Ridgway (1907), Hartert & Goodson (1917), Bangs & Penard (1921a), Zimmer (1937b), Dickey & van Rossem (1938), Traylor (1979b), Binford (1985), Pyle (1997c, in press). One other subspecies occurs in S.Am.

T.m. melancholicus (br & wint S.Am; vag to CA): Crown medium-dark gray; upperparts dark olive; throat dark gray, contrasting distinctly with the white chin.
T.m. occidentalis (br s.AZ; vag to coastal se.AK-CA): Tail moderately forked (r6 – r1 6-12 mm; *cf.* Fig. 167); crown pale gray; upperparts medium-dull olive; chin and throat uniformly whitish; underparts pale yellow; 1st PB more extensive (see **Molt**).
T.m. satrapa (br e.Mex; vag to ME & probably TX): Tail deeply forked (r6 – r1 8-15 mm; Fig. 167); crown pale gray; upperparts medium-bright olive; chin and throat uniformly grayish white; underparts deep yellow; 1st PB less extensive (see **Molt**).

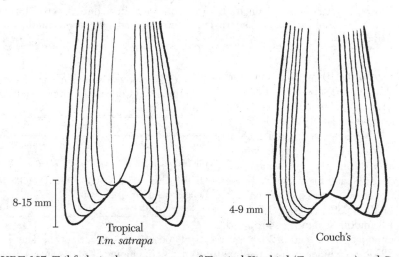

FIGURE 167. Tail forks in the eastern race of Tropical Kingbird (*T.m. satrapa*) and Couch's Kingbird for identification. The fork of the western race of Tropical (*occidentalis*) is intermediate, being 6-12 mm.

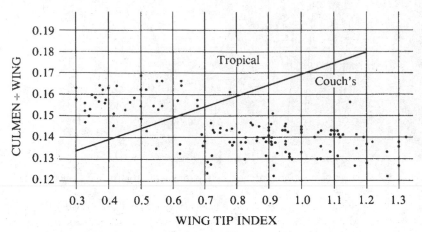

FIGURE 168. A scatter diagram plotting (bill form nares to tip) ÷ wing chord against a wing formula equation, for the separation of Tropical and Couch's kingbirds (from Traylor 1979). The wing tip index = (longest p − p5) ÷ (longest p − p10). **Note that the criteria presented in Figures 166-168 apply to AHY/ASYs only; more study is needed on HY/SYs.**

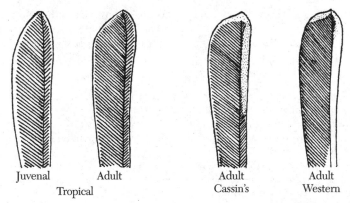

FIGURE 169. The outer rectrices (r6) of kingbirds for identification. In all three species, the juvenal rectrices are similar to the adult rectrices in pattern, being narrower and more tapered at the tip as in juv-HY Tropical Kingbird.

Molt—Details need to be worked out, but extents differ among the subspecies. For *T.m. occidentalis:* PB HY incomplete (Sep-Nov), AHY incomplete-complete (Jul-Nov); PA SY incomplete (Feb-May), ASY partial-incomplete (Feb-Apr). The PBs occur on the winter grounds. Molts during the first winter are eccentric (see p. 208 and Figs. 136A & 172A-C), occurring in two stages. The 1st PB includes 3 to 10 (~25%) gr covs, 1-3 terts, sometimes 1-3 middle ss (among s4-s6), 1-5

TABLE 5. Some measurement ranges (in mm) of Tropical and Couch's kingbirds (derived from Traylor 1979).

	Tropical	Couch's
Wg	108-122	115-131
Bill from nares	16.3-21.7	14.2-18.3
Bill from nares ÷ wg	0.143-0.183	0.128-0.147
Longest p − p5 ÷ longest p − p4	0.51-1.63	0.19-0.75

middle pp (among p4-p8), and 1-2 central rects (r1; occasionally other rects). The 1st PA includes 0 (~23%) to 6 inner gr covs, the innermost 4-7 ss (including 1-3 terts again), the outermost 2-5 pp (continuing where the 1st PB was suspended), and 2 to all 12 (~17%) rects. The adult PB usually is complete, but s5 and/or s6 occasionally can be retained until the adult PA. The adult PA occasionally (in ~14% of birds) can include 1-2 terts, as well. In *T.m. satrapa* the molts are similar but, on average, fewer flight feathers are replaced during the first year (0-4 inner ss, 0-3 middle pp, and occasionally 1-2 central rects), some birds retaining all juvenal pp and rects through the 2nd PB. The molt of *satrapa* may be more similar to that of Couch's Kingbird (which see), but more study is needed.

Skull—Pneumaticization completes in HY from 15 Oct through Dec. Look for windows (> 3 mm; see Figs. 11**D** & 204) in some birds through spring or summer.

Age—Juv (May-Oct) lacks concealed red in the crown and has upperparts washed brownish, uppertail covs tipped buff, outer pp with blunt tips (Fig. 170), and rects with buff edging (Fig. 169); juv ♀ = ♂. The following refers to western birds only *(T.m. occidentalis)*. Some of these criteria also apply to *T.m. satrapa* (see **Molt**), but the account of Couch's Kingbird (which see) may more accurately pertain to this subspecies; more study is needed.

Juvenal (May-Oct) and Basic (Oct-Apr) plumages (*T.m. occidentalis* only)

Juv-HY/SY (May-Apr): Crown with a reduced amount or no concealed red; 1-6 inner ss replaced in Sep-Oct and fresh, contrasting with the rest of the uniformly juvenal ss (Figs. 136**A** & 172**A**); pp covs narrow, relatively faded, and brown with buff tips when fresh (Figs. 138**A** & 172**A**); pp uniformly juvenal or molting, beginning with p4-p6 in Sep-Nov (see **Molt**), and with 1-4 middle pp (among p4-p8) freshly replaced (Fig. 172**A**) in Dec-Apr; some or all outer pp (among p6-p10) not notched (Fig. 170); rects tapered (Figs. 139**C** & 169), edged buff when fresh (Aug-Oct; Fig. 169), and uniformly juvenal or with the central pair sometimes contrastingly fresh. **Note: HYs on fall migration are easily separated from SY/ASYs by skull condition (see Skull), outer pp not notched, and flight feathers much fresher. Also, see above regarding age in *T.m. satrapa*.**

AHY/ASY (Aug-Apr): Crown with a substantial number of concealed red or yellow feathers; most or all ss uniformly adult, s5 and/or s6 sometimes contrastingly worn (see Fig. 161**A**); pp covs broad (Fig. 138**B**), dark brown to dusky, and without buff tips (see Fig. 172**D**); replacement of pp and ss proceeds in typical sequence (see p. 14 and Fig. 13) from p1 and s1 in Oct-Nov (see **Molt**), thereafter uniformly fresh (Fig. 133**F**) and with p6-p10 deeply notched (Fig. 170; see **Sex**); rects uniformly fresh and truncate (Figs. 139**C** & 169), the central rects (r1) not edged buff (Fig. 169). **Note: See above regarding age in *T.m. satrapa*.**

Alternate Plumage (Apr-Oct; *T.m. occidentalis* only)

SY (Apr-Oct): The innermost 3-7 pp and the outermost 3-6 ss retained, juvenal feathers, contrasting with the fresher, adult, outermost 3-7 pp and innermost 3-6 ss (Fig. 136**A**), two generations of adult feathers being present (Fig. 172**B-C**); pp covs narrow, faded brown, and abraded (Figs. 138**C** & 172**B-C**); rects (sometimes) uniformly adult or with one or more juvenal feathers retained, contrastingly abraded, and tapered (Figs. 139**C** & 169). **Note: AHYs showing extensive replacement of outer pp in Feb-May should be SYs. Also, see above regarding age in *T.m. satrapa*.**

ASY (Apr-Oct): Flight feathers uniformly adult (Fig. 133**F**) or, at most, 1-2 terts, s5,

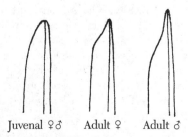

Juvenal ♀♂   Adult ♀   Adult ♂

FIGURE 170. The shape of the outer primary (p10) by age and sex in Tropical and Couch's kingbirds. Look for a slight, sex-specific difference in the shape of the juvenal feather, as in other kingbirds (see Figs. 173 & 177).

and/or s6 replaced at the PA, slightly fresher than the rest of the ss (Fig. 172**D**); pp covs broad, dark brown, and relatively fresh (Figs. 138**D** & 172**D**); rects uniformly adult and truncate (Figs. 139**C** & 169). **Note: See SY and see above regarding age in *T.m. satrapa*.**

Sex—♀ = ♂ by plumage. CP/BP (Apr-Jul); CP may be poorly developed. ♀ wg(n60) 108-118, tl(n35) 84-97; ♂ wg(n100) 111-122, tl(n69) 90-105.

AHY ♀: Notches on p6-p10 < 8 mm from the tip (Fig. 170). **Note: This is reliable only on adult pp. Look for slight differences in the shape of pp 6-10 on juv-HY/SYs prior to the 1st PA, as with Cassin's Kingbird (see Fig. 173). HY/SYs that have replaced p6 (Fig. 172A) often can be sexed (see Fig. 174); this includes most *T.m. occidentalis* and some *satrapa* (see Geographic variation & Molt).**

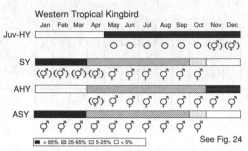

AHY ♂: Notches on p6-p10 ≥ 8 mm from the tip (Fig. 170). **Note: See AHY ♀.**

References—Ridgway (1907), Forbush (1927), Dickey & van Rossem (1938), Bent (1942), Rea (1969), Collins (1973, 1974a), Oberholser (1974), Traylor (1979b), Kaufman (1992b), Phillips (1994b), Pyle (1997c, in press); A.R. Phillips (pers. comm.); PRBO data.

COUCH'S KINGBIRD

Tyrannus couchii

COKI
Species # 4461
Band size: 1B-1A

Species—See Tropical Kingbird.

Geographic variation—No subspecies are recognized.

Molt—Details need to be worked out, but apparently as follows: PB HY partial-incomplete (Jul-Sep), AHY incomplete-complete (Jul-Sep); PA SY partial-incomplete (Feb-May), ASY partial-incomplete (Feb-Apr). The PBs occur on the summer grounds. The 1st year molt is eccentric (see p. 208 and Figs. 136**A** & 172**A-C**), as in Tropical Kingbird (*T.m. occidentalis*), but fewer gr covs, terts, and pp are replaced, some birds retaining all juvenal flight feathers until the 2nd PB. The 1st PB includes 2-5 inner gr covs, 2-4 inner ss, and often (in ~63% of birds) 1-2 central rects (r1). 1-4 middle pp sometimes are replaced during the 1st PB and/or PA, often leaving the outermost 1-3 pp (among p8-p10) juvenal. The 1st PA includes 0 (~33%) to 4 inner gr covs, often (in ~83% of birds) the innermost 1-4 ss (including 1-3 terts again), often (in ~83% of birds) 2-4 pp (continuing where the 1st PB was suspended), and often (in ~67% of birds) 2-8 rects. The adult PB often is complete, but 1-4 middle ss (among s1-s6) can be retained until the adult PA. The adult PA occasionally (in ~14% of birds) can include s8, as well. More study is needed.

Skull—Pneumaticization completes in HY from 15 Oct through Dec. Look for windows (> 3 mm; see Figs. 11**D** & 204) in some birds through spring or summer.

Age—Juv (May-Aug) lacks concealed red in the crown and has upperparts washed brownish, uppertail covs tipped buff, and outer pp with blunt tips (Fig. 170); juv ♀ = ♂.

HY/SY (Sep-Aug): Molt limits occur among the med and gr covs (Fig. 133**B-D**; see **Molt**), the replaced inner covs medium gray, without pale tips, contrasting with the brownish-gray and buff-tipped (when fresh), retained outer covs; pp covs narrow and relatively faded brown (Fig. 138) with buff tips when fresh (Fig. 172**A**); flight feathers primarily or entirely juvenal, 2-3 terts (sometimes s6, as well) contrastingly fresh (Fig. 133**D-E**), or 1-5 pp (among p4-p10) sometimes (Sep-Apr) to often (Apr-Aug) contrastingly fresh (Fig. 172**A**), three generations of feathers sometimes being present in Apr-Aug (Fig. 172**B-C**), but the outermost 1-5 pp (among p6-p10) usually retained and not notched (Figs. 170 & 172**A**); rects often uniformly juvenal and tapered (Figs. 139**C** & 169), the central rects (r1) edged buff when fresh (Fig. 169), or contrastingly fresh if replaced.

AHY/ASY (Sep-Aug): Wing covs and flight feathers primarily or entirely adult (Fig. 133**F**), medium gray (the terts and s6 can be contrastingly fresh in Apr-Aug; Fig. 172**D**); pp covs broad, relatively dark brown, and fresh (Fig. 138), without buff tips (Fig. 172**D**); p6-p10 uniformly adult, deeply notched (Fig. 170; see **Sex**); rects uniformly adult and truncate (Figs. 139**C** & 169), the central rects (r1) not edged buff (Fig. 169).

Sex—♀ = ♂ by plumage. CP/BP (Mar-Aug); CP may be poorly developed. ♀ wg(n62) 115-122, tl(n16) 90-102; ♂ wg(n100) 118-131, tl(n20) 95-108.

AHY ♀: Notches on p6-p10 < 8 mm from the tip (Fig. 170). **Note: This is useful only after the juvenal pp have been replaced (see Tropical Kingbird). HY/SYs that have replaced p6 often can be sexed (see Fig. 174); this includes some HY/SYs in Sep-Mar and many SYs in Apr-Aug (see Molt).**

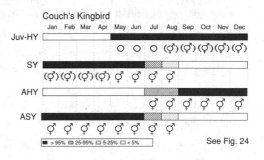

AHY ♂: Notches on p6-p10 ≥ 8 mm from the tip (Fig. 170). **Note: See AHY ♀.**

References—Ridgway (1907), Bent (1942), Rea (1969), Collins (1973, 1974a), Oberholser (1974), Traylor (1979b), Kaufman (1992b), Phillips (1994b), Pyle (1997c); A.R. Phillips (pers. comm.).

CASSIN'S KINGBIRD
Tyrannus vociferans

CAKI
Species # 4480
Band size: 1A

Species—From Tropical, Couch's, Thick-billed, and Western kingbirds by the combination of long wg (116-138) and short tl (84-99; see **Sex**); bill medium in width (at tip of nares 8.0-9.3 mm); p10 < p6 by 4-12 mm (Fig. 171); head and breast dark gray; back dark grayish olive; throat white; tail blackish; outer web of the outer rects (r6) with narrow, buff edging, not reaching the shaft (Fig. 169); tail slightly notched (r6 – r1 2-6 mm).

Geographic variation—Weak and clinal where ranges meet. Subspecies taxonomy follows Traylor (1979a); see Griscom (1934a), Sutton (1967). One other subspecies occurs in Mex.

T.v. vociferans (br & wint throughout range in N.Am): From *xenopterus* of sc.Mex by larger average size (see **Sex**, *vs* wg 119-131 in *xenopterus*); notches on the outer pp average longer and on more feathers by age/sex (see Fig. 173); plumage paler overall, the paler gray chest contrasting less markedly with the white throat.

Molt—PB: HY partial-incomplete (Sep-Dec), AHY complete (Aug-Oct); PA: SY absent-incomplete? (Mar-May), ASY absent-partial(?) Mar-May. The PBs can occur on either the summer or the winter grounds. Molts during the first winter are eccentric (see p. 208 and Figs. 136**A** & 172**A-C**), occurring in two stages. The 1st PB includes 0 (~27%) to 4 inner gr covs, often (in ~67% of birds) 1-3 terts, sometimes (in ~31% of birds) 1-2 of p4-p6, and occasionally (in ~20% of birds) 1-2 central rects (r1); the juvenal pp covs and most flight feathers are retained. The 1st PA usually (in ~78% of birds) includes 1-5 ss (among s5-s9, usually consecutive from the inside), the outermost

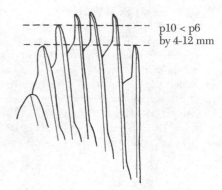

p10 < p6
by 4-12 mm

FIGURE 171. The wing formula of Cassin's Kingbird for identification.

0-5 pp (starting where the 1st PB suspended), and occasionally (in ~6% of birds) 1-2 central rects (r1). No flight feathers (except terts) are replaced during the first year in ~16% of birds. The 1st PA also includes 0 (~39%) to 6 inner gr covs and occasionally (in ~6% of birds) 1-2 central rects (r1). The adult PA includes 0 (~67%) to 4 inner gr covs and sometimes (in ~47% of birds) 1-2 terts, but no rects.

Skull—Pneumaticization completes in HY/SY from 1 Oct through Jan. Look for windows (> 3 mm; see Figs. 11**D** & 204) in some birds through spring or summer.

Age—Juv (May-Aug) lacks concealed red in the crown and has upperparts washed brownish, uppertail covs tipped buff, and outer pp with blunt tips (Fig. 173); some juvs can be sexed by the shape of the outer pp (see **Sex**).

HY/SY (Oct-Sep): Molt limits often occur among the med and gr covs (Figs. 133**A-D** & 135; see **Molt**), the replaced inner covs medium gray, without pale tips, contrasting markedly with

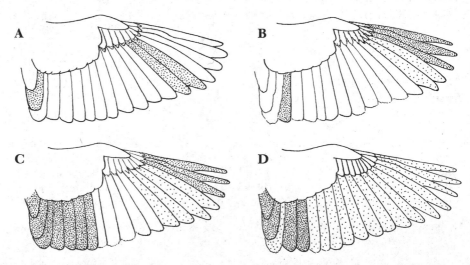

FIGURE 172. Examples of molt limits in HYs (**A**), SYs (**B-C**), and ASYs (**D**) of certain kingbirds. See text for details. Patterns in HYs and SYs result from suspended, eccentric replacement patterns. Suspended eccentric patterns (**A**) can also occur in orioles, siskins, and goldfinchs and should be looked for in other North American passerines that have eccentric molts.

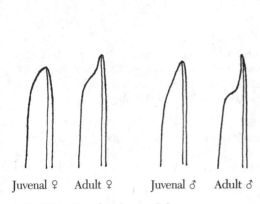

Juvenal ♀   Adult ♀   Juvenal ♂   Adult ♂

FIGURE 173. The shape of the outer primary (p10) by age and sex in Cassin's Kingbird.

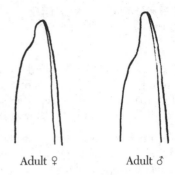

Adult ♀   Adult ♂

FIGURE 174. The shape of the non-juvenal p6 in Tropical and Cassin's kingbirds by sex. This is useful for sexing HY/SYs in winter, many of which have replaced this feather during the first prebasic molt (see Figure 172A).

the brownish gray and buff-tipped (when fresh), retained outer covs; pp covs narrow and relatively faded brown (Fig. 138) with buff tips when fresh (Fig. 172A); flight feathers primarily or entirely juvenal, 1-5 ss (among s5-s9) and/or 1-5 pp (among p6-p10; see **Molt**) often replaced, contrastingly fresh, with three generations of feathers often present in Apr-Sep (Fig. 172**A-C**), but one or more of p6-p10 often juvenal (Fig. 172A) and not notched (Fig. 173); most or all rects juvenal, tapered (Figs. 139**C** & 169), and relatively worn; central rects (r1) edged buff when fresh and juvenal, or contrastingly fresh if replaced (sometimes in Oct-Mar and often in Apr-Sep).

AHY/ASY (Oct-Sep): Wing covs and flight feathers entirely adult (Fig. 133**F**), uniformly medium gray (slight contrasts sometimes present among the terts (Fig. 172**D**; see **Molt**); pp covs broad, relatively fresh, and dark brown (Fig. 138), without buff tips (Fig. 172**D**); p6-p10 uniformly adult and deeply notched (Fig. 173; see **Sex**); rects uniformly adult and truncate (Figs. 139**C** & 169), the central rects (r1) not edged buff.

Sex— ♀ = ♂ by plumage. CP/BP (Apr-Aug); CP may be poorly developed. ♀ wg(n40) 116-132, tl(n20) 84-93; ♂ wg(n40) 125-138, tl(n20) 88-99.

♀: Tips of p6-p10 blunt (juvenal; Fig. 173; see **Age**) or with notches < 5 mm from the feather tip (adult; Fig. 173). **Note: Juv-HY/SYs that have not replaced any pp can be difficult to sex (compare with wg and tl lengths), although some to most HY/SYs that have replaced p6 (Fig. 172A; see Molt) can be more easily sexed by the shape of this feather (Fig. 174).**

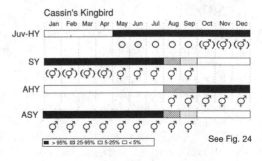

♂: Tips of p6-p10 tapered (juvenal; Fig. 173; see **Age**) or with notches > 8 mm from the feather tip (adult; Fig. 173). **Note: See ♀.**

References—Ridgway (1907), Swarth (1929), Bent (1942), Rea (1969), Collins (1973, 1974b), Oberholser (1974), Kaufman (1992b), Phillips (1994b), Pyle (1997c, in press).

THICK-BILLED KINGBIRD
Tyrannus crassirostris

TBKI
Species # 4451
Band size: 1A

Species—From the other kingbirds by large and thick bill (depth at tip of nares 9.3-11.0 mm, *vs* < 8 mm in the other kingbirds of N.Am); crown dusky, contrasting with the olive or grayish back; throat and breast white; lower underparts slightly to heavily washed yellow; outer rects (r6) without distinct white edging or tips; tail not notched (r6 – r1 0-5 mm).

Geographic variation—Subspecies taxonomy follows Monson & Phillips (1981), who considered the species monotypic (synonymizing a previously recognized subspecies); see also Bangs & Peters (1928), van Rossem (1941b). Birds of AZ *("T.c. sequestratus" or "pompalis")* may average paler than birds of c-s.Mex but differences, if present, are weak, broadly clinal, and obscured by rapid feather wear.

Molt—PB: HY partial (Jul-Sep), AHY incomplete-complete (Jul-Sep); PA: SY partial (Mar-Apr), ASY partial-incomplete (Feb-Apr). The PBs occur on the summer grounds. The 1st PB includes 0 (~29%) to 6 inner gr covs, sometimes (in ~47% of birds) 1-3 terts, and occasionally (in ~6% of birds) 1-2 central rects. The 1st PA includes 0 (87%) to 4 gr covs, 1-3 terts (sometimes s6, as well), and occasionally (in ~13% of birds) 1-2 central rects (r1). The adult PB usually is complete, but occasionally (in ~14% of birds) 1-3 middle ss (among s4-s6) can be retained until the adult PA. The adult PA includes those middle ss not replaced at the PB, 0 (~67%) to 2 inner gr covs, and sometimes (~33%) s8 and/or s9, but no rects.

Skull—Pneumaticization completes in HY from 15 Sep through Dec. Look for windows (> 3 mm; see Figs. 11**D** & 204) in some birds through spring or summer.

Age/Sex—Juv (May-Sep) lacks yellow in the crown and has wing and uppertail covs edged rusty; juv ♀ = ♂. CP/BP (Mar-Jul); CP may be poorly developed. ♀ wg(n30) 118-129, tl(n20) 90-101; ♂ wg(n30) 124-135, tl(n20) 94-105.

HY/SY ♀♂ (Oct-Sep): Molt limits occur among the med and gr covs (Figs. 133**B-D** & 135; see **Molt**), the replaced inner gr covs uniformly blackish, contrasting with the brownish black and rusty-tipped (when fresh), retained outer covs; pp covs narrow and relatively brownish (Fig. 138) with rusty tips; 1-3 terts (and sometimes s6 in Apr-Aug) often (Sep-Apr) to usually (Apr-Aug) contrastingly fresh (Fig. 133**D-E**); p8-p10 not notched (Fig. 175); ss and rects edged rufous; outer rects relatively abraded, brownish, and tapered (Figs. 139**C** & 169). **Note: In addition, fresh HYs average greener upperparts and yellower underparts than AHYs.**

AHY/ASY ♀ (Oct-Sep): Wing covs uniformly adult (Fig. 133**F**) and black or blackish, without rusty tips (inner 1-2 sometimes contrastingly fresh in Apr-Aug); pp covs broad and blackish (Fig. 138), without distinct, rusty tips (they can be narrowly edged rusty when very fresh); terts usually not contrastingly fresh; 1-3 middle ss (among s4-s6) occasionally are contrastingly worn in Sep-Mar (see Fig. 161**A**), and these and s8 or s9 sometimes are contrastingly fresh in Apr-Aug (Fig. 172**D**); p8-p10 pointed (Fig. 175); ss and rects not edged rufous; outer rects relatively fresh, blackish, and truncate (Figs. 139**C** & 169). **Note: See HY/SY ♀♂. Many intermediate AHY/ASYs**

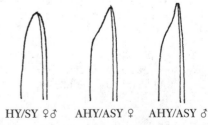

HY/SY ♀♂   AHY/ASY ♀   AHY/ASY ♂

FIGURE 175. The shape of the outer primary (p10) by age and sex in Thick-billed Kingbird.

may occur that are not reliably sexed; more study needed.

AHY/ASY ♂ (Oct-Sep): Like AHY/ASY ♀ but p8-p10 more acutely pointed (Fig. 175). **Note: See HY/SY ♀♂ and AHY/ASY ♀.**

References—Ridgway (1907), Rea (1969), Collins (1973), Phillips (1994b), Pyle (1997c, in press).

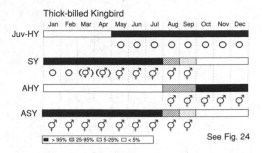

Thick-billed Kingbird

See Fig. 24

WESTERN KINGBIRD
Tyrannus verticalis

WEKI
Species # 4470
Band size: 1A

Species—From Tropical, Couch's, Cassin's, and Thick-billed kingbirds by the combination of long wg (112-135) and short tl (81-98; see **Sex**); bill narrow (width at tip of nares 6.9-8.3); p10 > p6 by 3-12 mm (Fig. 176); head, breast, and throat pale gray; back olive-gray; tail black; outer web of the outer rect (r6) distinctly white to the shaft (Fig. 169); tail not strongly notched (r6 – r1 1-5 mm).

Geographic variation—No subspecies are recognized.

Molt—PB: HY incomplete (Sep-Nov), AHY incomplete-complete (Jul-Oct); PA: SY incomplete (Feb-May), ASY partial-incomplete (Feb-Apr). The 1st PB occurs on the winter grounds whereas the adult PB can commence on the summer grounds and complete on the winter grounds. Molts during the first winter are eccentric (see p. 208 and Figs. 136**A** & 172**A-C**), occurring in two stages. The 1st PB includes 8 to 10 (~85%) inner gr covs, 1-3 terts (sometimes s6, as well), usually (in ~81% of birds) 1-3 middle pp (among p4-p8), and often (in ~70% of birds) 1-2 central rects (r1; sometimes other rects); the juvenal pp covs and most flight feathers are retained. The 1st PA includes 1-6 ss (among s4-s9, usually consecutive from the inside), the outermost 2-5 pp (continuing where the 1st PB suspended), 0 (~25%) to 4 inner gr covs, and often (in ~58% of birds) 1-2 central rects (r1). The adult PB sometimes is complete, but 1-4 middle ss (among s3-s6) often (in ~68% of birds) are retained until the adult PA. The adult PA includes any middle ss not replaced at the PB, 0 (~39%) to 3 inner gr covs, and often (in ~72% of birds) 1-2 terts, but usually not the central rects.

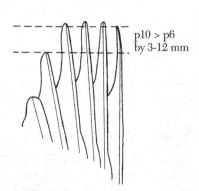

p10 > p6 by 3-12 mm

FIGURE 176. The wing formula of Western Kingbird for identification.

Skull—Pneumaticization completes in HY/SY from 15 Sep through Jan. Look for windows (> 3 mm; see Figs. 11**D** & 204) in some birds through spring or summer.

Age—Juv (Jun-Oct) lacks red or orange in the crown and has brownish-washed upperparts and outer pp with blunt tips (Fig. 177); some juvs can be sexed by the shape of the outer pp (see **Sex**).

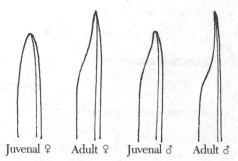

Juvenal ♀   Adult ♀   Juvenal ♂   Adult ♂   Adult ♀   Adult ♂

FIGURE 177. The shape of the outer primary (p10) by age and sex in Western Kingbird.

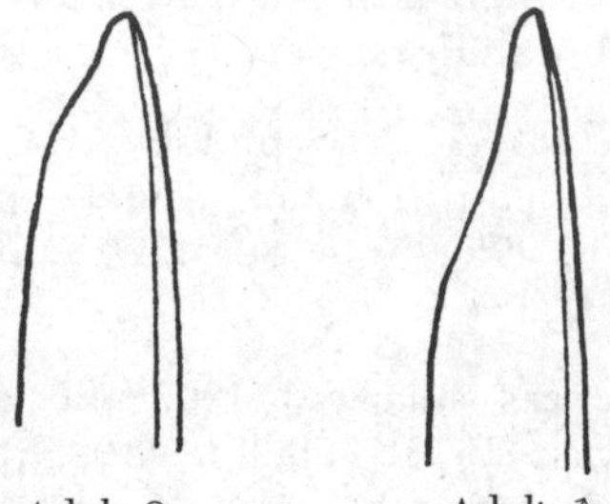

FIGURE 178. The shape of the non-juvenal p6 in Western Kingbird by sex. This is useful for sexing HY/SYs in winter, many of which have replaced this feather during the first prebasic molt (see Figure 172A).

Juvenal (Jun-Oct) and Basic (Oct-Apr) plumages

Juv-HY/SY (Jun-Apr): Crown without concealed red or orange feathers in Aug-Oct; 1-3 terts sometimes replaced in Sep-Oct, fresh, contrasting with the worn inner ss (Fig. 133**D-E**); pp covs narrow and relatively faded brown (Fig. 138**A**) with buff tips when fresh (Fig. 172**A**); pp uniformly juvenal, replacement beginning with p4-p6 in Sep-Oct (see **Molt**), or with 1-3 middle pp (among p4-p8) freshly replaced (Fig. 172**A**) in Dec-Apr; some or all outer pp (among p6-p10) not notched (Fig. 177); rects tapered (Figs. 139**C** & 169), edged buff when fresh (Aug-Oct), and uniformly juvenal and abraded, or with the central pair sometimes contrastingly fresh in Dec-Apr. **Note: HYs on fall migration are easily separated from SY/ASYs by skull condition (see Skull), outer pp not notched, and flight feathers much fresher.**

AHY/ASY (Aug-Apr): Crown with concealed red or orange feathers; most or all ss uniformly adult (Fig. 133**F**), 1-4 middle ss (among s3-s6) often contrastingly worn (Fig. 161**A**); pp covs broad and dark brown to dusky (Fig. 138**B**), without buff tips (see Fig. 172**D**); replacement of pp and ss proceeds in typical sequence (see p. 14 and Fig. 13) from p1 and s1 in Aug-Sep (see **Molt**), thereafter uniformly fresh (Fig. 133**F**); p6-p10 deeply notched (Fig. 177; see **Sex**); rects uniformly fresh and truncate (Figs. 139**C** & 169), the central rects (r1) not edged buff.

Alternate Plumage (Apr-Oct)

SY (Apr-Oct): Outer pp covs narrow, faded brown, and abraded (Figs. 138**C** & 172**C-D**); the juvenal innermost 3-7 pp and the outermost 2-6 ss retained, contrasting with the fresher, replaced, outermost 3-7 pp and innermost 3-6 ss (Fig. 136**A**), with three generations of feathers present (Fig. 172**B-C**); rects (sometimes) uniformly truncate or with one or more juvenal feathers retained, contrastingly abraded, and tapered (Figs. 139**C** & 169). **Note: AHYs showing extensive replacement of outer pp in Feb-May should be SYs.**

ASY (Apr-Oct): Outer pp covs broad, dark brown, and relatively fresh (Figs. 138**D** & 172**D**); flight feathers uniformly adult (Fig. 133**F**) or, at most, 1-4 middle ss (among s3-s6) and sometimes 1-2 terts replaced at the PA, slightly fresher than the rest of the ss (Fig. 172**D**); rects uniformly adult and truncate (Figs. 139**C** & 169). **Note: See SY.**

Sex— ♀ = ♂ by plumage. CP/BP (Apr-Aug); CP may be poorly developed. ♀ wg(n40) 112-128, tl(n20) 81-94; ♂ wg(n40) 120-135, tl(n28) 87-98.

AHY ♀: Notch on p10 < 10 mm from the tip (Fig. 177); p6-p9 slightly notched or pointed (Fig. 178). **Note: HY/SYs can be reliably sexed by the above after replacement of the juvenal outer pp (usually in Apr but sometimes in Oct; see Molt); with experience, some birds** can be sexed by the shape of the juvenal outer pp (Fig. 177) when combined with measurements. In addition, HY/SYs that have replaced p6 (including most HY/SYs in Sep-Mar; see Molt) usually can be sexed (Fig. 178).

AHY ♂: Notch on p10 ≥ 15 mm from the tip (Fig. 177); p6-p9 distinctly notched. **Note: See AHY ♀.**

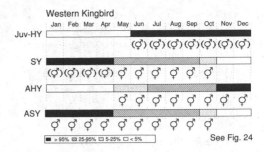

Hybrids reported—Scissor-tailed Flycatcher.

References—Dwight (1900a), Ridgway (1907), Forbush (1927), Dickey & van Rossem (1938), Bent (1942), Roberts (1955), Rea (1969), Davis & Webster (1970), Collins (1973, 1974c), Oberholser (1974), Kaufman (1992b), Tyler & Parkes (1992), Phillips (1994b), Gamble & Bergin (1996), Pyle (1997c, in press); PRBO data.

EASTERN KINGBIRD
Tyrannus tyrannus

EAKI
Species # 4440
Band size: 1B

Species—From the other kingbirds (including Gray Kingbird) by the small bill (depth at tip of nares 6.0-7.4); crown black or sooty, contrasting with the gray upperparts; rects with a distinct, white tip (which can wear off by late summer or fall); underparts without yellow.

Geographic variation—Subspecies taxonomy follows Traylor (1979a), who considered the species monotypic (synonymizing a previously recognized subspecies); see also Oberholser (1932, 1974), Zimmer (1937b), Miller (1941a), Todd (1963), Burleigh (1972), Van Wynsberghe *et al.* (1992). Northwestern birds *("T.t. hespericola")* are slightly larger and paler than southeastern birds, but variation is very slight, broadly clinal, and not consistent geographically.

Molt—Not well known, but possibly as follows: PB HY/SY incomplete-complete? (Sep-Mar), AHY/ASY complete (Sep-Feb); PA partial (Mar-May). Most if not all molting occurs on the winter grounds. The PBs are protracted through much of the winter, most flight feathers being replaced in Dec-Feb. The 1st PB apparently is nearly complete (including the pp covs?), although the innermost 1-2 pp, and 1-2 ss among s1-s6 occasionally can be retained. The PAs include 0 (~25%) to 4 inner gr covs and usually (in ~85% of birds) 1-3 terts, but no central rects (r1); more study is needed on variation in the extent of the PAs by age.

Skull—Pneumaticization completes in HY/SY from 15 Oct through Jan. Look for windows (> 3 mm; see Figs. 11**D** & 204) in some birds through spring or summer.

Age—Juv (Jun-Oct) lacks red or orange in the crown and has feathers of the upperparts edged cinnamon and outer pp with blunt tips (Fig. 179); juv ♀ = ♂.

Juvenal (Aug-Oct) and Basic (Oct-Apr) plumages

Juv-HY/SY (Aug-Apr): Crown without concealed red or orange feathers (through Nov?); unreplaced flight feathers fresh in Aug-Jan; wing covs edged buff or cinnamon when fresh; p9-p10 not notched (Fig. 179); ss and rects edged rufous; outer rects tapered (Figs. 139**C** & 169). **Note: Some birds can be aged by the shape of p10 through May.**

AHY/ASY (Aug-Apr): Crown with concealed orange or red feathers; wing covs without buff or cinnamon edging; unreplaced flight feathers abraded in Aug-Jan; p9-p10 deeply notched (Fig. 179); ss and rects not edged rufous; outer rects truncate (Fig. 139C & 169). **Note: See Juv-HY/SY.**

Alternate Plumage (Apr-Oct)

SY (Mar-Oct): The innermost 1-2 pp, and/or 1-2 ss (among s1-s6) occasionally retained juvenal feathers, contrastingly worn. **Note: Only a few SYs (~20% of birds) retain flight feathers and can be reliably aged (perhaps through Dec?); beware that birds of both age groups can show contrastingly fresh terts in spring. The juvenal pp covs also may be retained; if so, differences between these and adult pp covs in spring are difficult to detect (see Fig. 158).**

AHY (Apr-Oct): Pp and ss uniformly adult. **Note: See SY.**

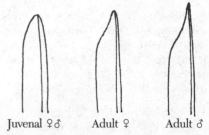

Juvenal ♀♂   Adult ♀   Adult ♂

FIGURE 179. The shape of the outer primary (p10) by age and sex in Eastern Kingbird. Look for a slight, sex-specific difference in the shape of the juvenal feather, as in other kingbirds (see Figs. 173 & 177).

Sex—♀ = ♂ by plumage. CP/BP (Apr-Aug); CP may be poorly developed. ♀ wg(n100) 106-120, tl(n51) 74-89; ♂ wg(n100) 113-128, tl(n45) 76-91.

AHY ♀: Notches on p9-p10 < 8 mm from the tip (Fig. 179). **Note: AHYs after the 1st replacement of the outer pp (usually after Dec) can be sexed; some HY/SYs previous to this might be reliably sexed by pp shape, as in other kingbirds (see Figs. 173 & 177), but this needs further investigation.**

AHY ♂: Notches on p9-p10 > 8 mm from the tip (Fig. 179). **Note: See AHY ♀.**

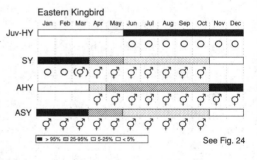

References—Stone (1896), Dwight (1900a), Ridgway (1907), Forbush (1927), Zimmer (1937b), Dickey & van Rossem (1938), Bent (1942), Roberts (1955), Blake (1962a), Rea (1969), Wood (1969), Collins (1973, 1974d), Oberholser (1974), Murphy (1988), Phillips (1994b), Murphy (1996), Pyle (1997c, in press); IBP (MAPS) data.

GRAY KINGBIRD
Tyrannus dominicensis

GRAK
Species # 4450
Band size: 1A

Species—From the other kingbirds of N.Am by the combination of the thick bill (depth at tip of nares 8.6-10.2 mm); crown and upperparts uniformly gray; rects without white tips; underparts without yellow.

Geographic variation—Weak to moderate (based on measurements only), and ranges well defined. Subspecies taxonomy follows Haberman *et al.* (1991); see also Brodkorb (1950), Monroe (1968). One other subspecies occurs in the W.Indies.

T.d. fugax (br throughout the range in N.Am; vag to BC, Ont, & NS): AHYs From non-migratory *domini-censis* of the s.W.Indies by longer wg (see **Sex**, *vs* 103-118 in *dominicensis*) and bill (exp culmen 26.4-32.3, *vs* 22.4-28.4); longest p – longest s longer (usually > 17 mm, *vs* usually < 17 mm in *dominicensis*). JuvHY/SYs have smaller measurements and can be difficult to separate. Also, see **Molt**. Birds of the n.W.Indies (*"sequax"*), probable vagrants to s.FL, average smaller, but this difference probably is too small for subspecies differentiation.

Molt—Not worked out in detail, but possibly as follows: PB HY/SY incomplete (Sep-Mar), AHY/ASY complete (Sep-Feb); PA absent (?). The PBs occur primarily on the winter grounds, although body-feather replacement can begin on the summer grounds. The 1st PB apparently is eccentric (see p. 208 and Figs. 136A & 172A-C), as in other kingbirds, with the outermost 1-6 pp and the innermost 1-5 ss replaced by some or most birds, and the pp covs retained by all birds. Some outermost pp occasionally can be retained until the 2nd PB, as in Cassin's Kingbird. The 1st PB may average more extensive in migratory *T.d. fugax* than in non-migratory *dominicensis* (see **Geographic variation**). Some birds in spring have 1-2 contrastingly fresh terts which likely represent a partial PA. More study is needed.

Skull—Pneumaticization completes in HY/SY from 15 Sep through Jan. Look for windows (> 3 mm; see Figs. 11D & 204) in some birds through spring or summer.

Age—Juv (Jun-Nov) lacks orange feathers in the crown, has upperparts washed brownish, and has outer pp with blunt tips (Fig. 180); juv ♀ = ♂.

Juv-HY/SY (Aug-2nd Nov): Pp covs narrow, relatively fresh, and grayish brown with buff tips in Aug-Dec (Figs. 138 & 172A), and relatively brown and abraded in Jan-2nd Nov (Figs. 138 & 172B-C); pp and ss uniformly juvenal in Aug-Oct, replacement beginning with p4-p6 and s3-s6 in Sep-Feb (see **Molt**), or the innermost 3-7 juvenal pp and the outermost 3-6 juvenal ss retained, contrasting with the fresher, replaced, outermost 3-7 pp and innermost 3-6 ss in Mar-2nd Nov (Fig. 136A), three generations of pp often being present (Fig. 172B-C); the outermost 5 pp (p6-p10) not notched in Aug-Feb (Fig. 180), p9-p10 sometimes not notched in Mar-Nov, as well; some or all rects juvenal and tapered (Figs. 139C & 169), or (sometimes) uniformly truncate in Jan-2nd Nov. **Note: Juv-HYs are easily separated from SY/ASY through fall migration by skull condition (see Skull), the above plumage criteria, and much fresher and blunt-tipped outer pp. The details for ageing in this species are somewhat tentative (see Molt), but should enable reliable separation of most SYs and ASYs through the fall.**

AHY/ASY (Dec-Nov): Pp covs broad, relatively fresh, and dark gray (Fig. 138), without buff tips (Fig. 172D); pp and ss uniformly adult and relatively fresh, the outermost 5 pp (p6-p10) deeply notched (Fig. 180); rects uniformly adult and truncate (Fig. 139C & 169). **Note: See Juv-HY/SY. In ASYs, look for replacement patterns of the ss in Apr-Nov similar to that of Fig. 172D, as in other kingbirds.**

Sex—♀ = ♂ by plumage. CP/BP (Apr-Aug); the CP may be poorly developed. ♀ wg(n100) 107-119, tl(n100) 80-93; ♂ wg(n100) 113-125, tl(n100) 86-99; measurements exclude HY/SYs with juvenal flight feathers.

AHY ♀: Notches on p6-p10 about 5 mm from the tip (Fig. 180). **Note: Only HY/SYs which have replaced the juve-**

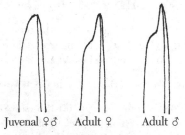

Juvenal ♀♂   Adult ♀   Adult ♂

FIGURE 180. The shape of the outer primary (p10) by age and sex in Gray Kingbird. Look for a slight, sex-specific difference in the shape of the juvenal feather, as in other kingbirds (See Figs. 173 & 177).

nal outer pp (see Molt) can be reliably sexed. Look for slight differences in the tips of the juvenal outer pp, as in other kingbirds (see Figs. 173 & 177). HY/SYs that have replaced p6 often can be sexed (see Fig. 174); this includes most HY/SYs in Sep-Mar (see Molt).

AHY ♂: Notches on p6-p10 about 8 mm from the tip (Fig. 180). **Note: See AHY ♀.**

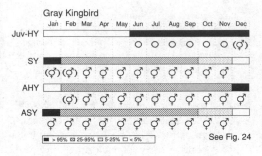

References—Ridgway (1907), Forbush (1927), Bent (1942), Brodkorb (1950), Rea (1969), Collins (1973), Phillips (1994b), Pyle (in press).

SCISSOR-TAILED FLYCATCHER
Tyrannus forficatus

STFL
Species # 4430
Band size: 1A

Geographic variation—No subspecies are recognized.

Molt—PB: HY partial-incomplete (Aug-Nov), AHY incomplete-complete (Jul-Sep); PA: SY incomplete (Feb-May), ASY partial-incomplete (Feb-Apr). The 1st PB begins on the summer grounds and completes on the winter grounds; the adult PB occurs primarily on the summer grounds. Molts during the first winter are eccentric (see p. 208 and Figs. 136A & 172A-C), occurring in two stages. The 1st PB is highly variable, including 2 to 10 (~27%) inner gr covs, usually (in ~95% of birds) 1-3 terts (sometimes s6 and/or s5, as well), often (in ~71% of birds) 1-5 middle pp (among p4-p8), and sometimes (in ~27% of birds) 1-2 central rects (r1; occasionally other rects); the juvenal pp covs, inner pp, and outer ss are retained. The 1st PA includes 1-4 ss (among s6-s9, usually consecutive from the inside), the outermost 2-5 pp (continuing where the 1st PB suspended), 0 (~18%) to 7 inner gr covs, often (in ~59% of birds) 1-2 central rects (r1), and occasionally other rects (but usually not the outermost). The adult PB sometimes is complete, but 1-3 middle ss (among s4-s6) often are retained until the adult PA. The adult PA includes those middle ss not replaced at the PB, 0 (~50%) to 3 inner gr covs, and often (in ~65% of birds) 1-2 terts, but no rects.

Skull—Pneumaticization completes in HY/SY from 15 Sep through Jan. Look for windows (> 3 mm; see Figs. 11D & 204) in some birds through spring or summer.

Age—Juv (May-Oct) lacks red in the crown and has upperparts washed brownish, outer pp with blunt tips (Fig. 181), and underparts buff, without pinkish or salmon; most juvs can be sexed by tl and plumage (see below).

Juvenal (Aug-Oct) and Basic (Oct-Apr) plumages

Juv-HY/SY (Aug-Apr): Tl 100-155 (see **Sex**); molt limits often occur among the med and gr covs (Fig. 133**B-E**, especially in Aug-Sep; see **Molt**); 1-3 terts (sometimes s5-s6, as well) often replaced in Sep-Oct, fresh, contrasting with the worn, retained ss (Fig. 133**D-E**); pp covs narrow and relatively faded brown (Fig.138**A**) with buff tips when fresh (Fig. 172**A**); pp uniformly juvenal in Aug-Sep, replacement beginning with p4-p6 in Sep-Oct (see **Molt**), or with 1-3 middle pp (among p4-p8) freshly replaced (Fig. 172**A**) in Dec-Apr; some or all outer pp (among p6-p10) not notched (Fig. 181); rects usually uniformly juvenal and relatively abraded. **Note: Juv-HYs are separated easily from SY/ASYs in Aug by skull condition (see Skull), outer pp not notched, and flight feathers much fresher.**

AHY/ASY (Aug-Apr): Tl 145-265 (see **Sex**); all gr covs and most or all ss uniformly adult (Fig. 133**F**), or 1-3 middle ss (among s4-s6) sometimes contrastingly worn (Fig. 161**A**); pp covs broad and dark brown to dusky (Fig. 138**B**), without buff tips; pp uniformly fresh (Fig. 133**F**) and with p6-p10 deeply notched (Fig. 181; see **Sex**); rects uniformly fresh.

Alternate Plumage (Apr-Aug)

SY (Apr-Aug): Tl 100-155 (see **Sex**); outer pp covs narrow, faded brown, and abraded (Figs. 138**C** & 172**B-C**); the innermost 3-7 pp and the outermost 3-6 ss retained, juvenal feathers, contrasting with the fresher, replaced, outermost 3-7 pp and innermost 1-6 ss (Fig. 136**A**), with three generations of feathers usually present (Fig. 172**B-C**); central rects (r1; sometimes others) often contrastingly fresh. **Note: Extensive pp and/or ss replacement in Feb-May indicates SY.**

ASY (Apr-Aug): Tl 145-265 (see **Sex**); outer pp covs broad, dark brown, and relatively fresh (Figs. 138**D** & 172**D**); pp and ss uniformly adult (Fig. 133**F**), or 1-2 terts and sometimes s5 and/or s6 replaced at the PA, slightly fresher than the rest of the ss (Fig. 172**D**); rects uniformly adult. **Note: See SY.**

Sex—CP/BP (Mar-Aug); CP may be poorly developed. Wg: ♀(n49) 105-120, ♂(n45) 110-129.

♀: Tl shorter by age (juv-HY/SY 100-130, AHY/ASY 145-182); flanks and underwing covs with little (juv-HY) to a moderate amount (AHY) of pink; p10 blunt (juvenal; Fig. 181) to moderately notched, 10-15 mm from the tip (adult; Fig. 181). **Note: See Molt regarding replacement of the outer pp. The shape of p6 cannot be used for sexing winter birds, as in other kingbirds.**

♂: Tl longer by age (juv-HY/SY 125-155, AHY/ASY 190-265); flanks and underwing covs with a moderate (juv-HY) to extensive (AHY), pink wash; p10 narrow and pointed (juvenal; Fig. 181) to extensively notched, 19-22 mm from the tip (adult; Fig. 181). **Note: See ♀.**

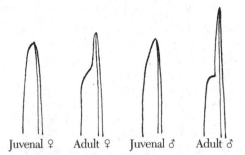

Juvenal ♀   Adult ♀   Juvenal ♂   Adult ♂

FIGURE 181. The shape of the outer primary (p10) by age and sex in Scissor-tailed Flycatcher.

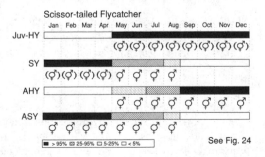

See Fig. 24

Hybrids reported—Western Kingbird.

References—Ridgway (1907), Forbush (1927), Bent (1942), Davis & Webster (1970), Oberholser (1974), Tyler & Parkes (1992), Phillips (1994b), Regosin & Pruett-Jones (1995), Pyle (1997c, in press); IBP (MAPS) data.

FORK-TAILED FLYCATCHER
Tyrannus savana

FTFL
Species # 4420
Band size: 1B-1

Geographic variation—Moderate, and ranges fairly well defined. Subspecies taxonomy follows Traylor (1979a); see also Ridgway (1907), Zimmer (1937b), Wetmore (1972), McCaskie & Patten (1994). One other subspecies occurs in S.Am.

    T.s. savana (vag from S.Am; probably to CA-NS; May-Nov): Molts primarily in Apr-Jul, so relatively fresh in Jun-Nov and worn in Dec-May; crown black, contrasting only moderately with the dark gray back; white collar averages less complete and less distinct; AHY/ASY ♂ with p8 distinctly notched, the notch on the outer web of p10 3-5 mm, and the notch on the inner web of p10 8-13 mm (see Fig. 182); p10 of AHY/ASY ♀ averages more tapered and pointed; underparts sometimes tinged yellow; flanks heavily washed gray.

    T.s. monarchus (vag from Mex, probably at least to TX; Dec-Apr): Molts primarily in Jul-Sep, so relatively fresh in Sep-Dec and worn in Jan-Aug; crown black, contrasting markedly with the pale gray back; white collar averages fuller and more distinct; AHY/ASY ♂ with p8 not notched, the notch on the outer web of p10 1-3 mm, and the notch on the inner web of p10 6-12 mm (see Fig. 182); p10 of AHY/ASY ♀ averages blunter and more rounded; underparts usually white; flanks with little or no gray.

    T.s. sanctaemartae (possible vag from S.Am to NJ; fall): Timing of molting presumably as in *savana*, but upperparts as in *monarchus*; AHY/ASY ♂ with p8 not distinctly notched, the notch on the inner web of p10 2-4 mm, and the notch on the outer web of p10 13-19 mm (see Fig. 182).

Molt—Unknown, but specimen examination indicates the following: PB HY/SY partial, AHY/ASY complete; PA absent-partial(?). The timing differs by subspecies (see **Geographic variation**). The PBs probably occur primarily on the non-breeding grounds (differing spatially and temporally with subspecies; see **Geographic variation**) and are protracted. All pp, ss (except perhaps the terts), and rects possibly are retained until the 2nd PB, at which time they are replaced in the typical sequence (see p. 14 and Fig. 13). More study is needed.

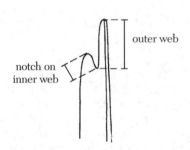

outer web

notch on inner web

FIGURE 182. Notch measurements in Fork-tailed Flycatcher, useful in separating subspecies.

Skull—Pneumaticization completes in HY/SY from 15 Mar through Sep *(T.s. savana)* or 15 Sep through Jan *(monarchus)*. Look for windows (> 3 mm; see Figs. 11**D** & 204) in some birds beyond these months.

Age—Juv (Jan-Jun in the nominate subspecies) lacks yellow in the crown and has upperparts and underparts washed brownish; some juv ♀♀ and ♂♂ can be separated by tl (see **Sex**) and the shape of p8-p10 (see below). Separation of non-juvs is complicated by winter breeding (in the nominate subspecies). In all subspecies the juvenal p6-p10 are not notched and the shorter juvenal tails by sex apparently are retained (see **Sex**); these apparently can be used to reliably age HY/SYs through the 2nd PB. Look also for HY/SYs to have molt limits among the wing covs and to average duller black crowns than AHY/ASYs. The timing of molt and ageing criteria varies by subspecies (see **Geographic variation**); it also is possible that molt extents may vary by subspecies, as well (*e.g.*, see Tropical Kingbird). More study is needed on molt and ageing in all kingbirds in C.Am-S.Am.

Sex—CP/BP reliable, but timing varies with subspecies. Wg: ♀(n8) 100-107, ♂(n12) 104-120.

♀: Tl shorter by age (juv-HY/SY 110-140, AHY 160-205); p10 blunt (juv-HY/SY; see Fig. 181) to tapered or slightly notched (AHY/ASY; p10 notch 0-6 mm; see Fig. 181).

♂: Tl longer by age (juv-HY/SY 150-210, ASY 195-290); p10 tapered (juv-HY/SY; see Fig. 181) or deeply notched (AHY/ASY; p10 notch 6-19 mm; see Fig. 181).

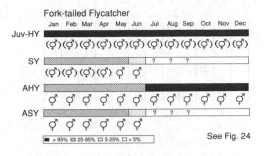

References—Dwight (1900a), Ridgway (1907), Forbush (1927), Zimmer (1937b), Bent (1942), Oberholser (1974), McCaskie & Patten (1994), Phillips (1994b).

ROSE-THROATED BECARD
Pachyramphus aglaiae

RTBE
Species # 4411
Band size: 1B-1

Species—♀♀ from Gray-collared Becard (*P. major*), a possible vagrant from Mex, by larger size (wg 86-98, tl 62-74; *vs* wg 76-85, tl 58-65 in ♀♀ Gray-collared Becard); r6 – r1 usually < 5 mm (*vs* > 15 mm); buffy supraloral stripe absent (*vs* present); back washed dusky (*vs* more cinnamon); gr covs uniformly brownish (*vs* blackish with distinct, cinnamon edges in Gray-collared Becard).

Geographic variation—Moderately well marked, and ranges in N.Am well defined. Subspecies taxonomy follows Traylor (1979a); see Ridgway (1907), van Rossem (1930c, 1938c), Dickey & van Rossem (1938), Webster (1963). Six other subspecies occur in Mex-C.Am.

> **P.a. albiventris** (br se.AZ-sw.NM): Small; bill short (exp culmen 13.8-16.2); ♀♀ with the cap blackish gray, the buff collar distinct, and the underparts buffy white; ♂♂ with the back pale gray and the throat patch pinkish rose. ♀ wg(n46) 86-93, tl(n10) 62-72; ♂ wg(n64) 87-94, tl(n10) 63-74. Northern birds, including those of N.Am ("*richmondi*") average slightly larger than southern birds, but variation is slight and broadly clinal.
>
> **P.a. gravis** (res s.TX): Large; bill long (exp culmen 14.4-18.0); ♀♀ with the cap black, the buff collar less distinct, and the underparts tawny-buff; ♂♂ with the back dark brownish gray and the throat patch deep rose. ♀ wg(n53) 8998, tl(n10) 64-74; ♂ wg(n58) 91-99, tl(n14) 66-76.

Molt—PB: HY partial (Jul-Dec), AHY complete (Jul-Sep); PA: SY absent-partial (Mar-May), ASY absent-limited (Mar-Apr). The PBs occur primarily on the summer grounds, although the 1st PB completes on the winter grounds. The 1st PB includes no gr covs and few if any med and lesser covs. The PAs appear to occur to a greater extent in SY ♂♂ than in ♀♀ and ASY ♂♂, at least in northern subspecies (see **Geographic variation**). The 1st PA includes 0 (~56%) to 2 inner gr covs, occasionally (in ~13% of birds) up to 4 inner ss (among s6-s9), and 1-2 central rects (r1); most to all juvenal wing covs and flight feathers are retained until the 2nd PB. The adult PA (if it occurs at all) includes no gr covs or flight feathers. More study is needed.

Skull—Pneumaticization completes in HY from 1 Oct through Dec. Look for windows (> 3 mm; see Figs. 11**D** & 204) in some birds through spring or summer.

Age/Sex—Juv (May-Aug) resembles HY/SY ♀, but has upperparts washed rufous and underparts buffier; juv ♀ = ♂, although occasional juv ♂♂ possibly can show one or more rose feathers on the throat and/or breast, and are reliably sexed. CP/BP (Apr-Jul). ♀ wg(n100) 86-98, tl(n20) 62-74; ♂ wg(n100) 87-99, tl(n24) 63-76; see **Geographic variation**.

HY/SY ♀ (Sep-Aug): Upperparts brown; underparts pale buff to cinnamon, without rose feathers; molt limits occur among the med and gr covs in some SYs in Apr Aug (Fig. 133**A-D**; see **Molt**); p9 full in length (*cf.* Fig. 183); outer rects relatively abraded and tapered (Fig. 139**B**). **Note: Intermediates may not be reliably aged by rect shape alone. Molting juvs in this plumage with incoming buffy breast feathers can be sexed ♀♀.**

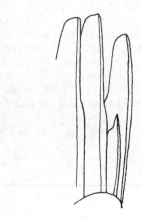

FIGURE 183. The unusual, abbreviated 9th primary of AHY/ASY ♂♂ Rose-throated Becards.

AHY/ASY ♀ (Sep-Aug): Like HY/SY ♀, but wing covs and terts uniformly adult in Apr-Aug (Fig. 133**F**); outer rects relatively fresh and truncate (Fig. 139**B**). **Note: See HY/SY ♀. Also, some AHY/ASY ♀♀ (particularly of *P.a. gravis*) can have a few to many rose feathers in the upper breast (see HY/SY ♂); these could be ASY/ATYs, but more study is needed.**

HY/SY ♂ (Sep-Aug): Upperparts primarily gray, with some rufous brown mixed in; most wing covs and flight feathers washed brownish; molt limits occur among the med and gr covs in some SYs in Apr-Aug (Fig. 133**A-D**; see **Molt**); p9 full in length (*cf.* Fig. 183); outer rects tapered (Fig. 139**B**); underwing covs buff; breast and/or throat with one or (variably) more rose feathers. **Note: Beware of some AHY/ASY ♀♀ with rose in the upper breast; confirm age (hence, sex) with the coloration of the upperparts, skull condition (see Skull), and rect shape.**

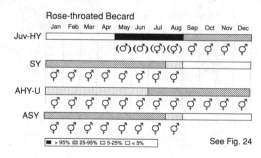

AHY/ASY ♂ (Sep-Aug): Upperparts blackish or slate gray; wing covs and flight feathers uniformly gray; p9 abbreviated (Fig. 183); underwing covs gray; breast gray with an extensive, rose patch.

References—Ridgway (1907), Dickey & van Rossem (1938), Bent (1942), Webster (1963), Oberholser (1974), Pyle (1997c).

SHRIKES

LANIIDAE

Two species. Family characters include large heads, heavy, toothed, and hooked beaks, short wings and legs, and fairly long tails. Shrikes have 10 primaries (the 10th reduced to shortened), 9 secondaries, and 12 rectrices. The first prebasic molt is partial to incomplete; ageing being accomplished with molt-related criteria. Prealternate molts are limited or partial. The sexes, alike in plumage, can be distinguished by breeding characters in spring/summer. Males average slightly to moderately larger than females.

NORTHERN SHRIKE
Lanius excubitor

NSHR
Species # 6210
Band size: 2

Species—From Loggerhead Shrike by much larger size (wg 106-121, tl 103-118; see **Sex**); bill long (nares to tip 13.0-14.3), the exp culmen > middle toe without claw; lores and nasal tufts gray or mixed gray and black (Fig. 184); underparts with extensive barring (moderately heavy and grayish on AHY, heavy and brownish on HY); lower mandible with a pale base (Fig. 184).

Geographic variation—Moderate and complex throughout the Holarctic range. Subspecies taxonomy in N.Am follows Phillips (1986), who synonymized a previously recognized subspecies; see also Ridgway (1904), Swarth (1926a), Miller (1931), Dement'ev & Gladkov (1954), Hubbard (1978), Svensson (1992), Cramp & Perrins (1993). Fifteen other subspecies occur in Eurasia and Africa.

L.e. borealis (br & wint throughout the range in N.Am): From *sibiricus* (a potential vagrant to w.AK) and the other Eurasian subspecies by upperparts slightly darker; lower eyelid usually with (vs often without) a white spot; bases of the ss without (vs often with some) white; r6 not entirely white; AHY with more distinct barring on the underparts. Within N.Am, birds of AK-Man to CA-TX (*"invictus"*) average larger, paler, and with more white on r6, but differences are slight, broadly clinal, and obscured by individual variation.

Molt—PB: HY partial (Oct-Dec), AHY complete (Jul-Sep); PA absent-partial (Mar-Apr). The 1st PB occurs on the winter grounds; the adult PB occurs on the summer grounds. The 1st PB includes some to all med covs, 0 (~8%) to 10 (~29%) inner gr covs and occasionally (in ~17% of birds) 1-3 terts, but no rects or other flight feathers. Look for some feathers (especially ss among s3-s6 and pp covs) to be retained during the adult PBs. The partial PA may occur only in SYs; more study is needed on the PA in ASYs. Look for the occurrence of a presupplemental molt in this species (see p. 16).

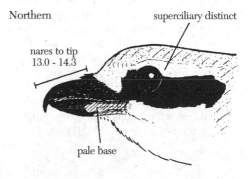

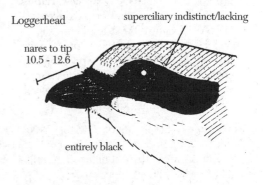

FIGURE 184. Facial features and bill size and color in Northern and Loggerhead shrikes.

271

Skull—Pneumaticization completes in HY/SY from 15 Oct through Jan. The skull can be difficult to see through the skin.

Age—Juv (Jun-Oct) has the plumage washed brownish, wing covs with cinnamon edging, and underparts with heavy, dusky barring; juv ♀ = ♂.

Juv-HY/SY (Sep-Aug): Face mask (especially lores) indistinct and brownish (through Mar); upperparts washed rufous-brown (through Nov) to dull olive-gray (through Mar?); molt limits usually occur among the med and gr covs (Fig. 133**A-E**; see **Molt**), the retained outer covs worn and brown with whitish to buff tips, contrasting with the fresher, black, and untipped, replaced inner covs; 1-3 terts occasionally replaced and black, contrasting with the older and brown, retained middle ss (s4-s6; Fig. 133**D-E**); outer pp covs narrow, tapered, relatively abraded (Fig. 138), and brown with buff tips; p6 with an indistinctly defined blackish center, extending to the base (Fig. 185); rects tapered (Fig. 139**B-C**); underparts brownish (Sep-Nov), or grayish (Nov-Aug), with moderately heavy to heavy barring; upper mandible brownish to dusky (through Mar). **Note: In addition, see Molt for age-related differences in the timing and location of the PBs.**

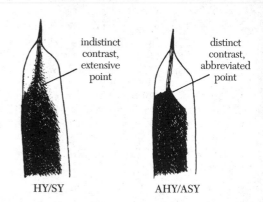

HY/SY   AHY/ASY

FIGURE 185. The base of p6 by age in Northern Shrike.

AHY/ASY (Sep-Aug): Face mask (including the lores) distinct and black; upperparts pearly gray; wing covs, terts, and middle ss (s4-s6) uniformly glossy black (Fig. 133**F**), the gr covs with narrow, white tips when fresh; outer pp covs broad, truncate, relatively fresh (Fig. 138), and black with white tips; p6 with a distinctly defined black center, not extending to the base (Fig. 185); rects truncate (Fig. 139**B-C**); underparts white with indistinct, dusky barring; upper mandible black. **Note: See HY/SY.**

Sex—CP/BP (May-Aug). ♀ wg(n30) 106-117, tl(n20) 103-114; ♂ wg(n54) 110-121, tl(n54) 105-118; see **Geographic variation**. HY/SY ♀♀ average browner and duller than HY/SY ♂♂, and AHY/ASY ♀♀ have slightly duller black flight feathers (on average) than AHY/ASY ♂♂, but these probably cannot be used to reliably sex individuals; more study is needed. Otherwise, no reliable plumage criteria are known for sexing.

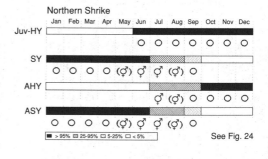

References—Stone (1896), Dwight (1900a), Ridgway (1904), Forbush (1929), Miller (1931), Bent (1950), Roberts (1955), Zimmerman (1955), Wood (1969), Oberholser (1974), Sheppard & Klimkiewicz (1976), Phillips *et al.* (1984), Svensson (1992), Cramp & Perrins (1993), Pyle (1997c); D.A. Sibley (pers. comm.).

LOGGERHEAD SHRIKE
Lanius ludovicianus

LOSH
Species # 6220
Band size: 1A

Species—From Northern Shrike by much smaller size (wg 85-105, tl 86-108; see **Geographic variation** & **Sex**); bill short (nares to tip 10.3-13.3), the exp culmen < middle toe without claw; lores and nasal tufts uniformly black (Fig. 184); underparts without extensive barring (slight and grayish on juv-HY); base of the lower mandible black (Fig. 184), occasionally slightly pale in juvs).

Geographic variation—Generally weak, geographically discordant, and clinal where ranges meet. Subspecies taxonomy follows A.R. Phillips and A.M. Rea *in* Phillips (1986); see also Ridgway (1904), Oberholser (1919f, 1922, 1974), Miller (1930, 1931), van Rossem (1931a), Bishop (1933), Van Tyne & Sutton (1937), Rand (1957), Phillips (1959b), Phillips *et al.* (1964), Unitt (1984), Behle (1985), Haas (1987), Stevenson & Anderson (1994), Collister & Wicklum (1996). Note that ♂♂ of all races average slightly paler upperparts than ♀♀. No other subspecies occur.

California Island *(L.l. anthonyi)* Group. Dark; white in the pp reduced.
L.l. anthonyi (res Channel Is, CA): Small; bill long (nares to tip 11.6-13.0, depth at tip of nares 7.8-8.8); upperparts medium-dark gray to slate; underparts grayish; white of the scapulars moderately extensive and moderately indistinct; uppertail covs gray with little to some white. ♀ wg(n10) 92-98, tl(n10) 94-102; ♂ wg(n13) 94-99, tl(n13) 96-103.
L.l. mearnsi (res San Clemente I, CA): Medium small; bill short (nares to tip 10.3-12.0, depth at tip of nares 8.2-8.7); upperparts dark gray; underparts whitish to gray; white of the scapulars extensive and moderately distinct; uppertail covs grayish with some to a substantial amount of white. ♀ wg(n8) 92-98, tl(n8) 86-100; ♂ wg(n10) 95-100, tl(n10) 93-102.
L.l. grinnelli (res San Diego County, CA): Large; bill long (nares to tip 11.6-13.2, depth at tip of nares 7.9-8.8); upperparts dark gray; underparts grayish white; white of the scapulars reduced and indistinct; uppertail covs medium-pale grayish with moderately little white. ♀ wg(n10) 92-100, tl(n10) 89-99; ♂ wg(n10) 99-103, tl(n10) 100-108.

Continental *(L.l. ludovicianus)* Group. Pale; white in the pp extensive.
L.l. mexicanus (br & wint WA-s.ID to s.CA-AZ & Man-NS to n.TX-VA, wint to s.TX-s.FL): Medium in size; bill slender (nares to tip 10.6-12.7, depth at tip of nares 7.9-8.7); upperparts medium-dark gray, contrasting slightly to moderately with the grayish-white underparts; white of the scapulars variable in extent and moderately indistinct; uppertail covs grayish white. ♀ wg(n87) 92-101, tl(n95) 88-104; ♂ wg(n100) 94-102, tl(n100) 89-106. In N.Am, birds of the western part of the range (*"gambeli"*) may average slightly darker upperparts and whiter uppertail covs than birds of the eastern part of the range (*"migrans"*), but differences are weak and obscured by individual variation.
L.l excubitorides (br Alb-Sask to AZ-w.TX, wint to OR & LA): Medium large; bill slender (nares to tip 10.8-12.7, depth at tip of nares 8.0-8.7); upperparts medium-pale gray; white of the scapulars extensive and distinct; uppertail covs white. ♀ wg(n57) 93-103, tl(n59) 92-106; ♂ wg(n82) 96-105, tl(n81) 94-108. Birds of desert se.CA-s.NV to w.TX (*"sonoriensis"*) average larger and birds of NV to e.CO-nw.NM (*"nevadensis"*) may average grayer, but differences are weak and broadly clinal.
L.l. ludovicianus (res s.LA to NC-c.FL): Medium small; bill large (nares to tip 10.8-13.3, depth at tip of nares 8.2-9.2); upperparts dark gray, contrasting moderately with the grayish-white underparts; white of the scapulars moderately broad and distinct; uppertail covs grayish white to dark gray. ♀ wg(n100) 89-99, tl(n100) 91-104; ♂ wg(n100) 93-101, tl(n100) 94-107.
L.l. miamensis (res s.FL): Small; bill large (nares to tip 11.3-13.3, depth at tip of nares 8.2-9.8); upperparts medium-pale gray, contrasting moderately with the white underparts; white of the scapulars narrow and indistinct; uppertail covs grayish white to gray. ♀ wg(n25) 85-94, tl(n25) 89-95; ♂ wg(n27) 92-98, tl(n27) 95-100.

Molt—HY partial-incomplete (Jun-Nov), AHY complete (Jun-Oct); PA absent-limited (Feb-Apr). The PBs occur primarily on the summer grounds. The 1st PB is variable, including 7 to

10 (~77%) inner gr covs, usually (in ~93% of birds) 1-3 terts, sometimes s6 and s5, and 0 (~13%) to all 12 (~73%) rects. Some (~50%) birds also show an eccentric replacement pattern (see p. 208 and Fig. 136), with the outermost 4-6 pp and the innermost 3-5 ss replaced; occasionally this molt can be arrested such that just 1-3 pp (e.g., p6-p7) are replaced. The pp covs are retained. The 1st PB averages more extensive in southern birds (e.g., *L.l. grinnelli, ludovicianus,* and *miamensis*) than in northern birds (*mexicanus* and *excubitorides*). Look for some feathers (especially ss among s3-s6 and pp covs) to be retained during the adult PBs. The PA probably is more extensive in SYs than in ASYs. Look for the occurrence of a presupplemental molt (see p. 16) in this species.

Skull—Pneumaticization completes in HY/SY from 15 Sep (as early as 1 Aug in southern birds) through Jan. The skull can be difficult to observe through the skin.

Age—Juv (Apr-Sep) has body feathers with indistinct barring and wing covs tipped buff; juv ♀ = ♂.

Juv-HY/SY (Oct-Sep): Molt limits sometimes occur among the gr covs (Fig. 133**D-E**; see **Molt**), the retained outer covs worn and brown with whitish to buff tips, contrasting with the fresher, black, and untipped, replaced inner covs; 1-3 terts (sometimes s5-s6, as well) usually replaced and black, contrasting with the older and brown, retained middle ss (s4-s6; Fig. 133**D-E**), 1-6 outer pp sometimes replaced (see **Molt**), contrasting with the juvenal, retained innermost (and sometimes the outermost) pp (Figs. 136**A-B** & 172**A**); outer pp covs narrow, tapered, relatively abraded (Fig. 138), and brown with narrow, buff tips; some or all rects juvenal, brown, and tapered (Fig. 139**B**), often mixed with black and truncate, replaced rects (see **Molt**). **Note: In addition, check the base of p6 for age-related differences, as in Northern Shrike (see Fig. 185).**

AHY/ASY (Oct-Sep): Wing covs and flight feathers uniformly glossy black (Fig. 133**F**; the terts tend to be darker but without distinct contrasts between adjacent feathers); outer pp covs broad, truncate, relatively fresh (Fig. 138), and black with white tips; rects uniformly black and truncate (Fig. 139**B**). **Note: See HY/SY.**

Sex—CP/BP (Feb-Aug). ♀ wg(n100) 85-103, tl(n100) 86-106; ♂ wg(n100) 92-105, tl(n100) 89-108; see **Geographic variation**. See Collister and Wicklum (1996) for a discriminant function analysis, based on live birds, using tl, bill depth at the tip of the nares, and distance from the wrist to the end of the white on the pp, that correctly sexed 77% of Alb (*L.l. excubitorides*) birds. ♀♀ average slightly darker upperparts and heavier barring to the underparts than ♂♂, but there is much overlap; otherwise, no other plumage criteria for sexing are known. Mouth color appears to average paler and grayer in ♀♀ and blacker in ♂♂, but more study is needed on the usefulness of this for sexing.

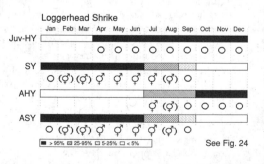

References—Stone (1896), Dwight (1900a), Ridgway (1904), Miller (1928, 1931), Forbush (1929), Bent (1950), Roberts (1955), Zimmerman (1955), Wood (1969), Oberholser (1974), Sheppard & Klimkiewicz (1976), Slack (1994), Collister & Wicklum (1996), Yosef (1996), Pyle (1997c); S.R. Blackshaw (pers. comm.); PRBO data.

VIREOS   *VIREONIDAE*

Twelve species. Family characters include stout and hooked beaks, short tails (wing chord > tail length), and fleshy, scaled legs. Vireos have 10 primaries (the 10th is variable, reduced in seven species and vestigial to minute in four such that there are only 9 visible primaries), 9 secondaries, and 12 rectrices. The first prebasic molt is partial to incomplete, being eccentric in two species. A protracted, winter adult prebasic molt occurs in four species, and limited to partial prealternate molts occur in most species. Windows in the pneumaticization of the skull often are retained into the first spring or later. Otherwise, ageing through spring is difficult, but can be accomplished in many birds by molt limits, rectrix shape, eye color and (especially) the condition of the primary coverts. Males average only slightly larger than females in size. Only one species shows marked sex-related plumage characters. Breeding characters are reliable in spring and summer, although males of most species develop a partial brood patch.

WHITE-EYED VIREO   WEVI
Vireo griseus   Species # 6310
                                            Band size: 0-0A

Species—From Bell's and the other vireos of N.Am by medium-small size (wg 54-65, tl 42-53; see **Sex**); p10 – pp covs 6-12 mm; spectacles prominent and yellow; wing bars distinct; flanks washed yellow; iris brownish gray (juv-HYs) to white (AHYs). From Thick-billed Vireo (*V. crassirostris*, alpha code **TBVI**, **Species # 9130**) a vagrant to s.FL, by bill blackish to black and smaller (nares to tip 6.6-8.1, depth at tip of nares 3.7-4.4, width at tip of nares 3.4-4.2, bill length × depth × width 91-132 mm, *vs* bill brownish and larger, 7.9-8.9, 4.2-4.8, 4.0-4.8, and 154-181 mm, respectively, in Thick-billed Vireo); throat to the center of the belly usually white (*vs* yellow); iris color (dark in all ages of Thick-billed Vireo). The inexperienced should also beware of mistaking HY White-eyed Vireos with *Empidonax* flycatchers (see p. 219).

Geographic variation—Moderate to well marked and ranges fairly well defined. Subspecies taxonomy follows Phillips (1991); see also Ridgway (1904), Worthington & Todd (1926), Todd (1933), Wetmore (1940), Burleigh & Lowery (1945), Hamilton (1958), Oberholser (1974), Stevenson & Anderson (1994), Remsen *et al.* (1996). Three other subspecies occur in Mex and Bermuda.

V.g. *micrus* (br & wint s.TX; vag to LA): Small; p8 usually ≤ p5; plumage dull; flanks olive with a yellow tinge. ♀ wg(n13) 54-58, tl(n10) 42-49; ♂ wg(n24) 55-59, tl(n24) 44-50.

V.g. *griseus* (br & wint throughout most of the range in N.Am): Large; bill small (exp culmen 9.1-11.4, depth at gonys 3.5-3.9); p8 > p5; plumage bright; yellow spectacles usually complete; flanks bright yellow with an olive tinge. ♀ wg(n60) 57-63, tl(n55) 44-52; ♂ wg(n86) 58-65, tl(n78) 46-53. Birds of coastal TX-FL-NC average slightly duller and grayer than those in the rest of N.Am ("*noveboracensis*"), but differences are slight and broadly clinal.

V.g. *maynardi* (res. s.FL Is): Size as in griseus, but bill large (exp culmen 10.3-12.8, depth at gonys 3.8-4.6); p8 usually ≤ p5; plumage medium bright; yellow spectacles usually broken above the eye; flanks pale yellow with an olive tinge.

Molt—PB: HY partial-incomplete (Jul-Sep); AHY complete (Jun-Sep); PA absent. The PBs occur on the summer grounds, often after postbreeding dispersal. The 1st PB usually (in ~83% of birds) is eccentric (see p. 208 and Fig. 136), including the innermost 1-5 ss, the outermost 1-8 pp, and usually (in ~80% of birds) all 12 rects; the pp covs are retained. Replacement of the pp commences with p4-p6 and often completes through p10, but sometimes will arrest after just 1-3 pp have been replaced; thus, *e.g.*, p6-p7 can be the only pp replaced. Other birds (the ~17% of birds not replacing pp) replace 8 to 10 (~75%) inner gr covs and 1-3 terts, but no rects. Birds of southern populations (including V.g. *micrus* and *maynardi*) replace more flight feathers on average than northern birds (*griseus*).

Skull—Pneumaticization completes in HY/SY from 1 Nov through Mar. Windows (> 2 mm; Fig. 11**D**) can occur in some SYs through spring.

Age—Juv (Apr-Aug) has brownish-buff head plumage (including the lores and eye ring), buff wing bars, and a grayish-brown iris; juv ♀ = ♂.

HY/SY (Aug-Jul): Iris brownish gray to grayish (through at least Feb); molt limits sometimes occur among the gr covs (Fig. 133**D-E**; see **Molt**), the retained outer covs worn and brownish with dull buffy-lemon tips, contrasting with the fresher, duskier, and lemon-tipped, replaced inner covs; 1-3 terts usually replaced (sometimes s6-s5, as well), contrasting with the older middle ss (s4-s6; Fig. 133**D-E**; the contrast can become difficult to see in Mar-Jul); 1-6 pp (among p4-p10) usually replaced, contrasting with the innermost (and sometimes the outermost), retained pp (Fig. 136**A**); outer pp covs narrow, tapered, relatively abraded, and brownish with indistinct, relatively narrow, or no greenish edging (Fig. 138); juvenal outer rects occasionally retained, tapered, and relatively abraded in spring (Fig. 139**A**). **Note: Caution is advised with the use of eye color, especially in southern populations (ASYs with gray irises have been reported in FL). On the other hand, spring birds with grayish or beige outer rings may be reliably aged SY; more study is needed. In addition, check for p10 to be longer (relative to the pp covs) and more rounded in HY/SYs than in AHY/ASYs (see Fig. 234), and for the roof of the mouth (upper mandible lining) to show color differences, as in the Solitary, Philadelphia, or Red-eyed vireos.**

AHY/ASY (Aug-Jul): Iris usually white, or white with a slight grayish wash; wing covs and flight feathers uniformly adult (Fig. 133**F**) and dusky with distinct, greenish edging; outer pp covs broad, truncate, relatively fresh, and dusky with distinct, relatively broad, greenish edging (Fig. 138); outer rects uniformly truncate and relatively fresh (Fig. 139**A**). **Note: See HY/SY.**

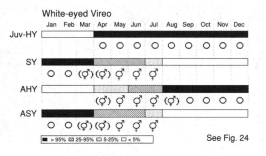

Sex—♀ = ♂ by plumage. CP/BP (Mar-Aug); ♂♂ develop a partial BP (Fig. 22**B**). ♀ wg(n100) 54-63, tl(n77) 42-52; ♂ wg(n100) 55-65, tl(n100) 44-53.

References—Stone (1896), Dwight (1900a), Ridgway (1904), Forbush (1929), Bent (1950), Roberts (1955), Blake (1962a), Wood (1969), Fisk (1972), George (1973), Thompson (1973), Oberholser (1974), Sheppard & Klimkiewicz (1976), Lloyd-Evans (1983), Phillips *et al.* (1983), Smith *et al.* (1990), Hopp *et al.* (1995), Pyle (1997c); C.S. Robbins, E.J. Fisk (*in litt.* to the BBL); H. Smith, C.W. Thompson, B. Walker (pers. comm.); IBP (MAPS) data, PNR data.

BELL'S VIREO   BEVI
Vireo bellii   Species # 6330
                                                                Band size: 0

Least Bell's Vireo (LBVI)   Species # 6334

Species—From Northern Beardless-Tyrannulet by tarsus long (> 17 mm); p9 < p6, p9 < p5 by 2-7 mm, and p10 reduced (Fig. 186); distinct crest lacking; wing bars indistinct and pale gray or tinged yellow; basal half of the lower mandible dark. From White-eyed, Gray, Hutton's, and the other vireos of N.Am by small size (wg 51-59, tl 41-54; see **Geographic variation**); p10 >

pp covs by 6-11 mm (Fig. 186); spectacles indistinct and pale yellowish or grayish; wing bars indistinct to moderately distinct; flanks grayish or tinged yellow; iris dark.

Geographic variation—Moderate, but clinal where ranges meet. Subspecies taxonomy follows Phillips (1991); see also Ridgway (1904), Oberholser (1917d, 1974), Phillips *et al.* (1964), Unitt (1985). One other possible subspecies occurs in Mex. Measurements of sexes are combined due to little dimorphism (see **Sex**). Note that birds become duller and grayer with wear.

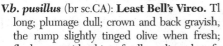

p9 < p6
p9 < p5 by 2-7 mm

6.5-11.0 mm

FIGURE 186. The wing morphology of Bell's Vireo. See Figure 10 for measurement techniques.

V.b. pusillus (br sc.CA): **Least Bell's Vireo.** Tl long; plumage dull; crown and back grayish, the rump slightly tinged olive when fresh; flanks gray with a hint of yellow-olive when fresh. Tl ♀♂(n26) 47-54.

V.b. arizonae (br desert sw.UT-se.CA to sw.NM): Tl long; plumage medium dull; crown grayish; back grayish olive to grayish; flanks grayish or with a light, pale yellow-olive wash when fresh. Tl ♀♂(n25) 47-54.

V.b. medius (br s.NM-sw.TX; vag to c.AZ, LA): Tl medium in length; plumage medium bright; crown grayish olive to grayish; back olive to grayish olive; flanks with a moderately pale yellow-olive wash. Tl ♀♂(n12) 45-49.

V.b. bellii (br ND-se.TX to w.OH-w.MS; vag to NY-FL): Tl short; plumage bright; crown tinged olive; back greenish olive to olive; flanks with a heavy yellow-olive wash. Tl ♀♂(n25) 41-47.

Molt—PB: HY partial-incomplete (Jul-Sep), AHY complete (Jun-Aug); PA absent. The PBs occur on the summer grounds. The 1st PB includes 8 to 10 (~85%) inner gr covs, usually (in ~81% of birds) 1-3 terts, and 0 (~54%) to all 12 (~38%) rects; it sometimes (in ~38% of birds) can be eccentric (see p. 208 and Fig. 136), including the innermost 4-5 ss and the outermost 4-5 pp; the pp covs are retained. Replacement of the pp (when it occurs) commences with p5-p6 and usually completes; look for some birds to arrest this molt, as in White-eyed Vireo.

Skull—Pneumaticization completes in HY/SY from 1 Nov (as early as 1 Oct in *V.b. pusillus*). Windows (> 2 mm; Fig. 11**D**) can occur in some SYs through spring.

Age—Juv (May-Aug) has a brownish wash to the upperparts, whiter underparts, and relatively distinct wing bars; juv ♀ = ♂.

HY/SY (Aug-Jul): Molt limits occasionally occur among the gr covs (Fig. 133**D-E**; see **Molt**), the retained outer covs worn and brownish with dull, buffy-greenish to buffy-grayish tips, contrasting with the fresher, duskier, and brighter, greenish-tipped to grayish-tipped, replaced inner covs; 1-3 terts usually replaced (sometimes s6-s5, as well), contrasting with the older middle ss (Fig. 133**D-E**; the limit can become difficult to see in Mar-Jul); the outermost 4-5 pp sometimes replaced, contrasting with the innermost, retained pp (Fig. 136**A**); outer pp covs narrow, tapered, relatively abraded, and brownish with indistinct, relatively narrow, or no greenish edging (Fig. 138), contrasting with the slightly fresher, replaced gr covs (Fig. 134); juvenal outer rects often retained, tapered, and relatively abraded (Fig. 139**A**) in spring. **Note: Ageing can be difficult in spring, when plumage can become quite worn; many intermediates may not be reliably aged in Mar-Jul. In addition, check for p10 to be longer (relative to the pp covs) and more rounded in HY/SYs than in AHY/ASYs (see Fig. 234), and for the roof of the mouth (upper mandible lining) to show color differences, as in the Solitary, Philadelphia, or Red-eyed vireos.**

AHY/ASY (Aug-Jul): Wing covs and flight feathers uniformly adult (Fig. 133**F**) and dusky with distinct, greenish or grayish edging; outer pp covs broad, truncate, relatively fresh, and dusky with distinct, relatively broad, greenish or grayish edging (Fig. 138), not contrasting in wear with the gr covs (Fig. 133**F**); outer rects truncate and relatively fresh (Fig. 139**A**). **Note: See HY/SY.**

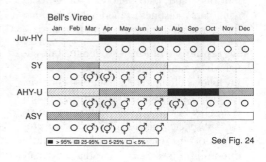

Sex—♀ = ♂ by plumage. CP/BP (Mar-Aug); ♂♂ can develop a partial BP (Fig. 22**B**). ♀ wg(n54) 51-58, tl(n28) 41-53; ♂ wg(n67) 52-59, tl(n49) 42-54.

References—Ridgway (1904), Forbush (1929), Bent (1950), Roberts (1955), Oberholser (1974), Phillips *et al.* (1983), Stallcup (1984), Unitt (1985), Brown (1993), Pyle (1997c); IBP (MAPS) data.

BLACK-CAPPED VIREO

Vireo atricapillus

BCVI
Species # 6300
Band size: 0-1C

Species—HY ♀♀ from the other vireos of N.Am by the combination of small size (wg 51-59, tl 39-47; see **Age/Sex**); p10 > pp covs by 7-13 mm; crown and face washed dusky; spectacles distinct (especially in front of the eye) and whitish.

Geographic variation—No subspecies are recognized.

Molt—PB: HY partial-incomplete (Jun-Aug), AHY complete (Jun-Aug); PA limited-partial (Feb-Mar). The PBs occur on the summer grounds. The 1st PB includes 9 to 10 (~83%) inner gr covs and 1-3 terts (occasionally s6, as well), but no rects or pp covs. The 1st PA includes 0 (~71%) to 2 inner gr covs, 1-3 terts, and occasionally (in ~14% of birds) 1-2 central rects (r1). The adult PA includes 0 (~25%) to 5 inner gr covs, often (in ~75% of birds) 1-3 terts, and sometimes (in ~25% of birds) 1-2 central rects (r1).

Skull—Pneumaticization completes in HY/SY from 15 Oct. Windows (> 2 mm; Fig. 11**D**) can occur in some SYs through spring.

Age/Sex—Juv (May-Jul) has plumage washed with buff and spectacles light buff; juv ♀ = ♂. CP/BP (Mar-Aug); ♂♂ can develop a partial BP (Fig. 22**B**). ♀ wg(n34) 51-57, tl(n20) 39-45; ♂ wg(n100) 52-59, tl(n100) 40-47.

Basic Plumage (Aug-Mar)

HY/SY ♀♂ (Aug-Mar): Iris brown (through Dec); Crown and nape dull brownish gray, showing little or no contrast with the brownish-olive back; molt limits occasionally occur among the outer gr covs (Fig. 133**D-E**; see **Molt**), the retained outermost cov worn and brownish with buffy-lemon edging, contrasting with the fresher, dusky, and bright lemon-edged, replaced inner covs; 1-3 terts (and occasionally s6) replaced, contrasting with the older middle ss (s4-s6; Fig. 133**D-E**); outer pp covs narrow, tapered, relatively abraded, and dusky brownish with indistinct, relatively narrow, yellow-olive edging (Fig. 138**A**); outer rects tapered and relatively abraded (Fig. 139**A**); underparts, especially the upper breast, washed with buff or yellow. **Note: In Aug-Mar, HY/SY ♂♂ average grayer crowns and whiter spectacles than HY/SY ♀♀, but more study is needed on the reliability of these plumage differences for sexing individuals. A few intermediates can occur which are not reliably aged by plumage alone. In addition, check for p10 to be longer (relative to the pp covs) and more rounded in HY/SYs than in AHY/ASYs (see Fig. 234), and for the roof of the mouth (upper mandible lining) to show color differences, as in the Solitary, Philadelphia, or Red-eyed vireos.**

AHY/ASY ♀ (Aug-Mar): Iris red; crown and nape slate-gray to dull black, contrasting fairly markedly with the olive-green back; wing covs, terts, and middle ss (s4-s6) uniformly adult (Fig. 133**F**), the feathers dusky with distinct, yellow or yellow-olive edging; pp covs broad, truncate, relatively fresh, and dusky with distinct, relatively broad, yellow-olive edging (Fig. 138**B**); outer rects truncate and relatively fresh (Fig. 139**A**); underparts (except the lemon-yellow flanks) white or whitish. **Note: See HY/SY ♀♂.**

AHY/ASY ♂ (Aug-Mar): Crown and nape glossy black, the feathers tipped gray when fresh; wing covs and flight feathers as in AHY/ASY ♀. **Note: See HY/SY ♀♂.**

Alternate Plumage (Mar-Jul)

SY ♀ (Mar-Jul): Crown and nape uniformly dull slate gray to dull blackish; outer pp covs narrow, tapered, relatively abraded, and brownish with indistinct, relatively narrow, or no yellow-olive edging (Fig. 138**C**); outer rects tapered and relatively abraded (Fig. 139**A**). **Note: Beware that both age groups show similar molt limits in Mar-Jul (see Molt), although occasional SYs have retained the innermost juvenal gr cov and this is still visible in spring. The pp-cov criteria probably are the best for ageing ♀♀. In addition, see HY/SY ♀ (above) regarding possible differences in the size and shape of p10.**

ASY ♀ (Mar-Jul): Crown and nape uniformly slate-gray to dull black; outer pp covs broad, truncate, relatively fresh, and dusky brownish with distinct, relatively broad, yellow-olive edging (Fig. 138**D**); outer rects truncate and relatively fresh (Fig. 139**A**). **Note: See SY ♀.**

SY ♂ (Mar-Jul): Crown and nape black with variable amounts of gray, especially in the nape; pp covs and rects as in SY ♀. **Note: See SY ♀.**

ASY ♂ (Mar-Jul): Crown and nape uniformly glossy black; pp covs and rects as in ASY ♀. **Note: See SY ♀.**

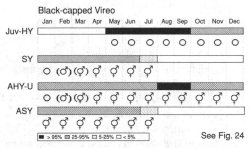

Black-capped Vireo

Note: In Oct-Dec, AHYs can be sexed but birds of unknown age should be left unsexed. ♂♂ should be reliably aged SY and ASY through Jul, whereas some ♀♀ should be aged U/AHY.

See Fig. 24

References—Ridgway (1904), Bent (1950), Sutton (1967), Oberholser (1974), Grzybowski (1991, 1995), Pyle (1997c); P. Ashman (pers. comm.).

GRAY VIREO

Vireo vicinior

GRVI
Species # 6340
Band size: 1

Species—From the other vireos of N.Am (including Bell's and Plumbeous Solitary vireos) by medium size but long tl (wg 59-68, tl 54-62; see **Sex**), wg – tl 6-13 mm; p9 < p5 by 4-7 mm and p10 > pp covs by 8-14 mm (Fig. 187); bill small (exp culmen 8.8-10.7); upperparts gray or brownish gray with a slight or no olive tinge; spectacles (eye ring) thin, white, and complete in front of the eye; wing bars indistinct, and grayish or tinted olive; underparts white, with a slight or no yellow-olive tinge to the flanks when fresh.

Geographic variation—Very weak and geographically complex; subspecies probably are not separated reliably. Subspecies taxonomy follows Phillips (1991); see also Ridgway (1904), Grinnell & Swarth (1913), Phillips *et al.* (1964). One other possible subspecies occurs in Mex, which may have a blacker bill than subspecies of N.Am.

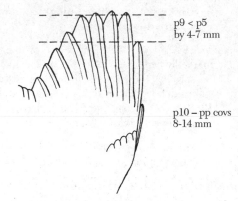

p9 < p5
by 4-7 mm

p10 – pp covs
8-14 mm

V.v. californicus (br s.CA-nw.AZ): Upperparts medium-dark gray.

V.v. vicinior (br & wint UT-CO to s.AZ-sw.TX): Upperparts medium-pale gray.

Molt—PB: HY partial-incomplete (Jul-Sep), AHY complete (Jul-Sep); PA absent-partial (Feb-Apr). The PBs occur on the summer grounds. The 1st PB includes 4 to 10

FIGURE 187. The wing morphology of Gray Vireo. See Figure 10 for measurement techniques.

(~50%) inner gr covs, 1-3 terts (sometimes s6, as well), and 0 (~50%) to all 12 (~50%) rects. The 1st PA includes 0 (~33%) to 3 inner gr covs, often (in ~73% of birds) 1-2 terts, and occasionally (in ~13% of birds) 1-2 central rects. The adult PA possibly is absent to limited, with few if any wing covs or flight feathers replaced; more study is needed.

Skull—Pneumaticization completes in HY/SY from 15 Oct. Windows (> 2 mm; Fig. 11D) can occur in some SYs through spring.

Age—Juv (May-Aug) has plumage washed brown and wing bars relatively distinct; juv ♀ = ♂.

HY/SY (Aug-Jul): Molt limits often occur among the gr covs (Fig. 133C-E; see **Molt**), the retained outer covs worn and brownish with indistinct, buff edging, contrasting with the fresher and grayer, replaced inner covs; 1-3 terts (and sometimes s6) replaced, contrasting with the older middle ss (s4-s6; Fig. 133D-E); outer pp covs narrow, tapered, relatively abraded, and brownish with indistinct, relatively narrow, or no buff edging (Fig. 138); outer rects tapered and relatively abraded (Fig. 139A). **Note: In addition, check for p10 to be longer (relative to the pp covs) and more rounded in HY/SYs than in AHY/ASYs (see Fig. 234), and for the roof of the mouth (upper mandible lining) to show color differences, as in the Solitary, Philadelphia, or Red-eyed vireos.**

AHY/ASY (Aug-Jul): Wing covs, terts, and middle ss (s4-s6) uniformly adult (Fig. 133F), the feathers grayish with indistinct or no pale gray edging; outer pp covs broad, truncate, relatively fresh, and dusky with distinct, relatively broad, pale gray edging (Fig. 138); outer rects truncate and relatively fresh (Fig. 139A). **Note: See HY/SY.**

Sex—♀ = ♂ by plumage. CP/BP (Mar-Aug); ♂ develops a partial BP (Fig. 22B). Wg: ♀ wg(n30) 59-66, tl(n20) 54-59; ♂ wg(n30) 61-68, tl(n20) 57-62.

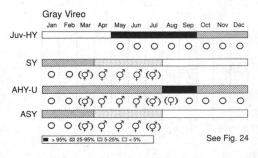

Gray Vireo

Jan Feb Mar Apr May Jun Jul Aug Sep Oct Nov Dec

Juv-HY

SY

AHY-U

ASY

■ > 95% ▨ 25-95% ▨ 5-25% □ < 5%   See Fig. 24

References—Ridgway (1904), W .Taber *in* Bent (1950), Oberholser (1974), Phillips *et al.* (1983), Pyle (1997c).

SOLITARY VIREO

SOVI
Species # 6299
Band size: 1C-1

BLUE-HEADED VIREO
Vireo solitarius

BHVI
Species # 6290

CASSIN'S VIREO
Vireo cassinii

CAVI
Species # 6291

PLUMBEOUS VIREO
Vireo plumbeus

PLVI
Species # 6292

Species—The "Solitary Vireos" are separated from the other vireos of N.Am, including Gray (from Plumbeous Vireo) and Hutton's (from Cassin's Vireo), by large size and relatively short tl (wg 67-85, tl 47-61; see **Geographic variation**); wg – tl 17-30 mm (see **Geographic variation**); bill variable (exp culmen 9.0-12.2; larger in Plumbeous Vireo; see **Geographic variation**); p9 ≥ p5 by 0-6 mm and p10 – pp covs -3 to 6 mm (Fig. 188); lores and eye ring bold, white, and broken in front of the eye; wing bars distinct, and white or tinged yellow; underparts white. See **Geographic variation** for criteria separating the (recently split) Solitary Vireos.

Geographic variation—Well marked and ranges well defined; few intermediates have been reported. Subspecies taxonomy follows Phillips (1991); see also Ridgway (1904), van Rossem (1934a), Wetmore (1937), Hamilton (1958), Phillips *et al.* (1964, 1983), Oberholser (1974), Browning (1978, 1990), Behle (1985), Johnson (1995), Heindel (1996). Four other subspecies occur in Mex-C.Am.

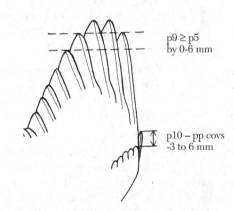

p9 ≥ p5
by 0-6 mm

p10 – pp covs
-3 to 6 mm

FIGURE 188. Wing morphology in the Solitary Vireos. See Figure 10 for measurement techniques.

Blue-headed (*V.s. solitarius*) Group. Bright.
V.s. solitarius (br n.BC to NS-s.PA, wint coastal se.TX-FL-GA; vag to CA): Small; wg – tl 19-27; bill medium in size (exp culmen 9.5-11.3); crown and face bright bluish, contrasting with the bright greenish nape and back; wing edging bright green; outer rects (r6) with distinct, white edges when fresh; flanks heavily washed yellow or yellowish olive, contrasting distinctly with the white underparts. ♀ wg(n26) 69-76, tl(n10) 47-54; ♂ wg(n24) 70-78, tl(n10) 48-55.
V.s. alticola (br montane c.WV-n.GA, wint coastal LA-FL-SC): Medium-large; bill large (exp culmen 11.2-12.2); plumage as in *solitarius*, except darker overall, the back mixed gray and olive. ♀ wg(n27) 74-82, tl(n15) 50-58; ♂ wg(n33) 76-83, tl(n21) 51-59.
Cassin's Vireo
V. cassini (br c.BC-c.ID to s.CA, wint s.CA-s.AZ): Small; wg – tl 17-26 mm; bill small (exp culmen 9.0-10.7); crown, nape, and face dull grayish to olive with a dusky wash, contrasting slightly with the dull olive back; wing edging dull greenish; outer rects (r6) with indistinct or no whitish edges; flanks washed dull olive, contrasting indistinctly with the whitish underparts. ♀ wg(n100) 67-75, tl(n10) 49-54; ♂ wg(n100) 69-77, tl(n19) 50-56.

Plumbeous Vireo

V. plumbeus (br s.ID-s.MT to se.CA-sw.TX, wint s.AZ; vag to LA): Large; wg – tl 23-30; bill large (exp culmen 11.2-12.2); crown, face, and back uniformly gray, usually without olive (sometimes with a slight olive tinge when fresh); wing edging whitish; outer rects (r6) with distinct, white edges; flanks washed grayish, sometimes tinged olive when fresh, contrasting distinctly with the white underparts. ♀ wg(n30) 77-84, tl(n30) 55-60; ♂ wg(n30) 78-85, tl(n30) 56-61. Birds of s.ID-s.MT to AZ ("*V.p. jacksoni*") may average darker (more olive) and with larger bills, but differences, if present, are very slight.

Molt—PB: HY partial (Jul-Sep), AHY complete (Jul-Aug); PA absent-partial (Mar-Apr). The PBs occur on the summer grounds. The 1st PB usually includes all gr covs (~7% retain the outer-most), but no terts or rects. The 1st PA includes 0 (~84%) to 2 outer gr covs and sometimes (in ~42% of birds) 1-3 terts, but no rects. The adult PA is similar, including 0 (~90%) to 2 outer gr covs and sometimes (in ~38% of birds) 1-2 terts, but no rects.

Skull—Pneumaticization completes in HY/SY from 15 Oct. Windows (> 2 mm; Fig. 11**D**), on the top or at the rear of the skull, can be retained by some SYs through summer and even into fall.

Age—Juv (May-Aug) averages browner and drabber in all subspecies; juv ♀ = ♂.

HY/SY (Aug-Jul): Outer pp covs narrow, tapered, relatively abraded, and brownish with indistinct, relatively narrow, or no greenish or grayish edging (Fig. 138), contrasting with the slightly fresher gr covs (Fig. 134); outer rects tapered and relatively abraded (Fig. 139**A**); roof of the mouth (upper mandible lining) whitish to grayish white (through Mar?). **Note: A few intermediates can be difficult to age, especially in Blue-headed Vireo and in Mar-Jul. Look also for p10 to be longer (relative to the pp covs) and more rounded in HY/SYs than in AHY/ASYs (see Fig. 234).**

AHY/ASY (Aug-Jul): Outer pp covs broad, truncate, relatively fresh, and dusky with distinct, relatively broad, green or gray edging (Fig. 138), not contrasting with the gr covs (Fig. 133**F**); outer rects truncate and relatively fresh (Fig. 139**A**); roof of the mouth dark gray to black. **Note: See HY/SY.**

Sex—CP/BP (Mar-Aug); ♂ develops a partial BP (Fig. 22**B**). See **Geographic variation** for measurements. Blue-headed and Cassin's vireos average duller than ♂♂, but variation is slight and confounded by age; thus, sexing of individuals probably is unreliable. Otherwise, ♀ = ♂ by plumage.

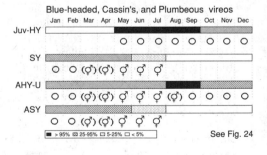

Blue-headed, Cassin's, and Plumbeous vireos

Hybrids reported—Yellow-throated Vireo (with Blue-headed Vireo).

References—Stone (1896), Dwight (1900a), Ridgway (1904), Forbush (1929), Bent (1950), Roberts (1955), Wood (1969), Oberholser (1974), Phillips *et al.* (1983), Phillips (1991), Heindel (1996), Pyle (1997c), M.S. Dugdale (unpublished ms., pers. comm.); C.A. Ely (*in litt.* to the BBL); IBP (MAPS) data, PNR data, PRBO data.

YELLOW-THROATED VIREO

Vireo flavifrons

YTVI
Species # 6280
Band size: 1C-1

Species—From the other vireos of N.Am by the combination of large size, but relatively short tl (wg 70-81, tl 44-53); wg – tl 26-34 mm; p10 minute, < pp covs by 6-9 mm; rump gray, contrasting with the green back; spectacles distinct and yellow; wing bars distinct and white; throat and breast yellow, contrasting with the white belly and undertail covs; iris dark.

Geographic variation—Subspecies taxonomy follows Phillips (1991), who considered the species monotypic (synonymizing a previously recognized subspecies); see also Ridgway (1904), Hamilton (1958), Oberholser (1974), Browning (1978), Cramp & Perrins (1994a). Birds breeding north of se.TX-GA ("*V.f. sylvicola*") may average larger and less golden or tinged orange, but differences, if present, are very slight and broadly clinal.

Molt—PB: HY partial (Jun-Sep), AHY complete (Jul-Sep); PA partial (Jan-Apr). The PBs occur on the summer grounds. The possible occurrence of a presupplemental molt in this species requires further study. The 1st PB begins soon after fledging, before flight feathers are fully grown. It usually includes all wing covs (the gr covs dropping all at once), but no terts or rects. The 1st PA includes 0 (~40%) to 4 inner gr covs and 2-3 terts, and the adult PA includes 0 (~64%) to 3 inner gr covs and often (in ~64% of birds) 1-3 terts; no rects are replaced during PAs.

Skull—Pneumaticization completes in HY/SY from 1 Nov. Windows (> 2 mm; Fig. 11**D**) at the rear of the skull occur on some SYs through Jul.

Age—Juv (May-Aug) has the upperparts washed brownish, and the throat pale buffy-yellow; juv ♀ = ♂.

HY/SY (Aug-Jul): Outer pp covs narrow, tapered, relatively abraded, and brownish with indistinct, relatively narrow, or no greenish edging (Fig. 138), contrasting with the slightly fresher gr covs (Fig. 134); outer rects tapered and relatively abraded (Fig. 139**A**). **Note: Molt limits (Fig. 133) probably are not reliable for ageing in Mar-Jul; however, SYs replace more feathers on average than ASYs during the PA (see Molt) and this might help in ageing some birds. In addition, check for the p10 to be longer (relative to the pp covs) and more rounded in HY/SYs than in AHY/ASYs (see Fig. 234), and for the roof of the mouth (upper mandible lining) to show color differences, as in the Solitary, Philadelphia, or Red-eyed vireos.**

AHY/ASY ♀ (Aug-Jul): Outer pp covs broad, truncate, relatively fresh, and dusky with distinct, relatively broad, green edging (Fig. 138), not contrasting with the gr covs (Fig. 133**F**); outer rects truncate and relatively fresh (Fig. 139**A**). **Note: See HY/SY.**

Sex—♀ = ♂ by plumage. CP/BP (Apr-Aug); ♂♂ can develop a partial BP (Fig. 22**B**). ♀ wg(n72) 70-79, tl(n44) 44-52; ♂ wg(n94) 71-81, tl(n74) 45-53.

Hybrids reported—Blue-headed Vireo.

Yellow-throated Vireo

	Jan	Feb	Mar	Apr	May	Jun	Jul	Aug	Sep	Oct	Nov	Dec
Juv-HY					○	○	○	○	○	○	○	○
SY				○ ○ ○ (♀) ♂ ♂ ♂								
AHY-U				○ ○ ○ (♀) ♂ ♂ ♂ (♀) ○ ○ ○ ○								
ASY				○ ○ ○ (♂) ♂ ♂ ♂								

References—Stone (1896), Dwight (1900a), Ridgway (1904), Forbush (1929), Sutton (1949), Bent (1950), Roberts (1955), Wood (1969), Oberholser (1974), Cramp & Perrins (1994a), Rodewald & James (1996), Pyle (1997c); IBP (MAPS) data, PNR data.

HUTTON'S VIREO
Vireo huttoni

HUVI
Species # 6320
Band size: 0

Species—From Northern Beardless-Tyrannulet and *Empidonax* flycatchers (see p. 219) by tarsus long (> 17 mm); p10 reduced and p9 ≤ p4 (Fig. 189); crest lacking; wing bars distinct and whitish to pale gray; basal half of the lower mandible dark. From Ruby-crowned Kinglet by longer tl (41-56; see **Sex**), p9 ≤ p4; bases of the pp uniformly dusky, not forming a distinct, black bar distal to the wing bars; bill and legs thicker and bluish gray; soles of the feet grayish. From Bell's, Gray, Solitary, and the other vireos of N.Am by medium size (wg 54-71, tl 41-56; see **Geographic variation** & **Sex**); p9 < p5 by 7-13 mm and p10 > pp covs by 8-13 (Fig. 189); spectacles (eye ring) moderately distinct, broken at the top but complete in the front, and whitish with an olive or gray tinge; wing bars moderately distinct, and whitish or tinged olive; flanks olive or tinged yellow; iris dark.

Geographic variation—Moderate and ranges are well defined between subspecies groups, but weak and clinal within groups. Subspecies taxonomy follows A.M. Rea and A.R. Phillips *in* Phillips (1991); see also Ridgway (1904), Bishop (1905a), Grinnell (1922, 1935), Oberholser (1922, 1974), Brandt (1938), Miller (1955a), Hamilton (1958), Phillips (1966d), Davis (1995). Five other subspecies occur in Mex-C.Am. Note that birds become paler with wear, and specimens become duller with time.

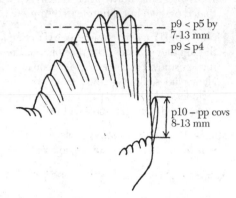

FIGURE 189. The wing morphology of Hutton's Vireo. See Figure 10 for measurement techniques.

Pacific (*V.h. huttoni*) Group. Small (wg 54-66, tl 41-52); greenish.

V.h. obscurus (br & wint coastal sw.BC to s.OR-nc.CA, Lake Co): Wg – tl 10-15 mm; upperparts fairly uniformly, dark greenish olive with a gray tinge; eye ring and wing bars moderately indistinct, and yellowish to yellowish olive; underparts brightish olive, the flanks washed buffy when fresh. Birds of Vancouver I, BC ("*insularis*") may average darker, but this difference is slight; the subspecies designation also may have been based on discolored specimens.

V.h. parkesi (br & wint coastal nw.CA, Del Norte-Marin Cos): Wg – tl 10-16 mm; crown and back bright grayish olive with a yellowish tinge, contrasting with the brighter and yellowish-green rump; eye ring and wing bars distinct and yellowish; underparts (including the flanks) bright yellowish olive.

V.h. huttoni (br & wint coastal c-sw.CA, San Francisco-Santa Barbara Cos, including Santa Cruz I): Wg – tl 11-17 mm; upperparts fairly uniformly, dull olive; eye ring and wing bars distinct, and whitish to cream; underparts dull whitish olive, the flanks washed dull buffy yellow.

V.h. unitti (res Santa Catalina I, CA): Upperparts uniformly dark dusky olive; eye ring and wing bars indistinct, and dull olive to grayish olive; underparts medium-dark olive with little or no yellowish.

V.h. sierrae (br & wint montane nc-sc.CA): Wg – tl 12-18 mm; crown and back fairly uniform, medium-pale grayish olive; eye ring and wing bars distinct and pale olive; underparts (including the flanks) whitish with a yellow-olive tinge.

V.h. oberholseri (br & wint interior ec-coastal sw.CA e.Monterey-San Diego Cos): Wg – tl 15-20 mm; crown and nape dull, medium-dark grayish olive, contrasting with the dull olive back and rump; eye ring and wing bars indistinct and pale olive; underparts pale whitish olive, the flanks washed medium-pale olive with little or no buff.

Interior or Stephen's (*V.h. stephensi*) Group. Large (wg 62-71, tl 48-56); grayish.

V.h. stephensi (br & wint AZ-NM): Large; wg – tl 16-22 mm; crown pale grayish olive, contrasting slightly with the pale grayish-olive back; eye ring and wing bars distinct and whitish; underparts (including the flanks) whitish with an olive tinge. ♀ wg(n43) 63-70, tl(n43) 49-55; ♂ wg(n81) 64-71, tl(n80) 50-56.

V.h. carolinae (br & wint sw.TX): Medium-large; wg – tl 15-20 mm; crown and back fairly uniformly olive with a grayish-green tinge; eye ring and wing bars distinct and whitish; underparts (including the flanks) grayish white with an olive tinge. ♀ wg(n17) 62-67, tl(n17) 48-53; ♂ wg(n28) 62-68, tl(n21) 49-54.

Molt—PB: HY partial (Jul-Sep), AHY complete (Jul-Sep); PA absent. The PBs occur on the summer grounds. The 1st PB includes 7 to 10 (~40%) inner gr covs and occasionally (in ~13% of birds) s8, but no rects.

Skull—Pneumaticization completes in HY/SY from 1 Oct. Some SYs retain windows (> 2 mm; Fig. 11**D**) through spring.

Age—Juv (Apr-Aug) has the upperparts relatively pale and washed brownish, and the wing bars relatively distinct and buffy; juv ♀ = ♂.

HY/SY (Aug-Jul): Molt limits often occur among the gr covs (Fig. 133**C-E**; see **Molt**), the retained outer covs worn and brownish with indistinct, pale edging, contrasting with the fresher, duskier, and greener-edged, replaced inner covs; s8 occasionally replaced, contrasting with the older middle ss (s4-s6; Fig. 133**D**); outer pp covs narrow, tapered, relatively abraded, and brownish with indistinct, relatively narrow, or no greenish edging (Fig. 138); outer rects tapered and relatively abraded (Fig. 139**A**). **Note: In addition, check for p10 to be longer (relative to the pp covs) and more rounded in HY/SYs than in AHY/ASYs (see Fig. 234), and for the roof of the mouth (upper mandible lining) to show color differences, as in the Solitary, Philadelphia, or Red-eyed vireos.**

AHY/ASY (Aug-Jul): Wing covs, terts, and middle ss (s4-s6) uniformly adult (Fig. 133**F**), the feathers dusky with relatively broad, greenish edging; outer pp covs broad, truncate, relatively fresh, and dusky with distinct, relatively broad, greenish edging (Fig. 138); outer rects truncate and relatively fresh (Fig. 139**A**). **Note: See HY/SY.**

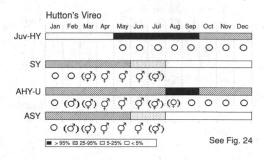

Sex—♀ = ♂ by plumage. CP/BP (Feb-Aug); ♂♂ can develop a partial BP (Fig. 22**B**). ♀ wg(n100) 54-70, tl(n100) 41-55; ♂ wg(n100) 55-71, tl(n100) 42-56; see **Geographic variation**.

References—Ridgway (1904), Bent (1950), Oberholser (1974), Kaufman (1979b, 1993b), Paulsen (1995), Pyle (1997c); PRBO data.

WARBLING VIREO
Vireo gilvus

WAVI
Species # 6270
Band size: 0-1C

Species—From Philadelphia Vireo and Red-eyed Vireo (which see for separation from Yellow-green Vireo) by the combination of small size but tl relatively long (wg 62-75, tl 46-56; see **Sex**); bill small (exp culmen 8.9-11.4, < middle toe without claw); p10 > pp covs by 2-8 mm (Fig. 190); crown and upperparts fairly uniformly grayish olive (see **Geographic variation**); supercilium indistinct to moderately distinct and dull whitish, contrasting indistinctly with the dull grayish eye line, face, and lateral crown; loral area pale grayish and uniform in color or only slightly darker than the supercilium and throat; under-

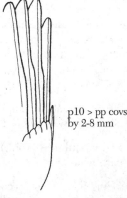

p10 > pp covs
by 2-8 mm

FIGURE 190. The wing morphology of Warbling Vireo. See Figure 10 for measurement techniques.

parts with a small amount to some yellow, usually excluding the central breast and brightest on the sides and flanks; iris dark.

Geographic variation—Weak to moderate and clinal where ranges meet. Subspecies taxonomy follows Phillips (1991); see also Ridgway (1904), Oberholser (1932, 1974), Sibley (1940), Sutton & Burleigh (1940), Rand (1948b), Hamilton (1958), Phillips *et al.* (1964), Oberholser (1974), Browning (1974, 1990), Behle (1985), Remsen *et al.* (1996). Two other subspecies occur in Mex. The following applies to birds in fresh plumage; spring birds become increasingly difficult to distinguish due to wear. In addition, check for p10 to be longer (*vs* the pp covs) in the Western than in the Eastern Subspecies Group (but see also **Age**).

Western (*V.g. swainsoni*) Group. Small to large; thin-billed; dull.

V.g. swainsoni (br se.AK-s.NWT to CA; vag to FL): Small; bill small and slender (Fig. 191; nares to tip 6.5-7.9, depth at tip of nares 3.3-3.8); crown and back dull olive-gray, contrasting with the olive rump; flanks washed olive when fresh; upper mandible grayish and lower mandible dusky horn (Fig. 191). ♀ wg(n100) 62-69, tl(n10) 46-52; ♂ wg(n100) 64-71, tl(n10) 47-53. Breeding birds of sc.OR-wc.NV ("*leucopolius*") may average paler and grayer, but differences probably are due to slight intergradation with *brewsteri*.

V.g. brewsteri (br s.ID-w.SD to AZ-sw.TX; vag to CA): Large; bill characters and wing morphology as in swainsoni; crown dull gray, contrasting with the grayish-olive back; flanks washed grayish olive when fresh. ♀ wg(n43) 66-73, tl(n10) 49-54; ♂ wg(n33) 68-75, tl(n10) 50-56. Birds breeding north of AZ-NM ("*petrorus*") may average slightly smaller and grayer, but differences are weak and broadly clinal.

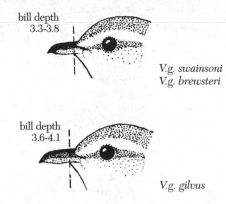

FIGURE 191. The depth and color of the bill by subspecies in Warbling Vireo. Note the pale coloration to the upper mandible in *V.g. gilvus*.

Eastern (*V.g. gilvus*) Group. Large; thick-billed; bright.

V.g. gilvus (br sc.Alb-LA to ME-NC): Large; bill large and thick (Fig. 191; nares to tip 7.5-8.8, depth at tip of nares 3.6-4.1); crown and back fairly uniformly grayish with a brown or olive tinge; flanks washed yellow when fresh; upper mandible dusky horn and lower mandible pale horn (Fig. 191). ♀ wg(n39) 66-72, tl(n15) 47-53; ♂ wg(n51) 68-74, tl(n22) 49-55.

Molt—PB: HY partial (Jun-Sep), AHY complete (Jun-Nov?); PA limited (Feb-Apr). The PBs occur mostly on the summer grounds, although they may occur partly on the winter grounds (at least in the Western Subspecies Group). The 1st PB begins very soon after fledging, before flight feathers are full-grown, and usually includes all gr covs and often the terts (on the winter grounds only?) but no other flight feathers. The PAs include no wing covs or flight feathers, although some inner ss (among s4-s6) might be suspended until the PA (or next PB) in some ASYs. More study is needed on molt of this species on the winter grounds.

Skull—Pneumaticization completes in HY/SY from 1 Nov (as early as 15 Oct in birds of CA). Some SYs retain windows (> 2 mm; Fig. 11**D**) on the top of the skull through Jun.

Age—Juv (May-Jul; see **Molt**) has the upperparts brown, gr covs tipped cinnamon-buff, and underparts white; juv ♀ = ♂.

HY/SY (Aug-Jul): Outer pp covs narrow, tapered, relatively abraded, and brownish with indistinct, narrow, or no greenish or grayish edging (Fig 138), contrasting with the slightly fresher gr covs (Fig. 134); outer rects tapered and relatively abraded (Fig. 139**A**). **Note: In addi-**

tion, check for p10 to be longer (relative to the pp covs) and more rounded in HY/SYs than in AHY/ASYs (see Fig. 234), and for the roof of the mouth (upper mandible lining) to show color differences, as in the Solitary, Philadelphia, or Red-eyed vireos. See also AHY/ASY.

AHY/ASY (Aug-Jul): Outer pp covs broad, truncate, relatively fresh, and dusky with distinct, relatively broad, green or grayish-green edging (Fig. 138), not contrasting with the gr covs (Fig. 133F); rects truncate and relatively fresh (Fig. 139A). **Note: See HY/SY. Look for a few birds with retained ss (among s4-s6) in Oct-Jul that may be reliably aged SY/TY; more study is needed. Also, if the adult PB occurs mostly on the winter grounds (see Molt; in the Western Subspecies Group only?), look for age-related differences in the relative contrasts of s7-s6, as in Red-eyed Vireo (Fig. 193).**

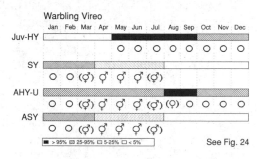

See Fig. 24

Sex— ♀ = ♂ by plumage. CP/BP (Mar-Aug); ♂♂ can show sparse feathering on the abdomen, giving the appearance of a partial BP (Fig. 22**B**). ♀ wg(n100) 62-73, tl(n35) 46-54; ♂ wg(n100) 64-75, tl(n42) 47-56; see **Geographic variation**.

References—Stone (1896), Dwight (1900a), Ridgway (1904), Dearborn (1907), Forbush (1929), Dickey & van Rossem (1938), Sutton (1948b, 1949), Bent (1950), Roberts (1955), Wood (1969), Oberholser (1974), Terrill & Terrill (1981), Phillips *et al.* (1983), Kaufman (1990a), Pyle (1997c); R.S. Mulvihill (pers. comm.); IBP (MAPS) data, PNR data, PRBO data.

PHILADELPHIA VIREO
Vireo philadelphicus

PHVI
Species # 6260
Band size: 0-0A

Species—From Warbling and Red-eyed vireos (which see for separation from Yellow-green and Black-whiskered vireos) by the combination of small size and relatively short tl (wg 61-70, tl 40-49; see **Sex**); bill short (exp culmen 9.5-10.5, < middle toe without claw); p10 vestigial or minute, 2-5 mm < pp covs if present (Fig. 192); upperparts fairly uniformly olive to greenish olive; supercilium distinct and whitish, contrasting distinctly with the dusky eye line and the grayish-olive face and lateral crown; loral area dusky, contrasting with the paler supercilium and throat; yellow of the underparts moderately extensive to extensive, including and usually brightest on the breast; iris dark. From Tennessee Warbler by p9 < p8 and ≤ p6 (see Fig. 192); bill blunt and hooked; eye line not narrowing behind eye; legs thick, fleshy, and gray.

Geographic variation—No subspecies are recognized. Western birds average slightly larger and duller than eastern birds, but differences are broadly clinal and not enough to warrant subspecies recognition. See Barlow & Power (1970), Phillips (1991).

Molt—PB: HY partial (Jul-Sep), AHY complete (Jul-Sep); PA absent(?). The PBs occur mostly on the summer grounds. The 1st PB usually includes all gr covs but no terts or rects. Some middle ss (among s4-s6) might be suspended until the PA or subsequent PB in some ASYs. More study is needed on the possible occurrence of PAs.

Skull—Pneumaticization completes in HY/SY from 15 Nov. Windows (> 2 mm; Fig. 11**D**) can be retained by some SYs through spring.

Age—Juv (Jun-Aug) generally is drabber, with a brownish wash to the plumage and more distinct wing bars; juv ♀ = ♂.

HY/SY (Aug-Jul): Outer pp covs narrow, tapered, relatively abraded, and brownish with indistinct, narrow, or no greenish edging (Fig. 138), contrasting with the slightly fresher gr covs (Fig. 134); outer rects tapered and relatively abraded (Fig. 139**A**); roof of the mouth (upper mandible lining) pinkish to grayish white (through Feb?). **Note: In addition, check for p10 to be present in HY/SYs and absent or shorter in AHY/ASYs (see Fig. 234).**

AHY/ASY (Aug-Jul): Outer pp covs broad, truncate, relatively fresh, and dusky with distinct, relatively broad, green edging (Fig. 138), not contrasting in wear with the gr covs (Fig. 133**F**); rects truncate and relatively fresh (Fig. 139**A**); roof of the mouth medium gray. **Note: See HY/SY.**

Sex—♀ = ♂ by plumage. CP/BP (May-Aug); ♂♂ can show sparse feathering on the abdomen, giving the appearance of a partial BP (Fig. 22**B**). ♀ wg(n52) 61-68, tl(n24) 40-46; ♂ wg(n55) 63-70, tl(n31) 43-49.

Hybrids reported—Red-eyed Vireo.

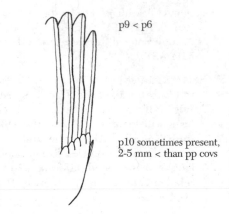

p9 < p6

p10 sometimes present, 2-5 mm < than pp covs

FIGURE 192. The wing morphology of Philadelphia Vireo. See Figure 10 for measurement techniques.

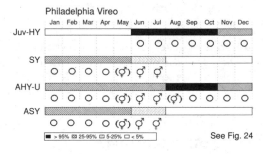

Philadelphia Vireo

See Fig. 24

References—Stone (1896), Dwight (1900a), Ridgway (1904), Forbush (1929), Bent (1950), Roberts (1955), Wood (1969), Oberholser (1974), Terrill & Terrill (1981), Phillips *et al.* (1983), Kaufman (1990a), Phillips (1991), Cramp & Perrins (1994a), Moskoff & Robinson (1996), Pyle (1997c), M.S. Dugdale (unpublished ms., pers. comm.); S.F. Bailey, R.S. Mulvihill (pers. comm.); IBP (MAPS) data, PNR data, PRBO data.

RED-EYED VIREO
Vireo olivaceus

REVI
Species # 6240
Band size: 1C-1-0

Species—From the other vireos by large size (wg 72-85, tl 47-60; see **Sex**); bill medium in size (exp culmen 11.6-13.6, > middle toe without claw); upper mandible dusky; p9 – p5 4-8 mm; p10 vestigial or minute, < pp covs by 3-9 mm (if present); crown grayish to grayish olive, contrasting with the olive (sometimes tinged yellowish) back and rump; rects olive without yellow edging; supercilium distinct and white or whitish, contrasting distinctly with the dusky to blackish eye line and the blackish lateral crown stripe; malar stripe lacking; underparts white with a small amount to some olive or yellow, restricted to the sides of the breast and flanks and usually not extending uninterrupted to the auricular; iris reddish brown (HY) to red (AHY). From Warbling Vireo by larger size, shorter p10, brighter plumage, and redder iris color. From

Philadelphia Vireo by larger size, whiter coloration of the underparts, and redder iris. From Yellow-green Vireo by smaller and darker bill, wing morphology, lack of a yellow wash or edging to the plumage, and presence of a distinct lateral crown stripe. From Black-whiskered Vireo by shorter bill, wing morphology, and lack of a malar stripe.

Geographic variation—Weak and clinal within the North American Subspecies Group. Subspecies taxonomy follows E.R. Blake *in* Paynter (1968), as modified by Phillips (1991); see also Todd (1931), Zimmer (1941), Hamilton (1958), Burleigh (1960c), Monroe (1968), Barlow & Power (1970), Hubbard & Banks (1970), Barlow & Williams (1971), Oberholser (1974), Wetmore *et al.* (1984), Johnson & Zink (1985), Browning (1990), Cramp & Perrins (1994a). Five other subspecies occur in S.Am; this (*V.o. chivi*) subspecies group separated by smaller size (wg 63-74), p9 usually < p5, and iris of AHY possibly reddish brown; molt strategies also possibly differ and could provide further clues to identification.

V.o. caniviridis (br WA-e.OR to nc.ID): Upperparts dull, medium-pale, grayish olive; underparts white with a reduced yellow-olive wash when fresh.

V.o. olivaceus (br throughout most of the range in N.Am, except as above): Upperparts bright, medium-dark, greenish olive when fresh; flanks with a moderately extensive, yellow-olive wash when fresh. Birds of montane VA ("*scotti*") may have larger eggs and different vocalizations, but differences at the subspecies level are doubtful.

Molt—PB: HY partial (Jul-Oct), AHY complete (Jul-Apr); PA absent (but see below). The PBs commence on the summer grounds and complete on the winter grounds. The 1st PB usually includes all gr covs and usually the greater alula but no terts or rects. The adult PB includes a variable number of wing covs (from none to all) and flight feathers (often just 1-3 terts and the central or other rects; occasionally other ss and inner pp) on the summer grounds, completing on the winter grounds in Jan-Apr, after suspension in Sep-Dec. The winter molt of ASYs may possibly involve complete replacement of all feathers, including those replaced before migrating, in which case it possibly should be considered a PA, although a homologous molt does not occur in SYs. More study is needed on this interesting molt strategy (see Cramp & Perrins 1994a, Mulvihill & Rimmer 1997).

Skull—Pneumaticization completes in HY/SY from 1 Nov. Windows (> 3 mm; Fig. 11**D**) can be retained through summer by some SYs and small windows (< 3 mm; see Fig. 186) also can be retained by ASYs (possibly TYs only); more study is needed.

Age—Juv (May-Aug) has brownish-tinged plumage, indistinct wing bars, and a brown or gray-brown iris; juv ♀ = ♂.

HY/SY (Aug-2nd Sep): Flight feathers fresh and not molting in Aug-Apr, to relatively abraded in Apr-Jul, s9 to s3 evenly worn (becoming slightly fresher distally), without well-marked contrasts between adjacent feathers (Fig. 193); outer pp covs narrow, tapered, and brownish with indistinct, narrow, or no greenish edging (Fig. 138), contrasting with the slightly fresher gr covs (Fig. 134); rects uniformly tapered and relatively fresh (Oct-Dec) to relatively abraded (Jan-Sep; Fig. 139**A**); roof of the mouth (upper mandible lining) pinkish gray to grayish white (through Feb?); iris gray-brown, brown, or reddish brown (through Mar, possibly later in some birds). **Note: Some spring birds show a brownish cast to the iris; these may be SYs or possibly ASYs that never acquire the full red color; more study is needed. Many intermediates may be difficult to age in spring. Look also for p10 to be present in HY/SYs and absent or shorter in AHY/ASYs (see Fig. 234).**

AHY/ASY (Oct-Sep): Flight feathers relatively worn or molting in Aug-Apr and relatively fresh in Apr-Jul, the terts usually distinctly more worn (due to exposure) than the middle ss (s4-s6) in Apr-Jul, with a distinct contrast between adjacent feathers (*e.g.*, a worn s7 and a fresh s6; Fig. 193; see **Molt**); outer pp covs broad, truncate, and dusky with distinct, relatively broad,

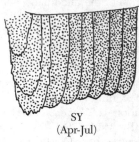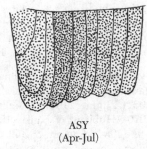

SY
(Apr-Jul)

ASY
(Apr-Jul)

FIGURE 193. Contrasts in the secondaries by age in Red-eyed Vireos in spring. This difference results from the prolonged adult prebasic molt on the winter grounds (see text); note that in ASYs, s7 is much more abraded than s6, having been replaced 4-7 months earlier and often before the fall migration. These feathers are all of uniform age (juvenal) in SYs, showing increased wear with increased exposure to the inside, as is typical. Look for this pattern in other species that have adult prebasic molts on the winter grounds; *e.g.*, certain flycatchers and thrashers.

green edging (Fig. 138); rects truncate and relatively worn (Oct-Dec) to molting or relatively fresh (Jan-Sep; Fig. 139**A**); roof of the mouth dark gray; iris bright red. **Note: See HY/SY.**

Sex—♀ = ♂ by plumage. CP/BP (Apr-Aug); ♂♂ can show sparse feathering on the abdomen, giving the appearance of a partial BP (Fig. 22**B**). ♀ wg(n100) 72-82, tl(n60) 47-56; ♂ wg(n100) 75-85, tl(n74) 51-60; includes subspecies of N.Am only (see **Geographic variation**).

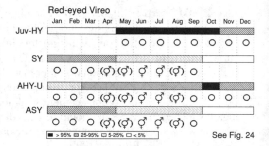

Red-eyed Vireo

See Fig. 24

Hybrids reported—Philadelphia Vireo.

References—Stone (1896), Dwight (1900a), Ridgway (1904), Forbush (1929), Zimmer (1941), Sutton (1949), Bent (1950), Roberts (1955), Blake (1962a), Goodpasture (1963), Wood & Wood (1972), Oberholser (1974), Sheppard & Klimkiewicz (1976), Terrill & Terrill (1981), Parkes (1988b), CWS & USFWS (1991), Phillips (1991), Cramp & Perrins (1994a), Mulvihill & Rimmer (1997), Pyle (1997c), M.S. Dugdale (unpublished ms., pers. comm.); C.S. Robbins (*in litt.* to the BBL); K. Convery, R.S. Mulvihill, B. Walker (pers. comm.); IBP (MAPS) data, PNR data.

YELLOW-GREEN VIREO
Vireo flavoviridis

YGVI
Species # 6250
Band size: 1

Species—From Red-eyed Vireo (which see for separation from other vireos) by bill long (exp culmen 12.9-15.3); upper mandible often pale horn to pale dusky; p9 – p5 1-5 mm; back and rump yellowish olive to yellowish green; rects edged yellowish; supercilium moderately distinct and whitish, contrasting indistinctly with the dusky eye line and variably indistinct (see **Geographic variation**) dusky lateral crown stripe; underparts with an extensive yellowish wash to the sides, approaching or meeting across the breast and usually extending uninterrupted to the auricular.

Geographic variation—Weak and obscured by individual variation. Subspecies taxonomy follows Phillips (1991); see also Ridgway (1904), Peters (1931), van Rossem & Hachisuka (1937b),

Zimmer (1941), Hamilton (1958), Monson & Phillips (1981), Remsen *et al.* (1996). Three other subspecies occur in Mex-C.Am.

V.f. hypoleucus (vag to CA-AZ): Bill medium small (exp culmen 12.9-14.3); crown medium-pale grayish, the lateral stripe indistinct and dusky, or lacking; upperparts dull yellow-green to yellowish-olive, paler on the rump; sides of the underparts washed dull yellow-olive.

V.f. flavoviridis (br s.TX, vag to w.TX-FL): Bill medium large (exp culmen 13.6-15.3); crown medium-dark grayish, lateral stripe indistinct and dusky; upperparts fairly uniformly, bright yellow-green; sides of the underparts washed bright olive-yellow.

Molt—Little-studied, but likely similar to that of Red-eyed Vireo: PB HY partial (Jun-Aug), AHY complete (May-Mar?); PA absent. The PBs may commence earlier and are more extensive on the summer grounds than in Red-eyed Vireo. More study is needed.

Skull—Pneumaticization completes in HY/SY from 1 Oct. Windows (> 2 mm; see Figs. 11**D** & 186) can be retained through spring by some SYs and ASYs (see Red-eyed Vireo).

Age—Juv (May-Aug) has brownish-tinged plumage, indistinct wing bars, and a brown iris; juv ♀ = ♂. Ageing is probably very similar to that of Red-eyed Vireo, although the pp-cov criteria and contrasts in the terts and middle ss appear harder to distinguish in this species; thus, many intermediates may exist.

Sex—♀ = ♂ by plumage. CP/BP (Mar-Jul); ♂♂ can have sparse feathering on the abdomen, giving the appearance of a partial BP (Fig. 22**B**). ♀ wg(n100) 71-80, tl(n30) 49-57; ♂ wg(n100) 74-83, tl(n50) 52-60.

References—Ridgway (1904), Peters (1931), Dickey & van Rossem (1938), Zimmer (1941), A.F. Skutch *in* Bent (1950), Sutton *et al.* (1950), Oberholser (1974), Morton (1977), Terrill & Terrill (1981), Phillips (1991), Pyle (1997c).

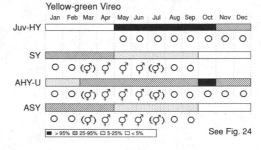

BLACK-WHISKERED VIREO
Vireo altiloquus

BWVI
Species # 6230
Band size: 1C

Species—From Red-eyed Vireo (which see for separation from other vireos) by bill large (exp culmen 12.7-15.6, depth at tip of nares 4.2-5.2; even larger in some subspecies of the W.Indies); p9 – p5 -1 to 5 mm; dark malar stripe present and distinct to indistinct.

Geographic variation—Moderate and breeding ranges well defined. Subspecies taxonomy follows Phillips (1991); see also Ridgway (1904), Hamilton (1958), Voous (1983), Wetmore *et al.* (1984). Two other subspecies occur in the W.Indies.

V.a. barbatulus (br throughout the range in N.Am): Small (see Sex), bill small (exp culmen 12.7-15.5, depth at tip of nares 4.0-5.0); crown grayish; back and rump uniformly dull olive with a gray tinge; supercilium distinct and whitish; central underparts white.

V.a. altiloquus (vag to FL,LA): Large; bill large (exp culmen 14.6-17.3, depth at tip of nares 4.5-5.5); crown brownish gray; back and rump medium-bright olive; supercilium indistinct and brownish gray; central underparts dull whitish. ♀ wg(n16) 76-83, tl(n16) 49-58; ♂ wg(n31) 77-85, tl(n31) 52-59.

Molt—Undescribed, but likely similar to that of Red-eyed Vireo; PB: HY partial (Jul-Oct?), AHY complete (Jun-Mar?); PA absent. The PBs may commence earlier. More study is needed.

Skull—Pneumaticization completes in HY/SY from 1 Nov. Some SYs probably retain Windows (> 2 mm) through spring.

Age—The same criteria found in Red-eyed Vireo appear to apply.

Sex—♀ = ♂ by plumage. CP/BP (Mar-Jul). ♀ wg(n39) 73-80, tl(n26) 47-56; ♂ wg(n40) 75-83, tl(n35) 51-61; includes *V.a. barbatulus* only (see **Geographic variation**).

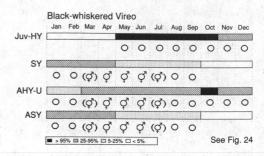

References—Ridgway (1904), Bent (1950), Oberholser (1974), Pyle (1997c).

JAYS, MAGPIES, AND CROWS — *CORVIDAE*

Eighteen species. Family characters include rounded wings, long and graduated tails, and powerful bills and legs. Jays and crows have 10 primaries (the 10th reduced), 9 secondaries, and 12 rectrices. The first prebasic molt almost always is partial (incomplete in southern populations of a few species), adult prebasic molts are complete, and prealternate molts are absent. In some species the timing of the second prebasic molt has been documented to occur up to a month before that of subsequent prebasic molts and this may be the rule in *Corvidae*. Corvids are reliably aged through the second prebasic molt: wing covert contrasts, the shape of the rectrices, and the color of the roof of the mouth (upper mandible lining) are useful with all species and should be combined for age determinations. More study is needed on the roof of the mouth color in the different species (see Fig. 193); many SY/TYs and possibly some ASY/ATYs might be aged by this criterion. Look also for tail fork differences between HY/SY and AHY/ASY in all species, as is found in Scrub Jay and Clark's Nutcracker. The skull, which typically may not completely ossify until the second spring, is difficult to view, and thus is less useful than plumage for ageing. Sexes are alike in plumage and males average moderately larger than females, considerably so in some measurements of certain species.

GRAY JAY   GRAJ
Perisoreus canadensis   Species # 4840
                                                               Band size: 3-2

Geographic variation—Highly variable, but generally weak and clinal where ranges of most forms meet. Subspecies taxonomy follows Ouellet *in* Strickland & Ouellet (1993); see also Ridgway (1904), Swarth (1912b, 1918a), Oberholser (1914a, 1917b), Brooks (1920), Peters (1920), Miller (1933a, 1943a), Aldrich (1943a), Burleigh & Peters (1948), Rand (1948b), Dickinson (1953), Todd (1963), Phillips (1986). No other subspecies occur. Understanding of the geographic variation in this species has been obscured by rapid discoloration of specimens.

P.c. pacificus (=*"fumifrons"*; res AK to Yuk-nw.BC): Medium small; crown with an extensive amount of brownish gray (Fig. 194A); upperparts washed brown; underparts heavily washed brownish gray. ♀ wg(n43) 132-142, tl(n40) 132-146; ♂ wg(n56) 133-152, tl(n52) 130-151. Birds of nw.BC (*"arcus"*) average darker and less brown, but differences are slight and broadly clinal.

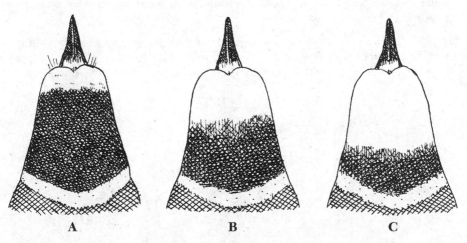

A   B   C

FIGURE 194. Variation in the head plumage in Gray Jays by subspecies (see text).

293

P.c. obscurus (res coastal sw.BC-CA): Variable in size; crown with extensive brownish gray (Fig. 194A); upperparts dark brownish gray, the feathers with white shafts; wing edging obscured; underparts white. ♀ wg(n77) 130-149, tl(n73) 123-150; ♂ wg(n76) 133-152, tl(n76) 129-152. Birds of sc.BC-nc.WA (*"connexus"*) average larger and less gray in the head, birds of nw.WA (*"rathbuni"*) average smaller and have slightly paler upperparts, and birds of c.WA-ne.CA (*"griseus"*) average larger and have paler upperparts, but in all cases differences are weak, broadly clinal and obscured by individual variation.

P.c. bicolor (res se.BC-ne.OR to w.MT): Medium in size; crown whitish with little to a moderate amount of pale gray (Fig. 194**B-C**); upperparts pale gray, the feathers with dark shafts; breast white; belly washed gray. ♀ wg(n29) 140-149, tl(n25) 136-150; ♂ wg(n48) 138-153, tl(n22) 137-152.

P.c. capitalis (res e.ID-AZ to c.CO-NM): Large; crown white with little or no gray (Fig. 194**C**); upperparts moderately pale gray; wing edging frosty white; underparts whitish. ♀ wg(n19) 144-157, tl(n19) 138-149; ♂ wg(n35) 147-159, tl(n28) 138-153.

P.c. albescens (res se.Yuk-ec.BC to ne.WY-w.SD & to c.Man-nw.MN): Medium in size; crown with a moderate amount of pale gray (Fig. 194**B**); upperparts pale gray; wing edging frosty pale; underparts white. ♀ wg(n16) 137-143, tl(n16) 133-145; ♂ wg(n25) 140-148, tl(n18) 140-148.

P.c. canadensis (br & wint NWT-n.Alb to Nfl-PA): Variable in size; crown with a moderate amount of medium gray (Fig. 194**B**); upperparts medium gray, the feathers with dark shafts; wing edging moderately pale; underparts with a moderate grayish wash. ♀ wg(n14) 133-146, tl(n14) 129-148; ♂ wg(n34) 136-149, tl(n20) 133-151. Birds of Lab-n.Que (*"nigricapillus"*) average darker gray, birds of Nfl (*"sanfordi"*) average slightly smaller and browner, and birds of Anticosti I, Que (*"barbouri"*) may average blacker and with darker underparts, but in all cases differences are weak and/or obscured by individual variation.

Molt—PB: HY partial (Jul-Sep), AHY complete (Jul-Aug); PA absent. The 1st PB includes no gr covs or flight feathers.

Skull—Pneumaticization completes in HY/SY from 15 Sep through Dec, probably later in some birds. The skull can be difficult or impossible to see through the skin.

Age—Juv (Apr-Aug) is slate-colored or brownish gray overall and has the roof of the mouth (upper mandible lining) entirely pinkish (Fig. 195A); juv ♀ = ♂.

HY/SY (Sep-Aug): Outer pp covs narrow and brownish, usually without gray edges in Feb-Jul (Fig. 138); rects narrow and tapered (Fig. 139**C**), often highly abraded in Jan-Jul; roof of the mouth entirely pinkish to mixed gray and black (Fig. 195A-B; through at least Jan). **Note: In addition, molt limits probably occur among the lesser and med covs (Fig. 133A), the retained outer covs brown and worn, contrasting with the grayer and fresher, replaced inner covs, but contrasts, if present, are difficult to see in this species; more study is needed.**

AHY/ASY (Sep-Aug): Outer pp covs broad and dusky, with pale gray edges in spring (Fig. 138); rects broad and truncate (Fig. 139**C**), relatively fresh in Jan-Jul; roof of the mouth primarily to entirely black (Fig. 195**C**), sometimes with a small horn-colored area near the tip. **Note:**

Juv-HY   HY/SY?   AHY/ASY

FIGURE 195. The roof of the mouth (lining of the upper mandible) in corvids. More study is needed on the use of this in ageing (see Common Raven).

See **HY/SY**. Some AHY/ASYs possibly can be aged SY/TY by having AHY/ASY plumage but substantial, pale coloration in the roof of the mouth (see Fig. 195B and Common Raven).

Sex—♀=♂ by plumage. CP/BP (Mar-Jul); SYs of both sexes can defer breeding and thus may not develop CP/BPs. ♀ wg(n100) 130-157, tl(n100) 123-150; ♂ wg(n100) 133-159, tl(n100) 129-153; see **Geographic variation**.

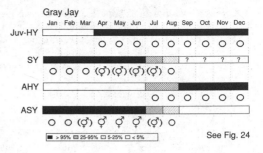

Gray Jay

See Fig. 24

References—Stone (1896), Dwight (1900a), Ridgway (1904), Forbush (1927), Bent (1946), Roberts (1955), Todd (1963), Goodwin (1976), Waite (1990), Strickland & Ouellet (1993), Pyle (1997c); IBP (MAPS) data.

STELLER'S JAY
Cyanocitta stelleri

STJA
Species # 4780
Band size: 3-2

Geographic variation—Moderate overall, although weak and clinal among the many adjacent forms. Subspecies taxonomy follows Phillips (1986); see also Ridgway (1904), Swarth (1911, 1912b), Taverner (1919a), Brooks (1923), van Rossem (1931b), Oberholser (1932, 1937b, 1974), Stevenson (1934), Miller (1941a), Phillips (1950a), Behle (1960, 1985), Brown (1963), Phillips *et al.* (1964), Browning (1979a, 1993b), Godfrey (1986). Nine other subspecies occur in Mex-C.Am. Note that the blues of the plumage become darker with wear.

C.s. stelleri (res coastal s.AK-sw.BC): Medium large; head blackish, with a few or no blue streaks on the forehead and throat; crest medium short (40-50 mm from the back of the eye) and not tinged blue; lower body moderately dark blue. ♀ wg(n10) 143-157, tl(n10) 129-147; ♂ wg(n49) 144-161, tl(n12) 133-150.

C.s. carlottae (res Queen Charlotte Is, BC): Large; head black, with some or no dark blue streaks on the forehead only; lower body dark purplish blue. ♀ wg(n10) 143-158, tl(n10) 134-146; ♂ wg(n14) 145-161, tl(n10) 138-152. Suggested three-letter subspecies code (see pp. 30-31): "crl".

C.s. paralia (res coastal sw.BC-sw.OR): Medium small; head blackish, usually with some blue streaks on the forehead and (sometimes) the throat; crest medium short (40-50 from the back of the eye); lower body medium-dark blue. ♀ wg(n21) 136-147, tl(n10) 122-138; ♂ wg(n31) 140-155, tl(n10) 130-143.

C.s. carbonacea (res coastal wc.CA): Small; head blackish, with a moderate amount of pale blue streaking on the forehead and (often) the throat; crest medium in length (42-52 from the back of the eye); lower body medium blue. ♀ wg(n50) 130-147, tl(n10) 125-138; ♂ wg(n10) 138-152, tl(n10) 134-146. Suggested three-letter subspecies code (see pp. 30-31): "crb".

C.s. frontalis (br & wint montane c.OR-s.CA): Small; head brownish dusky, with substantial, pale blue (but no white) streaking on the forehead or throat; crest short (36-48 from the back of the eye), occasionally tinged blue; lower body medium-dark blue. ♀ wg(n19) 133-148, tl(n10) 130-141; ♂ wg(n10) 141-153, tl(n10) 134-145. Birds of sc.OR (*"syncolla"*) average slightly larger and darker, but this results from intergradation with *paralia*.

C.s. annectens (br & wint c.BC-ne.OR to s.Sask-nw.NE): Large; head blackish, usually with some bluish-white or white streaking on the forehead, and often with some whitish or gray above the eyes; crest medium in length (42-52 from the back of the eye); lower body medium-dark blue. ♀ wg(n10) 142-154, tl(n10) 134-147; ♂ wg(n10) 147-163, tl(n10) 141-158.

C.s. macrolopha (br & wint n.UT-s.WY to s.NV-n.NM): Medium large; head dusky, with substantial white streaking on the forehead and bold white crescents above the eyes; crest medium long (44-55 from the back of the eye); lower body medium blue. ♀ wg(n47) 140-155, tl(n46) 126-148; ♂ wg(n70) 143-160, tl(n70) 130-160. Birds from n.UT (*"cottami"*) may average larger and darker, and birds from se.NV (*"percontatrix"*) may average darker gray backs, but differences are slight and obscured by individual variation.

C.s. diademata (br & wint AZ to c.NM-sw.TX): Medium small; head medium gray with a contrastingly black crest, substantial white streaking on the forehead, and bold white crescents above the eyes; crest long (46-57 from the back of the eye); lower body medium-pale blue. ♀ wg(n14) 141-149, tl(n14) 122-137; ♂ wg(n42) 142-156, tl(n20) 127-143. Birds from the U.S. (*"browni"*) average slightly duller and grayer than birds of Mex, but variation is slight and broadly clinal.

Molt—PB: HY partial (Jul-Sep), AHY complete (Jun-Aug); PA absent. The 1st PB includes 0 (~8%) to 9 inner gr covs, occasionally (in ~18% of birds) 1-2 terts, and occasionally (in ~10% of birds) 1-2 central rects (r1). There appears to be little geographic variation in the extent of the 1st PB among the subspecies of N.Am.

Skull—Pneumaticization completes in HY/SY from 15 Oct through Jan, probably later in some birds. The skull may be difficult or impossible to see through the skin.

Age—Juv (May-Aug) has the upperparts washed brownish or grayish, underparts grayish, without blue tones, and the roof of the mouth (upper mandible lining) grayish white (Fig. 195**A**); juv ♀ = ♂.

HY/SY (Sep-Aug): Molt limits occur among the med and gr covs (see **Molt**; Fig. 133**A-D**), the retained outer covs brownish or sooty and worn, contrasting with the markedly bluer, replaced inner covs; 1-2 terts often replaced and bluer, contrasting with the older adjacent ss (Fig. 133**D**); outer pp covs narrow (Fig. 138), washed brownish or sooty; rects narrow and tapered (Fig. 139**C**); 1-2 central rects (r1) occasionally replaced and contrastingly fresh; gape white to grayish (through Feb); roof of the mouth pinkish to mixed black and grayish white (Fig. 195**A-B**; through at least Mar).

AHY/ASY (Sep-Aug): Wing covs and flight feathers uniformly bright blue (Fig. 133**F**); outer pp covs broad, truncate (Fig. 139**C**), and bright blue; rects uniformly broad and truncate (Fig. 139**C**); gape dark grayish to black; roof of the mouth primarily to entirely black (Fig. 195**C**). **Note: Some AHY/ASYs possibly are reliably aged SY/TY by having AHY/ASY plumage but substantial, pale to the roof of the mouth (see Fig. 195B and Common Raven).**

Sex—♀ = ♂ by plumage. CP/BP (Mar-Jul); SYs of both sexes can defer breeding and thus may not develop CP/BPs. ♀ wg(n100) 130-162, tl(n100) 122-151; ♂ wg(n100) 140-165, tl(n100) 127-160; see **Geographic variation**. Also, for *C.s. macrolopha*, the bill length is reported to be useful (♂ exp culmen ≥ 27.5 mm, ♀ exp culmen ≤ 27.5 mm); however, bill length seems not as useful for sexing the other subspecies.

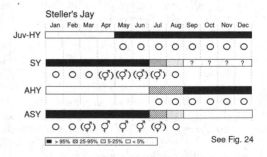

Hybrids reported—Blue Jay.

References—Ridgway (1904), Swarth (1912b), Bent (1946), McMannama (1950), Pitelka (1958, 1961a), Williams & Wheat (1971), Oberholser (1974), Pustmueller (1975), Goodwin (1976), Wheat (1981), Pyle (1997c); J.L. Brown (*in litt.* to the BBL); E. Jones (pers. comm.); IBP (MAPS) data, PRBO data.

BLUE JAY
Cyanocitta cristata

BLJA
Species # 4770
Band size: 2-3

Geographic variation—Weak, clinal where ranges meet, and differences possibly are obscured by substantial mixing. Subspecies taxonomy follows Phillips (1986), as modified by Stevenson & Anderson (1994); see also Ridgway (1904), Oberholser (1921a, 1974), Bailey (1928), Todd (1928), Sutton (1935b, 1967), Bond (1962), Mengel (1965), Browning (1990), Godfrey (1986). No other subspecies occur. Note that blues become darker with wear. See also **Molt**.

> **C.c. bromia** (br c.Alb-ne.NE to Nfl-sc.VA, wint to LA-n.FL): Large; upperparts bright and dark blue with a slight or no purplish wash; white marks on the non-juvenal terts extensive (8-16 mm from the tip along the shaft, when fresh). ♀ wg(n87) 120-139, tl(n17) 117-130; ♂ wg(n20) 125-148, tl(n20) 120-148. Birds of Nfl *("burleighi")* average darker, but variation is obscured by individual variation.
>
> **C.c. cyanotephra** (br & wint se.WY-NM to NE-s.TX): Medium large; upperparts dull and pale blue, without a purplish wash; white marks on the non-juvenal terts extensive (8-13 mm from the tip along the shaft). ♀ wg(n37) 124-134, tl(n29) 121-131; ♂ wg(n30) 127-140, tl(n30) 122-137.
>
> **C.c. cristata** (res s.IL-se.TX to sw.VA-FL): Medium in size; upperparts medium dull blue with a purplish wash; white marks on the non-juvenal terts reduced (5-11 mm from the tip along the shaft). ♀ wg(n38) 115-127, tl(n39) 106-117; ♂ wg(n37) 117-136, tl(n37) 114-132. Birds of s.FL *("semplei")* average slightly smaller and with whiter underparts, but differences are too weak for subspecies differentiation.

Molt—PB: HY partial-incomplete (Jun-Oct), AHY complete (Jun-Sep); PA absent. The PBs occur on the breeding grounds. The 1st PB includes 4 to 10 (~20%) inner gr covs, usually (in ~90% of birds) 1-3 terts (sometimes s6, as well), and sometimes (in ~50% of birds) 1-2 central rects (r1; occasionally other rects). Southern birds (*e.g.*, *C.c. cristata*) replace more feathers on average than northern birds (*e.g.*, *bromia*).

Skull—Pneumaticization completes in HY/SY from 1 Nov (possibly as early as 1 Oct in some birds of FL) through Feb, probably later in some birds. The skull can be difficult or impossible to see through the skin.

Age—Juv (May-Aug) has the upperparts relatively grayish, lores gray, gr covs dull blue-gray with thin, white tipping, and roof of the mouth (upper mandible lining) whitish (Fig. 195**A**); juv ♀ = ♂.

HY/SY (Sep-Aug): Molt limits often occur among the alula feathers and gr covs (Figs. 133**C-E** & 196; see **Molt**), the retained outer covs grayish blue with little or no dusky barring, con-

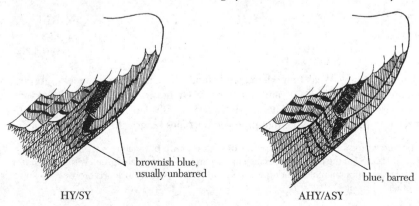

brownish blue,
usually unbarred

blue, barred

HY/SY

AHY/ASY

FIGURE 196. The pattern of the alula and primary coverts by age in Blue Jay. In this case, the HY/SY bird has replaced all 10 greater coverts (see text).

trasting with the brighter blue and blackish-barred, replaced inner covs; 1-3 terts (and some-times s6) usually replaced, contrasting with the older middle ss (s4-s6; Fig. 133**D-E**); alula and outer pp covs narrow, tapered, relatively abraded (Fig. 138), and dull blue with a gray-ish or brownish wash and little if any barring (Fig. 196); rects narrow and tapered (Fig. 139**C**), the central rects (r1; occasionally others) often contrastingly fresh; roof of the mouth whitish to mixed white and black (Fig. 195**A-B**; through at least Jan); iris often with a gray edge (through fall). **Note: In addition, look for larger white tips to s1 and s2 in AHY/ASYs than in HY/SYs (see Yunick 1992a), although this likely varies by subspecies, as does the white on the terts (see Geographic variation).**

AHY/ASY (Sep-Aug): Alula, wing covs, and ss uniformly bright blue, usually with distinct, black barring (Figs 133F & 196); outer pp covs broad, truncate, relatively fresh (Fig. 138), and bright blue, often with dusky barring (Fig. 196); rects uniformly broad and truncate (Fig. 139**C**); roof of the mouth primarily to entirely black (Fig. 195**B-C**); iris usually uniformly brown, without a grayish edge. **Note: See HY/SY. Some AHY/ASYs possibly can be aged SY/TY by having AHY/ASY plumage but substantial, pale coloration to the roof of the mouth (see Fig. 195B and Common Raven).**

Sex—♀ = ♂ by plumage. CP/BP (Mar-Aug); some SYs of both sexes probably defer breeding and thus may not develop CP/BPs. ♀ wg(n100) 115-139, tl(n100) 106-131; ♂ wg(n100) 117-148, tl(n100) 114-148; measurements can be useful on known sub-species; see **Geographic variation**.

Hybrids reported—Steller's Jay. Green Jay in captivity.

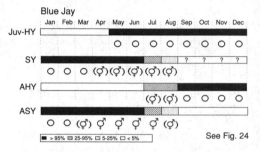

References—Stone (1896), Dwight (1900a), Ridgway (1904), Forbush (1927), Bent (1946), Pitelka (1946), Nichols (1955), Roberts (1955), Wood (1969), Dater (1970), Williams & Wheat (1971), Gebhardt (1971), Oberholser (1974), Briggs (1975), Goodwin (1976), Sheppard & Klimkiewicz (1976), Olyphant (1977), Lamb *et al.* (1978), Pulich & Dellinger (1981), Wheat (1981), Bancroft & Woolfenden (1982), Jewell (1986), CWS & USFWS (1991), Yunick (1992a), Pyle (1997c); R.M. Dellinger, C. Dowd, E.J. Fisk, B. Hilton, M.K. Klimkiewicz, T. Lloyd-Evans, R.P. Yunick (*in litt.* to the BBL); C.W. Thompson (pers. comm.); IBP (MAPS) data.

GREEN JAY
Cyanocorax yncas

GREJ
Species # 4830
Band size: 2

Geographic variation—Weak to moderate and clinal where most ranges meet. Subspecies tax-onomy follows E.R. Blake & C. Vaurie *in* Mayr & Greenway (1962), as modified by Phillips (1986); see also Ridgway (1904), Sutton (1947, 1951a), Oberholser (1974). Eleven other sub-species occur in Mex-S.Am. Note that plumage becomes bluer with wear.

C.y. glaucescens (res s.TX): From subspecies of Mex & S.Am by smaller average size (see **Sex**, *vs* wg 112-131, tl 122-153 in the other subspecies); upperparts duller and paler green with a bluish tinge; blue of the malar and auricular paler; underparts paler and mixed with whitish; iris brown (vs yellow in some of the other subspecies).

Molt—PB: HY partial-incomplete (Jun-Sep), AHY complete (Jun-Sep); PA absent. The 1st PB can include no (~30%), most, or (rarely) all ss, pp, and pp covs, beginning with the terts and apparently continuing distally (outward), in order, from the inner ss to the outer pp; more study is needed on this interesting replacement pattern. The 1st PB also includes all gr covs (occasionally 1-2 outer covs can be retained) and (usually) 2-4 central rects (r1-r2; sometimes more?). The above month ranges pertain to northern birds (*C.y. glaucescens*); among birds of tropical populations molts are more protracted, if not year-round, and may be more extensive.

Skull—Probably completes in HY/SY from 1 Oct through Jun. The skull can be difficult or impossible to see through the skin.

Age—Juv (May-Jul) has the head, chin, and throat brownish, upperparts relatively dull green, underparts relatively pale yellow, undertail covs washed with buff, and the roof of the mouth (upper mandible lining) white (Fig. 195A); juv ♀ = ♂.

HY/SY (Aug-Jul): Crown often with some dull bluish feathers; nasal tufts average smaller; molt limits usually occur, some or all outer pp, pp covs, ss, and/or sometimes 1-2 outer gr covs juvenal, dull or dusky brownish with green edging, and faded, contrasting with the relatively fresher, greener, and brighter, replaced, inner pp, pp covs, ss, gr covs, and/or med covs (see **Molt**); rects narrow and tapered (Fig. 139C), the central 1-4 (sometimes others) usually contrastingly fresh; roof of the mouth probably whitish to mixed grayish and white (Fig. 195A-B; through at least Jan).

AHY/ASY (Aug-Jul): Crown uniformly green; nasal tufts average fuller; pp, ss, and wing covs uniformly adult (Fig. 133F) and bright green, without well-marked contrasts; rects uniformly broad and truncate (Fig. 139C); roof of the mouth usually black (Fig. 195C). **Note: Some AHY/ASYs possibly can be aged SY/TY by having AHY/ASY plumage but substantial, pale coloration to the roof of the mouth (see Fig. 195B and Common Raven).**

Sex—♀ = ♂ by plumage. CP/BP (Mar-Jul); SYs of both sexes can defer breeding and thus may not develop CP/BPs. ♀ wg(n77) 107-118, tl(n47) 117-133; ♂ wg(n76) 110-122, tl(n46) 118-136; measurements restricted to *C.y. glaucescens* of TX (see **Geographic variation**).

Green Jay

See Fig. 24

Hybrids reported: Blue Jay in captivity.

References—Ridgway (1904), Bent (1946), Sutton (1951a), Pitelka (1961a), Oberholser (1974), Alvarez (1975), Goodwin (1976), Pulich & Dellinger (1981), Johnson & Jones (1993), Gayou (1995), Pyle (1997c); K. Burton, F.A. Pitelka (pers. comm.).

BROWN JAY
Cyanocorax morio

BRJA
Species # 4832
Band size: 4A-4-3

Geographic variation—Weak, clinal, and confused by polychromatism. Subspecies taxonomy follows Phillips (1986); see also Ridgway (1904), van Rossem (1934a), Davis (1951a), Selander (1959). Four other subspecies occur in Mex-C.Am.

C.m. palliatus (res s.TX): From the other subspecies of Mex-C.Am by wg large (see **Sex**, *vs* 182-216 in the other subspecies) but bill slender (depth at tip of nares 13.8-16.3, *vs* 15.2-17.6); rects of all birds uniformly dark, without white tips, and with a bluish sheen; belly whitish with a sooty wash (vs uniformly dark or uniformly white in subspecies of Mex-C.Am).

Molt—PB: HY partial (Jun-Sep), AHY complete (Jun-Sep); PA absent. The 1st PB includes some to most med covs and 0 (~15%) to 4 inner gr covs, but no flight feathers. This applies to northern populations; the molt may average more extensive in southern populations.

Skull—Pneumaticization completes in HY/SY from 1 Oct through Dec, probably later in some birds. The skull can be difficult or impossible to see through the skin.

Age—Juv (May-Jul) resembles HY/SY but is duller, has loosely textured undertail covs, bill and feet yellow or primarily yellow (see Fig. 197), roof of the mouth (upper mandible lining) white (Fig. 195**A**), and iris gray; juv ♀=♂.

HY/SY (Aug-Jul): Molt limits occur among the med and gr covs (see **Molt**; Fig. 133**A-C**), the retained outer covs pale brown, contrasting with the darker brown, replaced inner covs; outer pp covs narrow, tapered, and relatively abraded (Fig. 138); rects narrow and tapered (Fig. 139**C**); bill yellow, becoming partially (or rarely fully?) black by Jun (see Fig. 197); roof of the mouth probably pinkish or yellowish, becoming mixed grayish and white (Fig. 195**A-B**; through at least Jan); iris gray to brownish gray. **Note: Color of the soft parts should be used as a guide and not relied on entirely, as this appears to be quite variable in this species; more study is needed.**

AHY/ASY (Aug-Jul): Wing covs uniformly adult (Fig. 133**F**) and dark brown; outer pp covs broad, truncate, and relatively fresh (Fig. 138); rects broad and truncate (Fig. 139**C**); bill partially or fully black (see Fig. 197); roof of the mouth usually black (Fig. 195**C**); iris brown. **Note: See HY/SY. Some AHY/ASYs possibly can be aged SY/TY by having AHY/ASY plumage but substantial pale coloration to the roof of the mouth (see Fig. 195B and Common Raven). Also, some SY/TYs and/or ASY/ATYs might be reliably aged by partly yellow bills, as in Mexican Jay (Fig. 197) but with the rect shape of adult or, perhaps, intermediate between HY/SY and AHY/ASY (see Fig. 139C). Likewise, AHY/ASYs with entirely black soft parts may be ASY/ATYs (or even ATY/A4Ys), but more study is needed to confirm the reliability of these criteria (see Lawton & Guindon 1981).**

Sex—♀=♂ by plumage. CP/BP (Mar-Jul); SYs usually defer breeding and lack or show reduced CPs or BPs. ♀ wg(n19) 196-214, tl(n19) 194-215; ♂ wg(n22) 202-219, tl(n22) 200-220; measurements restricted to *C.m. palliatus* (see **Geographic variation**).

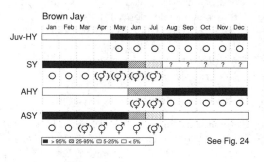

Hybrids reported: White-throated Magpie-Jay *(Calocitta formosa).*

References—Ridgway (1904), Pitelka *et al.* (1956), Selander (1959), Goodwin (1976), Lawton & Guindon (1981), Lawton & Lawton (1985), Pyle (1997c).

FLORIDA SCRUB-JAY
Aphelocoma coerulescens

FLSJ
Species # 4790
Band size: 3-2

Species—From Western Scrub-Jay (which see for separation from the other *Aphelocoma* jays) by small size (wg 102-122, tl 123-152; see **Sex**); crown pale blue, often with whitish streaks;

back pale gray, contrasting markedly with the darker blue wings.

Geographic variation—No subspecies are recognized. See Pitelka (1951b).

Molt—PB: HY partial-incomplete (Jun-Sep), AHY complete (May-Sep); PA absent. The 1st PB includes 9 to 10 (~67%) inner gr covs, 2-3 terts, and the central rects (sometimes other rects).

Skull—Pneumaticization completes in HY/SY from 1 Oct through Jan, probably later in some birds. The skull can be difficult or impossible to see through the skin.

Age—Juv (Mar-Aug) has the underparts washed sooty and roof of the mouth (upper mandible lining) grayish white (Fig. 195**A**); juv ♀ = ♂.

HY/SY (Aug-Jul): Molt limits sometimes occur among the gr covs (see **Molt**; Fig. 133**D-E**), the retained outermost cov worn and blue with a slight brownish cast, contrasting with the brighter blue and fresher, replaced inner covs; 2-3 terts replaced, contrastingly fresh and blue (Fig. 133**D-E**); outer pp covs narrow, tapered, relatively abraded (Fig. 138), and tinged brownish; outer rects narrow and tapered (Fig. 139**C**), the central rects (r1; sometimes other rects) contrastingly fresh; tail relatively graduated (longest r – r5 usually 8-18 mm); roof of the mouth whitish to mixed grayish and black (Fig. 195**A-B**; through at least Jan).

AHY/ASY (Aug-Jul): Gr covs, terts, and ss uniformly adult (Fig. 133**F**) and bright blue; outer pp covs broad, truncate, relatively fresh (Fig. 138), and blue without a brownish tinge; rects uniformly adult, broad, and truncate (Fig. 139**C**); tail moderately graduated (longest r – r5 usually 3-13 mm); roof of the mouth primarily to entirely black (Fig. 195**C**). **Note: Some AHY/ASYs possibly may be reliably aged SY/TY by having AHY/ASY plumage but substantial, pale coloration to the roof of the mouth (see Fig. 195B and Common Raven).**

Sex—♀ = ♂ by plumage. CP/BP (Feb-Aug); SYs of both sexes often defer breeding and may not develop CP/BPs. Measurements are useful: ♀ wg(n100) 102-118, tl(n100) 123-145; ♂ wg(n100) 105-122, tl(n100) 128-152. Also, see Tiersch & Mumme (1993) for sexing of this species using flow cytometry.

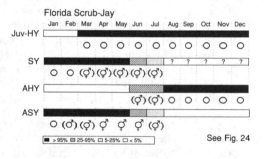

Florida Scrub-Jay

See Fig. 24

References—Ridgway (1904), Pitelka (1945b, 1951b), A. Sprunt Jr. *in* Bent (1946), Goodwin (1976), Bancroft & Woolfenden (1982), Phillips (1986), Tiersch & Mumme (1993), Woolfenden & Fitzpatrick (1996), Pyle (1997c).

ISLAND SCRUB-JAY
Aphelocoma insularis

ISSJ
Species # 4811
Band size: 3B-3

Species—From Western Scrub-Jay (which see for separation from the other *Aphelocoma* jays) by large size (wg 126-143, tl 138-163; see **Sex**); crown and wings dark blue; undertail covs blue.

Geographic variation—No subspecies are recognized.

Molt—PB: HY partial (Jun-Oct), AHY complete (Jun-Sep); PA absent. The 1st PB includes 7 to 10 (~8%) inner gr covs, but usually no terts or central rects.

Skull—Pneumaticization completes in HY/SY from 15 Oct through Jan, probably later in some birds. The skull can be difficult or impossible to see through the skin.

Age—Except for minor differences in the extent of the 1st PB (see **Molt**), thus, position of the molt limits (Fig. 133**C-D**), ageing follows that of Western Scrub-Jay (which see, below).

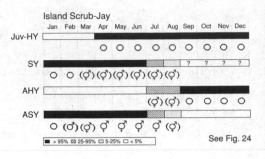

Sex—♀ = ♂ by plumage. CP/BP (Feb-Aug); SYs of both sexes probably defer breeding and may not develop CP/BPs. Measurements are useful: ♀ wg(n56) 126-137, tl(n54) 138-153; ♂ wg(n73) 131-143, tl(n69) 144-163.

References—Ridgway (1904), Swarth (1918b), Pitelka (1945b, 1951b), Bent (1946), Goodwin (1976), Phillips (1986), Pyle (1997c).

WESTERN SCRUB-JAY
Aphelocoma californica

WESJ
Species # 4810
Band size: 2-3

Species—From Florida Scrub-Jay by larger size (wg 109-136, tl 116-152; see **Geographic variation & Sex**); crown medium-pale to medium-dark blue, without whitish streaks; back darker gray, contrasting in color (but not hue) with the medium-dark blue wings. From Island Scrub-Jay by smaller average size (see above); crown and wings average paler blue; undertail covs whitish or (at most) tinged blue. Dull subspecies (especially *A.c. woodhouseii*) from Mexican Jay by shorter wg (see above); wg < tl; rects narrower (width of r1: HY/SY 18-22, AHY/ASY 20-24); plumage more contrasting; back with a distinct, gray patch; breast usually with distinct, blue or dusky markings; juv-HY/SYs with bill black.

Geographic variation—Weak to moderate, but clinal where ranges meet. Subspecies taxonomy follows Phillips (1986); see also Ridgway (1904), Grinnell & Swarth (1913), Oberholser (1917c, 1974), Swarth (1918b), Linsdale (1938), Pitelka (1945a, 1945b, 1951b, 1961b), Behle (1948, 1985), Phillips (1964), Browning (1978, 1990). Six to seven other subspecies occur in Mex. Note that the blues of the plumage become darker with wear. See also **Molt**.

Coastal *(A.c. californica)* Group. Bright blue; underparts whitish.

A.c. californica (br & wint s.WA to coastal wc.CA, Ventura Co): Medium in size; crown, nape, and rump medium-dark blue with a purplish tinge; underparts whitish with a gray wash; undertail covs usually whitish, without or slightly tinged blue. ♀ wg(n100) 112-127, tl(n100) 123-143; ♂ wg(n100) 117-131, tl(n100) 127-147. Birds from s.WA-s.OR (*"immanis"*) average larger, paler, and sometimes with bluish-tinged undertail covs, birds from coastal sw.OR-nw.CA (*"caurina"*) average darker overall, and birds from the San Francisco, CA region ("occleptica") average larger, but variation is weak and broadly clinal in all cases.

A.c. superciliosa (br & wint interior s.OR-w.NV to sc.CA, Ventura Co): Medium in size; crown medium-pale blue, contrasting with the darker blue and purplish-tinged wings; underparts and undertail covs whitish gray. ♀ wg(n100) 112-127, tl(n100) 117-141; ♂ wg(n100) 116-134, tl(n100) 126-151.

A.c. obscura (res sw.CA, Los Angeles-San Diego Cos): Medium small; crown and wings dark purplish blue; underparts whitish with a gray wash; undertail covs often tinged blue. ♀ wg(n100) 109-122, tl(n100) 116-137; ♂ wg(n100) 115-126, tl(n100) 124-144.

Interior *(A.c. woodhouseii)* **Group. Dull blue; underparts grayish.**

A.c. woodhouseii (="*nevadae*" in the nomenclature of the AOU [1957]; br & wint se.OR-se.CA to s.ID-sw.NM): Medium large; crown and wings uniformly dull, medium-pale blue; underparts medium gray; undertail covs tinged pale blue. ♀ wg(n100) 117-128, tl(n100) 123-143; ♂ wg(n100) 123-136, tl(n100) 132-152. Birds of sc.CA (*"cana"*) average darker and slightly larger, but variation is slight and due to intergradation with obscura.

A.c. suttoni (="*woodhouseii*" in nomenclature of the AOU [1957]; br & wint se.ID-s.WY to s.NM-sw.TX): Medium large; crown and wings uniformly medium blue; underparts dark gray; undertail covs usually with a pale blue wash. ♀ wg(n81) 119-130, tl(n72) 124-143; ♂ wg(n100) 124-136, tl(n100) 131-151. Birds of se.NM-sw.TX (*"mesolega"*) average slightly smaller and paler, but variation is slight.

A.c. texana (br & wint c.TX): Medium large; crown and wings uniformly medium blue; underparts dark gray; undertail covs whitish, often tinged blue. ♀ wg(n45) 119-128, tl(n45) 126-139; ♂ wg(n66) 124-136, tl(n66) 134-152.

Molt—PB: HY partial (Jun-Oct), AHY complete (Jun-Sep); PA absent. The 1st PB includes 3-9 inner gr covs and occasionally (in ~7% of birds) 1-2 terts, but no rects.

Skull—Pneumaticization completes in HY/SY from 15 Oct (possibly as early as 1 Sep in some birds of CA) through Jan, and probably later in some birds. The skull can be difficult or impossible to see through the skin.

Age—Juv (Apr-Aug) has relatively grayish upperparts with only slight bluish tones, underparts washed sooty, and roof of the mouth (upper mandible lining) grayish white (Fig. 195**A**); juv ♀=♂.

HY/SY (Sep-Aug): Molt limits usually occur among the gr covs (see **Molt**; Fig. 133**B-D**), the retained outer covs worn and blue with a slight brownish cast, contrasting with the brighter blue and fresher, replaced inner covs; 1-2 terts occasionally contrastingly fresh and blue (Fig. 133**D**); outer pp covs narrow, tapered, relatively abraded (Fig. 138), and tinged brownish; rects narrow and tapered (Fig. 139**C**); tail relatively graduated (longest r – r5 usually 10-20 mm); roof of the mouth whitish to mixed grayish and black (Fig. 195**A-B**; through at least Jan). **Note: The above can be subtle; a few intermediates may not be reliably aged.**

AHY/ASY (Sep-Aug): Gr covs, terts, and middle ss (s4-s6) uniformly adult (Fig. 133**F**) and bright blue; outer pp covs broad, truncate, relatively fresh (Fig. 138), and blue without a brownish tinge; rects broad and truncate (Fig. 139**C**); tail moderately graduated (longest r – r5 usually 3-15 mm); roof of the mouth primarily to entirely black (Fig. 195**C**). **Note: See HY/SY. It is probable that some AHY/ASYs can be reliably aged SY/TY by having AHY/ASY plumage but substantial, pale coloration to the roof of the mouth (see Fig. 195B and Common Raven).**

Sex—♀=♂ by plumage. CP/BP (Feb-Aug); SYs of both sexes often defer breeding and may not develop CP/BPs. Measurements, especially tl, helpful for sexing within each subspecies (see **Geographic variation**): ♀ wg(n100) 109-130, tl(n100) 116-143; ♂ wg(n100) 115-136, tl(n100) 124-152.

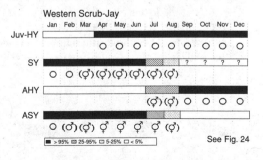

References—Ridgway (1904), Pitelka (1945b, 1951b), Bent (1946), Oberholser (1974), Goodwin (1976), Kaufman (1990b), Pyle (1997c); J.L. Brown, L. Salata (*in litt.* to the BBL); IBP (MAPS) data, PRBO data.

MEXICAN JAY
Aphelocoma ultramarina

MEJA
Species # 4820
Band size: 3B

Species—From dull Western Scrub-Jays by longer wg (139-174; see **Geographic variation**); wg > tl; rects broader (width of r1: HY/SY 21-26, AHY/ASY 24-29); plumage less contrasting; back without gray, or with an indistinct gray wash; breast whitish without distinct, blue or dusky markings; some juv-HY/SYs (see **Geographic variation**) with the bill primarily or partly whitish to pinkish.

Geographic variation—Well marked and ranges in N.Am well defined (weaker and clinal in Mex). Subspecies taxonomy follows Phillips (1986); see also Ridgway (1904), Van Tyne & Sutton (1937), Pitelka (1945b, 1951b, 1961b), Brown & Horvath (1989), Peterson (1991). Five other subspecies occur in Mex.

> **A.u. arizonae** (res c.AZ-sw.NM): Large; upperparts dull, pale, grayish blue; throat and breast uniformly gray; juv-HY/SY and SY/TY with the bill partly whitish to pinkish (Fig. 197). ♀ wg(n100) 150-169, tl(n100) 130-151; ♂ wg(n100) 154-174, tl(n100) 135-157.
>
> **A.u. couchii** (res sw.TX): Small; upperparts bright, dark blue; throat whitish, contrasting with the gray breast; juv-HY/SY with the bill black (*cf.* Fig. 197). ♀ wg(n32) 139-155, tl(n32) 117-131; ♂ wg(n52) 140-158, tl(n51) 123-141.

Molt—PB: HY partial (Jun-Oct), AHY complete (Jun-Nov); PA absent. The 1st PB includes 2-9 inner gr covs and can include the terts and central rects (r1) in subspecies of Mex, but not (except for rarely s8) in subspecies of N.Am. Birds of AZ (*A.u. arizonae*) replace fewer gr covs on average than birds of TX *(couchii)*. Mean timing of molt in *arizonae* also is later than that of *couchii* by 15-30 days.

Skull—Pneumaticization completes in HY/SY from 1 Oct through Dec, probably later in some birds. The skull can be difficult or impossible to see through the skin.

Age—Juv (May-Sep) has relatively grayish upperparts with only slight bluish tones, underparts washed sooty, bill pale whitish to pinkish in *A.u. arizonae* (*cf.* Fig. 197), and the roof of the mouth (upper mandible lining) grayish white (Fig. 195A); juv ♀ = ♂.

> HY/SY (Sep-Aug): Molt limits occur among the gr covs (see **Molt**; Fig. 133**B-D**), the retained outer covs worn and blue with a slight brownish cast, contrasting with the brighter blue and fresher, replaced inner covs; outer pp covs narrow, tapered, relatively abraded (Fig. 138), and tinged brownish; rects narrow and tapered (Fig. 139**C**); base of the upper mandible and much of the lower mandible whitish or pinkish, with black mottling (Fig. 197; in *arizonae* only); roof of the mouth whitish to mixed grayish and black (Fig. 195**A-B**; through at least Jan). **Note: The above plumage differences can be subtle, and a few intermediates (especially of *A.u. couchii*) may not be reliably aged.**

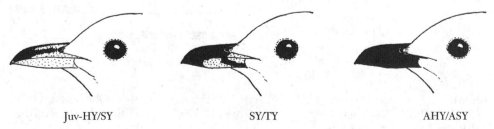

Juv-HY/SY   SY/TY   AHY/ASY

FIGURE 197. Bill color by age in the western subspecies of Mexican Jay, *A.u. arizonae*. All ages of the eastern subspecies *(A.u. couchii)* have black bills.

AHY/ASY (Sep-Aug): Wing covs uniformly adult (Fig. 133**F**) and bright blue; outer pp covs broad, truncate, relatively fresh (Fig. 138), and blue without a brownish cast; rects broad and truncate (Fig. 139**C**); upper and lower mandibles entirely black (Fig. 197; sometimes with slight, pale coloration at the base of the lower mandible in *arizonae);* roof of the mouth primarily to entirely black (Fig. 195**C**). **Note: See HY/SY. Some AHY/ASYs possibly can be aged SY/TY by having AHY/ASY plumage but substantial, pale coloration to the roof of the mouth (see Fig. 195B, SY/TY, and Common Raven); compare with bill color in *arizonae*. AHY/ASYs with entirely black lower mandibles possibly may be aged ASY/ATY (see SY/TY), but more study is needed.**

SY/TY (Sep-May; *arizonae* only): Plumage as in AHY/ASY, but base of the lower mandible pale, this coloration distinct and extending at least 5 mm from base (Fig. 197). Note: See HY/SY.

Not all SY/TYs in AZ (and no SY/TYs in TX) can be reliably aged, and SY/TY probably should be assigned only with some experience; ♂♂ typically retain more pale coloration to the bill than ♀♀, within each age group. **Note: See AHY/ASY.**

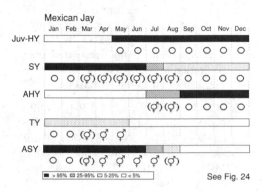

Sex— ♀ = ♂ by plumage. CP/BP (Mar-Aug); SYs and many TYs defer breeding and thus may not develop CP/BPs. See **Geographic variation** for measurements, which vary greatly by subspecies.

References—Ridgway (1904), Swarth (1904a, 1929), Van Tyne & Sutton (1937), Pitelka (1945b, 1951b), Bent (1946), Oberholser (1974), Goodwin (1976), Kaufman (1990b), Pyle (1997c); J.L. Brown (*in litt.* to the BBL); J.P. Church (pers. comm.).

PINYON JAY
Gymnorhinus cyanocephalus

PIJA
Species # 4920
Band size: 3-2

Geographic variation—Weak, clinal, and differences are obscured by individual variation and probable mixing. Subspecies taxonomy follows Phillips (1986); see also Brodkorb (1936), Oberholser (1974), Austin & Rea (1976). No other subspecies occur.

G.c. cassini (br & wint nc.OR-s.ID to s.NV-c.NM): Bill straight, long, and narrow (exp culmen ♀ 29.9-36.1, ♂ 33.0-37.1; width at tip of nares 7.5-8.2); culmen from base ≈ tarsus; plumage relatively dark.

G.c. rostratus (br & wint se.CA): Bill long and wide (exp culmen ♀ 31.5-36.2, ♂ 34.8-39.1; width at tip of nares 7.7-8.5); culmen from base usually > tarsus; plumage medium in hue.

G.c. cyanocephalus (br & wint c.MT-w.ND to n.CO): Bill decurved and short (exp culmen ♀ 27.8-34.1, ♂ 31.0-36.1); exp culmen from base usually < tarsus; plumage relatively pale.

Molt—PB: HY partial-incomplete (Jun-Sep), AHY complete (May-Sep); PA absent. The 1st PB is variable, including up to all gr covs and 6 inner ss. Spring-hatched birds replace many more feathers than late summer-hatched birds; look for some of the former to replace 1-2 central rects (r1) and perhaps others. Among the majority of birds, most lesser covs, no to most med covs, 0-3 inner gr covs, and no terts are replaced. The adult PB sometimes is suspended over late summer breeding. More study is needed.

Skull—Pneumaticization completes in HY/SY from 15 Aug through Dec, probably later in some birds. The skull can be difficult or impossible to see through the skin.

Age—Juv (Mar-Aug) has ashy-gray underparts, without a bluish cast, and the roof of the mouth (upper mandible lining) probably whitish (Fig. 195**A**); juv ♀ = ♂.

HY/SY (Sep-Aug): Molt limits usually occur among the wing covs (see **Molt**; Fig. 133**A-E**), the retained outer covs dull grayish and worn, contrasting with the bluer and fresher, replaced inner covs; 1-6 inner ss sometimes replaced in spring-hatched HY/SYs (see **Molt**), contrasting with the older outer ss (Fig. 133**E**); pp covs narrow, tapered, relatively abraded (Fig. 138), and dull grayish; breast dull grayish; rects narrow and tapered (Fig. 139**C**); roof of the mouth probably whitish to mixed gray and black (Fig. 195**A-B**).

AHY/ASY (Aug-Jul): Wing covs and ss uniformly adult (Fig. 133**F**) and blue; outer pp covs broad, truncate, relatively fresh (Fig. 138), and blue; breast blue; rects broad and truncate (Fig. 139**C**); roof of the mouth primarily to entirely black (Fig. 195**C**). **Note: Some AHY/ASYs possibly can be aged SY/TY by having AHY/ASY plumage but substantial, pale coloration to the roof of the mouth (see Fig. 195B and Common Raven).**

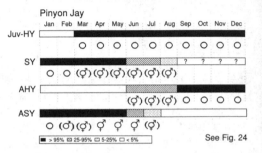

Sex—♀ = ♂ by plumage. CP/BP (Feb-Jul); ♂♂ assist with incubation and can develop a partial BP (Fig. 22**B**); SYs may defer breeding and thus may not develop CP/BPs. ♀ wg(n100) 136-154, tl(n48) 98-116; ♂ wg(n100) 142-161, tl(n59) 102-119.

References—Ridgway (1904), Bent (1946), Ligon (1971), Bateman & Balda (1973), Ligon & White (1974), Oberholser (1974), Goodwin (1976), Pyle (1997c).

CLARK'S NUTCRACKER
Nucifraga columbiana

CLNU
Species # 4910
Band size: 3B

Geographic variation—No subspecies are recognized. See Phillips (1986).

Molt—PB: HY/SY partial (Jul-Jan), AHY complete (Mar-Oct); PA absent. The 1st PB includes no to all (usually 3-6) med covs, but no gr covs or flight feathers. The 2nd PB occurs earlier (Mar-Sep) than subsequent PBs (Apr-Oct). Molts of adults occur concurrently with breeding.

Skull—Pneumaticization completes in HY/SY from 15 Sep through Dec, probably later in some birds. The skull can be difficult (if not impossible) to see through the skin.

Age—Juv (Apr-Sep) has plumage generally washed with brownish, the white eye ring and supercilium indistinct or lacking, and roof of the mouth (upper mandible lining) probably grayish white (Fig. 195**A**); juv ♀ = ♂.

HY/SY (Sep-Aug): Molt limits usually occur among the lesser and med covs (see **Molt**; Fig. 133**A**), the retained gr, outer med, and outer lesser covs dull black or brownish and worn, contrasting with the blacker and fresher, replaced inner med and lesser covs; outer pp covs narrow, tapered, relatively abraded (Fig. 138), and dull black to brownish; rects narrow and tapered (Fig. 139**C**); tail fork shallow (Fig. 198; r6 – r1 usually 3-15 mm); roof of the mouth probably whitish to mixed gray and black (Fig. 195**A-B**; through at least Jan). **Note: The protracted PB molt (see Molt) should be considered in ageing summer and fall birds.**

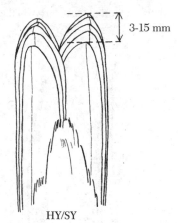

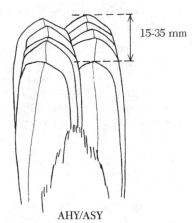

FIGURE 198. Shape of the rectrices and degree of the tail fork by age in Clark's Nutcracker. Similar differences in tail fork length should be looked for in other species of corvids.

AHY/ASY (Aug-Jul): Wing covs uniformly black; outer pp covs broad, truncate, relatively fresh (Fig. 138), and black; rects broad and truncate (Fig. 139C); tail fork deep (Fig. 198; r6 – r1 usually 15-35 mm); roof of the mouth primarily to entirely black (Fig. 195C). **Note: See HY/SY. Some AHY/ASYs possibly can be aged SY/TY by having AHY/ASY plumage but substantial, pale coloration to the roof of the mouth (see Fig. 195B and Common Raven).**

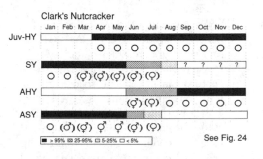

Sex— ♀ = ♂ by plumage. CP (Feb-Jun); BP (Mar-Jul) is developed by both sexes (slightly more fully in ♀♀; Fig. 22C), and it probably should not be used alone for sexing. ♀ wg(n100) 173-196, tl(n20) 108-122; ♂ wg(n100) 180-202, tl(n20) 112-126.

References—Ridgway (1904), Bent (1946), Mewaldt (1952, 1958), Roberts (1955), Oberholser (1974), Tomback (1978), Pyle (1997c).

BLACK-BILLED MAGPIE
Pica pica

BBMA
Species # 4750
Band size: 3B-4-3

Species—From Yellow-billed Magpie by larger average size (wg 177-216, tl 231-302; see **Sex**); bill black in all plumages. Reported differences in the iris color between the two magpies likely was based on seasonal changes rather than species-specific variation.

Geographic variation—Subspecies taxonomy follows Cramp & Perrins (1994a); see also Ridgway (1904), W.S. Brooks (1915), A. Brooks (1931), Linsdale (1937), Dement'ev & Gladkov (1954), Phillips (1986). Eleven other subspecies occur in Eurasia and Africa.

P.p. hudsonia (br & wint throughout range in N.Am): From the other subspecies of Eurasia by longer average tl (see **Sex**, *vs* 210-283 in the other subspecies); white of p1 averages smaller (usually 10-60 mm, *vs* 40-80 mm in length in Eurasian subspecies) and does not extend to the edge of the outer web;

throat feathers with concealed white bases; iris with a whitish outer ring (vs all brown in the other subspecies).

Molt—PB: HY partial (Jul-Oct), AHY complete (May-Sep); PA absent. The 1st PB includes 5 to 10 (~40%) inner gr covs and occasionally (in ~20% of birds) 1-2 terts, but not the central rects. The 2nd PB occurs earlier (May-Aug) than subsequent PBs (Jun-Sep).

Skull—Pneumaticization completes in HY/SY from 15 Sep through Nov, probably later in some birds (completion by 15 Aug has been reported for this species in Europe). The skull can be difficult (if not impossible) to see through the skin.

Age—Juv (May-Sep) has the upperparts washed dull brownish, underparts creamy, iris gray, and roof of the mouth (upper mandible lining) grayish white (Fig. 195**A**); juv ♀ = ♂.

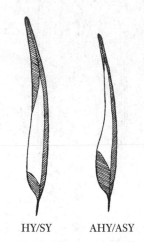

HY/SY   AHY/ASY

FIGURE 199. The outermost, reduced primary (p10) by age in magpies.

HY/SY (Aug-2nd Oct): Molt limits often occur among the gr covs (Fig. 133**C-E**, see **Molt**), the retained outer covs less glossy than the replaced inner covs (the contrast can be difficult to detect); 1-2 terts sometimes contrastingly fresh (Fig. 133**D**); p10 broadly shaped at the tip (Fig. 199); white of p9 indistinctly defined and usually extending > 20 mm from the tip (Fig. 200); outer rects narrow and tapered (Fig. 139**C**); roof of the mouth probably whitish to mixed gray and black (Fig. 195**A-B**; through at least Jan). **Note: Molt limits can be difficult to detect; however, shape and pattern differences in the outer pp and rects are apparent. SYs can be aged until p9-p10 are dropped, by Sep in most SYs and Oct in some.**

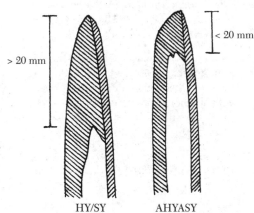

> 20 mm   < 20 mm

HY/SY   AHYASY

FIGURE 200. P9 by age in magpies.

These can be separated from HYs during this period by skull condition (see Skull), active flight-feather replacement, and extremely worn (juvenal) p9-p10.

AHY/ASY (Sep-Aug): Gr covs and terts uniformly adult (Fig. 133**F**); p10 attenuate (Fig. 199); white of p9 sharply defined and usually < 20 mm from the tip (Fig. 200); outer rects broad and truncate (Fig. 139**C**); roof of the mouth primarily to entirely black (Fig. 195**C**). **Note: See HY/SY. Some AHY/ASYs possibly can be aged SY/TY by having AHY/ASY plumage but substantial, pale coloration to the roof of the mouth (see Fig. 195B and Common Raven).**

Sex— ♀ = ♂ by plumage. CP/BP (Mar-Aug). Measurements are helpful, although subject to some geographic variation: ♀ wg(n100) 177-209, tl(n30) 231-283; ♂ wg(n100) 191-216, tl(n30) 245-

302; beware of free-flying juvs, which can resemble adults before reaching full size. Also, see Reese & Kadlec (1982) for a discriminant function analysis, based on live birds, using wg, bill nares to tip, and weight, that distinguished 95% of the sexes in a UT population, and Scharf (1987) for an analysis based on specimens, using wg and bill depth at the tip of the nares, that correctly sexed 95% of all birds and 98% of adults in an Alberta population. Formulas based on similar analyses probably are useful for sexing throughout the range.

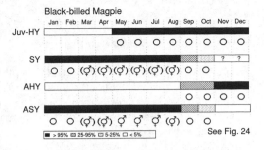

References—Ridgway (1904), Brooks (1931), Linsdale (1937), J.M. Linsdale *in* Bent (1946), Roberts (1955), Erpino (1968), Oberholser (1974), Reese & Kadlec (1982), Scharf (1987), Birkehead (1991), Svensson (1992), Cramp & Perrins (1994a), Pyle (1997c); J.N. Mugaas (*in litt.* to the BBL); C.H. Trost (pers. comm.).

YELLOW-BILLED MAGPIE
Pica nuttalli

YBMA
Species # 4760
Band size: 3A

Species—From Black-billed Magpie (which see) by smaller average size (wg 173-197, tl 215-268; see **Sex**); bill yellow in all plumages.

Geographic variation—No subspecies are recognized.

Molt—PB: HY partial (Jul-Nov), AHY complete (May-Nov); PA absent. The 1st PB includes 5 to 10 (~45%) inner gr covs, sometimes (in ~27% of birds) 1-2 terts, and occasionally (in ~9% of birds) 1-2 central rects (r1). Molt of SYs probably averages earlier in timing; see Black-billed Magpie.

Skull—Pneumaticization completes in HY/SY from 15 Sep through Nov, probably later in some birds. The skull can be difficult (if not impossible) to see through the skin.

Age—Ageing criteria follow those of Black-billed Magpie; also, HY/SY Yellow-billed Magpies occasionally can replace 1-2 central rects (r1), these being contrastingly fresh.

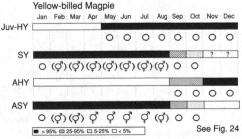

Sex—♀ = ♂ by plumage. CP/BP (Feb-Aug). Measurements are useful: ♀ wg(n100) 173-187, tl(n25) 215-250; ♂ wg(n84) 180-197, tl(n29) 223-268; beware of free-flying juvs, which can resemble adults before reaching full size.

References—Ridgway (1904), Brooks (1931), Linsdale (1937), J.M. Linsdale *in* Bent (1946), Verbeek (1973a, 1976), Oberholser (1974), Phillips (1986), Birkehead (1991), Reynolds (1995), Pyle (1997c); C.H. Trost (pers. comm.).

AMERICAN CROW   AMCR
Corvus brachyrhynchos   Species # 4880
                                                     Band size: 5

Species—From Fish Crow and the ravens by medium size (wg 272-341, tl 147-199; see **Geographic variation & Sex**); tarsus medium-short (53.0-66.5 mm); bill medium in size (exp culmen 43.0-53.5, nares to tip 28.3-44.0, depth at tip of nares 15.0-20.5); p5 > p9; r1 – r6 12-22 mm when fresh; length of the longest throat feathers 15-26 mm; centers of the crown and back feathers glossy violet, creating a scaled appearance, contrasting with the uniformly flat-black nape feathers; iridescence of the underparts restricted to the breast and flanks; bases of the neck and breast feathers gray.

Adults of the northwestern subspecies *(C.b. hesperis;* see **Geographic variation**) perhaps are not safely separated from Northwestern Crow by in-hand criteria alone. Measurements (especially tarsus; see above) can distinguish about 50% of unsexed birds and 70% of known-sex birds, but birds in the overlap zone can be difficult or impossible to separate. The nasal bristles may be more laterally situated in American Crow, lying along the sides of the bill *vs* along the culmen in Northwestern Crow, but there appears to be overlap in this difference, if it exists at all. The underparts average glossier in American Crow and flatter black in Northwestern Crow. In juvs, look for the mouth lining to be pinker *(vs* orange) and the nessoptiles of the spinal tract to average shorter in American than in Northwestern Crow. See Rhoads (1893), Swarth (1912b), Oberholser (1919c), Meinertzhagen (1926), Brooks (1942), L.I. Davis (1958), Johnston (1961), Ratti (1984), A.M. Rea *in* Phillips (1986), Parkes (1988b), Bayer (1989a, 1989b), Patterson (1989), Paulsen (1989), Paulson (1989), Roberts (1990), and Verbeek (1991) for more on separating these two species of crows.

Geographic variation—Weak (based on measurements only), geographically discordant, and clinal where ranges meet. Subspecies taxonomy follows Phillips (1986); see also Ridgway (1904), Howell (1913), Taverner (1919b), Bailey (1923b), Meinertzhagen (1926), Phillips (1942b), Johnston (1961), Todd (1963), Sutton (1967), Richards (1971), Oberholser (1974), Behle (1985). No other subspecies occur. Winter birds can be impossible to distinguish to subspecies, especially in the eastern parts of the range. In the following, all measurements pertain to AHY/ASYs. HY/SYs average 15-20 mm shorter wg, 5-10 mm shorter tl, 1-3 mm shorter bill nares to tip, and 1-2 mm shorter tarsus than AHY/ASYs.

   C.b. hesperis (br & wint interior & lowland n.BC-s.Sask to s.CA & to s.NV-c.KS, & AR-LA to MD-n.FL): Small; bill small, straight, and sharp (nares to tip 28.3-40.1); tarsus relatively long (48.8-63.5); length of the longest throat feathers 15-21 mm. AHY/ASY ♀ wg(n100) 272-317, tl(n100) 147-179; AHY/ASY ♂ wg(n100) 277-330, tl(n100) 153-188. Birds breeding in AR-LA to MD-n.FL *("paulus"),* although geographically separated by *brachyrhynchos,* are inseparable from *hesperis* based on measurements.

   C.b. hargravei (br & wint montane s.ID to c.AZ-c.NM): Large; bill small, straight, and sharp (nares to tip 30.0-38.0); tarsus relatively short (50.5-65.3); wg ÷ cube root of the weight (gms) 40.5-44.1. AHY/ASY ♀ wg(n15) 305-323, tl(n14) 169-183; AHY/ASY ♂ wg(n15) 310-333, tl(n14) 178-196.

   C.b. brachyrhynchos (br NWT-Nfl to s.TX-NJ, wint to LA-n.FL): Large; bill long, decurved, and blunt (nares to tip 31.4-44.0); tarsus relatively short (50.8-64.4); wg ÷ cube root of the weight (gms) 37.0-40.4; length of the longest throat feathers 19-26 mm. AHY/ASY ♀ wg(n100) 284-327, tl(n100) 158-187; AHY/ASY ♂ wg(n75) 295-341, tl(n71) 162-199.

   C.b. pascuus (res c-s.FL): Large; bill medium in size (nares to tip 32.7-41.9); tarsus relatively long (55.4-65.9). AHY/ASY ♀ wg(n49) 278-320, tl(n48) 156-179; AHY/ASY ♂ wg(n32) 288-327, tl(n32) 159-188.

Molt—PB: HY partial (Jul-Sep), AHY complete (Jul-Sep); PA absent. The 1st PB includes 0 (~24%) to 3 inner gr covs, but no terts or rects.

Skull—Pneumaticization completes in HY/SY from 1 Sep through Dec, and probably later in

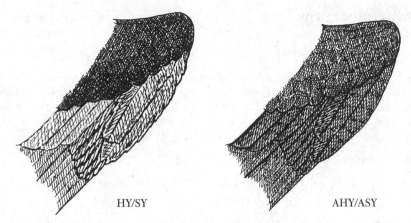

HY/SY   AHY/ASY

FIGURE 201. Wing covert contrasts by age in crows and ravens.

some birds. The skull is very difficult (if not impossible) to see through the skin.

Age—Juv (May-Aug) has a brownish cast (lacking gloss) to the plumage, and roof of the mouth (upper mandible lining) pinkish (Fig. 195**A**); juv ♀ = ♂.

HY/SY (Sep-Aug): Molt limits occur among the med covs and often among the gr covs (see **Molt** and Figs. 133**A-C** & 201), the retained outer covs brownish and worn, contrasting with the black and fresher, replaced inner covs; outer pp covs narrow, tapered, relatively abraded (Fig. 138), and brownish; rects narrow and tapered (Fig. 139**C**); roof of the mouth pinkish to mixed whitish and black (Fig. 195**A-B**; Aug to at least Jan).

AHY/ASY (Sep-Aug): Wing covs uniformly glossy black (Figs. 133F & 201); outer pp covs broad, truncate, relatively fresh (Fig. 138), and black; rects broad and truncate (Fig. 139**C**); roof of the mouth variable, primarily pink to entirely black (Fig. 195**B-C**). **Note: Some AHY/ASYs possibly can be aged SY/TY by having AHY/ASY plumage but substantial, pale coloration to the roof of the mouth (see Fig. 195B and Common Raven).**

Sex—♀ = ♂ by plumage. CP/BP (Feb-Aug); SYs (and some TYs?) may defer breeding and thus may not develop CP/BPs. ♀ wg(n100) 272-327, tl(n100) 147-187; ♂ wg(n100) 277-341, tl(n100) 153-199; see **Geographic variation**. Also, see Clark et al. (1991) for a discriminant function analysis, based on specimens, using wg, tarsus, and head-bill length, that distinguished the sexes in 92% of adults in a population from Sask.

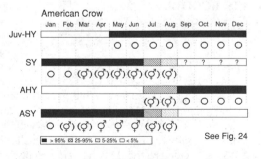

Hybrids reported—Hybrids with Northwestern Crow have been suspected, but not fully documented.

References—Stone (1896), Dwight (1900a), Ridgway (1904), Meinertzhagen (1926), Forbush (1927), Emlen (1936), Pitelka (1945b), A.O. Gross *in* Bent (1946), Roberts (1955), Johnston (1961), Rea (1967), Rea & Kanteena (1968), Saiza (1968), Wood (1969), Oberholser (1974), Clark *et al.* (1991), Pyle (1997c); C. Caffrey (pers. comm.).

NORTHWESTERN CROW
Corvus caurinus

NOCR
Species # 4890
Band size: 4-4A

Species—From American Crow (which see for separation from the other crows and ravens) by smaller size (wg 257-302, tl 134-167; see **Sex**); tarsus shorter (41.5-53.0 mm); bill smaller (exp culmen 41.5-49.0, nares to tip 26.9-37.2, depth at tip of nares 15.0-17.5); length of the longest throat feathers 14-21 mm. Some to many birds probably are not safely separated from the small western subspecies of American Crow by in-hand criteria alone. See American Crow.

Geographic variation—No subspecies are recognized.

Molt—PB: HY partial (Jul-Sep), AHY complete (Jul-Sep); PA absent. The 1st PB includes 0 (~67%) to 2 inner gr covs, but no terts or rects.

Skull—Pneumaticization completes in HY from 15 Oct through Dec, and probably later in some birds. The skull is very difficult, (if not impossible) to see through the skin.

Age—Ageing criteria follow those of American Crow.

Sex—♀ = ♂ by plumage. CP/BP (Apr-Aug); see American Crow. ♀ wg(n66) 257-289, tl(n33) 134-160, tarsus(n39) 41.5-50.2; ♂ wg(n91) 268-302, tl(n64) 144-167, tarsus(n83) 43.6-53.0.

Northwestern Crow

See Fig. 24

Hybrids reported—See Common Crow.

References—Rhoads (1893), Ridgway (1904), Swarth (1912b), Oberholser (1919c), Meinertzhagen (1926), Forbush (1927), Brooks (1942), Bent (1946), Johnston (1961), Rea & Kanteena (1968), Godfrey (1986), Phillips (1986), Parkes (1988b), Bayer (1989a, 1989b), Patterson (1989), Paulsen (1989), Paulson (1989), Roberts (1990), Verbeek (1991), Pyle (1997c).

FISH CROW
Corvus ossifragus

FICR
Species # 4900
Band size: 4A

Species—From American Crow (which see for separation from the other crows and ravens) by small size (wg 254-310, tl 137-175; see **Sex**, and **Geographic variation** for American Crow); tarsus short (41.5-49.6 mm); bill small (exp culmen 41.5-48.5, nares to tip 25.7-34.2, depth at tip of nares 13.5-15.5); crown, back, nape, and underparts uniformly, glossy blackish violet, lacking a scaled appearance or contrasts with flat black plumage. Tamaulipas Crow *(C. imparatus),* a non-breeding visitor to s.TX, is smaller but with a relatively long tl (wg 231-263, tl 136-155, exp culmen 37.5-42.0, bill nares to tip 25.2-32.4, tarsus 36.2-43.0), and has even glossier plumage.

Geographic variation—No subspecies are recognized.

Molt—PB: HY partial (Jul-Sep), AHY complete (Jul-Sep); PA absent. The 1st PB includes 0 (~17%) to 3 inner gr covs, but no terts or rects.

Skull—Pneumaticization completes in HY/SY from 15 Oct through Dec, probably later in some birds. The skull is very difficult (if not impossible) to see through the skin.

Age—Ageing criteria follow those of American Crow.

Sex—♀ = ♂ by plumage. CP/BP (Apr-Aug); see American Crow. ♀ wg(n100) 254-288, tl(n70) 137-160; ♂ wg(n100) 260-310, tl(n82) 147-175.

Fish Crow

	Jan	Feb	Mar	Apr	May	Jun	Jul	Aug	Sep	Oct	Nov	Dec
Juv-HY						○	○	○	○	○	○	○
SY							?	?	?	?		
	○	○	○	(♀)(♀)(♀)(♀)(♀)								
AHY												
ASY				(♀)(♀)	○	○	○	○				
	○	○	○	(♀) ♂ ♂ (♀)(♀)								

■ > 95% ▨ 25-95% ▥ 5-25% □ < 5%   See Fig. 24

References—Stone (1896), Dwight (1900a), Ridgway (1904), Forbush (1927), Bent (1946), Baumel (1957), Johnston (1961), Rea & Kanteena (1968), Oberholser (1974), Pyle (1997c).

CHIHUAHUAN RAVEN
Corvus cryptoleucus

CHRA
Species # 4870
Band size: 5

Species—From American Crow and Common Raven by medium-large size (wg 321-380, tl 179-214; see **Sex**); tarsus medium long (55.5-68.5 mm); bill medium large (exp culmen 49.5-59.0, depth at tip of nares 20.0-22.5); p5 usually ≤ p9; r1 – r6 25-45 mm when fresh; length of the longest throat feathers 29-42 mm; bases of the neck and breast feathers whitish. Beware that the throat and breast plumage differences can be subtle, particularly without direct comparison.

Geographic variation—Subspecies taxonomy follows Browning (1990), who considered the species monotypic (synonymizing a previously recognized subspecies); see also Phillips (1986). Birds of c-s.TX average smaller than western birds (*"C.c. reai"*), but variation is slight and in need of more study.

Molt—PB: partial (Sep-Nov), AHY complete (Sep-Nov); PA absent. The 1st PB includes 1-3 inner gr covs, but no terts or rects.

Skull—Pneumaticization completes in HY/SY from 15 Sep through Dec, and probably later in some birds. The skull is very difficult (if not impossible) to see through the skin.

Age—Ageing criteria follow those of American Crow; combine with the slightly later timing of molt in this species. Juvs of this species have some pale color at the base of the lower mandible.

Sex—♀ = ♂ by plumage. CP/BP (Mar-Aug); see American Crow. ♀ wg(n100) 321-361, tl(n20) 179-205; ♂ wg(n100) 332-380, tl(n20) 181-214.

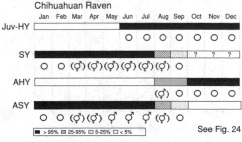

Chihuahuan Raven

	Jan	Feb	Mar	Apr	May	Jun	Jul	Aug	Sep	Oct	Nov	Dec
Juv-HY						○	○	○	○	○	○	○
SY								?	?	?		
	○	○	(♀)(♀)(♀)(♀)(♀)(♀)	○								
AHY												
ASY				(♀)	○	○	○	○				
	○	○	(♀)(♀) ♂ ♂ ♂ (♀) ○									

■ > 95% ▨ 25-95% ▥ 5-25% □ < 5%   See Fig. 24

References—Ridgway (1904), Swarth (1904a), Bent (1946), Baumel (1953), Rea & Kanteena (1968), Saiza (1968), Oberholser (1974), Goodwin (1976), Pyle (1997c).

COMMON RAVEN
Corvus corax

CORA
Species # 4860
Band size: 6-7A

Species—From the other crows and ravens by large size (wg 383-468, tl 206-263; see **Geographic variation & Sex**); tarsus long (63-74 mm); bill large (exp culmen 65-92, depth at tip of nares 23.0-31.5); r1 – r6 34-63 mm when fresh; length of the longest throat feathers 42-75 mm; bases of the neck and breast feathers grayish.

Geographic variation—Weak (based on measurements only) and clinal where most ranges meet. Subspecies taxonomy in N.Am follows A.M. Rea *in* Phillips (1986); see also Ridgway (1904), Brooks (1915), Oberholser (1918c), Meinertzhagen (1926), Swarth (1929), Willett (1941), Dement'ev & Gladkov (1954), Todd (1963), Rea (1983), Cramp & Perrins (1994a). Seven other subspecies occur in Eurasia, which differ in size, have less glossy plumage, and have longer throat feathers. The following measurements include all age groups; note that HY/SYs can average up to 10% shorter measurements than AHY/ASYs.

C.c. kamtschaticus (br & wint w.AK) Large; bill thick (nares to tip 47.7-53.8, depth at tip of nares 27.3-32.1); tarsus medium in length (63.4-71.8) and thick (depth at widest point 10.9-12.5). ♀ wg(n10) 418-455, tl(n10) 226-249; ♂ wg(n14) 425-480, tl(n10) 240-262.

C.c. principalis (br & wint n.AK-sw.BC to Nfl-se.ME & montane PA-n.GA): Large; bill long and medium in depth (nares to tip 44.0-55.9, depth at tip of nares 23.0-30.0); tarsus medium in length (60.5-72.8) and thin (depth at deepest point 8.7-11.9); length of the longest throat feathers long (57-75 mm). ♀ wg(n28) 395-439, tl(n28) 218-253; ♂ wg(n29) 403-468, tl(n30) 231-263. Birds east of c.Ont-AR (*"europhilus"*) may average smaller and with a relatively larger bill than northwestern birds, but differences are slight and obscured by individual variation.

C.c. sinuatus (br & wint e.WA-MT to sc.AZ-TX): Medium in size; bill medium small and slender (nares to tip 42.1-52.3, depth at tip of nares 21.7-26.1); tarsus long (55.8-78.2) and thin (depth at deepest point 8.8-11.3); length of the longest throat feathers medium short (39-56 mm). ♀ wg(n19) 390-425, tl(n19) 218-242; ♂ wg(n17) 412-440, tl(n17) 225-250.

C.c. clarionensis (br & wint w.WA to s.CA-sw.AZ): Small; bill short and slender (nares to tip 39.1-49.8, depth at tip of nares 20.9-24.3); tarsus medium short (60.0-71.8) and thin (depth at deepest point 8.3-11.3); length of the longest throat feathers short (34-50 mm). ♀ wg(n17) 383-415, tl(n17) 206-228; ♂ wg(n13) 386-419, tl(n13) 207-233.

Molt—PB: HY partial (Jun-Oct), AHY complete (May-Oct); PA absent. The 1st PB includes 0 (~54%) to 2 inner gr covs, but no terts or rects.

Skull—Pneumaticization completes in HY/SY from 1 Sep through Nov, probably later in some birds. The skull is very difficult (if not impossible) to see through the skin.

Age—Ageing criteria follow those of American Crow; combine with differences in the timing of molt for this species. In captive birds, color change of the roof of the mouth (upper mandible lining) has been found to vary substantially (relating to both age and social dominance), some SYs attaining entirely black mouths by Jan while some TY/4Ys still retain some pink in the mouths (Heinrich & Marzluff 1992; see Fig. 195). It is probable that some AHY/ASYs can be aged SY/TY by having adult plumage but retaining a certain amount of pink in the mouth (*e.g.*, Fig. 195**B**). More study is needed on mouth color change in relation to age of wild Common Ravens and other species of jays and crows.

Sex—♀ = ♂ by plumage. CP/BP (Feb-Aug); see American Crow. Measurements are useful within subspecies (see **Geographic variation**): ♀ wg(n100) 383-438, tl(n100) 206-253; ♂ wg(n100) 386-468, tl(n100) 207-263.

Hybrids reported—Carrion Crow (*C. corone*).

References—Stone (1896), Dwight (1900a), Ridgway (1904), Forbush (1927), Bent (1946), Roberts (1955), Rea & Kanteena (1968), Wood (1969), Oberholser (1974), Goodwin (1976), Heinrich & Marzluff (1992), Svensson (1992), Cramp & Perrins (1994a), Heinrich (1994), Pyle (1997c).

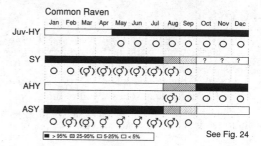

Common Raven

See Fig. 24

LARKS   *ALAUDIDAE*

One geographically variable species. Family characters include long wings, a small bill, and short legs and tail. Larks have 9 visible primaries (the 10th vestigial), 9 secondaries and 12 rectrices. A single annual prebasic molt is completed on the summer grounds in both HYs and AHYs. Skull pneumaticization and breeding characters are reliable for ageing and sexing, respectively. Plumage usually does not allow separation of the age classes (beyond juvenal plumage), but is reliable for separation of the sexes, in most cases. Males also average substantially larger than females, within a given subspecies.

HORNED LARK
Eremophila alpestris

HOLA
Species # 4740
Band size: 1B

Species—Juvs are very nondescript and might be confused with other species. From all sparrows, longspurs and other nondescript brown passerines by long wg (87-115) and wg – tl (25-50 mm); upperparts with white or silvery spots; bill somewhat conical (see Fig. 203); tarsus laterally rounded *(vs* acute in most other species).

Geographic variation—Highly variable in distinctiveness and range; intermediates occur among the many widespread populations whereas ranges of local populations often are distinctly defined. Subspecies taxonomy follows J.L. Peters *in* Mayr & Greenway (1960); see Dwight (1890), Oberholser (1902, 1919b, 1932, 1974), Ridgway (1907), Walker & Trautman (1936), Behle (1938, 1942a, 1942b, 1948, 1985), Green (1940), Jewett (1943), Montagna (1943), Dement'ev & Gladkov (1954), Dickerman (1964), Phillips *et al.* (1964), Sutton (1967), Phillips (1970), Niles (1973a), Browning (1979a), Monson & Phillips (1981), Rea (1983), Unitt (1984), Cramp (1988), Beason (1995). Nineteen other subspecies occur in Eurasia and Mex-S.Am. The following pertain primarily to spring (Feb-Jun) birds, when plumage differences are most marked due to the loss through abrasion of the brown or buff feather tips. Differentiation of fall birds (Aug-Jan), as well as juvs, can be difficult (if not impossible). The extent of the black mask of ♂♂ varies among subspecies, on average, but differences in this feature are largely obscured by substantial individual variation.

Western Rufous *(E.a. strigata)* Group. Small.
E.a. strigata (res coastal s.BC-c.OR, wint to e.WA & c.CA): Small; nape washed rufous; back brown; streak on the longest uppertail cov distinct (Fig. 184**D-E**); throat and face washed yellow; breast (below the black) tinged yellow. ♀ wg(n13) 89-94, tl(n13) 55-64; ♂ wg(n32) 95-102, tl(n32) 62-69.

E.a. actia (res coastal CA): Small; nape washed pale rufous; back brown with a pinkish-rufous tinge; streak on the longest uppertail cov moderately distinct (Fig. 184**C-D**); throat and face yellow; breast without yellow. ♀ wg(n47) 86-96, tl(n47) 54-63; ♂ wg(n100) 93-103, tl(n100) 62-70.

E.a. insularis (res Channel Is, CA; wint to sw.CA): Small; nape brownish rufous; back dark brown; streak on the longest uppertail cov distinct (Fig. 184**E**); throat and face tinged yellow; breast (below the black) whitish or slightly tinged yellow. ♀ wg(n41) 86-97, tl(n46) 54-63; ♂ wg(n57) 93-101, tl(n57) 59-68.

E.a. sierrae (br & wint montane nc.CA): Medium small; nape washed rufous; back brown; streak on the longest uppertail cov indistinct to moderately indistinct (Fig. 184**B-D**); throat and face washed yellow; breast (below the black) without (or slightly tinged) yellow. ♀ wg(n10) 89-97, tl(n10) 58-65; ♂ wg(n31) 95-104, tl(n31) 63-71.

E.a. rubea (res c.CA, Tehama-Solano Cos): Medium small; nape pinkish rufous; back moderately pale brown with a rufous wash; streak on the longest uppertail cov indistinct to moderately indistinct (Fig. 184**B-D**); throat and face washed yellow; breast without yellow. ♀ wg(n30) 89-96, tl(n30) 55-63; ♂ wg(n44) 94-105, tl(n44) 64-71.

E.a. adusta (br & wint s.AZ-sw.NM): Medium small; upperparts burnt pinkish brown; streak on the longest uppertail cov lacking to indistinct (Fig. 184**A-B**); throat and face washed yellow; breast without yellow. ♀ wg(n34) 92-99, tl(n34) 57-65; ♂ wg(n64) 96-106, tl(n64) 64-73.

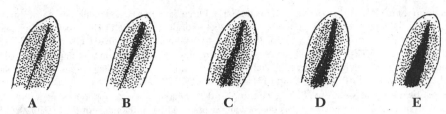

FIGURE 202. Variation in the distinctness of the streaks on the uppertail coverts in Horned Lark, useful in identifying subspecies.

Western Pale *(E.a. arcticola)* Group. Large.

E.a. arcticola (br nw.AK-w.NWT to n.BC, wint sc.BC-ne.CA to w.MT-w.UT): Large; upperparts pale grayish brown; streak on the longest uppertail cov moderately distinct (Fig. 202**C-D**); throat, face, and breast without yellow. ♀ wg(n20) 99-106, tl(n20) 62-67; ♂ wg(n50) 106-115, tl(n50) 66-74.

E.a. alpina (br & wint c.WA): Large; upperparts pale grayish; streak on the longest uppertail cov moderately distinct (Fig. 202**C-D**); throat, face, and breast without yellow. ♀ wg(n10) 95-105, tl(n10) 57-66; ♂ wg(n10) 107-112, tl(n15) 66-72. Suggested three-letter subspecies code (see pp. 30-31): "aln".

E.a. ammophila (br & wint sw.NV-s.CA): Medium small; nape washed pinkish rufous; back moderately pale, buffy brown; streak on the longest uppertail cov lacking to indistinct (Fig. 202**A-B**); throat and face tinged yellow; breast without yellow. ♀ wg(n37) 89-96, tl(n37) 55-64; ♂ wg(n100) 96-103, tl(n100) 62-72.

E.a. leucansiptila (res desert sw.NV to se.CA-sw.AZ): Medium in size; nape pale pinkish cinnamon; back pale buffy brown; streak on the longest uppertail cov indistinct (Fig. 202**A-B**); throat and face tinged yellow; breast without yellow. ♀ wg(n13) 92-98, tl(n13) 57-63; ♂ wg(n24) 98-104, tl(n24) 65-73. Suggested three-letter subspecies code (see pp. 30-31): "lcn".

E.a. merrilli (res sc.BC-n.ID to cn.CA, wint to c.CA-UT): Medium in size; upperparts medium brown; pinkish on the rump reduced; streak on the longest uppertail cov moderately indistinct (Fig. 202**B-C**); throat and face washed yellow; breast (below the black) without yellow or with a slight yellow tinge. ♀ wg(n32) 92-102, tl(n32) 58-66; ♂ wg(n64) 97-106, tl(n64) 63-73.

E.a. lamprochroma (res se.WA-ec.CA to w.ID-w.NV, wint to sw.CA-s.AZ): Medium in size with a relatively short tl; nape pinkish cinnamon; back medium gray-brown with a pinkish tinge; streak on the longest uppertail cov indistinct to distinct (Fig. 202**B-E**); throat and face washed yellow; breast (below the black) without yellow or with a slight yellow tinge. ♀ wg(n57) 92-99, tl(n57) 56-64; ♂ wg(n85) 98-107, tl(n85) 61-72.

E.a. utahensis (res s.ID to e.NV-w.UT, wint to se.CA-AZ): Medium in size; nape cinnamon; back pale brownish gray; streak on the longest uppertail cov moderately distinct (Fig. 202**C-D**); throat and face tinged yellow; breast without yellow. ♀ wg(n12) 94-99, tl(n12) 60-66; ♂ wg(n38) 100-107, tl(n38) 66-74.

E.a. leucolaema (res s.Alb-c.UT to sw.Sask-nw.TX, wint to se.CA-s.TX): Medium large; nape pale rufous; back moderately pale brown with a pinkish tinge; streak on the longest uppertail cov indistinct (Fig. 202**B**); throat and face tinged yellow; breast without yellow. ♀ wg(n15) 98-103, tl(n15) 60-67; ♂ wg(n15) 103-111, tl(n15) 70-77. Suggested three-letter subspecies code (see pp. 30-31): "lcl".

E.a. occidentalis (res s.UT-s.CO to AZ-NM): Medium in size; nape medium rufous; back medium brown with a pinkish tinge; streak on the longest uppertail cov moderately indistinct (Fig. 202**C**); throat and face washed yellow; breast usually without yellow. ♀ wg(n25) 95-100, tl(n25) 58-68; ♂ wg(n45) 100-110, tl(n45) 66-75.

E.a. enthymia (res Sask-c.ID to w.Ont-nw.TX, wint to se.CA-s.TX): Medium in size; nape cinnamon; back pale brownish gray; streak on the longest uppertail cov moderately distinct (Fig. 202**C-D**); throat and face without yellow or with a slight yellow tinge; breast without yellow. ♀ wg(n10) 93-101, tl(n10) 59-67; ♂ wg(n10) 101-109, tl(n10) 67-75.

Eastern Dark *(E.a. alpestris)* Group. Variable in size.

E.a. flava (Eurasia; vag to Aleutian Is, AK): Large; nape washed pinkish cinnamon; back medium brown with a grayish tinge; streak on the longest uppertail cov moderately distinct to distinct (Fig. 202**D-E**); throat and face yellow; breast without yellow. ♀ wg(n53) 99-107, tl(n33) 56-67; ♂ wg(n47) 108-116, tl(n47) 64-74.

E.a. hoyti (br n.NWT-n.Alb to n.Ont, wint to Ont-MD): Large; upperparts moderately dark brownish gray; streak on the longest uppertail cov moderately distinct to distinct (Fig. 202**D-E**); throat and face tinged yellow; breast without yellow. ♀ wg(n13) 102-107, tl(n13) 60-69; ♂ wg(n15) 104-116, tl(n15) 66-75.

E.a. giraudi (res se.TX-s.LA): Small; upperparts medium gray-brown; streak on the longest uppertail cov indistinct to moderately indistinct (Fig. 202**B-D**); throat and face bright yellow; breast without yellow. ♀ wg(n15) 87-94, tl(n15) 53-59; ♂ wg(n15) 92-102, tl(n15) 57-66.

E.a. praticola (res MN-e.KS to NS-NC, wint to TX-n.FL): Medium in size; upperparts medium brown; pinkish on the rump extensive; streak on the longest uppertail cov moderately distinct (Fig. 202**C-D**); throat and face whitish, sometimes washed yellow; breast without yellow. ♀ wg(n15) 95-105, tl(n15) 59-66; ♂ wg(n15) 100-108, tl(n15) 67-73. Birds of coastal MA *("atlantica")* may average smaller, grayer, and darker on the underparts, but differences, if present, probably are too slight for subspecies recognition.

E.a. alpestris (br n.Ont-n.Que-Nfl, wint Man-KS to Nfl-GA): Large; nape washed rufous; back moderately dark brown with a pinkish tinge; streak on the longest uppertail cov moderately distinct (Fig. 202**C-D**); throat and face yellow; upper breast without yellow or with a slight yellow tinge. ♀ wg(n15) 101-109, tl(n15) 61-67; ♂ wg(n15) 107-116, tl(n15) 67-75. Suggested three-letter subspecies code (see pp. 30-31): "als".

Molt—PB: HY complete (Jul-Sep), AHY complete (Jun-Aug); PA absent-limited (Feb-Mar). The PBs occur primarily on the summer grounds, although the 1st PB sometimes can be completed on the winter grounds. The PAs include, if anything, a few yellow head feathers.

Skull—Pneumaticization completes in HY/SY from 1 Sep through Jan; most birds (excepting *E.a. actia, insularis,* and *giraudi;* see **Geographic variation**) from 15 Oct.

Age—Juv (Apr-Aug) has white flecks on the upperparts, wide, buff fringes to the ss and pp covs, and lacks black on the head and breast; juv ♀ = ♂. No reliable plumage criteria are known for ageing after the 1st PB. A few HYs can retain partial juvenal plumage through migration; look also for retained flight feathers (especially s6) on these. Also, HY/SYs average duller and with more spots on the breast than AHY/ASYs, within each subspecies and sex, but overlap precludes reliable ageing based on plumage alone. See Skull.

Sex—CP/BP (Feb-Aug). Measurements are very useful within subspecies (see **Geographic variation**), with little or no overlap between the sexes; overall: ♀ wg(n100) 86-109, tl(n100) 53-69; ♂ wg(n100) 92-116, tl(n100) 57-77.

♀: Black areas of the chest and head indistinct, less extensive, and often mixed with yellow, whitish, or buff (Fig. 203); "horns" short or lacking (Fig. 203); pinkish of the nape reduced (by subspecies) and indistinctly streaked brownish; wing covs primarily brown with some pink in the outer webs and often with indistinct streaks. **Note: Intermediates occur, especially in fresh plumage (Aug-Nov) that may not be safely sexed; compare with measurements and Geographic variation**.

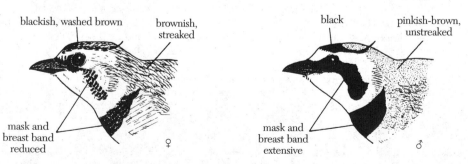

FIGURE 203. The head pattern by sex in Horned Lark.

♂: Black areas of the chest and head distinct, uniform, and more extensive, contrasting markedly with the paler areas (Fig. 203); "horns" prominent (Fig. 203); nape and wing covs distinctly pinkish and unstreaked. **Note: See** ♀.

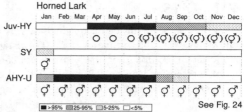

References—Dwight (1890, 1900a), Stone (1896), Ridgway (1907), Forbush (1927), Behle (1942a), Bent (1942), Roberts (1955), Davis (1969a), Oberholser (1974), Phillips & Chase (1982), Cramp (1988), Svensson (1992), Jenni & Winkler (1994), Beason (1995).

SWALLOWS   *HIRUNDINIDAE*

Eight species. Family characters include very long wings, short and wide bills, and short legs. Swallows have 9 visible primaries (the 10th vestigial), 9 secondaries, and 12 rectrices. The first prebasic molt is complete or nearly so, often takes place on the winter grounds, and (in at least some of the species) can be 1-2 months later than the adult molt. Limited prealternate molts occur in certain species, possibly all. SYs (and some ASYs) often show windows (> 2 mm; see Figs. 11**D** & 204) in the skull pneumaticization through the spring; thus, the size of the windows should be assessed when ageing by skull (*e.g.*, see Barn Swallow). More study is needed on pneumaticization rates and its completion in swallows and the other North American passerines. Plumage patterns among the age/sex classes vary from completely different to practically identical. More study is needed on the variation in color patterns of the distal marginal coverts by age and sex (see Fig. 205). Breeding characters are reliable indicators of sex. Males average slightly larger than females in most species, whereas juveniles of both sexes have much shorter wings in all species.

PURPLE MARTIN   PUMA
Progne subis   Species # 6110
                                                             Band size: 1A-2

Species—Juvs and ♀♀ from the other swallows by larger size (wg 131-154, tl 63-78; see **Age/Sex**); underparts primarily dark gray. HY/SY ♂ and ♀ from other martins (from Mex-S.Am), possible vagrants to N.Am, by moderate size (see above); throat, chest and/or upperparts grayish or sooty; forehead and abdomen sometimes whitish (see **Geographic variation**); nape with a distinct and full collar. AHY/ASY ♂♂ from other martins by tl (64-81) and tail fork (r6 – r1 15-22 mm) moderate in length; underparts entirely dark steely purplish; lower abdomen without concealed white feathers.

Geographic variation—Weak to moderate and differences are partly obscured by individual variation, but breeding ranges are well defined. Subspecies taxonomy follows Phillips (1986); see also Ridgway (1904), Grinnell (1928d), Brandt (1951), Phillips (1959b), Phillips *et al.* (1964), Johnston (1966), Behle (1968), Monroe (1968), Hubbard (1972a), Rohwer & Niles (1979), Unitt (1984), Wetmore *et al.* (1984), Browning (1990), Stutchbury (1991a, 1991b), Brown (1997). No other subspecies occur. Note that AHY/ASY ♂♂ are indistinguishable to subspecies on plumage alone.

P.s. arboricola (br coastal sw.BC to s.CA-NM): Large; plumage averages duller; forehead and throat of ♀♀ and HY/SY ♂♂ medium brownish to whitish; SY ♂♂ usually with dark steely purplish on the forehead and with a moderate amount of steely purplish on the underparts (3-10 cm²). ♀ wg(n37) 140-154, tl(n22) 66-78; ♂ wg(n72) 143-156, tl(n41) 72-81. Pacific coastal birds average darker underparts than interior birds, and northern birds are larger than southern birds, but in both cases differences are slight and obscured by individual variation; differentiation from *subis* also is weak.

P.s. hesperia (br desert s.AZ): Small; forehead and throat of ♀♀ and HY/SY ♂♂ pale brownish to whitish; SY ♂♂ without dark steely purplish on the forehead and with little to a moderate amount of steely purplish on the underparts (< 5 cm²). ♀ wg(n32) 131-141, tl(n30) 63-71; ♂ wg(n42) 133-145, tl(n42) 66-73. Birds of AZ (*"oberholseri"*) may average smaller and darker than birds of Mex, but variation probably is too slight for subspecies recognition.

P.s. subis (br ec.BC-s.TX to Nfl-FL): Medium large; plumage averages brighter; forehead and throat of ♀♀ and HY/SY ♂♂ medium silvery brownish to sooty; SY ♂♂ usually with dark steely purplish on the forehead and with substantial steely purplish on the underparts (> 5 cm²). ♀ wg(n54) 137-150, tl(n44) 65-75; ♂ wg(n69) 138-152, tl(n59) 70-79.

Molt—PB: HY/SY complete (Jul-Apr), AHY/ASY complete (Jul-Mar); PA absent. The PBs suspend over fall migration. The 1st flight-feather replacement occurs entirely on the winter grounds, whereas adult flight-feather replacement begins on the summer grounds and completes on the winter grounds.

Skull—Pneumaticization completes in HY/SY from 15 Oct. Most SYs and probably many ASYs can retain windows (> 2 mm; see Figs. 11**D** & 204) through spring. More study is needed on the size of windows by age (see Fig. 204, the family account, Barn Swallow, and Niles 1972b).

Age/Sex—Juv (Apr-Aug) is like HY/SY ♀ (below), but has a greenish tinge to the forehead, fresher and pale-edged terts and middle ss (s4-s6), a shallower tail fork (r6 – r1 usually < 12 mm), and yellower mouth lining; juv ♀ = ♂. CP/BP (Mar-Jul); some to many SY ♀♀ may not develop BPs. ♀ wg(n100) 131-154, tl(n100) 63-78; ♂ wg(n100) 133-156, tl(n100) 66-81; see **Geographic variation**.

FIGURE 204. "Windows" in the pneumaticization pattern on the skull of swallows. Windows of this size can be found in both HY/SYs and AHY/ASYs. Birds with larger windows can probably be aged reliably as HY/SY. More study is needed on retention of windows (above the occipital triangle; see Collier & Wallace 1989) by AHY/ASY swallows and other passerines, including the sizes at which HY/SYs can be reliably aged.

HY/SY ♀ (Sep-Aug): Flight feathers not molting in Aug-Oct before birds reach the winter grounds; upperparts brown with a slight bluish-green tinge; forehead and underparts brownish, without purple feathers; distal marginal covs (under alula) may average paler brown and without a bluish tinge (see Fig. 205); terts with pale edging through Jan-Mar; tail fork shallow (r6 – r1 usually < 12 mm) through Mar; mouth lining horn colored; undertail covs without dusky centers (Fig. 206). **Note: Differences between HY/SYs and AHY/ASYs in the timing of molt (as reflected by replacement patterns and contrasts among the ss) may be helpful in ageing ♀♀; more study is needed. Caution is advised in sexing HY ♀ on the summer grounds; see HY/SY ♂.**

AHY/ASY ♀ (Sep-Aug): Like HY/SY ♀, but flight feathers usually molting in Aug-Oct before birds reach the winter grounds; upperparts dark steely purplish, often mixed with gray; forehead and underparts grayish to whitish; distal marginal covs may average darker brown and

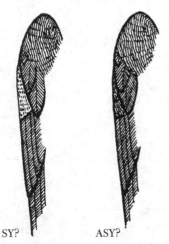

SY?   ASY?

FIGURE 205. Variation in the distal marginal coverts in swallows. These are viewed by moving the alula feathers proximally. It appears as though SYs average browner marginal coverts than ASYs, sex for sex, but more study is needed to confirm this.

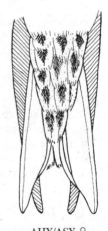

HY/SY ♀   AHY/ASY ♀

FIGURE 206. Undertail covert patterns in HY/SY and AHY/ASY ♀ Purple Martins.

with a bluish tinge (see Fig. 205); terts without pale edging; tail fork deep (r6 – r1 usually > 13 mm); undertail covs with distinct, dusky centers (Fig. 206). **Note: See HY/SY ♀.**

HY/SY ♂ (Sep-Aug): Flight feathers not molting in Aug-Oct before birds reach the winter grounds; upperparts and underparts as in AHY/ASY ♀, but a few (Sep-Jan) to many (Feb-Aug) dark steely purplish feathers present; distal marginal covs may average medium brown and sometimes with a slight bluish tinge (see Fig. 205); terts with pale edging through Jan-Mar; tail fork shallow (r6 – r1 usually < 12 mm) through Mar; undertail covs without dusky centers (Fig. 206). **Note: Occasional HY/SY ♂♂, especially of *P.s. hesperia* (see Geographic variation), can lack steely purplish feathers in Sep-Jan and can be difficult to separate from HY/SY ♀♀; compare with measurements.**

SY/TY ♂ (Sep-Apr): Like HY/SY ♂ in Feb-Aug, but flight feathers often molting in Aug-Oct before birds reach the winter grounds; upperparts and underparts with many dark steely purplish feathers (Sep-Dec), to primarily but not entirely steely purplish (Jan-Apr); distal marginal covs may average darker brown and with a bluish tinge (see Fig. 205); terts without pale edging.

ASY/ATY ♂ (May-Apr): Upperparts, underparts and distal marginal covs entirely dark steely purplish.

Purple Martin

	Jan	Feb	Mar	Apr	May	Jun	Jul	Aug	Sep	Oct	Nov	Dec
Juv-HY												
					o	o	o	o	(♂)(♂)(♀)(♀)(♀)			
SY												
	(♀) ♂ ♂ ♂ ♂ ♂ ♂ ♂ ♂ ♂ ♂ ♂ ♂											
TY												
	♂ ♂ ♂ ♂											
AHY												
	♀ ♀ ♀ ♀ ♀ ♀ ♀ ♀ ♀ ♀											
ASY												
	♀ ♀ ♂ ♂ ♂ ♂ ♂ ♂ ♂ ♂ ♂ ♂											
ATY												
	♂ ♂ ♂ ♂											

■ > 95% ▨ 25-95% ▢ 5-25% ☐ < 5%   See Fig. 24

References—Stone (1896), Dwight (1900a), Ridgway (1904), Forbush (1929), Bent (1942), Roberts (1955), Eisenmann (1959), Wood (1969), Niles (1972a, 1972b), Oberholser (1974), Saner (1975), Brown (1978), Phillips (1986), Turner & Rose (1989), CWS & USFWS (1991), Stutchbury (1991), Brown (1997); D.M. Niles, E.J. Fisk, J.M. Sheppard (*in litt.* to the BBL).

TREE SWALLOW
Tachycineta bicolor

TRES
Species # 6140
Band size: 1C-1

Species—Juv from juv Purple Martin by shorter wg (98-116; see **Age/Sex**); underparts white. Juv from juv Violet-green Swallow by larger size (wg 98-116, tl 49-57; see **Age/Sex**); white of the rump confined to the immediate sides. Juv from Northern Rough-winged and Bank swallows by the combination of longer average wg and tl (see above); upperparts uniformly brown except for white along the sides of the rump; terts tipped white; throat white, contrasting distinctly with the dark crown; breast band lacking or indistinct and thinnest in the center if present; hind tarsus without feathering; operculum present over nostrils.

Geographic variation—Subspecies taxonomy follows Phillips (1986), who recognized no subspecies; see also Ridgway (1904), Oberholser (1974), Browning (1978). Birds breeding in CA (*"T.b. vespertina"*) average very slightly smaller than birds from the rest of the range, but this difference is not sufficient for subspecies recognition. See also **Molt**.

Molt—PB: HY complete (Jul-Nov), AHY complete (Jul-Nov); PA absent-limited (Feb-May). Both the 1st and the adult PBs commence on the summer grounds and complete on the winter grounds. The PA occurs in some (~35%) birds of all age/sex groups and includes feathers of the chin, sometimes the crown, and occasionally the back and rump. The timing of the PA in western birds is later, on average, than in eastern birds.

Skull—Pneumaticization completes in HY/SY from 1 Nov. Most SYs (and possibly some ASYs) retain windows (> 2 mm; see Figs. 11**D** & 204) in the rear of the skull through at least May. More study on the relative size of windows by age is needed in this species (see Fig. 204, the family account, and Barn Swallow), as this could assist with ageing (and thus sexing) uniformly bluish birds (see **Age/Sex**).

Age/Sex—Juv (May-Sep) has sooty upperparts and whitish underparts with an indistinctly defined, dusky wash across breast; juv ♀ = ♂. CP/BP (Apr-Jul); a partial BP (Fig. 22**B**) can be developed by some ♂♂, but is much less swollen than in ♀♀ (Fig. 22**C**). AHY/ASY ♀ wg(n100) 106-122, tl(n24) 49-57; AHY/ASY ♂ wg(n100) 110-125, tl(n26) 51-60; HYs average much shorter measurements (wg: ♀ 98-109, ♂ 104-116, n=15 each); see also **Geographic variation**.

HY/SY ♀ (Sep-Aug): Upperparts entirely or largely brownish or non-iridescent greenish, with 0-60% iridescent green feathers; distal marginal covs may average paler brown, without a green tinge, contrasting markedly with the rest of the wing covs (see Fig. 205). **Note: Intermediates occur which may not be reliably aged and/or sexed, especially without experience with this species; combine all ageing and sexing criteria. The color of both new and old feathers should be considered carefully on molting birds. In May-Sep, SYs are separated from juvs and HYs by skull condition (see Skull), more faded plumage, and worn flight feathers. Molting HYs in Aug-Oct can be sexed ♀ by mixed sooty and brownish feathers to the upperparts. See SY/TY ♀.**

AHY/ASY ♀ (Sep-Aug): Upperparts primarily or entirely dull to brightish iridescent blue, sometimes with a greenish cast, and without non-iridescent brown or greenish feathers in most of the upperparts; some or all feathers of the forehead sometimes non-iridescent brownish or greenish; distal marginal covs may average darker brown with a greenish tinge, contrasting slightly with the rest of the wing covs (see Fig. 205). **Note: See HY/SY ♀. The brightest ♀♀, without brownish in the head, may not be distinguishable from U/AHY ♂♂, especially without experience; compare with CP/BP, wg, and skull (see above). ♀♀ with uniformly bright blue heads and upperparts probably are at least ASY/ATY in age but more study is needed. Also, see Cohen (1984) for methods of sexing birds in this plumage prior to capture at a nest box.**

SY/TY ♀ (Sep-Aug): Like AHY/ASY ♀, but a few (1-20%) brownish or non-iridescent greenish feathers present in the upperparts (other than forehead). **Note: See HY/SY ♀. This plumage only occurs in occasional (~15%) SY/TY ♀♀. ♀♀ with 60-80% iridescent green in the upperparts (see HY/SY ♀) can be either HY/SY or SY/TY and therefore should be aged AHY/ASY.**

HY ♂ (Aug-Nov): Outer pp fresh; upperparts (including the head) sooty, with incoming iridescent blue feathers. **Note: This category only applies to HYs in active molt, although some HY/SY ♂ can be identified through at least Jan by skull condition in combination with plumage. See HY/SY ♀ and U/AHY ♂.**

U/AHY ♂ (Nov-Oct): Outer pp abraded in Aug-Oct; upperparts (including the forehead) uniformly bright iridescent blue. **Note: See HY/SY ♀ and HY ♂. HY/SYs probably average slightly duller than AHY/ASYs and also may be aged by the distal marginal covs (HY/SYs brownish, contrasting with the other wing covs, AHY/ASYs bluish with little or no contrast; see Fig. 205), but more study is needed. Also, duller individuals may not be reliably sexed; see AHY/ASY ♀.**

Hybrids reported—Cliff Swallow. Also, observed paired with Violet-green Swallow.

References—Stone (1896), Dwight (1900a), Ridgway (1904), Forbush (1929), Kuerzi (1941), Bent (1942), Roberts (1955), Wood (1969), Collins (1972a), Oberholser (1974), Sheppard & Klimkiewicz (1976), Cohen (1980, 1984), Hussell (1983), Wilds (1985b), Phillips (1986), Stutchbury & Robertson (1987), Turner & Rose (1989), Stutchbury & Rohwer (1990), CWS & USFWS (1991), Robertson et al. (1992), Johnson & Moskoff (1995), Wiggins & Pärt (1995), Lethaby (1996); R.R. Cohen, M.T. Donnald, K. Heidel, D.J.T. Hussell, M. Mauritz, W.D. Merritt, K.C. Parkes, F.S. Schaeffer (*in litt.* to the BBL); IBP (MAPS) data, PNR data, PRBO data.

Tree Swallow

See Fig. 24

Note: In Oct-Dec, most ♂♂ should be aged U whereas ♀♀ can be aged AHY. SY ♂♂ during these months can only be determined by incompletely pneumaticized skulls.

VIOLET-GREEN SWALLOW
Tachycineta thalassina

VGSW
Species # 6150
Band size: 1C

Species—In all plumages (including juvenal) from the other swallows of N.Am by small size (wg 98-108, tl 42-51; see **Age/Sex**); white of the sides of the rump forming distinct, white patches, almost meeting across the center.

Geographic variation—Moderately weak (based on measurements only), but breeding ranges moderately well defined. Subspecies taxonomy follows Phillips (1986); see also Ridgway (1904). No other subspecies occur.

> **T.t. thalassina** (br and wint throughout range in N.Am): Large. ♀ wg(n30) 106-116, tl(n13) 42-49; ♂ wg(n30) 113-125, tl(n26) 44-51. Juvs average smaller (see **Sex**). Birds of N.Am-n.Mex (*"lepida"*) may average slightly smaller and more greenish (less purplish and/or bluish) on the back than birds of s-c.Mex, but variation is affected by wear and not geographically consistent.
> **T.t. brachyptera** (br & wint nw.Mex; vag to s.AZ): Small. ♀ wg(n10) 98-105, tl(n10) 38-44; ♂ wg(n10) 101-109, tl(n10) 41-46. Juvs average smaller (see **Sex**).

Molt—PB: HY complete (Aug-Oct), AHY complete (Aug-Sep); PA absent(?). The PBs occur primarily on the summer grounds. A limited PA, as in Tree Swallow, should be looked for.

Skull—Pneumaticization completes in HY/SY from 1 Nov. Most SYs (and possibly some ASYs) retain windows (> 2 mm; see Figs. 11**D** & 204) through spring; see Figure 204, the family account, and Barn Swallow.

Age/Sex—Juv (May-Oct) has upperparts gray-brown, sometimes tinged greenish, and underparts washed gray; juv ♀ = ♂. CP/BP (Apr-Jul); the BP can develop in both sexes, but is more pronounced in ♀♀ (see Fig. 22**B-C**). Non-juv ♀ wg(n71) 105-116, tl(n33) 42-49; non-juv ♂ wg(n87) 112-125, tl(n46) 44-51; juvs average shorter (♀ 98-108, ♂ 104-116, n=15 each); measurements include the nominate subspecies only (see **Geographic variation**).

HY/SY ♀ (Sep-Aug): Upperparts dull green and purple, with substantial brownish mixed in the crown and rump; postocular area and cheek dusky gray-brown, contrasting gradually with the darker crown (Fig. 207); distal marginal covs may average paler brown and without a violet tinge, contrasting markedly with the other wing covs (see Fig. 205). **Note: Some ♀♀ may be difficult to age; more study is needed.**

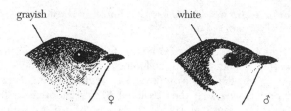

FIGURE 207. The face pattern by sex in Violet-green Swallow.

AHY/ASY ♀ (Sep-Aug): Like HY/SY ♀, but upperparts dull to brightish green and purple, with some olive mixed in the crown and grayish in the rump; distal marginal covs may average darker brown and with a violet tinge, contrasting only slightly with the other wing covs (see Fig. 205). **Note: See HY/SY ♀.**

U/AHY ♂ (Sep-Aug): Upperparts (including the crown and rump) entirely iridescent green and purple; postocular area and cheek bright white, contrasting markedly with the darker crown (Fig. 207). **Note: At least some HY/SY ♂♂ possibly may be separated from AHY/ASY ♂♂ by the distal marginal covs (HY/SY as in AHY/ASY ♀, AHY/ASY uniformly green-violet, not contrasting with the wing covs; see Fig. 205), but more study is needed. Otherwise, no plumage criteria are known for ageing ♂♂ after completion of the PB (see Skull).**

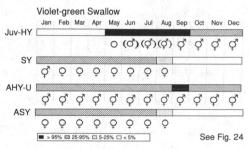

Hybrids reported—Observed paired with Tree Swallow.

References—Ridgway (1904), Bent (1942), Collins (1972b), Oberholser (1974), Sheppard & Klimkiewicz (1976), Phillips (1986), Turner & Rose (1989), CWS & USFWS (1991), Brown *et al.* (1992), Johnson & Moskoff (1995); IBP (MAPS) data, PRBO data.

NORTHERN ROUGH-WINGED SWALLOW
Stelgidopteryx serripennis

NRWS
Species # 6170
Band size: 0

Species—From the other swallows of N.Am by the combination of medium-large measurements (wg 95-118, tl 44-54; see **Age/Sex**); throat dusky brown, not contrasting distinctly with the head; lack of an operculum over the nostrils.

Geographic variation—Weak and clinal within N.Am. Subspecies taxonomy follows Phillips (1986); see also Ridgway (1904), Griscom (1929b), van Rossem (1931a, 1934a), Oberholser (1932, 1974), Miller (1941a), Brodkorb (1942), Lowery & Dalquest (1951), Phillips *et al.* (1964), Stiles (1981), Rea (1983), Wetmore *et al.* (1984), Behle (1985), Johnson (1994), Phillips (1994a), DeJong (1996). Two to four other subspecies occur in Mex-C.Am, depending on the species taxonomy. See also Yuri & Rohwer (1997) for geographic variation in molt patterns.

S.s. serripennis (br BC-c.CA to ME-FL): Upperparts, throat, breast, and rump fairly uniformly dark brown. Western birds (*"aphractus"*) may average larger and with the upperparts and underparts more contrasting than eastern birds, but variation is very slight.

S.s. psammochrous (br c-s.CA to se.TX): Upperparts, throat, and breast pale grayish brown, contrasting with the paler (usually) crown and rump.

Molt—PB: HY/SY complete (Aug-Jan), AHY complete (Jul-Dec); PA absent-limited (Feb-May). The PBs begin on the summer grounds (including some flight feathers) and complete during migration (western population), at a stopover site (eastern populations), or on the winter grounds. Western populations begin the PBs about 40 days later than eastern populations. The PAs include feathers of the crown and chin, and may occur in SYs only; more study is needed.

Skull—Pneumaticization completes in HY/SY from 1 Oct. Most SYs (and possibly some ASYs) retain windows (> 2 mm; see Figs. 11**D** & 204) at the rear of the skull through at least May; see Figure 204, the family account, and Barn Swallow.

Age/Sex—Juv (May-Oct) has the feathers of the upperparts edged cinnamon and the barbs on the outer p (p9) reduced by sex (Fig. 208); juv ♀=♂, although some may be distinguished by the barbs on p9, as in juv-HYs (Fig. 208). CP/BP (Apr-Jul). AHY/ASY ♀ wg(n100) 100-112, tl(n100) 44-52; AHY/ASY ♂ wg(n100) 105-118, tl(n100) 46-54; juv-HYs are smaller (♀ 95-107, ♂ 100-112, n=15 each).

Juv-HY ♀ (May-Dec): Feathers of the upperparts, wing covs, and terts edged cinnamon; flight feathers relatively fresh; barbs on the outer edge of the juvenal outer p (p9) lacking or very short and not naked at the point (Fig. 208). **Note: All autumn birds north of the winter grounds can be reliably aged, but ageing can become increasingly difficult thereafter (see Molt). Many intermediate juv-HYs (and possibly some U/AHYs) also can be difficult to sex. The distal marginal covs likely average slightly paler and more contrasting in HY/SYs than in AHY/ASYs (see Fig. 205) and some HY/SYs may show a slight buffy tinge to the throat, but more study is needed on the usefulness of these for ageing after Nov.**

U/AHY ♀ (Dec-Nov): Feathers of the upperparts, wing covs, and terts without cinnamon edging; unreplaced flight feathers relatively abraded in May-Oct; barbs of the outer edge of the adult outer p (p9) short, naked at the point, and weakly hooked (Fig. 208). **Note: See Juv-HY ♀.**

Juv-HY ♂ (May-Dec): Plumage as in Juv-HY ♀; barbs on the juvenal outer p (p9) short to medium in length, not naked at the point, and straight or weakly hooked (Fig. 208). **Note: See Juv-HY ♀.**

U/AHY ♂ (Dec-Nov): Plumage as in AHY/ASY ♀; barbs on the adult outer p (p9) long, naked at the point, and strongly hooked (Fig. 208). **Note: See Juv-HY ♀ and U/AHY ♀.**

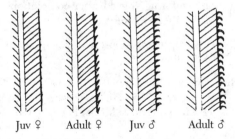

Juv ♀   Adult ♀   Juv ♂   Adult ♂

FIGURE 208. Variation in the barbs on the outer edge of the outer primary (p9) by age and sex in Northern Rough-winged Swallow. Note that some overlap between groups occurs.

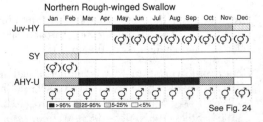

References—Stone (1896), Dwight (1900a), Ridgway (1904), Forbush (1929), Griscom (1929b), E.S. Dingle *in* Bent (1942), Brodkorb (1942), Lunk (1962), Snow & Snow (1964), Wood (1969), Ricklefs (1972), Oberholser (1974), Sheppard & Klimkiewicz (1976), Stiles (1981), Wilds (1985b), Phillips (1986), Turner & Rose (1989), CWS & USFWS (1991), DeJong (1996), Lethaby (1996), Yuri & Rohwer (1997) ; M.T. Donnald (*in litt.* to the BBL); IBP (MAPS) data, PNR data, PRBO data.

BANK SWALLOW
Riparia riparia

BANS
Species # 6160
Band size: 0

Species—From juv Tree and Northern Rough-winged swallows by the combination of smaller average size (wg 85-106, tl 43-52; see **Age/Sex**); upperparts (including the sides of the rump) grayish brown, contrasting with the darker wings; terts entirely brown or brown with pale edging; throat white, contrasting with the dark crown; breast band distinct and thickest in the center; hind tarsus with feathering; operculum present over nostrils.

Geographic variation—Weak and clinal where breeding ranges meet. Subspecies taxonomy follows Cramp (1988) and Phillips (1986); see also Oberholser (1938, 1974), Wetmore (1939), Arny (1952), Dement'ev & Gladkov (1954). One to two other subspecies occurs in Asia.

   R.r. riparia (br Eurasia and throughout the range in N.Am): Upperparts moderately dark brown; breast band dark and distinct. Birds of N.Am (*"maximiliani"*) may average smaller and have more rufous feather edging in juvs than birds of Eurasia but size variation is broadly clinal (western birds > eastern birds in N.Am). Breeding birds of sw.TX average smaller but with a larger bill and may warrant subspecies recognition, but more study is needed.

   R.r. diluta (br & wint c.Asia; vag to AK): Upperparts moderately pale gray-brown; breast band faded and indistinct.

Molt—PB: HY/SY complete (Aug-Apr), AHY complete (Jul-Mar); PA absent(?). The 1st PB can commence with the body feathers on the breeding grounds, but most molting (including the replacement of all flight feathers) occurs on the winter grounds. The adult PBs occur primarily on the winter grounds, but can be suspended over fall migration, with the innermost 2-4 pp (occasionally to 6) sometimes replaced on the summer grounds. Replacement of pp during the 1st PB averages about one month later than that of the adult PB and this difference may be useful for ageing. Very limited PAs may occur in Apr-May, but this might be difficult to distinguish from the completion of the PBs.

Skull—Pneumaticization completes in HY/SY from 1 Oct. Some SYs (20% reported), and probably occasional ASYs (as in other swallows), can retain windows (> 2 mm; see Figs. 11**D** & 204) through spring; see Figure 204, the family account, and Barn Swallow.

Age—Juv (Jun-Oct) has the feathers of the upperparts edged buff or whitish, and a buffy-pinkish wash to the throat; juv ♀ = ♂.

Juv-HY/SY (May-Mar): Feathers of the upperparts, wing covs, and terts edged with buff or whitish (through Dec); unreplaced flight feathers relatively fresh; chin and throat washed pinkish (through Sep), sometimes with faint, dusky spotting. **Note: AHYs still replacing outer pp in Apr can be reliably aged SY (see Molt) and the timing of the replacement of pp, in general, probably is useful, but more study is needed. No reliable plumage criteria are known after completion of the 1st PB, although check the distal marginal covs (see Fig. 205) for possible separation of some SY/TYs from AHY/ASYs.**

AHY/ASY (Apr-Mar): Feathers of the upperparts, wing covs, and terts without buff or whitish edging; chin and throat white; unreplaced flight feathers relatively worn in Jun-Mar. **Note: See Juv-HY/SY.**

Sex—♀ = ♂ by plumage. CP/BP (Apr-Aug). ♀ wg(n100) 94-105, tl(n30) 43-50; ♂ wg(n100) 95-106, tl(n30) 45-52; juv-HY/SYs are smaller (♀ 85-97, ♂ 87-99, n=15 each).

Hybrids reported—Common House-Martin (*Delichon urbica*).

References—Stone (1896), Dwight (1900a), Ridgway (1904), Forbush (1929), A.O. Gross *in* Bent (1942), Roberts (1955), Wood (1969), Yunick (1970a), Oberholser (1974), Sheppard & Klimkiewicz (1976), Freer & Belanger (1981), Wilds (1985b), Phillips (1986), Cramp (1988), Turner & Rose (1989), CWS & USFWS (1991), Svensson (1992), Jenni & Winkler (1994), MacBriar (1995), Lethaby (1996); M.T. Donnald (*in litt.* to the BBL); R.P. Yunick data.

Bank Swallow

	Jan	Feb	Mar	Apr	May	Jun	Jul	Aug	Sep	Oct	Nov	Dec

Juv-HY

SY

AHY-U

ASY

■ > 95%   ▨ 25-95%   ▢ 5-25%   ▢ < 5%

See Fig. 24

BARN SWALLOW
Hirundo rustica

BARS
Species # 6130
Band size: 0-1C

Geographic variation—Weak, but ranges are well defined within N.Am; moderate between continents. Subspecies taxonomy in N.Am follows Phillips (1986); see also Ridgway (1904), Burleigh (1942), Dement'ev & Gladkov (1954), Monroe (1968), Patterson (1981), Cramp (1988), Svensson (1992). Four other subspecies occur in Africa and Asia.

H.r. rustica (Eurasia; vag to AK): Large; dark chest band broad and not interrupted by the rufous of the throat; underparts white (worn birds and juvs) to pale buff (fresh). ♀ wg(n31) 118-125, tl(n35) 72-99; ♂ wg(n71) 120-129, tl(n80) 89-119; juvs average 5 mm shorter wg and ~15 mm shorter tl.

H.r. gutturalis (Asia; vag to AK): Small; dark chest band thin and complete or interrupted narrowly in the center by the rufous throat; underparts white (worn birds and juvs) to pale buff (fresh). ♀ wg(n17) 110-118, tl(n10) 71-82; ♂ wg(n37) 111-122, tl(n10) 76-96; juvs average 4 mm shorter wg and ~14 mm shorter tl. Also, this subspecies molts much earlier than the other subspecies, in Apr-Nov.

H.r. erythrogaster (br throughout the range in n.Am, except islands of LA-AL): Medium in size (see **Sex**); upperparts of juvs blackish; dark chest band interrupted in the center by the dark rufous throat or confined to the sides; underparts creamy buff (worn birds and juvs) to rusty buff (fresh). Note that this subspecies varies clinally in size, northern birds having longer wg and tl than southern birds.

H.r. insularis (br Is off LA-AL): Weakly separated from *erythrogaster* by upperparts of juvs average duskier or more heavily washed olive; underparts white (worn birds and juvs) to pale buff (fresh).

Molt—PB: HY/SY complete (Oct-Apr); AHY/ASY complete (Aug-Feb); PA absent(?). Molt occurs primarily on the winter grounds, although it can commence in some AHYs on the summer grounds. Protracted flight-feather replacement occurs in Oct-Feb in AHY/ASYs and Nov-Apr in HY/SYs.

Skull—Pneumaticization completes in HY/SY from 1 Nov (or later?). Many SYs and some ASYs (up to 29% in Europe) retain apneumaticized areas or windows (> 2 mm; Figs. 11**D** & 204) for one or more years, such that the use of skulling for ageing requires caution. Birds in May-Dec or later with the patterns of Figure 11**A-C** are reliably aged HY/SY by skull whereas birds with the patterns of Figures 11**D** & 204 should not be aged by skull alone. Birds with fully pneumaticized skulls might be reliably aged AHY/ASY through winter/spring, but more study is needed. The above information is based on European birds; birds of N.Am probably show the same patterns, but this needs confirmation. Similar patterns may occur in the other swallows, especially the larger ones. More study is needed on the reliability of skull pneumaticization patterns for ageing all birds.

Age—Juv (Jun-Dec) has the upperparts brownish, throat buffy orange, and underparts averaging paler (see **Geographic variation**); juv ♀ = ♂.

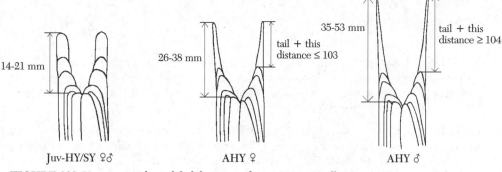

FIGURE 209. Variation in the tail fork by age and sex in Barn Swallow.

Juv-HY/SY (Jun-Apr): Tl usually < 68; tail notch shallow (Fig. 209; r6 – r1 14-21 mm); upperparts brownish or mixed steel blue and brownish; wing covs and terts broadly edged reddish brown (Jun-Nov), or buff (Nov-Feb, later if not worn off); flight feathers relatively fresh in Jun-Nov; outer pp usually retained through Mar, brown and relatively short. **Note: The above is reliable on autumn birds north of the winter grounds, but thereafter should be used with caution and consideration of molt. Also, check the distal marginal covs (see Fig. 205) for possible separation of SY/TY (May-Apr; pale grayish brown, contrasting with the other wing covs) from ASY/ATY (dark brown or bluish, sometimes with cinnamon edging). More study is needed.**

AHY/ASY (Apr-Mar): Tl > 68; tail fork deep (Fig. 209; r6 – r1 > 26-53 mm); upperparts uniformly steel blue or mixed with faded blue feathers; wing covs and terts with thin, whitish edging when fresh; flight feathers relatively abraded in Jun-Nov; outer pp usually replaced by Mar, dusky or bluish and not relatively short. **Note: See Juv-HY/SY.**

Sex—CP/BP (Mar-Aug). ♀ wg(n100) 113-123, tl(n43) 70-88; ♂ wg(n100) 115-127, tl(n40) 79-106; juvs average 5 mm shorter wg and ~15 mm shorter tl; measurements include subspecies of N.Am only (see **Geographic variation**).

AHY ♀: Upperparts relatively dull blue; breast relatively pale cinnamon or buff; tl 68-84 mm; tl + (r6 – r5) usually < 103 mm (Fig. 191); r6 – r1 26-38 mm (Fig 209). **Note: The above sexing criteria are useful only for birds after the 1st PB; occasional intermediates may not be reliably sexed, especially without previous experience (combine with information from the skull; these possibly are all SY ♂♂). Also, beware of large ♀♀ from northern populations. Some HY/SYs that have not replaced the rects possibly are sexed by the length of the tail fork (see Fig. 209; ♀ r6 – r1 14-18 mm, ♂ r6 – r1 17-21 mm), but more study is needed to confirm this.**

AHY ♂: Upperparts relatively glossy blue; breast relatively dark rusty; tl 79-106; tl + (r6 – r5) > 104 mm (Fig. 209; check both sides of the tail); r6 – r1 35-53 mm (Fig 191). **Note: See AHY ♀.**

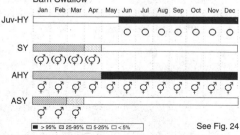

Hybrids reported—Cliff Swallow, Cave Swallow, Common House-Martin.

References—Stone (1896), Dwight (1900a), Ridgway (1904), Forbush (1929), Bent (1942), Roberts (1955), Wood (1969), Oberholser (1974), Schaeffer (1968), Samuel (1971a, 1971b), Martin & Selander (1975), Sheppard & Klimkiewicz (1976), Martin (1980), Patterson (1981), Turner & Rose (1989), CWS & USFWS (1991), Svensson (1992), Jenni & Winkler (1994); C.N. Rose (*in litt.* to the BBL); IBP (MAPS) data, PNR data, PRBO data.

CLIFF SWALLOW
Petrochelidon pyrrhonota

CLSW
Species # 6120
Band size: 1C-1

Species—From Cave Swallow by forehead buffy or reddish (see **Geographic variation**); throat with a blackish or brownish patch, darker than the cheeks, which is variable, but present in all plumages (see **Geographic variation**); juv with the throat and breast washed dark brownish. Also, see differences in molt strategies.

Geographic variation—Moderate to well marked, but clinal where ranges meet, and differences are obscured by individual variation. Subspecies taxonomy follows Phillips (1986), as modified by Browning (1992a); see also Ridgway (1904), Oberholser (1920a, 1932, 1974), van Rossem (1936c), Van Tyne & Sutton (1937), van Rossem & Hachisuka (1938b), Miller (1941a), Behle (1948, 1976), Rand (1948b), Jewett *et al.* (1953), Selander & Baker (1957), Jeter (1959), Phillips *et al.* (1964), Sutton (1967), Browning (1978, 1979a, 1990), Wetmore *et al.* (1984). No other subspecies occur. Sexes are similar in size (see **Sex**) and have been lumped in the following.

P.p. pyrrhonota (br AK-c.CA to Nfl-VA): Large; AHYs with forehead buffy to whitish; blackish breast patch extensive (10-17 mm wide). ♀♂ wg(n100) 103-117, tl(n100) 44-54; juv-HY/SYs average 5 mm shorter wg. Birds of coastal sw.AK-cw.CA (*"hypopolia"*) average slightly larger and with whiter foreheads and grayer breasts, but differences are obscured by individual variation. Birds of sc.OR (*"aprophata"*) may average buffier foreheads and paler underparts, but variation, if present, is very slight.

P.p. tachina (br c.CA-n.NM to s.CA-sw.TX, vag to AK): Medium in size; AHYs with the forehead pale buffy to cinnamon; blackish throat patch extensive. ♀♂ wg(n90) 100-110, tl(n90) 43-50; juv-HY/SYs average 5 mm shorter wg.

P.p. swainsoni (=*"melanogaster"*; br se.AZ & sw TX): Small; AHYs with the forehead pale brownish cinnamon to chestnut; blackish throat patch extensive. ♀♂ wg(n30) 96-108, tl(n30) 40-49; juv-HY/SYs average 5 mm shorter wg. Birds of AZ-nw.Mex (*"minima"*) may average slightly larger and with the underparts slightly paler but subspecies characters are weak and/or opposite to those originally described. Beware that juv-HY/SYs (Jun-Mar) of the other subspecies sometimes can have chestnut in the forehead (see **Age**).

P.p. ganieri (br OK-s.TX to wc.TN): Medium in size; AHYs with the forehead buffy to whitish; blackish throat patch reduced (~7-13 mm wide). ♀♂ wg(n40) 101-109, tl(n20) 43-49; juv-HY/SYs average 5 mm shorter wg.

Molt—PB: HY/SY complete (Aug-Mar?), AHY/ASY complete (Jul-Mar?); PA absent. The PBs occur primarily on the winter grounds, although body molt can commence on the summer grounds or during migration. Flight-feather replacement does not commence until at least Nov in HY/SYs, and could be earlier in AHY/ASYs (as in other swallows); more study is needed.

Skull—Pneumaticization completes in HY/SY from 1 Oct. Most SYs (and probably some ASYs) retain windows (> 2 mm; see Figs. 11**D** & 204) through spring; see Figure 204, the family account, and Barn Swallow.

Age—Juv (Jun-Dec) has the forehead dark brown to rufous and the throat and cheeks washed brownish; juv ♀ = ♂.

Juv-HY/SY (Jun-Mar): Forehead patch brownish and not distinctly defined; head, back, cheeks, and throat washed brown; terts with buffy-rufous edging; unreplaced flight feathers relatively fresh. **Note: Body plumage may assume that of AHY/ASY by Dec. AHYs molting flight feathers in Feb-Mar possibly can be reliably aged SY, but more study is needed. No plumage criteria are known after completion of the PBs in Jan-Mar(?); however, the edges of the terts may average slightly whiter in ASY/ATYs (Mar-Feb) than in SY/TYs. Check the distal marginal covs (see Fig. 205) for possible ageing, as well.**

AHY/ASY (Mar-Feb): Forehead patch buffy to chestnut (see **Geographic variation**) and distinctly defined; head and back primarily steel blue; cheeks and throat pale orangish to chestnut; terts with whitish edging; unreplaced flight feathers relatively abraded in (Jun-Feb). **Note: See Juv-HY/SY. AHYs having finished molt in Feb-Mar probably are reliably aged ASY.**

Sex— ♀ = ♂ by plumage, although the blackish throat patch averages larger in ♂♂ than in ♀♀, within each subspecies (see **Geographic variation**). CP/BP (Mar-Aug); ♂♂ share in incubation and can develop a partial BP (Fig. 22**B**). ♀ wg(n100) 96-114, tl(n100) 40-52; ♂ wg(n100) 99-117, tl(n100) 42-54; juv-HY/SYs average 5 mm shorter wg; see **Geographic variation**.

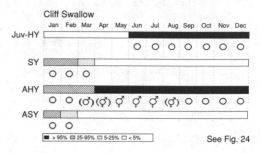

Hybrids reported: Tree Swallow, Barn Swallow. Probably Cave Swallow.

References—Stone (1896), Dwight (1900a), Ridgway (1904), Forbush (1929), Dickey & van Rossem (1938), A.O. Gross & A.C. Bent *in* Bent (1942), Roberts (1955), Wood (1969), Samuel (1971a), Oberholser (1974), Sheppard & Klimkiewicz (1976), Martin (1980), Huels (1985), Phillips (1986), Turner & Rose (1989), CWS & USFWS (1991), Brown & Brown (1995); IBP (MAPS) data, PRBO data, R.P. Yunick data.

CAVE SWALLOW
Petrochelidon fulva

CASW
Species # 6121
Band size: 1C-1

Species—From Cliff Swallow by forehead reddish; throat uniformly pale buffy orange, without blackish (sometimes with a few dark brownish feather tips when fresh), and paler than or uniform in color with the cheeks; juv with breast and throat whitish, sometimes tinged buff. Also, see differences in molt strategies.

Geographic variation—Weak to moderate, but breeding ranges fairly well defined. Subspecies taxonomy follows J.L. Peters *in* Mayr & Greenway (1960), as modified by Phillips (1986); see also Ridgway (1904), Barbour & Brooks (1917), Selander & Baker (1957), Martin *et al.* (1986), Smith & Robertson (1988). Two to three other subspecies occur in Mex-S.Am (depending on the species taxonomy). Sexes are similar in size (see **Sex**) and have been lumped in the following. In addition to the following, juvs of northern subspecies average more pale coloration in the forehead than juvs of southern subspecies.

P.f. pelodoma (=*"pallida"*; br s.AZ-c.TX; vag to s.FL): Large; tl long; cheeks and throat buff to pale cinnamon; rump pale cinnamon. ♀♂ wg(n60) 106-113, tl(n60) 45-52; juv-HY/SYs average 4-5 mm shorter wg.

P.f. fulva (br s.FL; vag to NS): Small; tl short; cheeks and throat cinnamon; rump cinnamon-rufous. ♀♂ wg(n10) 97-103, tl(n10) 37-45; juv-HY/SYs average 4-5 mm shorter wg.

P.f. cavicola (br Cuba; vag to s.FL): Medium in size; cheeks and throat cinnamon-rufous; rump rufous. ♀♂ wg(n20) 101-108, tl(n20) 42-48; juv-HY/SYs average 4-5 mm shorter wg.

Molt—PB: HY/SY complete (Jul-Mar?), AHY/ASY complete (Jun-Oct); PA absent(?). The 1st PB probably occurs primarily on the non-breeding grounds, although body molt can commence on the summer grounds or during migration. The adult PB occurs on the summer grounds.

Skull—Pneumaticization completes in HY/SY from 1 Nov. Most SYs (and possibly some ASYs) retain windows (> 2 mm; see Figs. 11**D** & 204) through spring; see Figure 204, the family account, and Barn Swallow.

Age—Juv (Jun-Dec) has the forehead and crown with a variable amount of whitish, back brownish, and throat dingy; juv ♀ = ♂.

Juv-HY/SY (Jun-Mar): Crown and back brownish; terts with buffy-rufous edging; flight feathers not in molt in Jul-Aug but molting in Sep-Mar. **Note: Body plumage may assume that of AHY/ASY by Dec. No plumage criteria are known after completion of the PBs in Jan-Mar; however, the edges of the terts may average slightly whiter on ASY/ATYs (Mar-Feb) than on SY/TYs. Check the distal marginal covs (see Fig. 205) for possible ageing, as well.**

AHY/ASY (Mar-Feb): Crown and back primarily steel blue; terts with whitish edging; flight feathers in molt in Jul-Sep but not in Oct-Mar. **Note: See Juv-HY/SY. Also, SYs should average fresher flight feathers in Mar-Jul than ASYs but more study is needed on the usefulness of this for ageing.**

Sex—♀ = ♂ by plumage. CP/BP (Mar-Sep); ♂♂ may help incubate (see Cliff Swallow). ♀ wg(n30) 103-113, tl(n30) 42-50; ♂ wg(n30) 104-115, tl(n30) 43-52; measurements include *H.f. pelodoma* only (see **Geographic variation**). Juv-HY/SYs average 4-5 mm shorter wg by subspecies.

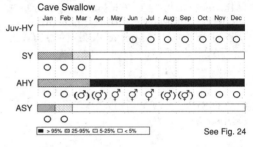

Hybrids reported—Barn Swallow. Probably Cliff Swallow.

References—Ridgway (1904), Selander & Baker (1957), Oberholser (1974), Martin & Selander (1975), Martin (1980), Walters (1983b), Huels (1985), Phillips (1986), Turner & Rose (1989), West (1995).

CHICKADEES AND TITMICE   *PARIDAE*

Eleven species. Family characters include small size, small and sharp beaks, distinct rictal bristles, relatively short tarsi, and strong legs. Titmice have 10 primaries (the 10th reduced), 9 secondaries, and 12 rectrices. The first prebasic molt is partial to incomplete, sometimes including the tertials, some to all rectrices, and some to all secondaries and primaries in southern populations. Prealternate molts do not occur. All plumages (including juvenal) generally are similar in appearance; molt limits and the shape and condition of the rectrices are the best criteria for ageing. The color of the roof of the mouth (upper mandible lining) may be helpful in ageing birds in some or all species; this should be examined further. Breeding characters are reliable for sexing, and males average slightly larger than females.

CAROLINA CHICKADEE
Poecile carolinensis

CACH
Species # 7360
Band size: 0-0A-1C

Species—Wg 53-69, tl 46-63 (see **Geographic variation**); bill short (exp culmen 6.6-9.5) crown and bib black; upperparts gray with an olive wash; ss and terts with indistinct, whitish edging (see **Geographic variation**), contrasting with the gr covs without pure white edging (Fig. 211); outer rects (r6) without distinct white edging (see Fig. 210); flanks pale grayish buff (fall) to brownish gray (spring), not contrasting markedly with the remainder of the underparts. From all chickadees, except Black-capped Chickadee, by measurements and plumage. See Black-capped Chickadee for separation from that species.

Geographic variation—Weak and clinal where ranges meet. Subspecies taxonomy follows Phillips (1986); see also Ridgway (1904), Todd & Sutton (1936), Wetmore (1937, 1939), Oberholser (1938, 1974), Lunk (1952), Stevenson & Anderson (1994), Harrap & Quinn (1995). No other subspecies occur. Also, see **Molt**.

P.c. atricapilloides (res s.KS-c.TX): Large; tl relatively short; upperparts pale gray with a slight or no olive tinge; gr covs edged whitish gray; edging to the ss distinct and whitish; flanks with a moderate grayish-buff tinge. ♀ wg(n71) 59-68, tl(n17) 52-62; ♂ wg(n64) 61-69, tl(n54) 54-63.

P.c. agilis (res s.AR to se.TX-s.LA): Medium in size; upperparts pale gray with a slight or no olive tinge; gr covs edged buffy gray; edging to the ss moderately distinct and whitish, often tinged buffy; flanks lightly tinged grayish. ♀ wg(n100) 57-66, tl(n100) 49-60; ♂ wg(n100) 59-68, tl(n100) 50-61.

P.c. extimus (res ec.IL-ec.MO & NJ to w.TN-cn.NC): Medium in size; upperparts medium gray with an olive tinge; gr covs indistinctly edged buffy gray; edging to the ss moderately distinct and whitish; flanks with a moderate buff wash. ♀ wg(n100) 56-65, tl(n57) 49-58; ♂ wg(n100) 59-67, tl(n72) 51-60.

P.c. carolinensis (n.AR-se.LA to se.VA-FL): Small; upperparts dark gray with an olive tinge; gr covs edged gray; edging to the ss indistinct and grayish-white; flanks with a moderate grayish-buff wash. ♀ wg(n65) 53-63, tl(n49) 46-52; ♂ wg(n100) 55-65, tl(n89) 48-54. Birds west of AL-MS ("*guilloti*") may average smaller, and birds of FL ("*impiger*") may average darker and smaller, but variation, if present, is slight and broadly clinal.

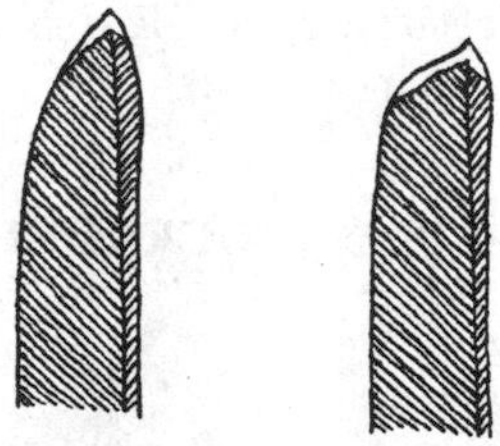

Molt—PB: HY partial-incomplete (Jul-Sep), AHY complete (Jun-Sep); PA absent. The

HY/SY   AHY/ASY

FIGURE 210. The shape and color pattern of the outer rectrix (r6) by age in Carolina and Mountain chickadees. The pattern of white can be helpful in identification, as well.

333

1st PB includes 6 to 10 (~67%) inner gr covs, sometimes (in ~22% of birds) 1-2 terts, and occasionally (in ~18% of birds) 1-2 central rects (r1; rarely to all rects in southern populations).

Skull—Pneumaticization completes in HY from 1 Oct (possibly as early as 15 Aug in birds of TX) through Dec. Look for some HY/SYs to retain windows (> 2 mm; Fig. 11**D**) on the top of the skull through early spring.

Age—Juv (May-Aug) differs only in having a slightly duller (sootier) black cap and more loosely textured body feathers, especially the undertail covs; juv ♀ = ♂.

HY/SY (Sep-Aug): Molt limits often occur among the gr covs (Fig. 133**C-E**; see **Molt**), the retained outer covs tinged brownish and worn, contrasting with the grayer, fresher, and more distinctly pale-edged, replaced inner covs; 1-2 terts sometimes replaced, contrasting with the older, juvenal middle ss (s4-s6; Fig. 133**D**); outer pp covs narrow, tapered, relatively abraded, and brownish with indistinct, narrow, or no pale grayish-brown edging (Fig. 138); central rects (r1; rarely others) occasionally contrastingly fresh; outer rects (r6) relatively abraded, tapered, and pointed (Fig. 139**A**), the white tips reduced (Fig. 210). **Note: In addition, the roof of the mouth (upper mandible lining) color also may vary with age; see Mountain Chickadee and Tufted Titmouse. Beware that some HY/SYs of southeastern populations (*P.c. carolinensis*) may replace all rects (see Molt) and cannot be distinguished by rect shape; these should also replace 1-2 terts.**

AHY/ASY (Sep-Aug): Gr covs and terts uniformly adult (Fig. 133**F**) and gray; outer pp covs broad, truncate, relatively fresh, and dark gray with relatively broad, pale grayish edging (Fig. 138); rects uniformly adult, the outer rect (r6) relatively fresh and truncate (Fig. 139**A**), with an extensive white tip, when fresh (Fig. 210). **Note: See HY/SY.**

Sex—♀ = ♂ by plumage. CP/BP (Mar-Jul). ♀ wg(n100) 53-68, tl(n100) 46-62; ♂ wg(n100) 55-69, tl(n100) 48-63; see **Geographic variation**.

Carolina Chickadee

	Jan	Feb	Mar	Apr	May	Jun	Jul	Aug	Sep	Oct	Nov	Dec
Juv-HY									o	o	o	o	o	o	o	o
SY												
AHY-U	o	o	(♀)	♂	♂	♂	(♀)	o				
ASY	o	o	(♀)	♂	♂	♂	(♀)	o				

■ > 95% ▨ 25-95% ▢ 5-25% □ < 5%   See Fig. 24

Hybrids reported—Black-capped Chickadee. Hybrid chickadees (HYCH) are given species # 7356.

References—Stone (1896), Dwight (1900a), Ridgway (1904), Bent (1946), Lunk (1952), Tanner (1952), Simon (1959), Brewer (1961, 1963), Blake (1965b), Rising (1968), Wiseman (1969), Wood (1969), Hubbard (1970a), Johnston (1971), Oberholser (1974), Merritt (1978), Balch *et al.* (1979), Robbins *et al.* (1986), Parkes (1987b, 1988b), Kaufman (1990a), Harrap & Quinn (1995), Pyle (1997c); C.H. Blake, J.P. Hubbard (*in litt.* to the BBL); C.W. Thompson (pers. comm.).

BLACK-CAPPED CHICKADEE
Poecile atricapillus

BCCH
Species # 7350
Band size: 0-1C

Species—Wg 57-73, tl 53-72 (see **Geographic variation**); bill medium short (exp culmen 7.6-10.5); crown and bib black (rarely brownish in anomalous birds); upperparts pure gray to buffy gray; ss, terts, and gr covs with white edging when fresh (Fig. 211; see **Geographic variation**); outer rects (r6) with white edging when fresh (see Fig. 213); flanks usually washed pinkish buff (fall) to pinkish gray (spring), contrasting distinctly with the gray belly and breast. From all

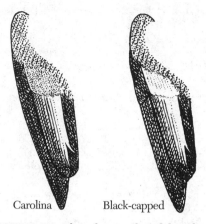

Carolina   Black-capped

FIGURE 211. The relative color of the edging on the greater coverts and inner secondaries (including the tertials) of Black-capped and Carolina chickadee.

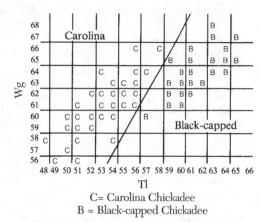

Tl

C= Carolina Chickadee
B = Black-capped Chickadee

FIGURE 212. A scatter diagram of wg *vs* tl in Black-capped and Carolina chickadees from MD (from Simon 1959).

chickadees except Carolina by plumage and measurements (see the other species). Best separated from Carolina Chickadee by the white edging to the gr covs being fairly uniform with the edging to the ss (Fig. 211), the white edging to the outer rects (r6; see Fig. 213), the color and contrast of the underparts, and the relative wg and tl (Fig. 212). In areas of overlap (see **Geographic variation**), the tl length is the most useful character: 56-66 in Black-capped, 49-61 in Carolina. The tail/wg ratio can then provide further means for separation: 0.886-1.032 (usually > 0.9) for Black-capped, 0.819-0.922 (usually < 0.9) for Carolina. Also, wg – tl < exp culmen in Black-capped Chickadee, *vs* wg – tl usually > exp culmen in Carolina Chickadee. A very few individuals may not be separated reliably with these criteria; also, beware of hybrids, especially where breeding ranges overlap. For more information see Simon (1959), Brewer (1963), Rising (1968), Johnston (1971), Merritt (1978), and Robbins *et al.* (1986).

Geographic variation—Moderate, but clinal where many ranges meet. Subspecies taxonomy follows Phillips (1986); see also Ridgway (1904), Dawson & Bowles (1909), Oberholser (1937c, 1974), Linsdale (1938), Todd (1938, 1963), Aldrich & Nutt (1939), Wetmore (1939), Braund & McCullagh (1940), Taverner (1940), Duvall (1945a), Behle (1948, 1951, 1985), Rand (1948b), Dickinson (1953), Parkes (1954), Godfrey (1986), Smith (1991, 1993), Harrap & Quinn (1995), Cooper (1996). No other subspecies occur.

Northwestern (*P.a. occidentalis*) Group. Small; dark; wing edging indistinct.

P.a. fortuitus (br & wint s.BC-nc.OR to nw.MT-c.ID): Medium small; upperparts medium olive gray with a buff tinge; wing edging narrow, white (sometimes tinged pinkish), and distinct; flanks heavily washed buffy tan when fresh. ♀ wg(n75) 59-67, tl(n32) 56-64; ♂ wg(n41) 60-69, tl(n37) 58-66.

P.a. occidentalis (res coastal sw.BC-nw.CA): Small; upperparts dark olive-gray; wing edging narrow, pale grayish, and fairly indistinct; flanks heavily washed pinkish brown when fresh. ♀ wg(n61) 57-63, tl(n54) 53-60; ♂ wg(n70) 58-64, tl(n70) 54-61.

Interior Western (*P.a. septentrionalis*) Group. Large; pale; wing edging distinct.

P.a. turneri (br & wint AK-sw.Yuk): Medium in size; tl relatively long; upperparts pale buffy gray; wing edging white; flanks whitish and lightly tinged buff when fresh. ♀ wg(n43) 61-67, tl(n30) 60-67; ♂ wg(n37) 62-68, tl(n35) 62-69.

P.a. nevadensis (br & wint e.OR-sc.ID to c.UT): Large; tl relatively long; upperparts pale gray without or with a slight buff tinge; wing edging extensive, whitish, and distinct; flanks tinged pale buffy tan when fresh. ♀ wg(n13) 63-71, tl(n13) 63-71; ♂ wg(n22) 64-72, tl(n22) 64-72.

P.a. septentrionalis (br s.Yuk-ne.CO to c.Man-c.KS): Large; upperparts medium-pale gray, lightly washed buff; wing edging extensive, white, and distinct; flanks lightly washed buff to grayish buff, when fresh. ♀ wg(n74) 62-71, tl(n45) 64-71; ♂ wg(n100) 64-73, tl(n94) 64-72.

P.a. garrinus (br montane c.ID-sc.MT to se.UT-c.NM, wint to ne.AZ): Medium large; tl relatively long; upperparts medium-pale gray, the back washed brown, contrasting with the buff-tinged rump; wing edging extensive, whitish to buffy white, and distinct; flanks lightly washed buff when fresh. ♀ wg(n35) 60-69, tl(n10) 61-69; ♂ wg(n26) 62-71, tl(n27) 62-70.

Eastern (*P.a. atricapillus*) Group. Medium-sized; upperparts medium dark; wing edging relatively distinct.

P.a. atricapillus (br se.Man-e.KS to PEI-n.NJ, wint to se.MO-n.VA): Medium in size; upperparts medium-dark olive-gray, slightly tinged buff; wing edging whitish to buffy white and moderately distinct; flanks with a moderate buff wash when fresh. ♀ wg(n100) 58-68, tl(n36) 57-64; ♂ wg(n100) 60-69, tl(n46) 59-66. Birds of Anticosti I, Que ("*aldrichi*") may average larger, darker, and with more distinct wing edging but variation, if present, is very slight.

P.a. anamesus (br & wint ne.Ont): Medium in size; upperparts medium gray; wing edging white and distinct; flanks tinged buffy tan when fresh. ♀ wg(n12) 61-68, tl(n12) 60-69; ♂ wg(n14) 62-70, tl(n14) 61-70.

P.a. bartletti (res. Nfl & Miquelon I): Medium large; tl relatively short; upperparts dark gray tinged brownish; wing edging narrow, white, and indistinct; flanks heavily washed buffy tan when fresh. ♀ wg(n12) 61-68, tl(n10) 56-63; ♂ wg(n15) 63-69, tl(n15) 58-65.

P.a. practicus (br montane c.PA-ne.TN): Medium in size; tl relatively short; upperparts dark gray, slightly tinged brownish; wing edging narrow, white, and indistinct; flanks with a moderate pinkish wash when fresh. ♀ wg(n12) 59-66, tl(n12) 56-62; ♂ wg(n12) 61-67, tl(n12) 57-63.

Molt—PB: HY partial (Jul-Oct), AHY complete (Jun-Oct); PA absent. The 1st PB includes 6 to 10 (~54%) inner gr covs and occasionally (in ~8% of birds) 1-2 terts, but no rects.

Skull—Pneumaticization completes in HY/SY from 1 Oct. Some HY/SYs can retain windows (> 2 mm; Fig. 11**D**) on the top of the skull through Apr.

HY/SY   AHY/ASY

FIGURE 213. The shape and color pattern of the outer rectrix (r6) by age in Black-capped Chickadee. The pattern of white can be helpful in identification, as well.

Age—Juv (May-Aug) differs only in having a slightly duller (sootier) black cap and more loosely textured body feathers, especially the undertail covs; juv ♀ = ♂.

HY/SY (Sep-Aug): Molt limits sometimes occur among the gr covs (Fig. 133**C-E**; see **Molt**), the retained outer covs tinged brownish and worn, contrasting with the grayer, fresher, and whiter-edged, replaced inner covs; 1-2 terts occasionally contrastingly fresh (Fig. 133**D**); outer pp covs narrow, tapered, relatively abraded, and brownish with indistinct, narrow, or no pale grayish-brown edging (Fig. 138); outer rects (r6) relatively abraded, tapered, and pointed (Fig. 139**A**), the white edge of the outer web not extending substantially onto the inner web (Fig. 213). **Note: In addition, the roof of the mouth (upper mandible lining) color also may vary by age; see Mountain Chickadee and Tufted Titmouse.**

AHY/ASY (Sep-Aug): Gr covs and terts uniformly adult (Fig. 133**F**) and gray; outer pp covs broad, truncate, relatively fresh, and dark gray with relatively broad, pale grayish edging (Fig. 138); outer rects (r6) relatively fresh and truncate (Fig. 139**A**), the white edge of the outer web usually extending substantially onto the inner web when fresh (Fig. 213). **Note: See HY/SY.**

Sex—♀ = ♂ by plumage. CP/BP (Apr-Aug). ♀ wg(n100) 57-71, tl(n100) 53-71; ♂ wg(n100) 58-73, tl(n100) 54-72; see **Geographic variation**. The shape of the bib and cap has been suggested as helpful in separating the sexes, with experience (see Mosher & Lane 1972), but see Gochfeld (1977) and Smith (1991). See Desrochers (1990) for a discriminant function analysis, based on live birds, using wg (flat), outer rect (r6) length, and weight, that separated 92-95% of the sexes in an Alberta population.

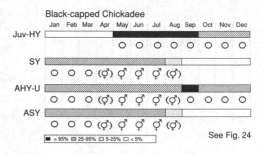

See Fig. 24

Hybrids reported—Carolina Chickadee, Mountain Chickadee. Possibly Tufted Titmouse. Varied Tit (*Parus varius*) in captivity.

References—Stone (1896), Dwight (1900a), Ridgway (1904), Forbush (1929), Odum (1941, 1943), Bent (1946), Lunk (1952), Tanner (1952), Roberts (1955), Simon (1959), Brewer (1961, 1963), Blake (1965b), Rising (1968), Wiseman (1969), Wood (1969), Banks (1970a), Hubbard (1970a), Taylor (1970), Johnston (1971), Mosher & Lane (1972), Glase (1973), Oberholser (1974), Sheppard & Klimkiewicz (1976), Gochfeld (1977), Merritt (1978), Balch *et al.* (1979), Weise (1979), Yunick (1980, 1981b), Meigs *et al.* (1983), Robbins *et al.* (1986), Parkes (1987b, 1988b), Desrochers (1990), Kaufman (1990a), Smith (1991, 1993), Harrap & Quinn (1995), Cooper (1996), Martin & Martin (1996), Pyle (1997c); J.P. Hubbard, M.K. Waddington, C.M. Weise (*in litt.* to the BBL); D. Agro, E. Jones (pers. comm.); IBP (MAPS) data, PNR data, R.P. Yunick data.

MOUNTAIN CHICKADEE
Poecile gambeli

MOCH
Species # 7380
Band size: 0-0A

Species—Worn birds can lack a supercilium (which consists of white feather tips only); these from Black-capped and Carolina chickadees by large average wg (60-75) but short relative tl (52-67; see **Sex**); bill large (exp culmen 8.6-12.3); upperparts more heavily washed olive or tan; gr covs indistinctly edged pale gray to buffy gray; ss without distinct whitish edging; flanks washed dark gray to olive.

Geographic variation—Weak to moderate, but clinal where ranges meet. Subspecies taxonomy follows Phillips (1986); see also Grinnell (1908, 1918a), Grinnell & Swarth (1926b), van Rossem (1928), Behle (1950a, 1956, 1985), Phillips *et al.* (1964), Panza & Parkes (1992), Harrap & Quinn (1995). One other subspecies occurs in Mex.

P.g. baileyae (br & wint sw.Yuk-sw.Alb to c.OR-s.CA): Small to medium in size; tl relatively long; upperparts dark gray with a slight or no buff tinge; flanks washed grayish with a slight-olive or buff tinge. ♀ wg(n100) 60-70, tl(n100) 52-62; ♂ wg(n100) 62-73, tl(n100) 55-65. Birds of interior BC to e.WA-w.MT ("*grinnelli*") average smaller, more olive, and with pinker flanks, and birds of c.WA-n.CA ("*abbreviatus*") average shorter-billed and with slightly paler and buffier flanks than birds of c-s.CA, but in each case variation is slight, broadly clinal, and due to intergradation with other subspecies. Birds of n.Baja CA (*atratus*), potential vagrants to s.CA, have upperparts dark gray with a dusky-olive tinge; supercilium less distinct; flanks and belly washed darker gray.

P.g. inyoensis (br & wint se.OR-sc.ID to ec.CA-nc.AZ): Medium in size; upperparts pale gray, slightly washed tan; gr covs edged buffy whitish; flanks washed pale buffy gray. ♀ wg(n100) 63-70, tl(n100) 55-64; ♂ wg(n100) 65-73, tl(n100) 56-67.

P.g. gambeli (br & wint se.ID-c.MT to s.AZ-sw.TX): Large; upperparts gray with an olive wash; supercilium distinct; gr covs edged pale grayish olive; flanks washed grayish olive. ♀ wg(n76) 64-74, tl(n76) 57-

66; ♂ wg(n100) 66-75, tl(n100) 58-67. Birds of se.ID-UT ("*wasatchensis*") average paler and longer-billed, but variation is slight and broadly clinal. Birds of sw.TX average smaller but potential distinction to subspecies has yet to be documented.

Molt—PB: HY partial (Jul-Sep), AHY complete (Jun-Sep); PA absent. The 1st PB includes 4 to 10 (~36%) inner gr covs, rarely (in ~4% of birds) 1-2 terts, and occasionally (in ~7% of birds) 1-2 central rects (r1).

Skull—Pneumaticization completes in HY/SY from 1 Oct through Jan. Look for some HY/SYs to retain windows (> 2 mm; Fig. 11**D**) on the top of the skull through early spring.

Age—Juv (May-Aug) differs only in having a slightly duller (sootier) black cap and more loosely textured body feathers, especially the undertail covs; juv ♀ = ♂.

HY/SY (Sep-Aug): Molt limits often occur among the gr covs (Fig. 133**C-D**; see **Molt**), the retained outer covs tinged brownish and worn, contrasting with the grayer, fresher, and more distinctly grayish-edged, replaced inner covs; outer pp covs narrow, tapered, relatively abraded, and brownish with indistinct, narrow, or no pale grayish-brown edging (Fig. 138); central rects (r1) occasionally contrastingly fresh; outer rects (r6) relatively abraded, tapered, and pointed (Fig. 139**A**), with the white tip reduced (Fig. 210). **Note: In addition, most juv-HYs may be separated from AHY through fall by the dark gray roof of the mouth (upper mandible lining), *vs* white in AHYs. This needs further study, in this and the other species of parids (see Tufted Titmouse).**

AHY/ASY (Sep-Aug): Gr covs uniformly adult (Fig. 133**F**) and gray; outer pp covs broad, truncate, relatively fresh, and dark gray with relatively broad, pale grayish edging (Fig. 138); rects uniformly adult, the outer rects (r6) relatively fresh and truncate (Fig. 139**A**), with an extensive white tip when fresh (Fig. 210). **Note: See HY/SY.**

Sex—♀ = ♂ by plumage. CP/BP (Mar-Aug). ♀ wg(n100) 60-74, tl(n100) 52-66; ♂ wg(n100) 62-75, tl(n100) 55-67; see **Geographic variation**.

Mountain Chickadee

See Fig. 24

Hybrids reported—Black-capped Chickadee.

References—Ridgway (1904), Bent (1946), Felt (1967), Banks (1970a), Taylor (1970), Oberholser (1974), Kaufman (1990a), Harrap & Quinn (1995), Martin & Martin (1996), Pyle (1997c); IBP (MAPS) data.

MEXICAN CHICKADEE
Poecile sclateri

MECH
Species # 7370
Band size: 0

Species—From all other chickadees by crown and bib black, the latter extending to the upper breast; flanks extensively washed olive-gray without brown or pinkish tones.

Geographic variation—Weak and clinal where ranges meet. Subspecies taxonomy follows Phillips (1986); see also Ridgway (1904), Peters (1927a), Traylor (1949), Miller & Storer (1950), Ficken & Nocedal (1992), Harrap & Quinn (1995). Three other subspecies occur in Mex.

P.s. eidos (res se.AZ-sw.NM): From subspecies of Mex by larger size (see **Sex**, *vs* wg 59-70, tl 51-61 in the subspecies of Mex); paler, grayer (less olive) coloration, flanks tinged relatively pale olive-gray (*vs* darker olive in the subspecies of Mex).

Molt—PB: HY partial (Jul-Sep), AHY complete (May-Sep); PA absent. The 1st PB appears to include just 0 (~72%) to 3 inner gr covs and no flight feathers.

Skull—Pneumaticization completes in HY from 1 Oct through Dec. Look for some HY/SYs to retain windows (> 2 mm; Fig. 11**D**) on the top of the skull through early spring.

Age—Juv (May-Aug) differs only in having a slightly duller (sootier) black cap and more loosely textured body feathers, especially the undertail covs; juv ♀ = ♂.

HY/SY (Sep-Aug): Molt limits probably occur among the med covs and sometimes among the gr covs (Fig. 133**A-B**; see **Molt**), the retained outer covs brownish gray and worn, contrasting with the darker gray and fresher, replaced inner covs; outer pp covs narrow, tapered, relatively abraded, and tinged brownish, with indistinct, narrow, or no brownish-gray edging (Fig. 138); outer rects relatively abraded, tapered, and pointed (Fig. 139A). **Note: In addition, the roof of the mouth (upper mandible lining) color also may vary by age; see Mountain Chickadee and Tufted Titmouse.**

AHY/ASY (Sep-Aug): Med and gr covs uniformly adult (Fig. 133**F**) and dark gray; outer pp covs broad, truncate, relatively fresh, and dark gray with relatively broad, pale grayish edging (Fig. 138); outer rects relatively fresh and truncate (Fig. 139A). **Note: See HY/SY.**

Sex—♀ = ♂ by plumage. CP/BP (Mar-Jun). ♀ wg(n26) 63-72, tl(n21) 55-63; ♂ wg(n28) 65-74, tl(n21) 57-64; measurements include subspecies of N.Am only (see **Geographic variation**).

Mexical Chickadee — seasonal occurrence and age/sex chart (Jan–Dec). Legend: ■ > 95%, ▨ 25-95%, ▥ 5-25%, ☐ < 5%. See Fig. 24

References—Ridgway (1904), Bent (1946), Kaufman (1990a), Ficken & Nocedal (1992), Harrap & Quinn (1995), Pyle (1997c).

CHESTNUT-BACKED CHICKADEE
Poecile rufescens

CBCH
Species # 7410
Band size: 0-0A

Geographic variation—Moderate, but clinal where ranges meet. Subspecies taxonomy follows Phillips (1986); see also Ridgway (1904), Grinnell (1910a), Burleigh (1959a), Browning (1990), Harrap & Quinn (1995). No other subspecies occur.

P.r. rufescens (res coastal se.AK-nw.CA to nw.MT & nc.CA): Back and flanks washed bright rufous, the flank wash extensive and contrasting distinctly with the white belly; gr covs edged white. Birds of s.AK (*"vivax"*) average larger and birds of WA-sw.MT (*"levyi"* = *"caliginosus"*) may average darker, but differences are broadly clinal and/or obscured by individual variation.

P.r. neglectus (res coastal c.CA, Marin Co): Back and flanks washed pale chestnut, the flank wash reduced and contrasting indistinctly with the whitish belly; gr covs edged whitish.

P.r. barlowi (res coastal c-s.CA, San Francisco-San Luis Obispo Cos): Back moderately bright chestnut; flanks washed dull olive-brown; gr covs edged dull whitish.

Molt—PB: HY partial (Jul-Sep), AHY complete (Jul-Sep); PA absent. The 1st PB includes 6 to 10 (~22%) inner gr covs, but no terts or rects.

Skull—Pneumaticization completes in HY from 1 Sep through Dec. Look for some HY/SYs to retain windows (> 2 mm; Fig. 11**D**) on the top of the skull through early spring.

Age—Juv (May-Aug) differs in being drabber overall and having a slightly duller (sootier) blackish cap and more loosely textured body feathers, especially the undertail covs; juv ♀ = ♂.

HY/SY (Sep-Aug): Molt limits often occur among the gr covs (Fig. 133**C-D**; see **Molt**), the retained outer covs worn and with dull buff edging, contrasting with the fresher and more distinctly whitish-edged to buff-edged, replaced inner covs; outer pp covs narrow, tapered, relatively abraded, and brownish with indistinct, narrow, or no pale brown edging (Fig. 138); outer rects relatively abraded, tapered, and pointed (Fig. 139**A**). **Note: In addition, the roof of the mouth (upper mandible lining) color also may vary by age; see Mountain Chickadee and Tufted Titmouse.**

AHY/ASY (Sep-Aug): Gr covs uniformly adult (Fig. 133**F**) and grayish with distinct, buff to white edging; outer pp covs broad, trun-cate, relatively fresh, and dark grayish and chestnut, with relatively broad, brownish edging (Fig. 138); outer rects relatively fresh and truncate (Fig. 139**A**). **Note: See HY/SY.**

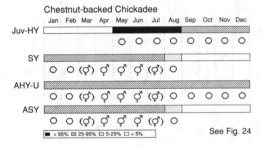

Sex—♀ = ♂ by plumage. CP/BP (Mar-Jul). ♀ wg(n100) 54-63, tl(n20) 44-52; ♂ wg(n100) 57-66, tl(n25) 46-53.

References—Ridgway (1904), Bent (1946), Harrap & Quinn (1995), Pyle (1997c); IBP (MAPS) data, PRBO data.

BOREAL CHICKADEE
Poecile hudsonicus

BOCH
Species # 7400
Band size: 0

Species—From the other chickadees (including Siberian Tit) by small average size (wg 52-70, tl 54-71; see **Geographic variation** & **Sex**); crown brownish; gr covs indistinctly edged brownish olive; ss and gr covs without pale edging; auricular washed gray, without white; bib brown; flanks extensively washed brownish olive to rufous (see **Geographic variation**).

Geographic variation—Moderate, but obscured by individual variation and clinal where ranges meet. Subspecies taxonomy follows Phillips (1986); see also Ridgway (1904), Townsend (1916), Miller (1943b), Burleigh & Peters (1948), Todd (1950, 1963), Godfrey (1951a, 1986), Harrap & Quinn (1995). No other subspecies occur.

Grayish-backed (*P.h. columbianus*) Group.

P.h. stoneyi (br & wint n.AK-n.NWT): Large; bill relatively short (nares to tip 6.4-7.8); crown, rump, and flanks pale olive-brown; back and neck pale gray. ♀ wg(n2) 62-67, tl(n2) 64-68; ♂ wg(n3) 63-69, tl(n3) 65-70.

P.h. columbianus (res s.AK-s.Yuk to ne.WA-nw.MT): Large; bill long (nares to tip 6.9-8.4); back brown with a gray tinge; sides of the neck distinctly slaty gray; flanks dull tawny chestnut. ♀ wg(n10) 62-68, tl(n10) 59-67; ♂ wg(n35) 64-69, tl(n35) 60-68. Birds of WA ("*cascadensis*") may average darker, but apparent variation possibly was due to comparison of fresh and worn specimens.

Brown-backed (*P.h. hudsonicus*) Group.

P.h. hudsonicus (br c.AK-MN to Nfl-s.Ont, wint to IL-MD): Medium small; bill nares to tip 6.8-8.1; back brown with an olive tinge; sides of the neck indistinctly slaty gray; flanks brightish tawny. ♀ wg(n29) 59-68, tl(n20) 56-66; ♂ wg(n38) 60-70, tl(n31) 60-70. Birds of Labrador ("*nigricans*" and "*labradorius*") may average duller brown with whiter underparts, and birds of Nfl ("*rabbittsi*") may average slightly paler, but differences, if present, are slight and obscured by individual variation.

P.h. farleyi (res s.NWT-Alb to sw.Man): Large; bill nares to tip 7.0-8.0; crown, back, rump, and flanks pale brown with a reddish tinge; sides of the neck indistinctly pale gray. ♀ wg(n11) 62-66, tl(n11) 59-64; ♂ wg(n10) 64-70, tl(n10) 62-71.

P.h. littoralis (res s.Que-PEI to ne.NY-ME): Small; tl relatively short; bill small (nares to tip 5.8-7.7); back olive-brown; rump brown with a reddish tinge; sides of the neck indistinctly dusky gray; flanks dull tawny. ♀ wg(n20) 52-61, tl(n20) 54-61; ♂ wg(n23) 58-67, tl(n23) 55-64.

Molt—PB: HY partial (Jul-Sep), AHY complete (Jun-Sep); PA absent. The 1st PB includes 7 to 10 (~31%) inner gr covs but no terts or central rects (r1).

Skull—Pneumaticization completes in HY from 1 Nov through Dec. Look for some HY/SYs to retain windows (> 2 mm; Fig. 11**D**) on the top of the skull through early spring.

Age—Juv (Jun-Sep) differs only in having more loosely textured body feathers, especially the undertail covs; juv ♀ = ♂.

HY/SY (Sep-Aug): Molt limits often occur among the gr covs (Fig. 133**D**; see **Molt**), the retained outer covs worn, with indistinct edging, contrasting with the fresher and more distinctly olive-edged, replaced inner covs; outer pp covs narrow, tapered, relatively abraded, and brownish with indistinct, narrow, or no pale brown edging (Fig. 138); outer rects relatively abraded, tapered, and pointed (Fig. 139A). **Note: In addition, the roof of the mouth (upper mandible lining) color also may vary by age; see Mountain Chickadee and Tufted Titmouse.**

AHY/ASY (Sep-Aug): Gr covs uniformly adult (Fig. 133**F**) and grayish with distinct, brownish-olive edging; outer pp covs broad, truncate, relatively fresh, and dark grayish or brownish with relatively broad, brownish-olive edging (Fig. 138); outer rects relatively fresh and truncate (Fig. 139A). **Note: See HY/SY.**

Sex—♀ = ♂ by plumage. CP/BP (May-Jul). ♀ wg(n61) 52-69, tl(n61) 54-68; ♂ wg(n100) 58-70, tl(n100) 55-71.

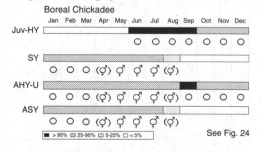

References—Dwight (1900a), Ridgway (1904), Forbush (1929), Bent (1946), Roberts (1955), Cherry & Cannell (1984), Kaufman (1990a), Ficken *et al.* (1996), Harrap & Quinn (1995), Pyle (1997c); IBP (MAPS) data.

GRAY-HEADED CHICKADEE
Poecile cinctus

GHCH
Species # 7390
Band size: 1C-0

Species—From the other chickadees (including Black-capped and Boreal chickadees) by the combination of large average size (wg 65-73, tl 62-69; see **Sex**); crown pale brown with a buffy-olive wash; gr covs and ss distinctly edged buffy white; auricular white; bib brown; flanks brown with a tawny tinge; rects without distinct, white edging.

Geographic variation—Weak, although the subspecies of N.Am is allopatric. Subspecies taxonomy follows Cramp & Perrins (1993); see also Ridgway (1904), Dement'ev & Gladkov (1954), Phillips (1986), Svensson (1992), Harrap & Quinn (1995). Three other subspecies occur in Eurasia.

P.c. lathami (br & wint throughout range in N.Am): From Eurasian subspecies by bill small (exp culmen 8.8-9.9, *vs* usually > 9.5 in the other subspecies); upperparts and underparts average paler and grayer; flanks average darker cinnamon.

Molt—PB: HY partial (Jul-Sep), AHY complete (Jun-Sep); PA absent. The 1st PB includes 4-8 inner gr covs in *P.c. lathami*. Look for 1-2 terts and/or central rects to be replaced in occasional birds, as has been found in Europe (*P.c. lapponicus*).

Skull—Pneumaticization completes in HY from 1 Oct through Dec. Look for some HY/SYs to retain windows (> 2 mm; Fig. 11D) on the top of the skull through early spring.

Age—Juv (Jun-Sep) differs in being drabber overall and having more loosely textured body feathers, especially the undertail covs; juv ♀ = ♂.

HY/SY (Sep-Aug): Molt limits occur among the gr covs (Fig. 133C-D; see **Molt**), the retained outer covs tinged brownish and worn, contrasting with the grayer, fresher, and whiter-edged, replaced inner covs; outer pp covs narrow, tapered, relatively abraded, and brownish with indistinct, narrow, or no pale grayish-brown edging (Fig. 138); outer rects relatively abraded, tapered, and pointed (Fig. 139A). **Note: In addition, the roof of the mouth (upper mandible lining) color also may vary by age; see Mountain Chickadee and Tufted Titmouse.**

AHY/ASY (Sep-Aug): Gr covs uniformly adult (Fig. 133F) and grayish with distinct, white edging; outer pp covs broad, truncate, relatively fresh, and dark gray with relatively broad, pale grayish edging (Fig. 138); outer rects relatively fresh and truncate (Fig. 139A). **Note: See HY/SY.**

Sex—♀ = ♂ by plumage. CP/BP (Apr-Aug). ♀ wg(n19) 64-70, tl(n19) 62-68; ♂ wg(n22) 67-73, tl(n22) 64-70.

Hybrids reported—Willow Tit (*P. montanus*).

Siberian Tit

	Jan	Feb	Mar	Apr	May	Jun	Jul	Aug	Sep	Oct	Nov	Dec
Juv-HY						o	o	o	o	o	o	o
SY	o	o	o	(♂)	♂	♂	♂	(♂)				
AHY-U	o	o	o	(♂)	♂	♂	♂	(♂)	o	o	o	o
ASY	o	o	o	(♂)	♂	♂	♂	(♂)				

■ > 95% ▨ 25-95% ▥ 5-25% □ < 5%   See Fig. 24

References—Ridgway (1904), Bent (1946), Kaufman (1990a), Svensson (1992), Cramp & Perrins (1993), Hailman & Haftorn (1995), Harrap & Quinn (1995).

BRIDLED TITMOUSE
Baeolophus wollweberi

BRTI
Species # 7340
Band size: 1

Geographic variation—Weak and clinal where ranges meet. Subspecies taxonomy follows A.M. Rea & A.R. Phillips *in* Phillips (1986); see also Ridgway (1904), Oberholser (1917d), van Rossem (1947b), Harrap & Quinn (1995). Two other subspecies occur in Mex.

B.w. vandevenderi (br & wint c.AZ-sw.NM): Upperparts (including the rump) dark gray with a dull olive wash; breast and flanks with a grayish-olive wash; belly without a yellow tinge.

B.w. phillipsi (br & wint se.AZ): Upperparts medium gray washed brightish olive, the rump contrastingly olive; breast and flanks with little or no grayish; belly tinged yellow when fresh.

Molt—PB: HY partial-incomplete (Jul-Oct), AHY complete (Jun-Sep); PA absent. The 1st PB includes 4 to 10 (~50%) inner gr covs, often (in ~56% of birds) 1-3 terts, and sometimes (in ~50% of birds) 1-4 rects, occasionally as many as all rects.

Skull—Pneumaticization completes in HY/SY from 1 Oct through Jan. Look for some SYs to retain windows (> 2 mm; Fig. 11**D**) on the top or at the rear of the skull through summer.

Age—Juv (May-Aug) has an indistinct head pattern, throat mixed black and grayish, more loose-ly textured undertail covs, and roof of the mouth (upper mandible lining) probably yellowish to pinkish gray; juv ♀ = ♂.

HY/SY (Sep-Aug): Molt limits often occur among the gr covs (Fig. 133**C-E**; see **Molt**), the retained outer covs tinged buff and worn, contrasting with the olive-tinged and fresher, replaced inner covs; 1-3 terts often replaced, contrasting with the older, juvenal middle ss (s4-s6; Fig. 133**D-E**); outer pp covs narrow, tapered, and relatively abraded, with reduced or no pale edging (Fig. 138), and with buff tips when fresh; central rects (r1; sometimes other rects) often replaced, contrastingly fresh; outer rects usually relatively abraded and tapered (Fig. 139**A**); roof of the mouth probably mixed gray and pink, gray, or grayish black (through Jan-Apr; see Fig. 195). **Note: Intermediates can occur that are difficult to reliably age.**

AHY/ASY (Sep-Aug): Wing covs and terts uniformly adult (Fig. 133**F**) and dark gray with an olive tinge; outer pp covs broad, truncate, relatively fresh, and dark gray with pale gray edging (Fig. 138); rects uniformly adult, relatively fresh, and truncate (Fig. 139**A**); roof of the mouth probably blackish to black (see Fig. 195). **Note: See HY/SY.**

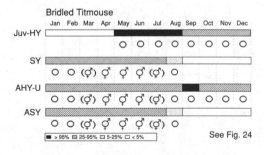

Sex—♀ = ♂ by plumage. CP/BP (Mar-Jul); ♂♂ can develop a partial BP (Fig. 22**B**). ♀ wg(n34) 58-65, tl(n20) 53-60; ♂ wg(n54) 62-68, tl(n24) 58-63.

References—Ridgway (1904), Bent (1946), Harrap & Quinn (1995), Pyle (1997c).

PLAIN TITMOUSE	See Below Band size: 1
OAK TITMOUSE *Baeolophus inornatus*	OATI Species # 7330
JUNIPER TITMOUSE *Baeolophus ridgwayi*	JUTI Species # 7331

Species—From Tufted Titmouse by the lack of black in the head; flanks without pinkish or rufous coloration. See **Geographic variation** for criteria separating the recently split, Oak from Juniper titmouse.

Geographic variation—Weak and clinal within both species. Subspecies taxonomy follows Cicero (1996); see also Ridgway (1904), Oberholser (1917d, 1932), Grinnell & Swarth (1926b), Grinnell (1928b, 1934a), Grinnell & Behle (1937a), Linsdale (1938), Miller (1946b), Phillips (1959a, 1986), Phillips *et al.* (1964), Behle (1985), Harrap & Quinn (1995). One other subspecies of Oak Titmouse occurs in Baja CA.

Oak Titmouse

B.i. inornatus (res coastal sw. OR-sc.CA, Santa Barbara-Kern Cos): Bill short (exp culmen 9.9-11.8); upperparts medium brownish gray; underparts pale gray, the flanks sometimes tinged light brown. Birds of sw.OR-nw.CA ("*sequestratus*") average darker, birds of the San Francisco, CA area ("*restrictus*") may average grayer, and birds of the southern extreme of the range in CA ("*kernensis*") may average paler and less brownish, but in all cases variation is weak and based on intergradation; the previous nomenclature also possibly was based on specimen discolorations.

B.i. affabilis (= "*murinus*"; res sw.CA): Bill medium long (exp culmen 11.5-12.9); upperparts dark, dusky grayish brown; underparts medium-dark gray, the flanks washed brownish dusky. Birds of sw.CA ("*transpositus*") may average darker and browner than birds of Mex, but variation is weak or possibly based on specimen discolorations.

B.i. mohavensis (res sc.CA, Riverside-San Bernadino Cos): Bill medium long (exp culmen 11.8-12.9); upperparts medium-dark grayish with a brownish wash; underparts medium-dark gray, the flanks washed pale gray.

Juniper Titmouse

B.r. zaleptus (res interior s.OR-se.CA to NV): Bill medium long (exp culmen 10.9-13.0); upperparts pale gray with a slight brown tinge; underparts whitish gray with a slight or no buff tinge to the flanks.

B.r. ridgwayi (res s.ID-AZ to w.OK-w.TX): Bill long (exp culmen 11.5-14.4); upperparts medium gray without a brown tinge; underparts pale gray. Birds of e.AZ-NM ("*plumbescens*") may average darker and with a shorter culmen, but variation is broadly clinal or based on specimen discoloration.

Molt—PB: HY partial-incomplete (Jul-Oct), AHY complete (Jun-Oct); PA absent. The 1st PB includes 8 to 10 (~84%) gr covs; usually (in ~89% of birds) 1-3 terts, sometimes s5-s6, rarely 1-3 outer ss, occasionally (in ~11% of birds) 1-3 inner pp (and corresponding pp covs), and usually (in ~89% of birds) the rects; those that do not replace all rects typically may replace only the central rects (r1), but more study is needed. Birds of southern populations may molt more flight feathers, on average; more study is needed.

Skull—Pneumaticization completes in HY/SY from 1 Dec (as early as 1 Oct in some birds of s.CA) through Feb. Look for some SYs to retain windows (> 2 mm; Fig. 11**D**) on the top or at the rear of the skull through summer.

Age—Juv (May-Sep) has more loosely textured undertail covs and the roof of the mouth (upper mandible lining) probably yellowish to pinkish gray (see Fig. 195 and Tufted Titmouse); juv ♀ = ♂.

HY/SY (Sep-Aug): Molt limits occasionally occur among the gr covs (Fig. 133**D-E**; see **Molt**), the retained outer covs brownish gray and worn, contrasting with the grayer and fresher, replaced inner covs; 1-3 terts (and occasionally other ss and/or inner pp) usually replaced (see **Molt**), contrasting with the older, juvenal middle ss (s4-s6; Figs. 133**D-E** & 137**A**); outer pp covs narrow, tapered, relatively abraded (Fig. 138), and edged brown; roof of the mouth probably mixed gray and pink, to gray or grayish black (see Fig. 195; through Jan-Apr). **Note: Intermediates can occur (especially in May-Jul) that are not reliably aged. Occasional HY/SYs also retain rects which are relatively tapered, pointed, and worn (Fig. 139A), but most HY/SYs obtain fresh and truncate rects at the 1st PB.**

AHY/ASY (Sep-Aug): Gr covs, ss, and pp uniformly adult (Fig. 133**F**), gray, and fresh; outer pp covs broad, truncate, relatively fresh, and gray with relatively broad, pale gray edging (Fig. 138); roof of the mouth probably blackish to black (see Fig. 195). **Note: See HY/SY.**

Sex— ♀ = ♂ by plumage. CP/BP (Mar-Aug); ♂♂ can develop a partial BP (Fig. 22**B**). ♀ wg(n68) 64-75, tl(n68) 52-61; ♂ wg(n88) 67-75, tl(n88) 55-64.

References—Ridgway (1904), Bent (1946), Dixon (1962), Oberholser (1974), Harrap & Quinn (1995), Pyle (1997c); IBP (MAPS) data.

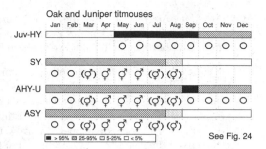

Oak and Juniper titmouses

See Fig. 24

TUFTED TITMOUSE
Baeolophus bicolor

See below
Band size: 1B

Black-crested Titmouse (BCTI)
Eastern Tufted Titmouse (ETTI)

Species # 7320
Species # 7310

Geographic variation—Well marked (between the subspecies groups), but weak and obscured by individual variation (within the Black-crested Group). Subspecies taxonomy follows Phillips (1986); see also Ridgway (1904), Van Tyne & Sutton (1937), Stevenson (1940), Van Tyne (1954), Dixon (1955, 1978, 1990), Sutton (1967), Oberholser (1974), Browning (1978), Harrap & Quinn (1995), Pyle (1997c). No other subspecies occur. With the following, note that juvs of all subspecies lack black in the crest and thus must be separated based on other criteria. See also **Molt**.

Black-crested (*B.b. atricristatus*) Group.
B.b. paloduro (res sw. & n.TX): **Black-crested Titmouse.** Medium in size; forehead (just above the bill) whitish, usually without a cinnamon wash; crown, crest, and sometimes the nape black; back moderately dark gray without an olive tinge. ♀ wg(n40) 69-78, tl(n33) 62-70; ♂ wg(n73) 72-80, tl(n69) 63-72. Birds of sw.TX (*"dysleptus"*) average smaller (shorter-tailed) and slightly paler, and have black more often extending to the nape, but differences probably are too slight for subspecies distinction.
B.b. castaneifrons (= *"sennetti"*; res sw.OK-c.TX): **Black-crested Titmouse.** Medium in size; forehead whitish to pale cinnamon, blending with the blackish-slate crown and crest; nape and back medium gray with a slight brownish-olive tinge. ♀ wg(n100) 69-78, tl(n100) 58-69; ♂ wg(n100) 71-82, tl(n100) 61-72.
B.b. atricristatus (res s.TX): **Black-crested Titmouse.** Small; forehead white to tan; crown and crest black; nape and back moderately dark gray with an olive tinge. ♀ wg(n80) 65-72, tl(n73) 57-66; ♂ wg(n100) 66-75, tl(n100) 57-67.

Eastern Tufted (*P.b. bicolor*) Group.
B.b. bicolor (br & wint NE-se.TX to VT-FL; vag to e.CO,w.TX,s.Que-ME): **Eastern Tufted Titmouse.** Large; forehead black; crown, tuft, and back uniformly pale gray. ♀ wg(n100) 73-84, tl(n32) 64-74; ♂ wg(n100) 76-86, tl(n52) 66-79. Birds south of n.TX-n.GA (*"floridanus"*) may average smaller, paler, and grayer, but differences, if present, are very slight and broadly clinal.

Molt—PB: HY partial-incomplete (Jun-Oct), AHY complete (May-Sep); PA absent. The 1st PB includes 8 to 10 (~75%) inner gr covs, often (in ~75% of birds) 1-3 terts, sometimes other inner and/or outer ss (rarely all?), occasionally (in ~6% of birds) up to 5 inner pp (and most or all corresponding pp covs), and the rects. Molt averages more extensive in the Black-crested than in the Eastern Tufted group; pp and ss other than the terts rarely (if ever) are replaced by the latter. More study is needed, especially in the Black-crested Group.

Skull—Pneumaticization completes in HY/SY from 1 Nov. Some SYs retain windows (> 2 mm; Fig. 11**D**) on the top or at the rear of the skull through summer or even fall.

Age—Juv (May-Aug) has a dusky forehead (Eastern Tufted Group), or a brownish wash to the crest (Black-crested Group), a buff eye ring, more loosely textured undertail covs, and roof of the mouth (upper mandible lining) yellowish to pinkish gray (see Fig. 195); juv ♀ = ♂.

HY/SY (Sep-Aug): Molt limits sometimes occur among the gr covs (Fig. 133**D-E**; see **Molt**), the retained outer covs tinged brownish and worn, contrasting with the grayer and fresher, replaced inner covs; 1-3 terts (sometimes other ss and/or inner pp in the Black-crested Group) usually replaced (see **Molt**), contrasting with the older, juvenal middle ss (s4-s6; Figs. 133**D-E** & 137**A**); some or all pp covs narrow, tapered, relatively abraded, and brownish with reduced or no pale edging (Fig. 138); roof of the mouth mixed gray and pink, gray, or grayish black (see Fig. 195; through Jan-Apr). **Note: Intermediates can occur that are not reliably aged. Rect shape is not useful for ageing after the 1st PB.**

AHY/ASY (Sep-Aug): Gr covs, pp, and ss uniformly adult (Fig. 133**F**), gray, and fresh; pp covs uniformly broad, truncate, relatively fresh, and gray with relatively broad, pale gray edging (Fig. 138); roof of the mouth blackish to black (see Fig. 195). **Note: See HY/SY. More study is needed on the roof of the mouth color, which may be useful in ageing some SYs through fall.**

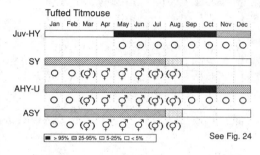

Sex—♀ = ♂ by plumage. CP/BP (Mar-Aug); ♂♂ can develop a partial BP (Fig. 22**B**) which is not as swollen as in ♀♀. See **Geographic variation** for measurements, which vary substantially among the subspecies groups.

Hybrids reported—Possibly Black-capped Chickadee.

References—Stone (1896), Dwight (1900a), Ridgway (1904), Forbush (1929), Bent (1946), Dixon (1955), Roberts (1955), Katholi (1966), Wood (1969), Leberman (1973), Oberholser (1974), Woodward (1975), Sheppard & Klimkiewicz (1976), Parkes (1988b), Grubb & Pravosudov (1994), Harrap & Quinn (1995), Pyle (1997c); R.W. Condee, A.T. Tarbell (in litt. to the BBL); E. Ruhlen, H. Smith, C.W. Thompson (pers. comm.); IBP (MAPS) data, PNR data.

VERDINS   *REMIZIDAE*

One species. Family characters include very small size, obsolete rictal bristles, short wings, and a moderately long tail. Verdins have 10 primaries (the 10th minute), 9 secondaries, and 12 rectrices. The first prebasic molt is incomplete and eccentric. No prealternate molt occurs. Sexing and (especially) ageing by plumage is quite subtle; more study is needed on the reliability of these criteria. Breeding characters are reliable for sexing in Feb-Jul, and males average slightly larger than females.

VERDIN   VERD
Auriparus flaviceps   Species # 7460
                                               Band size: 0A

Species—Juv from Northern Beardless-Tyrannulet by much longer tl (43-50, when fully grown); p10 rudimentary; p9 ≈ p4; eye line and supercilium absent; bill straight and sharp (Fig. 214). From juv Bushtit by shorter average tl (43-50); p9 ≈ p4; longest p – p9 2-4 mm; bill straight and sharp (Fig. 214). From juv Lucy's Warbler by bill short (exp culmen < 6 mm); rudimentary p10 present; wing morphology short (longest p – longest s < 10 mm).

Geographic variation—Weak and clinal where ranges meet. Subspecies taxonomy follows Phillips (1986); see also Ridgway (1904), van Rossem (1930d), Grinnell (1931), Rea (1983), Harrap & Quinn (1995). Five other subspecies occur in Mex.

   A.f. acaciarum (res sw.UT-s.CA to sw.NM): Upperparts (especially rump) washed tan; lower underparts grayish white.
   A.f. ornatus (res s.NM-se.TX): Upperparts with a slight or no brownish tinge; lower underparts white.

Molt—PB: HY incomplete (Jun-Sep), AHY complete (Jul-Sep); PA absent. The 1st PB is eccentric (see p. 208 and Fig. 136**A-C**), with all gr covs, the outermost 4-7 pp, the innermost 4-6 ss, occasionally (in ~6% of birds) 1-2 outer pp covs, and the rects replaced.

Skull—Pneumaticization completes in HY from 1 Sep through Dec.

Age—Juv (Apr-Sep) lacks yellow in the head and has lesser covs without chestnut; juv ♀ = ♂.

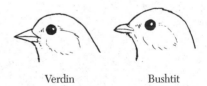

Verdin   Bushtit

FIGURE 214. The bill and head shape in Verdin and Bushtit for the separation of juveniles.

   HY/SY (Aug-Jul): Outer pp covs narrow, tapered, relatively abraded, and brownish with reduced or no pale edging (Fig. 138), occasionally with the outermost 1-2 feathers contrastingly fresh (see Fig. 136**C**); the innermost 3-6 pp and the outermost 3-5 ss brownish and faded, contrasting with the grayer and fresher, outer pp and inner ss (Fig. 136**A-B**). **Note: Compare with the intensity of yellow on the head (HY/SYs average duller yellow than AHY/ASYs, within each sex). Also, the chestnut lesser covs are often replaced later during the 1st PB, mixed gray and chestnut covs indicating HY through Sep.**

   AHY/ASY (Aug-Jul): Outer pp covs uniformly broad, truncate, relatively fresh, and gray with relatively broad, pale gray to brownish-gray edging (Fig. 138); pp and ss uniformly adult (Fig. 133**F**) and gray. **Note: See HY/SY.**

Sex—CP/BP (Feb-Jul). ♀ wg(n46) 48-54, tl(n20) 43-48; ♂ wg(n30) 50-57, tl(n23) 46-50; includes birds of N.Am only (see **Geographic variation**).

♀: Yellow of the head relatively dull and often washed brownish; yellow of the throat abbreviated (extending 6-15 mm below the bill); lesser covs relatively pale reddish brown or tawny. **Note: Plumage distinctions are very subtle and probably unreliable for sexing some intermediate birds (compare with measurements and age), especially without previous experience.**

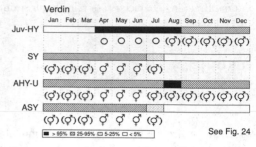

See Fig. 24

♂: Yellow of the head relatively bright and usually without a brownish wash; yellow of the throat extended (12-23 mm below the bill); lesser covs relatively rich reddish brown. **Note: See ♀.**

References—Ridgway (1904), Bent (1946), Taylor (1970), Austin & Rea (1971), Oberholser (1974), Kaufman (1990a), Harrap & Quinn (1995), Pyle (1997c).

BUSHTITS   *AEGITHALIDAE*

One species. Family characters include very small size, long tails, and very small beaks. Bushtits have 10 primaries (the 10th reduced), 9 secondaries, and 12 rectrices. The first prebasic molt is complete, after which birds of most populations cannot be aged by plumage. No prealternate molt occurs. Sexing is accomplished by eye color, plumage, and breeding characters. Males average moderately larger than females.

BUSHTIT   BUSH
Psaltriparus minimus   Species # 7430
                                               Band size: 0A

Species—Juv from Northern Beardless-Tyrannulet by much longer tl (46-61, when fully grown); p10 reduced; p9 ≈ p1; eye line and supercilium absent; bill small and decurved (see Fig. 214). From juv Verdin by longer average tl (46-61); p9 ≈ p1; longest p – p9 6-8 mm; bill decurved and blunt (Fig. 214).

Geographic variation—Weak (within subspecies groups) to moderate (between groups), but clinal, geographically discordant, and the nomenclature has been confused by plumage polychromatism and specimen discoloration. Subspecies taxonomy follows A.M. Rea & A.R. Phillips *in* Phillips (1986); see also Ridgway (1904), Thayer & Bangs (1906), Swarth (1913a, 1914a), Grinnell & Swarth (1926b), Grinnell *et al.* (1930), van Rossem (1936c, 1936d), Van Tyne & Sutton (1937), van Rossem & Hachisuka (1938c), Arvey (1941), Miller (1946b, 1955a), Behle (1948, 1985), Jewett *et al.* (1953), Heimerdinger (1955), Phillips (1958, 1959a), Phillips *et al.* (1964), Raitt (1967), Oberholser (1974), Rea (1983), Harrap & Quinn (1995). Three other subspecies occur in Mex. Note that plumage in this species becomes substantially paler with wear. In addition to the following, the two subspecies groups differ slightly in size (see **Sex**).

Brown-crowned (*P.m. minimus*) Group. Juv ♂♂ without black in the auricular.
P.m. saturatus (res sw.BC-sw.WA): Crown dark blackish brown, contrasting with the dusky and brown-tinged back; flanks washed dark brownish; juv ♂♂ without black in the auricular (Fig. 215A). This subspecies is indistinguishable from *melanurus*, except by its allopatric range.
P.m. minimus (res coastal nw.OR-Los Angeles Co, CA): Crown medium-pale brown contrasting with the medium-gray (with little or no brownish) back; flanks washed gray (♀) or pale brown (♂); juv ♂♂ without black in the auricular (Fig. 215A).
P.m. melanurus (res sw.CA): Crown dark dusky brown, contrasting with the dark gray and slightly brown-tinged back; flanks washed dark brownish; juv ♂♂ without black in the auricular (Fig. 215A). See *saturatus*.
P.m. californicus (res interior s.OR-sc.CA): Crown pale brown, contrasting with the pale brownish-gray back; flanks white to slightly washed tan (some ♂♂); juv ♂♂ without black in the auricular (Fig. 215A).

Gray-crowned (*P.m. plumbeus*) Group. Some juv ♂♂ with black in the auricular.
P.m. plumbeus (res ec.OR-se.CA to w.OK-w. & c.TX): Crown and back gray with an olive tinge; face and auricular of some juv ♂♂ and occasional non-juv ♂♂ (especially in the southern portion of the range) partly blackish (Fig. 215**B-C**), face and auricular of ♀♀ brown. Birds of s.NV to s.CA ("*providentialis*") may average grayer upperparts and paler underparts, birds of se.CA ("*sociabilis*") may have the crown slightly tinged brownish, and birds of sc.AZ ("*cecaumenorum*") may average slightly smaller, but differences, if present, are weak, broadly clinal, and/or due to intergradation with *californicus*.

Black-eared (*P.m. melanotis*) Group. Crown gray; all juv ♂♂ with black in the auricular.
P.m. dimorphicus (res sw.TX): Crown and back gray; face and auricular of all juv ♂♂ partly to entirely black (Fig. 215**C-D**), those of non-juv ♂♂ and juv ♀♀ with some to no black (Fig. 215**A-C**), and those of non-juv ♀♀ with little or no black (Fig. 215**A-B**).

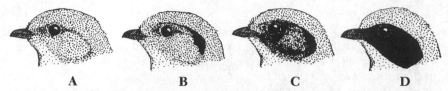

A   **B**   **C**   **D**

FIGURE 215. Variation in the amount of black in the auricular, by age, sex, and subspecies, in Bushtit. See text for details.

Molt—PB: HY complete (Jul-Oct), AHY complete (Jul-Oct); PA absent.

Skull—Pneumaticization completes in HY from 15 Aug through Dec. The skull can be difficult to see due to the dark skin.

Age—Juv (Apr-Aug) has loosely textured undertail covs and the p10 larger (11.5-14.0 mm from the longest pp covs, *vs* 8.0-12.0 in non-juvs) and more rounded (Fig. 216); some juv ♂♂ of *P.m. plumbeus* and all juvs of *dimorphicus*

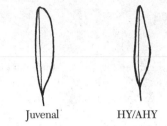

Juvenal   HY/AHY

FIGURE 216. The shape of p10 in juvenile and basic-plumaged (HY/AHY) Bushtits.

can be sexed by the presence of black in the face of ♂♂; otherwise, juv ♀♀ of *plumbeus* and juvs of all other races are not reliably sexed until eye color changes occur (see **Sex**). No plumage criteria are known for ageing after the 1st PB, although the amount of black in the face and auricular of non-juvs, by geography (see **Geographic variation**) probably is useful for ageing some HY/SY ♂♂ and perhaps some HY/SY ♀♀ and AHY/ASY ♂♂ of certain populations (see Fig. 215 and Raitt 1967); more study is needed. Otherwise, see **Skull** for ageing some HYs through Dec.

Sex—CP/BP (Apr-Aug). Brown-crowned ♀ wg(n100) 43-48, tl(n17) 46-54; ♂ wg(n100) 44-49, tl(n53) 48-55; Gray-crowned and Black-eared ♀ wg(n100) 45-51, tl(n28) 50-58; ♂ wg(n100) 46-52, tl(n73) 51-61; see **Geographic variation**.

♀: Throat gray; flanks grayish white; iris pale grayish, white, or yellow. **Note: See ♂.**

♂: Throat white; flanks (when fresh) washed brown, tan, or pinkish; iris entirely dark brown. **Note: Plumage distinctions are greater in the Brown-crowned and Black-eared subspecies groups than in the Gray-crowned group. The iris color is reliable for sexing HY ♂♂ only after completion of the 1st PB; the iris initially is dark in juvs of both ♂ and ♀. In addition to the above, any bird (in N.Am) in non-juv plumage showing substantial black in the face and/or auricular (Fig. 215C-D) can be reliably sexed ♂ (see Geographic variation & Age).**

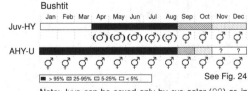

Bushtit

Note: Juvs can be sexed only by eye color (♀♀) or, in southern subspecies, the presence of black in the face (♂♂).

References—Ridgway (1904), Swarth (1914a), van Rossem (1935a), Van Tyne & Sutton (1937), Bent (1946), Phillips (1958, 1961b), Phillips *et al.* (1964), Raitt (1967), Radke *et al.* (1968), McKnight (1969), Oberholser (1974), Ervin (1975), Collins & Ervin (1979), Harrap & Quinn (1995), Pyle (1997c); IBP (MAPS) data, PRBO data.

NUTHATCHES

SITTIDAE

Four species. Family characters include slender and sharp bills, short tails, and short legs. Nuthatches have 10 primaries (the 10th reduced), 9 secondaries, and 12 rectrices. The first prebasic molt is partial, yet age-related differences in the shape and condition of the rectrices are not apparent. Limited prealternate molts occur in three species. Ageing by plumage is reliable for most birds through spring, and ageing by skull is reliable into fall, although beware of persistent small windows (1-2 mm; see Figs. 11D & 186) in certain species. Plumage is reliable for sexing two of the species, and breeding characters can be used for sexing in spring. Males average only slightly larger than females.

RED-BREASTED NUTHATCH
Sitta canadensis

RBNU
Species #7280
Band size: 0-1C

Geographic variation—Subspecies taxonomy follows Phillips (1986), who considered the species monotypic (synonymizing a previously recognized subspecies); see also Burleigh (1960c), Todd (1963), Banks (1970b), Browning (1990). Birds west of Alb-c.AZ ("*S.c. clariterga*") may have paler and bluer upperparts, but variation, if present, is slight and the nomenclature (at least partly) was based on specimen wear and discolorations. Birds of AZ also average slightly shorter bills.

Molt—PB: HY partial (Jul-Sep), AHY complete (Jun-Sep); PA absent-limited (Mar-Apr). The PBs occur primarily on the summer grounds. The 1st PB includes no to some lesser covs, few if any med covs and no gr covs, terts, or rects.

Skull—Pneumaticization completes in HY/SY from 15 Oct through Jan or later. AHY/ASYs can show persistent windows (Fig. 11D; up to 4 mm across) throughout adulthood; thus, birds found with these during Jan-Sep are not reliably aged SY.

Age—Juv (Jun-Aug) has the crown relatively pale by sex, head and throat of some birds with black speckling, and lower mandible with a yellow base, changing to white after 2-4 weeks; many juvs can be sexed by crown color (see **Sex**).

HY/SY (Aug-Jul): Most wing covs, ss, and pp brownish gray with little or no bluish edging, contrasting with the blue-gray back and (often) some inner lesser covs (see Fig. 133A); pp covs narrow, tapered, relatively abraded, and brownish with little or no bluish edging (Fig. 138). **Note: Rect shape seems unhelpful for ageing despite the retention of the juvenal tail. Some intermediates may be impossible to age, especially in Jun-Jul when plumage becomes worn.**

AHY/ASY (Aug-Jul): Wing covs, ss, and pp uniformly dusky with bluish edging (Fig. 133F), and not contrasting markedly in color with the blue-gray back; pp covs broad, truncate, relatively fresh, and dusky with relatively broad, bluish edging (Fig. 138). **Note: See HY/SY.**

Sex—CP/BP (Apr-Aug); ♂ can develop a partial BP (Fig. 22B). ♀ wg(n100) 60-70, tl(n20) 33-38; ♂ wg(n100) 64-73, tl(n22) 35-39.

♀: Crown gray (juv), lead colored, or dull black, contrasting little to moderately with the gray back. **Note: A few intermediates (probably juv-HY/SY ♂♂ and AHY/ASY ♀♀) may not be reliably sexed, especially without experience; compare the crown color with wg and age, if known.**

♂: Crown dull (juv) to glossy black, contrasting markedly with the gray back. **Note: See ♀.**

References—Stone (1896), Dwight (1900a), Ridgway (1904), Forbush (1929), Bent (1948), Roberts (1955), Wood (1969), Banks (1970b, 1978), Oberholser (1974), Sheppard & Klimkiewicz (1976), Yunick (1980), CWS & USFWS (1991), Cramp & Perrins (1993), Harrap & Quinn (1995), Pyle (1995b, 1997c); A.M. Rea, R.P. Yunick (*in litt.* to the BBL); A. Knox (pers. comm.); IBP (MAPS) data, PNR data, PRBO data, R.P. Yunick data.

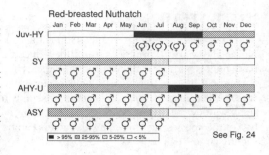

Red-breasted Nuthatch

See Fig. 24

WHITE-BREASTED NUTHATCH
Sitta carolinensis

WBNU
Species # 7270
Band size: 1B-1

Geographic variation—Weak to moderate and clinal where most ranges meet. Subspecies taxonomy follows Phillips (1986), as modified by Wood (1992); see also Ridgway (1904), Maynard (1916 *in* Phillips 1986), Oberholser (1917e, 1974), Grinnell (1918b, 1926b), Grinnell *et al.* (1930), Brandt (1938), van Rossem (1939b), Twomey (1942), Aldrich (1944a), Hawbecker (1948), Phillips (1959b), Mengel (1965), Sutton (1967), Behle (1985), Godfrey (1986), Harrap & Quinn (1995). Four other subspecies occur in Mex. Movement patterns of this species are poorly known; watch for the occurrence of non-resident subspecies, especially in fall and winter.

- **S.c. aculeata** (br & wint coastal sw.BC-sw.CA): Wg short; bill medium short (exp culmen 16.3-19.2); crown of ♀♀ gray; back medium-pale, brownish gray (♀) or blue-gray (♂); sides of the breast and flanks (especially in ♀♀) washed brownish gray. Wg: ♀(n40) 80-86, ♂(n87) 82-88. Birds of n.Baja CA (*alexandrae*), potential vagrants to s.CA, differ only in having a much longer bill (exp culmen 20.8-23.0).
- **S.c. tenuissima** (br se.BC-w.WY to se.CA, wint to NM & KS): Wg medium long; bill long (exp culmen 18.4-22.5); crown of ♀♀ gray; back dark, brownish gray (♀) or blue-gray (♂); sides of the breast and flanks whitish, without brown. Wg: ♀(n50) 82-91, ♂(n88) 85-93.
- **S.c. nelsoni** (br & wint MT-AZ to w.OK-w.TX): Wg long; bill medium long (exp culmen 16.9-21.7); back medium-dark, brownish gray (♀) or blue-gray (♂), the crown of ♀♀ gray; inner webs of the terts brownish black; sides of the breast and flanks grayish white, without brown. Wg: ♀(n73) 85-92, ♂(n100) 87-96. Birds of se.UT (*"uintaensis"*) may average paler, but variation is obscured by substantial individual variation.
- **S.c. oberholseri** (res sw.TX): Wg medium in length; bill medium short (exp culmen 16.8-19.2); crown of ♀♀ gray; back dark, brownish gray (♀) or blue-gray (♂); sides of the breast and flanks washed grayish, with little or no brown. Wg: ♀(n3) 84-89, ♂(n6) 86-91.
- **S.c. carolinensis** (br & wint Sask-se.TX to NB-n.FL; vag to Alb): Wg variable in size; bill short (exp culmen 15.4-19.5); crown of ♀♀ gray to partly (occasionally completely) dull black; back pale to medium, brownish gray (♀) or blue-gray (♂); inner webs of the terts black; sides of the breast and flanks white to grayish white with a brown tinge. Wg: ♀(n58) 82-94, ♂(n100) 84-96. Birds breeding north of NC-AR (*"cookei"*) are larger, average paler overall, and have ♀♀ averaging less black on the crowns than southern birds (*"atkinsi"*), but differences are broadly clinal.

Molt—PB: HY partial (Jul-Sep), AHY complete (Jun-Sep); PA absent. The 1st PB includes few to some lesser covs but no med covs, gr covs, or flight feathers. Beware of pseudolimits (see p. 207) between s6-s8 that cause the terts to appear newer.

Skull—Pneumaticization completes in HY/SY from 15 Sep to Feb or later. AHY/ASYs can show persistent windows (Fig. 11**D**; up to 4 mm across) throughout adulthood; thus, birds found with these during Jan-Sep are not reliably aged SY.

Age—Juv (May-Aug) is relatively paler, especially on the crown (sex for sex), has more pronounced wing bars, and has loosely textured undertail covs; most juvs can be sexed by crown color (see **Sex**).

HY/SY (Aug-Jul): Most wing covs (see **Molt**) and all ss and pp brownish gray with little or no brownish (♀) or bluish (♂) edging, contrasting with the fresher and gray or blue-gray back; a few of more lesser covs sometimes replaced, contrastingly fresh and with dusky centers (see Fig. 133A); pp covs narrow, tapered, relatively abraded, and brownish black with little or no grayish edging (Fig. 138). **Note: Many intermediates occur that are not reliably aged.**

AHY/ASY (Aug-Jul): Wing covs, ss, and pp uniformly dusky with bluish edging (Fig. 133F), not contrasting markedly in color with the gray or blue-gray back; pp covs broad, truncate, relatively fresh, and black with relatively broad, grayish edging (Fig. 138). **Note: See HY/SY.**

Sex—CP/BP (Mar-Aug); ♂♂ can develop partial BPs (Fig. 22B). ♀ wg(n100) 80-94, tl(n100) 39-51; ♂ wg(n100) 82-96, tl(n100) 41-52; see **Geographic variation**.

♀: Crown lead colored (usually), to dull black, with at least a few gray feathers, often contrasting with the blacker nape; upperparts dull gray; wing edging dull gray with a brownish or olive tinge. **Note: See ♂. Only ♀♀ of southeastern populations ("S.c. atkinsi"; see Geographic variation) develop primarily blackish crowns. These ♀♀ occasionally can have crowns entirely black, but can be sexed by their duller overall plumage, and a brownish or grayish tinge to the wing-feather edging; on intermediates compare crown color with measurements and age (if known), as AHY/ASYs average blacker crowns than HY/SYs.**

♂: Crown and nape uniformly dull black (primarily juvs) to glossy black; upperparts bluish gray when fresh; wing edging blue-gray without a brownish or dull olive tinge. **Note: See ♀. Beware that some HY/SY ♂♂ of western subspecies (*e.g.*, *nelsoni* and *oberholseri*; see Geographic variation) can have grayishwashed crowns; these should be sexed by overall brighter plumage (especially back color) and wing-cov edging, as compared with HY/SY ♀♀.**

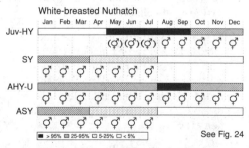

White-breasted Nuthatch

References—Stone (1896), Dwight (1900a), Ridgway (1904), Forbush (1929), Bent (1948), Roberts (1955), Wood (1969), Oberholser (1974), Sheppard & Klimkiewicz (1976), Banks (1978), Parkes (1988b), CWS & USFWS (1991), Wood (1992), Pravosudov & Grubb (1993), Harrap & Quinn (1995), Pyle (1995b, 1997c); J. Church, E.J. Fisk, R.P. Yunick (*in litt.* to the BBL); IBP (MAPS) data, PNR data, PRBO data, R.P. Yunick data.

PYGMY NUTHATCH
Sitta pygmaea

PYNU
Species # 7300
Band size: 0

Species—From Brown-headed Nuthatch by shorter wing morphology (longest p – longest s 11-16 mm); crown dusky olive; entire base of the central rects (r1) distinctly white.

Geographic variation—Moderate and ranges in N.Am fairly well defined. Subspecies taxonomy follows Phillips (1986); see also Ridgway (1904), van Rossem (1929, 1931b), Norris (1958a), Austin & Rea (1976), Behle (1985), Harrap & Quinn (1995). Two other subspecies occur in Mex.

S.p. melanotis (br & wint montane BC-sc.CA to sw.SD-sw.TX): Medium small; lores and postocular line blackish, contrasting distinctly with the olive crown; flanks with a moderate buffy-gray wash. ♀ wg(n100) 60-66, tl(n100) 29-33; ♂ wg(n100) 61-67, tl(n100) 30-35. Birds of s.NV ("*canescens*") may average paler and grayer, but differences, if present, are slight.

S.p. pygmaea (res coastal c.CA): Small; lores and postocular area dusky, contrasting indistinctly with the grayish-olive crown; flanks heavily washed buff. ♀ wg(n65) 58-63, tl(n65) 28-32; ♂ wg(n100) 60-65, tl(n100) 30-34.

S.p. leuconucha (res montane San Diego Co, CA): Large; lores, postocular, and crown uniformly grayish olive; flanks lightly washed buffy gray. ♀ wg(n49) 64-70, tl(n48) 32-37; ♂ wg(n82) 65-71, tl(n82) 34-39.

Molt—PB: HY partial (Jul-Oct), AHY complete (Jul-Oct); PA limited (Feb-May). The 1st PB includes no to some lesser covs, few if any med covs, and no gr covs, terts, or rects.

Skull—Pneumaticization completes in HY/SY from 15 Sep through Dec or later. More study is needed on the possible occurrence of windows (2-4 mm; see Figs. 11**D** & 186) at all times of the year in both HY/SYs and AHY/ASYs (see Red-breasted Nuthatch).

Age—Juv (May-Aug) has a drab and grayish crown, dull and brown-washed upperparts, and loosely textured undertail covs; juv ♀ = ♂.

HY/SY (Aug-Jul): Most wing covs, ss, and pp brownish gray to grayish, with little or no bluish edging, contrasting with the bluish back and (often) some lesser covs (see Fig. 133**A**); pp covs narrow, tapered, relatively abraded, and brownish with little or no bluish edging (Fig. 138); base of the lower mandible pink to whitish (through Nov). **Note: Some intermediates occur that are not reliably aged.**

AHY/ASY (Aug-Jul): Wing covs, ss, and pp bluish, not contrasting markedly in color with the back; pp covs broad, truncate, relatively fresh, and dusky with relatively broad, bluish edging (Fig. 138); base of the lower mandible gray to black. **Note: See HY/SY.**

Sex—♀ = ♂ by plumage. CP/BP (Mar-Aug). ♀ wg(n30) 58-70, tl(n30) 29-37; ♂ wg(n68) 60-71, tl(n58) 30-39; see **Geographic variation**.

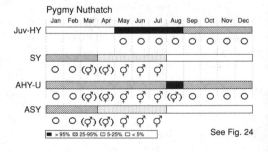

References—Ridgway (1904), Bent (1948), Norris (1958a), Oberholser (1974), Banks (1978), Harrap & Quinn (1995), Pyle (1995b, 1997c); PRBO data.

BROWN-HEADED NUTHATCH
Sitta pusilla

BHNU
Species #7290
Band size: 0

Species—From Pygmy Nuthatch by longer wing morphology (longest p – longest s 17-21 mm); crown brown to chestnut; base of the central rects (r1) without white, or with an indistinct white patch close to the feather shaft.

Geographic variation—Weak and clinal in N.Am. Subspecies taxonomy follows Stevenson & Anderson (1994); see also Ridgway (1904), Howell (1930), Bond (1931), Norris (1958a), Phillips (1986), Harrap & Quinn (1995). One other subspecies occurs in the W.Indies.

S.p. pusilla (br & wint throughout most of the range in N.Am): Wg long; bill short (exp culmen 11.0-14.3); crown chestnut. Wg: ♀(n30) 58-68, ♂(n48) 60-69.

S.p. caniceps (res s.FL): Wg short; bill long (exp culmen 12.4-15.0); crown brown. Wg: ♀(n10) 55-61, ♂(n10) 57-63.

Molt—PB: HY partial (Jul-Oct), AHY complete (Jul-Sep); PA limited (Feb-Apr). The 1st PB includes most to all med covs, 0 (~67%) to 3 inner gr covs, and sometimes (in ~43% of birds) 1-3 terts.

Skull—Pneumaticization completes in HY/SY from 1 Sep through Dec or later. See Pygmy Nuthatch.

Age—Juv (Apr-Jul) is paler, with a grayer crown and loosely textured undertail covs; juv ♀ = ♂.

HY/SY (Aug-Jul): Molt limits usually occur among the med covs and sometimes among the gr covs (Fig. 133**A-B**; see **Molt**), the retained outer covs brownish gray and worn, contrasting with the bluer and fresher, replaced inner covs and back; 1-3 terts often replaced, contrasting with the older, juvenal middle ss (s4-s6; Fig. 133**D-E**); pp covs narrow, tapered, relatively abraded, and brownish with little or no bluish edging (Fig. 138); base of the lower mandible probably pink to whitish (through Nov).

AHY/ASY (Aug-Jul): Wing covs, terts, and middle ss (s4-s6) uniformly bluish (Fig. 133**F**) and not contrasting markedly in color with the back; pp covs broad, truncate, relatively fresh, and dusky with relatively broad, bluish edging (Fig. 138); base of the lower mandible gray to black.

Sex—♀ = ♂ by plumage. CP/BP (Feb-Aug). ♀ wg(n40) 55-68, tl(n20) 28-33; ♂ wg(n58) 57-69, tl(n20) 29-35; see **Geographic variation**.

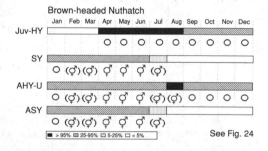

Brown-headed Nuthatch

References—Dwight (1900a), Ridgway (1904), Bent (1948), Norris (1958a), Oberholser (1974), Banks (1978), Harrap & Quinn (1995), Pyle (1995b, 1997c).

TREECREEPERS

CERTHIIDAE

One geographically variable species. Family characters include a slender, decurved beak, short legs, long claws, and a long tail, with individual rectrices being stiff and pointed. Treecreepers have 10 primaries (the 10th reduced), 9 secondaries, and 12 rectrices. The first prebasic molt is incomplete, the rectrices apparently being replaced. No prealternate molt occurs. No plumage-related ageing or sexing criteria are known, although the shape (and perhaps the pattern) of the outer primary coverts may be of use in ageing. Breeding characters are useful for sexing in spring and summer, and males average slightly larger than females.

BROWN CREEPER
Certhia americana

BRCR
Species # 7260
Band size: 0A-0

Species—Probably not distinguishable from European species of *Certhia* due to intraspecific variation in all species. See Harrap & Quinn (1995) for more details.

Geographic variation—Moderate, but broadly clinal where ranges meet and taxonomy confused by variation in plumage polychromatism (brown, gray, and reddish plumages) among the subspecies. Subspecies taxonomy follows J.D. Webster *in* Phillips (1986), as modified by Browning (1990) and Unitt & Rea (1997); see also Ridgway (1904), van Rossem (1931b), Burleigh (1935), Braund & McCullagh (1940), Aldrich (1946), Behle (1948, 1985), Burleigh & Peters (1948), Dickinson (1953), Marshall (1956), Phillips *et al.* (1964), Oberholser (1974), Austin & Rea (1976), Browning (1978), Rea (1983), Harrap & Quinn (1995). Three other subspecies occur in Mex-C.Am. In the following, beware that the bill (from base) of ♀♀ average 1-2 mm shorter than that of ♂♂ (see **Sex**).

C.a. alascensis (br sc.AK, wint to AZ-AR): Averages medium in size; bill averages medium short (from base 12.2-17.2); upperparts pale grayish brown; underparts white; undertail covs tinged buff. Wg: ♀(n5) 61-65, ♂(n17) 62-66.

C.a. occidentalis (br & wint coastal se.AK-c.CA, Marin Co): Averages small; bill averages medium long (from base 12.9-18.7); upperparts medium-dark buffy brown to warm reddish brown with narrow buffy streaking; rump dark cinnamon; underparts white to pale buff; undertail covs and flanks with a dull cinnamon-buff wash. Wg: ♀(n34) 57-64; ♂(n100) 59-66.

C.a. stewarti (res Queen Charlotte Is & n.Vancouver I?, BC): Averages small; bill averages medium short (from base 12.4-16.9); upperparts medium-bright rufous to warm reddish brown; underparts whitish; undertail covs and flanks with a light, dull buff tinge. Wg: ♀(n5) 58-65, ♂(n20) 59-66.

C.a. phillipsi (res wc.CA, San Mateo-San Luis Obispo Cos): Averages medium in size; upperparts medium-dark grayish brown with a rufous cap and narrow whitish streaking; rump golden cinnamon; underparts grayish brown contrasting with the white throat. Wg: ♀(n10) 54-61, ♂(n14) 59-64.

C.a. zelotes (br montane sc.OR to w.NV-s.CA): Averages medium in size; bill averages long (from base 13.5-19.6); dichromatic; upperparts dull, brown or reddish brown, with little or no buff and narrow white streaking; rump dark cinnamon; underparts white to grayish white; undertail covs and flanks with a dull cinnamon wash. Wg: ♀(n81) 58-65, ♂(n100) 59-67.

C.a. montana (br wc.BC-Alb to s.AZ-w.TX, wint to CA & LA): Averages medium large; bill averages long (from base 13.5-19.3); dichromatic; upperparts dark, cold, reddish brown or brownish gray with broad white streaking; rump pale tawny; supercilium whitish; underparts white; flanks and undertail covs with a grayish to cinnamon wash. Wg: ♀(n26) 58-67, ♂(n100) 61-68. A complexly variable population, which accounts for several other described, synonymized, incorrectly assigned, and/or possibly recognizable subspecies (see Browning 1990): warmer and buffier birds of wc.BC-ne.CA ("*caurina*"), redder and shorter-billed birds of Alb to n.ID-nw.MT ("*idahoensis*") paler birds of s.NV-sw.UT ("*leucosticta*"), and smaller birds of w.TX ("*iletica*").

C.a. albescens (res se.AZ-sw.NM): Averages medium small; bill averages medium in length (from base 12.5-17.2); upperparts dull grayish to reddish brown; underparts grayish; undertail covs and flanks with

356

a pale buffy-cinnamon wash. Wg: ♀(n5) 58-64, ♂(n72) 60-66. Formerly known as *alticola*, the latter is now restricted to Mex.

C.a. americana (br n.Sask-n.WS to Nfl-n.WV, wint to CA-FL): Averages large; bill averages short (from base 11.7-16.9); weakly dichromatic; upperparts medium brown, sometimes slightly tinged reddish, and with broad white streaking; rump pale tawny; supercilium buffy to whitish; underparts white; undertail covs with a cinnamon tinge or wash. Wg: ♀(n25) 59-67, ♂(n100) 62-69. Birds of Anticosti I, Que (*"anticostiensis"*) may average grayer upperparts (especially nape) and whiter underparts, but differences, if present, are slight.

C.a. nigrescens (br montane s.WV to e.TN-w.NC, wint to LA-GA): Averages large; bill averages short (from base 11.8-15.8); upperparts dark, brown to reddish brown; underparts grayish white; undertail covs with a grayish-cinnamon wash. Wg: ♀(n3) 60-67, ♂(n11) 63-69.

Molt—PB: HY incomplete (Jul-Sep), AHY complete (Jul-Sep); PA absent. The PBs occur on the summer grounds. The 1st PB includes few if any lesser or med covs, and no gr covs or terts, but apparently the rects(?); more study is needed.

Skull—Pneumaticization completes in HY from 1 Oct (as early as 1 Sep in some birds of CA) through Dec.

Age—Juv (May-Aug) is buffier, with buff edging to the wing covs on some birds, and loosely textured undertail covs; juv ♀=♂. The pp covs average slightly narrower and more worn in HY/SYs than in AHY/ASYs (Fig. 138), and the longest pp cov may have larger and more wedge-shaped whitish tips (extending along feather shaft) in HY/SYs than in AHY/ASYs (see Svensson 1992), but the reliability of these criteria for ageing Brown Creeper is in need of further study. Otherwise, no plumage criteria are known; see **Skull**.

Sex—♀=♂ by plumage. CP/BP (Mar-Aug). ♀ wg(n100) 57-67, tl(n48) 53-67; ♂ (n100) 59-69, tl(n53) 55-69; see **Geographic variation**. Bill length seems to show the most sexual dimorphism (see **Geographic variation**); more study (including larger samples of ♀♀ by subspecies) is needed.

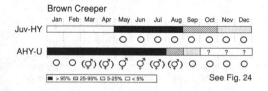

References—Dwight (1900a), Ridgway (1904), Forbush (1929), Bent (1948), Roberts (1955), Wood (1969), Oberholser (1974), Sheppard & Klimkiewicz (1976), Svensson (1992), Cramp & Perrins (1993), Jenni & Winkler (1994), Harrap & Quinn (1995), Pyle (1997c); D.F. DeSante, J.B. Miles (*in litt.* to the BBL); J.R. King (pers. comm.); IBP (MAPS) data, PRBO data.

WRENS

TROGLODYTIDAE

Nine species. Family characters include generally small size, slender bills, and short, rounded wings. Wrens have 10 primaries (the 10th reduced), 9 secondaries, and 12 rectrices. The extent of the first prebasic molt is quite variable, with different species showing partial, eccentric, or nearly complete replacement; two species have extensive prealternate molts, as well. There are few plumage differences among the age and sex classes. Breeding characters are reliable for sexing in spring, and males average slightly to moderately larger than females.

CACTUS WREN
Campylorhynchus brunneicapillus

CACW
Species # 7130
Band size: 1B-1A

Geographic variation—Moderate, but broadly clinal where ranges meet. Subspecies taxonomy follows A.M. Rea & A.R. Phillips *in* Phillips (1986), as modified by Rea & Weaver (1990); see also Ridgway (1904), Stephens (1904), Swarth (1904b), Grinnell (1921), Bancroft (1923), Selander (1964), Oberholser (1974), Rea (1983), Browning (1990). Five other subspecies occur in Mex.

C.b. sandiegense (res coastal sw.CA): Crown and back warm brownish; back medium-pale brownish gray; chin and upper throat primarily whitish, without black marks; chest and lower underparts with a moderate amount of black spots, the chest without a single, centrally located concentration of spots; flanks washed pale cinnamon-buff when fresh; non-juvenal r5 with an extensive white marking below the subterminal band (Fig. 217).

C.b. anthonyi (res sw.UT to s.CA-s.AZ): Crown washed rufous; back medium-pale brownish gray; chin and upper throat primarily whitish, without black marks; chest feathers with a single, centrally located concentration of black spots; lower underparts streaked black; flanks washed dark cinnamon when fresh; non-juvenal r5 with few or no white markings below the subterminal band (Fig. 217).

C.b. couesi (res se.AZ-se.TX): Crown dark brown; back dark brownish gray; underparts and r5 (Fig. 217) as in *anthonyi*; chin and upper throat heavily marked blackish; flanks washed dull cinnamon when fresh.

C.b. sandiegense *C.b. anthonyi*
C.b. couesi

FIGURE 217. The pattern of r5 by subspecies in Cactus Wren.

Molt—PB: HY incomplete (Jul-Oct), AHY complete (Jul-Oct); PA absent. The 1st PB is eccentric (see p. 208 and Fig. 136), with 7 to 10 (~87%) inner gr covs, the outermost 4-8 pp, the innermost 3-9 ss (all ss in ~8% of birds), 0 (~87%) to 3 outer pp covs, and some to all 12 (~83%) rects replaced. Look for occasional birds to retain the outermost pp (*e.g.*, p9-p10, having replaced middle pp) or, perhaps, for some birds to replace all pp and ss (having retained some pp covs) during the 1st PB.

Skull—Pneumaticization completes in HY/SY from 1 Sep through Jan. Look for windows (> 3 mm; Fig. 11**D**) in some SYs through spring.

Age—Juv (Apr-Aug) has buffier upperparts, less distinct spotting on the throat and upper breast, loosely textured undertail covs, and a gray iris; juv ♀=♂.

HY/SY (Sep-Aug): Most or all pp covs retained, the middle feathers (at least) narrow, tapered, relatively abraded (Fig. 138), and tipped buff (Fig. 218), occasionally contrasting with the fresher, replaced outer 1-3 feathers (see Fig. 136C) without buff tips (Fig. 218); the innermost 2-6 pp, the outermost 1-6 ss and occasionally 1-3 outer gr covs contrastingly faded (Fig. 136A-B); iris gray to reddish brown (through Nov). **Note: Ageing can become difficult in Apr-Aug due to feather wear; some intermediates likely are not reliably aged during this period.**

HY/SY   AHY/ASY

FIGURE 218. The color pattern on the outer primary coverts by age in the Cactus Wren.

AHY/ASY (Sep-Aug): Pp covs uniformly adult, broad, truncate (Fig. 138), not tipped buff (Fig. 218), and relatively fresh; pp, ss, and gr covs uniformly adult (Fig. 133F) and dusky brown. **Note: See HY/SY.**

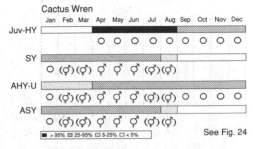

Sex—♀ = ♂ by plumage. CP/BP (Feb-Aug). ♀ wg(n32) 78-88, tl(n30) 71-84; ♂ wg(n31) 80-92, tl(n32) 76-86; see **Geographic variation**.

References—Ridgway (1904), R.S. Woods & A.C. Bent *in* Bent (1948), Selander (1964), Oberholser (1974), Rea & Weaver (1990), Pyle (1997c).

ROCK WREN
Salpinctes obsoletus

ROWR
Species # 7150
Band size: 1-0-1C

Geographic variation—Weak and differences are greatly obscured by individual variation. Subspecies taxonomy follows Phillips (1986); see also Ridgway (1904), Willett (1912), Swarth (1914b), Oberholser (1919d), Grinnell (1927b, 1928b), Griscom (1932), Moore (1941b), Phillips (1966d). Nine other subspecies occur in Mex-C.Am. When using the following, beware that juv-HYs may not obtain full-length bills for several months after fledging.

   S.o. obsoletus (br & wint throughout most of the range in N.Am): Bill small and thin (exp culmen 15.5-18.8, depth at tip of nares 3.1-3.5); upperparts variably pale to medium grayish.
   S.o. pulverius (res San Nicolas I, CA): Bill large and thick (exp culmen 17.3-20.8, depth at tip of nares 3.3-3.8); upperparts pale grayish buff.

Molt—PB: HY partial-incomplete (Jul-Oct), AHY complete (Jul-Oct); PA absent. The PBs occur on the summer grounds. The 1st PB is variable: it can be eccentric (see p. 208 and Fig. 136), primarily in California offshore island populations (~44% of island birds), with the outermost 2-8 pp, the innermost 2-6 ss, and the outermost 0 (in ~57% of birds showing eccentric replacement patterns) to 3 pp covs replaced. All gr covs in these birds usually are replaced and the central rects (r1) are rarely (?) replaced. Mainland populations occasionally (in ~5% of birds) can show an eccentric pattern but more typically replace 8 to 10 (~25%) inner gr covs and usually (in ~91% of birds) 1-3 terts, but not the central rects (r1). More study is needed.

Skull—Pneumaticization completes in HY from 15 Sep (as early as 15 Jul in some birds of s.CA) through Dec. Look for windows (> 2 mm; Fig. 11**D**) in some SYs through spring.

Age—Juv (Mar-Aug) is duller (and often darker), has buff tips to the gr covs, little or no streaking or spotting on the breast, and loosely textured undertail covs; juv ♀ = ♂.

HY/SY (Aug-Jul): Molt limits sometimes occur among the gr covs (Fig. 133**D-E**; see **Molt**), the retained outer covs worn and tipped buff, contrasting with the fresher and white-tipped, replaced inner covs; 1-3 terts usually replaced, contrasting with the older, juvenal middle ss (s4-s6; Fig. 133**D-E**, although beware of pseudolimits in AHY/ASYs); outer pp covs narrow, tapered, relatively abraded (Fig. 138), and grayish with indistinct and even, pale edges (Fig. 219); central rects (r1; rarely other rects) sometimes replaced, contrastingly fresh; lower mandible color flesh (through Oct or later?). **Note: Rect shape seems unhelpful for ageing despite the retention of the juvenal tail. Intermediates can become difficult to age in May-Jul due to wear. HY/SYs of island populations also can show eccentric molt patterns (see p. 208 and Fig. 136A-B), ageing as in Cactus Wren.**

AHY/ASY (Aug-Jul): Wing feathers and rects uniformly adult (Fig. 133**F**, although beware of pseudolimits; see p. 207) and dark grayish brown; outer pp covs broad, truncate, relatively fresh (Fig. 138), and dusky with indistinct, dusky markings among uneven pale edges (Fig. 209); lower mandible color flesh-gray or blackish with a yellow base. **Note: See HY/SY.**

Sex—♀ = ♂ by plumage. CP/BP (Jan-Aug). ♀ wg(n37) 66-73, tl(n20) 49-58; ♂ wg(n43) 68-77, tl(n32) 51-59; see **Geographic variation**.

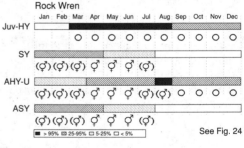

FIGURE 219. The color pattern of the outer primary coverts by age in Rock Wren. Look for similar (although less diagnostic) patterns in Bewick's and House wrens.

References—Ridgway (1904), Dickey & van Rossem (1938), Bent (1948), Oberholser (1974), Pyle (1997c); PRBO data.

CANYON WREN
Catherpes mexicanus

CANW
Species # 7170
Band size: 1

Geographic variation—Weak and differences are obscured by substantial individual variation. Subspecies taxonomy follows Phillips (1986); see also Oberholser (1903a, 1930a, 1974),

Ridgway (1904), Grinnell & Behle (1935), Aldrich (1946), Miller (1948), Phillips (1966d), Behle (1985), Browning (1990), Jones & Dieni (1995). Four other subspecies occur in Mex.

C.m. griseus (br & wint s.BC-s.OR to w.ID-nw.UT): Crown with a heavy dusky wash; back, rump, and belly dull grayish brown with a rufous wash.

C.m. punctulatus (br & wint nc-sc.CA): Crown with a moderate dusky wash; back, rump, and belly dark rufous with a brown tinge.

C.m. conspersus (res NV-sw.CA to c.CO-TX): Crown with a variable dusky wash; back, rump, and belly variable, pale rufous-brown. Birds of se.AZ can approach subspecies of Mex, which generally average darker.

C.m. pallidior (br & wint c.ID-sw.SD to ne.UT-nw.CO): Crown whitish, sometimes tinged dusky; back, rump, and belly pale brown with a rufous wash.

Molt—PB: HY partial (Aug-Oct), AHY complete (Jul-Oct); PA absent. The 1st PB includes 2 to 10 (~8%) inner gr covs and usually (in ~92% of birds) 1-3 terts, but typically no rects.

Skull—Pneumaticization completes in HY/SY from 1 Sep through Jan. Look for windows (> 2 mm; Fig. 11**D**) in some SYs through spring.

Age—Juv (Apr-Aug) has little or no white spotting on the upperparts and belly, and loosely textured undertail covs; juv ♀=♂.

HY/SY (Sep-Aug): Molt limits usually occur among the gr covs (Fig. 133**B-E**; see **Molt**), the retained outer covs worn and tipped cinnamon-rufous (Fig. 220), contrasting with the fresher and whitish-tipped or cinnamon-tipped, replaced inner covs (Fig. 220); 1-3 terts usually replaced, contrasting with the older, juvenal middle ss (s4-s6; Fig. 133**D-E**); outer pp covs narrow, tapered, relatively abraded (Fig. 138), and pale brown with substantial, bar-like, blackish markings (Fig. 220). **Note: Rect shape seems unhelpful for ageing despite the retention of the juvenal tail. A few intermediates can be difficult to age, especially in May-Aug when plumage can become quite worn.**

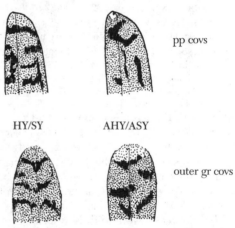

pp covs

HY/SY   AHY/ASY

outer gr covs

FIGURE 220. The color patterns of the outer primary coverts and outer greater coverts by age in Canyon Wren.

AHY/ASY (Sep-Aug): Wing covs and ss uniformly adult (Fig. 133**F**) and relatively fresh, the outer gr covs with pale whitish or cinnamon tips (Fig. 220); outer pp covs broad, truncate, relatively fresh (Fig. 138), and dark brown with reduced and irregular, blackish markings and sometimes with small white tips (Fig. 220). **Note: See HY/SY.**

Sex—♀=♂ by plumage. CP/BP (Feb-Aug). ♀ wg(n100) 53-65, tl(n100) 44-56; ♂ wg(n100) 55-68, tl(n100) 46-59.

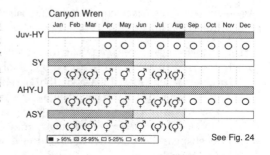

Canyon Wren

	Jan	Feb	Mar	Apr	May	Jun	Jul	Aug	Sep	Oct	Nov	Dec
Juv-HY					○	○	○	○	○	○	○	○
SY		○	(♀)	(♀)	♂	♀	♀	(♀)	(♀)			
AHY-U		○	(♀)	(♀)	♂	♀	♀	(♀)	(♀)	○	○	○
ASY		○	(♀)	(♀)	♂	♀	♀	(♀)	(♀)			

■ > 95% ▨ 25-95% ▢ 5-25% □ < 5%   See Fig. 24

References—Ridgway (1904), Bent (1948), Oberholser (1974), Jones & Dieni (1995), Pyle (1997c).

CAROLINA WREN
Thryothorus ludovicianus

CARW
Species # 7180
Band size: 1B

Geographic variation—Weak and differences are obscured by individual variation, but ranges are moderately well defined. Subspecies taxonomy follows Phillips (1986); see also Ridgway (1904), Lowery (1940), Godfrey (1946), Mengel (1965), Sutton (1967), Hubbard & Banks (1970), Stevenson (1973), Oberholser (1974), Browning (1990), Stevenson & Anderson (1994). Two to five other subspecies (depending on the species taxonomy) occur in Mex-C.Am.

T.l. ludovicianus (br & wint s.IA-se.TX to MA-nc.FL; vag to NM & s.Man-ME): Averages medium large; bill short (exp culmen 13.6-17.6); upperparts bright rufous-brown; underparts with a moderate tawny-buff wash. ♀ wg(n100) 53-62, tl(n100) 45-52; ♂ wg(n100) 56-64, tl(n100) 47-55. Birds north of s.OK-s.VA ("*carolinianus*") may average larger and paler, birds of se.TX ("*alamoensis*") may average paler and grayer, and birds of se.LA-s.GA ("*euronotus*") may average smaller and darker, but variation is weak, broadly clinal, and/or due to intergradation with other subspecies. The name "*alleghani*" for birds of montane MD-SC probably was based on comparison of juvs with non-juvs.

T.l. oberholseri (res wc-sc.TX): Averages medium small; upperparts medium-dull brown with a rufous wash. ♀ wg(n28) 53-62, tl(n4) 45-50; ♂ wg(n14) 56-64, tl(n3) 49-53.

T.l. lomitensis (res s.TX): Averages small; upperparts dull brown with a rufous tinge; underparts medium buffy brown. ♀ wg(n8) 52-58, tl(n8) 42-48; ♂ wg(n10) 56-60, tl(n10) 46-52.

T.l. burleighi (res Cat I, MS): Averages medium small; upperparts (especially crown) pale rufous-brown. ♀ wg(n4) 56-59, tl(n4) 46-49; ♂ wg(n7) 59-63, tl(n7) 48-52.

T.l. nesophilus (res Dog I, FL): Averages medium in size; upperparts medium rufous-brown; underparts pale buff. ♀ wg(n7) 54-58, tl(n7) 43-47; ♂ wg(n12) 56-62, tl(n12) 45-52.

T.l. miamensis (res se.GA-s.FL): Averages large; bill long (exp culmen 16.4-19.0); upperparts dark rufous-brown; underparts with a heavy tawny wash. ♀ wg(n12) 56-62, tl(n12) 46-54; ♂ wg(n13) 61-67, tl(n13) 49-55.

Molt—PB: HY partial-incomplete (Jul-Oct), AHY complete (Jul-Sep); PA absent. The 1st PB is variable, often (in ~53% of birds) being eccentric (see p. 208, Fig. 136), with the outermost 4-6 pp and the innermost 3-6 ss, but usually no pp covs, replaced. Other HYs follow this pattern, but also can replace some inner pp (among p1-p3) and outer ss (among s1-s3); see Fig. 136**D**. Still others replace just 4-10 gr covs and 0-3 terts (occasionally s6, as well). The rects vary from none replaced (in ~53% of birds) to all replaced (in ~40% of birds). Southern birds (*e.g.*, *T.l. oberholseri*, *lomitensis* and *miamensis*) replace more feathers on average than northern birds (*ludovicianus*). More study is needed.

Skull—Pneumaticization completes in HY/SY from 1 Oct (as early as 1 Sep in southern birds; see **Molt**) through Jan. Some SYs retain windows (> 2 mm; Fig. 11**D**) on the top of the skull through Mar.

Age—Juv (Apr-Aug) has relatively duller and paler plumage, buff tips to the wing covs, and loosely textured and unbarred undertail covs; juv ♀ = ♂.

HY/SY (Sep-Aug): Outer pp covs narrow, faded, abraded, and brown to cinnamon-brown, with buff tips when fresh (Fig. 138); 1-6 pp (among p1-p6) and 1-6 ss among (s1-s6) often contrastingly faded (Figs. 136**A-B** or 136**D**); molt limits often occur among the gr covs (Fig. 133**C-E**; see **Molt**), the retained outer covs brownish cinnamon and worn, contrasting with the more rufous and fresher, replaced inner covs; rects often retained, juvenal, and relatively abraded. **Note: Many intermediates may occur that are difficult or impossible to age. Rect shape is not useful for ageing after the 1st PB, despite the retention of the juvenal tail in many birds.**

AHY/ASY (Sep-Aug): Outer pp covs broad, truncate, and relatively fresh, with relatively broad, pale gray edging (Fig. 138); wing covs, ss, pp, and rects uniformly adult (Fig.

133F), fresh, and rufous. **Note: See HY/SY.**

Sex—♀=♂ by plumage. CP/BP (Mar-Aug). Measurements are useful for sexing within subspecies (see **Geographic variation**): ♀ wg(n100) 52-62, tl(n100) 43-54; ♂ wg(n100) 56-67, tl(n100) 45-55.

References—Stone (1896), Dwight (1900a), Ridgway (1904), Forbush (1929), Bent (1948), Roberts (1955), Wood (1969), Oberholser (1974), Sheppard & Klimkiewicz (1976), CWS & USFWS (1991), Haggerty & Morton (1995), Pyle (1997c); C.W. Thompson (pers. comm.); IBP (MAPS) data.

Carolina Wren

See Fig. 24

BEWICK'S WREN
Thryomanes bewickii

BEWR
Species # 7190
Band size: 1

Geographic variation—Weak to moderate, and differences are obscured by partial dichromatism (gray and reddish-brown phases) and substantial individual variation; the nomenclature also has been confused by specimen discolorations. Subspecies taxonomy follows A.M. Rea & A.R. Phillips *in* Phillips (1986); see also Oberholser (1898, 1920b, 1932, 1974), Ridgway (1904), Grinnell (1910b, 1927a, 1928b), Swarth (1916b), Sutton (1934, 1967), Van Tyne & Sutton (1937), Miller (1941b), Aldrich (1944b), Jewett (1944a), Mengel (1965), D.M. Power (1980), Browning (1990). Three other (extant) subspecies occur in Mex.

Pacific Coastal (*T.b. drymoecus*) Group. Small; dark brown with a reddish tinge.

T.b. calophonus (res coastal sw.BC-nw.OR): Medium small; bill large (exp culmen 14.3-15.7); upperparts (including the rump) dark brown, variously tinged reddish; underparts gray. ♀ wg(n10) 49-53, tl(n10) 48-54; ♂ wg(n10) 51-56, tl(n10) 51-56. Birds of sw.BC-nw.WA ("*ariborius*") may average more reddish and birds of c.WA ("*hurleyi*") may average more olive-brown, but variation is weak and the subspecies designations were partly due to plumage dichromatism, specimen wear, and/or specimen discolorations.

T.b. marinensis (res coastal nw-wc.CA, s.Humboldt-Marin Cos): Small; bill small (exp culmen 13.3-15.2); upperparts medium brown, the rump tinged reddish brown; underparts dingy whitish. ♀ wg(n50) 47-53, tl(n10) 46-51; ♂ wg(n50) 49-54, tl(n10) 49-53.

T.b. spilurus (res coastal wc.CA, San Francisco-Monterey Cos): Small; upperparts moderately dull brown, the rump slightly tinged reddish; underparts dingy grayish white. ♀ wg(n37) 47-53, tl(n10) 46-50; ♂ wg(n14) 49-55, tl(n10) 47-53.

T.b. drymoecus (br & wint interior sc.OR to w.NV-sw.CA): Small; upperparts (including the rump) variably medium-pale, brownish to reddish brown; underparts grayish. ♀ wg(n10) 48-53, tl(n10) 47-53; ♂ wg(n20) 49-55, tl(n20) 49-55. Birds of s.OR ("*atrestus*") may average slightly larger and grayer, but the designation was based (at least partly) on specimen discoloration.

T.b. charienturus (br & wint sw-s.CA, Los Angeles-San Diego Cos, including offshore Is.): Medium small; upperparts (including the rump) dark grayish brown; underparts dingy whitish. ♀ wg(n27) 47-53, tl(n15) 47-53; ♂ wg(n32) 50-56, tl(n19) 49-56. Birds from Santa Catalina I ("*catalinae*") may average darker and larger-billed, birds of Santa Cruz I ("*nesophilus*") may average browner and shorter-tailed, birds of the San Diego area ("*correctus*") may average paler, birds of San Clemente I ("*leucophrys*" = "*anthonyi*"), now extinct, may have averaged grayer and with larger bills, and birds of n.Baja CA ("*carbonarius*") may average slightly smaller and grayer, but in all cases differences are weak and obscured by individual variation and specimen discoloration.

Interior West (*T.b. eremophilus*) Group. Large; pale grayish.

T.b. eremophilus (br e.CA-ne.CO to s.AZ-TX): Medium large; bill medium long (exp culmen 12.8-15.5);

partially dichromatic, the upperparts medium-pale brown or grayish with a slight reddish tinge and the rump usually paler; underparts whitish. ♀ wg(n39) 51-58, tl(n10) 51-58; ♂ wg(n28) 53-60, tl(n10) 53-62. Birds of sw.NM-TX average browner, but this may be due to variation in dichromatism rather than geography.

T.b. cryptus (br e.CO-w.OK, wint to TX): Large; bill short (exp culmen 12.3-13.4); upperparts (including the rump) dull, medium grayish brown; underparts whitish. ♀ wg(n12) 51-56, tl(n12) 50-58; ♂ wg(n18) 55-60, tl(n18) 55-61. Birds of se.UT-ne.AZ to w.KS-nw.TX ("*niceae*") may average grayer, but this difference is broadly clinal and the designation was based (at least partly) on specimen wear and discoloration.

T.b. sadai (res s.TX): Medium in size; upperparts brown, the rump tinged grayish tawny; underparts whitish. ♀ wg(n10) 49-54, tl(n10) 48-54; ♂ wg(n10) 52-56, tl(n10) 50-55.

T.b. pulichi (br wc.OK-KS, wint to TX): Medium large; tl long; bill short (12.5-13.5); upperparts (including the rump) medium-pale reddish brown; underparts whitish. ♀ wg(n18) 50-58, tl(n2) 55-58; ♂ wg(n12) 52-60, tl(n5) 56-60.

Eastern (T.b. bewickii) Group. Medium in size; reddish brown.

T.b. bewickii (br se.NE-AR to s.PA-w.TN, wint to sc.TX-FL): Medium in size; bill medium short (exp culmen 12.4-14.4); upperparts (including the rump) moderately bright, dark reddish brown; underparts dingy whitish. ♀ wg(n30) 49-54, tl(n30) 47-53; ♂ wg(n50) 52-57, tl(n50) 48-56. Birds of montane PA-n.GA ("*altus*") may average darker, but differences are broadly clinal and the designation was probably based (at least partly) on specimen discoloration.

Molt—PB: HY partial-incomplete (Jul-Sep), AHY complete (Jul-Sep); PA absent. The PBs occur on the summer grounds. The 1st PB is variable, sometimes (in ~34% of birds) being eccentric (see p. 208 and Fig. 136), with the outermost 4-7 pp and the innermost 3-6 ss, but usually no pp covs replaced. Others replace 6 to 10 (~91%) inner gr covs and 1-3 terts (s6 in some birds), but no pp. The rects vary from none replaced (in ~13% of birds) to all replaced (in ~28% of birds). Southern birds (*e.g.*, *T.b. charienturus* and *sadai*) molt more feathers on average than northern birds (*e.g.*, *calophonus*, *drymoecus*, *cryptus*, and *bewickii*). Molt limits are hard to detect in this species; thus, more study is needed.

Skull—Pneumaticization completes in HY from 1 Sep through Dec. Look for windows (> 2 mm; Fig. 11**D**) in some SYs through spring.

Age—Juv (Apr-Aug) has relatively paler plumage, often with dusky edging to the feathers of the underparts, and loosely textured undertail covs; juv ♀ = ♂.

HY/SY (Sep-Aug): Outer pp covs narrow, abraded, and faded brown to grayish, with a reduced, pale edge (Fig. 138; see also Fig. 209); the innermost 3-5 pp and/or the outermost 3-6 ss contrastingly faded (Fig. 136**A**); molt limits occasionally occur among the gr covs and terts (Fig. 133**C-E**; see **Molt**), the retained outer covs brownish and worn, contrasting with the fresher, replaced inner covs; the central and other rects often replaced, contrasting with the more abraded, retained juvenal rects. **Note: Many intermediates occur, especially in Apr-Jul.**

AHY/ASY (Sep-Aug): Outer pp covs broad, truncate, relatively fresh, and dark brown or gray, with relatively broad, brownish to tawny edging (Fig. 138; see also Fig. 209); wing covs, ss, pp, and rects uniformly adult (Fig. 133**F**), fresh, and grayish brown to brownish rufous. **Note: See HY/SY; AHY/ASYs can be especially hard to reliably age.**

Sex—♀ = ♂ by plumage. CP/BP (Mar-Aug). Measurements are useful within subspecies (see **Geographic variation**): overall, ♀ wg(n100) 47-58, tl(n100) 46-58; ♂ wg(n100) 49-60, tl(n100) 47-62.

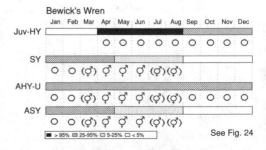

References—Ridgway (1904), Forbush (1929), Bent (1948), Roberts (1955), Wood (1969), Oberholser (1974), Pyle (1997c); C.W. Thompson (pers. comm.); IBP (MAPS) data, PRBO data.

HOUSE WREN   HOWR
Troglodytes aedon   Species # 7210
                                                  Band size: 0-1C

Species—From Winter Wren by longer tl (38-48; see **Sex**); barring on the flanks usually not extending forward of the legs; undertail covs (non-juvs) barred whitish and dusky.

Geographic variation—Moderate, but differences are obscured by substantial individual variation. Subspecies taxonomy follows R.A. Paynter *in* Mayr & Greenway (1960), as modified by Phillips (1986); see also Ridgway (1904), Chapman & Griscom (1924), Oberholser (1934, 1974), van Rossem (1938d), Brandt (1945), Miller (1955a), Marshall (1956), Paynter (1957), Phillips (1959b, 1961a), Lanyon (1960b), Todd (1963), Phillips *et al.* (1964), Mengel (1965), Binford (1985), Godfrey (1986). About 27 other subspecies occur in Mex-S.Am.

   T.a. parkmanii (br ec.BC-s.CA to c.Ont-c.KY, wint wc-sw.CA to nw.FL): Upperparts grayish brown with a slight or no rufous tinge, the back feathers usually with dusky barring; underparts grayish white to brownish. Birds of se.AZ ("*vorhiesi*") average buffier supercilia and browner breasts, but variation is broadly clinal and due to intergradation with *cahooni* of Mex, the latter of which (in purer form) also could occur as a vagrant to N.Am.
   T.a. aedon (= "*domesticus*"; br c.MI-NB to ne.TN-SC, wint sc.TX-e.NC to FL): Upperparts brown with a rufous wash, the back feathers usually unmarked; underparts whitish to buffy. Breeding birds of c.MI-s.Que to TN ("*baldwini*") may average darker and grayer, but differences are broadly clinal and the subspecies designation likely was based (at least partly) on specimen discoloration.

Molt—PB: HY partial-incomplete (Jul-Oct), AHY complete (Jul-Sep); PA absent. The PBs occur on the summer grounds, although substantial post-breeding dispersal can occur (usually upslope in western populations). The 1st PB includes 3 to 10 (~7%) inner gr covs, usually (in ~93% of birds) 1-3 terts (occasionally s6, as well), and occasionally (in ~20% of birds) 1-2 central rects. It may also be eccentric (see p. 208 and Fig. 136) in some individuals, with some outer pp, inner ss, and most or all rects replaced. Molt limits are difficult to detect in this species; thus, more study is needed.

Skull—Pneumaticization completes in HY/SY from 15 Oct (possibly as early as 15 Sep in some birds of s.CA) through Jan. Look for windows (> 2 mm; Fig. 11**D**) in some SYs through spring.

Age—Juv (May-Aug) has dusky mottling on the breast and less distinct barring on the flanks, vent, and undertail covs (the latter also loosely textured); juv ♀ = ♂.

   HY/SY (Aug-Jul): Molt limits usually occur among the gr covs (Fig. 133**C-E**; see **Molt**), the retained outer covs worn and brown with indistinct, dusky bars, and without white tips, contrasting with the fresher, darker brown, distinctly blackish-barred, and often white-tipped, replaced inner covs; 1-3 terts (occasionally s6, as well) usually replaced, contrasting with the older, juvenal middle ss (s4-s6; Fig. 133**D-E**); outer pp covs narrow, tapered, relatively abraded (Fig. 138), and brown with pale edges and few or no dusky marks (see Fig. 209); central rects (r1) occasionally replaced and contrastingly fresh. **Note: Some or many birds may also show an eccentric molt pattern; see Molt and Figure 136. Rect shape seems unhelpful for ageing despite retention of the juvenal tail. Ageing in this species is difficult and many intermediates should not be reliably aged, especially in Mar-Jul.**

AHY/ASY (Aug-Jul): Gr covs, terts, and middle ss (s4-s6) uniformly adult (Fig. 133F) and dark brown with distinct, blackish bars; gr covs often tipped white; outer pp covs broad, truncate, relatively fresh (Fig. 138), and brownish rufous with indistinct, dusky marks (see Fig. 209). **Note: See HY/SY; ASYs in Mar-Jul can be especially difficult to reliably age.**

Sex— ♀ = ♂ by plumage. CP/BP (Apr-Aug). ♀ wg(n100) 46-53, tl(n100) 38-45; ♂ wg(n100) 48-55, tl(n100) 40-48; measurements include birds of N.Am only (see **Geographic variation**).

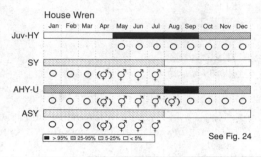

See Fig. 24

References—Stone (1896), Dwight (1900a), Ridgway (1904), Forbush (1929), A.O. Gross *in* Bent (1948), Roberts (1955), Wood (1969), Fisk (1972), Oberholser (1974), Sheppard & Klimkiewicz (1976), CWS & USFWS (1991), Pyle (1997c); IBP (MAPS) data, PNR data, PRBO data.

WINTER WREN
Troglodytes troglodytes

WIWR
Species # 7220
Band size: 0A-0

Species—From House Wren by shorter tl (25-36; see **Sex**); barring on the flanks usually extending forward of the legs; undertail covs dusky and rufous.

Geographic variation—Weak to moderate and differences are obscured by broad intergradation and individual variation. Subspecies taxonomy in N.Am follows A.R. Phillips & A.M. Rea *in* Phillips (1986), as modified by Browning (1990); see also Ridgway (1904), Brooks (1915), Oberholser (1919e, 1930b, 1974), Swarth (1934b), Burleigh (1935, 1959a), Burleigh & Peters (1948), Gabrielson & Lincoln (1951a), Dement'ev & Gladkov (1954), Paynter (1957), Mengel (1965), Cramp (1988). Fourteen other subspecies occur in Eurasia and Africa.

Alaskan Island (*T.t. alascensis*) Group. Large; bill long; uniform pale brownish.

T.t. alascensis (res Pribilof Is, AK): Large; bill medium in size (exp culmen 12.1-13.7); upperparts medium brown; throat and breast medium-pale brown. Wg: ♀(n9) 49-53, ♂(n10) 51-55. Siberian subspecies (*e.g., pallescens* or *dauricus*), which could occur as vagrants, generally are smaller (wg 45-54) and darker than Alaskan Island subspecies.

T.t. meligerus (res Attu-Buldir Is, AK): Large; bill medium long (exp culmen 13.8-15.3); upperparts dull, dark dusky brown; throat and breast dull, medium-dark brown. Wg: ♀(n3) 50-55, ♂(n11) 52-57. See *alascensis* regarding Siberian subspecies.

T.t. kiskensis (res Kiska-Unalaska Is, AK): Large; bill medium long (exp culmen 12.5-16.1); upperparts medium brown; throat and breast medium-pale brown. Wg: ♀(n33) 47-54, ♂(n44) 50-56. Birds of Tanaga I (*"tanagensis"*) may average slightly larger and redder, birds of Seguam-Yunaska Is (*"seguamensis"*) may average paler and grayer, birds of Amat-Amagat Is (*"stevensoni"*) may average slightly paler and grayer, and birds of the Unalaska Is (*"petrophilus"*) may average shorter billed and redder, but in all cases differences may be attributed to specimen wear or, if present, are too slight for subspecies recognition.

T.t. semidiensis (res Semidi I, AK): Large; bill long (exp culmen 14.6-16.5); upperparts medium grayish brown; throat and breast pale grayish brown. Wg: ♀(n6) 48-53, ♂(n5) 52-55.

Western (*T.t. pacificus*) Group. Small; bill short; uniform dark brownish.

T.t. helleri (res Kodiak Is, AK): Medium in size; bill medium short (exp culmen 10.4-12.8); upperparts medium-dark brown; throat and breast medium brownish. Wg: ♀(n4) 46-48, ♂(n20) 47-50.

T.t. pacificus (br & wint coastal sw.AK to sw.CA & montane sc.CA): Small; bill short (exp culmen 9.8-12.7); upperparts dark rufous-brown to dusky rufous; throat and breast dull rufous-brown. Wg: ♀(n100) 42-48, ♂(n100) 44-50. Smaller and grayer birds of se.AK Is ("*ochroleucus*"), smaller and paler birds of wc.CA ("*muiri*") and darker birds of ec-sw.CA ("*obscurior*"), along with other populations within *pacificus*, may warrant subspecies recognition, but more study is needed.

T.t. salebrosus (br interior c.BC-w.MT to e.OR, wint to s.CA-sw.AZ): Small; bill short (exp culmen 10.0-12.0); upperparts medium brown with a rufous wash; throat and breast medium-pale brown. Wg: ♀(n12) 42-48, ♂(n10) 45-50. Grayer birds of w.ID-WY may be distinct at the subspecies level, but more study is needed.

Eastern (*T.t. hiemalis*) Group. Medium in size; reddish brown; throat whitish.

T.t. hiemalis (br e.BC-WS to Nfl-PA, wint to c.NM-FL): Medium in size; bill medium short (exp culmen 10.5-12.3); upperparts medium brown with a rufous tinge; throat whitish; breast lightly washed brownish. Wg: ♀(n41) 44-49, ♂(n11) 46-51. Birds of Nfl ("*aquilonaris*") may average darker and grayer, but variation is slight.

T.t. pullus (br WV-n.GA, wint to MS-FL?): Medium in size; bill short (exp culmen 10.1-11.4); upperparts medium-dark reddish brown; throat whitish; breast with a moderate brownish wash. Wg: ♀(n2) 44-50, ♂(n5) 47-52.

Molt—PB: HY partial-incomplete (Jul-Oct), AHY complete (Jul-Sep); PA absent. The PBs occur on the summer grounds. The 1st PB includes 4 to 10 (~13%) inner gr covs, usually (in ~92% of birds) 1-3 terts (occasionally s6, as well), and occasionally (in ~8% of birds) 1-2 central rects (r1). Molt limits are very difficult to see; thus, more study is needed.

Skull—Pneumaticization completes in HY/SY from 1 Nov (as early as 1 Oct in birds of w.CA) through Jan. Look for windows (> 2 mm; Fig. 11**D**) in some SYs through spring.

Age—Juv (May-Aug) has the breast mottled indistinctly with dusky and has less distinct barring on the flanks, vent, and undertail covs (the latter also loosely textured); juv ♀ = ♂.

HY/SY (Aug-Jul): Molt limits usually occur among the gr covs (Fig. 133**C-E**, but these can be difficult to detect; see **Molt**), the retained outer covs worn, buffy rufous, usually without white tips, contrasting with the fresher and indistinctly white-tipped, replaced inner covs; 1-3 terts usually replaced, contrasting with the older, juvenal middle ss (s4-s6; Fig. 133**D-E**); outer pp covs narrow, tapered, relatively abraded (Fig. 138) and brownish with indistinct, pale cinnamon or whitish fringes; central rects (r1) occasionally replaced, contrastingly fresh; upper mandible brown to brownish black; lower mandible yellowish to pale brown (through Oct-Nov?). **Note: Rect shape seems unhelpful for ageing, despite the retention of the juvenal tail. Molt limits in this species can be very difficult to see; thus, many intermediates (especially in Apr-Jul) will be difficult or impossible to age reliably.**

AHY/ASY (Aug-Jul): Wing covs, terts, and rects uniformly adult (Fig. 133**F**) and fresh, the gr covs (except for the outer 3 feathers) often tipped white; outer pp covs broad, truncate, relatively fresh, and dusky with distinct, cinnamon-buff edging (Fig. 138); upper mandible black; lower mandible brown. **Note: See HY/SY; ASYs in Mar-Jul can be especially difficult to age reliably.**

Sex—♀ = ♂ by plumage. CP/BP (Mar-Aug). ♀ wg(n100) 42-50, tl(n30) 25-33; ♂ wg(n100) 44-52, tl(n35) 28-36; measurements exclude birds of Alaskan Island Subspecies Group (see **Geographic variation**).

References—Stone (1896), Dwight (1900a), Ridgway (1904), Forbush (1929), Bent (1948), Roberts (1955), Wood (1969), Hawthorn (1972), Oberholser (1974), Cramp (1988), Svensson (1992), Jenni & Winkler (1994), Pyle (1997c); J.R. King (pers. comm.); IBP (MAPS) data, PNR data, PRBO data.

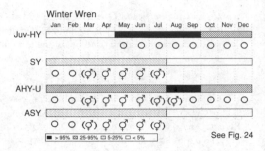

Winter Wren

See Fig. 24

SEDGE WREN
Cistothorus platensis

SEWR
Species # 7240
Band size: 0A-0

Species—From the other wrens (including Marsh Wren) by the combination of small size (wg 40-48, tl 34-41; see **Sex**); exp culmen < middle toe without claw; crown and rump with white streaking (in all plumages); supercilium indistinct and buff; undertail covs without bars.

Geographic variation—The subspecies of N.Am is well defined. Subspecies taxonomy follows Mayr & Greenway (1960), as modified by Phillips (1986); see also Ridgway (1904). About nineteen other subspecies occur in Mex-S.Am.

  C.p. stellaris (br & wint throughout range in N.Am): From subspecies of Mex-S.Am by wg averages longer (see **Sex**, *vs* 36-45 in the other subspecies); blackish streaking on the crown extending forward of the eyes (*vs* absent or restricted to the central crown); rump dusky and cinnamon with white streaking (*vs* primarily or entirely tawny in the other subspecies).

Molt—PB: HY partial-incomplete (Jul-Oct), AHY complete (Jul-Sep); PA partial-incomplete (Mar-Apr). The PBs occur on the summer grounds. The 1st PB is variable: in most birds it includes 7 to 10 (~85%) inner gr covs, usually (in ~92% of birds) 1-3 terts (sometimes s6, as well), and sometimes (in ~42% of birds) 1-2 central rects (r1). Occasional birds (probably from southern populations only) also can replace the innermost 1-2 pp and the outermost 1-2 ss. The 1st PA includes 2-8 inner gr covs, 1-3 terts, and often (in ~67% of birds) 1-2 central rects (r1), sometimes more, and occasionally (in ~8% of birds), all 12 rects. The adult PA includes 3-9 gr covs, 2-3 terts (sometimes s6, as well), and 0 (~9%) to all 12 (~27%) rects.

Skull—Pneumaticization completes in HY/SY from 15 Oct through Jan. Look for windows (> 2 mm; Fig. 11**D**) in some SYs through spring.

Age—Juv (Jun-Aug) has less white streaking to the upperparts (especially the crown), relatively paler underparts, and loosely textured undertail covs; juv ♀ = ♂.

  HY/SY (Aug-Jul): Outer pp covs narrow, tapered, and relatively abraded, with relatively indistinct, narrow, or no pale cinnamon to whitish edging (Fig. 138); molt limits occasionally occur among the gr covs in Aug-Mar (Fig. 133**D-E**), the outer covs contrastingly worn; 2-3 terts and sometimes s6 replaced at the 1st PB, contrasting with the older, juvenal middle ss (s4-s6) in Aug-Mar (Fig. 133**D-E**; but beware of pseudolimits between s6-s8 that cause terts to appear newer in AHY/ASYs); central rects (r1; sometimes other rects and rarely all) often replaced at the 1st PB, contrastingly fresh in Aug-Mar. **Note: Rect shape seems unhelpful for ageing despite the retention of the juvenal tail in most birds until at least the 1st PA. Molt limits among the gr covs, terts, and rects are found in both SY and ASY in Mar-Jul and should not be used for ageing during this period; use the pp-cov criteria at this** time. **Differences in the extent of the 1st and adult PAs (see Molt) also may provide some clues; more study is needed. Caution is advised, especially in Apr-Jul, when many or most birds probably should not be aged.**

AHY/ASY (Aug-Jul): Outer pp covs broad, truncate, and relatively fresh, with relatively broad and distinct, medium-dark cinnamon edging (Fig. 138); gr covs, terts, middle ss (s4-s6), and rects uniformly adult (Fig. 133**F**) and fresh in Aug-Mar (but beware of pseudolimits between s6-s8 that cause terts to appear newer; see p. 207). **Note: See HY/SY.**

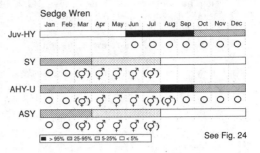

Sex—♀ = ♂ by plumage. CP/BP (May-Aug). ♀ wg(n30) 40-46, tl(n20) 34-39; ♂ wg(n30) 42-48, tl(n20) 36-41; measurements include birds of N.Am only (see **Geographic variation**).

References—Stone (1896), Dwight (1900a), Ridgway (1904), Forbush (1929), Bent (1948), Roberts (1955), Wood (1969), Oberholser (1974), Pyle (1997c).

MARSH WREN
Cistothorus palustris

MAWR
Species # 7250
Band size: 1C-1

Species—From the other wrens (including Sedge Wren) by the combination of medium-small size (wg 42-57, tl 35-51; see **Sex**); exp culmen ≥ middle toe without claw; crown and rump without white streaks (in all plumages); undertail covs whitish with blackish bars.

Geographic variation—Weak to moderate and largely clinal throughout range. Subspecies taxonomy primarily follows A.R. Phillips & A.M. Rea *in* Phillips (1986); see also Ridgway (1904), Swarth (1917b), Harper (1926), Wheeler (1931), Dingle & Sprunt (1932), Welter (1935), Todd (1937), Aldrich (1946), Behle (1948, 1985), Parkes (1952a, 1959), Sutton (1967), Oberholser (1974), Browning (1978, 1990), Rea (1983), Unitt (1984), Godfrey (1986). One other subspecies occurs in Mex. The following applies to birds in fresh plumage after molts. Worn birds (Feb and, especially, Jun-Jul) become extremely faded and impossible to distinguish.

Coastal Pacific (*C.p. paludicola*) Group. Medium in size; dark rufous-brown.

C.p. browningi (res coastal sw.BC-wc.WA, wint to sw.WA): Medium in size; crown and lower back medium-dark grayish brown; rump tinged rufous; flanks brownish, without dusky markings. ♀ wg(n3) 47-52, tl(n3) 41-46; ♂ wg(n5) 50-54, tl(n5) 45-49.

C.p. paludicola (br & wint coastal sw.WA-sw.CA): Medium small; crown mixed brown and blackish; lower back moderately dark brown with a variable rufous wash; rump dark cinnamon to rufous; uppertail covs with moderately distinct, dusky barring; flanks medium brown with a rufous to dark rufous tinge and without dusky markings. ♀ wg(n30) 45-50, tl(n29) 39-44; ♂ wg(n40) 46-52, tl(n40) 42-45. Birds of coastal CA are brighter and probably distinct at the subspecies level, but more study is needed. Suggest three-letter subspecies code (see p. 30-31): "pld".

Interior Western (*C.p. plesius*) Group. Large; pale brownish with a rufous tinge.

C.p. pulverius (br interior sc.BC to ne.CA-w.NV, wint to s.CA-TX): Medium large; lower back pale brown with little or no rufous tinge; uppertail covs with indistinct, dusky barring; flanks pale brownish, without dusky markings. ♀ wg(n10) 49-54, tl(n10) 42-45; ♂ wg(n20) 51-56, tl(n14) 44-49.

C.p. aestuarinus (res interior c.CA, wint to coastal CA): Medium in size; crown primarily blackish; lower back washed rufous, with narrow to indistinct, white streaks; rump dusky rufous; uppertail covs usually with dusky barring; flanks moderately dark brown with a rufous tinge and without dusky markings. ♀ wg(n10) 46-52, tl(n10) 42-48; ♂ wg(n21) 50-54, tl(n21) 44-49.

C.p. deserticola (res desert s.NV to se.CA-sc.AZ): Medium large; crown primarily blackish; lower back and rump rufous-brown; uppertail covs with distinct, dusky barring; flanks medium brown with a rufous tinge and without dusky markings. ♀ wg(n13) 48-52, tl(n13) 44-49; ♂ wg(n12) 51-55, tl(n12) 46-51.

C.p. plesius (br se.ID-WY to sc.CO, NM? & sw.TX?; wint w.WA-s.CA to KS-TX): Large; lower back and rump moderately pale and dull brown with a rufous tinge; uppertail covs usually with distinct, dusky barring; flanks medium brownish, without dusky markings. ♀ wg(n45) 50-54, tl(n36) 43-48; ♂ wg(n50) 53-57, tl(n45) 45-51.

C.p. laingi (br n.Alb-n.MT to s.Man, wint NM-s.CO-TX): Medium large; lower back pale brownish cinnamon; rump cinnamon; uppertail covs without dusky bars; flanks brightish pale cinnamon, without dusky markings ♀ wg(n10) 47-53, tl(n10) 38-45; ♂ wg(n41) 51-55, tl(n41) 42-48.

C.p. iliacus (= "*cryphius*"; br se.Man-e.KS to MI-c.OH, wint se.TX-FL): Medium in size; lower back and rump medium reddish brown; uppertail covs without barring or with indistinct, dusky barring; flanks rufous, without dusky markings. ♀ wg(n32) 47-52, tl(n32) 39-44; ♂ wg(n32) 50-54, tl(n32) 43-47.

Eastern (*C.p. palustris*) Group. Small; dull brown tinged rufous.

C.p. dissaeptus (br s.Ont-NB to n.OH-WV, wint LA-FL-se.NY?): Medium small; lower back and rump dull, moderately dark brown with a rufous wash; uppertail covs without dusky barring; flanks buffy cinnamon, without dusky markings. ♀ wg(n25) 45-51, tl(n25) 39-44; ♂ wg(n48) 49-55, tl(n48) 42-47. Birds of OH-nw.PA ("*canniphonus*") may average slightly larger and darker, but differences are slight and substantially obscured by individual variation.

C.p. marianae (res coastal e.TX-w.FL): Medium small; lower back and rump dark dusky brown with little or no rufous; uppertail covs without dusky markings; flanks dusky brownish with dusky spotting. ♀ wg(n16) 43-49, tl(n16) 35-41; ♂ wg(n18) 45-51, tl(n18) 36-43. Birds of se.TX-LA ("*thryophilus*") average smaller and paler, but differences are slight.

C.p. palustris (br & wint coastal RI-c.VA; vag to NS): Medium small; lower back and rump dull, grayish brown with a rufous wash; uppertail covs without dusky or (sometimes) with indistinct, dusky barring; flanks mixed dark buffy gray and brownish, usually without dusky marks. ♀ wg(n32) 45-51, tl(n32) 37-42; ♂ wg(n47) 47-52, tl(n47) 39-44. Suggested three-letter subspecies code (see p. 30-31): "pls".

C.p. waynei (res coastal s.VA-NC; vag to NB & FL?): Medium small; lower back and rump dull, dark rufous; uppertail covs with indistinct, dusky barring; flanks dusky cinnamon, sometimes with dusky spotting. ♀ wg(n10) 42-48, tl(n10) 34-39; ♂ wg(n14) 46-50, tl(n14) 37-41.

C.p. griseus (res coastal SC-ec.FL): Small; upperparts pale gray with a brownish tinge; uppertail covs with distinct, dusky barring; flanks pale brownish gray with dusky barring. ♀ wg(n4) 42-44, tl(n4) 33-37; ♂ wg(n5) 45-49, tl(n5) 37-41.

Molt—PB: HY incomplete (Jul-Oct), AHY complete (Jul-Aug); PA partial-incomplete (Feb-Apr). The PBs occur on the summer grounds. The 1st PB is variable, often (in ~65% of birds) being eccentric (see p. 208 and Fig. 136), with the outermost 5-7 pp, the innermost 3-6 ss, and the outermost 0 (~85%) to 4 pp covs replaced. Others replace 5 to 10 gr covs (~58% replacing all 10) and 1-3 terts (plus s6 in ~29% of birds), but no pp. All rects appear to be replaced in most or all birds. Southern and western birds (*e.g.*, *C.p. paludicola*, *marianae* and *griseus*) appear to replace more feathers on average than northern and eastern birds (*e.g.*, *laingi*, *dissaeptus* and *palustris*). The 1st PA includes 4 to 10 (~15%) inner gr covs, usually (in ~95% of birds) 1-3 terts, and 0 (~40%) to all 12 (~15%) rects. The adult PA includes 5 to 10 (~30%) inner gr covs, 1-3 terts (occasionally s6, as well), and 0 (~9%) to all 12 (~27%) rects. More study is needed.

Skull—Pneumaticization completes in HY/SY from 1 Oct (as early as 1 Sep in coastal Pacific populations) through Jan. Look for windows (> 2 mm; Fig. 11**D**) in some SYs through spring.

Age—Juv (May-Aug) has a relatively dark crown, less distinct or no white streaking on the back, a less distinct supercilium, and loosely textured undertail covs; juv ♀ = ♂.

HY/SY (Aug-Jul): Outer pp covs narrow, tapered, relatively abraded (Fig. 138), and pale brown; molt limits usually occur among the gr covs, pp, and ss (Figs. 133**C-E** & 136**A-B**; see **Molt**) in Aug-Mar, the retained, 0-4 outer gr covs, 3-5 inner pp, and 3-7 outer ss brown and faded, contrasting with the fresher and duskier, replaced feathers. **Note: Beware of pseudolimits (see p. 207) between s6-s8 that cause the terts to appear newer in AHY/ASYs. Molt limits among the gr covs, terts, and rects are found in both SY and ASY in Mar-Jul and should not be used for ageing during this period; use the pp and pp-cov criteria at this time. Differences in the extent of the 1st and adult PAs (see Molt) also may provide some clues; more study is needed. Caution is advised, especially in Apr-Jul when feathers become extremely worn, and many or most birds probably should not be aged.**

AHY/ASY (Aug-Jul): Outer pp covs broad, truncate, relatively fresh (Fig. 138), and dusky with a brownish tinge; gr covs, pp, and ss uniformly adult (Fig. 133**F**) in Aug-Mar. **Note: See HY/SY.**

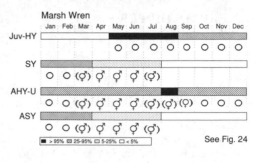

Sex—♀ = ♂ by plumage. CP/BP (Mar-Sep). ♀ wg(n100) 42-54, tl(n100) 35-49; ♂ wg(n100) 45-57, tl(n100) 37-51; measurements are useful for sexing within each subspecies (see **Geographic variation**).

References—Stone (1896), Dwight (1900a), Ridgway (1904), Forbush (1929), Welter (1936), Bent (1948), Roberts (1955), Kale (1966), Wood (1969), Oberholser (1974), Pyle (1997c).

DIPPERS   *CINCLIDAE*

One species. Family characters include stocky proportions, soft plumage, strong legs, and short wings and tail. Dippers have 10 primaries (the 10th reduced), 9 secondaries, and 12 rectrices. The first prebasic molt is partial and no prealternate molt occurs. Ages and sexes are similar in plumage. Breeding characters can be used to sex spring/summer birds, and males average moderately larger than females.

AMERICAN DIPPER
Cinclus mexicanus

AMDI
Species # 7010
Band size: 2-1A

Geographic variation—Weak and clinal where ranges meet. Subspecies taxonomy follows Phillips (1986); see also Ridgway (1904). Three other subspecies occur in Mex-C.Am.

  C.m. unicolor (br & wint throughout the range in N.Am): Crown moderately pale gray with a brownish wash; juv with throat and chin white. Birds of coastal AK-CA (*"mortoni"*) may average slightly darker and smaller, but variation probably is too slight to warrant subspecies recognition.

  C.m. mexicanus (br & wint Mex, vag to se.AZ): Crown medium-dark gray with a brownish wash; throat and chin usually gray, juvs sometimes with a whitish chin.

Molt—PB: HY partial (Aug-Oct), AHY complete (Jun-Aug); PA absent-limited(?). The sequence of molt is not typical in this species. The 1st PB includes 2-6 gr covs (0-4 inner covs and 0-3 outer covs) and sometimes (in ~21% of birds) 1-2 terts; the rects are retained. During the adult PB, two blocks of pp can be dropped consecutively, usually p2-p5 or p6 followed by p1 and the outermost pp, when the former have completed growth. The ss can molt irregularly, s5 often being the last replaced. SYs (possibly non-breeders) also can molt earlier than ASYs, beginning in Jun.

Skull—Pneumaticization completes in HY from 15 Sep through Dec. Look for windows (> 3 mm; Fig. 11**D**) in some SYs through spring.

Age—Juv (May-Sep) has a whitish to pale grayish throat, underparts mottled whitish, and pale buffy-whitish edging to the gr covs; juv ♀ = ♂.

  HY/SY (Sep-Aug): Molt limits occur among the gr covs (Fig. 133**B-D**; see **Molt**), the retained middle covs worn and brownish gray with indistinct, dingy-whitish tips, contrasting with the fresher, slate-colored, and whiter-tipped, replaced inner and outer covs; 1-2 terts occasionally replaced, contrasting with the older, juvenal middle ss (s4-s6; Fig. 133**D**) or, if all juvenal terts are retained, these are relatively worn and brownish gray, especially in spring; outer pp covs quite narrow, tapered, relatively abraded (Figs. 138 & 221), and brownish gray with dingy-whitish tips when fresh. **Note: Rect shape seems unhelpful for ageing despite the retention of the juvenal tail. The extent or brightness of yellow in the bill may be useful for separating HY/SY from AHY through winter (although the bills of AHY/ASYs become yellower in the winter, as well); more study is needed.**

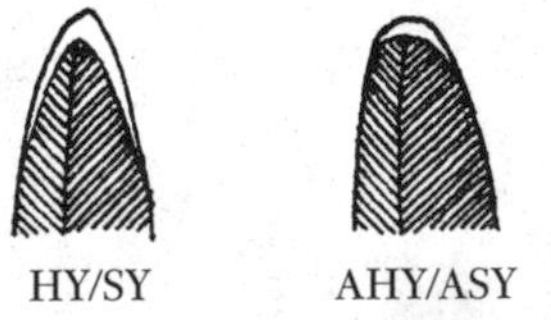

HY/SY   AHY/ASY

FIGURE 221. The shape and pattern of the primary coverts by age in American Dipper.

AHY/ASY (Sep-Aug): Wing covs uniformly adult (Fig. 133F) and slaty gray with whitish tips when fresh; terts uniformly adult, slate, and relatively fresh in spring; outer pp covs quite broad, truncate, relatively fresh (Figs. 138 & 221), and slate gray with whitish tipping when fresh. **Note: See HY/SY.**

American Dipper

See Fig. 24

Sex—♀ = ♂ by plumage. CP/BP (Mar-Aug). Measurements are moderately helpful for sexing: ♀ wg(n89) 80-94, tl(n25) 41-55; ♂ wg(n44) 86-102, tl(n22) 43-56.

References—Ridgway (1904), Bent (1948), Bakus (1959), Sullivan (1965), Oberholser (1974), Svensson (1992), Kingery (1996), Pyle (1997c); F.E. Price (*in litt.* to the BBL).

KINGLETS

REGULIDAE

Two species. Subfamily characters include very small size and delicate features. Kinglets have 10 primaries (the 10th reduced), 9 secondaries, and 12 rectrices. The first prebasic molt is partial to incomplete, and prealternate molts, if they occur at all, are very limited. Because of their small size, skull pneumatization completes relatively early, by September in most birds. Ageing of most birds is possible by differences between juvenal and adult flight feathers, and sexing by plumage and breeding condition is reliable. Males average moderately larger than females.

GOLDEN-CROWNED KINGLET
Regulus satrapa

GCKI
Species # 7480
Band size: 0A

Species—Juv from juv Ruby-crowned Kinglet by crown primarily dusky; indistinct supercilium present.

Geographic variation—Moderate and ranges fairly well defined. Subspecies taxonomy follows Phillips (1991); see also Ridgway (1904), Jenks (1936), van Rossem (1945b), Dickinson (1953), Jewett *et al.* (1953), Phillips *et al.* (1964), Oberholser (1974), Behle (1985), Godfrey (1986). Two other subspecies occur in Mex.

>**R.s. apache** (br & wint s.AK-s.Yuk to sw.CA-s.NM): Medium small; bill long (nares to tip 5.0-7.1); back and rump bright yellowish olive; white supercilium extends to the posterior of the crown stripe and auricular; wing bars narrow (1-2 mm wide when fresh) and dingy whitish with a lemon or olive tinge. ♀ wg(n100) 50-56, tl(n10) 39-44; ♂ wg(n44) 53-59, tl(n44) 41-46. Birds north and west of AZ-NM ("*amoenus*") may average smaller billed, brighter, and less grayish, but differences are obscured by individual variation.

>**R.s. olivaceus** (br coastal se.AK-sw.OR, wint to ID,sw.CA): Small; bill medium long (nares to tip 4.7-6.5); back and rump dark greenish olive; white supercilium extends to the posterior of the crown stripe and auricular; wing bars as in *apache*. ♀ wg(n53) 49-55, tl(n10) 37-42; ♂ wg(n100) 52-57, tl(n79) 39-44.

>**R.s. satrapa** (br n.Alb-WS to Nfl-NC, wint to se.CA-FL): Large; bill short (nares to tip 4.4-5.2); back and rump olive with a grayish wash; white supercilium abbreviated at the middle of the crown stripe and auricular; wing bars wide (2-3 mm when fresh) and white or slightly tinged lemon. ♀ wg(n23) 54-59, tl(n20) 41-45; ♂ wg(n27) 56-62, tl(n26) 42-47.

Molt—PB: HY partial (Jul-Sep), AHY complete (Jul-Aug); PA absent. The PBs occur on the summer grounds. The 1st PB includes 0 (~59%) to 4 inner gr covs, but usually no terts or rects.

Skull—Pneumaticization completes in HY from 1 Oct (as early as 1 Sep in coastal Pacific populations) through Dec.

Age—Juv (Jun-Aug) lacks yellow or orange in the crown and has a brownish cast to the upperparts, loosely textured undertail covs, and a yellowish roof of the mouth (upper mandible lining); juv ♀ = ♂.

>HY/SY (Aug-Jul): Molt limits sometimes occur (but are very indistinct) among the med and gr covs (Fig. 133A-C; see **Molt**), the retained outer covs worn and brownish with indistinct, dingy-whitish tips, contrasting with the fresher, duskier and distinctly white-tipped, replaced inner covs; outer pp covs narrow, tapered, relatively abraded, and brownish with indistinct, relatively narrow, or no dingy-olive edging (Fig. 138); rects tapered and pointed (Fig. 222). **Note: Many intermediates can occur, especially in May-Jul when feathers become worn.**

AHY/ASY (Aug-Jul): Wing covs uniformly adult (Fig. 133F), dusky with fresh green edging and distinct, white tips; outer pp covs broad, truncate, relatively fresh, and dusky with distinct, relatively wide, greenish-olive edging (Fig. 138); rects broad and truncate (Fig. 222; they can have small point at the shaft). **Note: See HY/SY.**

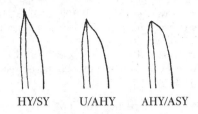

HY/SY   U/AHY   AHY/ASY

FIGURE 222. The shape of the outer rectrices (r4-r6) by age in Golden-crowned and Ruby-crowned kinglets.

Sex—CP/BP (Apr-Aug). ♀ wg(n100) 49-59, tl(n36) 37-45; ♂ wg(n100) 52-62, tl(n100) 39-47; see **Geographic variation**.

♀: Crown yellow, without orange-red feathers. **Note: Sexing by crown plumage is reliable after the 1st PB; beware that juv ♂♂ lack red feathers. Also, occasional birds with one or two orange-red feathers may not be reliably sexed by plumage alone. Compare with age; these either should be HY/SY ♂♂ or, more probably, AHY/ASY ♀♀.**

♂: Crown yellow with at least a few orange-red feathers. **Note: See ♀.**

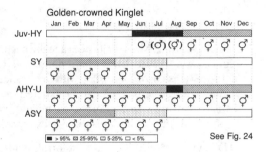

Hybrids reported—Possibly Ruby-crowned Kinglet.

References—Stone (1896), Dwight (1900a), Ridgway (1904), Forbush (1929), Bent (1949), Roberts (1955), Wood (1969), Leberman (1970), Collins (1974e), Oberholser (1974), Sheppard & Klimkiewicz (1976), Fairfield & Shirokoff (1978), Smith (1979), Prescott (1980b), CWS & USFWS (1991), Jackson (1992), Svensson (1992), Jenni & Winkler (1994), Pyle (1997c); D.M. Fairfield, P.A. Shirokoff & R. Engs, M. Wood (*in litt.* to the BBL); J.R. King, G. Wallace (pers. comm.); IBP (MAPS) data, PNR data, PRBO data.

RUBY-CROWNED KINGLET
Regulus calendula

RCKI
Species # 7490
Band size: 0A

Species— ♀♀ from Northern Beardless-Tyrannulet by p10 reduced; p9 < p6; crest lacking; wing bars distinct; bill small and slender; basal half of the lower mandible blackish. From Hutton's Vireo by shorter tl (38-47; see **Sex**); p9 ≈ p4 and p9 > p3; bases of the pp blackish, forming a black bar 3-6 mm beyond the gr covs; bill and legs thin and blackish; soles of the feet yellowish. Juv from juv Golden-crowned Kinglet by crown grayish olive; supercilium absent.

Geographic variation—Moderately well marked, but differences are obscured by variation in the nominate form. Subspecies taxonomy follows Phillips (1991); see also Ridgway (1904), Bishop (1926), Phillips (1964), Phillips *et al.* (1964), Hubbard & Crossin (1974), Oberholser (1974), Browning (1979b, 1990), D.M. Power (1980), Behle (1985). One other extinct subspecies formerly occurred in Baja CA.

R.c. calendula (br & wint throughout most of the range in N.Am): Variably large; upperparts medium olive; underparts grayish olive, with the vent tinged dull whitish olive. ♀ wg(n100) 52-59, tl(n100) 40-47; ♂ wg(n100) 55-63, tl(n100) 43-51. Birds breeding in montane w.N.Am (*"cineraceus"*) may average grayer and birds of AZ (*"arizonensis"*) may average shorter-winged, but differences are slight and broadly clinal.

R.c. grinnelli (br coastal se.AK-BC, wint to coastal sw.CA): Small; upperparts dark greenish olive; underparts buffy olive, with the vent tinged yellowish. ♀ wg(n20) 50-56, tl(n10) 38-44; ♂ wg(n30) 53-58, tl(n20) 40-46.

Molt—PB: HY partial (Jul-Sep), AHY complete (Jul-Aug); PA absent-limited (Feb-Apr). The PBs occur on the summer grounds. The 1st PB includes 0 (~88%) to 3 inner gr covs, but no terts or rects.

Skull—Pneumaticization completes in HY from 1 Oct through Nov.

Age—Juv (Jun-Aug) lacks red in the crown and has a brownish cast to the upperparts, buffy-brown wing bars, loosely textured undertail covs, and the roof of the mouth (upper mandible lining) yellowish; juv ♀ = ♂.

HY/SY (Aug-Jul): Molt limits occasionally occur (but are very indistinct) among the med and gr covs (Fig. 133**A-C**; see **Molt**), the retained outer covs worn and brownish with indistinct, dingy-whitish tips, contrasting with the fresher, duskier, and distinctly white-tipped, replaced inner covs; outer pp covs narrow, tapered, relatively abraded, and brownish with indistinct, relatively narrow, or no dingy-olive edging (Fig. 138); rects tapered and pointed (Fig. 222). **Note: Many intermediates can occur, especially in May-Jul when feathers become worn.**

AHY/ASY (Aug-Jul): Wing covs uniformly adult (Fig. 133**F**) and dusky with fresh green edging and distinct, white tips; outer pp covs broad, truncate, relatively fresh, and dusky with distinct and relatively wide, greenish-olive edging (Fig. 138); rects broad and truncate (Fig. 222; they can have small point at the shaft). **Note: See HY/SY.**

Sex—CP/BP (Apr-Aug). Wg: ♀ wg(n100) 50-59, tl(n100) 38-47; ♂ wg(n100) 53-63, tl(n100) 40-51; see **Geographic variation**.

♀: Crown without red or orange-red feathers. **Note: Sexing by crown plumage is reliable after the 1st PB, but beware that juv ♂♂ lack red feathers. Occasional birds with one or two red or orange-red feathers may not be reliably sexed by plumage alone; compare with age, these likely are either HY/SY ♂♂ or, more probably, AHY/ASY ♀♀.**

♂: Crown with at least a few red or orange-red feathers. **Note: See ♀.**

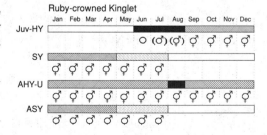

Hybrids reported—Possibly Golden-crowned Kinglet.

References—Stone (1896), Dwight (1900a), Ridgway (1904), Forbush (1929), Bent (1949), Roberts (1955), Sawyer (1961), Wood (1969), Leberman (1970), Collins (1974e), Oberholser (1974), Sheppard & Klimkiewicz (1976), Fairfield & Shirokoff (1978), Kaufman (1979b, 1993b), Smith (1979), Prescott (1980a), CWS & USFWS (1991), Cramp (1992), Svensson (1992), Paulsen (1995), Pyle (1997c); D.M. Fairfield, P.A. Shirokoff & R. Engs, C.S. Robbins, M. Wood (*in litt.* to the BBL); IBP (MAPS) data, PNR data, PRBO data.

MUSCICAPIDS   *MUSCICAPIDAE*

Twenty-one species. Family characters include generally small and delicate bills, relatively pointed wings, and delicate legs. For convenience, this family is divided into three subfamilies.

Old World Warblers and Gnatcatchers   *Sylviinae*

Five species. Subfamily characters include small size, delicate features, and prominent rictal bristles. Old World warblers have 10 primaries (the 10th reduced), 9 secondaries, and 12 rectrices. In North American species, the first prebasic molt is partial to incomplete, and partial to incomplete prealternate molts also occur in most species. Because of their small size, skull pneumaticization completes relatively early. Ageing of most birds is possible by differences between juvenal and adult flight feathers. Sexing by plumage also is possible for most North American species, and breeding condition is reliable for sexing during the nesting seasons. Males average moderately larger than females.

ARCTIC WARBLER   ARWA
Phylloscopus borealis   Species # 7470
                                                        Band size: 0A

Species—All *Phylloscopus* warblers are separated from American wood-warblers (*e.g.*, Tennessee and Orange-crowned warblers) by the presence of a reduced p10. From other Eurasian species of *Phylloscopus* (potential vagrants to N.Am) by the combination of large size (wg 58-70, tl 42-52; see **Sex**) and bill (nares to tip 6.5-8.2); p10 – pp covs -2 to 3 mm; p9 ≈ p5; 7 pp tips extend beyond the longest ss; supercilium long and distinct; one distinct wing bar (on the gr covs) present (a small bar on the med covs sometimes can be present).

Geographic variation—Weak, but the range in N.Am is well defined. Subspecies taxonomy follows Cramp (1992); see also Ridgway (1904), Dement'ev & Gladkov (1954), Gibson (1981), Phillips (1991), Svensson (1992). No other subspecies occur.

> *P.b. xanthodryas* (vag to w.AK Is): Wing long; bill large (nares to tip 7.0-8.2); upperparts green without a grayish tinge; underparts with a heavy, yellow wash. Wg: ♀(n30) 66-72, ♂(n30) 70-76. *P.b. borealis*, a possible vagrant to w.AK Is, has wg medium long (♀ 61-68, ♂ 64-71), bill medium large (nares to tip 6.6-8.0), upperparts grayish green, and underparts whitish with little yellow wash.
>
> *P.b. kennicotti* (br w.AK): Wg short (see **Sex**); bill small (nares to tip 6.5-7.8); upperparts green without a grayish tinge; underparts whitish with a moderate yellow wash.

Molt—PB: HY partial (Jul-Aug), AHY partial (Jul-Aug); PA complete (Jan-Apr). The PBs occur on the summer grounds. The 1st PB sometimes can include the central rects (r1) and the adult PB often includes up to two terts (s8-s9) and the central rects (r1; rarely other rects). Look for some SYs to retain a few flight feathers (*e.g.*, ss among s4-s6) during the 1st PA. More study is needed on this interesting molt strategy.

Skull—Pneumaticization completes in HY from 1 Oct through Dec.

Age—Juv (Jun-Aug) has the upperparts washed grayish brown and the sides of the underparts washed brown, with little or no yellow; juv ♀ = ♂.

> HY/SY (Aug-Mar): Flight feathers uniformly fresh through fall migration; tips to retained, juvenal med covs yellow; rects narrow and tapered (Fig. 139**A**).
>
> AHY/ASY (Apr-Mar): Flight feathers relatively worn through at least fall migration, the inner 1-2 ss (s8-s9) and/or central rects (r1) often contrastingly fresh; tips to the med covs whitish

(or worn off through fall migration); outer rects broad and truncate (Fig. 139A; but they can have small points at the shafts). **Note: Look also for some SY/TYs (Apr-Mar) to possibly retain some juvenal middle ss (among s3-s6), contrastingly abraded and worn.**

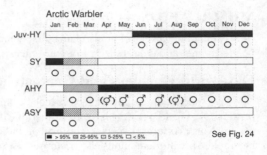

Arctic Warbler

Sex—♀ = ♂ by plumage. CP/BP (Apr-Aug). ♀ wg(n39) 58-67, tl(n20) 42-49; ♂ wg(n59) 62-70, tl(n20) 44-52; wg includes *P.b. kennicotti* only (see **Geographic variation**).

References—Ridgway (1904), Oberholser (1919d), B.W. Tucker *in* Bent (1949), Cramp (1992), Svensson (1992); J.R. King (pers. comm.); IBP (MAPS) data.

BLUE-GRAY GNATCATCHER
Polioptila caerulea

BGGN
Species # 7510
Band size: 0A

Species—Wing pointed (Fig. 223; p8 – p4 3-5 mm, p9 – p10 16-23 mm); tail graduation slight (Fig. 224; r1 – r6 5-9 mm); bill medium small (exp culmen ♀ 8.8-10.5, ♂ 9.3-11.2); upperparts of ♀♀ without brown or with relatively little brown wash, not contrasting markedly with the head color; ♂♂ with black on the forehead and lores in Feb-Jul (Fig. 228B); otherwise, ♀♀ and ♂♂ without black in the rest of the crown (Fig. 228A); outer 2 rects (r5-r6) with a substantial amount of white, including most of the outer webs (Fig. 224); underparts primarily white; base of the mandible usually flesh. From Black-tailed and California gnatcatchers by slightly longer bill, head plumage (♂♂), pattern to the outer rects, and color of the underparts. From Black-capped Gnatcatcher by wing and tail morphology, shorter bill, head plumage (♂♂), and mandible color.

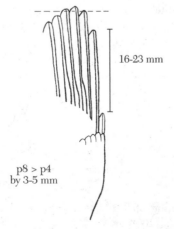

FIGURE 223. The wing morphology of Blue-gray Gnatcatcher. See Figure 10 for measurement techniques.

FIGURE 224. The tail morphology and pattern of white in the rectrices of Blue-gray Gnatcatcher.

Geographic variation—Moderate and ranges fairly well defined. Subspecies taxonomy follows Phillips (1991); see also Ridgway (1904), Grinnell (1926c), van Rossem (1934a), van Rossem & Hachisuka (1937a), Oberholser (1974). Four other subspecies occur in Mex-C.Am.

P.c. obscura (br & wint CA to WY-w.TX; vag to LA): Upperparts dark grayish to brownish gray by age/sex class (see **Age/Sex**); black at the base of the inner web of r6 (see Fig. 224) often extends distal to the tip of the undertail covs. Birds of N.Am ("*amoenissima*") may average larger and with paler crowns than birds of Baja CA, but differences are obscured by individual variation.

P.c. deppei (br extreme s.TX): Smaller than the other subspecies of N.Am; coloration otherwise as in *caerulea*, perhaps averaging paler. ♀ wg(n10) 43-48, tl(n10) 41-47; ♂ wg(n10) 47-52, tl(n10) 45-50.

P.c. caerulea (br & wint KS-c.TX to NH-FL; vag to s.CA): Upperparts bright blue-gray to medium brownish gray by age/sex class (see **Age/Sex**); black at the base of the inner web of r6 (see Fig. 224) rarely extends distal to the tip of the undertail covs.

Molt—PB: HY partial-incomplete (Jul-Aug), AHY complete (Jul-Aug); PA: SY partial-incomplete (Feb-Apr), ASY partial (Jan-Mar). The PBs occur on the summer grounds. The 1st PB includes 5 to 10 (~71%) inner gr covs, often (in ~82% of birds) 1-3 terts (occasionally s6, as well), and 0 (~86%) to all 12 (~7%) rects. The 1st PA includes 0 (~89%) to 3 inner gr covs, often (in ~53% of birds) 1-3 terts (rarely s6, as well), and sometimes (in ~21% of birds) 1-4 central rects (r1). The replacement of 1-2 pp covs (usually among the 4th to the 2nd from the outside) occasionally (~5-10%) can be suspended (until the winter grounds?), resulting in slight contrasts among these feathers (Fig. 225); more study is needed on this. The adult PA includes 0 (~61%) to 3 inner gr covs and often (in ~61% of birds) 1-2 terts, but no rects.

Skull—Pneumaticization completes in HY from 1 Oct (as early as 15 Sep in birds of s.N.Am) through Dec.

Age—Juv (May-Jul) has the crown and upperparts brownish gray, and loosely textured undertail covs; juv ♀ = ♂.

HY/SY (Jul-Jun): Outer pp covs uniformly narrow, tapered, relatively abraded, and brownish with indistinct, relatively narrow, or no grayish edging (Fig. 138, see also Fig. 225); molt limits sometimes occur among the outer gr covs (Fig. 133C-E; see **Molt**), the retained outer covs worn and brownish with paler brown edging, contrasting with the fresher, darker brown and bluish-edged to grayish-edged, replaced inner covs; 1-3 terts (occasionally s6, as well) often replaced, contrasting with the older, juvenal middle ss (s4-s6) in Jul-Feb (Fig. 133D-E), or if the juvenal terts are retained, these are relatively worn and brownish; rects occasionally with mixed, retained and replaced feathers, or inner rects brownish and relatively worn, especially in Mar-Jun. **Note: Both SYs and ASYs can replace inner gr covs and terts during the PA, showing molt limits in MarJun; ageing in spring thus relies on the outer gr covs, pp covs, and rects. Rect shape seems unhelpful for ageing, despite the usual retention of the juvenal tail, but look for retained juvenal crown feathers or (loosely textured) undertail covs on some birds through at least fall. Some intermediates, especially nesting ♀♀ in summer,**

FIGURE 225. An interesting pattern of primary covert replacement found in a small proportion of gnatcatchers and House Finches. It is possible that the replacement of 2-3 coverts (see text) during the adult prebasic molt is suspended over the fall migration; more study is needed. Look for this pattern in other passerines, as well.

may be indistinguishable; compare relative color and wear with season. Also, see AHY/ASY.

AHY/ASY (Jul-Jun): Outer pp covs broad, truncate, relatively fresh, and dark brown with distinct, relatively broad, bluish to grayish edging (Fig. 138), and sometimes with 1-2 feathers contrastingly fresh as in Figure 225; wing covs, terts, and middle ss (s4-s6) uniformly adult (Fig. 133F) in Jul-Feb, the outer gr covs without limits in Mar-Jun; rects uniformly adult, the inner rects relatively blackish and fresh. **Note: See HY/SY. Occasional ♂♂ showing one or two black flecks in the forehead in Sep-Dec also can be aged AHY/ASY.**

Sex—CP/BP (Mar-Aug). ♀ wg(n85) 46-53, tl(n24) 47-54; ♂ wg(n50) 49-56, tl(n42) 48-55; measurements exclude *P.c. deppei* (see **Geographic variation**).

Alternate Plumage

AHY ♀ (Mar-Jul): Forehead and supercilium region uniformly blue-gray or whitish (Fig. 228A). **Note: Sexing by plumage is reliable with alternate-plumaged birds only; no plumage criteria are known for sexing basic-plumaged birds, although a very small proportion (< 5%) of ♂♂ (AHY/ASY only) can have one or more black feathers in the forehead during Sep-Dec and are reliably sexed. ♀♀, especially of *P.c. obscura* (see Geographic variation), also average browner upperparts than ♂♂; some birds may be reliably sexed, with experience, but more study is needed.**

AHY ♂ (Jan-Aug): Forehead with a black supercilium extending from the bill to behind the eye (Fig. 228B). **Note: See ♀.**

Hybrids reported—Possibly Black-tailed Gnatcatcher.

Blue-gray Gnatcatcher

Jan Feb Mar Apr May Jun Jul Aug Sep Oct Nov Dec

Juv-HY ○ ○ ○ ○ ○ ○ ○ ○

SY ○ (♂) (♀) ♂ ♂ ♂

AHY-U ○ (♂) (♀) ♂ ♂ ♂ ♂ (♀) ○ ○ ○ ○

ASY (♂)(♂)(♀) ♂ ♂ ♂

■ > 95% ▨ 25-95% ☐ 5-25% □ < 5%   See Fig. 24

References—Stone (1896), Dwight (1900a), Ridgway (1904), Forbush (1929), Bent (1949), Roberts (1955), Wood (1969), Fisk (1972), Phillips *et al.* (1973), Collins & Phillips (1974), Oberholser (1974), Sheppard & Klimkiewicz (1976), Rappole *et al.* (1979), Parkes (1985a), Dunn & Garrett (1987), Howell (1987), Ellison (1992), Pyle (1997c); Pyle & Unitt (in press), E.J. Fisk (*in litt.* to the BBL); D. Cimprich (pers. comm.); IBP (MAPS) data, PRBO data.

CALIFORNIA GNATCATCHER
Polioptila californica

CAGN
Species # 7530
Band size: 0A

Species—From Black-tailed Gnatcatcher (which see for separation from Blue-gray and Black-capped gnatcatchers) by white eye ring of alternate-plumaged ♂♂ usually restricted to lower half (Fig. 228F); upperparts of ♀♀ strongly washed brown, contrasting distinctly with the grayish head; outer 2 rects with a reduced amount of white, that on the inner web of r6 rarely extending > 6 mm proximal to the tip and usually angled proximal-laterally (Fig. 227); underparts relatively dark gray. The above information applies to California Gnatcatchers of N.Am; birds of Mex (especially s.Baja CA) have plumage features closer to Black-tailed Gnatcatcher (see **Geographic variation**).

Geographic variation—Moderate and ranges fairly well defined. Subspecies taxonomy follows Atwood (1991), as modified by Mellink & Rea (1994); see also Ridgway (1904), Grinnell

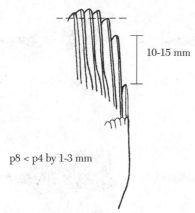

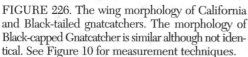

10-15 mm

p8 < p4 by 1-3 mm

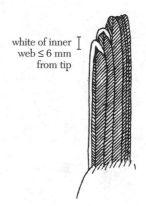

white of inner
web ≤ 6 mm
from tip

FIGURE 226. The wing morphology of California and Black-tailed gnatcatchers. The morphology of Black-capped Gnatcatcher is similar although not identical. See Figure 10 for measurement techniques.

FIGURE 227. The pattern of white in the rectrices of California Gnatcatcher.

(1926c), van Rossem (1931c), Atwood (1988), Phillips (1991). Two other subspecies occur in Baja CA.

P.c. californica (res throughout range in N.Am): From subspecies of Mex by tl long (see **Age/Sex**, *vs* 44-50 in subspecies of Mex); plumage darker; ♀♀ with the back more heavily washed brown and the flanks with a moderate (*vs* light) brown wash; ♂♂ with the upperparts dark gray, often slightly tinged brown (*vs* pale gray with little or no brown); wing edging buff to whitish (*vs* whitish to white); r6 with the white tip on the inner web usually < 3 mm and the outer web usually < 60% white (*vs* usually > 3 and > 60% in birds of s.Baja CA). Birds of n.Baja CA, *atwoodi*, potential vagrants to s.CA(?), have plumage and measurements as in *californica*, but ♀♀ with the upperparts and flanks slightly paler and less brown; ♂♂ with the upperparts grayer, without a brown tinge; wing edging whitish to white.

Molt—PB: HY partial-incomplete (Jul-Sep), AHY complete (Jul-Aug); PA: SY partial-incomplete (Feb-Apr), ASY partial (Jan-Mar). The 1st PB includes 8 to 10 (~75%) inner gr covs, usually (in ~95% of birds) 1-3 terts (sometimes s6 and occasionally s5, as well), and 0 (~40%) to all 12 (~15%) rects. The 1st PA includes 0 (~75%) to 3 inner gr covs, often (in ~65% of birds) 1-3 terts (rarely s6, as well), and occasionally (in ~20% of birds) 1-2 central rects (r1). The replacement of 1-2 pp covs (usually among the 4th to the 2nd from the outside) occasionally (~5-10%) can be suspended (until the winter grounds?), resulting in slight contrasts among these feathers (Fig. 225); more study is needed on this. The adult PA includes 0 (~50%) to 3 inner gr covs and sometimes (in ~50% of birds) 1-2 terts, but no rects.

Skull—Pneumaticization completes in HY from 1 Sep through Dec.

Age/Sex—Juv (May-Jul) has the crown and upperparts brownish gray and loosely textured undertail covs; juv ♀ = ♂, although ♂♂ may average slightly grayer head plumage and can obtain black in the eyebrow stripe (see below) as early as mid-Jun. CP/BP (Mar-Aug). ♀ wg(n30) 44-48, tl(n30) 47-51; ♂ wg(n30) 46-50, tl(n30) 48-53.

HY/SY ♀ (Jul-Jun): Crown and eyebrow stripe without black (Fig. 228A); back strongly washed brown, contrasting distinctly with the grayish head; 1-3 terts (sometimes s6, as well) often replaced (see **Molt**), contrasting with the older middle ss (s4-s6) in Jul-Feb (Fig. 133C-D); outer pp covs narrow, tapered, relatively abraded, and brownish dusky with indistinct and relatively narrow, brownish to brownish-gray edging (Fig. 138), contrasting with the slightly fresher, replaced gr covs (Fig. 134); outer pp tapered and relatively worn (Fig. 140A); central rects (r1; sometimes other rects) often replaced at the PB and/or PA (see **Molt**), con-

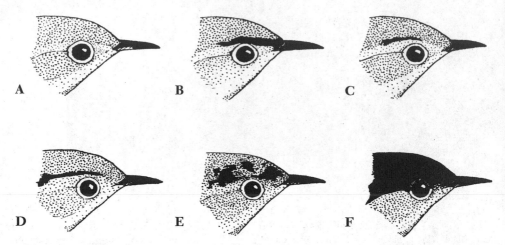

FIGURE 228. Variation in the pattern of black or blackish in the crowns of gnatcatchers, for identification, ageing, and sexing. Note that the partial eye ring featured in illustration **F** represents that of California Gnatcatcher.

trastingly fresh. **Note: Contrasting gr covs and terts are not indicative of SY in Mar-Jun (see Molt). Rect shape seems unhelpful for ageing, despite the retention of the juvenal tail. Some intermediates, especially nesting ♀♀ in summer, can be difficult or impossible to age; compare the relative color and wear with season.**

AHY/ASY ♀ (Jul-Jun): Crown, eyebrow stripe, and upperparts as in HY/SY ♀; terts and middle ss (s4-s6) uniformly adult in Jul-Feb (Fig. 133F); outer pp covs broad, truncate, relatively fresh, and dusky with distinct, relatively broad, brownish-gray edging (Fig. 138), not contrasting in wear with the gr covs (Fig. 133F); 1-2 pp sometimes contrastingly fresh as in Figure 225; outer pp truncate and relatively fresh (Fig. 140A); rects uniformly adult and fresh. **Note: See HY/SY ♀.**

HY/SY ♂ (Jul-Jun): Molt-limit, pp-cov, and rect criteria as in HY/SY ♀; eyebrow with a thin black stripe and crown without black (Fig. 228C) in Jul-Jan, or crown glossy black in Feb-Jul (Fig. 228F), occasionally mixed with dull black or a few dull gray feathers; back without brown or tinged brown, not contrasting distinctly with the grayish head. **Note: See HY/SY ♀.**

AHY/ASY ♂ (Jul-Jun): Molt-limit, pp-cov, and rect criteria as in AHY/ASY ♀; eyebrow with a thick black stripe and crown often (in ~72% of birds) with one or more (up to 70%) dull black feathers (Fig. 228D-E) in Jul-Jan, or crown uniformly shiny black, without gray or dull black feathers (Fig. 228F) in Jan-Jul; upperparts with little or no brown. **Note: See HY/SY ♀.**

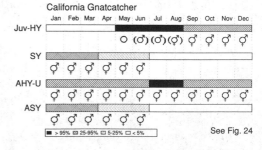

Hybrids reported—Possibly Black-tailed Gnatcatcher.

References—Swarth (1902), Ridgway (1904), R.S. Woods *in* Bent (1949), Phillips *et al.* (1973), Collins & Phillips (1974), Dunn & Garrett (1987), Atwood (1988, 1991), Pyle (1997c), Pyle & Unitt (in press); R.A. Erickson, P. Unitt (pers. comm.).

BLACK-TAILED GNATCATCHER
Polioptila melanura

BTGN
Species # 7520
Band size: 0A

Species—Wing rounded (Fig. 226; p8 – p4 1-3 mm, p9 – p10 10-15 mm); bill small (exp culmen ♀ 8.3-9.6, ♂ 9.1-11.1); ♂♂ with the cap black in Feb-Jul and at least a black eyebrow stripe (Fig. 228**C-E**; see **Age**) in Aug-Jan, but ♀♀ without black in the crown (Fig. 228**A**); white eye ring of alternate-plumaged ♂♂ usually extending to upper half, sometimes nearly complete (*cf.* Fig. 228**F**); amount of white in the outer 2 rects moderately reduced, that of the inner web of r6 usually extending > 5 mm proximal to the tip (when fresh) and usually angled distal-laterally or roughly laterally (Fig. 229); underparts moderately dark gray. From Blue-gray and Black-capped gnatcatchers by shorter bill, crown pattern (♂ from Blue-gray), pattern of the outer rects (r5-r6), and darker underparts. From California Gnatcatcher by pattern of white in the outer rects (r5-r6), and paler (less brownish) underparts. See California Gnatcatcher.

Geographic variation—Moderate and ranges in N.Am well defined. Subspecies taxonomy follows Phillips (1991); see also van Rossem (1931c), Atwood (1988). One other subspecies occurs in Mex.

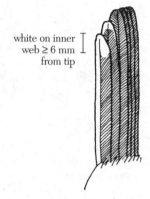

white on inner web ≥ 6 mm from tip

P.m. lucida (res desert s.NV to se.CA-s.AZ): Upperparts pale grayish, the back of ♀♀ with a moderate brown wash; length of white on the inner web of r6 (at shaft) usually 6-9 mm; base of the lower mandible grayish.

P.m. melanura (res. s.NM-s.TX): Upperparts medium gray, the back of ♀♀ with a light brown wash; length of white on the inner web of r6 (at shaft) usually 8-12 mm; lower mandible entirely black.

FIGURE 229. The pattern of white in the rectrices of Black-tailed Gnatcatcher.

Molt—PB: HY partial-incomplete (Jul-Sep), AHY complete (Jul-Aug); PA partial (Jan-Apr). The 1st PB includes all gr covs, 1-3 terts (occasionally s6 and/or s5, as well), and 0 (~13%) to all 12 (~13%) rects. Some birds of Mex also can replace the innermost 1-2 pp and the outermost 1-2 ss (Fig. 137**A**); look for this in birds of N.Am, as well. The 1st PA includes no gr covs, sometimes (in ~36% of birds) 1-2 terts, and occasionally (in ~18% of birds) 1-2 central rects. The replacement of 1-2 pp covs (usually among the 4th to the 2nd from the outside) occasionally (~5-10%) can be suspended (until the winter grounds?), resulting in slight contrasts among these feathers (Fig. 225); more study is needed on this. The adult PA includes 0 (~58%) to 3 inner gr covs and sometimes (in ~25% of birds) 1-3 terts but no rects.

Skull—Pneumaticization completes in HY from 1 Sep through Dec.

Age/Sex—♀ wg(n30) 43-48, tl(n20) 44-53; ♂ wg(n30) 45-50, tl(n30) 47-55. The backs of ♀♀ are only moderately different (browner) than those of ♂♂, with some overlap possible between HY/SY ♂♂ and AHY/ASY ♀♀. Otherwise, juvenal plumages and all subsequent ageing and sexing follows that of California Gnatcatcher (see **Molt** for slight differences in the extents of partial-incomplete molts).

Hybrids reported—Possibly Blue-gray and California gnatcatchers.

References—Ridgway (1904), Bent (1949), Phillips *et al.* (1973), Collins & Phillips (1974), Dunn & Garrett (1987), Howell (1987), Atwood (1988), Pyle (1997c), Pyle & Unitt (in press); R.A. Erickson, P. Unitt (pers. comm.).

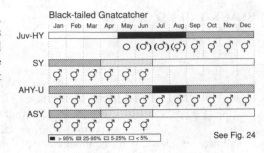

Black-tailed Gnatcatcher

See Fig. 24

BLACK-CAPPED GNATCATCHER

Polioptila nigriceps

BCGN
Species # 7531
Band size: 0A

Species—From Blue-gray Gnatcatcher (which see for separation from California and Black-tailed gnatcatchers) by wing rounded; p8 – p4 1-3 mm, p9 – p10 12-16 mm, see Fig. 226); tail graduation substantial (Fig. 230; r1 – r6 9-12 mm); bill large (exp culmen ♀ 10.4-11.6, ♂ 10.8-12.2); ♂♂ with a full black cap and white eye ring usually restricted to below the eye in Feb-Jul (Fig. 228**F**), and with at least a black eyebrow stripe (Fig. 228**C-E**) in Aug-Feb; base of the mandible grayish.

Geographic variation—Weak and probably clinal. Subspecies taxonomy follows Phillips (1991); see also van Rossem (1931d). One other subspecies occurs in Mex.

> ***P.n. restricta*** (br vag to s.AZ): From the nominate subspecies of Mex by tl longer (see **Sex**, *vs* 47-53 in the nominate subspecies); plumage averages paler; black cap of ♂♂ averages less extensive on the nape.

Molt—Unknown, but presumably similar to Blue-gray and Black-tailed gnatcatchers, although breeding and molt cycles may begin earlier. More study is needed.

Skull—Pneumaticization completes in HY from 1 Sep through Dec.

Age/Sex—♀ wg(n7) 44-48, tl(n7) 50-55; ♂ wg(n13) 46-52, tl(n10) 51-57. Otherwise, presumably as in California Gnatcatcher, with less sexual dichromatism present in the back coloration (♂♂ bluish gray, ♀♀ brownish gray); more study is needed.

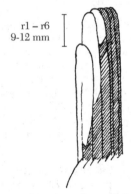

r1 – r6
9-12 mm

FIGURE 230. The tail morphology and pattern of white in the rectrices of Black-capped Gnatcatcher.

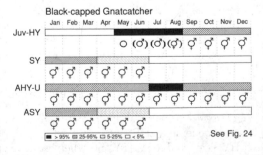

Black-capped Gnatcatcher

See Fig. 24

References—Ridgway (1904), Phillips *et al.* (1973), Collins & Phillips (1974), Dunn & Garrett (1987), Howell (1987).

Thrushes
Turdinae

Fifteen species. Subfamily characters include plump postures, short and medium-statured bills, moderately short tails, and spotted juvenal plumages. Thrushes have 10 primaries (the 10th reduced), 9 secondaries, and 12 rectrices. The first prebasic molt usually is partial, with complete rectrix molt being recorded in only two species. Complete adult molts occur on the summer grounds and prealternate molts (in North American species) usually are absent or, at best, limited. Ageing generally is possible by combining skull condition and wing-covert plumage with the shape of the rectrices and primaries. More study is needed on the roof of the mouth (upper mandible lining) color in thrushes; juv-HY/SYs probably have yellower mouths than AHY/ASYs, in some or all species. Sexing by plumage is reliable with seven of the 15 species, and all species can be sexed by breeding characters in the spring and summer. Males average moderately larger than females.

BLUETHROAT
Luscinia svecica

BLUE
Species # 7640
Band size: 1

Species—From the other Eurasian thrushes in all plumages by basal half of r2-r6 rufous; throat and/or breast usually with at least some blue and red.

Geographic variation—Moderate, but complicated by individual variation and broad intergradation. Subspecies taxonomy follows Cramp (1988); see also Friedmann (1946), Dement'ev & Gladkov (1954), Phillips (1991), Svensson (1992). Five other subspecies occur in Eurasia.

> **L.s. svecica** (br throughout range in N.Am): From the other subspecies by alternate-plumaged ♂♂ with the center of the breast uniformly deep rufous and lower breast band rufous, not separated from the black central band by white; ♀♀ and basic-plumaged ♂♂ average buffier (but generally are inseparable from the other subspecies).

Molt—PB: HY partial (Jul-Oct), AHY complete (Jul-Oct); PA absent-limited (Feb-Apr). The PBs can occur on the summer grounds and/or the winter grounds, being suspended for migration in some individuals; the body molt of HYs usually completes on the summer grounds. The 1st PB usually includes 1-7 gr covs and rarely can include 1-2 terts. The PA usually is limited to the head and breast and is more extensive in ASYs and ♂♂ than in SYs and ♀♀.

Skull—Pneumaticization completes in HY/SY from 15 Oct through Feb.

Age—Juv (Jun-Aug) has the feathers of the upperparts brown with buff or cinnamon tipping, and the underparts largely buffy; juv ♀ = ♂.

> HY/SY (Aug-Jul): Molt limits occur among the gr covs (Fig. 133**B-D**; see **Molt**), the retained outer covs worn and brownish with cinnamon tips, contrasting with the fresher, grayer, and uniformly brown, replaced inner covs; 1-2 terts occasionally replaced, contrasting with the older, juvenal middle ss (s4-s6; Fig. 133**D**); outer pp covs narrow, tapered, relatively abraded (Fig. 138), and brownish with buff tips when fresh; pp and rects uniformly fresh in Aug-Oct; rects narrow, tapered (Fig. 139**B**), and relatively worn in Nov-Jul; breast of ♀♀ with little or no blue and red; red and blue of the throat and central breast of ♂♂ mixed with whitish. **Note: Intermediates can be difficult to age, especially when plumage is worn in May-Jul.**

> AHY/ASY (Aug-Jul): Gr covs, terts, and middle ss (s4-s6) uniformly grayish, usually without distinct, cinnamon edging or tips; outer pp covs broad, truncate, relatively fresh (Fig. 138), and

grayish, without buff tips; pp and rects mostly or uniformly worn in Aug-Oct, and relatively fresh in Nov-Jul; breast of ♀♀ with some blue and red; red and blue of the throat and central breast of ♂♂ without whitish. **Note: See HY/SY.**

Sex—CP/BP (May-Jul). ♀ wg(n15) 70-77, tl(n15) 49-54; ♂ wg(n34) 72-81, tl(n34) 51-57; measurements include *L.s. svecica* throughout the range in Europe-N.Am; birds of N.Am may average slightly larger.

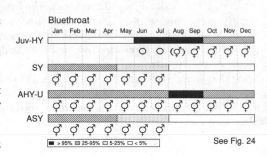

♀: Malar region without blue; single breast band dusky, usually tinged or lightly mixed with blue and red.

♂: Malar region with at least some blue; breast with distinct bands of blue, black, and red.

References—Ridgway (1907), B.W. Tucker *in* Bent (1949), Cramp (1988), Svensson (1992), Jenni & Winkler (1994).

NORTHERN WHEATEAR
Oenanthe oenanthe

NOWH
Species # 7650
Band size: 1B

Species—From the other species of wheatears (see Svensson 1992) by different wing morphology (p10 < longest pp cov by 0-7 mm, p9 > p6, p6 indistinctly or not emarginated); upperparts gray to gray-brown; supercilium usually distinct; r1 uniformly dark; r2-r5 white, contrasting sharply with the uniformly dark, distal third.

Geographic variation—Weak to moderate, but subspecies of N.Am relatively well defined. Subspecies taxonomy follows Cramp (1988); see also Ridgway (1907), Godfrey (1986), Phillips (1991), Svensson (1992). Two other subspecies occur in Eurasia.

O.o. oenanthe (br AK-nw.NWT; vag to CA, NY): Small; upperparts of ♀♀ grayish to brownish-gray; underparts whitish (AHYs) to white with an uneven cinnamon wash (HYs in fall). ♀ wg(n30) 88-96, tl(n15) 49-55; ♂ wg(n100) 92-101, tl(n36) 52-58. Birds of AK-NWT ("*oenanthoides*") average larger than those of Eurasia, as a whole, but distinction to subspecies requires further study.

O.o. leucorhoa (br ne.NWT-Nfl; presumed vag to AR-FL): Large; upperparts of ♀♀ brownish; underparts whitish with a cinnamon wash (AHYs) to uniformly rich cinnamon (HYs in fall). ♀ wg(n100) 98-108, tl(n23) 53-58; ♂ wg(n100) 100-110, tl(n29) 54-60.

Molt—PB: HY partial (Jul-Oct), AHY complete (Jul-Sep); PA partial (Jan-Apr). The 1st PB often occurs on the summer grounds, but sometimes (~25% of birds) can be suspended, completing on the winter grounds. The adult PBs usually occur entirely on the summer grounds, although they occasionally are completed on the winter grounds. The 1st PB includes 0 (~70%) to 5 inner gr covs and occasionally 1-2 terts. The PAs occasionally can include some gr covs and 1-2 terts.

Skull—Pneumaticization completes in HY/SY from 1 Sep through Dec.

Age/Sex—Juv (Jun-Aug) has the feathers of the upperparts brownish with buff or cinnamon tipping; juv ♀ = ♂. CP/BP (May-Jul). ♀ wg(n100) 88-108, tl(n38) 49-58; ♂ wg(n100) 92-110, tl(n65) 52-60; see **Geographic variation**

Basic Plumage (Aug-Mar)

HY/SY ♀♂ (Aug-Mar): Upperparts heavily washed brownish or cinnamon; dusky mask indistinctly defined; supercilium buff; wing feathers uniformly juvenal and brown (noticeably browner than the mask of alternate-plumaged ♂♂), or one or more inner gr or med covs replaced and dark brown to blackish, contrasting with the brownish, retained outer covs (Fig. 133A-C); outer gr covs edged buff to cinnamon when fresh; outer pp covs narrow, tapered, relatively abraded (Fig. 138A), and brownish; roof of the mouth (upper mandible lining) with yellowish (through Oct-Mar). **Note: Most HY/SYs are not reliably sexed in Aug-Feb, although some SY ♂♂ in Jan-Feb with incoming black mask feathers can be sexed. Also, the replaced inner wing covs may average blacker on ♂♂ than on ♀♀ and this could be useful in sexing some birds; more study is needed. Intermediates can be difficult or impossible to age, especially ♀♀.**

AHY/ASY ♀ (Aug-Mar): Upperparts heavily washed brownish or cinnamon; dusky mask indistinctly defined; supercilium buffy; wing feathers uniformly adult (Fig. 133F) and dark brown; gr covs with narrow or no buff to cinnamon edging; outer pp covs broad, truncate, fresh (Fig. 138B), and brownish black; roof of the mouth gray or black, without yellowish. **Note: See HY/SY ♀♂.**

AHY/ASY ♂ (Aug-Mar): Upperparts gray with a brownish or cinnamon wash; black mask distinctly defined; supercilium white; wing feathers uniformly adult (Fig. 133F) and blackish; gr covs edged gray; outer pp covs broad, truncate, fresh (Fig. 138B), and black; roof of the mouth gray or black, without yellowish. **Note: See HY/SY ♀♂.**

Alternate Plumage (Mar-Aug)

SY ♀ (Mar-Aug): Upperparts with a light to moderate, brownish or cinnamon wash; dusky mask indistinctly defined; supercilium whitish to buff; outer wing covs mostly pale brown, often contrasting with one or two generations of darker brown inner covs (see Fig. 135); outer pp covs narrow, tapered, abraded (Fig. 138C), and brownish. **Note: Intermediate ♀♀ can be difficult or impossible to age, especially when plumage is worn, in May-Aug.**

ASY ♀ (Mar-Aug): Body plumage as in SY ♀; outer wing covs mostly dark brown, sometimes contrasting slightly (in wear) with one generation of fresher inner covs (Fig. 133B-D, *cf.* Fig. 135); outer pp covs broad, truncate, relatively fresh (Fig. 138D), and brownish black. **Note: See SY ♀.**

SY ♂ (Mar-Aug): Upperparts gray, sometimes lightly washed brownish or cinnamon; blackish mask distinctly defined; supercilium whitish to white; wing covs and pp covs as in SY ♀, except that the recently replaced, inner med and gr covs are blackish, contrasting with the browner pp and retained juvenal covs.

ASY ♂ (Mar-Aug): Upperparts gray (Mar-Jul); black mask distinctly defined; supercilium white; wing covs uniformly adult (Fig. 133F) and blackish (sometimes with slightly fresher inner covs; Fig. 133B-D, *cf.* Fig. 135), not contrasting markedly with the blackish pp; outer pp covs broad, truncate, relatively fresh (Fig. 138D), and black.

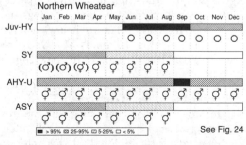

Northern Wheatear

Note: In Oct-Dec, AHYs can be sexed but birds of unknown age should be left unsexed.

References—Dwight (1900a), Ridgway (1907), B.W. Tucker *in* Bent (1949), K. Williamson (1957), Cramp (1988), Svensson (1992), Jenni & Winkler (1994).

EASTERN BLUEBIRD
Sialia sialis

EABL
Species # 7660
Band size: 1B-1

Species—From Western Bluebird by smaller size (wg 91-109, tl 57-70; see **Geographic variation** & **Age/Sex**); longest p – longest s 25-34 mm; ♀♀ with upperparts uniformly dull grayish brown with a blue tinge, throat whitish to pale chestnut, and lower belly and undertail covs white, separated distinctly from the pale chestnut of the flanks and upper belly; ♂♂ with some or no rusty in the upperparts (see **Geographic variation**) and chin and throat chestnut; juvs (and non-juvs when fresh) with the terts fringed cinnamon. ♀♀ from ♀ Mountain Bluebirds (which can have underparts tinged cinnamon) by smaller size (see above); wing covs primarily dark blue, often with brownish edging; flanks with an extensive pale chestnut wash.

Geographic variation—Weak to moderate and clinal where ranges meet. Subspecies taxonomy follows Phillips (1991); see also Ridgway (1907), Oberholser (1917f, 1974), Griscom (1932), Webster (1973), Stevenson & Anderson (1994). Three other subspecies occur in Bermuda and Mex-C.Am.

    S.s. fulva (res se.AZ): Large; ♂♂ with upperparts medium blue, the feathers edged cinnamon when fresh; underparts of both ♂ & ♀ relatively pale, cinnamon to rufous. ♀ wg(n17) 94-102, tl(n12) 59-67; ♂ wg(n39) 98-109, tl(n34) 61-70.

    S.s. nidificans (res s.TX): Large; ♂♂ with upperparts dark blue, the feathers edged cinnamon-chestnut when fresh; underparts of both ♂ & ♀ relatively rich and dark, rufous to chestnut. ♀ wg(n4) 97-104, tl(n4) 60-68; ♂ wg(n14) 100-109, tl(n14) 61-70.

    S.s. sialis (br & wint s.Man-e.AZ to NB-FL): Small; bill short (nares to tip 7.8-9.7); ♂♂ with upperparts dark purplish blue, the feathers usually not edged cinnamon-chestnut; underparts of both ♂ & ♀ relatively dark but dull, rufous to chestnut. ♀ wg(n100) 91-101, tl(n41) 57-66; ♂ wg(n100) 95-105, tl(n100) 58-68. Birds of s.TX ("*episcopus*") may represent intermediates with *nidificans*.

    S.s. grata (res s.FL): Size and plumage as in *sialis*, but bill longer (nares to tip 9.0-10.2).

Molt—PB: HY partial-incomplete (Jul-Oct), AHY complete (Jul-Oct); PA absent. The PBs occur on the summer grounds. The 1st PB includes 3 to 10 (~27%) inner gr covs, sometimes (in ~50% of birds) 1-3 terts (occasionally s6 and rarely s5, as well), and 0 (~50%) to all 12 (~31%) rects. ♂♂ may average more feathers replaced than ♀♀, but more study is needed.

Skull—Pneumaticization completes in HY/SY from 1 Nov (as early as 1 Oct in *S.s. nidificans* and *grata*) through Feb. Look for some SYs to retain windows (> 3 mm; Fig. 11**D**) through spring. The skull can be difficult to see through the skin.

Age/Sex—Juv (May-Aug) has the upperparts primarily brown with white streaking and the underparts with dusky mottling; nestlings and juvs can be sexed by the color of the pp, wing covs, and rects (as in HYs; see below), and the width of the buff border on the outer rects (r6: < 0.5 mm in ♂♂, > 0.5 mm in ♀♀). CP/BP (Mar-Aug). ♀ wg(n100) 91-104, tl(n57) 57-68; ♂ wg(n100) 95-109, tl(n100) 58-70; see **Geographic variation**.

HY/SY ♀ (Sep-Aug): Upperparts grayish with a slight to moderate blue wash; molt limits often occur among the gr covs (Fig. 133**B-E**; see **Molt**), the retained outer covs worn and brown to brownish blue, contrasting with the fresher and bright bluish, replaced inner covs; 1-3 terts (sometimes s6 and/or s5, as well) often replaced, contrasting with the older and browner middle ss (s4-s6; Fig. 133**D-E**); outer pp covs narrow, tapered, relatively abraded (Figs. 138), and brownish with a blue tinge, the outermost pp cov rounded, without blue, and with broad buffy fringes (Fig. 231); pp faded gray with a slight bluish wash; rects tapered (Fig. 139**B**) and bluish dusky, truncate, or mixed tapered and truncate (see **Molt**).

AHY/ASY ♀ (Sep-Aug): Upperparts gray-ish with a heavy, blue wash; gr covs, terts, and middle ss (s4-s6) uniformly adult (Fig. 133**F**) and bluish; outer pp covs broad, truncate, relatively fresh (Fig. 138), and dusky blue, the outer-most pp cov relatively pointed and bluish with a narrow buffy or cinnamon fringe (Fig. 231); pp dusky with a bluish wash; rects uniformly adult, truncate (Fig. 139**B**), and dusky blue.

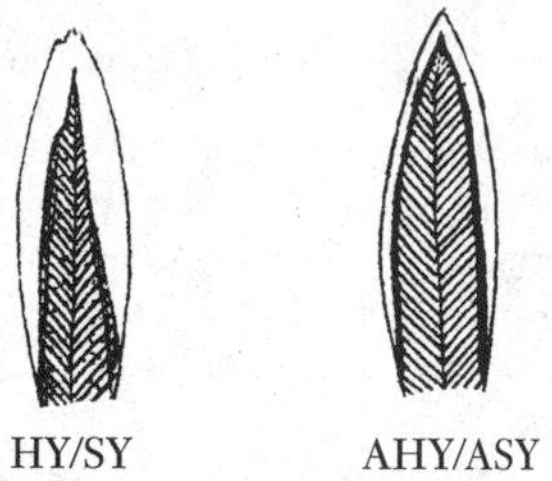

HY/SY   AHY/ASY

FIGURE 231. The pattern of the outermost (reduced) primary covert by age in Eastern and Western bluebirds.

HY/SY ♂ (Sep-Aug): Upperparts and pp relatively dull or faded blue; molt-limit and pp-cov criteria as in HY/SY ♀, except that the pp covs are bluish brown to blue, with indistinct, dusky tips; rects tapered (Fig. 139**B**) and blue with indistinct, dusky tips, truncate, or mixed tapered and truncate (see **Molt**); underparts relatively pale rufous.

AHY/ASY ♂ (Sep-Aug): Upperparts and pp relatively bright blue; gr covs, terts, and middle ss (s4-s6) uniformly adult (Fig. 133**F**) and bright blue; outer pp covs as in AHY/ASY ♀, except that the color is uniformly bright blue without tips, or with slight and indistinct, dusky tips; rects uniform-ly adult, truncate (Fig. 139**B**), and blue without dusky tips; underparts relatively deep rufous.

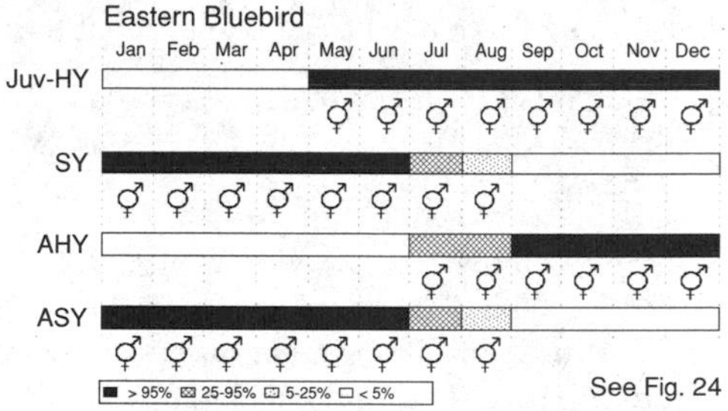

Hybrids reported—Mountain Bluebird. Western Bluebird in captivity.

Eastern Bluebird

	Jan	Feb	Mar	Apr	May	Jun	Jul	Aug	Sep	Oct	Nov	Dec
Juv-HY					♂	♂	♂	♂	♂	♂	♂	♂
SY								♂ ♂ ♂ ♂ ♂ ♂ ♂ ♂ ♂				
AHY								♂ ♂ ♂ ♂ ♂ ♂				
ASY			♂ ♂ ♂ ♂ ♂ ♂ ♂ ♂									

■ > 95% ▨ 25-95% ▦ 5-25% □ < 5%   See Fig. 24

References—Stone (1896), Dwight (1900a), Ridgway (1907), Forbush (1929), Bent (1949), Roberts (1955), Lane (1968), Wood (1969), Webster (1973), Oberholser (1974), Pinkowski (1974, 1976), Dunn (1981), Rounds & Munro (1982), Pitts (1985), CWS & USFWS (1991), Phillips (1991), Kaufman (1992c), Plissner *et al.* (1994), Pyle (1997c); D. Agro (*in litt.* to the BBL); IBP (MAPS) data.

WESTERN BLUEBIRD
Sialia mexicana

WEBL
Species # 7670
Band size: 1B

Species—From Eastern Bluebird (which see for separation from Mountain Bluebird) by larger size (wg 98-117, tl 56-71; see **Geographic variation** & **Age/Sex**); longest p − longest s 33-40 mm; ♀♀ with the crown and nape dull bluish gray, contrasting with the dull grayish-brown back, throat whitish to dull grayish with a blue tinge, and lower belly and undertail covs gray, sepa-rated indistinctly from the chestnut of the flanks and upper belly; ♂♂ with substantial rusty to the upperparts (see **Geographic variation**) and chin and throat dark blue; juvs (and non-juvs when fresh) with the terts fringed grayish to grayish buff.

Geographic variation—Weak, clinal where ranges meet, and differences are obscured by indi-vidual variation. Subspecies taxonomy follows Phillips (1991); see also Ridgway (1907), Grinnell & Swarth (1913), Moore (1939c), Phillips *et al.* (1964), Rea (1983), Behle (1985).

Three other subspecies occur in Mex.

S.m. occidentalis (br s.BC-sc.MT to s.CA-NV, wint to s.NM): Averages small; upperparts and throat grayish in ♀♀, or medium blue with a moderate chestnut wash to the back, becoming indistinct by the lower scapulars in ♂♂; breast band of ♂♂ dark and rich chestnut. ♀ wg(n49) 98-107, tl(n10) 56-64; ♂ wg(n55) 100-112, tl(n10) 60-68. Birds of s.CA ("*anabelae*") average larger, deeper blue, and paler chestnut, but differences are slight and the subspecies designation possibly was based on relatively worn specimens.

S.m. bairdi (br c.UT-c.CO to s.AZ-sw.NM, wint to s.TX): Averages large; upperparts and throat grayish in ♀♀, or medium blue with an extensive chestnut wash to the back and interscapular region in ♂♂; breast band of ♂♂ pale and dull chestnut. ♀ wg(n25) 102-110, tl(n18) 58-68; ♂ wg(n28) 105-117, tl(n21) 64-71. Breeding birds of sw.CO average paler, duller, and (possibly) smaller than surrounding birds, but potential distinction to subspecies requires further study.

S.m. jacoti (res se.NM-sw.TX): Medium small(?); Upperparts and throat grayish in ♀♀, or dull blue with a moderate, dark chestnut wash to the back, extending distinctly to the lower scapulars in ♂♂. Wg: ♀(n4) 102-107, ♂(n3) 107-111.

Molt—PB: HY partial-incomplete (Jul-Oct), AHY complete (Jul-Sep); PA absent. The PBs occur on the summer grounds. The 1st PB includes 2 to 10 (~10%) inner gr covs, occasionally (in ~17% of birds) 1-3 terts (rarely s6, as well), and 0 (~77%) to all 12 (10%) rects. ♂♂ may average more feathers replaced than ♀♀, but more study is needed.

Skull—Pneumaticization completes in HY/SY from 1 Oct through Jan. Look for some SYs to retain windows (> 3 mm; Fig. 11**D**) through spring. The skull can be difficult to see through the skin.

Age/Sex—CP/BP (Mar-Aug). ♀ wg(n100) 98-110, tl(n28) 56-68; ♂ wg(n100) 100-117, tl(n32) 60-71; see **Geographic variation**. Age and sex criteria (including that of juvs) is the same as in Eastern Bluebird, although the extent of the 1st PB averages less (see **Molt**) and the blue coloration averages darker.

Western Bluebird

See Fig. 24

Hybrids reported—Mountain Bluebird. Eastern Bluebird in captivity.

References—Ridgway (1907), Bent (1949), Oberholser (1974), Dunn (1981), Phillips (1991), Kaufman (1992c), Pyle (1997c); IBP (MAPS) data, PRBO data.

MOUNTAIN BLUEBIRD
Sialia currucoides

MOBL
Species # 7680
Band size: 1B-1A

Species— ♀♀ from ♀♀ Eastern and Western bluebirds by larger size (wg 101-121, tl 63-76; see **Age/Sex**); longest p – longest s 38-47 mm; wing covs grayish brown with whitish edging; flanks brownish, without cinnamon or chestnut.

Geographic variation—No subspecies are recognized.

Molt—PB: HY partial (Jul-Sep), AHY complete (Jul-Sep); PA absent. The PBs occur on the summer grounds. The 1st PB includes 1-8 inner gr covs and rarely (in ~4% of birds) 1-2 central rects (r1), but no terts.

Skull—Pneumaticization completes in HY/SY from 1 Oct through Jan. Look for some SYs to retain windows (> 3 mm; Fig. 11**D**) through spring. The skull can be difficult to see through the skin.

Age/Sex—Juv (May-Aug) has grayish upperparts with white streaking, and underparts with dusky mottling; most juvs can be sexed by the color of the central rects (bright bluish in ♂♂, dusky with a bluish wash at the base in ♀♀). CP/BP (Mar-Aug). Wg is useful for sexing: ♀ wg(n85) 101-116, tl(n20) 63-72; ♂ wg(n100) 108-121, tl(n20) 66-76.

HY/SY ♀ (Sep-Aug): Body plumage dull brownish to grayish; molt limits occur among the gr covs (Fig. 133**B-D**; see **Molt**), the retained outer covs worn and brownish with a blue tinge, contrasting with the fresher and bluish-gray, replaced inner covs; outer pp covs narrow, tapered, relatively abraded (Fig. 138), and dull brownish blue; alula brownish; rects tapered (Fig. 139**B**) and relatively abraded.

AHY/ASY ♀ (Sep-Aug): Body plumage dull bluish gray; gr covs uniformly bluish gray (Fig. 133**F**); outer pp covs broad, truncate, relatively fresh (Fig. 138), and bluish with indistinct, dusky tips; alula blue with a brownish wash; rects truncate (Fig. 139**B**) and relatively fresh.

HY/SY ♂ (Sep-Aug): Body plumage bluish to mixed brown and blue; molt limits as in HY/SY ♀ (Fig. 133**B-D**), the retained outer covs worn and brownish blue, contrasting with the fresher and bright blue, replaced inner covs; outer pp covs narrow, tapered, relatively abraded (Fig. 138), and bluish with indistinct, dusky tips; alula brownish blue; rects tapered (Fig. 139**B**) and relatively abraded.

AHY/ASY ♂ (Sep-Aug): Plumage (including the wing covs and alula) uniformly bright, sky blue; outer pp covs broad, truncate, relatively fresh (Fig. 138), and uniformly blue; rects truncate (Fig. 139**B**) and relatively fresh.

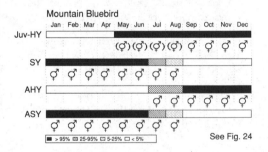

Mountain Bluebird

See Fig. 24

Hybrids reported—Eastern Bluebird, Western Bluebird.

References—Ridgway (1907), Bent (1949), Lane (1968), Oberholser (1974), H.W. Power (1980), Dunn (1981), Kaufman (1992c), Power & Lombardo (1996), Pyle (1997c); IBP (MAPS) data.

TOWNSEND'S SOLITAIRE
Myadestes townsendi

TOSO
Species # 7540
Band size: 1B

Geographic variation—Weak, but ranges well defined. Subspecies taxonomy follows Phillips (1991); see also Griscom (1932), Moore (1937), van Rossem (1945a). No other subspecies occur. Beware that specimens can become darker with age.

> **M.t. townsendi** (br & wint throughout the range in N.Am): Crown and rump medium-pale brownish gray; bases of the pp and ss medium buff.
>
> **M.t. calophonus** (br & wint nc.Mex, possible vag to NY): Crown and rump medium-dark grayish brown; bases of the pp and ss tawny.

Molt—PB: HY partial-incomplete (Jul-Oct), AHY complete (Jul-Sep); PA absent. The PBs occur primarily if not entirely on the summer grounds. The 1st PB includes some to all med covs, 0 (~31%) to 8 gr covs and occasionally (in ~7% of birds) 1-4 central rects (r1), but usually no terts.

Skull—Pneumaticization completes in HY/SY from 15 Sep through Feb. Look for some SYs to retain windows (> 3 mm; Fig. 11**D**) through spring.

Age—Juv (Jun-Sep) has heavily spotted upperparts and heavily scaled underparts; juv ♀ = ♂.

HY/SY (Aug-Jul): Some juv body feathers in the back and breast sometimes retained and tipped buff; molt limits occur (but are difficult to see) among the med and gr covs (Fig. 133**A-D**; see **Molt**), the retained outer covs worn, with distinct (> 1 mm) buff or whitish tips (when fresh), contrasting with the fresher, replaced inner covs without edging, or with thin, whitish edging; outer pp covs narrow, tapered, and relatively abraded (Fig. 138); roof of the mouth (upper mandible lining) yellow to pinkish yellow (through Jan-Jun). **Note: The shape of the rects (Fig. 139B) may be somewhat helpful for ageing, but substantial overlap occurs in this species. Some intermediates will be difficult or impossible to age.**

AHY/ASY (Aug-Jul): Body feathers and wing covs uniformly adult (Fig. 133**F**) and without buff or whitish tips (gr covs sometimes with indistinct tips, < 1 mm wide); outer pp covs broad, truncate, and relatively fresh (Fig. 138); roof of the mouth pink. **Note: See HY/SY.**

Sex—♀ = ♂ by plumage. CP/BP (Apr-Sep). ♀ wg(n79) 107-117, tl(n20) 94-106; ♂ wg(n84) 109-123, tl(n22) 98-110.

Townsend's Solitaire

Jan Feb Mar Apr May Jun Jul Aug Sep Oct Nov Dec

Juv-HY

SY

AHY-U

ASY

■ > 95% ▨ 25-95% ▢ 5-25% ▢ < 5%

See Fig. 24

References—Ridgway (1907), Bent (1949), Roberts (1955), Sutton (1967), Oberholser (1974), Salomonson & Balda (1977), Bowen (1997), Pyle (1997c); R. Bowen (unpublished ms., pers. comm.); IBP (MAPS) data.

VEERY
Catharus fuscescens

VEER
Species # 7560
Band size: 1B

Species—Wg 89-106, tl 62-79 (see **Sex**); pp covs – p10 -2 to 9 mm (see **Age**); p9 > p6, p6 slightly emarginated, p8 – p6 5-7 mm, p8 – p5 10-14 mm, and p8 – p1 23-29 mm (Fig. 232); upperparts and tail uniformly reddish to reddish brown; face grayish, without a distinct, buffy eye ring; breast with a pinkish wash and indistinct to moderately distinct, reddish brown to brownish spotting confined primarily to the upper breast; flanks washed pale gray, contrasting distinctly with the white belly and reddish-brown upperparts. From Gray-cheeked Thrush (which see for separation from Bicknell's Thrush) and Hermit Thrush by the combination of wing morphology and plumage. From Swainson's Thrush (with caution, as the color of the upperparts can overlap with the western subspecies of Veery, *C.f. salicicola*; see **Geographic variation**) by longer relative tl length; shorter wing morphology and slight emargination of p6 (Fig. 232); upperparts and flanks contrasting distinctly; eye ring reduced; breast markings indistinct; and belly white.

Geographic variation—Weak to moderate, clinal where ranges meet, and differences are obscured somewhat by individual variation. Subspecies taxonomy follows Phillips (1991); see also Ridgway (1907), Noble (1919), Aldrich (1939), Griscom & Snyder (1955), Burleigh & Duvall (1959), Monroe (1968), Oberholser (1974), Wetmore *et al.* (1984), Godfrey (1986), Cramp (1988), Browning (1990), Dickerman & Parkes (1997), Patten (1997). No other subspecies occur. Beware that specimens fox with age.

C.f. salicicola (br BC to AZ-CO): Upperparts dull, moderately dark brown with a reddish tinge; breast lightly washed dull buff; brownish chest spots distinct. Birds of e.WA-ne.OR to n.ID-MT ("*subpallidus*") average slightly grayer and with a darker crown, but the subspecies designation was possibly based on foxed specimens.

C.f. levyi (br Alb to n.MI-WS): Upperparts medium-dull reddish brown; breast lightly washed dull buff; reddish-brown chest spots distinct.

C.f. fuliginosus (br Que-Nfl, probably n.ME-s.NS): Upperparts deep, bright reddish brown; breast lightly washed bright buff; reddish-brown chest spots distinct.

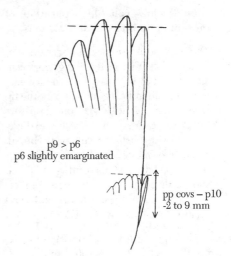

p9 > p6
p6 slightly emarginated

pp covs – p10
-2 to 9 mm

FIGURE 232. The wing morphology of Veery. See Figure 10 for measurement techniques and Fig. 234 for age-related differences in pp covs – p10.

C.f. fuscescens (br s.Ont-s.ME to lowland MD): Upperparts medium-bright reddish brown; breast heavily washed bright pinkish buff; reddish chest spots indistinct.

C.f. pulichorum (br montane WV-n.GA): Upperparts dark reddish brown; breast lightly washed bright pinkish buff to buff; brownish-red chest spots moderately distinct.

Molt—PB: HY partial (Jul-Sep), AHY complete (Jul-Sep); PA absent. The PBs occur on the summer grounds. The 1st PB includes some to all med covs and 0 (~10%) to 5 inner gr covs, but no terts or rects.

Skull—Pneumaticization completes in HY/SY from 15 Oct. Some SYs retain large windows (> 3 mm; see Fig. 11**D**) at the rear of the skull (above the occipital triangle; see Collier and Wallace 1989) through September and some ASYs can retain small windows (< 3 mm) there.

Age—Juv (Jun-Aug) has the feathers of the upperparts with buff tipping; juv ♀ = ♂.

HY/SY (Sep-Aug): Molt limits occur among the med and gr covs (Fig. 133**A-C**; see **Molt**), the retained outer covs worn, paler, and usually (in ~92% of birds) with buff tips when fresh (Fig. 233**A-C**), contrasting with the fresher and darker (usually without buff tips), replaced inner covs; outer pp covs narrow, tapered, relatively abraded, and brownish with indistinct and relatively thin or no pale brownish edging (Fig. 138); p10 broad, rounded, and measuring -2 to 5 mm shorter than the pp covs (Fig. 234); rects and pp tapered (Figs. 139**B** & 140**B**) and relatively abraded. **Note: The buff tipping to the juvenal gr covs can be lacking and wear off in many birds by spring; however, the other criteria**

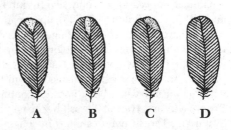

A   B   C   D

FIGURE 233. Variation in the pattern on juvenal and adult greater coverts (see text) in *Catharus* thrushes.

should allow reliable separation of most of these birds from AHY/ASYs.

AHY/ASY (Sep-Aug): Med and gr covs uniformly adult (Fig. 133**F**), the gr covs usually without distinct, buff tips (occasionally with an an indistinct pale spot at the tip when fresh; Fig. 233**C-D**); outer pp covs broad, truncate, relatively fresh, and dusky brown with distinct, relatively broad, rufous-brown edging (Fig. 138); p10 narrow, tapered, and measuring 4-9 mm shorter than the pp covs (Fig. 234); rects and pp truncate (Figs. 139**B** & 140**B**) and relatively fresh. **Note: See HY/SY.**

Sex—♀ = ♂ by plumage. CP/BP (Apr-Jul). ♀ wg(n100) 89-103, tl(n100) 62-74; ♂ wg(n100) 91-106, tl(n100) 65-79.

Hybrids reported—Possibly Gray-cheeked Thrush.

References—Stone (1896), Dwight (1900a), Ridgway (1907), Forbush (1929), Bent (1949), Roberts (1955), Dilger (1956), Blake (1962a), Wood (1969), Oberholser (1974), Phillips (1975a, 1991), Robbins (1975), Phillips & Holmgren (1980), Cramp (1988), Collier & Wallace (1989), CWS & USFWS (1991), Suthers (1993), Yong & Moore (1994), Moskoff (1995), Patten (1997), Pyle (1997c); C.S. Robbins (*in litt.* to the BBL); IBP (MAPS) data, PNR data.

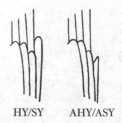

HY/SY   AHY/ASY

FIGURE 234. Variation in the shape and size of the reduced outer primary (p10) by age in *Catharus* thrushes. The distance between the tip of p10 and the tip of the longest primary covert varies by age (see text). This figure represents this difference in Veery; the other species have longer or shorter p10s (see accounts) but the relative differences in size and shape are similar.

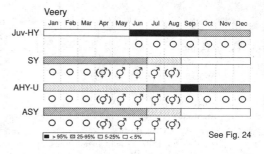

See Fig. 24

GRAY-CHEEKED THRUSH
Catharus minimus

GCTH
Species # 7570
Band size: 1B

Species—Wg 93-109, tl 63-79 (see **Sex**); pp covs – p10 3-12 mm (see **Age**), p9 > p6, p6 usually emarginated (occasionally only slightly, rarely lacking), p8 – p6 5-10 mm, p8 – p5 12-18 mm, and p8 – p1 27-35 mm (Fig. 235); upperparts and tail uniformly brownish or grayish olive (the tail can have a slight chestnut tinge, especially in *C.m. minimus*; see **Geographic variation**); face grayish, fairly uniform in color with the back, and with the eye ring lacking or partial and whitish (but see Juv under **Age**); auricular streaked whitish; throat white; breast with distinct, blackish, triangular spotting; flanks brownish gray to brownish olive, contrasting moderately with the creamy-white belly, and not contrasting distinctly with the color of the upperparts. From Veery and Hermit Thrush by the combination of wing morphology and plumage. From Swainson's Thrush (with caution) by longer relative tl length; longer average length of p10; emargination of p6; facial plumage grayer; eye ring partial or absent; and breast spots smaller, more distinct, and blackish.

From Bicknell's Thrush (with caution) by larger size (wg 93-109, tl 63-79; see **Sex**); wing morphology longer (p8 – p6 5-10 mm and p8 – p1 27-35 mm; Fig. 235); tail not strongly tinged chestnut and uniform in color (or nearly so) with the grayish brown back; throat and underparts average whiter; pale area of the lower mandible reduced (usually extending to ~1/2 the mandible length at most) and dull flesh to yellowish flesh; legs pale flesh with a dusky wash, paler than the toes. The subspecies *minimus* (see **Geographic variation**) can approach Bicknell's Thrush in plumage coloration but also has a duller lower mandible than *aliciae*. Birds of the Gray-cheeked Thrush complex not identified to species can be recorded with alpha code **GCBT** and **Species # 7579**.

Geographic variation—Weak, and variation possibly confused by slight dichromatism (grayish and olive plumages), but breeding ranges are fairly well defined. Subspecies taxonomy follows Phillips (1991); see also Wallace (1939), Burleigh & Peters (1948), Todd (1958, 1963), Ouellet (1993), Knox (1996), Patten (1997). No other subspecies occur.

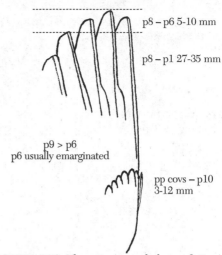

FIGURE 235. The wing morphology of Gray-cheeked Thrush. See Figure 10 for measurement techniques and *cf.* Fig. 234 for age-related differences in pp covs – p10.

    C.m. aliciae (br AK-n.Alb to Lab): Upperparts and flanks grayish olive; breast lightly washed cream; pale base to the lower mandible reduced (usually not extending beyond the nostril) and with a dull yellow tinge.

    C.m. minimus (br Nfl & possibly ne.Que): Upperparts brownish olive; flanks washed grayish brown to brownish olive; breast with a moderate cream wash; pale base to the lower mandible relatively extensive (usually extending beyond the nostril) and with a bright yellow tinge.

Molt—PB: HY partial (Jul-Sep), AHY complete (Jul-Aug); PA absent. The PBs occur on the summer grounds. The 1st PB includes some to all med covs and 0 (~11%) to 5 inner gr covs, but no terts or rects.

Skull—Pneumaticization completes in HY/SY from 1 Nov. Some SYs retain large windows (> 3 mm; see Fig. 11**D**) at the rear of the skull (above the occipital triangle; see Collier and Wallace 1989) through October and some ASYs can retain small windows (< 3 mm) there.

Age—Juv (Jun-Aug) has the feathers of the upperparts with buff tipping and a moderately distinct, buffy eye ring; juv ♀ = ♂.

    HY/SY (Sep-Aug): Molt limits occur among the med and gr covs (Fig. 133**A-C**; see **Molt**), the retained outer covs worn, paler, and usually (in ~90% of birds) with buff tips when fresh (Fig. 233**A-C**), contrasting with the fresher, darker (and usually without buff tips), replaced inner covs; outer pp covs narrow, tapered, relatively abraded, and brownish with indistinct and relatively thin or no pale brownish edging (Fig. 138); p10 broad, rounded, and measuring 3-7 mm shorter than the pp covs (see Fig. 234); rects and pp tapered (Figs. 139**B** & 140**B**) and relatively abraded. **Note: See Veery regarding the buff tips to the gr covs.**

    AHY/ASY (Sep-Aug): Med and gr covs uniformly adult (Fig. 133**F**), the gr covs without distinct, buff tips (occasionally with an indistinct pale spot at the tip when fresh; Fig. 233**C-D**); outer pp covs broad, truncate, relatively fresh, and dusky brown with distinct, relatively broad, grayish-brown edging (Fig. 138); p10 narrow and tapered, 5-12 mm shorter than the

pp covs (see Fig. 234); rects and pp truncate (Figs. 139**B** & 140**B**) and relatively
fresh. **Note: See HY/SY.**

Sex—♀ = ♂ by plumage. CP/BP (May-Aug).
♀ wg(n100) 93-106, tl(n85) 63-76; ♂
wg(n100) 96-109, tl(n100) 68-79.

Hybrids reported—Possibly Veery and
Swainson's Thrush.

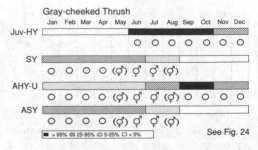

References—Stone (1896), Dwight (1900a), Ridgway (1907), Forbush (1929), Wallace (1939),
Bent (1949), Parkes (1954, 1995b), Roberts (1955), Dilger (1956), Payne (1961), Blake
(1962a), Wood (1969), Oberholser (1974), Phillips (1975a, 1991), Robbins (1975), Phillips &
Holmgren (1980), Cramp (1988), Collier & Wallace (1989), CWS & USFWS (1991), Ouellet
(1993), Curson (1994), Yong & Moore (1994), McLaren (1995), McMinn (1995), Knox (1996),
Patten (1997), Pyle (1997c); C.S. Robbins (*in litt.* to the BBL); IBP (MAPS) data, PNR data.

BICKNELL'S THRUSH
Catharus bicknelli

BITH
Species # 7571
Band size: 1B

Species—Averages much smaller than the other *Catharus*; see Gray-cheeked Thrush for differences other than measurements. From Gray-cheeked Thrush (especially *C.m. minimus*), with
caution, by smaller size (wg 80-98, tl 59-74; see **Sex**); wing morphology shorter (p8 – p6 3-7
mm and p8 – p1 24-29 mm; Fig. 236); tail with a noticeable chestnut tinge, contrasting with
the olive-brown back; throat washed buffy; underparts tinged grayish; pale base of the lower
mandible extensive (usually > 1/2 the mandible length) and brightish yellow; legs flesh with a

purplish tinge or a brownish-dusky wash,
darker than toes. Birds of the Gray-cheeked
Thrush complex not identified to species
can be recorded with alpha code **GCBT**
and **Species # 7579.**

Geographic variation—No subspecies are
recognized.

Molt—PB: HY partial (Jul-Sep), AHY complete (Jul-Aug); PA absent. The PBs occur
on the summer grounds. The 1st PB
includes some to all med covs and 0 (~13%)
to 4 inner gr covs, but no terts or rects.

Skull—Pneumaticization completes in HY/SY
from 1 Nov. Some SYs probably retain large
windows (> 3 mm; Fig. 11**D**) at the rear of
the skull (above the occipital triangle; see
Collier and Wallace 1989) through spring
and some ASYs probably retain small windows (< 3 mm; see Fig. 186).

Age—See Gray-cheeked Thrush. Pp cov –
p10 is 0-6 mm in HY/SYs and 4-10 mm in

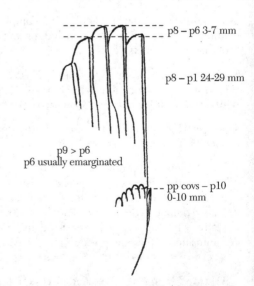

FIGURE 236. The wing morphology of Bicknell's
Thrush. See Figure 10 for measurement techniques
and *cf.* Fig. 234 for age-related differences in pp
covs – p10.

AHY/ASYs. Otherwise all criteria (including molt limits) appear to be similar.

Sex—♀ = ♂ by plumage. CP/BP (Apr-Aug). ♀ wg(n30) 80-96, tl(n28) 59-71; ♂ wg(n84) 87-98, tl(n84) 62-74.

References—Dwight (1900a), Ridgway (1907), Forbush (1929), Wallace (1939), G.J. Wallace *in* Bent (1949), Parkes (1954, 1995b), Oberholser (1974), Cramp (1988), Phillips (1991), Ouellet (1993), Curson (1994), McLaren (1995), Knox (1996), Patten (1997), Pyle (1997c).

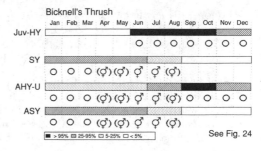

Bicknell's Thrush

See Fig. 24

SWAINSON'S THRUSH
Catharus ustulatus

SWTH
Species # 7580
Band size: 1B

Species—Wg 87-104, tl 61-78 (see **Sex**); pp covs – p10 -3 to 8 mm (see **Age**), p9 > p6, p6 not emarginated, p8 – p6 7-12 mm, p8 – p5 13-18 mm, and p8 – p1 27-30 mm (Fig. 237); upperparts and tail uniformly brown with a reddish tinge or olive-brown to grayish olive (the uppertail covs can be tinged rufous in Pacific coastal subspecies; see **Geographic variation**); face buffy or olive, contrasting with the browner or grayer upperparts; eye ring distinct and buffy; auricular streaked buffy; throat tinged buffy; breast with fairly distinct, large, oval, and brownish spotting; flanks brownish or olive-brown, contrasting moderately with the creamy white belly, and not contrasting distinctly with the color of the upperparts.

From Veery (with caution, as color of the upperparts can approach overlap with Pacific coast subspecies; see **Geographic variation**) by shorter relative tl length; longer wing morphology; lack of emargination on p6; lack of a distinct contrast between the color of the upperparts and the flank wash; buffy eye ring distinct; breast markings olive to brownish; belly creamier. From Gray-cheeked and Bicknell's thrushes (with caution) by shorter relative tl length; shorter average length of p10; lack of emargination on p6; facial plumage buffier; buffy eye ring full and distinct; brownish breast spots larger and less distinct. From Hermit Thrush (with caution, as contrast between back and uppertail covs can approach overlap in Pacific coastal subspecies; see **Geographic variation**) by (especially) the longer wing morphology; tail not distinctly redder than back; eye ring buffier and more distinct.

Geographic variation—Weak to moderate, but certain breeding ranges (and especially winter ranges) are fairly well defined. Subspecies taxonomy follows Rea *in* Phillips (1991); see also Ridgway (1907),

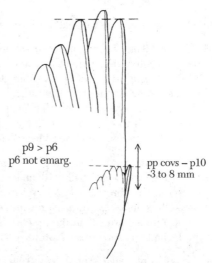

p9 > p6
p6 not emarg.

pp covs – p10
-3 to 8 mm

FIGURE 237. The wing morphology of Swainson's Thrush. See Figure 10 for measurement techniques and *cf.* Fig. 234 for age-related differences in pp covs – p10.

Wetmore (1940), Burleigh & Peters (1948), Godfrey & Wilk (1948), Godfrey (1951b, 1986), Jewett *et al.* (1953), Parkes (1954), Bond (1963), Todd (1963), Phillips *et al.* (1964), Sutton (1967), Monroe (1968), Oberholser (1974), Ramos & Warner (1980), Wetmore *et al.* (1984), Behle (1985), Cramp (1988), Marshall (1988), Patten (1997). No other subspecies occur.

Russet-backed (*C.u. ustulatus*) Group.

C.u. incanus (br w.AK-w.NWT to n.BC-nc.Alb): Back, rump, and uppertail covs uniformly pale grayish brown with an olive tinge; breast whitish with moderately dense, distinct, brownish-black spots.

C.u. ustulatus (br coastal se.AK-nw.CA): Back and rump brown, slightly tinged reddish, contrasting with the reddish uppertail covs; breast washed pale brownish, with moderately sparse, indistinct, brown spots.

C.u. phillipsi (br Queen Charlotte Is, BC): Back and rump brown with a moderate reddish tinge, contrasting with the reddish uppertail covs; breast washed medium brownish, with sparse, indistinct, brown spots.

C.u. oedicus (br c-sw.CA): Back and rump pale brown with a slight or no reddish tinge, contrasting with the paler and slightly reddish uppertail covs; breast washed pale buff, with moderately sparse, indistinct, brown spots.

Olive-backed (*C.u. swainsoni*) Group.

C.u. swainsoni (br interior c.BC-AZ to Nfl-NH): Back and rump medium brownish olive to grayish olive, the uppertail covs uniform in color or only slightly browner; breast whitish or tinged buff, with dense, distinct, blackish-brown spots. Birds of BC to AZ-NM ("*almae*") and birds of Nfl-NS ("*clarescens*") may have upperparts averaging grayer, but differences are slight and broadly clinal.

C.u. appalachiensis (br montane NH-VA): Back and rump dark brownish olive, the uppertail covs uniform in color or only slightly browner; underparts as in *swainsoni*.

Molt—PB: HY partial (Jul-Sep), AHY complete (Jul-Sep); PA absent. The PBs occur on the summer grounds and/or during the early part of fall migration. The 1st PB includes some to all med covs and 0 (~4%) to 5 inner gr covs, but no terts or rects.

Skull—Pneumaticization completes in HY/SY from 1 Nov (as early as 1 Oct in birds of CA). Some SYs retain large windows (> 3 mm; see Fig. 11**D**) at the rear of the skull (above the occipital triangle; see Collier and Wallace 1989) through October and some ASYs can retain small windows (< 3 mm) there.

Age—Juv (Jun-Aug) has the feathers of the upperparts with buff tipping; juv ♀ = ♂.

HY/SY (Sep-Aug): Molt limits occur among the med and gr covs (Fig. 133**A-C**; see **Molt**), the retained outer covs worn, paler, and often (in ~75% of birds) with buff tips when fresh (Fig. 233**A-C**), contrasting with the fresher, darker (and usually without buff tips), replaced inner covs; outer pp covs narrow, tapered, relatively abraded, and brownish with indistinct and relatively thin or no pale brownish edging (Fig. 138); p10 broad, rounded, and measuring -1 to 6 mm shorter than the pp covs (see Fig. 234); rects and pp tapered (Figs. 139**B** & 140**B**) and relatively abraded. **Note: See Veery regarding the buff tips to the gr covs.**

AHY/ASY (Sep-Aug): Med and gr covs uniformly adult (Fig. 133**F**), the gr covs without distinct, buff tips (occasionally with an indistinct pale spot at the tip when fresh; Fig. 233**C-D**); outer pp covs broad, truncate, relatively fresh, and dusky brown with distinct, relatively broad, brownish olive or pale brownish edging (Fig. 138); p10 narrow, tapered, and measuring 4-9 mm shorter than the pp covs (see Fig. 234); rects and pp truncate (Figs. 139**B** & 140**B**) and relatively fresh. **Note: See HY/SY.**

Sex—♀ = ♂ by plumage. CP/BP (Apr-Aug). ♀ wg(n100) 87-100, tl(n100) 61-73; ♂ wg(n100) 91-104, tl(n100) 67-78.

Hybrids reported—Possibly Veery and Gray-cheeked Thrush.

References—Stone (1896), Dwight (1900a), Ridgway (1907), Forbush (1929), Bent (1949), Roberts (1955), Dilger (1956), Payne (1961), Blake (1962a), Wood (1969), Stewart (1971, 1972a), Oberholser (1974), Phillips (1975a, 1991), Robbins (1975), Phillips & Holmgren (1980), Cherry (1985), Cramp (1988), Collier & Wallace (1989), CWS & USFWS (1991), Winkler *et al.* (1992), Yong & Moore (1994), Patten (1997), Pyle (1997c); C.S. Robbins (*in litt.* to the BBL); IBP (MAPS) data, PNR data, PRBO data.

Swainson's Thrush

	Jan	Feb	Mar	Apr	May	Jun	Jul	Aug	Sep	Oct	Nov	Dec
Juv-HY						○	○	○	○	○	○	○
SY				○ ○ ○ (♀) (♀) ♂ ♂ (♀)								
AHY-U				○ ○ ○ (♀) (♀) ♂ ♂ (♀) ○ ○ ○ ○								
ASY				○ ○ ○ (♀) (♀) ♂ ♂ (♀)								

■ > 95%   ▨ 25-95%   ▨ 5-25%   □ < 5%   See Fig. 24

HERMIT THRUSH
Catharus guttatus

HETH
Species # 7590
Band size: 1B-1

Species—Wg 78-110, tl 58-79 (see **Geographic variation & Sex**); pp covs – p10 -5 to 4 mm (see **Age**), p9 < p6, p6 emarginated, p8 – p6 5-6 mm, p8 – p5 11-13 mm, and p8 – p1 20-22 mm (Fig. 238); upperparts brown to grayish brown, contrasting distinctly with the rufous or reddish uppertail covs and tail (this contrast can be slight in the subspecies of CA, *e.g., C.g. slevini*; see **Geographic variation**); eye ring variable, but often fairly distinct and whitish; face, breast, and flank plumage variable (see **Geographic variation**); belly creamy white. From Veery and Gray-cheeked thrushes by the combination of the shorter wing morphology and plumage. From Swainson's Thrush (with caution, as uppertail cov/back contrast can approach overlap in subspecies of CA; see **Geographic variation**) by (especially) the shorter wing morphology; tail distinctly redder than the back; and eye ring usually whiter and less distinct.

Geographic variation—Variably weak (among subspecies groups) to well marked (between groups), at times confused by plumage dichromatism (grayish and reddish-brown plumages), with ranges variably defined. Subspecies taxonomy follows Phillips (1991) as modified by Dickerman & Parkes (1997); see also Ridgway (1907), Grinnell (1918b), Bangs & Penard (1921c), Swarth (1922), McCabe & McCabe (1932, 1933), Oberholser (1932, 1956, 1974), Bishop (1933), Cumming (1933), Miller (1941a), Behle (1948, 1985), Burleigh & Peters (1948), Jewett *et al.* (1953), Phillips (1959b, 1961a), Todd (1963), Phillips *et al.* (1964), Bailey & Niedrach (1965), Sutton (1967), Aldrich (1968), Austin & Rea (1976), Browning (1979a, 1990), Monson & Phillips (1981), Rea (1983), Godfrey (1986), Unitt & Estrella (1996). No other subspecies occur. Beware that specimens fox with age.

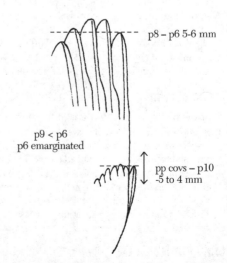

p8 – p6 5-6 mm

p9 < p6
p6 emarginated

pp covs – p10
-5 to 4 mm

FIGURE 238. The wing morphology of Hermit Thrush. See Figure 10 for measurement techniques and *cf.* Fig. 234 for age-related differences in pp covs – p10.

In addition to the following, leg and foot color differs among subspecies and should be noted on all live birds. Breast spotting also varies with subspecies, but the usefulness of this feature is reduced by individual variation.

Western Lowland (*C.g. guttatus*) Group. Small; brownish.

C.g. guttatus (br coastal s.AK-w.BC, wint n.CA-AZ to w.TX): Medium small; bill moderately narrow at the base; back moderately dark grayish brown; rump washed pale rufous; flanks washed brownish gray. ♀ wg(n61) 81-90, tl(n27) 61-68; ♂ wg(n73) 84-94, tl(n30) 63-71.

C.g. nanus (= "*osgoodi*"; br s.AK Is & possibly to coastal se.AK-w.BC, wint coastal WA-s.CA to AZ): Medium small; bill moderately narrow at the base; back medium brown; rump washed dull rufous; flanks washed dark brownish gray. ♀ wg(n10) 83-88, tl(n10) 61-66; ♂ wg(n10) 85-90, tl(n10) 63-70.

C.g. verecundas (br Queen Charlotte Is, BC; wint to coastal n.CA) Medium small; bill moderately narrow at the base; back dark brown; rump washed dull rufous; flanks washed dark brownish gray. ♀ wg(n10) 82-88, tl(n10) 62-68; ♂ wg(n10) 85-92, tl(n10) 65-70.

C.g. vaccinius (br coastal sw.BC-nw.WA, wint coastal CA): Medium small; bill moderately narrow at the base; back dark brown with a dusky wash; flanks washed dark grayish brown. ♀ wg(n20) 82-90, tl(n20) 61-68; ♂ wg(n36) 87-94, tl(n36) 64-71.

C.g. jewetti (br coastal nw.WA-nw.CA, wint s.CA-sw.NM): Small; bill narrow at the base; back pale, warm grayish brown, the crown darker, and the uppertail covs paler (cinnamon); flanks washed pale grayish. ♀ wg(n16) 79-87, tl(n10) 61-68; ♂ wg(n25) 82-91, tl(n10) 65-72.

C.g. slevini (br interior sc.WA-wc.CA, wint s.NV to se.CA-se.AZ): Small; bill moderately narrow at the base; back medium-pale grayish brown; rump relatively dull rufous; flanks washed medium-pale grayish brown. ♀ wg(n55) 78-87, tl(n23) 58-67; ♂ wg(n74) 81-90, tl(n30) 62-69.

C.g. munroi (br c.BC-w.Alb to n.MT, wint sw.OK-s.TX to LA): Medium in size; bill moderately wide at the base; back brown with a dull rufous tinge; flanks washed pale brown with a tawny tinge. ♀ wg(n10) 87-94, tl(n10) 69-72; ♂ wg(n10) 90-96, tl(n10) 67-75.

C.g. oromelus (= "*dwighti*"; br interior s.BC-nw.MT to ne.CA, wint s.NM-s.TX): Medium small; bill narrow at the base; back moderately pale brownish gray, without rufous; flanks washed pale grayish. ♀ wg(n39) 84-91, tl(n39) 63-72; ♂ wg(n53) 88-94, tl(n53) 64-74.

Western Mountain (*C.g. auduboni*) Group. Large; grayish brown.

C.g. sequoiensis (br montane nc-sc.CA, wint se.AZ): Medium large; bill moderately narrow at the base; back medium-pale grayish brown; rump bright rufous; flanks washed medium-pale grayish brown. ♀ wg(n37) 86-96, tl(n16) 64-70; ♂ wg(n62) 89-99, tl(n46) 67-74.

C.g. polionotus (br e.CA to nw.UT-AZ, wint s.AZ): Large; bill moderately narrow at the base; back pale grayish brown; rump dull rufous; flanks washed pale grayish brown; undertail covs white. ♀ wg(n27) 92-101, tl(n17) 67-72; ♂ wg(n47) 97-105, tl(n47) 69-78.

C.g. auduboni (br montane se.WA-s.MT to s.NM-w.TX, possibly wint s.TX): Large; bill moderately narrow at the base; back medium-pale grayish brown; tail medium-bright rufous; flanks washed medium-pale grayish brown; undertail covs pale buff. ♀ wg(n58) 94-103, tl(n46) 67-74; ♂ wg(n78) 98-110, tl(n70) 71-79.

Northern (*C.g. nanus*) Group. Medium in size; reddish brown; gr covs with paler tips by age.

C.g. euborius (br c.AK-n.BC, possibly further east; wint OK-TX to NC-n.FL): Medium in size; bill moderately wide at the base; back moderately dark brown with a medium-dull rufous wash; flanks washed grayish brown, sometimes tinged tawny. ♀ wg(n20) 88-95, tl(n18) 68-73; ♂ wg(n34) 90-97, tl(n30) 66-76.

C.g. faxoni (br s.NWT-s.Alb to Nfl-MD, wint MO-LA to NJ-FL; vag to AZ): Medium in size; bill wide at the base; back brown with a medium-bright rufous wash; flanks washed tawny brown. ♀ wg(n83) 84-94, tl(n63) 62-71; ♂ wg(n100) 88-98, tl(n100) 66-75. Eastern birds within the subspecies range may average redder than western birds, but differences are broadly clinal. Birds of Nfl ("*crymophilus*") may average darker, but the subspecies designation likely was based on foxed specimens.

Molt—PB: HY partial (Jul-Oct), AHY complete (Jul-Sep); PA absent. The PBs occur on the summer grounds. The 1st PB includes some to all med covs and 0 (~28%) to 4 inner gr covs, but no terts or rects. The extent of the 1st PB appears not to vary among subspecies.

Skull—Pneumaticization completes in HY/SY from 1 Nov. Some SYs retain large windows (> 3 mm; see Fig. 11**D**) at the rear of the skull (above the occipital triangle; see Collier and Wallace

1989) through at least July and some ASYs can retain small windows (< 3 mm) there.

Age—Juv (Jun-Aug) has the feathers of the upperparts with buff tipping; juv ♀=♂.

HY/SY (Sep-Aug): Molt limits occur among the med and gr covs (Fig. 133**A-C**; see **Molt**), the retained outer covs worn, paler, and usually (in ~87% of birds) with buff tips when fresh (Fig. 233**A-C**), contrasting with the fresher, darker (and usually without buff tips), replaced inner covs; outer pp covs narrow, tapered, relatively abraded, and brownish with indistinct and relatively thin or no pale brownish edging (Fig. 138); p10 broad, rounded, and measuring -5 to 2 mm shorter than the pp covs (see Fig. 234); rects and pp tapered (Figs. 139**B** & 140**B**) and relatively abraded. **Note: See Veery regarding the buff tips to the gr covs. Also, beware that the Northern Subspecies Group (see Geographic variation) averages paler gr cov tips (in both age groups) than the western subspecies groups.**

AHY/ASY (Sep-Aug): Med and gr covs uniformly adult (Fig. 133**F**), the gr covs without distinct, buff tips (occasionally with an indistinct pale spot at the tip when fresh; Fig. 233**C-D**); outer pp covs broad, truncate, relatively fresh, and dusky brown with distinct, relatively broad, grayish-brown to rufous-brown edging (Fig. 138); p10 narrow, tapered, and measuring -1 to 4 mm shorter than the pp covs (see Fig. 234); rects and pp truncate (Figs. 139**B** & 140**B**) and relatively fresh. **Note: See HY/SY.**

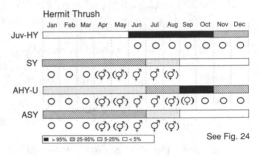

Sex—♀ = ♂ by plumage. CP/BP (Apr-Sep). ♀ wg(n100) 78-103, tl(n100) 58-74; ♂ wg(n100) 81-110, tl(n100) 62-79; see **Geographic variation**.

References—Stone (1896), Dwight (1900a), Ridgway (1907), Forbush (1929), A.O. Gross & A.C. Bent *in* Bent (1949), Roberts (1955), Dilger (1956), Payne (1961), Blake (1962a), Aldrich (1968), Wood (1969), Stewart (1972a), Oberholser (1974), Phillips (1975a, 1991), Robbins (1975), Phillips & Holmgren (1980), Cramp (1988), Collier & Wallace (1989), CWS & USFWS (1991), Jones & Donovan (1996), Pyle (1997c); C.S. Robbins (*in litt.* to the BBL); B. Murphy (unpublished ms); D.A. Sibley (pers. comm.); IBP (MAPS) data, PNR data, PRBO data.

WOOD THRUSH
Hylocichla mustelina

WOTH
Species # 7550
Band size: 1A

Species—From all *Catharus* thrushes by larger wg (96-116; see **Sex**); pp covs – p10 0-6 mm; p8 – p6 3-5 mm; upperparts reddish, brightest on the crown and dullest on the rump (*vs* brightest on the rump in most *Catharus*); underparts white, with large, oval, black spots.

Geographic variation—Subspecies taxonomy follows Browning (1978), who considered the species monotypic (synonymizing a previously recognized subspecies); see also Oberholser (1974). Breeding birds of OK-TX to SC-FL (*"H.m. densa"*) average duller and smaller, but differences are very slight and broadly clinal.

Molt—PB: HY partial (Jul-Aug), AHY complete (Jul-Aug); PA absent-limited (Feb-Apr). The PBs occur on the summer grounds. The 1st PB includes some to all med covs and 0 (~50%) to 4 inner gr covs, but no terts or rects. The occurrence and extent of the PA in the wild requires more investigation.

Skull—Pneumaticization completes in HY/SY from 15 Oct. Some SYs retain large windows (> 3 mm; see Fig. 11**D**) at the rear of the skull (above the occipital triangle; see Collier and Wallace 1989) through August and some ASYs can retain small windows (< 3 mm) there. The skull can be difficult to see through the skin.

Age—Juv (May-Aug) has the feathers of the upperparts with buff spots; juv ♀ = ♂.

HY/SY (Sep-Aug): Molt limits occur among the med and gr covs (Fig. 133**A-C**; see **Molt**), the retained outer covs worn and pale brown with indistinct to distinct, pale cinnamon tips when fresh (Fig. 233**A-C**), contrasting with the fresher, darker, and (usually) untipped, replaced inner covs; outer pp covs narrow, tapered, relatively abraded, and brownish with indistinct and relatively thin or no pale rufous-brown edging (Fig. 138); p10 broad, rounded, and measuring 0-4 mm shorter than the pp covs (see Fig. 234); rects and pp tapered (Figs. 139**B** & 140**B**) and relatively abraded. **Note: Caution is advised, as distinctions are not as clear as in _Catharus_ thrushes. Note that AHY/ASYs can show buff tips to the gr covs (Fig. 233C), although these usually are less numerous and less distinct than in HY/SYs.**

AHY/ASY (Sep-Aug): Med and gr covs uniformly adult (Fig. 133**F**), the gr covs without distinct, buff tips, or with an indistinct pale spot at the tip when fresh (Fig. 233**C-D**); outer pp covs broad, truncate, relatively fresh, and dusky brown with distinct, relatively broad, rufous edging (Fig. 138); p10 narrow, tapered, and measuring 3-6 mm shorter than the pp covs (see Fig. 234); rects and pp truncate (Figs. 139**B** & 140**B**) and relatively fresh. **Note: See HY/SY.**

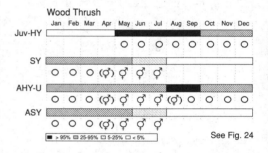

Sex—♀ = ♂ by plumage. CP/BP (Apr-Aug). ♀ wg(n100) 96-112, tl(n86) 62-75; ♂ wg(n100) 100-116, tl(n100) 64-77.

References—Stone (1896), Dwight (1900a), Ridgway (1907), Forbush (1929), F.G. Weaver _in_ Bent (1949), Roberts (1955), Dilger (1956), Norris (1958b), Blake (1962a), Wood (1969), Oberholser (1974), Sheppard & Klimkiewicz (1976), Cramp (1988), Winker _et al._ (1990), CWS & USFWS (1991), Suthers (1993), Weinberg & Roth (1994), Roth _et al._ (1996), Pyle (1997c); C.S. Robbins (_in litt._ to the BBL); IBP (MAPS) data, PNR data.

CLAY-COLORED ROBIN
Turdus grayi

CCRO
Species # 7621
Band size: 2

Species—From similar Mex species of robins by upperparts and underparts fairly uniformly warm brown to yellowish brown; undertail covs without white; bill yellowish; legs pinkish; p9 usually < p4.

Geographic variation—Moderate, but largely clinal where ranges meet. Subspecies taxonomy follows Phillips (1991); see also Ridgway (1907), Miller & Griscom (1925b), Griscom (1930c), Lowery & Newman (1949), Phillips (1966d), Dickerman (1981). Six to seven other subspecies occur in Mex-C.Am.

T.g. tamaulipensis (res s.TX): From other Mex-C.Am subspecies by overall plumage pale and strongly washed buff to pinkish (_vs_ darker and tinged reddish in the other subspecies).

Molt—PB: HY partial (Jul-Oct), AHY complete (Jul-Sep); PA absent. The PBs occur on the summer grounds. The 1st PB includes 2 to 10 (~6%) inner gr covs and occasionally (in ~6% of birds) 1-2 terts, but not the rects. These proportions include birds from throughout the range of the species; northern birds (*T.g. tamaulipensis*) may average fewer feathers replaced (more study is needed).

Skull—Pneumaticization completes in HY/SY from 15 Sep. Some SYs probably retain large windows (> 3 mm; Fig. 11**D**) through spring and some ASYs probably retain small windows (< 3 mm; see Fig. 186). The skull probably is difficult to see through the skin, as in other robins.

Age—Juv (May-Sep) has buff spotting to the upperparts and indistinct, dusky spotting to the underparts; juv ♀ = ♂.

HY/SY (Sep-Aug): Molt limits usually occur among the med and gr covs (Fig. 133**B-D**; see **Molt**), the retained outer covs worn and distinctly tipped buff, contrasting with the fresher and untipped, replaced inner covs; outer pp covs narrow, tapered, relatively abraded, and pale brownish with indistinct, relatively narrow, or no pale buff edging (Fig. 138); rects and pp tapered (Figs. 139**C** & 140**B**) and relatively abraded.

AHY/ASY (Sep-Aug): Med and gr covs uniformly adult (Fig. 133**F**), without buff tips; outer pp covs broad, truncate, relatively fresh, and medium brown with distinct, relatively broad, clay-colored edging (Fig. 138); rects and pp truncate (Figs. 139**C** & 140**B**) and relatively fresh.

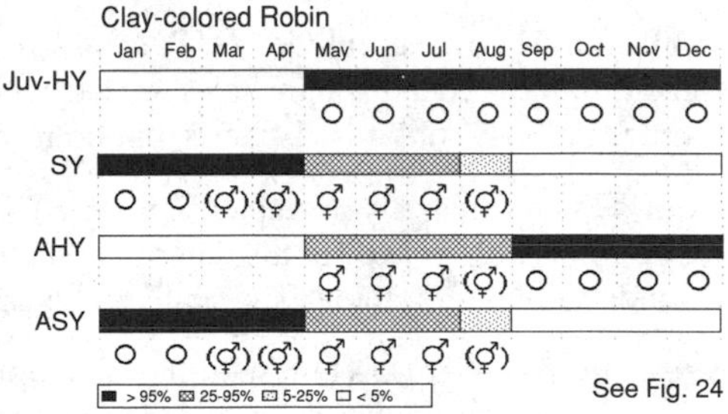
Clay-colored Robin
Jan Feb Mar Apr May Jun Jul Aug Sep Oct Nov Dec
Juv-HY
SY
AHY
ASY
> 95% 25-95% 5-25% < 5%
See Fig. 24

Sex—♀ = ♂ by plumage. CP/BP (Mar-Aug). ♀ wg(n11) 113-126, tl(n11) 92-103; ♂ wg(n30) 118-129, tl(n29) 95-109; measurements include *T.g. tamaulipensis* only; see **Geographic variation**.

References—Ridgway (1907), Dickey & van Rossem (1938), Oberholser (1974), Wetmore *et al.* (1984), Howell & Webb (1995), Pyle (1997c).

AMERICAN ROBIN
Turdus migratorius

AMRO
Species # 7610
Band size: 2

Geographic variation—Weak to moderate and clinal where ranges meet. Subspecies taxonomy follows Phillips (1991); see also Ridgway (1907), Grinnell *et al.* (1909), Swarth (1912b), Oberholser (1917a), Aldrich & Nutt (1939), Rand (1948a, 1948c), Webster (1959a), Todd (1963), Mengel (1965), Sutton (1967), Browning (1974, 1990), Oberholser (1974), Godfrey (1986), Cramp (1988), Aldrich & James (1991). Two other subspecies occur in Mex.

T.m. caurinus (br coastal se.AK-nw.OR, wint to s.CA): Small; tl relatively short; upperparts pale brownish gray (♀♀ and HY/SYs) to medium brownish dusky (AHY/ASY ♂♂); underparts medium-pale (♀♀ and HY/SYs) to medium-dark (AHY/ASY ♂♂) rufous-orange; outer rect (r6) without white, or with an indistinct and medium-small white spot (0-5 mm from the tip in HY/SYs, 3-8 mm in AHY/ASYs, when fresh). ♀ wg(n39) 115-132, tl(n10) 85-98; ♂ wg(n37) 120-137, tl(n10) 88-103.

T.m. propinquus (br & wint interior sc.BC-s.Sask to coastal sw.CA-w.TX): Large; upperparts pale (♀♀ and HY/SYs) to medium (AHY/ASY ♂♂) brownish gray; underparts pale (♀♀ and HY/SYs) to medium (AHY/ASY ♂♂) rufous without an orange tinge; outer rect (r6) without white, or with a moderately indistinct and small white spot (0-3 mm in HY/SYs, 1-7 mm in AHY/ASYs, when fresh). ♀ wg(n100) 124-140, tl(n18) 90-106; ♂ wg(n100) 128-145, tl(n21) 95-112. Birds of OR-CA ("*aleucus*") average smaller, slightly darker, and browner, with less white in the tail than birds of the Rocky Mts. but differences are slight and broadly clinal.

T.m. migratorius (br AK-c.BC to c.Que-NJ, wint to NM-FL): Medium in size; upperparts medium brownish gray (♀♀ and HY/SYs) to dark brownish dusky (AHY/ASY ♂♂); underparts medium-pale (♀♀ and HY/SYs) to medium-dark (AHY/ASY ♂♂) rufous with an orange tinge; outer rect (r6) with a moderately distinct to distinct, and large white spot (4-11 mm in HY/SYs, 7-15 mm in AHY/ASYs, when fresh). ♀ wg(n100) 118-132, tl(n19) 93-101; ♂ wg(n100) 120-140, tl(n38) 96-107.

T.m. nigrideus (br n.Que-Nfl, wint to MS-n.FL): Medium in size; upperparts dark brownish dusky (♀♀ and HY/SYs) to blackish (AHY/ASY ♂♂); underparts medium (♀♀ and HY/SYs) to deep (AHY/ASY ♂♂) rufous without an orange tinge; outer rect (r6) with a moderately distinct to distinct, and medium-sized white spot (1-8 mm in HY/SYs, 6-11 mm in AHY/ASYs, when fresh). ♀ wg(n10) 123-131, tl(n10) 91-102; ♂ wg(n10) 128-136, tl(n10) 96-107.

T.m. achrusterus (br & wint se.OK-s.TX to MD-n.FL): Small; tl relatively long; upperparts brownish gray (♀♀ and HY/SYs) to medium brownish dusky (AHY/ASY ♂♂); underparts medium (♀♀ and HY/SYs) to deep (AHY/ASY ♂♂) rufous with an orange tinge; outer rect (r6) with a moderately indistinct to distinct, and medium-small white spot (0-7 mm in HY/SYs, 3-10 mm in AHY/ASYs, when fresh). ♀ wg(n54) 116-129, tl(n21) 88-97; ♂ wg(n50) 119-133, tl(n13) 94-103.

Molt—PB: HY partial (Jul-Oct), AHY complete (Jul-Sep); PA absent. The PBs occur on the summer grounds. The 1st PB includes some to all med covs, 0 (~12%) to 9 inner gr covs, and sometimes (in ~24% of birds) 1-2 terts, but no rects.

Skull—Pneumaticization completes in HY/SY from 15 Oct. Some SYs can retain large windows (> 3 mm; see Fig. 11**D**) at the rear of the skull through August and some ASYs can retain small windows (< 3 mm) there. The skull can be difficult to see through the skin.

Age—Juv (May-Sep) has buff spotting to the upperparts and black spotting to the underparts; juv ♀ = ♂, although ♂♂ may average darker upperparts, fewer white spots in the crown, and larger and blacker spots on the breast; more study is needed.

HY/SY (Sep-Aug): Molt limits occur among the med and gr covs (Fig. 133**A-D**; see **Molt**), the retained outer covs worn and brownish gray with buff to buffy-white tips, contrasting with the fresher, medium-dark gray and buffy-tipped to whitish-tipped, replaced inner covs; 1-3 terts sometimes replaced, contrasting with the older, juvenal middle ss (s4-s6; Fig. 133**D**); outer pp covs narrow, tapered, relatively abraded, and brownish gray with indistinct, relatively narrow, brownish edging (Fig. 138); rects and pp grayish to grayish brown, tapered (Figs. 139**C** & 140**B**), and relatively abraded. **Note: In addition, HY/SYs of both sexes average paler and duller, and have smaller white spots in the outer rects (r6) than AHY/ASYs, but this varies with subspecies (see Geographic variation). Also, look for a few black (juvenal) spots on the breast of occasional HY/SYs through spring. Some intermediates are difficult to age, especially in May-Jul when feathers become worn.**

AHY/ASY (Sep-Aug): Wing covs and terts uniformly adult (Fig. 133**F**) and medium gray, the gr covs often with narrow, whitish tips; outer pp covs broad, truncate, relatively fresh, and dusky with distinct, relatively broad, gray edging (Fig. 138); rects and pp dark dusky to blackish, truncate (Figs. 139**C** & 140**B**), and relatively fresh. **Note: See HY/SY.**

Sex—CP/BP (Mar-Aug). ♀ wg(n100) 115-140, tl(n78) 85-106; ♂ wg(n100) 119-145, tl(n92) 88-112; see **Geographic variation**.

♀: Crown dark brown; upperparts light brown or pale grayish; underparts medium to pale rufous or rufous-orange, the feathers of the upper breast usually with paler edging. **Note: Sexing should be performed with caution and in combination with information on subspecies, age, and wg; intermediates (especially HY/SY ♂♂ & AHY/ASY ♀♀) occur which** are not reliably sexed by plumage alone. Note that some ♀♀ of *T.m. nigrideus* can be as dark as ♂♂ of the other subspecies, and that some ♂♂ of *propinquus* can be as pale as ♀♀ of the other subspecies; see Geographic variation.

♂: Crown black; upperparts deep grayish to dark brown; underparts rich to medium-dark rufous or cinnamon-rufous, the feathers of the upper breast usually without paler edging. **Note: See ♀.**

Hybrids reported—Song Thrush (*T. philomelos*), Redwing (*T. iliacus*), and Pale-breasted Thrush (*T. leucomelas*), all in captivity.

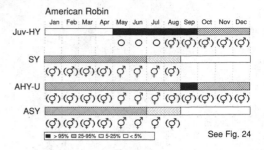

American Robin

See Fig. 24

References—Dwight (1900a), Ridgway (1907), Forbush (1929), Bent (1949), Roberts (1955), Dilger (1956), Wood (1969), Oberholser (1974), Sheppard & Klimkiewicz (1976), Bartel (1987), Cramp (1988), Parkes (1988b), Lewington *et al.* (1991), Phillips (1991), Pyle (1997c); IBP (MAPS) data, PNR data, PRBO data.

VARIED THRUSH
Ixoreus naevius

VATH
Species # 7630
Band size: 2

Geographic variation—Weak, clinal, and based on the plumage of ♀♀ almost exclusively. Subspecies taxonomy follows Phillips (1991); see also Ridgway (1907), Dickinson (1953), Burleigh (1972), Godfrey (1986). No other subspecies occur. Few helpful criteria are known for separating ♂♂, although differences in the hue of ♀♀ are slightly evident in ♂♂.

I.n. meruloides (br AK-NWT, wint WA-ID to s.CA, vag to NM & NJ): ♀♀ with the upperparts uniformly medium-pale, dull brown with a grayish tinge, and the underparts pale orange.

I.n. naevius (br coastal se.AK-nw.CA, wint to sw.CA): ♀♀ with the upperparts uniformly medium-dark brown with a tawny tinge, and the underparts deep orange.

I.n. carlottae (br Queen Charlotte Is, wint to coastal BC-c.CA): ♀♀ with the upperparts dark brown with a tawny tinge, the crown sometimes paler, and the underparts deep orange.

I.n. godfreii (br interior BC to e.WA-w.MT, wint to s.CA?): ♀♀ with the upperparts uniformly medium brown with a reddish tinge, and the underparts pale to medium orange.

Molt—PB: HY partial (Jul-Sep), AHY complete (Jul-Sep); PA absent(?). The PBs occur on the summer grounds. The 1st PB includes some to all med covs, 0 (~7%) to 5 inner gr covs and occasionally (in ~7% of birds) s8, but no rects. Look for a limited or partial PA, perhaps in SYs only.

Skull—Pneumaticization completes in HY/SY from 1 Oct. Some SYs retain large windows (> 3 mm; Fig. 11**D**) through spring and some ASYs can retain small windows (< 3 mm; see Fig. 186).

Age/Sex—Juv (May-Aug) has heavy, dusky mottling on the upper breast, not forming a breast band; some juvs can be sexed by the color of the rects, as in HY/SYs (see below). CP/BP (Mar-Aug). ♀ wg(n100) 118-133, tl(n17) 78-90; ♂ wg(n100) 121-136, tl(n20) 83-94.

HY/SY ♀ (Sep-Aug): Upperparts brown; molt limits occur among the med and gr covs (Fig. 133**A-D**; see **Molt**), the retained outer covs worn and edged brownish, contrasting with the fresher, darker, and brown-edged to tawny-edged, replaced inner covs; outer pp covs narrow, tapered, relatively abraded (Fig. 138), and dusky brownish; rects and pp tapered (Figs.

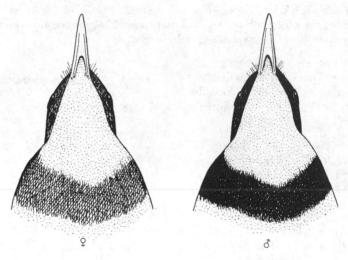

FIGURE 239. The distinctness of the breast band by sex in Varied Thrush. Within each sex, HY/SYs have less distinct bands than AHY/ASYs.

139**C** & 140**B**); rects brown without a grayish tinge; breast band brownish and indistinct (Fig. 239) or nearly obscure. **Note: In addition, HY/SYs average duller in both sexes. A few intermediates can occur (especially worn ♀♀) which are not reliably aged and/or sexed by plumage alone (combine all criteria).**

AHY/ASY ♀ (Sep-Aug): Upperparts brownish olive to brownish gray; wing covs uniformly adult (Fig. 133**F**) and edged dark olive-brown to tawny brown; outer pp covs broad, truncate, relatively fresh (Fig. 138), and brownish black; rects and pp truncate (Figs. 139**C** & 140**B**) and relatively fresh; rects brownish gray; breast band brownish and indistinct (Fig. 239). **Note: See HY/SY ♀.**

HY/SY ♂ (Sep-Aug): Upperparts bluish gray, often tinged brownish; molt limits occur among the med and gr covs (Fig. 133**A-D**; see **Molt**), the retained outer covs worn and edged brownish, contrasting with the fresher, darker, and bluish-edged, replaced inner covs; outer pp covs narrow, tapered, relatively abraded (Fig. 138), and blackish; rects and pp tapered (Figs. 139**C** & 140**B**) and relatively abraded; rects grayish brown with a blue tinge at the base; breast band blackish and fairly distinctly defined (Fig. 239). **Note: See HY/SY ♀.**

AHY/ASY ♂ (Sep-Aug): Upperparts deep bluish gray; wing covs uniformly adult (Fig. 133**F**) and edged bluish gray; rects and pp truncate (Figs. 139**C** & 140**B**) and relatively fresh; rects deep bluish gray; breast band black and distinctly defined (Fig. 239). **Note: See HY/SY ♀.**

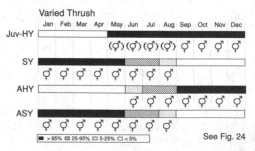

See Fig. 24

References—Dwight (1900a), Ridgway (1907), Forbush (1929), Bent (1949), Sorrie (1977), Madge *et al.* (1990), Lewington *et al.* (1991), Pyle (1997c); A. Knox, B. Walker (pers. comm.); IBP (MAPS) data, PRBO data.

Babblers   *Timaliinae*

One species. Subfamily characters include very short wings (p9 < the secondaries) and a long, graduated tail. Wrentits have 10 primaries (the 10th reduced), 9 secondaries, and 12 rectrices. The first prebasic molt is complete and no prealternate molt occurs. Except for skull and iris color, no reliable, in-hand, ageing or sexing criteria are known for this species. Both sexes develop brood patches and at least partial cloacal protuberances, and males and females are similar in size.

WRENTIT
Chamaea fasciata

WREN
Species # 7420
Band size: 1C

Geographic variation—Moderate, but broadly clinal, resulting in subspecies boundaries difficult to define (they are related more to climate than to geography *per se*). Subspecies taxonomy follows Phillips (1986), as modified by Browning (1992b); see also Ridgway (1907), Grinnell & Swarth (1926b), Bowers (1960). No other subspecies occur.

C.f. phaea (res coastal nw.OR-nw.CA): Tl short (74-83); upperparts and underparts dark brown with a chestnut tinge, the crown washed dusky.

C.f. margra (res interior cs.OR): Tl short (74-83); upperparts and underparts dark brown without a chestnut tinge, the crown washed dusky, and the flanks tinged pale pinkish brown.

C.f. rufula (res coastal nw.CA, Humboldt-w.Marin Cos): Tl short (72-85); upperparts and underparts medium brown slightly tinged chestnut, the crown tinged dusky, and the flanks washed tawny brown.

C.f. fasciata (res coastal c.CA, e.Sonoma-Santa Barbara Cos): Tl long (80-87); upperparts medium brown with a grayish tinge, the crown slightly tinged dusky; underparts brown with a grayish tinge, the flanks washed pinkish brown. Birds of the e-s.San Francisco Bay area (*"intermedia"*) have plumage tending towards *henshawi*, but only slightly.

C.f. henshawi (res interior nc.CA-coastal sw.CA): Tl medium long to long (75-89); upperparts uniformly medium to pale grayish brown, the crown sometimes slightly tinged grayish; underparts uniformly pale grayish brown. Birds of nw.Baja CA to the U.S. border (*"canicauda"*) may average paler and grayer, but differences, if not supposed from worn specimens, are very slight and broadly clinal.

Molt—PB: HY complete (Jul-Oct), AHY complete (Jul-Sep); PA absent.

Skull—Pneumaticization completes in HY from 1 Sep through Dec.

Age—Juv (Apr-Aug) resembles adult in plumage, but has slightly more loosely textured undertail covs; juv ♀ = ♂.

Juv-HY (Apr-Oct): Outer iris brownish gray to brown, sometimes with reddish flecking. **Note: The feathers around the eye should be pulled back gently when examining the outer iris. Otherwise, no plumage criteria are known for ageing (see Skull).**

U/AHY (Sep-Aug): Outer iris reddish brown to maroon. **Note: See Juv-HY.**

Sex—♀ = ♂ by plumage. CP/BP (Feb-Aug) are not reliably used for sexing, as both sexes develop both breeding characters. Subtle differences in the shape of the CP (Mar-Jul) may be of some use, with experience. No differences occur in the BP. Wg: ♀ wg(n100) 52-61, tl(n100) 71-84; ♂ wg(n100) 54-63, tl(n100) 73-89; see **Geographic variation**. This species is not reliably sexed in the hand by external characters (except, perhaps, measurements on occasional extremes).

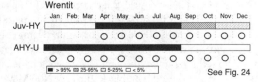

References—Ridgway (1904), Bent (1948), Bowers (1960), Pyle (1997c); PRBO data.

CATBIRDS, MOCKINGBIRDS, AND THRASHERS   *MIMIDAE*

Ten species. Family characters include longish, slightly to strongly decurved beaks, short and rounded wings, and long and (often) graduated tails. Mimids have 10 primaries (the 10th reduced), 9 secondaries, and 12 rectrices. The first prebasic molt tends to be partial, but can be incomplete and eccentric in certain species, especially in juveniles of earlier broods. No (or possibly very limited) prealternate molts occur. Wing-covert contrasts, flight-feather condition, and iris color are the primary ageing criteria. No reliable plumage differences are known for sexing; breeding characters are reliable in spring/summer, although beware that males of certain species can develop partial brood patches. Males average moderately larger than females.

GRAY CATBIRD

Dumetella carolinensis

GRCA
Species # 7040
Band size: 1A

Geographic variation—Weak and clinal where ranges meet. Subspecies taxonomy follows Phillips (1986); see also Aldrich (1946), Rand (1948b), Rand & Traylor (1949), Burleigh (1959b), Phillips (1962), Phillips *et al.* (1964), Monroe (1968), Mayr & Short (1970), Burleigh (1972), Oberholser (1974), Ramos & Warner (1980), Binford (1985), Browning (1990). No other subspecies occur.

D.c. ruficrissa (br BC-w.Man to nw.TX): Undertail covs pale (♀ and HY/SY) to medium-pale (AHY/ASY ♂), rufous-chestnut.

D.c. carolinensis (br e.Man-se.TX to NS-n.FL, wint coastal TX-FL-NJ; vag to s.CA): Undertail covs medium-dark (♀ and HY/SY) to dark (AHY/ASY ♂), chestnut. Breeding birds of e.TX to sw.MD-n.FL ("*meridianus*") may average paler, but differences, if present, are slight and broadly clinal.

Molt—PB: HY partial (Jul-Oct), AHY complete (Jul-Sep); PA absent-limited (Feb-May). The PBs occur primarily on the summer grounds, although they can complete on the winter grounds. The 1st PB includes 0 (~4%) to 10 (~12%) inner gr covs, occasionally (in ~19% of birds) 1-2 terts, and occasionally (in ~10% of birds) 1-2 central rects (r1). Abnormal retention of the juvenal undertail covs through the 1st PB has also been recorded. More study is needed on the occurrence and extent of the PA, which at most includes a limited amount of body plumage only.

Skull—Pneumaticization completes in HY/SY from 1 Nov. Some SYs retain windows (> 3 mm) at the rear of the skull through Jun.

Age—Juv (Jun-Aug) has the upperparts with a brownish wash, undertail covs pale rufous to grayish and loosely textured, iris gray to gray-brown, mouth lining extensively whitish, and tongue yellowish; juv ♀ = ♂.

HY/SY (Aug-Jul): Crown sometimes with retained, grayish juvenal feathers; molt limits usually occur among the gr covs (Fig. 133**B-E**; see **Molt**), the retained outer covs worn and brownish gray with indistinct, rusty tips (when fresh), contrasting with the fresher, dark pearly gray, and untipped, replaced inner covs; 1-2 terts occasionally replaced, contrasting with the older, juvenal middle ss (s4-s6; Fig. 133**D**); outer pp covs narrow, tapered, relatively abraded, and brownish with indistinct, relatively narrow, or no brownish-gray edging (Fig. 138); 1-2 central rects (r1) occasionally replaced and contrastingly fresh; outer rects tapered (Figs. 139**B**) and relatively abraded; iris grayish brown to reddish brown (through Dec-May); tongue and mouth lining primarily whitish, pinkish, and/or pale gray mixed with black (through Nov-May). **Note: Some intermediate individuals may not be reliably aged, especially in May-Jul; also, beware of abnormal AHY/ASYs with gray irises.**

408

See Suthers & Suthers (1990) for a discriminant function analysis, based on live migrants in NJ, using the above and other characters, that separated 88.5% of SYs from ASYs.

AHY/ASY (Aug-Jul): Crown usually uniformly black; wing covs uniformly adult (Fig. 133**F**) and pearly gray, without rusty tips; outer pp covs broad, truncate, relatively fresh, and dusky with distinct, relatively broad, grayish edging (Fig. 138); rects uniformly blackish, the outer rects truncate (Fig. 138) and relatively fresh; iris dark maroon; mouth lining primarily black, paler at the base. **Note: See HY/SY.**

Sex—CP/BP (Apr-Sep). ♀ wg(n100) 81-95, tl(n23) 85-97; ♂ wg(n100) 83-99, tl(n33) 90-104. See Suthers & Suthers (1990) for a discriminant function analysis, based on live birds, using exp culmen, mouth and tongue color, and length of the chestnut on the longest undertail cov, that accurately separated 78% of the sexes. These and other plumage criteria differ on average between the sexes (by age and subspecies), but no reliable in-hand criteria are known to sex individuals.

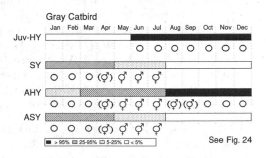

References—Stone (1896), Dwight (1900a), Ridgway (1907), Forbush (1929), A.O. Gross *in* Bent (1948), Roberts (1955), Blake (1962a), Parkes & Leberman (1967), M. Wood (1969), Fisk (1972), D.S. Wood (1973), Oberholser (1974), Sheppard & Klimkiewicz (1976), Crawford (1978), Carpenter (1979), Raynor (1979), Prescott (1982), Cramp (1988), Suthers & Suthers (1990), CWS & USFWS (1991), Cimprich & Moore (1995), Pyle (1997c); J. Baird, C.S. Robbins, J.S. Weske (*in litt.* to the BBL); D. Cimprich, G.E. Wallace (pers. comm.); IBP (MAPS) data, PNR data.

NORTHERN MOCKINGBIRD
Mimus polyglottos

NOMO
Species # 7030
Band size: 2-1A

Geographic variation—Subspecies taxonomy follows Phillips (1986), who considered the species monotypic (synonymizing a previously recognized subspecies); see also Ridgway (1907), Phillips (1961a), Phillips *et al.* (1964), Sutton (1967), Oberholser (1974), Rea (1983), Godfrey (1986). Birds west of c.SD-c.TX (*"M.p. leucopterus"*) may average slightly larger, paler, and buffier than eastern birds, but differences are weak and the subspecies designation possibly was based on feather wear or discoloration.

Molt—PB: HY partial-incomplete (Aug-Nov), AHY complete (Jul-Oct); PA absent. The PBs occur primarily on the summer grounds, but some (to all?) replacement also can occur on the winter grounds. The 1st PB includes 8 to 10 (~77%) inner gr covs, 0 (~4%) to all 9 (~4%) ss, 0 (~74%) to 4 inner pp (and most or all of their corresponding pp covs), and 0 (~46%) to all 12 (~27%) rects. Replacement of the ss proceeds from both the terts and s1, such that s3-s5 are the last feathers replaced (Fig. 137); when 1-4 inner ss are replaced this usually is accompanied by replacement of 1-4 inner pp and pp covs.

Skull—Pneumaticization completes in HY/SY from 1 Oct (as early as 15 Aug in birds of southern populations) through Feb.

Age—Juv (Apr-Sep) has dusky spotting on the throat and breast and a gray to grayish-olive iris; juv ♀ = ♂.

HY/SY (Aug-Jul): Molt limits sometimes occur among the outer gr covs (Fig. 133**D-E**; see **Molt**), the retained outer covs worn and brownish, contrasting with the fresher and dusky, replaced inner covs; 1-8 outer and/or inner ss usually replaced (see **Molt**), contrasting with the older, juvenal middle ss (Fig. 137; often among at least s3-s5); outer pp covs narrow, tapered, relatively abraded (Fig. 138), and mixed brownish and faded white, contrasting with the slightly fresher gr covs (Fig. 134); 1-4 inner pp and pp covs sometimes replaced, contrasting with the more worn outer pp and pp covs (Fig. 137); some or all outer rects juvenal and tapered (Fig. 139**C**; see **Molt**); iris usually grayish to greenish gray (through Nov-May). **Note: Except in very young birds, iris color should not be used for reliable ageing without consulting other criteria, as AHYs occasionally can retain grayish or greenish irises. The pattern and amount of white in the flight feathers and pp covs possibly are of some use in ageing (AHY/ASY averaging more white than HY/SY), but this varies considerably with the individual (see Michener 1953) and probably geographically, as well (see Geographic variation).**

AHY/ASY (Aug-Jul): Gr covs, ss, pp, and rects uniformly adult (Fig. 133**F**) and dusky to dark gray; outer pp covs broad, truncate, relatively fresh (Fig. 138), and mixed dusky and bright white, not contrasting in wear with the gr covs (Fig. 133**F**); outer rects truncate (Fig. 139**C**) and relatively fresh; iris usually greenish yellow to yellowish orange. **Note: See HY/SY.**

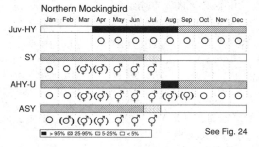

Northern Mockingbird

Sex—♀ = ♂ by plumage. CP/BP (Feb-Sep); ♂♂ can develop partial BPs (Fig. 22**B**). ♀ wg(n100) 99-118, tl(n74) 100-127; ♂ wg(n100) 103-122, tl(n100) 106-134.

References—Stone (1896), Dwight (1900a), Ridgway (1907), Forbush (1929), Bent (1948), Michener (1953), Roberts (1955), Blake (1962a), Wood (1969), Prescott (1972), Fisk (1973a), Oberholser (1974), Sheppard & Klimkiewicz (1976), Zaias & Breitwisch (1990), CWS & USFWS (1991), Derrickson & Breitwisch (1992), Pyle (1997c); C.W. Thompson (pers. comm.); E.J. Fisk (*in litt.* to the BBL); IBP (MAPS) data, PNR data, PRBO data.

SAGE THRASHER
Oreoscoptes montanus

SATH
Species # 7020
Band size: 1B-1A

Species—From Bendire's Thrasher (which see for separation from other thrashers) by small size (wg 93-103, tl 84-95; see **Sex**); wg > tl; p10 – pp covs 6-10 mm and p9 > p4 by 3-10 mm (Fig. 240); tail relatively square (r1 – r6 7-11 mm); bill straight and short (nares to tip 11.0-13.5); throat usually streaked, when fresh; breast with more distinct streaks. From similar-plumaged Gray Thrasher (*T. cinereum*) of Baja CA by smaller size (see above; wg 95-105, tl 96-114 in Gray Thrasher) and much shorter and straighter bill (nares to tip 19-26 in Gray Thrasher).

Geographic variation—No subspecies are recognized.

Molt—PB: HY partial (Jul-Oct), AHY complete (Jul-Oct); PA absent. The PBs occur on the summer grounds. The 1st PB includes 1-7 gr covs, sometimes (in ~35% of birds) 1-3 terts, and occasionally (in ~5% of birds) 1-2 central rects (r1).

Skull—Pneumaticization completes in HY/SY from 15 Oct through Jan.

Age—Juv (Jun-Sep) has a browner and dusky-streaked back, and broad, buffy-white edging to the terts; juv ♀ = ♂.

HY/SY (Aug-Jul): Molt limits occur among the gr covs (Fig. 133**B-D**; see **Molt**), the retained outer covs worn and brownish dusky, contrasting (slightly) with the fresher and dusky, replaced inner covs; 1-3 terts sometimes replaced, contrasting with the older, juvenal middle ss (s4-s6; Fig. 133**D-E**), or if all juvenal terts retained, these are quite worn and pale brownish, especially in spring; outer pp covs narrow, tapered, relatively abraded (Fig. 138), and brownish gray with cinnamon or buff tips when fresh; central rects (r1) occasionally replaced, contrastingly fresh; outer rects tapered (Figs. 139**B**) and relatively abraded. **Note: Molt limits can be hard to detect, thus many intermediates may not be reliably aged, especially in May-Jul when plumage becomes worn.**

AHY/ASY (Aug-Jul): Gr covs and terts uniformly adult (Fig. 133**F**), the gr covs dusky and the terts medium-dark grayish brown and relatively fresh; outer pp covs broad, truncate, relatively fresh (Fig. 138), and dusky with narrow, whitish edging; outer rects uniformly truncate (Fig. 139**B**) and relatively fresh. **Note: See HY/SY.**

Sex—♀ = ♂ by plumage. CP/BP (Apr-Aug); ♂♂ can develop partial BPs (Fig. 22**B**). ♀ wg(n30) 93-100, tl(n20) 84-92; ♂ wg(n30) 96-103, tl(n20) 87-95.

References—Ridgway (1907), Bent (1948), Sutton (1967), Oberholser (1974), Morlan (1986), Kaufman (1990a), Kaufman & Bowers (1990), Pyle (1997c); PRBO data.

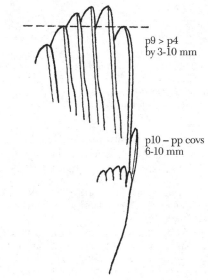

p9 > p4
by 3-10 mm

p10 – pp covs
6-10 mm

FIGURE 240. The wing morphology of Sage Thrasher. See Figure 10 for measurement techniques.

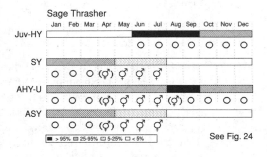

BROWN THRASHER
Toxostoma rufum

BRTH
Species # 7050
Band size: 2-3

Species—From Long-billed Thrasher by longest p – longest s 10-20 mm (Fig. 241); bill averages shorter (exp culmen 22.1-28.8); upperparts (including the forecrown) uniformly bright rufous; malar stripe indistinct; undertail covs buff, occasionally with indistinct, dusky centers (Fig. 242); base of the lower mandible extensively pale yellowish; iris of AHY yellow.

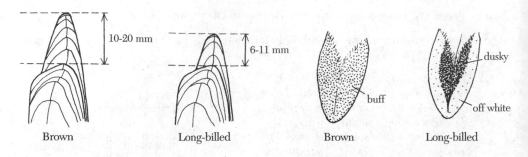

FIGURE 241. The longest p – longest s in Brown and Long-billed thrashers.

FIGURE 242. The pattern of the undertail coverts in Brown and Long-billed thrashers.

Geographic variation—Weak and clinal where ranges meet. Subspecies taxonomy follows Phillips (1986); see also Ridgway (1907), Oberholser (1938, 1974), Wetmore (1939), Bent (1948), Rand & Traylor (1950), Phillips (1962), Sutton (1967). No other subspecies occur.

> **T.r. longicauda** (br s.Alb-s.Man to ne.NM-c.OK, wint to s.TX-nw.FL): Large; upperparts cinnamon-rufous; wing bars whitish to buffy white. ♀ wg(n20) 103-114, tl(n23) 119-138; ♂ wg(n36) 105-117, tl(n45) 121-141.
>
> **T.r. rufum** (br & wint Ont-ME to se.TX-FL): Small; upperparts deep rufous; wing bars buffy white to buff. ♀ wg(n100) 94-105, tl(n47) 111-131; ♂ wg(n100) 98-111, tl(n81) 114-136.

Molt—PB: HY partial (Jul-Sep), AHY complete (Jul-Aug); PA absent. The PBs occur on the summer grounds. The 1st PB includes 2-9 inner gr covs and usually (in ~78% of birds) 1-3 terts, but no rects.

Skull—Pneumaticization completes in HY/SY from 1 Nov (as early as 1 Oct in birds of FL) through Jan. The skull can be difficult to see through the skin.

Age—Juv (May-Aug) has the upperparts usually with indistinct, buff spotting, loosely textured undertail covs, and a gray to grayish-olive iris; juv ♀ = ♂.

> HY/SY (Aug-Jul): Molt limits occur among the gr covs (Fig. 133**B-D**; see **Molt**), the retained outer covs worn and pale cinnamon-rufous at the base, contrasting with the fresher, darker, and rufous-based, replaced inner covs; 1-3 terts usually replaced, contrasting with the older, juvenal middle ss (s4-s6; Fig. 133**D-E**), or if the juvenal terts are retained, these are tipped buff (fall) and relatively abraded (spring); outer pp covs narrow, tapered, relatively abraded (Fig. 138), and rufous-brown with pale buff tips when fresh; outer rects tapered (Fig. 139**C**) and relatively abraded; iris brownish to grayish yellow (through Mar). **Note: Some intermediates can occur, especially HY/SYs that have not replaced terts, and/or worn birds in May-Jul, that are difficult if not impossible to age.**
>
> AHY/ASY (Aug-Jul): Wing covs and terts uniformly adult (Fig. 133**F**), the gr covs deep rufous at the base (beware of a pseudolimit among the outer covs; see p. 207, the terts tipped whitish (fall) and relatively fresh (spring); outer pp covs broad, truncate, relatively fresh (Fig. 138), and rufous-dusky to uniformly deep rufous; outer rects truncate (Fig. 139**C**) and relatively fresh; iris yellow to yellowish orange. **Note: See HY/SY.**

Sex—♀ = ♂ by plumage. CP/BP (Mar-Aug); ♂♂ can develop partial BPs (Fig. 22**B**) and sometimes have reduced CPs. ♀ wg(n100) 94-114, tl(n80) 111-138; ♂ wg(n100) 98-117, tl(n100) 114-141; see **Geographic variation**.

Hybrids reported—Possibly Curve-billed Thrasher.

References—Stone (1896), Dwight (1900a), Ridgway (1907), Forbush (1929), Engels (1940), Bent (1948), Weston (1952), Nichols (1953b), Roberts (1955), Blake (1962a), Wood (1969), Oberholser (1974), Sheppard & Klimkiewicz (1976), Fisher (1979), Cramp (1988), CWS & USFWS (1991), Lewington *et al.* (1991), Pyle (1997c); C.S. Robbins (*in litt.* to the BBL); IBP (MAPS) data, PNR data.

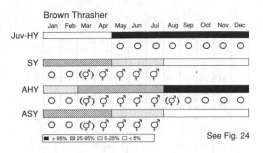

Brown Thrasher

See Fig. 24

LONG-BILLED THRASHER
Toxostoma longirostre

LBTH
Species # 7060
Band size: 2

Species—From Brown Thrasher by longest p – longest s 6-11 mm (Fig. 241); bill averages longer (exp culmen 25.3-32.0); forecrown and nape with a variable amount of grayish, contrasting with the medium bright chestnut to grayish rufous, crown and back; malar stripe distinct; undertail covs whitish with distinct, dusky centers (Fig. 242); base of the lower mandible dusky with a reduced, pale area; iris of AHY yellow-orange to orange.

Geographic variation—Moderate, but somewhat complicated by individual variation. Subspecies taxonomy follows Phillips (1986); see also Ridgway (1907). One other subspecies occurs in Mex.

> **T.l. sennetti** (res s.TX): From the nominate subspecies of Mex by bill shorter (exp culmen 25.3-29.0, *vs* 27.8-32.0 in *longirostre*); upperparts paler and grayer chestnut; black streaks on the flanks average narrower and more distinct.

Molt—PB: HY partial-incomplete (Jul-Sep), AHY complete (Jul-Aug); PA absent. The 1st PB includes 6 to 10 (~33%) inner gr covs and often (in ~67% of birds) 1-3 terts (occasionally s6, as well), but no rects. More study is needed.

Skull—Pneumaticization completes in HY/SY from 15 Oct through Jan. The skull can be difficult to see through the skin.

Age—Juv (May-Aug) has dusky streaking to the rump and loosely textured and relatively buffy undertail covs; juv ♀ = ♂.

> HY/SY (Aug-Jul): Molt limits usually occur among the gr covs (Fig. 133**C-E**; see **Molt**), the retained outer covs worn and pale rufous at the base, contrasting with the fresher, darker, and chestnut-based, replaced inner covs; 1-3 terts (occasionally s6) usually replaced, contrasting with the older, juvenal middle ss (Fig. 133**D-E**), or if the juvenal terts are retained, these tipped grayish buff (fall) to relatively abraded (spring); outer pp covs narrow, tapered, relatively abraded (Fig. 138), and rufous-brown with pale grayish-buff tips when fresh; outer rects tapered (Fig. 139**C**) and relatively abraded; iris grayish to grayish yellow or dull orange (through Mar). **Note: Some intermediates can occur, especially HY/SYs that have not replaced terts, and/or worn birds in May-Jul, that are difficult if not impossible to age.**

> AHY/ASY (Aug-Jul): Wing covs and terts uniformly adult (Fig. 133**F**), the gr covs dark chestnut at the base (beware of a pseudolimit among the outer covs; see p. 207), terts without

grayish-buff tips (fall) and relatively fresh (spring); outer pp covs broad, truncate, relatively fresh (Fig. 138), and uniformly deep chestnut to dusky chestnut; outer rects truncate (Fig. 139C) and relatively fresh; iris yellowish orange to orange. **Note: See HY/SY.**

Sex—♀ = ♂ by plumage. CP/BP (Mar-Jul); ♂♂ probably develop partial BPs (Fig. 22**B**), as in Brown Thrasher. ♀ wg(n30) 92-102, tl(n20) 118-128; ♂ wg(n30) 95-105, tl(n20) 120-132.

References—Ridgway (1907), Engels (1940), Bent (1948), Oberholser (1974), Fisher (1979), Pyle (1997c).

Long-billed Thrasher

	Jan	Feb	Mar	Apr	May	Jun	Jul	Aug	Sep	Oct	Nov	Dec
Juv-HY					○	○	○	○	○	○	○	○
SY			○ ○ (♀) ♂ ♂ ♂ (♀)									
AHY			○ ○ (♀) ♂ ♂ ♂ (♀) ○ ○ ○ ○ ○									
ASY			○ ○ (♀) ♂ ♂ ♂ (♀)									

■ > 95% ▨ 25-95% ▢ 5-25% ▢ < 5%   See Fig. 24

BENDIRE'S THRASHER
Toxostoma bendirei

BETH
Species # 7080
Band size: 2

Species—Wg usually < tl; p10 – pp covs 15-22 mm, p9 – p4 -2 to 6 mm, longest p – longest s 17-22 mm and longest p – p9 6-10 mm (Fig. 243); tail relatively graduated (r1 – r6 14-26 mm); bill slightly decurved (the lower mandible straight) and medium in length (nares to tip 17.5-19.5, when fully grown); outer rects (r6) with moderately distinct, whitish tips (see Fig. 246); throat usually unstreaked when fresh; upper breast with small, moderately indistinct, triangular spots; flanks washed buffy brown; gonydeal angle (under lower mandible) rounded and lower mandible with an extensive pale base (> 5 mm from the feather tips; Fig. 244). From Sage Thrasher by larger size (wg 97-110, tl 101-115; see **Sex**); longer and slightly more decurved bill; wing and tail morphology; breast with less distinct spots, and throat unstreaked. From Curve-billed Thrasher (which see for caution regarding juvs) by longer wing morphology, lower mandible features, shorter and straighter bill, and plumage of the underparts and rects.

Geographic variation—Subspecies taxonomy follows Phillips (1986), who considered the species monotypic (synonymizing two previously recognized subspecies); see also van Rossem (1942c), Phillips (1962). Recognition of subspecies of Mex (darker *"T.b. rubricatum"* and paler *"candidum"*) likely was based on comparisons of specimens in different stages of wear.

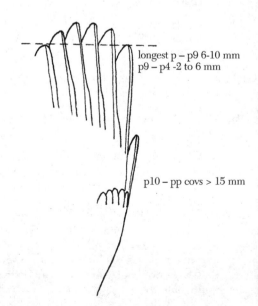

longest p – p9 6-10 mm
p9 – p4 -2 to 6 mm

p10 – pp covs > 15 mm

FIGURE 243. The wing morphology of Bendire's Thrasher. See Figure 10 for measurement techniques.

Molt—Not well known, but apparently as follows: PB HY partial-incomplete (Jun-Nov), AHY complete (Jul-Oct); PA absent. The PBs occur primarily on the winter grounds, but can commence on the summer grounds (in early-hatched HYs only). The 1st PB probably is variable and can include some to all gr covs, usually 1-3 terts, and usually the rects. Early-hatched birds (perhaps ~25% of all HYs) also appear to have an eccentric replacement pattern (see p. 208, Fig. 136), with the outermost 4-6 pp, the innermost 1-6 ss, and up to 3 outermost pp covs replaced, but more study is needed to confirm this.

Skull—Pneumaticization completes in HY/SY from 15 Aug through Feb. The skull can be difficult to see through the skin.

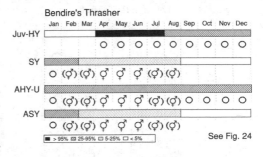

Bendire's   Curve-billed

FIGURE 244. The color and shape of the base of the underside of the mandible in Bendire's and Curve-billed thrashers. The difference between the two species in the gonydeal angle is subtle.

Age—Juv (Apr-Aug) has a slightly reddish-brown wash to the upperparts, buff or cinnamon-buff edging to the gr covs and terts, and little or no distinct whitish to the outer rects (r6; Fig. 246); juv ♀ = ♂.

HY/SY (Sep-Aug): Pp covs narrow, tapered, abraded (Fig. 138), and faded brown to grayish, with indistinct, buff to tawny edging (1-4 outer feathers sometimes replaced and contrastingly fresh); the innermost 3-5 ss and the outermost 3-5 pp sometimes contrastingly fresh (Fig. 136**A**; see **Molt**), s6 not distinctly fresher than s7 (see Fig. 193); molt limits occasionally occur among the gr covs (Fig. 133**B-E**; see **Molt**), the retained outer covs worn and brownish with wide, indistinct, buff tips, contrasting with the fresher, darker, and thinly whitish-tipped or untipped, replaced inner covs. **Note: In addition check for a grayer iris in younger birds. Birds become difficult, if not impossible to age in Mar-Jul due to wear.**

AHY/ASY (Sep-Aug): Pp covs uniformly broad, truncate, relatively fresh (Fig. 138), and dark brown or gray with distinct, paler brown or gray edging; wing covs, ss, pp, and rects uniformly adult (Fig. 133**F**), fresh, and medium-dark grayish brown; s6 usually distinctly fresher than s7 (see Fig. 193). **Note: See HY/SY.**

Sex—♀ = ♂ by plumage. CP/BP (Feb-Aug); ♂♂ can develop partial BPs (Fig. 22**B**), as in other thrashers. ♀ wg(n30) 97-106, tl(n20) 101-111; ♂ wg(n30) 100-110, tl(n20) 105-115.

Bendire's Thrasher

	Jan	Feb	Mar	Apr	May	Jun	Jul	Aug	Sep	Oct	Nov	Dec
Juv-HY				○	○	○	○	○	○	○	○	○
SY												
	○	(♀)	(♀)	♂	♂	♂	(♀)	(♀)				
AHY-U												
	○	(♀)	(♀)	♂	♂	♂	(♀)	(♀)	○	○	○	○
ASY												
	○	(♀)	(♀)	♂	♂	♂	(♀)	(♀)				

■ > 95% ▨ 25-95% ▢ 5-25% □ < 5%   See Fig. 24

References—Ridgway (1907), Engels (1940), Bent (1948), Phillips (1962), Phillips *et al.* (1964), Phillips & Holmgren (1980), Morlan (1986), Kaufman (1990a), Kaufman & Bowers (1990), England & Laudenslayer (1993), Pyle (1997c).

CURVE-BILLED THRASHER
Toxostoma curvirostre

CBTH
Species # 7070
Band size: 3

Species—From Bendire's Thrasher (which see for separation from Sage Thrasher) by p9 < p4 by 6-12 mm, longest p – longest s 13-18 mm and longest p – p9 8-15 mm (Fig. 245); bill strongly decurved (including the lower mandible) and long (nares to tip 20.0-25.5, when fully grown); outer rects (r6) with or without distinct, whitish tips (Fig. 246; see **Geographic variation**); upper breast with large, indistinct, round spots; flanks washed gray; lower mandible with an acute gonydeal angle and the base entirely dark (Fig. 244). Beware especially of juvs, which can show overlap in plumage of the underparts and shape and length of the bill; on these use gonydeal angle, lack of a distinct pale area at the base of the lower mandible, and wing morphology.

Geographic variation—Well marked between the two subspecies of N.Am (but weaker among the subspecies of Mex) and clinal where ranges in N.Am meet. Subspecies taxonomy follows Phillips (1986); see also Ridgway (1907), Law (1928), Swarth (1929), van Rossem (1931a, 1945a), Van Tyne & Sutton (1937), Moore (1941c), Sutton (1948a), Phillips (1962), Phillips *et al.* (1964), Oberholser (1974). Two to four other subspecies occur in Mex.

T.c. palmeri (res wc-s.AZ; vag to CA, NE & FL): Tl long; wing bars indistinct and pale grayish; rects with little or no indistinct white (Fig. 246; on the outer rect [r6] usually < 7 mm when fresh); throat and breast gray, not contrasting distinctly with the grayish breast spots. Tl: ♀(n58) 110-121, ♂(n91) 115-130.

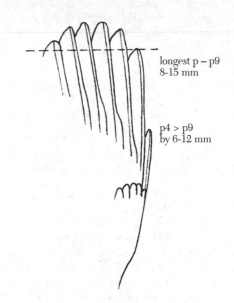

longest p – p9
8-15 mm

p4 > p9
by 6-12 mm

FIGURE 245. The wing morphology of Curve-billed Thrasher. See Figure 10 for measurement techniques.

Juvenal Bendire's and Curve-billed / Adult Bendire's / Adult Curve-billed *T.c. palmeri* / Adult Curve-billed *T.c. oberholseri*

FIGURE 246. The shape and pattern of the outer rectrix (r6) by species, subspecies, and age in Bendire's and Curve-billed thrashers.

T.c. oberholseri (res se.AZ to se.CO-w.TX; vag to FL): Tl short; wing bars distinct and whitish; rects with distinct and extensive white tips (Fig. 246; on the outer rect [r6] usually > 7 mm when fresh); throat and breast white to whitish, contrasting distinctly with the dark gray breast spots. Tl: ♀(n44) 99-111, ♂(n47) 103-117. Birds of w.TX average smaller than other birds ("*celsum*"), but differences are broadly clinal.

Molt—PB: HY partial-incomplete (Jun-Oct), AHY complete (Jun-Oct); PA absent. The 1st PB includes 3 to 10 (~63%) inner gr covs, often (in ~75% of birds) 1-3 terts (sometimes s6 and s5, as well), and from 0 (~19%) to all 12 (~50%) rects. Some birds (~44%) show an eccentric molt pattern (see p. 208 and Fig. 136) with the innermost 4-5 ss, the outermost 2-5 pp, and the outermost 1-3 pp covs replaced. More study is needed.

Skull—Pneumaticization completes in HY/SY from 1 Sep through Feb. The skull can be difficult to see through the skin.

Age—Juv (Apr-Aug) has the upperparts and upper breast washed rufous, undertail covs loosely textured, and rects without white tips (Fig. 246); juv ♀ = ♂.

HY/SY (Aug-Jul): Pp covs narrow, abraded (Fig. 138), and faded brown to grayish, with indistinct, buff to tawny edging (1-3 outer feathers sometimes replaced and contrastingly fresh); the innermost 1-5 ss and the outermost 2-5 pp sometimes contrastingly fresh (Fig. 136**A**), s6 not distinctly fresher than s7 (see Fig. 193); molt limits sometimes occur among the gr covs (Fig. 133**B-E**), the retained outer covs worn and brownish with wide, indistinct, tawny tips, contrasting with the fresher, darker, and thinly whitish-tipped or untipped, replaced inner covs; rects sometimes mixed fresh and worn (see **Molt**), the outer rects (if juvenal) tapered (Fig. 139**C**), without a distinctly defined white tip (Fig. 246; see **Geographic variation**), and relatively abraded; iris gray, cream, or yellowish (through Oct). **Note: Ageing becomes increasingly difficult through spring, as feathers rapidly become faded and abraded.**

AHY/ASY (Aug-Jul): Pp covs uniformly broad, truncate, relatively fresh (Fig. 138), and dark brown or gray, with distinct, whitish edging; wing covs, ss, pp, and rects uniformly adult (Fig. 133**F**), fresh, and medium-dark grayish brown; s6 usually distinctly fresher than s7 (see Fig. 193); rects uniformly truncate (Fig. 139**C**), the outer rects (r6) with a variable amount of distinctly defined white (Fig. 246; see **Geographic variation**) and relatively fresh; iris orange-yellow. **Note: See HY/SY.**

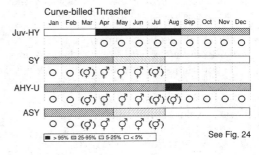

Sex—♀ = ♂ by plumage. CP/BP (Mar-Aug); ♂♂ can develop partial or nearly complete BPs (Fig. 22**B**). ♀ wg(n100) 96-111, tl(n100) 99-121; ♂ wg(n100) 102-115, tl(n100) 103-130.

Hybrids reported—Possibly Brown Thrasher.

References—Ridgway (1907), Engels (1940), Bent (1948), Weston (1952), Phillips *et al.* (1964), Oberholser (1974), Phillips & Holmgren (1980), Walters & Lamm (1986), Kaufman (1990a), Kaufman & Bowers (1990), Fink & DeNeal (1993), Tweit (1996), Pyle (1997c).

CALIFORNIA THRASHER
Toxostoma redivivum

CATH
Species # 7100
Band size: 3

Species—From Crissal and Le Conte's thrashers by the combination of short tl (117-138; see **Sex**); upperparts dark dusky brown; indistinct supercilium present; malar stripe narrow, broken, and/or indistinct; undertail covs tan, contrasting indistinctly with the lower belly.

Geographic variation—Weak and clinal where ranges meet. Subspecies taxonomy follows Phillips (1986); see also Ridgway (1907), Grinnell (1915b), Oberholser (1918d). One other subspecies occurs in Mex.

> ***T.r. sonomae*** (res n-c.CA, Humboldt-Santa Cruz Cos): Underparts dark dusky brown; chest band indistinct.
> ***T.r. redivivum*** (res c-s.CA): Underparts medium dusky brown; chest band fairly distinct.

Molt—PB: HY partial-incomplete (Jul-Oct), AHY complete (Jul-Oct); PA absent. The 1st PB includes 4 to 10 (~19%) inner gr covs, often (in ~67% of birds) 1-3 terts, and sometimes (in ~29% of birds) the central rects (r1), occasionally as many as 8 rects.

Skull—Completion in HY/SY can occur as early as 1 Jul, but generally takes place from 15 Sep through Jan. The skull can be difficult to see through the skin.

Age—Juv (Feb-Aug) has buffy-cinnamon edging to the gr covs and terts, and loosely textured undertail covs; juv ♀ = ♂.

HY/SY (Aug-Jul): Molt limits usually occur among the gr covs (Fig. 133C-E; see **Molt**), the retained outer covs worn and brownish with indistinct, tawny tips, contrasting with the fresher and dark dusky-brown and whitish-tipped or buff-tipped, replaced inner covs; 1-3 terts often replaced, contrasting with the older, juvenal middle ss (s4-s6; Fig. 133D-E) or, if all juvenal terts are retained, these are tipped tawny (fall) to relatively abraded (spring); outer pp covs narrow, tapered, relatively abraded (Fig. 138), and brownish with indistinct, tawny tips; one or more rects sometimes contrastingly worn; outer rects tapered (Fig. 139C) and relatively abraded. **Note: Ageing can be difficult, especially in Mar-Jul when plumage becomes worn; many intermediates may not be reliably aged. In addition, look for changes in eye color, as in other thrashers.**

AHY/ASY (Aug-Jul): Wing covs and terts uniformly adult (Fig. 133F), the gr covs dark brown with distinct, whitish to grayish-cinnamon tips (beware of a pseudolimit among the outer covs; see p. 207); terts without tawny tips (fall) and relatively fresh (spring); outer pp covs broad, truncate, relatively fresh (Fig. 138), and dark brown with distinct, grayish tips; rects uniformly adult, the outer rects (r6) truncate (Fig. 139C) and relatively fresh. **Note: See HY/SY.**

Sex—♀ = ♂ by plumage. CP/BP (Dec-Jul); ♂♂ can develop partial or perhaps nearly complete BPs (see Fig. 22D). ♀ wg(n35) 92-105, tl(n20) 117-132; ♂ wg(n35) 95-108, tl(n20) 120-138.

California Thrasher

	Jan	Feb	Mar	Apr	May	Jun	Jul	Aug	Sep	Oct	Nov	Dec
Juv-HY												
	○	○	○	○	○	○	○	○	○	○	○	○
SY												
	(♂)	(♂)	♂	♂	♂	(♂)	(♀)					
AHY-U												
	(♂)	(♂)	♂	♂	♂	(♂)	(♀)	○	○	○	○	(♂)
ASY												
	(♂)	(♂)	♂	♂	♂	(♂)	(♀)					

■ > 95%   ▨ 25-95%   ▥ 5-25%   □ < 5%   See Fig. 24

Hybrids reported—See Le Conte's Thrasher.

References—Ridgway (1907), Grinnell & Swarth (1913), Engels (1940), Bent (1948), Sheppard (1996), Pyle (1997c).

CRISSAL THRASHER
Toxostoma crissale

CRTH
Species # 7120
Band size: 2

Species—From California and Le Conte's thrashers by longer average tl (126-150; see **Sex**); upperparts medium grayish brown; indistinct supercilium present or lacking; malar stripe broad and distinct; undertail covs deep chestnut, contrasting markedly with the pale gray lower belly.

Geographic variation—Weak and clinal where ranges meet. Subspecies taxonomy follows Phillips (1986); see also Moore (1941d), Burleigh & Lowery (1942), van Rossem (1946a), Phillips (1962), Hubbard & Crossin (1974), Rea (1983). One other subspecies occurs in Mex.

T.c. coloradense (res desert se.CA-sw.AZ): Upperparts and underparts medium-pale grayish brown.
T.c. crissale (res sw.UT-sc.AZ to w.TX): Upperparts and underparts medium-dark grayish brown.

Molt—PB: HY partial-incomplete (Jun-Oct), AHY complete (Jun-Sep); PA absent. The 1st PB usually (in ~85% of birds) is eccentric (see p. 208 and Fig. 136), with the outermost 3-8 pp and the innermost 3-7 ss, but no outer pp covs replaced. Other birds retain all pp but replace all gr covs (rarely the outermost can be retained) and 2-3 terts. The rects usually are replaced, but can be retained in occasional (~15%) birds. More study is needed.

Skull—Pneumaticization completes in HY/SY from 1 Sep through Jan. The skull can be difficult to see through the skin.

Age—Juv (Mar-Aug) has buffy-cinnamon edging to the gr covs and terts and paler and loosely textured undertail covs; juv ♀ = ♂.

HY/SY (Sep-Aug): Outer pp covs narrow, tapered, abraded (Fig. 138), and pale brown with tawny edging, contrasting with the slightly fresher gr covs (Fig. 134); the outermost 2-6 ss and the innermost 2-7 pp usually contrastingly fresh (Fig. 136**A-B**), s6 not distinctly fresher than s7 (see Fig. 193); one or more rects sometimes contrastingly worn, the outer rects (if juvenal) tapered (Fig. 139**C**) and relatively abraded.

AHY/ASY (Sep-Aug): Outer pp covs uniformly broad, truncate, relatively fresh (Fig. 138), and medium-dark grayish brown with distinct, whitish to buffy-whitish edging, not contrasting in wear with the gr covs (Fig. 133**F**); ss and pp uniformly adult (Fig. 133**F**), fresh, and medium-dark grayish brown; s6 usually distinctly fresher than s7 (see Fig. 193); rects uniformly truncate (Fig. 139**C**) and relatively fresh.

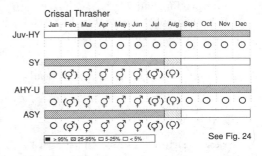

Sex— ♀ = ♂ by plumage. CP/BP (Feb-Aug); ♂♂ probably develop partial and perhaps nearly complete BPs (see Fig. 22**B**), as in other thrashers. ♀ wg(n32) 93-101, tl(n20) 126-145; ♂ wg(n34) 97-105, tl(n20) 133-150.

References—Ridgway (1907), Engels (1940), Bent (1948), Oberholser (1974), Pyle (1997c).

LE CONTE'S THRASHER
Toxostoma lecontei

LCTH
Species # 7110
Band size: 2

Species—From California and Crissal thrashers by the combination of short tl (113-131; see **Sex**); upperparts pale grayish brown to gray; supercilium lacking; malar stripe narrow and indistinct; undertail covs pale tan, contrasting indistinctly with the pale gray lower belly.

Geographic variation—Moderate and ranges well-defined. Subspecies taxonomy follows Sheppard (1996); see also Grinnell (1933), Phillips (1964, 1986), Browning (1990), Zink *et al.* (1997). One other subspecies occurs in Mex.

> **T.l. lecontei** (res throughout range in N.Am): From *arenicola* of w.Baja CA by tl longer (see **Sex**, *vs* 107-117 in *arenicola*); coloration averages paler. Birds of c.CA ("*macmillanorum*") may average darker but this difference is broadly clinal.

Molt—PB: HY partial-incomplete (Jul-Oct), AHY complete (May-Oct); PA absent. The 1st PB includes 8 to 10 (~61%) inner gr covs, 1-3 terts (sometimes s6-s5, as well), and 0 (~77%) to all 12 (~11%) rects. Occasional birds (~11%) show an eccentric replacement pattern (see p. 208 and Fig. 136), with the outermost 3-5 pp and the innermost 3-5 ss replaced; the pp covs are retained.

Skull—Pneumaticization completes in HY/SY from 1 Aug through Jan. The skull can be difficult to see through the skin.

Age—Juv (Feb-Aug) has slightly darker brown upperparts (compared with faded AHYs) with relatively paler and loosely textured undertail covs; juv ♀ = ♂.

> HY/SY (Sep-Aug): Outer pp covs narrow, tapered, and abraded (Fig. 138), with tawny tips; the innermost 4-6 ss and the outermost 5-7 pp occasionally contrastingly fresh (Fig. 136**A-B**; see **Molt**), s6 not distinctly fresher than s7 (see Fig. 193); molt limits occasionally occur among the gr covs (see **Molt**, Fig. 133**D-E**), the retained outer covs worn with wide, indistinct, buff tips, contrasting with the fresher, darker, and thinly whitish-tipped or untipped, replaced inner covs; outer rects usually juvenal, tapered (Fig. 139**C**), and relatively abraded. **Note: Many intermediates will be difficult or impossible to age.**

> AHY/ASY (Sep-Aug): Outer pp covs uniformly broad, truncate, and relatively fresh (Fig. 138), with distinct, whitish edging; wing covs, ss, and pp uniformly adult (Fig. 133**F**), relatively fresh, and medium-dark grayish brown; s6 usually distinctly fresher than s7 (see Fig. 193); rects uniformly truncate (Fig. 139**C**) and relatively fresh. **Note: See HY/SY.**

Sex—♀ = ♂ by plumage. CP/BP (Jan-Aug); ♂♂ develop partial and perhaps nearly complete BPs (see Fig. 22**B**). ♀ wg(n100) 91-101, tl(n100) 113-129; ♂ wg(n100) 93-103, tl(n100) 115-131.

Hybrids reported—A supposed hybrid with California Thrasher was probably based on a dark (fresh basic-plumaged) Le Conte's Thrasher.

Le Conte's Thrasher

	Jan	Feb	Mar	Apr	May	Jun	Jul	Aug	Sep	Oct	Nov	Dec
Juv-HY												
	○	○	○	○	○	○	○	○	○	○	○	○
SY												
	(♀)	(♀)	♂	♂	♂	(♀)	(♀)	(♀)				
AHY-U												
	(♀)	(♀)	♂	♂	♂	(♀)	(♀)	(♀)	○	○	○	○
ASY												
	(♀)	(♀)	♂	♂	♂	(♀)	(♀)	(♀)				

■ > 95% ▨ 25-95% ▥ 5-25% □ < 5%   See Fig. 24

References—Ridgway (1907), Grinnell & Swarth (1913), Engels (1940), Bent (1948), Sheppard (1996), Pyle (1997c).

STARLINGS

STURNIDAE

One species. Family characters include a robust body, strong legs, and a short tail. Starlings have 10 primaries (the 10th minute), 9 secondaries, and 12 rectrices. The first prebasic molt is complete, or nearly so. Almost all birds should be reliably aged and sexed when all of the many criteria are combined. Males average moderately larger than females.

EUROPEAN STARLING
Sturnus vulgaris

EUST
Species # 4930
Band size: 2-3

Geographic variation—Weak to moderate and complex through the Eurasian range. Subspecies taxonomy follows Cramp & Perrins (1994a); see also Svensson (1992). Eleven to twelve other subspecies occur in Eurasia. See Blem (1981a) for details on slight variation in size within N.Am.

S.v. vulgaris (br & wint throughout the range in N.Am): From other Eurasian subspecies by large size (see Sex); p10 medium short (10-15 mm); gloss of the nape and breast purplish, contrasting with the greenish gloss of the rest of the plumage; whitish spots of fresh feathers larger; underwing covs dark gray with buff edging.

Molt—PB: HY complete (Jul-Nov), AHY complete (Jun-Oct); PA absent. The alula, a few outer ss, and/or a few inner pp occasionally can be retained during the 1st PB.

Skull—Pneumaticization completes in HY/SY from 1 Dec through Apr. The skull can be difficult to see through the skin.

Age—Juv (May-Oct) has entirely gray-brown plumage; many juvs can be sexed by eye color, as in HYs (see below).

HY/SY (Sep-Aug): Length of the iridescence on the throat feathers shorter by sex (Fig. 248); a few gray, juvenal flight feathers occasionally retained (see **Molt**); rects relatively rounded, the central rect with indistinct, black subterminal edging and buff terminal edging (Fig. 247); outer rect (r6) with narrow or indistinct, cinnamon edging; tongue with at least some yellow (through Oct-Nov). **Note: The shape of the rects is useful for ageing, despite replacement of the juvenal tail during the 1st PB, although some overlap exists. Intermediates will occur (especially with ♀♀) that are not reliably aged; it is best to sex birds first before ageing.**

AHY/ASY (Sep-Aug): Length of the iridescence on the throat feathers longer by sex (Fig. 248); flight feathers uniformly adult; rects relatively pointed, the central rect with distinctly defined black subterminal edging and cinnamon terminal edging (Fig. 247); outer rect (r6) with wide, distinct, cinnamon edging; tongue without yellow coloration. **Note: See HY/SY.**

Sex—CP/BP (Mar-Sep); ♂♂ can develop a partial BP (Fig. 22**B**). ♀ wg(n100) 120-133, tl(n100) 58-65; ♂ wg(n100) 124-138, tl(n100) 60-68; measurements based on birds of N.Am (*S.v. vulgaris*) only.

♀: Length of the iridescence on the throat feathers shorter by age (Fig. 248); iris pale grayish with a yellow tinge (juv) to

HY/SY

AHY/ASY

FIGURE 249. The central rectrix (r1) by age in European Starling.

brown with a distinct (occasionally indistinct), yellow outer ring; base of the lower mandible pinkish in Jan-Jun (sometimes in Jul-Dec, as well). **Note: Beware of occasional birds (3-7% of non-juvs) showing conflicting iris and bill color characters; these should be sexed only in combination with measurements, throat feather, and ageing criteria.**

♂: Length of the iridescence on the throat feathers longer by age (Fig. 248); iris dark brownish gray (juv) to uniformly dark brown; base of the lower mandible blue or bluish gray in Jan-Jun (sometimes in Jul-Dec, as well). **Note: See ♀.**

Hybrids reported—Brahminy Starling (*S. pagodarum*) in captivity.

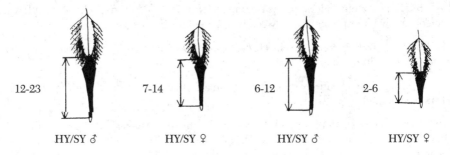

References—Ridgway (1907), Forbush (1927), Hicks (1934), Nichols (1945), Bent (1950), Kessel (1951, 1957), Roberts (1955), Davis (1959, 1960), Parks (1962), Lloyd (1965), Schwab & Marsh (1967), Wood (1969), Oberholser (1974), Suthers (1978), Svensson (1992), Cabe (1993), Cramp & Perrins (1994a), Jenni & Winkler (1994); PRBO data.

12-23	7-14	6-12	2-6
HY/SY ♂	HY/SY ♀	HY/SY ♂	HY/SY ♀

FIGURE 248. Lengths of the iridescence on the throat feathers of European Starlings by age/sex category.

WAGTAILS AND PIPITS   *MOTACILLIDAE*

Six species. Family characters include slender bills, pointed wings, elongated tertials, and long hind claws. Wagtails and pipits have 10 primaries (the 10th reduced), 9 secondaries, and 12 rectrices. The first prebasic molt is partial to incomplete, and prealternate molts are limited to incomplete. The shape of the rectrices does not appear to be useful for ageing; however, plumage coupled with molt limits can be used to age most birds in the fall and some birds in the spring. The plumages of the sexes differ in the wagtails but are similar in the pipits. Breeding condition can be used to sex birds in spring and summer, and males average moderately to substantially larger than females.

YELLOW WAGTAIL
Motacilla flava

YWAG
Species # 6960
Band size: 1

Species—P7 – p6 3-7 mm; emargination of p8 extends 16-18 mm from the tip and is ≥ the tip of p3; tl short (62-72 in *M.f. tschutschensis*; see **Age/Sex**); forehead and crown uniformly dark gray to brownish olive; auricular dark gray, not bordered posteriorly with pale edging; upper wing bar distinct but narrow (tips to the med covs 1.5-2.5 mm), often tinged yellow; rump olive or pale grayish, the feathers often edged yellow; underparts (including the throat and under-tail covs) usually with yellow; breast without distinct black coloration; lower mandible with a slight, pale pink or gray base. Juv-HY from juv-HY Citrine Wagtail (*M. citreola*), a potential vagrant to N.Am, with caution: Citrine usually has p7 – p6 1-4 mm; emargination of p8 extending 18-24 mm from the tip and ≤ p3; forehead paler than the crown; auricular bordered posteriorly with pale edging; rump dark gray to blackish; lower mandible black. Gray Wagtail (*M. cinerea*; alpha code **GRAW**, **Species # 6961**) has a much longer tl (84-106); upper wing bar usually lacking; throat white or gray, contrasting with the pale yellow underparts, which in turn contrast with the darker yellow undertail covs. Juv-HY ♀ Yellow Wagtail (which can lack yellow to the underparts) from White and Black-backed wagtails by smaller size (wg 72-83, tl 63-72; see **Age/Sex**) and the plumage of the forehead, auricular, and breast.

Geographic variation—Moderate to well marked, but complex. Subspecies taxonomy follows Cramp (1988); see also Ridgway (1904), Dement'ev & Gladkov (1954), D. Gibson *in* Phillips (1991), Svensson (1992). Seventeen other subspecies occur in Eurasia.

> **M.f. simillima** (vag or mig to w.AK Is): Large; wg long; back bright olive or grayish; chin and throat of AHY/ASY ♂ white; breast bright and deep yellow with indistinct or no dusky markings. ♀ wg(n10) 76-82, tl(n10) 63-68; ♂ wg(n13) 80-86, tl(n10) 67-73.

> **M.f. tschutschensis** (br AK-Yuk): Small; wg short (see **Age/Sex**); back dull olive or grayish; chin and throat of AHY/ASY ♂ yellow; breast dull and pale yellow with indistinct to distinct, dusky spots, sometimes forming a collar. Breeding birds of N.Am ("*alascensis*") may average slightly smaller, paler, and browner than Siberian birds, but differences are weak and the subspecies designation was possibly based on worn specimens. Subspecies of N.Am from other Eurasian subspecies (possible vagrants to N.Am) by their generally darker coloration; crown gray; supercilium distinct; auricular dusky (HY/SYs & ♀♀) to black (AHY/ASY ♂♂).

Molt—PB: HY partial (Jul-Dec), AHY complete (Jun-Oct); PA partial-incomplete (Jan-Apr). There is evidence that a presupplemental molt (see p. 16) may occur in HYs, with body feathers replaced once on the summer grounds and twice on the winter grounds (Oct-Dec, and again in Mar-Apr during the PA), at least in Africa; more study is needed. Adult PBs occur primarily on the summer grounds. The 1st PB includes all med covs (rarely 1-2 outer ones are retained), 0 (~50%) to 9 (rarely all) inner gr covs, occasionally (in ~10% of birds) 1-3 terts, occasionally (in ~10% of birds) the central rects (r1), and rarely (in ~3% of birds) other rects. Both the 1st and the adult PAs are also highly variable, including 4 to 10 (~6%) inner gr covs, 1-3 terts (usually all) and perhaps all rects. Proportions are based on European populations and may differ, somewhat, in birds of Asia and N.Am.

Skull—Pneumaticization completes in HY/SY from 1 Nov through Mar.

Age/Sex—Juv (Jun-Aug) has brownish-washed upperparts and pale buffy-yellow underparts, with a relatively distinct, blackish malar stripe and a dusky breast collar; juv ♀ = ♂. CP/BP (May-Aug). ♀ wg(n30) 72-80, tl(n20) 62-70; ♂ wg(n30) 74-83, tl(n20) 64-72; includes *M.f. tschutschensis* only (see **Geographic variation**).

Basic Plumage (Aug-Mar)

HY/SY ♀♂ (Aug-Mar): Crown and auricular uniformly dull brownish, often tinged grayish; molt limits usually occur among the med and gr covs (Fig. 133A-D; see **Molt**), the retained outer gr covs worn, with distinct, white tips, contrasting with the fresher and buff-edged, replaced med and inner gr covs; 1-3 terts sometimes replaced, contrasting with the older middle ss (s4-s6; Fig. 133D-E), or if all juvenal terts retained, these are relatively worn and brown with buffy-white edging; outer pp covs narrow, tapered, relatively abraded (Fig. 138A), and brownish dusky; central rects (r1; rarely other rects) occasionally replaced and contrastingly fresh; underparts with little or no yellow. **Note: Most HY/SYs in Aug-Mar probably are not reliably sexed, although those without yellow on the underparts likely are ♀♀ and those strongly washed yellow likely are ♂♂; compare with wg and tl. Also, many intermediates can occur that are difficult if not impossible to age.**

AHY/ASY ♀ (Aug-Mar): Crown and auricular uniformly brownish olive; wing covs and terts uniformly adult (Fig. 133F) and dusky with buff or yellowish-white tips or edging; outer pp covs broad, truncate, relatively fresh (Fig. 138B), and dusky; rects uniform in wear; underparts pale yellow with a variable buff tinge. **Note: See HY/SY ♀♂.**

AHY/ASY ♂ (Aug-Mar): Crown gray with a brownish tinge; gr covs and flight feathers as in AHY/ASY ♀; auricular blackish; underparts bright yellow. **Note: See HY/SY ♀♂.**

Alternate Plumage (Mar-Jul)

SY ♀ (Mar-Jul): Crown and auricular dull brownish, sometimes tinged grayish; 1-5 juvenal outer gr covs usually retained and brown, with the white tips often worn off, contrasting markedly with the adjacent, first-alternate covs renewed in spring (Fig. 133C-D; occasionally 3 generations of gr covs are present; see Fig. 135); pp covs narrow, tapered, relatively abraded (Fig. 138C), and brownish; underparts pale buffy yellow. **Note: Experience may be needed to age spring birds, as both age groups can show molt limits (see Molt); the differences in the pp covs appears to be the most reliable ageing criterion.**

ASY ♀ (Mar-Jul): Crown and auricular uniformly grayish olive; retained, adult outer gr covs dusky brownish with yellowish edging, contrasting only slightly with the adjacent, replaced covs (at most only two generations of gr covs present; *cf.* Fig. 135); outer pp covs broad, truncate, relatively fresh (Fig. 138D), and brownish dusky; underparts pale to medium yellow. **Note: See SY ♀.**

SY ♂ (Mar-Jul): Crown gray (sometimes mixed brownish), contrasting with the blackish auricular; gr covs and pp covs as in SY ♀; underparts bright yellow. **Note: See SY ♀.**

ASY ♂ (Aug-Jul): Crown gray, contrasting with the black auricular; gr covs and flight feathers as in ASY ♀; underparts bright yellow. Note: **See SY ♀.**

Hybrids reported—White Wagtail in captivity.

References—Ridgway (1904), Bent (1950), Dement'ev & Gladkov (1954), Cramp (1988), Svensson (1992), Jenni & Winkler (1994).

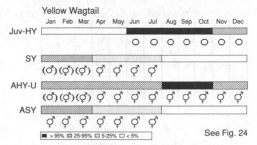

Note: In Nov-Dec, AHYs can be sexed but birds of unknown age should be left unsexed.

WHITE WAGTAIL
Motacilla alba

WHWA
Species # 6940
Band size: 1

Species—From HY/SY ♀ Yellow Wagtail (which can lack yellow on the underparts) by larger size (wg 84-98, tl 83-99; see **Age/Sex**); forecrown white, contrasting with the gray or black hindcrown; auricular primarily white; breast black or with a distinct, black chest collar.

From Black-backed Wagtail with caution, by bill averages shorter and thinner (nares to tip 8.5-10.2; depth at tip of nares 3.5-4.1); bases of the pp (under alula) without white, or with some white confined to the inner web (Fig. 249); replaced, first-basic or adult med covs dark at the bases with a moderately distinct, white tip (Fig. 250; forming wing bar); outer pp covs average less white by age (Fig. 251**A-D**; see **Age/Sex**); outer pp without distinct white base (Fig. 252; see also Fig. 249); base of the shaft of r4 dark (rarely with a slight whitish area); white areas of r5-r6 usually with dark streaks. The combination of these characters should separate most if not all birds, including juvs, HY/SYs, and AHY/ASY ♀♀ in Jun-Mar. Additional characters for AHYs in Mar-Aug include: Back pale bluish gray, without black (perhaps rarely with a few black flecks; in intergrades only?); rump dark gray, sometimes with black mottling; replaced first-alternate or adult gr covs (see **Molt**) dark with narrow to moderately broad, white edges; chin usually black or blackish, rarely to whitish in SYs. AHY/ASYs in Aug-Mar are similar to Mar-Aug birds, except that the chin and throat are white. Accurate identifications should rely on a synthesis of all information, including that of age and sex. Beware of hybrids (up to 10% may be expected in N.Am).

White   Black-backed

FIGURE 249. The base of the juvenal primaries in HY/SY White and Black-backed wagtails. Note that the greater alula must be pulled back to see this feature.

White   HY/SY ♀   AHY/ASY & ♂♂
                        Black-backed

FIGURE 250. The color pattern of the basic (adult) median coverts in White and Black-backed wagtails. The coverts are similar in all ages of White Wagtail. Note that the juvenal median coverts are similar in the two species, but most birds replace most or all of them at the first prebasic molt (see text).

Geographic variation—Well marked, but complex and clinal where ranges meet. Subspecies taxonomy follows Cramp (1988); see also Ridgway (1904), Dement'ev & Gladkov (1954), D. Gibson *in* Phillips (1991), Svensson (1992). Nine other subspecies occur in Eurasia.

M.a. ocularis (br throughout range in w.AK; vag to CA): Distinct, gray (HY/♀♀) to black (♂) eye line present.

M.a. alba (vag to NWT): Eye line absent. From alternate-plumaged birds of the other Eurasian subspecies (possible vagrants to N.Am?) by the combination of back gray, forehead white, chin and throat black, and wing covs with narrow edging.

Molt—PB: HY partial-incomplete (Jul-Sep), AHY complete (Jun-Sep); PA partial-incomplete (Jan-Apr). The PBs occur on the summer grounds. The 1st PB includes all med covs (rarely 1-2 outer ones can be retained); 0 (~10%) to 10 (5%) inner gr covs; often (in ~60% of birds) 1-3 terts; sometimes (in ~50% of birds) the central rects (r1), and sometimes (in ~35% of birds) other rects. Both the SY and the ASY PAs include 0 (~6%) to 7 inner gr covs, usually (in ~88% of birds) 1-3 terts, and sometimes (in ~50% of birds) one or more rects. Proportions of replaced feathers are based on European populations and these may differ somewhat in birds of N.Am (*M.a. ocularis*).

Skull—Pneumaticization completes in HY/SY from 15 Oct through Feb. The skull can be difficult to see through the skin.

Age/Sex—Juv (Jun-Aug) has uniformly brownish-washed upperparts and pale buffy-yellow underparts, with relatively indistinct facial features; juv ♀=♂. CP/BP (May-Aug). ♀ wg(n10) 84-94, tl(n10) 83-96; ♂ wg(n10) 87-98, tl(n10) 88-99; includes *M.a. ocularis* only (see **Geographic variation**).

Basic Plumage (Aug-Mar)

HY/SY ♀♂ (Aug-Mar): Forecrown and face mixed gray, and white or yellowish; hindcrown with no to a moderate amount of black; nape gray; molt limits usually occur among the med and gr covs (Fig. 133A-E; see **Molt**), the retained outer gr covs worn and brownish dusky with indistinct, buffy-white edging, contrasting with the fresher, grayer, and distinctly grayish-edged or white-edged, replaced inner covs; 1-3 terts often replaced, contrasting with the older middle ss (s4-s6; Fig. 133C-D), or if all juvenal terts retained these are relatively worn and brown with buffy-white edging; outer pp covs narrow, tapered, relatively abraded (Fig. 138A), and brownish dusky with little or no white, which (if present) is confined to the edging (Fig. 251A); central rects (r1; occasionally other rects) sometimes replaced, contrastingly fresh; breast band variable in width, blackish, and indistinctly defined; base of the bill washed pinkish (through Mar?). **Note: HY/SYs without black in the crown and rump are primarily ♀♀ whereas HY/SYs with substantial black mottling on the crown and rump are ♂♂, and the breast band probably averages wider and more distinct in HY/SY ♂♂ than in HY/SY ♀♀, but more study is needed before HY/SYs are reliably sexed by plumage alone. Also, intermediates can occur that are difficult to age.**

AHY/ASY ♀ (Aug-Mar): Forecrown and face white to mixed gray and white; hindcrown with a moderate dark gray to blackish wash; nape gray; wing covs and terts uniformly adult (Fig. 133F), the gr covs dusky with wide, white edging; outer pp covs broad, truncate, relatively fresh (Fig. 138B), and blackish with white edging and/or with some white to the inner web (Fig. 251B-C); rects uniform in wear; breast band moderately narrow, blackish, and distinctly defined; base of the bill blackish. **Note: See HY/SY ♀♂.**

AHY/ASY ♂ (Aug-Mar): Forecrown and face white; wing covs, flight feathers, and base of the bill as in AHY/ASY ♀, except that the amount of white in the pp covs averages greater (Fig. 251C-D); crown and nape extensively black (feathers tipped gray); breast band moderately broad, black, and distinctly defined. **Note: See HY/SY ♀♂.**

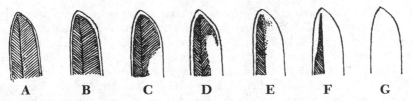

FIGURE 251. Variation in the color pattern of the outer primary coverts, by species and age (see text), in White and Black-backed wagtails.

Alternate Plumage (Mar-Jul)

SY ♀ (Mar-Jul): Center of the crown blackish, often with gray mottling, contrasting with the grayish nape; 1-8 juvenal outer gr covs often retained and brown with buffy-whitish edging (often worn off), contrasting markedly with the adjacent, first-alternate covs replaced in spring (Fig. 133**B-D**; occasionally three generations of gr covs present; see Fig. 135); outer pp covs narrow, tapered, relatively abraded (Fig. 138**C**), and brownish, without white (Fig. 251**A**). **Note: Experience may be needed to age spring birds, as both age groups can, or (occasionally) may not, show wing-cov contrasts (see Molt); differences in the pp covs seem to be the most reliable criteria.**

ASY ♀ (Mar-Jul): Center of the crown blackish, contrasting with the grayish nape; retained, adult outer gr covs dusky with white edging, contrasting only slightly with the adjacent, replaced covs (at most only two generations of gr covs present; *cf.* Fig. 135); outer pp covs broad, truncate, relatively fresh (Fig. 138**D**), and dusky blackish, with white edging and/or some white to the inner web (Fig. 251**B-C**). **Note: See SY ♀.**

SY ♂ (Mar-Jul): Center of the crown and nape uniformly blackish, occasionally with 1-2 grayish feathers mixed in; gr covs and flight feathers as in SY ♀. **Note: See SY ♀.**

ASY ♂ (Aug-Jul): Center of the crown and nape uniformly glossy black; gr covs and flight feathers as in ASY ♀, except that the amount of white in the pp covs averages greater (Fig. 251**C-D**). **Note: See SY ♀.**

Hybrids reported—Probably Black-backed Wagtail. Possibly Gray Wagtail (pairs mating). Gray Wagtail and Yellow Wagtail in captivity.

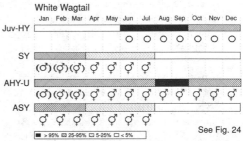

White Wagtail

See Fig. 24

Note: In Oct-Dec, AHYs can be sexed but birds of unknown age should be left unsexed.

References—Ridgway (1904), B.W. Tucker *in* Bent (1950), Dement'ev & Gladkov (1954), Morlan (1981), Nakamura (1985), Cramp (1988), Howell (1990), Phillips (1991), Svensson (1992), Jenni & Winkler (1994), Badyaev *et al.* (1996), Sibley & Howell (unpublished ms).

BLACK-BACKED WAGTAIL
Motacilla lugens

BWAG
Species # 6951
Band size: 1

Species—From White Wagtail (which see for separation from Yellow Wagtail), with caution, by bill averages longer and stouter (nares to tip 9.2-11.2, depth at tip of nares 3.9-4.5); bases of the pp (under alula) with large white patches spanning both webs (HY/SYs; Fig. 249) to entirely white (AHY/ASYs); replaced first-basic or adult med covs white, or irregularly dark at the bases, with distinct, white tips (Fig. 250); outer pp covs average more white by age/sex (Fig. 251A-G; see **Age/Sex**); outer pp of AHY/ASYs with extensive and distinct white bases (Fig. 252); base of shaft of r4 usually white (rarely dark); white areas of r5-r6 usually without dark streaks. The combination of these characters should separate most if not all birds (including juvs and HY/SYs) in Jun-Mar. Additional characters for AHYs in Mar-Aug include: Back and upper rump black, or dusky gray with some black (rarely with just a little mottling on the scapulars on some SY ♀♀); rump black, or gray with heavy, black mottling; replaced first-alternate or adult gr covs (see **Molt**) white or pale gray, with wide, white edges; chin usually white or blackish, rarely to black in some ASYs. AHY/ASYs in Aug-Mar are similar to Mar-Aug birds, except that the back is dark gray (usually with blackish mottling) and the chin and throat are extensively white. Accurate identifications should rely on a synthesis of all information, including that of age and sex. Beware of hybrids (up to 10% may be expected in N.Am).

Geographic variation—No subspecies are recognized.

Molt—Undocumented, but probably similar to White Wagtail; PB: HY partial-incomplete (Jul-Sep), AHY complete (Jun-Sep); PA partial-incomplete (Jan-Apr). See White Wagtail.

Skull—Pneumaticization completes in HY/SY from 15 Oct through Feb. The skull can be difficult to see through the skin.

Age/Sex—Juv (Jun-Aug) has uniformly brownish-washed upperparts and pale buffy-yellow underparts with relatively indistinct facial features; juv ♀ = ♂. CP/BP (May-Aug). ♀ wg(n30) 90-97, tl(n20) 84-95; ♂ wg(n50) 94-102, tl(n25) 88-102.

Basic Plumage (Aug-Mar)

HY/SY ♀♂ (Aug-Mar): Forecrown and face often tinged yellow; crown to rump medium gray, with a slight amount or no black mottling on the back and/or the rump; molt limits probably occur among the med and gr covs (Fig. 133A-E), the retained outer covs worn and brownish dusky with buffy-white edging, contrasting with the fresher, white or gray and extensively white-tipped, replaced inner covs (see Fig. 250); 1-3 terts probably replaced in at least some birds, contrasting with the older middle ss (s4-s6; Fig. 133C-D), or if all juvenal terts retained, these are relatively worn and brown with buffy-white edging; pp covs narrow, tapered, relatively abraded (Fig. 138A), and brownish dusky with little or no white edging and no to some white in the inner web (Fig. 251A-D); bases of the pp and ss with reduced, indistinct whitish coloration (Fig. 252; see also Fig. 249); base of the bill washed pinkish (through Feb-Apr). **Note: Some basic-plumaged HY/SY ♂♂ (and possibly ♀♀) can be reliably sexed by the combination of the amount of black in the back and rump (♀♀< ♂♂), the pattern of the med covs (Fig. 250), and the amount of white in the outer pp covs (Fig. 251A-C in ♀♀, & 251C-D in ♂♂), but more study is**

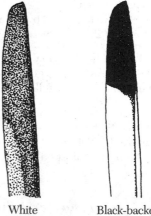

White   Black-backed
HY/SY Black-backed   AHY/ASY ♀

FIGURE 252. The pattern of the outer primaries (p6-p9), by species, age, and sex, in White and Black-backed wagtails. This pattern is similar in all White Wagtails. The primaries are mostly white in AHY/ASY ♂ Black-backed Wagtails.

needed; look also for HY/SY ♂♂ to average more black in the breast than HY/SY ♀♀.

AHY/ASY ♀ (Aug-Mar): Forecrown and face white or mixed gray and white, often without a yellow tinge; crown to rump dark gray with a moderate amount to a substantial amount of black mottling; wing covs and terts uniformly adult (Fig. 133**F**), the med and gr covs primarily white (Fig. 250); outer pp covs broad, truncate, relatively fresh (Fig. 138**B**), and black with some to a moderate amount of white to the inner web (Fig. 251**D-E**); bases of the pp and ss with extensive white coloration (Fig. 252); rects uniform in wear; base of the bill blackish.

AHY/ASY ♂ (Aug-Mar): Forecrown, terts, and base of the bill as in AHY/ASY ♀; crown to rump uniformly dark gray with black mottling, to blackish with gray mottling; med and gr covs primarily to entirely white (Fig. 250); pp covs primarily to entirely white (Fig. 251**E-G**); bases of the pp and ss extensively white (Fig. 252). **Note: It is possible that SY/TYs may be distinguished from ASY/ATYs by the amount of white in the pp and ss, but more study is needed.**

Alternate Plumage (Mar-Jul)

SY ♀ (Mar-Jul): Crown to rump dark gray, with a slight amount or no black mottling on the back and rump (back 0-15% black); 1-8 juvenal, outer gr covs probably retained and brownish with the buffy-whitish edging often worn off, contrasting markedly with the adjacent, primarily white covs, replaced in spring (Fig. 133**B-D**; occasionally three generations of gr covs present; see Fig. 135); outer pp covs narrow, tapered, relatively abraded (Fig. 138**C**), and brownish with little or no white edging, and a small amount or no white to the inner web (Fig. 251**A-C**); bases of the pp and ss with reduced, indistinct, white coloration (Fig. 252; see also Fig. 249).

ASY ♀ (Mar-Jul): Crown to rump dark gray, with no (rarely) to a moderate amount of black mottling on the back and rump (back 0-80% black); retained, adult outer gr covs extensively white, contrasting only slightly with the adjacent, replaced inner covs (at most only two generations of gr covs present; *cf.* Fig. 135); outer pp covs broad, truncate, relatively fresh (Fig. 138**D**), and blackish with some to a moderate amount of white (Fig. 251**D-E**); bases of the pp and ss with extensive white coloration (Fig. 252).

SY ♂ (Mar-Jul): Crown to rump uniformly blackish or dark gray, with a slight to a substantial amount of black mottling on the back and rump (back 15-100% black); wing covs and bases of the pp and ss as in SY ♀, except that the pp covs average more white (Fig. 251**C-D**) and both the juvenal and the replaced gr covs may average brighter and more extensively white.

ASY ♂ (Mar-Jul): Crown to rump uniformly glossy black, or primarily glossy black, with a slight to a moderate amount of gray mottling on the rump (back 95-100% black); wing covs and flight feathers as in ASY ♀, except that the adult gr covs can average more white, often entirely so, and the pp covs are primarily to entirely white (Fig. 251**E-G**); bases of the pp and ss extensively white (Fig. 252). **Note: AHY/ASY ♂ (above).**

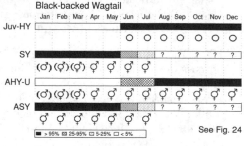

Black-backed Wagtail

Note: In Oct-Dec, AHYs can be sexed but birds of unknown age should be left unsexed.

Hybrids reported—Probably White Wagtail.

References—Bent (1950), Dement'ev & Gladkov (1954), Morlan (1981), Nakamura (1985), Cramp (1988), Howell (1990), Badyaev *et al.* (1996), Sibley & Howell (unpublished ms), Weintraub and Ryan (unpublished ms).

RED-THROATED PIPIT
Anthus cervinus

RTPI
Species # 6990
Band size: 1

Species—From American and Sprague's pipits by the combination of upperparts brown with distinct, black, buff and white streaks; outer rects (r5-r6) with reduced white (r5 usually without white) and with the outer web tinged brown (Fig. 253); throat and upper breast tinged to heavily washed reddish in spring; lower underparts buffy or tinged reddish, with bold, black streaks; legs yellowish to bright pink.

Geographic variation—No subspecies are recognized. See Cramp (1988).

Molt—PB: HY partial (Jul-Dec), AHY complete (Jul-Sep); PA limited-partial (Jan-May). There is a suggestion that a presupplemental molt (see p. 16) may occur in this species, with body feathers replaced once on the summer grounds and twice on the winter grounds (Oct-Dec and again in Mar-Apr, during the PA), at least in Africa; more study is needed. Adult PBs occur primarily on the summer grounds. The 1st PB includes all med covs (sometimes a few outer feathers are retained), no to some (rarely all?) inner gr covs, usually all 3 terts (occasionally fewer), and sometimes the central rects (r1). The PAs include no to a few inner gr covs, 1-3 terts on most birds, and the central rects (r1) on some birds.

Skull—Pneumaticization completes in HY/SY from 1 Nov through Jan.

Age—Juv (Jun-Aug) resembles HY/SYs, but the upperparts are washed darker brown and the underparts are washed buff; juv ♀ = ♂.

HY/SY (Aug-Jul): Molt limits occur among the med and gr covs (Fig. 133**A-E**; see **Molt**), the retained outer covs worn and brown with indistinct, buff edging (often worn off in spring), and without indentations on the corners of the outer webs (Fig. 254), contrasting (markedly in Mar-Jul and sometimes with three generations of feathers present; see Fig. 135) with the fresher and darker, replaced inner covs, with indentations at the corners (Fig. 254); 1-3 terts usually replaced, contrasting with the older, adjacent middle ss (s4-s6) in Aug-Mar (Fig. 133**C-D**; occurs in both age groups in Mar-Jul); outer pp covs narrow, tapered, relatively abraded (Fig. 138), and brownish; central rects (r1) sometimes contrastingly fresh in Aug-Mar; throat, face and upper breast without red (Aug-Mar; rarely with 1-2 red feathers; see **Sex**), or slightly to heavily washed red (Mar-Jul). **Note: Many intermediates will occur, especially later in spring, that are not reliably aged. Alternate-plumaged AHYs can be especially difficult to age, as both SY and ASY can replace gr covs, terts, and central rects (r1); differences in the outermost gr covs and the condition of the pp covs probably are the best criteria in Mar-Jul.**

AHY/ASY (Aug-Jul): Wing covs and flight feathers uniformly fresh (Aug-Mar; Fig. 133**F**), the gr covs with distinct, buff edging and indentations on the corners of the outer webs (Fig. 254), or gr covs with two generations of adult feathers in Mar-Jul (*cf.* Fig. 135), not contrasting markedly, as in SY; outer pp covs broad, truncate, relatively fresh (Fig. 138), and dusky; throat, face, and upper breast slightly (Aug-Mar), or heavily (Mar-Jul) washed red (see **Sex**), the feathers tipped buff in Aug-Dec. **Note: See HY/SY.**

Sex—CP/BP (May-Aug). ♀ wg(n55) 79-86, tl(n20) 54-60; ♂ wg(n100) 83-90, tl(n32) 56-63. Alternate-plumaged and AHY/ASY ♂♂ average more red in the face, throat, and breast than ♀♀, but substantial overlap precludes reliable ageing of individuals. Occasional confirmed HY/SYs in Aug-Jan with 1-2 red feathers probably are reliably sexed ♂; compare with wg and tl.

References—Ridgway (1904), B.W. Tucker *in* Bent (1950), King (1981), Cramp (1988), Svensson (1992), Jenni & Winkler (1994).

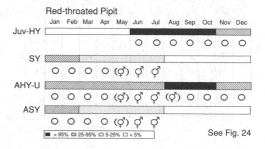

Red-throated Pipit

See Fig. 24

AMERICAN PIPIT
Anthus rubescens

AMPI
Species # 6970
Band size: 1

Species—From Red-throated, Sprague's and most other Eurasian pipits by the combination of longer average tl (53-68; see **Geographic variation** & **Sex**); upperparts uniformly grayish brown (basic plumage), or gray (alternate plumage) with indistinct or no dusky streaks; outer rects (r5-r6) with a moderate amount of white (including the outer web of r6), the white of r5 usually extending 15-40 mm from the tip (Fig. 253); auricular dark brown or gray, contrasting distinctly with the throat; throat and upper breast without reddish; underparts dull buff to pinkish, with indistinct to moderately distinct streaks, sometimes lacking; legs black or brownish black (pale brown in *A.r. japonicus*; see **Geographic variation**); hind claw short (6-11 mm), the hind toe and claw shorter than the central toe and claw.

From Water Pipit (*A. spinoletta*) of Eurasia, a possible vagrant to N.Am (with caution), by upperparts with less distinct, dusky (*vs* black) streaking; outer rects with substantial white coloration (Fig. 253; the white on r5 usually extends only 4-15 mm in Water Pipit); legs usually blackish or dark brown (*vs* pinkish, yellowish, brown, or rarely blackish in Water Pipit). Leg color also separates American Pipit from the other Eurasian pipits, although there is overlap in this character.

Geographic variation—Moderate and ranges well defined (between subspecies groups) to weak, obscured by individual variation and possible dichromatism (grayish and olive plumages), and clinal where ranges meet (among subspecies of the Northern Subspecies Group). Subspecies taxonomy follows Phillips (1991); see also Ridgway (1904), Todd (1935, 1963), Oberholser (1946, 1974), Jewett *et al.* (1953), Dement'ev & Gladkov (1954), Phillips *et al.* (1964), Phillips (1975a), Browning (1978), Webster (1978), Parkes (1982c), Behle (1985), Miller & Green (1987), Cramp (1988), Verbeek & Hendricks (1994). No other subspecies occur. Within each subspecies, note that ♀♀ average more streaking to the underparts than ♂♂ (see **Sex**).

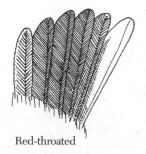
Red-throated

American

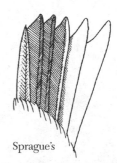
Sprague's

FIGURE 253. The pattern of white in the rectrices in Red-throated, American, and Sprague's pipits.

Asian (*A.r. japonicus*) Group. Dark grayish brown; underparts whitish; legs brownish to pinkish.

A.r. japonicus (vag to w.AK,CA,NM): Medium large; upperparts washed grayish (basic plumage), or dark brown (alternate plumage); underparts contrastingly whitish; breast streaks black, distinct, and extensive on the flanks; legs pale brownish pink to brownish. ♀ wg(n10) 79-87, tl (n10) 57-64; ♂ wg(n20) 82-92, tl (n10) 60-67.

Buff-bellied (*A.r. rubescens*) Group. Brown; legs black.

A.r. geophilus (br w-c.AK to w.NWT, wint s.BC-CA to w.TX): Small; tl relatively long; hind claw long (8.3-10.5); upperparts uniformly pale brownish with a gray (basic plumage), or pale brown (alternate plumage) tinge; chin white, contrasting with the pale whitish (basic plumage), or pinkish-buff (alternate plumage) underparts; breast streaks dusky and moderately indistinct; legs brownish black to black. ♀ wg(n10) 75-82, tl(n10) 58-64; ♂ wg(n10) 77-84, tl(n10) 61-68. Note that this subspecies is marginally distinct from *pacificus*.

A.r. pacificus (br BC-Alb to c.OR, wint c.AZ-w.TX): Small; tl relatively short; hind claw long (8.3-10.5); upperparts pale brownish gray (basic plumage), or pale gray (alternate plumage), the rump contrastingly pale; chin whitish, contrasting with the pale buff (basic plumage), or yellowish-buff to pinkish-buff (alternate plumage) underparts; breast streaks broad, dusky, and moderately indistinct; legs brownish black to black. ♀ wg(n23) 73-82, tl(n23) 53-59; ♂ wg(n24) 81-88, tl(n24) 56-64.

A.r. rubescens (br n.AK-Nfl, wint NM-MD): Medium large; hind claw long (8.8-10.8); upperparts dark brownish (basic plumage), or slaty (alternate plumage), the crown and rump slightly darker; chin whitish, contrasting with the buff (basic plumage), or pinkish-buff (alternate plumage) underparts; breast streaks dusky and moderately indistinct; legs brownish black to black. ♀ wg(n10) 78-86, tl(n10) 54-63; ♂ wg(n10) 82-91, tl(n10) 58-67. Birds of the Hudson Bay area (*"ludovicianus"*) may average paler and grayer, but differences, if present, are almost completely obscured by individual variation.

Western Montane (*A.r. alticola*) Group. Pale grayish; legs black.

A.r. alticola (br ne.OR-MT to e.CA-NM, wint AZ): Large; hind claw short (6.3-9.5); upperparts uniformly pale grayish brown (basic plumage), or medium gray (alternate plumage); chin and underparts pinkish buff (basic plumage), or deep pink (alternate plumage); breast streaks narrow and dusky, indistinct, or lacking; legs black. ♀ wg(n75) 78-87, tl(n75) 56-64; ♂ wg(n76) 84-94, tl(n76) 60-68.

Molt—PB: HY partial (Jul-Sep), AHY complete (Jul-Sep); PA partial (Jan-Apr). The PBs occur primarily on the summer grounds. The 1st PB includes no to all med covs, 0 (~55%) to 4 inner gr covs and sometimes (in ~25% of birds) 1-2 terts, but no rects. The 1st PA includes 0 (~23%) to 4 inner gr covs, usually (in ~85% of birds) 1-3 terts, and often (in ~62% of birds) 1-2 central rects (r1). The adult PA is similar to the 1st PA, including 0 (~13%) to 4 inner gr covs, 1-3 terts, and often (in ~73% of birds) 1-2 central rects (r1).

Skull—Pneumaticization completes in HY/SY from 1 Nov through Jan.

Age—Juv (Jun-Aug) has brownish-washed upperparts and relatively pale underparts; juv ♀ = ♂.

HY/SY (Aug-Jul): Molt limits usually occur among the med and gr covs (Fig. 133**A-D**; see **Molt**), the retained outer covs worn, pale brown with narrow, whitish fringes when fresh, and

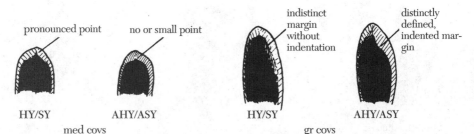

FIGURE 254. The patterns of the middle and greater coverts, by age, in Red-throated and American pipits. Check for these differences in Sprague's Pipit as well. Note that these differences can be very subtle.

with pronounced points extending from the center (med covs), or without indentations (gr covs; Fig. 254), contrasting (markedly in Mar-Jul) with the fresher, dark brown, and widely buff-edged, replaced inner covs with adult-like patterns (Fig. 254; three generations of wing feathers sometimes present in Mar-Jul; Fig. 135); 1-2 terts sometimes replaced, contrasting with the older middle ss (s4-s6) in Aug-Mar (Fig. 133**D**), or if all juvenal terts retained, these are relatively worn and brownish; outer pp covs narrow, tapered, and relatively abraded (Fig. 138); outer rects tapered (Fig. 139**B**) and relatively abraded. **Note: Many intermediates will occur that are not reliably aged. Ageing alternate-plumaged AHYs in Feb-Jul can be especially difficult, as both SYs and ASYs show molt limits; the shape and condition of the pp covs may provide the best clues at this time.**

AHY/ASY (Aug-Jul): Wing covs and terts uniformly fresh in Aug-Jan (Fig. 133**F**), or contrasting indistinctly with the replaced feathers in Feb-Jul (only two generations of coverts present; *cf.* Fig. 135), the med and gr covs with glossy blackish centers, contrasting distinctly with the pale brownish to buff edging, the med covs with no or small points extending from the tips of the dark centers, and the gr covs with distinct indentations on the corners of the outer webs (Fig. 254); outer pp covs broad, truncate, and relatively fresh (Fig. 138); outer rects truncate (Fig. 139**B**) and relatively fresh. **Note: See HY/SY.**

Sex—CP/BP (May-Aug). Measurements are useful within subspecies (see **Geographic variation**); overall, ♀ wg(n100) 73-87, tl(n100) 53-64; ♂ wg(n100) 77-94, tl(n100) 56-68. In alternate plumage (Mar-Jul), ♀♀ average heavier streaking on the underparts than ♂♂, but there is much overlap and individuals are not reliably sexed by this feature alone. Otherwise, ♀ = ♂ by plumage.

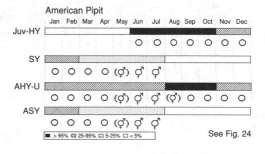

References—Stone (1896), Dwight (1900a), Ridgway (1904), Oberholser (1919d, 1974), Forbush (1929), Bent (1950), Shortt (1951), Roberts (1955), Phillips *et al.* (1964), Wood (1969), Verbeek (1973b), King (1981), Parkes (1982c), Cramp (1988), Knox (1988a), Svensson (1992), Verbeek & Hendricks (1994), Pyle (1997c); J.R. King (pers. comm.).

SPRAGUE'S PIPIT

Anthus spragueii

SPPI
Species # 7000
Band size: 1

Species—From American Pipit (which see for separation from other pipits) by shorter average tl 51-64; (see **Sex**); upperparts buffy brown with broad, dusky streaking; outer rects (r4-r6) with extensive white, the white of r5 extending > 40 mm from the tip (Fig. 253); auricular pale buff to whitish, not contrasting distinctly with the throat; underparts buffy and white, with narrow and moderately distinct streaks that do not extend to the flanks; legs pale brownish or yellow; hind claw long (10-15 mm), the hind toe and claw longer than the central toe and claw.

Geographic variation—No subspecies are recognized.

Molt—PB: HY partial-incomplete (Aug-Oct), AHY complete (Aug-Sep); PA partial (Mar-Apr). The PBs occur at least partially on migration and/or the winter grounds; more study is needed. The 1st PB includes no to all med covs, 5 to 10 (~20%) inner gr covs and usually (in ~80% of birds) 1-3 terts (occasionally s6, as well), but no rects. The 1st PA includes 0 (~25%) to 3 inner gr covs, often (in ~75% of birds) 1-3 terts, and sometimes (in ~25% of birds) 1-2 central rects (r1). The adult PA includes 3-5 inner gr covs, 2-3 terts, and often (in ~67% of birds) 1-2 central rects (r1).

Skull—Pneumaticization completes in HY from 15 Oct through Dec.

Age—Juv (Jun-Aug) has dull black spotting (rather than streaking) to the upperparts and pale tips to some or all back feathers; juv ♀ = ♂. The shape of the outer rects is lanceolate in both age groups, and thus is unhelpful for ageing, although relative wear may be of use. Otherwise, ageing criteria are similar to those of American Pipit, but with slight differences in the average placement of the molt limits (see **Molt**).

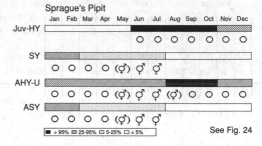

Sex—♀ = ♂ by plumage. CP/BP (May-Aug). ♀ wg(n30) 75-84, tl(n10) 51-60; ♂ wg(n30) 78-88, tl(n20) 54-64.

References—Ridgway (1904), Bent (1950), Shortt (1951), Roberts (1955), Sutton (1967), Oberholser (1974), King (1981), Pyle (1997c).

WAXWINGS   *BOMBYCILLIDAE*

Two species. Family characters include short tails and legs, plump bodies, crests, and waxy appendages to the secondaries (rarely to the greater coverts, primaries, and rectrices) in some juvenile and all adult birds. Waxwings have 10 primaries (the 10th minute), 9 secondaries, and 12 rectrices. The first prebasic molt is partial, with few wing coverts replaced, and prealternate molts are lacking. Males and females practically are identical in measurements; however, most birds should be reliably aged and sexed when all other criteria are combined.

BOHEMIAN WAXWING   BOWA
Bombycilla garrulus   Species # 6180
                                                             Band size: 1A

Species—From Cedar Waxwing by much larger size (wg 109-121, tl 59-70; see **Sex**); forehead washed chestnut; pp covs, pp, and ss tipped white or yellow (Fig. 255); undertail covs chestnut.

Geographic variation—Weak and obscured by individual variation, but range in N.Am well defined. Subspecies taxonomy follows Phillips (1991); see also Reichenow (1908), Oberholser (1917g), Swarth (1922), Cramp (1988). One other subspecies occurs in Europe.

> ***B.g. centralasiae*** (vag to w.AK Is): Forehead pale grayish cinnamon, not contrasting markedly with the grayish-brown head; malar region without cinnamon; back bright gray with a lilac tinge; flanks washed pale gray.
>
> ***B.g. pallidiceps*** (br & wint throughout the range in N.Am): Forehead medium cinnamon, contrasting with the grayish-brown to brown head; malar region with cinnamon; back grayish brown to brown, without a lilac tinge; flanks washed dark grayish. Nominate birds of Europe (potential vagrants to ne.Can?) are slightly darker and more richly colored.

Molt—PB: HY partial (Aug-Nov), AHY complete (Aug-Nov); PA absent. The PBs commence on the summer grounds, but many birds suspend molt, completing on the winter grounds. The 1st

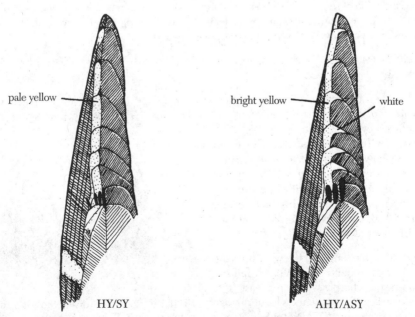

FIGURE 255. The pattern of the primaries by age in Bohemian Waxwing. Note also the difference in size of the waxy tips on the secondaries.

PB usually includes few if any wing covs, and no terts or rects. Look for a few middle ss (among s3-s6) to be retained by AHYs through winter and possibly until the subsequent PBs; more study is needed.

TABLE 6. Number and length of waxy appendages on one wing , and length of yellow tips to the central and outermost rectrices, in Bohemian Waxwing (all length measurements are in mm; derived from Svensson 1992).

	HY/SY ♀	AHY/ASY ♀	HY/SY ♂	AHY/ASY ♂
Number of waxy appendages to the ss	0-5	5-7	4-8	6-8
Length of the longest waxy appendage	0.0-3.5	3.0-7.5	3.5-5.5	6.0-9.5
Length of yellow at the tip of r1	2.0-5.0	4.0-6.0	5.0-8.0	5.5-8.5
Length of yellow at the tip of r5	3.0-6.0	5.0-8.0	7.0-10.5	7.0-11.0

Skull—Pneumaticization completes in HY/SY from 1 Nov through Feb.

Age—Juv (Jun-Oct) has a whitish throat and indistinct, dusky streaking to the underparts; juv ♀ = ♂, although extremes possibly are sexed by the waxy appendage and rect tip criteria as in HY/SYs (Table 6).

HY/SY (Nov-Oct): Number and length of the waxy tips smaller by sex (Table 6); pp without white tips to the inner webs (Fig. 255); outer pp covs narrow, tapered, and relatively abraded (Fig. 138); rects tapered, with the yellow tips often dull, washed with dusky, and reduced by sex (Table 6; see Fig. 257); breast sometimes with the dusky streaking of juv during Oct-Dec. **Note: See AHY/ASY.**

AHY/ASY (Nov-Oct): Number and length of the waxy tips larger by sex (Table 6); at least some pp (often p4-p7) with white extending to the tips of the inner webs (Fig. 255); outer pp covs broad, truncate, and relatively fresh (Fig. 138); rects truncate, usually with bright yellow tips, and longer by sex (Table 6; see Fig. 257); breast without dusky streaking. **Note: Also, look for occasional AHY/ASYs to retain 1-4 ss (among s3-s6) at least for migration if not until the summer. These are possibly SY/TYs but more study is needed**

Sex—CP/BP (May-Sep); ♂♂ can develop a partial BP (Fig. 22**B**). ♀ wg(n30) 109-119, tl(n20) 59-69; ♂ wg(n40) 111-121, tl(n30) 60-70.

♀: Number and length of the waxy tips smaller by age (Table 6); throat patch relatively restricted and contrasting indistinctly with the breast (Fig. 256); yellow tips to the rects reduced by age (Table 6; see Fig. 257).
Note: A few intermediates can occur (especially birds with the dusky streaking of juv remaining) which are not reliably sexed. Birds with intermediate throat patches probably are either HY/SY ♂♂ or AHY/ASY ♀♀; combine with age criteria.

♂: Number and length of the waxy tips larger by age (Table 6); throat patch full and contrasting sharply with the breast (Fig. 256); yellow tips to the rects longer by age (Table 6; see Fig. 257). **Note: See ♀.**

♀   ♂

FIGURE 256. The distinctness of the throat patch by sex in Bohemian Waxwing.

References—Dwight (1900a), Ridgway (1904), Cameron (1908), Swarth (1922), Forbush (1929), Bent (1950), Arvey (1951), Roberts (1955), Oberholser (1974), Cramp (1988), Svensson (1992), Pyle (1997c).

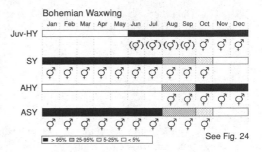

CEDAR WAXWING
Bombycilla cedrorum

CEDW
Species # 6190
Band size: 1B

Species—From Bohemian Waxwing by much smaller size (wg 88-100, tl 50-61; see **Sex**); forehead without a chestnut wash; pp covs, pp, and ss uniformly dark or dusky; undertail covs white or pale buff.

Geographic variation—Weak, clinal, and obscured by individual variation and (probably) frequent mixing. Subspecies taxonomy follows Phillips (1991); see also Burleigh (1963), Monroe (1968), Oberholser (1974), Behle (1985), Binford (1985), Browning (1990). No other subspecies occur.

> **B.c. larifuga** (br se.AK-nw.CA to Man-KS; wint range undefined): Plumage paler overall; crown and breast tinged grayish. Breeding birds of coastal se.AK-nw.CA average darker and likely are inseparable from *cedrorum* based on plumage.
>
> **B.c. cedrorum** (br Ont-Nfl to MO-VA; wint range undefined): Plumage darker overall; crown and breast tinged reddish. Breeding birds of Nfl (*"aquilonia"*) may average grayer, but this difference, if present, is almost completely obscured by individual variation.

Molt—PB: HY partial (Sep-Dec), AHY/ASY complete (Aug-Jan); PA absent. The PBs occur primarily on the winter grounds, but can commence during migration or post-breeding wandering. The 1st PB usually includes few if any wing covs, and no terts or rects. Watch for a few middle ss (among s3-s6) to be retained during the adult PB (see Bohemian Waxwing); more study is needed.

Skull—Pneumaticization completes in HY/SY from 15 Oct. Look for many SYs (and some ASYs) to retain windows (> 3 mm; see Figs. 11**D** & 204) at the rear of the skull through summer and even fall; more study is needed.

Age—Juv (Jun-Nov) has a whitish chin with distinct malar stripes, underparts with heavy, dusky streaking, and a grayish iris; juv ♀ = ♂, but some extremes possibly are sexed by the waxy tip and rect tip criteria as in HY/SYs (Table 7, Fig. 257).

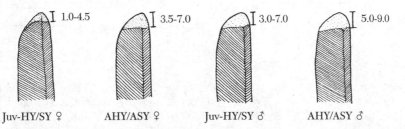

FIGURE 257. The width and distinctness of the yellow tips to the outer rectrices (r4-r6) in Cedar Waxwing. Bohemian Waxwing shows similar differences in distinctness by age and sex, but different widths (see Table 6). The width measurements refer to fresh feathers and become slightly shorter with wear.

TABLE 7. The range and mean number of waxy appendages on one wing of Cedar Waxwings by age and sex (derived from Yunick 1970c, PRBO data, and specimen examination).

	HY/SY ♀	AHY/ASY ♀	HY/SY ♂	AHY/ASY ♂
Sample	69	60	73	60
Range	0-3	1-7	0-7	3-9
Mean	0.1	3.3	0.4	6.2

HY/SY (Nov-Oct): Number and length of waxy tips on the wing smaller by sex (Table 7), often with none; outer pp covs narrow, tapered, relatively abraded (Fig. 138), and gray with a brown tinge; rects tapered, often with the yellow tips dull or washed with dusky and reduced by sex (Fig. 257); breast often with the dusky streaking of juv present during Oct-Dec; iris grayish brown to reddish brown (through Jan-May). **Note: The occurrence of orange-tipped rects may be age-related (as correlated with timing in the availability of certain non-native berries), but this timing (hence, in which age group it appears) varies geographically; thus, orange-tipped rects are of little help in ageing. See AHY/ASY.**

AHY/ASY (Nov-Oct): Number and length of waxy tips on the wing larger by sex (Table 7); outer pp covs broad, truncate, relatively fresh (Fig. 138), and dark gray; rects truncate, usually with brighter and longer yellow tips by sex (Fig. 257); breast without dusky streaking; iris deep reddish. **Note: See HY/SY. Also, look for occasional AHY/ASYs to retain 1-4 ss (among s3-s6) at least for migration if not until the summer.**

Sex—CP/BP (May-Oct); ♂♂ can develop a partial BP (Fig. 22**B**). ♀ wg(n100) 88-99, tl(n41) 50-60; ♂ wg(n100) 90-100, tl(n46) 52-61.

♀: Number and length of waxy tips on the wing smaller by age (Table 7); chin dull or brownish black, the base of the blackish patch 2-8 mm wide (Fig. 258); yellow tips to the rects shorter by age (Fig. 257). **Note: A few intermediates (especially birds with the dusky streaking of juv remaining) can occur which are not reliably sexed. Birds with intermediate throat patches (7-8 mm wide at the base) probably are either HY/SY ♂♂ or AHY/ASY ♀♀; combine with age criteria. In addition, ♀♀ average slightly grayer than ♂♂, but this difference is probably too slight to assist with sexing.**

♂: Number and length of the waxy tips larger by age (Table 7); chin glossy black, the base of the black patch 7-15 mm wide (Fig. 258); yellow tips to the rects longer by age (Fig. 257). **Note: See ♀.**

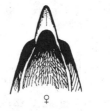

FIGURE 258. The throat patch by sex in Cedar Waxwing.

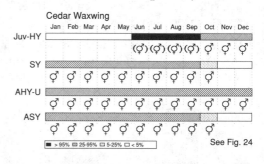

References—Stone (1896), Dwight (1900a), Ridgway (1904), Forbush (1929), Bent (1950), Arvey (1951), Roberts (1955), Myers & Myers (1967), Sutton (1967), Wood (1969), Yunick (1970c), Oberholser (1974), Sheppard & Klimkiewicz (1976), Mountjoy & Robertson (1988), Parkes (1988b), Stedman & Stedman (1989), CWS & USFWS (1991), Mulvihill *et al.* (1992), Witmer (1996), Pyle (1997c); M.H. Clench, E.J. Fisk, L.L. Hood, J.C. Howell, R.C. Leberman (*in litt.* to the BBL); M.R. Browning (pers. comm.); IBP (MAPS) data, PNR data, PRBO data.

SILKY-FLYCATCHERS   *PTILOGONATIDAE*

One species. Family characters include silky plumage, a crest, short legs, and unspotted juvenal plumage. Silky-flycatchers have 10 primaries (the 10th reduced), 9 secondaries, and 12 rectrices. A supplemental plumage occurs, the first prebasic molt varies from partial to complete, and no prealternate molt occurs. Reliable ageing and sexing by plumage is possible with most birds through at least mid-winter. Males average slightly larger than females.

PHAINOPEPLA   PHAI
Phainopepla nitens   Species # 6200
                                                      Band size: 1B

Geographic variation—Moderate, although based on measurements only, and the ranges are well defined but can overlap during different seasons (more study is needed). Subspecies taxonomy follows Phillips (1991); see also Van Tyne (1925), Oberholser (1974). No other subspecies occur.

   P.n. lepida (br & wint throughout the range in N.Am): Small. ♀ wg(n55) 86-94, tl(n55) 82-95; ♂ wg(n88) 88-96, tl(n88) 86-99.

   P.n. nitens (br & wint sw.TX; vag to CA, AZ, & NM): Large. ♀ wg(n17) 91-100, tl(n17) 91-100; ♂ wg(n23) 95-105, tl(n23) 95-107.

Molt—PS/PB: HY partial-complete (May-Nov), AHY complete (May-Nov); PA absent. A presupplemental molt (see p. 16) occurs in HYs, with the body plumage being replaced once in May-Jul and again with the flight feathers in Aug-Nov. The PS sometimes (in ~36% of birds) includes 1-3 inner gr covs, but no terts or rects. The PBs can be suspended over migration, completing on the winter grounds. The 1st PB is extremely variable, from just 2 inner gr covs and no flight feathers replaced, to complete replacement (reported in ~35% of ♂♂); the pp covs often are the last feathers replaced and one or more can be retained during otherwise complete molts. Incomplete replacement of the pp and ss (which occurs in ~70% of birds not having a complete molt) is not eccentric, but usually follows typical sequence (Fig. 137), beginning with the innermost p (p1) and outermost s (s1, along with the terts), although sometimes s6 and s5 can be replaced before the outer ss. This species may regularly breed twice per year in different localities, the variable timing of fledging explaining the variable extent of the 1st PB.

Skull—Pneumaticization completes in HY from 15 Aug through Dec.

Age/Sex—Juv (Apr-Jul) is gray, with relatively buffy wing bars and brown-washed upperparts; juv ♀ = ♂. CP/BP (Feb-Aug); ♂♂ can develop a partial BP (Fig. 22**B**). ♀ wg(n100) 86-100, tl(n87) 82-100; ♂ wg(n100) 88-105, tl(n100) 86-107; see **Geographic variation**.

Supplemental Plumage (Jul-Sep)

HY ♀♂ (Jul-Sep): Plumage gray, usually without glossy black feathers; molt limits often occur among the med covs and (sometimes) the gr covs (Fig. 133**A-B**; see **Molt**), most or all retained juvenal feathers brownish gray with distinct, buffy tips, contrasting with the fresher, dark gray, and untipped, replaced inner covs; outer rects tapered (Fig. 139**B**). **Note: Some if not all ♂♂ begin to acquire black plumage while in supplemental plumage and can be sexed; otherwise, HYs without black plumage should not be sexed ♀ until Sep.**

Basic and Alternate Plumage (Oct-Sep)

HY/SY ♀ (Sep-Aug): Plumage gray, without glossy black feathers; molt limits often occur among the gr covs, pp, pp covs, ss, and/or rects (Figs. 133**B-E** & Fig. 137**A-B**; see **Molt**), the retained juvenal feathers (often among the pp covs, if anywhere) faded, brownish gray, or (gr covs) with indistinct, buff tips, contrasting with the fresher and dark gray, replaced feathers; pp covs (if juvenal) narrow, tapered, relatively abraded (Fig. 138), and brownish gray with buff tips, the same color or paler than adjacent pp; outer rects (if juvenal) tapered (Fig. 139B). **Note: The whitish edging to the terts and undertail covs may average wider on HY/SYs than on AHY/ASYs but, if so, there appears to be too much overlap for reliable ageing. See also HY/SY ♂.**

U/AHY ♀ (Nov-Oct): Plumage gray, without glossy black feathers; wing covs and flight feathers entirely and uniformly gray; gr covs uniform in wear, without or with pale grayish tips when fresh (Fig. 133F); outer pp covs uniformly broad, truncate, relatively fresh (Fig. 138), and dusky without pale tips, and darker than adjacent pp; outer rects truncate (Fig. 139B). **Note: See HY/SY ♀.**

HY/SY ♂ (Oct-Sep): Body plumage varies from mixed gray and black to completely black (or nearly so); molt limits as in HY/SY ♀ except that replaced, first-basic wing covs and flight feathers black, contrasting markedly with the retained, juvenal gray feathers; pp with indistinct or no whitish patches; outer rects (if juvenal) gray and tapered (Fig. 139B). **Note: See HY/SY ♀ and U/AHY ♂. Jul-Sep SYs in this plumage should have very worn flight feathers and pneumaticized skulls, to separate them from molting juv-HYs.**

U/AHY ♂ (Nov-Oct): Plumage uniformly glossy black; pp with distinct, white patches; rects uniformly truncate (Fig. 139B). **Note: See HY/SY ♀. Birds in immaculate, glossy-black plumage are probably AHY/ASYs but more study is needed to distinguish these from HY/SYs with complete molts.**

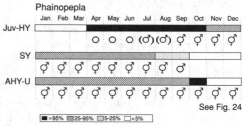

References—Ridgway (1904), R.S. Woods *in* Bent (1950), Oberholser (1974), Miller (1933b), Thompson & Leu (1994), Pyle (1997c).

OLIVE WARBLERS   *PEUCEDRAMIDAE*

One species, formerly considered a wood-warbler. Family characters include generally small size, delicate features, and slender bills. Olive Warblers have 10 primaries (the 10th reduced), 9 secondaries, and 12 rectrices. The first prebasic molt is partial, including few if any wing coverts, and prealternate molts are absent or very limited. Ageing and sexing by plumage and breeding condition are reliable for all males and most females in both fall and spring. Males average substantially larger than females.

OLIVE WARBLER   OLWA
Peucedramus taeniatus   Species # 6510
                                                    Band size: 0

Species—HY/SY ♀ from Hermit Warbler by longer wg (67-73); reduced p10 and white patch at the base of the pp (sometimes hidden by pp covs) present; tail with a deeper notch (r6 – r1 ≥ 4.5 mm).

Geographic variation—Weak and differences are obscured by individual variation, but ranges are well defined. Subspecies taxonomy follows Phillips (1991); see also Ridgway (1902), Miller & Griscom (1925b), Webster (1958b, 1962), George (1962), Curson *et al.* (1994), Dunn & Garrett (in press). Two other subspecies occur in Mex-C.Am. See also **Age/Sex**.

   P.t. arizonae (br & wint se.AZ-sw.NM): Nape and back medium gray; flanks lightly washed dull grayish brown; juv washed dull brownish olive.
   P.t. jaliscensis (vag to sw.TX): Nape and back dark dusky gray; flanks heavily washed brownish olive; juv washed dull grayish olive.

Molt—PB: HY partial (Jun-Aug), AHY complete (Jul-Aug); PA absent-limited (Jan-May). The PBs occur on the summer grounds. The 1st PB includes few if any wing covs and no terts or rects. The PA involves a few throat feathers on some ♂♂ (SY only?).

Skull—Pneumaticization completes in HY from 15 Oct through Dec.

Age/Sex—Juv (Jun-Jul) is washed brownish olive to grayish olive (see **Geographic variation**), and has buffy-brownish to yellowish wing bars. More study is needed on plumage by sex in juvs; some birds may be sexed by the amount of white at the base of the pp, as in HY/SYs (see below). Also, juv ♀♀ possibly average grayer and juv ♂♂ browner, but this may be related to geography more than sex (see **Geographic variation**). CP/BP (May-Aug). Measurements are useful: ♀ wg(n30) 67-75, tl(n20) 45-55; ♂ wg(n100) 73-81, tl(n100) 49-58; refers to subspecies of N.Am only (see **Geographic variation**).

HY/SY ♀ (Jul-Jun): Crown, nape, and auricular grayish suffused with yellowish buff; throat and upper breast pale buffy yellow; outer pp covs narrow, tapered, relatively abraded (Fig. 138), and brownish; white at the base of the pp falls -2 to 2 mm from the tip of the pp covs; outer rects relatively abraded, tapered (Fig. 139A), and dusky brown. **Note: The amount of white in the outer rects (r4-r6) shows average differences by age/sex (Fig. 262B-D), as in** *Dendroica* **warblers, but differences are slight and obscured by individual variation.**

AHY/ASY ♀ (Aug-Jul): Forecrown, throat, and upper breast yellowish; nape, lores, and auricular grayish, suffused with yellow; outer pp covs broad, truncate, relatively fresh (Fig. 138), and dusky; white at the base of the pp extends 1-4 mm distal to the pp covs; outer rects relatively fresh, truncate (Fig. 139A), and dusky. **Note: See HY/SY ♀.**

HY/SY ♂ (Aug-Jul): Forecrown, throat, and upper breast yellowish, slightly washed tawny, or with a few bright tawny feathers in Mar-Jul; nape, lores, and auricular grayish, suffused with yellow or pale tawny; pp-cov and rect criteria as in HY/SY ♀, except that the white at the base of the pp extends 0-4 mm distal to the pp covs. **Note: See HY/SY ♀. Also, plumage criteria for ageing ♂♂ apply to the subspecies of N.Am only; subspecies of s.Mex-C.Am differ in having HY/SY ♂ closer in plumage to AHY/ASY ♂.**

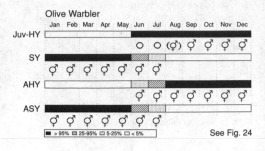

AHY/ASY ♂ (Aug-Jul): Crown, nape, throat, and upper breast rich tawny; lores and auricular black; pp-cov and rect criteria as in AHY/ASY ♀, except that the white at the base of the pp extends 3-8 mm distal to the pp covs. **Note: See HY/SY ♀ and HY/SY ♂.**

References—Ridgway (1902), Swarth (1904a), Bent (1953), Webster (1958b, 1962), George (1962), Curson *et al.* (1994), Dunn & Garrett (1997), Pyle (1997c).

WOOD-WARBLERS *PARULIDAE*

Fifty-three species. Family characters include generally small size, delicate features, and slender bills. Wood-warblers have 9 visible primaries, 9 secondaries, and 12 rectrices. The first prebasic molt generally is partial, but can be incomplete or complete in a few species, especially in southern populations. In many species the first prebasic molt typically includes all greater coverts, but no tertials or rectrices. In several species the first prebasic molt can commence before fledging, resulting in very short-lived, or "ephemeral" juvenal plumages. Many species have protracted prealternate molts in the tropics, continuous on a limited basis throughout the winter period in some species, and generally most extensive in HY/SY males. A few species replace greater coverts and/or tertials during the prealternate molt. Plumages generally are bright, and vary considerably by species, age, sex, and season. Some species show as many as nine distinct plumages; others as few as one or two. Most species can be aged in both spring and fall, when all criteria are considered. Many species also can be sexed at all times of the year, although in some species plumage does not vary by sex. Breeding characters are reliable for sexing spring birds, and males average moderately larger than females in most species.

BACHMAN'S WARBLER
Vermivora bachmanii

BAWA
Species # 6400
Band size: 0A-0

Species— ♀♀ separated from most other warblers by the combination of small size (wg 54-64, tl 37-47; see **Age/Sex**); wing bars or facial features lacking; white or whitish patches in the outer rects (r4-r6) present. From ♀ Hooded Warbler by shorter tl (see above); crown with gray; eye ring present.

Geographic variation—No subspecies are recognized.

Molt—PB: HY partial (May-Aug), AHY complete (May-Aug); PA limited (Feb-Apr). The PBs occur on the summer grounds. The 1st PB includes all med covs and 8 to 10 (~67%) inner gr covs, but no terts or rects. The PA is limited to feathers of the head and (sometimes) the throat.

Skull—Pneumaticization completes in HY from 1 Sep through Nov.

Age/Sex—Juv (May-Jul) has brownish-washed plumage and distinct, buff wing bars; some juvs can be sexed by the amount of white in the rects, as in HY/SYs (see below). CP/BP (Mar-Jul). ♀ wg(n93) 54-60, tl(n63) 37-44; ♂ wg(n100) 57-64, tl(n100) 39-47.

HY/SY ♀ (Aug-Jul): Forecrown and breast without black feathering, the breast with little to a moderate amount of yellow (especially in Jul-Mar) and no dusky speckling; molt limits sometimes occur among the gr covs (Fig. 13**D-E**; see **Molt**), the retained outer covs worn and pale brownish with buff tips, contrasting with the fresher and dusky-green, replaced inner covs; terts relatively worn, with buff tips when fresh; outer pp covs narrow, tapered, relatively abraded, and brownish with indistinct, narrow, or no buff edging (Fig. 13**8**); outer rects and pp relatively abraded, tapered (Figs. 139**A** & 140**A**), and washed brownish; outer rects (r5-r6) without white, or occasionally with a small, indistinct, whitish patch (Fig. 262**A**), confined to the feather edge. **Note: Ageing can be difficult (especially with ♀♀); many intermediates cannot be aged. Also, among HY/SYs in Aug-Dec, intermediates will occur that may not be reliably sexed; any black feathering on the breast or crown indicates a ♂, but those without black may be of either sex during this time period.**

AHY/ASY ♀ (Aug-Jul): Forecrown and breast usually without black feathering (a few older AHY/ASYs can acquire one to a few blackish to dusky feathers, especially in the forecrown); breast extensively yellow, often with indistinct, dusky speckling; wing covs, terts, and ss uni-

443

formly adult (Fig. 133**F**) and dark greenish without buff tips; outer pp covs broad, truncate, relatively fresh, and dusky with relatively distinct and broad, olive edging (Fig. 138); outer rects and pp relatively fresh, truncate (Figs. 139**A** & 140**A**), and dusky; outer rects (r5-r6) often with diffuse white patches (Fig. 262**A-B**). **Note: See HY/SY ♀.**

HY/SY ♂ (Aug-Jul): Forecrown with little or no black in Aug-Feb, or with a distinct, blackish patch in Feb-Jun; molt-limit, wing-cov, and flight-feather criteria as in HY/SY ♀, except that the outer rects (r4-r6) usually have diffuse white patches (Fig. 262**B-C**), contrasting indistinctly with the brownish-gray feather bases; breast with a distinct, blackish patch in Feb-Jun, sometimes mottled yellow and restricted to the center. **Note: See HY/SY ♀.**

AHY/ASY ♂ (Aug-Jul): Forecrown with a distinct, black patch; molt-limit, wing-cov and flight-feather criteria as in AHY/ASY ♀, except that the outer rects (r4-r6) have white patches (Fig. 262**B-D**), contrasting distinctly with the dark gray feather bases; black of the breast extensive (reaching across breast), the feathers with narrow, yellow tipping in Aug-Dec. **Note: See HY/SY ♀.**

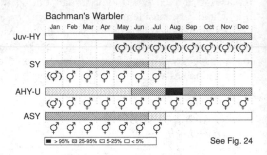

References—Brewster (1891, 1905), Ridgway (1902), Bent (1953), Robbins (1964), Hamel & Gauthreaux (1982), Barber (1985), Curson *et al.* (1994), Hamel (1995), Dunn & Garrett (1997), Pyle (1997c).

BLUE-WINGED WARBLER
Vermivora pinus

BWWA
Species # 6410
Band size: 0A-0

Geographic variation—No subspecies are recognized.

Molt—PB: HY partial (Jun-Aug), AHY complete (Jun-Aug); PA absent-limited? (Jan-Apr). The PBs occur on the summer grounds. The 1st PB usually includes all med and gr covs, but no terts or rects; 20-50% of birds replace the greater alula. A few head feathers may be replaced during the PA; more study is needed.

Skull—Pneumaticization completes in HY from 1 Oct through Nov.

Age/Sex—Juv (Jun-Jul) is washed olive, with the eye line indistinct and the wing bars washed or tinged yellow; juv ♀ = ♂. CP/BP (May-Aug). Wg is somewhat useful for sexing: ♀ wg(n100) 50-61, tl(n20) 41-47; ♂ wg(n100) 55-64, tl(n35) 43-49.

HY/SY ♀ (Aug-Jul): Forehead and crown greenish, sometimes with a diffuse patch of yellow (Fig. 259); eye line dusky; terts relatively worn and without broad, olive fringes; outer pp covs narrow, tapered, relatively abraded, and brownish gray with indistinct, narrow, or no buff edging (Fig. 138), contrasting with the slightly fresher gr covs (Fig. 134); outer rects and pp relatively abraded, tapered (Figs. 139**A** & 140**A**), and washed brownish; r4-r6 with relatively little white (Fig. 262**D**). **Note: In addition, ♀♀ may average thinner wing bars than ♂♂, but this difference is too variable to be of much use in sexing.**

AHY/ASY ♀ (Aug-Jul): Forehead and crown moderately bright yellow, grading into the green of the nape and back (Fig. 259); eye line dusky to dull blackish; terts relatively fresh, with

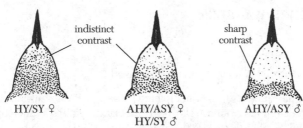

FIGURE 259. The crown plumage by age and sex in spring Blue-winged and Prothonotary warblers. Note that the crowns of all age/sex groups are greener in fall and yellower in spring.

broad, olive fringes; outer pp covs broad, truncate, relatively fresh, and blackish gray with relatively distinct and broad, gray (and sometimes olive) edging (Fig. 138), not contrasting in wear with the gr covs (Fig. 133**F**); outer rects and pp relatively fresh, truncate (Figs. 139**A** & 140**A**), and dusky; outer rects (r3-r6) with a relatively small to a moderate amount of white (Fig. 262**D-E**). **Note: See HY/SY ♀.**

HY/SY ♂ (Aug-Jul): Forehead and crown moderately bright yellow, grading into the green of the nape and back (Fig. 259); eye line dull blackish; pp-cov and rect criteria as in HY/SY ♀, except that the outer rects (r3-r6) average more white (Fig. 262**D-F**). **Note: See HY/SY ♀.**

AHY/ASY ♂ (Aug-Jul): Forehead and crown bright yellow, contrasting with the darker green nape and back (Fig. 259); eye line black; pp-cov and rect criteria as in AHY/ASY ♀, except that the outer rects (r2-r6) average more white (Fig. 262**E-F**). **Note: See HY/SY ♀.**

Hybrids reported—Golden-winged Warbler (see below), Kentucky Warbler. Probably Nashville Warbler. A reported hybrid with Mourning Warbler was based on a probable Blue-winged **X** Kentucky warbler.

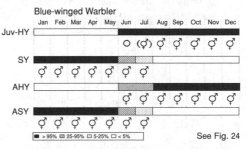

References—Stone (1896), Dwight (1900a), Ridgway (1902), Forbush (1929), McCamey (1950), Bent (1953), Roberts (1955), Robbins (1964), Wood (1969), Oberholser (1974), Graves (1988), Pyle & McCaskie (1992), Curson *et al.* (1994), Dunn & Garrett (1997), Pyle (1997c); F.B. Gill (*in litt.* to the BBL); IBP (MAPS) data, PNR data.

BLUE-WINGED X GOLDEN-WINGED WARBLER

Brewster's Warbler (BRWA)   Species # 6412
Lawrence's Warbler (LAWA)   Species # 6413

The information found in the accounts of Blue-winged and Golden-winged warblers should be carefully combined when ageing or sexing a hybrid between the two species. Generally, the most useful plumage criteria on hybrids are the amount of yellow in the crown (Brewster's and Lawrence's) and the coloration of the throat and auricular (Lawrence's). All ageing criteria related to molt and flight feathers should apply, as well. It should be kept in mind that intergrades can show any combination of characters between the two species, and that the ageing and sexing criteria should be weighted accordingly. For more information on the plumages of these hybrids, see Ridgway (1902), Bishop (1905b), Alexander (1919), Morss (1926), Parkes (1949, 1951, 1991), Short (1963, 1969b), Ficken & Ficken (1968), Gill (1980, 1987), Confer (1992), Curson *et al.* (1994), and Dunn & Garrett (in press).

GOLDEN-WINGED WARBLER
Vermivora chrysoptera

GWWA
Species # 6420
Band size: 0A-0

Geographic variation—No subspecies are recognized.

Molt—PB: HY partial (Jun-Aug), AHY complete (Jun-Aug); PA absent-limited? (Jan-Apr). The PBs occur on the summer grounds. The 1st PB usually includes all med and gr covs, but no terts or rects; 20-50% of birds replace the greater alula. The PA, if present, only includes head and body feathers; more study is needed.

Skull—Pneumaticization completes in HY/SY from 1 Oct. Look for windows (> 2 mm; Fig. 11**D**) on the top of the skull in some SYs through May.

Age—Juv (Jun-Jul) has upperparts grayish to brownish olive, olive-green wing bars, and underparts dingy yellow with a dusky throat; juv ♀ = ♂.

HY/SY (Aug-Jul): Outer pp covs narrow, tapered, relatively abraded, and brownish dusky with indistinct, narrow, or no pale brownish-gray edging (Fig. 138), contrasting with the slightly fresher gr covs (Fig. 134); outer rects and pp relatively abraded, tapered (Figs. 139**A** & 140**A**), and washed brownish; chin usually whitish, contrasting with the grayish (♀) or black (♂) throat. **Note: In addition, the amount of white in the outer rects (r3-r6) averages slightly less in ♀♀ and HY/SYs (Fig. 262C-D) than in ♂♂ and AHY/ASYs (Fig. 262C-E), but differences are too slight and variable to be of much use in ageing (or sexing). Some intermediates can be difficult to age.**

AHY/ASY (Aug-Jul): Outer pp covs broad, truncate, relatively fresh, and dusky blackish with relatively distinct and broad, gray edging (Fig. 138), not contrasting in wear with the gr covs (Fig. 133**F**); outer rects and pp relatively fresh, truncate (Figs. 139**A** & 140**A**), and dusky; chin and throat usually uniformly gray (♀) or black (♂). **Note: See HY/SY.**

Sex—CP/BP (May-Jul). ♀ wg(n43) 54-63, tl(n20) 40-47; ♂ wg(n81) 57-67, tl(n20) 43-50.

♀: Throat and cheeks dusky, not showing a well-marked contrast with the adjoining white; crown yellow suffused with green; gr covs with moderately dull yellow-olive margins to the outer webs. **Note: See HY/SY, above.**

♂: Throat and cheeks black (tipped gray in fall), contrasting markedly with the adjoining white; crown relatively bright yellow; gr covs with bright yellow margins to the outer webs. **Note: See HY/SY, above.**

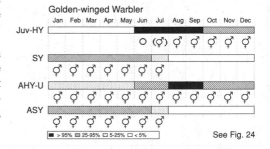

Hybrids reported—Blue-winged Warbler (see above).

References—Stone (1896), Dwight (1900a), Ridgway (1902), Forbush (1929), Bent (1953), Roberts (1955), Robbins (1964), Wood (1969), Oberholser (1974), Parkes (1988b), Francis & Wood (1989), Confer (1992), Cramp & Perrins (1994b), Curson *et al.* (1994), Dunn & Garrett (1997), Pyle (1997c); J.S. Weske (*in litt.* to the BBL); J. Curson (pers. comm.); IBP (MAPS) data, PNR data.

TENNESSEE WARBLER   TEWA
Vermivora peregrina   Species # 6470
                                               Band size: 0A-0

Species—From Old World warblers (*Phylloscopus*), potential vagrants to N.Am which resemble this species, by the lack of a reduced p10 (which *Phylloscopus* have), longest p – longest s 14-20 mm (*vs* < 15 mm in most *Phylloscopus* warblers), beak sharper, and legs darker; see Bradshaw (1992), Cramp (1992), Svensson (1992), Prowse (1993), and Cramp & Perrins (1994b) for more information. From Philadelphia Vireo by p9 ≥ p8 and > p6; bill sharp and pointed; eye line narrowing behind the eye; legs thin and blackish. From Orange-crowned Warbler by tl short (36-46; see **Age/Sex**); longest p – longest s 14-20 mm; upperparts green; undertail covs white. From dull Nashville Warblers by supercilium and eye line present; distinct eye ring absent.

Geographic variation—No subspecies are recognized. Within the breeding range, northern birds average slightly larger bills than southern birds (see Raveling 1965).

Molt—PB: HY partial (Jun-Aug), AHY complete (Jun-Sep); PA limited (Jan-Apr). The PBs occur primarily on the summer grounds, although AHY sometimes can suspend flight-feather replacement over migration. The 1st PB usually includes all med and gr covs, but no terts or rects; 20-50% replace the greater alula. The PA is limited to the head and throat.

Skull—Pneumaticization completes in HY from 1 Oct through Nov.

Age/Sex—Juv (Jun-Jul) is washed grayish and has distinct, yellow wing bars; juv ♀=♂. CP/BP (May-Aug). Measurements are useful for sexing: ♀ wg(n100) 58-64, tl(n20) 36-42; ♂ wg(n100) 62-68, tl(n20) 39-46.

Basic Plumage (Aug-Mar)

HY/SY ♀♂ (Aug-Mar): Crown dull green, usually without gray coloration; eye line and supercilium indistinct and dusky olive with a heavy, yellow wash; outer pp covs narrow, tapered, relatively abraded, and dusky brownish with indistinct, narrow, olive or buff edging (Fig. 138A), contrasting with the slightly fresher and dusky-olive gr covs (Fig. 134); outer rects and pp relatively abraded, tapered (Figs. 139A & 140A), and washed brownish, with little green edging; outer rect (r6) without white, or occasionally with small and indistinct patches (see Fig. 262A); underparts heavily washed yellow. **Note: All age/sex criteria should be combined for reliable determinations; some intermediates will not be aged and/or sexed, especially in basic plumage. It is easiest to age birds before sexing. Look for the gr covs to average larger white tips and yellow corners on HY/SYs than on AHY/ASYs. Also, basic-plumaged HY/SY ♀♀ average slightly duller green crowns, duskier eye lines, and less white in the outer rects (r4-r6; see SY ♀ & ♂, below) than HY/SY ♂♂, but differences are too variable for reliable sexing by plumage alone. Some extremes probably can be reliably sexed, with experience, by the combination of plumage and wg (see above).**

AHY/ASY ♀ (Aug-Mar): Crown medium-bright green; eye line and supercilium moderately distinct, and dusky and whitish with a yellow tinge; outer pp covs broad, truncate, relatively fresh, and dusky with distinct, olive edging (Fig. 138B), not contrasting markedly in color or wear with the gr covs (Fig. 133F); outer rects and pp relatively fresh, truncate (Figs. 139A & 140A), and dusky with green edging; outer rects (r6) without white, or sometimes with small and indistinct, whitish patches (Fig. 262A); underparts with a moderate yellow wash. **Note: See HY/SY ♀♂.**

AHY/ASY ♂ (Aug-Mar): Crown bluish gray with green mottling; eye line and supercilium distinct, and blackish and white; pp-cov and rect criteria as in AHY/ASY ♀, except that the outer rects (r5-r6) average more white (Fig. 262A-B); underparts lightly washed yellow. **Note: See HY/SY ♀♂.**

Alternate Plumage (Mar-Jul)

SY ♀ (Mar-Jul): Crown dull green with little or no gray coloration; eye line and supercilium indistinct and dusky olive with a light, yellow wash; outer pp covs narrow, tapered, relatively abraded, and brownish with little or no olive or buff edging (Fig. 138C), contrasting with the slightly fresher and dusky-olive gr covs (Fig. 134); outer rects and pp relatively abraded, tapered (Figs. 139A & 140A), and brownish with little or no green edging; outer rects (r5-r6) usually without white or whitish; underparts with a moderate yellow wash. **Note: All age/sex criteria should be combined for reliable determinations; some intermediates will not be reliably aged and/or sexed.**

ASY ♀ (Mar-Jul): Crown green with a gray wash; eye line and supercilium moderately distinct, and dusky and whitish; outer pp covs broad, truncate, relatively fresh, and dusky with olive edging (Fig. 138D), not contrasting in color or wear with the gr covs (Fig. 133F); outer rects and pp relatively fresh, truncate (Figs. 139A & 140A), and dusky with green edging; outer rects (r6) without white, or sometimes with small and indistinct patches (Fig. 262A); underparts white to lightly washed yellow. **Note: See SY ♀.**

SY ♂ (Mar-Jul): Crown primarily gray, often tinged green; eye line and supercilium moderately distinct and dusky and whitish; pp-cov and rect criteria as in SY ♀, except that the outer rects (r5-r6) average slightly more white (sometimes as in Fig. 262A); underparts lightly washed yellow. **Note: See SY ♀.**

ASY ♂ (Mar-Jul): Crown bluish gray, without green coloration; eye line and supercilium distinct and blackish and white; pp-cov and rect criteria as in ASY ♀, except that the outer rects (r5-r6) average larger and more distinct white patches (Fig. 262A-B); underparts white. **Note: See SY ♀. Also, look for some ♂♂ to have a small amount of rufous in the crown, probably in ASYs only; more study is needed.**

Tennessee Warbler

Note: In Oct-Dec, AHYs can be sexed but birds of unknown age should be left unsexed.

See Fig. 24

Hybrids reported—Nashville Warbler.

References—Stone (1896), Dwight (1900a), Ridgway (1902), Forbush (1929), Dickey & van Rossem (1938), Bent (1953), Roberts (1955), Goodpasture (1963), Robbins (1964), Raveling (1965), Raveling & Warner (1965), Baird (1967), Wood (1969), Oberholser (1974), Sheppard & Klimkiewicz (1976), Sealy (1985), Bledsoe (1988), Quay (1989), Kaufman (1990a), Prowse (1993), Winker (1993), Cramp & Perrins (1994b), Curson *et al.* (1994), Dick & James (1996), Parkes (1996), Dunn & Garrett (1997), Pyle (1997c); T. Smith (*in litt.* to the BBL); IBP (MAPS) data, PNR data, PRBO data.

ORANGE-CROWNED WARBLER
Vermivora celata

OCWA
Species # 6460
Band size: 0-0A

Species—From Tennessee Warbler (which see for separation from *Phylloscopus* warblers) by tl long (42-53; see **Age/Sex**); longest p – longest s 8-15 mm; upperparts olive to yellowish; undertail covs yellow. From dull Nashville Warblers by supercilium and eye line present; distinct eye ring absent. Eastern birds from Mourning Warbler by much smaller size (wg 51-66, tl 42-53; see **Age/Sex**); undertail covs usually brighter yellow than the belly; legs blackish.

Geographic variation—Moderate and ranges fairly well defined. Subspecies taxonomy follows G.H. Lowery & B.L. Monroe *in* Paynter (1968); see Ridgway (1902), Oberholser (1905, 1917d, 1974), Swarth (1935), Phillips *et al.* (1964), Phillips (1975a), Behle (1985), Godfrey (1986), Dunn & Garrett (in press). No other subspecies occur.

V.c. lutescens (br & wint coastal se.AK-s.CA; vag to OK): Averages small; bill short (exp culmen 8.5-10.3); head, upperparts, and underparts uniformly, moderately bright yellowish olive; undertail covs with very indistinct or no dusky. ♀ wg(n100) 51-59, tl(n10) 42-48; ♂ wg(n100) 55-62, tl(n16) 44-50.

V.c. sordida (res Channel Is, CA; wint to coastal CA): Averages medium small; bill long (exp culmen 10.1-12.0); head and upperparts uniformly dull dusky olive; underparts olive with a slight or no yellow wash; undertail covs with dusky centers. ♀ wg(n10) 54-60, tl(n10) 45-50; ♂ wg(n15) 57-63, tl(n15) 47-52. See also differences in molt strategy.

V.c. orestera (br & wint s.Yuk to e.CA-sw.TX; vag to SC,FL): Averages large; bill medium long (exp culmen 9.4-10.8); head yellow-olive with a grayish tinge when fresh; upperparts yellow-olive; underparts medium-bright greenish with a yellow tinge; undertail covs with indistinct or no dusky. ♀ wg(n55) 55-64, tl(n10) 46-51; ♂ wg(n43) 58-66, tl(n10) 48-53.

V.c. celata (br AK-c.Alb to Que; wint coastal s.CA to SC-FL): Averages medium in size; bill medium short (exp culmen 8.8-10.6); head grayish (fall) to grayish olive (spring); upperparts olive; underparts grayish with a greenish wash (fall) to dull yellowish green (spring); undertail covs with indistinct or no dusky centers. ♀ wg(n51) 54-62, tl(n10) 45-50; ♂ wg(n66) 57-65, tl(n17) 46-52.

Molt—PB: HY partial (May-Sep), AHY complete (Jun-Sep); PA absent-limited (Jan-May). The PBs occur primarily on the summer grounds (in *V.c. sordida* they occur on the winter grounds), although substantial, post-breeding dispersal can occur (usually upslope in western populations). The 1st PB usually includes all med and gr covs, sometimes (in ~25% of birds; perhaps in a greater proportion of *lutescens*, and in most or all *sordida*) 1-3 terts (rarely s6 and/or s5), and occasionally (in ~10% of birds) 1-2 central rects (r1; to all rects in *lutescens* and *sordida*). The PA is limited primarily to the head and chin, is more extensive in SY ♂♂ than in the other age/sex groups, and occurs in all subspecies except *sordida*.

Skull—Pneumaticization completes in HY/SY from 1 Oct (as early as 15 Aug in populations of CA). Look for occasional windows (> 2 mm; Fig. 11**D**) on the top of the skull through spring.

Age/Sex—Juv (Apr-Aug) has a brownish or grayish wash to the upperparts, a brownish-buff breast, and relatively distinct, buffy-yellow wing bars; juv ♀=♂. CP/BP (Mar-Aug). Measurements are useful for sexing (especially within subspecies): ♀ wg(n100) 51-64, tl(n40) 42-51; ♂ wg(n100) 55-66, tl(n58) 44-53; see **Geographic variation**.

HY/SY ♀ (Aug-Jul): Crown usually without orange or with a small concealed orange patch (0-6 mm in length; see Fig. 281); outer 2-5 gr covs with distinct, yellow to buffy-yellow tips when fresh (Aug-Feb); outer pp covs narrow, tapered, relatively abraded, and brownish dusky with indistinct, narrow, or no olive edging (Fig. 138), contrasting with the slightly fresher gr covs (Fig. 134); terts and central rects (r1) occasionally replaced (see **Molt**), contrastingly fresh; outer rects and pp relatively abraded, tapered (Figs. 139**A** & 140**A**), and washed brownish, with little or no olive edging. **Note: A few birds with intermediate crown-patch lengths may not be sexed, although most birds of known age should be sexed; combine with age and measurements.**

AHY/ASY ♀ (Aug-Jul): Crown sometimes without orange, but usually with a small concealed orange patch (0-12 mm); outer 2-5 gr covs with indistinct or no yellow tips when fresh; outer pp covs broad, truncate, relatively fresh, and dusky with relatively distinct and broad, olive edging (Fig. 138), not contrasting in wear with the gr covs (Fig. 133**F**); terts and rects uniformly adult; outer rects relatively fresh, truncate (Figs. 139**A** & 140**A**), and dusky with olive edging. **Note: See HY/SY ♀.**

HY/SY ♂ (Aug-Jul): Concealed orange crown patch moderately large (9-15 mm, possibly to 18 mm in Mar-Jul); pp-cov and rect criteria as in HY/SY ♀. **Note: See HY/SY ♀.**

AHY/ASY ♂ (Aug-Jul): Concealed orange crown patch large (13-18 mm); pp-cov and rect criteria as in AHY/ASY ♀. **Note: See HY/SY ♀.**

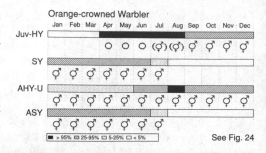

References—Dwight (1900a), Ridgway (1902), Forbush (1929), Dickey & van Rossem (1938), Bent (1953), Roberts (1955), Robbins (1964), Foster (1967a, 1967b), Wood (1969), Oberholser (1974), Bohlen & Kleen (1976), Collins (1974f), Kaufman (1990a), CWS & USFWS (1991), Curson *et al.* (1994), Sogge *et al.* (1994), Dunn & Garrett (1997), Pyle (1997c); K. Burton, J.R. King, E. Ruhlen, J. Steele, W. Wehtje (pers. comm.); M. San Miguel, B.A. Sorrie, G.C. West (*in litt.* to the BBL); IBP (MAPS) data, PRBO data.

NASHVILLE WARBLER
Vermivora ruficapilla

NAWA
Species # 6450
Band size: 0A-0

Species—From Tennessee and Orange-crowned warblers in all plumages by supercilium lacking; distinct eye-ring present; underparts with at least some bright yellow. HY/SY ♀♀ separated from HY/SY ♂ Virginia's Warbler by p6 not emarginated; throat and flanks with at least a slight yellowish wash, not contrasting sharply with the yellow of the breast. From Connecticut Warbler by much smaller size (wg 52-66, tl 38-48; see **Age/Sex**); belly and/or vent with white; legs blackish.

Geographic variation—Weak, but breeding ranges well defined. Subspecies taxonomy follows G.H. Lowery & B.L. Monroe *in* Paynter (1968); see Ridgway (1902), Phillips *et al.* (1964), Oberholser (1974), Phillips (1975a), Dunn & Garrett (in press). No other subspecies occur. Account for age and sex when using the following, as plumage features vary more by these than by subspecies.

V.r. ridgwayi (br s.BC-nw.MT to sc.CA): Tl averages long; back relatively bright greenish and rump bright greenish yellow by age/sex; underparts bright yellow. Tl: ♀(n10) 40-45, ♂(n10) 43-48.

V.r. ruficapilla (br Man-Nfl to montane WV): Tl averages short; back relatively dull olive and rump medium-dull yellow-green by age/sex; underparts medium-bright yellow with an olive tinge. Tl: ♀(n10) 38-43, ♂(n10) 41-46.

Molt—PB: HY partial (Jun-Sep), AHY complete (Jun-Sep); PA limited-partial (Jan-May). The PBs occur on the summer grounds, although post-breeding dispersal can occur (usually up-slope in western populations). The 1st PB usually includes all med and gr covs (a small proportion of birds can retain 1-3 juvenal, outer gr covs), occasionally (10%) 1-2 terts, and occasionally (in ~15% of birds) 1-2 central rects (r1; probably in *V.r. ridgwayi* only); 20-50% of birds replace the greater alula. The PA is limited to the head and may be more extensive in HY/SYs than in AHY/ASYs.

Skull—Pneumaticization completes in HY from 1 Oct through Dec.

Age/Sex—Juv (May-Aug) has upperparts and breast washed grayish or brownish and relatively distinct, buffy-yellow wing bars; juv ♀ = ♂. CP/BP (Apr-Aug). ♀ wg(n100) 52-63, tl(n20) 38-45; ♂ wg(n100) 55-66, tl(n26) 41-48; see **Geographic variation**.

HY/SY ♀ (Aug-Jul): Concealed crown patch absent (Aug-Mar), or indistinctly defined, small (0-8 mm in length; see Fig. 281), and pale rufous in Mar-Jul; crown grayish olive, contrasting slightly with the brownish-olive to dull olive back; eye ring buffy to whitish; molt limits occasionally occur among the gr covs and terts (Fig. 133**D-E**; see **Molt**), the retained outer covs worn and brownish olive with distinct, yellow corners, contrasting with the fresher and dusky-green, replaced inner covs with indistinct or no, yellow corners; outer pp covs narrow, tapered, relatively abraded, and dusky brownish with indistinct, narrow, or no yellow-green edging (Fig. 138); outer rects and pp relatively abraded, tapered (Figs. 139**A** & 140**A**), and washed brownish, with little or no olive edging; chin and throat buffy whitish to white; breast and flanks pale buffy yellow. **Note: A few intermediates can be difficult to age and/or sex; compare with measurements. It is easiest to age birds before sexing.**

AHY/ASY ♀ (Aug-Jul): Concealed crown patch indistinctly defined, moderately small (2-10 mm in length), and pale rufous; crown grayish to grayish olive, contrasting moderately with the olive back; eye ring whitish; gr covs uniformly adult (Fig. 133**F**), dusky with greenish edging, and with indistinct or no yellow corners; outer pp covs broad, truncate, relatively fresh, and dusky with relatively distinct and broad, yellow-green edging (Fig. 138); outer rects and pp relatively fresh, truncate (Figs. 139**A** & 140**A**), and dusky with distinct, greenish edging; chin and throat whitish or tinged yellow; breast and flanks medium-bright yellow. **Note: See HY/SY ♀.**

HY/SY ♂ (Aug-Jul): Concealed crown patch usually distinctly defined, moderate in size (2-12 mm in Aug-Mar to 5-13 mm in Mar-Jul), and medium-dark rufous, the rufous of individual feathers usually extending < 5 mm from the base (Fig. 260); crown grayish, contrasting moderately to markedly with the greenish-olive back; eye ring whitish to white; molt-limit and flight-feather criteria as in HY/SY ♀; chin, throat, breast, and flanks moderately bright yellow, often with paler yellow on the chin and throat. **Note: See HY/SY ♀.**

AHY/ASY ♂ (Aug-Jul): Concealed crown patch well defined, large (9-16 mm), and dark rufous, the rufous of individual feathers usually extending > 5 mm from the base (Fig. 260); crown gray, contrasting markedly with the brightish green back; eye ring white; molt-limit and flight-feather criteria as in AHY/ASY ♀; chin, throat, breast, and flanks uniformly bright yellow. **Note: See HY/SY ♀.**

Hybrids reported—Tennessee Warbler, Black-throated Blue Warbler. Probably Blue-winged Warbler. Possibly American Redstart.

FIGURE 260. The amount of rufous on the crown feathers by age in ♂ Nashville, Virginia's and Colima warblers. Lucy's Warbler show's a similar but less pronounced difference.

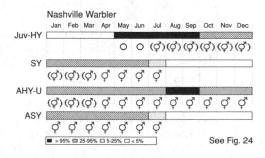

References—Stone (1896), Dwight (1900a), Ridgway (1902), Forbush (1929), Bent (1953), Roberts (1955), Robbins (1964), Wood (1969), Oberholser (1974), Bledsoe (1988), Curson *et al.* (1994), Parkes (1996), Williams (1996a), Dunn & Garrett (1997), Pyle (1997c); C.A. Ely, J.S. Weske (*in litt.* to the BBL); K. Burton, E. Ruhlen (pers. comm.); IBP (MAPS) data, PNR data, PRBO data.

VIRGINIA'S WARBLER
Vermivora virginiae

VIWA
Species # 6440
Band size: 0A

Species—HY/SY ♂ from HY/SY ♀ Nashville Warblers by p6 emarginated; throat and flanks white or whitish, contrasting markedly with the yellow breast. From Colima Warbler by smaller tl (41-50; see **Age/Sex**) and bill (nares to tip 8.9-10.9); p6 emarginated; plumage (especially flanks) with relatively little or no brown; breast with yellow in most birds. From Lucy's Warbler (including juvs) by larger size (wg 54-66, tl 41-50; see **Age/Sex**); p6 emarginated; rump and undertail covs with at least some yellow; outer rect without a white patch.

Geographic variation—No subspecies are recognized.

Molt—PB: HY partial (May-Aug), AHY complete (Jun-Aug); PA limited-partial (Jan-May). The PBs occur on the summer grounds. The 1st PB usually includes all med and gr covs (~9% of birds can retain the outermost juvenal gr cov), occasionally (in ~14% of birds) 1-3 terts, and occasionally (in ~14% of birds) 1-2 central rects (r1). The PA is limited to the head and sometimes the breast, and may be more extensive in HY/SYs than in AHY/ASYs.

Skull—Pneumaticization completes in HY from 1 Oct through Dec.

Age/Sex—Juv (May-Jul) has brownish plumage, lacks rufous in the crown and yellow on the breast, and has relatively distinct, buff wing bars; juv ♀ = ♂. CP/BP (Apr-Aug). ♀ wg(n48) 54-63, tl(n20) 41-47; ♂ wg(n37) 57-66, tl(n20) 43-50.

HY/SY ♀ (Aug-Jul): Concealed crown patch absent, or reduced to 1-2 pale orangish feathers (Aug-Mar), or indistinct, small (2-8 mm; see Fig. 281), and pale rufous (Mar-Jul); molt limits sometimes occur among the gr covs and terts (Fig. 133**D-E**; see **Molt**), the retained outermost covs worn and brownish with buff tips, contrasting with the fresher, duskier, and gray-edged, replaced inner covs; outer pp covs narrow, tapered, relatively abraded, and brownish with indistinct, narrow, or no pale grayish-brown edging (Fig. 138); outer rects and pp relatively abraded, tapered (Figs. 139**A** & 140**A**), and washed brownish; yellow on the breast lacking, or reduced to a small patch at the center. **Note: Birds become increasingly difficult to age in Apr-Jul due to wear of the flight feathers; many if not most birds may be indeterminable. It usually is easier to age birds before sexing.**

AHY/ASY ♀ (Aug-Jul): Concealed crown patch indistinct, moderately small (2-10 mm), and pale rufous; gr covs and terts uniformly adult (Fig. 133**F**), the gr covs dusky with gray edges; outer pp covs broad, truncate, relatively fresh, and dusky with relatively distinct and broad, gray edging (Fig. 138); outer rects and pp relatively fresh, truncate (Figs. 139**A** & 140**A**), and dusky; yellow patch on the breast reduced, usually confined to the center of the breast. **Note: See HY/SY ♀.**

HY/SY ♂ (Aug-Jul): Concealed rufous crown patch moderately indistinct and small (6-10 mm) in Aug-Mar, or distinct and moderately large (8-11 mm) in Mar-Jul, the rufous of individual feathers usually extending < 5 mm from the base (Fig. 260); molt-limit, wing-cov, and rect criteria as in HY/SY ♀; yellow patch on the breast reduced and usually confined to the center of the breast (Aug-Mar), to moderately extensive, but usually not extending across the breast or to the throat (Mar-Jul). **Note: See HY/SY ♀.**

AHY/ASY ♂ (Aug-Jul): Concealed crown patch distinct, large (8-13 mm), and deep rufous, the rufous of individual feathers usually extending > 5 mm from the base (Fig. 260); molt-limit, wing-cov, and rect criteria as in AHY/ASY ♀; yellow patch on the underparts extensive, spanning the width of the breast and sometimes extending to the throat. **Note: See HY/SY ♀.**

References—Ridgway (1902), Swarth (1904a), Bent (1953), Oberholser (1974), Curson *et al.* (1994), Dunn & Garrett (1997), Pyle (1997c); IBP (MAPS) data, PRBO data.

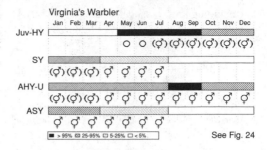

Virginia's Warbler

See Fig. 24

COLIMA WARBLER
Vermivora crissalis

COLW
Species # 6471
Band size: 1C

Species—From Virginia's Warbler (which see for separation from other warblers) by longer tl (47-57; see **Age/Sex**) and bill (nares to tip 10.7-11.9); p6 not emarginated; upperparts grayish brown; flanks strongly washed brown; breast with little or no yellow.

Geographic variation—No subspecies are recognized.

Molt—PB: HY partial (Jun-Aug), AHY complete (Jun-Aug); PA limited (Jan-May). The PBs occur on the summer grounds. The 1st PB usually includes all med and gr covs, but no terts or rects. Look for a few HY/SYs to retain the outermost gr cov, or to replace terts and/or central rects (r1), as in Virginia's Warbler. The PA is limited to the head and may be more extensive in HY/SYs than in AHY/ASYs.

Skull—Pneumaticization completes in HY from 1 Oct through Dec.

Age/Sex—Juv (Jun-Jul) is drab brownish overall, with two buff wing bars; juv ♀ = ♂. CP/BP (Apr-Aug). ♀ wg(n15) 57-65, tl(n8) 47-54; ♂ wg(n20) 60-69, tl(n10) 50-57. Little-studied, but plumage criteria (except for the yellow on the breast) appear to parallel those of Virginia Warbler. Within each age/sex class, the concealed crown patch appears to average 1-2 mm greater in Colima Warbler than in Virginia's Warbler.

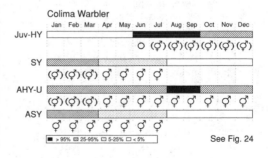

Colima Warbler

See Fig. 24

References—Ridgway (1902), Bangs (1925), Bent (1953), Oberholser (1974), Curson *et al.* (1994), Dunn & Garrett (1997), Pyle (1997c).

LUCY'S WARBLER
Vermivora luciae

LUWA
Species # 6430
Band size: 0A

Species—Juv from juv Verdin by bill long (exp culmen > 7 mm) and not conical (*cf.* Fig. 204); p10 absent; wing morphology longer (longest p – longest s > 15 mm). From Virginia's Warbler (including juvs) by smaller size (wg 49-60, tl 33-44; see **Age/Sex**); p6 not emarginated; rump with at least some rufous in all plumages; undertail covs white, without yellow; outer rect usually with a white patch (see **Age/Sex**).

Geographic variation—No subspecies are recognized.

Molt—PB: HY partial (Jun-Sep), AHY complete (Jun-Oct); PA absent. The PBs occur primarily on the summer grounds, although they apparently can complete on the winter grounds; more study is needed. The 1st PB usually includes all med and gr covs, occasionally (in ~20% of birds) 1-3 terts, and occasionally (in ~20% of birds) 1-2 central rects (r1). A limited PA may occur in some individuals, as in Virginia's Warbler.

Skull—Pneumaticization completes in HY from 1 Sep through Nov.

Age/Sex—Juv (May-Jul) lacks the crown patch entirely, generally is pale and tinged buff, and has distinct, buff to white wing bars; juv ♀ = ♂. CP/BP (Apr-Aug). Measurements are somewhat useful: ♀ wg(n66) 49-56, tl(n20) 33-40; ♂ wg(n100) 52-60, tl(n20) 36-44.

HY/SY ♀ (Aug-Jul): Concealed crown patch indistinct, reduced (2-7 mm; see Fig. 281), and pale orangish; outer pp covs narrow, tapered, relatively abraded, and brownish gray with indistinct, narrow, or no pale grayish edging (Fig. 138), contrasting with the slightly fresher gr covs (Fig. 134); 1-3 terts occasionally replaced, contrastingly fresh (Fig. 133**D-E**); rump pale buffy rufous; outer rects and pp relatively abraded, tapered (Figs. 139**A** & 140**A**), and washed brownish; outer rect with the whitish patch lacking or indistinct. **Note: Ageing of this species can be particularly difficult; many intermediates are to be expected at all times of the year, but especially in Apr-Jul when birds become increasingly worn.**

AHY/ASY ♀ (Aug-Jul): Concealed crown patch indistinct, moderately small (5-9 mm), and pale rufous; outer pp covs broad, truncate, relatively fresh, and dusky with relatively distinct and broad, grayish edging (Fig. 138), not contrasting in wear with the gr covs (Fig. 133**F**); terts uniformly adult (Fig. 133**F**); rump pale rufous; outer rects and pp relatively fresh, truncate (Figs. 139**A** & 140**A**), and dusky; outer rect with the white patch distinct. **Note: See HY/SY ♀.**

HY/SY ♂ (Aug-Jul): Concealed crown patch moderately indistinct, moderately large (6-12 mm), and rufous to deep rufous, the rufous of individual feathers usually extending < 5 mm from the base (Fig. 260); molt limit, pp-cov, and rect criteria as in HY/SY ♀, except that the whitish patch in the outer rect usually is present; rump moderately deep to deep rufous. **Note: See HY/SY ♀.**

AHY/ASY ♂ (Aug-Mar): Concealed crown patch distinct, large (9-14 mm), and deep rufous, the rufous of individual feathers usually extending > 5 mm from the base (Fig. 260); molt-limit, pp-cov, and flight-feather criteria as in AHY/ASY ♀; rump deep rufous. **Note: See HY/SY ♀.**

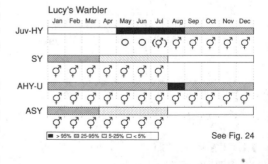

References—Ridgway (1902), Bent (1953), Oberholser (1974), Lamm (1991), Curson *et al.* (1994), Dunn & Garrett (1997), Pyle (1997c).

NORTHERN PARULA
Parula americana

Species—HY/SYs from Tropical Parula by white crescents present above and below the eye (including juvs); yellow of the breast not extending below the lower wing bar; breast usually with a distinct, orange wash and/or a blackish patch.

Geographic variation—Weak and clinal (on the basis of plumage and measurements). Subspecies taxonomy follows Moldenhauer (1992) who, primarily on the basis of vocalizations, resurrected two formerly recognized subspecies; see also Ridgway (1902), Chapman (1925), Oberholser (1938, 1974), Wetmore (1941), Parkes (1954), Sutton (1967), Monroe (1968). No other subspecies occur. Most individuals probably are not reliably distinguished to subspecies by in-hand criteria alone.

> ***P.a. ludoviciana*** (="*ramalinae*"; br sw.Ont-MI to e.TX-sw.AL): Size averages small; bill averages short (exp culmen 8.1-10.9); black and orange on the breast of AHY/ASY ♂ average more extensive and distinct; yellow of the underparts averages brighter. ♀ wg(n19) 50-56, tl(n13) 37-42; ♂ wg(n80) 53-60, tl(n66) 39-45.

> ***P.a. americana*** (br se.Ont-PEI to sc.AL-FL): Size averages medium small to large; bill averages long (exp culmen 9.0-11.4); black and orange on the breast of AHY/ASY ♂ average less extensive and distinct; yellow of the underparts averages duller. ♀ wg(n59) 52-59, tl(n35) 38-45; ♂ wg(n100) 56-64, tl(n73) 40-47. Birds breeding north of s.OH-s.MD ("*pusilla*") average larger and with more distinct breast markings than southern birds, but differences are weak and broadly clinal.

Molt—PB: HY partial (May-Aug), AHY complete (Jun-Aug); PA absent-limited (Jan-May). The PBs occur on the summer grounds. The 1st PB usually includes all med and gr covs and sometimes the greater alula, but no terts or rects; occasionally (in ~8% of birds) the outermost juvenal gr cov can be retained and rarely (in ~4% of birds) the longest tert (s8) can be replaced. The PA is limited to the head and breast, and may be more extensive in HY/SYs than AHY/ASYs.

Skull—Pneumaticization completes in HY from 1 Oct (as early as 15 Sep in southeastern populations) through Dec.

Age—Juv (May-Jul) is pale grayish to grayish brown, without yellow coloration; juv ♀ = ♂, although some birds perhaps can be sexed by the amount of white in the rects, as in HY/SYs (see below).

> HY/SY (Aug-Jul): Molt limits occasionally occur among the gr covs (Fig. 133**D-E**; see **Molt**), the retained outermost cov worn and brownish with pale green edging, contrasting with the fresher, dusky, blue-edged, and white-tipped, replaced inner covs; terts (if juvenal) edged green; alula (usually) and outer pp covs narrow, tapered, relatively abraded, and brownish with indistinct, narrow, or no greenish edging (Fig. 138), contrasting with the slightly fresher and blue-edged gr covs (Fig. 134); outer rects and pp relatively abraded, tapered (Figs. 139**A** & 140**A**), and brownish, with greenish edging when fresh; white patches in the outer rects (r5-r6) reduced by sex (♀, Fig. 262**A**; ♂, Fig. 262**A-B**). Note: **Most are reliably aged but ageing can become difficult, especially with ♀♀ in the spring/summer. See also Sex for further plumage indications.**

> AHY/ASY (Aug-Jul): Wing covs uniformly adult (Fig. 133**F**) and dusky with blue edging and white tips; alula and outer pp covs broad, truncate, relatively fresh, and black with relatively distinct and broad, blue edging (Fig. 138), not contrasting markedly in color or wear with the gr covs (Fig. 133**F**); rects and pp relatively fresh, truncate (Figs. 139**A** & 140**A**), dusky, and distinctly edged blue; white patches in the outer rects (r4-r6) more extensive by sex (♀, Fig. 262**A-B**; ♂, Fig. 262**B-C**). **Note: See HY/SY.**

Sex—CP/BP (Mar-Aug). Measurements are rather useful (especially when the subspecies is known): ♀ wg(n78) 50-59, tl(n48) 37-45; ♂ wg(n100) 53-64, tl(n100) 39-47; see **Geographic variation**.

♀: Breast usually uniformly yellow, sometimes with a slight tawny wash (AHY/ASYs), but without slate; outer rects (r5-r6) average less white by age (Fig. 262**A-B**; see **Age**).

♂: Tawny and slate breast bands distinct, or (in some HY/SYs) breast with a wide, tawny band and little or no slate; outer rects (r4-r6) average more white by age (Fig. 262**A-C**; see **Age**).

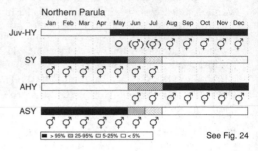

Hybrids reported—Yellow-rumped Warbler, Yellow-throated Warbler (resulting in "Sutton's Warbler", alpha code **SUWA**, **Species # 6634**), American Redstart.

References—Stone (1896), Dwight (1900a), Ridgway (1902), Forbush (1929), Haller (1940), Burleigh (1944), Bent (1953), Roberts (1955), Robbins (1964), Sutton (1967), Wood (1969), Oberholser (1974), Sheppard & Klimkiewicz (1976), CWS & USFWS (1991), Graves (1993), Cramp & Perrins (1994b), Curson *et al.* (1994), Moldenhauer & Regelski (1996), Dunn & Garrett (1997), Pyle (1997c); G.E. Wallace (pers. comm.); IBP (MAPS) data, PNR data, PRBO data.

TROPICAL PARULA
Parula pitiayumi

TRPA
Species # 6490
Band size: 0A

Geographic variation—Weak (between subspecies of N.Am) to moderate, and clinal where most ranges meet. Subspecies taxonomy follows G.H. Lowery & B.L. Monroe *in* Paynter (1968); see also Ridgway (1902), Chapman (1925), Curson *et al.* (1994), Howell & Webb (1995). Twelve other subspecies occur in Mex-S.Am. When using the following, beware that variation by age/sex is greater than that among subspecies.

P.p. pulchra (vag to s.AZ): Large; wing bars wide and distinct; underparts brightish yellow (♀) or deep yellow with a heavy orange wash on the breast (♂). ♀ wg(n5) 48-53, tl(n5) 36-40; ♂ wg(n8) 52-58, tl(n7) 39-44.

P.p. nigrilora (res s.TX): Small; wing bars narrow and indistinct; underparts dull yellow (♀) or medium yellow with a moderate orange wash on the breast (♂). ♀ wg(n3) 45-51, tl(n3) 33-38; ♂ wg(n10) 49-54, tl(n10) 36-42.

Molt—PB: HY partial (May-Aug), AHY complete (Jun-Aug); PA absent-partial (Jan-May). The PBs occur on the summer grounds. The 1st PB usually includes all med and gr covs and often the greater alula, but no terts or rects. The PA is limited to the head and breast, and may be more extensive in HY/SYs than in AHY/ASYs.

Skull—Pneumaticization completes in HY from 15 Sep through Nov.

Age/Sex—Juv (Apr-Jul) has upperparts and underparts washed dull gray with little or no blue or yellow coloration; juv ♀ = ♂, although some extremes may be sexed by the amount of white in the rects, as in HY/SYs (see below). CP/BP (Apr-Aug). Measurements are useful: ♀ wg(n30) 45-52, tl(n8) 33-40; ♂ wg(n43) 49-58, tl(n17) 36-44; see **Geographic variation**.

HY/SY ♀ (Aug-Jul): Lores and auricular medium-pale blue; greater alula (often) and outer pp covs narrow, tapered, relatively abraded, and brownish with indistinct, narrow, or no greenish edging (Fig. 138), contrasting with the slightly fresher, dusky-centered, and blue-edged gr covs (Fig. 134); outer rects relatively abraded, tapered (Fig. 139A), and brownish, with greenish edging when fresh; amount of white in the outer rects (r5-r6) reduced (Fig. 262A); breast pale yellow, without orange.

AHY/ASY ♀ (Aug-Jul): Lores and auricular medium-dark blue, sometimes tinged dusky; greater alula and outer pp covs broad, truncate, relatively fresh, and dusky with relatively distinct and broad, blue edging (Fig. 138), not contrasting in color or wear with the gr covs (Fig. 133F); rects relatively fresh, truncate (Fig. 139A), and dusky with blue edging; amount of white in the outer rects (r5-r6) moderately reduced (Fig. 262A-B); breast medium-bright yellow, sometimes tinged orange.

HY/SY ♂ (Aug-Jul): Lores and auricular dusky blue to blackish; pp-cov and rect criteria as in HY/SY ♀, except that the outer rects (r5-r6) averages more white (Fig. 262A-B); breast medium-bright yellow, often lightly washed orange.

AHY/ASY ♂ (Aug-Jul): Lores and auricular dusky blackish; pp-cov and rect criteria as in AHY/ASY ♀, except that the outer rects (r4-r6) average more white (Fig. 262B-C); breast bright yellow with a moderate orange wash.

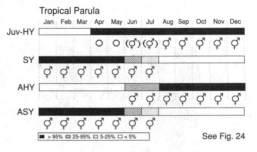

References—Ridgway (1902), Bent (1953), Oberholser (1974), Curson *et al.* (1994), Howell & Webb (1995), Dunn & Garrett (1997), Pyle (1997c), Regelski & Moldenhaur (1997).

Ageing and Sexing *Dendroica* Warblers

Ageing and sexing *Dendroica* warblers generally is complicated by much plumage overlap among the age/sex classes and the fact that most species change plumage at the prealternate molt. By combining plumage and skull with flight-feather condition, molt limits, and the amount of white in the outer rectrices, however, most individuals of this genus should be reliably aged and sexed in both basic and alternate plumages.

Fig. 139A illustrates typical differences in the shape and the amount of wear of the rectrices in both spring and fall. With experience, the shape of the outer primaries (Fig. 140A) is of secondary use, and both these and the rectrices will appear browner in HY/SY birds and blacker in AHY/ASYs, sex for sex (note that ♀♀ average slightly browner feathers than ♂♂, age for age). The shape of the rectrices can show overlap, and their use in ageing usually requires experience. In a few species (*e.g.*, Yellow-rumped, Palm, and Cerulean warblers) shape of the rectrices appears difficult or impossible to use for ageing.

The primary coverts provide one of the more consistent ageing methods; however, season must be considered. In HY/SYs the primary coverts tend to be brownish black with thin edging (the same color as the wings) in fall (Fig. 138A), abrading quickly to brownish with pale brownish edging in spring (Fig. 138C). These will contrast with the slightly fresher, replaced greater coverts (Fig. 134). In AHY/ASYs the primary coverts are black and distinctly edged in fall (Fig. 138B), wearing to brownish black and more thinly edged in spring (Fig. 138D). No contrasts with the greater coverts are apparent in fall and winter (Fig. 133F). A few *Dendroica* species (see accounts) can replace some or all greater coverts during prealternate molts. In these species, the

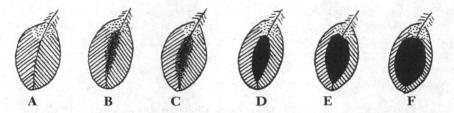

FIGURE 261. Variation in the distinctness of the centers to the back feathers and uppertail coverts, by age and sex (see text for each species), in certain *Dendroica* warblers. Back feathers are shown; see also Figure 268 for uppertail covert differences, and Figure 274 for differences in the back feathers of Bay-breasted and Blackpoll warblers.

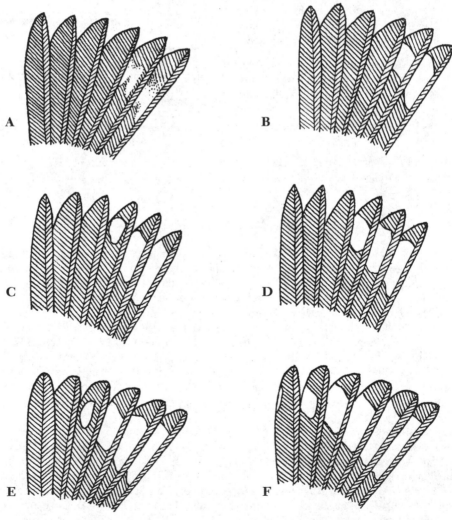

FIGURE 262. Variation in the amount of white in the rectrices, by age and sex (see text for each species), in *Dendroica* and other warblers. The exact patterns of white varies among the species.

primary-covert criteria remain the same; however, contrasts between these and the greater coverts can be found in both age groups (see Fig. 135), so caution is advised.

In many species the blackish centers to the back and uppertail coverts are useful for ageing and sexing (Fig. 261). HY/SY ♀♀ tend to have dusky and indistinct centers, AHY/ASY ♀♀ and HY/SY ♂♂ tend to have moderately distinct and medium sized centers, and AHY/ASY ♂♂ tend to have large and black centers. Note that there is variation in the pattern of the centers among species, and that, in some species, the back feathers and uppertail coverts can be replaced during prealternate molts, so the same criteria may not apply in both fall and spring.

The amount of white in the outer rectrices will provide a final clue for both ageing and sexing most *Dendroica* warblers (see accounts and Fig. 262). AHY/ASY ♂♂ average larger patches than both HY/SY ♂♂ and AHY/ASY ♀♀, which, in turn, average larger patches than HY/SY ♀♀. Age-specific and sex-specific differences in the sizes of these patches vary among the *Dendroica* species; in certain species (*e.g.*, Chestnut-sided, Bay-breasted, and Blackpoll warblers) differences are relatively slight. In all species, there also is significant individual variation within each age/sex class. The amount of white in the rectrices should never be relied upon alone. When combined with the other age/sex criteria, however, it can be quite useful. In the fall, for instance, when skull condition can provide the age, the amount of white in the rectrices should assist with sexing. In the spring, most *Dendroica* warblers are readily sexed by plumage, during which time the amount of white in the rectrices can help with ageing. Quantitative analyses of the amount of white in the rectrices by age and sex (*e.g.*, see Jackson *et al.* 1992) are needed for most species.

The criteria presented in the species accounts should coincide with each other in most cases. Individuals will be found with conflicting characters, however, and these are best left unaged and/or unsexed, especially without experience with the species. Birds in late spring and summer, especially ♀♀, can be difficult or impossible to reliably age due to the increased feather wear associated with breeding.

YELLOW WARBLER
Dendroica petechia

YWAR
Species # 6520
Band size: 0-0A-1C

Species—From all other warblers by medium-large size (wg 55-68, tl 38-50; see **Age/Sex**); indistinct eye ring present, but other facial features lacking; distinct wing bars lacking; outer rects (r5-r6) with a unique yellow pattern (Fig. 263).

Geographic variation—Moderate to well marked (between subspecies groups), but moderately weak and clinal where most ranges in N.Am meet. Subspecies taxonomy follows Browning (1994); see Ridgway (1902), Grinnell (1903, 1914a), Phillips (1911), Batchelder (1918), Swarth (1922, 1935), Peters (1927b), van Rossem (1931a), Griscom (1932), Dickey & van Rossem (1938), Oberholser (1938, 1974), Aldrich (1942), Twomey (1942), Behle (1948, 1985), Dickinson (1953), Phillips *et al.* (1964), Parkes & Dickerman (1967), Monroe (1968), Browning (1978, 1990), Raveling & Warner (1978), Ramos & Warner (1980), Wetmore *et al.* (1984), Godfrey (1986), Wiedenfeld (1991), Cramp & Perrins (1994b), Curson *et al.* (1994), Dunn & Garrett (in press). Twenty-eight other subspecies occur in the W.Indies and Mex-S.Am. Most HYs and ♀♀ will be impossible to separate with the following.

Northern *(D.p. aestiva)* Group. Crown without rufous; p9 ≈ p8 ≈ p7 > p6.

D.p. rubiginosa (br coastal s.AK-sw.BC; vag to FL): Bill long (nares to tip 7.2-8.6); AHY/ASY ♂ with the forecrown and back uniformly dull, dark olive with a yellow wash, and the underparts medium-dull, dark yellow with dark, narrow, and moderately distinct, red streaks; ♀ and HY with the upperparts medium-bright yellow-olive with a dusky wash, and the underparts pale lemon with an olive tinge.

D.p. brewsteri (br coastal WA-CA): AHY/ASY ♂ with the forecrown medium-bright yellow, contrasting slightly with the medium-dark yellow back, and the underparts medium-bright yellow with narrow and sparse, red streaking; ♀ and HY with the upperparts medium olive with a buff wash, and the under-parts medium-bright yellow with an olive wash.

D.p. banksi (br interior c.AK-Yuk): Bill medium in length (from nares to tip 7.1-8.3); AHY/ASY ♂ with the forecrown medium-bright yellow, sometimes washed green, contrasting slightly with the medium-bright yellow-olive back, and the underparts medium-dark yellow with dark, moderately wide, and distinct chestnut streaks; ♀ and HY with the upperparts bright olive with a slight grayish-yellow wash, and the underparts medium-dark yellow with an olive wash.

D.p. morcomi (br interior s.AK-s.CA to n.TX): AHY/ASY ♂ with the forecrown dull yellow, contrasting slightly with the dull, medium-dark yellow-olive back, and the underparts medium-bright yellow with moderately wide and indistinct, red streaking; ♀ and HY with the upperparts dull olive with a buff wash and the underparts pale yellow with an olive wash.

D.p. sonorana (br desert s.NV-se.CA to sw.TX): AHY/ASY ♂ with the forecrown pale lemon-yellow, con-trasting with the pale olive-yellow back, and the underparts pale yellow to whitish yellow, with pale, nar-row, and indistinct, red streaks; ♀ and HY with the upperparts pale grayish olive with a yellow tinge, and the underparts pale yellow to whitish with a buff wash. Birds of n.AZ-n.NM (*"hypochlora"*) may average smaller and darker, but differences represent slight intergradation toward *morcomi*.

D.p. parkesi (br n.AK-n.Ont): Bill short (from nares to tip 6.5-7.9); AHY/ASY ♂ with the forecrown medium-bright yellow, sometimes washed green, contrasting distinctly with the dark olive back, and the underparts medium-dark, dull yellow with dark, moderately wide, and distinct chestnut streaks; ♀ and HY with the upperparts bright olive with a slight grayish-yellow wash, and the underparts medium-dark yellow with an olive wash.

D.p. amnicola (br e.Yuk-ne.BC to Nfl): AHY/ASY ♂ with the forecrown medium-dull yellow, often washed green, contrasting slightly with the dull, dark yellow-olive back, and the underparts medium-dark yellow with dark, moderately wide, and moderately indistinct, red streaks; ♀ and HY with the upperparts dark olive with a grayish-yellow wash, and the underparts medium-dark yellow with an olive wash.

D.p. aestiva (br se.Alb-cs.OK to PEI-SC): AHY/ASY ♂ with the forecrown bright lemon-yellow (rarely tinged orangish), contrasting with the brightish olive-yellow back, and the underparts bright yellow with bright, broad, and moderately distinct, red streaks; ♀ and HY with the upperparts medium-bright olive-yellow, without a grayish tinge, and the underparts bright, pale yellow.

Mangrove (*D.p. erithachorides*) Group. Head of ♂♂ rufous; p9 < p8 ≈ p7 ≈ p6

D.p. oraria (res coastal e.Mex; vag to s.TX): AHY/ASY ♂ with the head rufous; ♀ and HY with the upper-parts pale olive-yellow and the underparts bright pale yellow.

Golden (*D.p. petechia*) Group. Crown of ♂♂ often with rufous; p9 < p8 ≈ p7 ≈ p6.

D.p. gundlachi (res s.FL Is): AHY/ASY ♂ with the forecrown bright yellow, sometimes washed orangish rufous, contrasting with the brightish yellow-olive back, and the underparts bright yellow with bright, broad, and distinct, red streaks; ♀ and HY with the upperparts medium-bright olive-yellow, and the underparts bright medium-pale yellow.

Molt—PB: HY partial (May-Sep), AHY complete (Jun-Sep); PA: SY partial-incomplete (Dec-Apr), ASY partial (Dec-Apr). The PBs occur primarily on the summer grounds; some AHYs occasionally suspend flight-feather replacement during fall migration. The 1st PB (which is largely underway before fledging) includes some to all med covs, 3 to 10 (~89%) inner gr covs, usually the greater alula, and usually (in ~77% of birds) 1-3 terts, but no rects. The 1st PA includes 3 to 10 (~22%) inner gr covs, usually (in ~87% of birds) 1-3 terts, sometimes (in ~22% of birds) s6 and occasionally (in ~8% of birds) s5, but no rects. The adult PA includes 8 to 10 (~88%) inner gr covs and 2-3 terts, but no rects. The PAs may involve continuous, limited body replacement on the winter grounds, from Oct-Apr, as in certain other warblers; however, the gr covs and terts are largely replaced in Mar-Apr.

Skull—Pneumaticization completes in HY from 15 Oct (as early as 15 Sep in populations of CA) through Dec.

Age/Sex—Juv (May-Aug) has plumage washed brownish, obscure dusky-olive streaking to the upperparts, and distinct, buffy-yellow wing bars; juv ♀ = ♂, although some ♂♂ (at least) can be distinguished by the amount of yellow in the rects and by having red streaks in the breast, as in HY/SYs (see below). CP/BP (Apr-Aug). ♀ wg(n100) 55-64, tl(n100) 38-47; ♂ wg(n100) 58-68, tl(n100) 41-50.

Basic Plumage (Aug-Mar)

HY/SY ♀ (Aug-Mar): Forecrown dull greenish yellow or grayish yellow; molt limits occasionally occur among the gr covs (Fig. 133**C-E**; see **Molt**), the retained outer covs worn and brownish yellow with distinct, lemon tips when fresh, contrasting with the slightly fresher, duskier, and indistinctly tipped, replaced inner covs; 1-3 terts often replaced, contrasting with the older middle ss (s4-s6; Fig. 133**D-E**); outer pp covs narrow, tapered, somewhat abraded, and brownish with indistinct, narrow, or no buffy-yellow edging (Fig. 138**A**); outer rects (r5-r6) relatively abraded, tapered (Fig. 139**A**), and brownish with relatively little yellow on the inner webs (Fig. 263**A**); underparts pale yellow, without reddish streaks; base of the lower mandible flesh (through Sep-May?). **Note: Only the dullest HY/SYs, with indicative short wings should be sexed. Many, bright HY/SY ♀♀ (possibly half or more) overlap in plumage with dull HY/SY ♂♂ and should be left unsexed; HY/SYs that lack red streaks are not necessarily ♀♀. See also Geographic variation; sexing is more reliable on HY/SYs of known subspecies.**

AHY/ASY ♀ (Aug-Mar): Forecrown dull to moderately bright yellow, often washed heavily with greenish; wing covs, terts, and ss uniformly adult (Fig. 133**F**) and dusky with yellow or yellow-olive edging; outer pp covs broad, truncate, fresh, and dusky brown with relatively distinct and broad, yellow-olive edging (Fig. 138**B**); rects fresh, truncate (Fig. 139**A**), and dusky with a moderately extensive to extensive amount of yellow on the inner webs (Fig. 263**B-C**); underparts pale to brightish yellow, usually with a few very indistinct, reddish streaks on the upper breast; lower mandible entirely black.

HY/SY ♂ (Aug-Mar): Forecrown dull to moderately bright yellow, often washed heavily with greenish; molt-limit, wing-cov, flight-feather, and mandible criteria as in HY/SY ♀, except that the outer rects (r5-r6) average more yellow to the inner webs (Fig. 263**A-B**); underparts pale to brightish yellow, sometimes with a few (but often no) indistinct, reddish streaks on the upper breast. **Note: Duller HY/SY ♂♂ (up to half) can overlap in plumage with HY/SY ♀♀ (which see), although known, basic-plumaged HY/SYs with reddish streaks on the breast are reliably sexed ♂.**

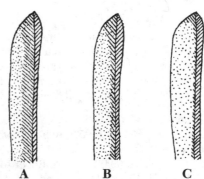

FIGURE 263. Variation in the amount of yellow and brown in the outer rectrices (r4-r6), by age and sex (see text), in Yellow Warbler.

AHY/ASY ♂ (Aug-Mar): Forecrown brightish yellow with a moderate green wash; molt-limit, wing-cov, flight-feather, and mandible criteria as in AHY/ASY ♀, except that the outer rects (r5-r6) average more yellow (Fig. 263**C**); underparts brightish yellow with moderately distinct to distinct, red streaking on the breast and flanks.

Alternate Plumage (Mar-Jul)

SY ♀ (Mar-Jul): Forecrown yellow with a greenish wash, not showing a well-marked contrast with the back coloration; molt limits usually occur among the gr covs (Fig. 133**B-E**; see

Molt), with two or three feather generations present, the retained, juvenal outer covs (if present) worn and brownish, contrasting markedly with the fresher, dusky, and yellow-edged, recently replaced inner covs, with 3-7 intermediate first-basic covs often being present, as well (see Fig. 135); outer pp covs narrow, tapered, abraded, and brown with little or no pale edging (Fig. 138**C**); outer rects (r5-r6) relatively abraded, tapered (Fig. 139**A**), and brownish with restricted yellow on the inner webs (Fig. 263**A**); red streaking of the underparts narrow and indistinct, or lacking. **Note: Intermediates will occur which are not reliably aged.**

ASY ♀ (Mar-Jul): Forecrown and back as in SY ♀; molt limits sometimes occur among the gr covs (Fig. 133**D-E**; see **Molt**), at most two generations present (*cf.* Fig. 135), the retained, adult outer covs dusky brown with moderately worn edging, contrasting slightly (in wear only) with the recently replaced inner covs; outer pp covs broad, truncate, relatively fresh, and dusky brown, usually with distinct but narrow, yellow-olive edging (Fig. 138**D**); outer rects (r5-r6) relatively fresh, truncate (Fig. 139**A**), and brownish dusky with moderately extensive to extensive yellow on the inner web (Fig. 263**B-C**); red streaking of the underparts narrow and moderately indistinct. **Note: See SY ♀.**

SY ♂ (Mar-Jul): Forecrown bright yellow, usually without an orange tinge, and usually contrasting in coloration with the greener back (see **Geographic variation**); molt-limit, wing-cov, and rect criteria as in SY ♀, except that the inner webs of the outer rects (r5-r6) average more yellow (Fig. 263**A-B**); red streaking of the breast and flanks broad and moderately distinct. **Note: See SY ♀.**

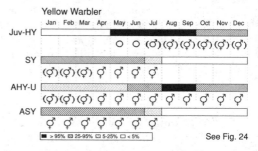

ASY ♂ (Mar-Jul): Forecrown and back as in SY ♂, except that the crown sometimes is tinged orange or red; molt-limit, wing-cov, and rect criteria as in ASY ♀, except that the inner webs of the outer rects (r5-r6) average more yellow (Fig. 263**C**); red streaking of the breast and flanks broad and distinct. **Note: See SY ♀.**

References—Stone (1896), Dwight (1900a), Ridgway (1902), Forbush (1929), Dickey & van Rossem (1938), Bent (1953), Roberts (1955), Southern (1961), Robbins (1964), Wood (1969), Stewart (1972a), Oberholser (1974), Sheppard & Klimkiewicz (1976), Raveling & Warner (1978), Yunick (1984), Studd & Robertson (1985), Rimmer (1988), Francis & Wood (1989), CWS & USFWS (1991), Kaufman (1991b), Parkes (1992a), Cramp & Perrins (1994b), Curson *et al.* (1994), Dunn & Garrett (1997), Pyle (1997c); Mundy & McCracken (unpublished ms.); D. Agro, J. Curson, J.R. King, R.G. McKinney, D. Spector, B. Walker (pers. comm.); IBP (MAPS) data, PNR data, PRBO data.

CHESTNUT-SIDED WARBLER
Dendroica pensylvanica

CSWA
Species # 6590
Band size: 0A-0

Geographic variation—No subspecies are recognized.

Molt—PB: HY partial (Jun-Sep), AHY complete (Jun-Oct); PA partial (Jan-May). The PBs occur mostly on the summer grounds, although the adult PB (at least) may complete on migration or the winter grounds. The 1st PB usually includes all med and gr covs and often the greater alula, but no terts or rects. The 1st PA includes 3 to 10 (~18%) inner gr covs and occasionally (in ~6% of birds) s8 or s9, but no rects. The adult PA includes 5 to 10 (~37%) inner gr covs and occasionally (in ~16% of birds) s8 or s9, but no rects. The PAs may involve continuous, limited body replacement on the winter grounds, from Oct-May, as in certain other warblers.

Skull—Pneumaticization completes in HY from 15 Oct through Dec.

Age/Sex—Juv (Jun-Jul) has brownish-olive upperparts, buffy-yellow wing bars, and dull white underparts; juv ♀ = ♂. CP/BP (May-Aug). ♀ wg(n100) 56-65, tl(n54) 42-49; ♂ wg(n100) 59-68, tl(n38) 44-52.

Basic Plumage (Aug-Mar)

HY/SY ♀ (Aug-Mar): Upperparts dull to medium olive-green, the feathers of the lower back without dusky, or with indistinct, dusky centers (Fig. 261**A-B**); uppertail covs with indistinct, dusky streaks (Fig. 261**B**); outer pp covs narrow, tapered, somewhat abraded, and brownish dusky with indistinct, narrow, or no buffy-grayish edging (Fig. 138**A**), contrasting with the slightly fresher and dusky-centered gr covs (Fig. 134); outer rects (r4-r6) relatively abraded, tapered (Fig. 139**A**), and dusky brown with a relatively small amount of white (Fig. 262**B-C**); sides of the underparts without chestnut. **Note: Only the dullest HY/SYs, with indicative short wings should be sexed. Many HY/SY ♀♀ (possibly half or more) overlap in plumage with dull HY/SY ♂♂ and should be left unsexed. HY/SYs that lack chestnut on the sides of the underparts are not necessarily ♀♀.**

AHY/ASY ♀ (Aug-Mar): Upperparts medium to medium-bright green, the feathers of the lower back with indistinct, blackish centers (Fig. 161**B-C**); uppertail covs with indistinct to distinct but relatively narrow, blackish centers (Fig. 261**C-D**); outer pp covs broad, truncate, fresh, and blackish with relatively distinct and broad, gray edging (Fig. 138**B**), not contrasting in color or wear with the gr covs; outer rects (r4-r6) fresh, truncate (Fig. 139**A**), and dusky with relatively little to a moderate amount of white (Fig. 262**B-D**); chestnut on the sides of the underparts indistinct and limited, sometimes lacking.

HY/SY ♂ (Aug-Mar): Upperparts medium to medium-bright green, the feathers of the back without dusky, or with indistinct, dusky centers (Fig. 261**A-C**); uppertail covs with indistinct to moderately distinct, narrow, blackish centers (Fig. 261**C-D**); pp-cov and rect criteria as in HY/SY ♀, except that the outer rects (r4-r6) average more white (Fig. 262**B-D**); sides of the underparts without chestnut, or with an indistinct chestnut wash. **Note: Dull HY/SY ♂♂ without chestnut on the sides (up to half) can overlap in plumage with HY/SY ♀♀ (which see), although known, basic-plumaged HY/SYs with chestnut in the sides of the underparts are reliably sexed ♂.**

AHY/ASY ♂ (Aug-Mar): Upperparts bright green, the feathers of the lower back with distinct, black centers (Fig. 261**C-D**); uppertail covs with distinct, black centers (Fig. 261**D-E**); pp-cov and rect criteria as in AHY/ASY ♀, except that the outer rects (r3-r6) average more white (Fig. 262**D-E**); sides of the underparts with relatively distinct and extensive chestnut coloration.

Alternate Plumage (Mar-Aug)

SY ♀ (Mar-Aug): Crown greenish yellow, often with some black streaking, and not contrasting with the greenish nape; lores and moustache dull black; outer pp covs narrow, tapered, abraded, and brown with little or no pale edging (Fig. 138**C**); outer rects (r4-r6) relatively abraded, tapered (Fig. 139**A**), and brownish with a relatively small amount of white (Fig. 262**B-C**); chestnut on the sides of the underparts relatively indistinct and restricted, usually not reaching the base of the legs. **Note: Beware that both SYs and ASYs can show contrasting gr covs (and occasionally s8 or s9) in spring (Fig. 133B-D; see Molt). Inter-**

mediates will occur which cannot be reliably aged.

ASY ♀ (Mar-Aug): Crown, lores, moustache, and sides of the underparts as in SY ♀ (perhaps averaging more distinct); outer pp covs broad, truncate, relatively fresh, and dusky brown, usually with distinct but narrow, grayish edging (Fig. 138**D**); outer rects (r4-r6) relatively fresh, truncate (Fig. 139**A**), brownish dusky, and with a relatively large amount of white (Fig. 262**B-D**). **Note: See SY ♀.**

SY ♂ (Mar-Aug): Crown bright yellow and without streaking, contrasting with the blackish nape; lores and moustache black and distinct; pp-cov and rect criteria as in SY ♀, except that the outer rects (r4-r6) average more white (Fig. 262**B-D**); chestnut on the sides of the underparts relatively bold and extensive, usually extending beyond the base of the legs. **Note: See SY ♀.**

ASY ♂ (Mar-Aug): Crown, lores, moustache, and sides of the underparts as in SY ♂ (but averaging bolder and more distinct); pp-cov and rect criteria as in ASY ♀, except that the outer rects (r3-r6) average more white (Fig. 262**D-E**). **Note: See SY ♀.**

Chestnut-sided Warbler

	Jan	Feb	Mar	Apr	May	Jun	Jul	Aug	Sep	Oct	Nov	Dec
Juv-HY						O	(♂)	(♀)	(♀)	(♀)	(♀)	(♀)
SY	(♀)	(♀)	(♀)	♂	♂	♂	♂	♂				
AHY-U	(♀)	(♀)	(♀)	♂	♂	♂	♂	♂	♂	♂	♂	♂
ASY	♂	♂	♂	♂	♂	♂	♂	♂	♂			

■ > 95%   ▨ 25-95%   ▢ 5-25%   ▢ < 5%   See Fig. 24

References—Stone (1896), Dwight (1900a), Ridgway (1902), Forbush (1929), Bent (1953), Roberts (1955), Robbins (1964), Wood (1969), Oberholser (1974), Sheppard & Klimkiewicz (1976), Cramp & Perrins (1994b), Curson *et al.* (1994), Richardson & Brauning (1995), Dunn & Garrett (1997), Pyle (1997c); D. Holmes (pers. comm.); IBP (MAPS) data, PNR data, PRBO data.

MAGNOLIA WARBLER
Dendroica magnolia

MAWA
Species # 6570
Band size: 0A-0

Species—From all other warblers by unique pattern of white in the rects (see Fig. 264).

Geographic variation—No subspecies are recognized.

Molt—PB: HY partial (Jun-Aug), AHY complete (Jun-Sep); PA partial (Jan-May). The PBs occur on the summer grounds. The 1st PB (which largely can complete before fledging) usually includes all med and gr covs and often the greater alula, but no terts or rects. The 1st PA includes 3-9 inner gr covs and occasionally (in ~6% of birds) s8 or s9, but no rects. The adult PA includes 4 to 10 (~25%) inner gr covs and occasionally (in ~20% of birds) s8 or s9, but no rects. The PAs may involve continuous, limited body replacement on the winter grounds, from Oct-May, as in certain other warblers.

Skull—Pneumaticization completes in HY from 15 Oct through Dec.

Age/Sex—Juv (Jun-Aug) has brownish upperparts with distinct, buff wing bars, and buffy-olive underparts that lack streaking; sexing may be possible on some birds by the amount of white on r2, as in HY/SYs (see below). CP/BP (May-Aug). ♀ wg(n100) 53-61, tl(n57) 41-48; ♂ wg(n100) 55-64, tl(n100) 44-51.

Basic Plumage (Aug-Mar)

HY/SY ♀♂ (Aug-Mar): Back feathers without dusky, or with indistinct, dusky centers (Fig.

261**A-B**); outer pp covs narrow, tapered, somewhat abraded, and dusky with indistinct, narrow, or no grayish edging (Fig. 138**A**), contrasting with the slightly fresher and black-centered gr covs (Fig. 134); uppertail covs with indistinct, narrow, dusky centers (Fig. 261**B**), and dull, greenish to bluish edging; outer rects relatively abraded, tapered (Fig. 139**A**), and washed brownish; r2 with a relatively small amount of white (Fig. 264**A**); streaks on the flanks indistinct. **Note: ♀♀ average slightly duller and average slightly smaller white patches on r2 than ♂♂ (Fig. 264A-B), but HY/SYs gen-**

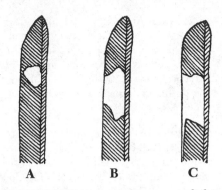

A   B   C

FIGURE 264. Variation in the amount of white in r2, by age and sex (see text), in Magnolia Warbler.

erally are not reliably sexed, except, perhaps, extremes, when all criteria (including wg and tl) are combined. More study is needed on the color of the edging to the uppertail covs (greenish in ♀♀, bluish in ♂♂), as this may prove the most useful sexing criterion for basic-plumaged HY/SYs.

AHY/ASY ♀ (Aug-Mar): Back feathers with small but distinct, black centers (Fig. 261**B-C**); outer pp covs broad, truncate, fresh, and blackish with relatively distinct and broad, blue-gray edging (Fig. 138**B**), not contrasting in wear with the gr covs; uppertail covs with distinct, small blackish centers (Fig. 261**C-D**), and greenish to bluish edging; rects fresh, truncate (Fig. 139**A**), and blackish; r2 with a moderate amount of white (Fig. 264**B**); streaks on the flanks narrow and moderately indistinct.

AHY/ASY ♂ (Aug-Mar): Back feathers with large and distinct, black centers (Fig. 261**D-E**); pp-cov and rect criteria as in AHY/ASY ♀, except that r2 averages blacker and with more white (Fig. 264**C**); uppertail covs with distinct, large black centers (Fig. 261**D-E**) and bluish edging; streaks on the flanks wide and distinct.

Alternate Plumage (Mar-Aug)

SY ♀ (Mar-Aug): Crown usually greenish gray; upper back greenish, the feathers with small and indistinct, black centers (Fig. 261**B-C**); lores and auricular grayish; outer pp covs narrow, tapered, abraded, and brown with little or no pale edging (Fig. 138**C**); outer rects relatively abraded, tapered (Fig. 139**A**), and brownish; r2 with a relatively small amount of white (Fig. 264**A**); streaking on the underparts narrow and relatively indistinct. **Note: Both SYs and ASYs can show contrasting gr covs and (occasionally) s8 or s9 in spring (Fig. 133B-D; see Molt).**

ASY ♀ (Mar-Aug): Crown greenish gray to grayish; upper back greenish to blackish, the feathers with distinct, black centers (Fig. 261**C-F**); lores and auricular grayish to blackish; outer pp covs broad, truncate, relatively fresh, and dusky, usually with distinct but narrow, blue-gray edging (Fig. 138**D**); outer rects relatively fresh, truncate (Fig. 139**A**), and dusky; r2 with a moderate amount of white (Fig. 264**B**); streaking on the underparts narrow and relatively indistinct. **Note: See SY ♀. Also, the plumage of the upperparts and head of bright AHY/ASY ♀♀ can approach that of dull SY ♂♂; confirm sex only after considering age and the boldness of the streaking on the underparts.**

SY ♂ (Mar-Aug): Crown grayish to bluish gray; upper back dull black to greenish with black mottling (Fig. 261**F**); pp-cov and rect criteria as in SY ♀, except that the amount of white on r2 averages more white (Fig. 264**A-B**); lores and auricular blackish; streaking on the underparts moderately wide and distinct. **Note: See SY ♀ and ASY ♀.**

ASY ♂ (Mar-Aug): Crown bluish gray; upper back black; lores and auricular black; pp-cov and rect criteria as in ASY ♀, except that the amount of white on r2 averages more white (Fig. 264C); streaking on the underparts wide and distinct. **Note: See SY ♀.**

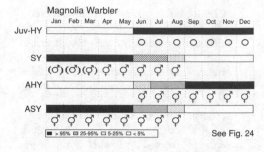

References—Stone (1896), Dwight (1900a), Ridgway (1902), Forbush (1929), Dickey & van Rossem (1938), Bent (1953), Roberts (1955), Woodford & Lovesy (1958), Goodpasture (1963), Robbins (1964), Wood (1969), Oberholser (1974), Sheppard & Klimkiewicz (1976), Smith (1983), Curson *et al.* (1994), Hall (1994), Dunn & Garrett (1997), Pyle (1997c); R.C. Leberman, J.M. Sheppard, R.D. Weir, J.S. Weske (*in litt.* to the BBL); J. Curson, J. Statz (pers. comm.); IBP (MAPS) data, PNR data, PRBO data.

CAPE MAY WARBLER
Dendroica tigrina

CMWA
Species # 6500
Band size: 0-0A-1C

Species—HY/SY ♀ from HY/SY Yellow-rumped Warbler by shorter tl (61-72; see **Age/Sex**); plumage generally tinged greenish; auricular often with some yellow; yellow rump patch indistinct and tinged greenish.

Geographic variation—No subspecies are recognized.

Molt—PB: HY partial (Jun-Aug), AHY complete (Jun-Sep); PA limited (Jan-May). The PBs occur on the summer grounds. The 1st PB usually includes all med and gr covs and often the greater alula, but no terts or rects. The PAs are limited to the body plumage, no wing covs or flight feathers normally being replaced. The PAs may be continuous on the winter grounds, from Oct-May, as in certain other warblers.

Skull—Pneumaticization completes in HY from 15 Oct through Dec.

Age/Sex—Juv (Jun-Aug) has olive-brown upperparts and grayish underparts with dusky mottling or streaking; juv ♀ = ♂, although some extremes possibly can be sexed by the amount of white in the rects, as in HY/SYs (see below). CP/BP (May-Aug). ♀ wg(n39) 61-70, tl(n20) 41-47; ♂ wg(n41) 64-72, tl(n26) 44-49.

HY/SY ♀ (Aug-Jul): Upperparts and underparts washed grayish in Aug-Mar; feathers of the lower back with indistinct or no dusky centers (Fig. 261A-B); auricular and hind neck grayish with little or no yellow in Aug-Mar (tinged yellow in Mar-Aug), auricular without chestnut; gr and med covs with narrow, pale edging (Fig.

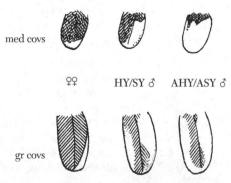

FIGURE 265. The amount of white in the median and greater coverts by age and sex in Cape May Warbler. All juveniles and some HY/SY ♂♂ have coverts resembling those of ♀♀.

265); outer pp covs narrow, tapered, somewhat abraded, and brownish with indistinct, narrow, or no buffy-yellow edging (Fig. 138), contrasting with the slightly fresher and duskier gr covs (Fig. 134); outer rects (r5-r6) relatively abraded, tapered (Fig. 139A), and dusky brown with a relatively small amount of white (Fig. 262A-B). **Note: A few intermediate ♀♀ can occur that are not reliably aged; however, most birds are readily sexed and most ♂♂ aged, in all plumages, by the wing-cov criteria.**

AHY/ASY ♀ (Aug-Jul): Upperparts and underparts washed brownish in Aug-Mar; feathers of the lower back with small and distinct, blackish centers (Fig. 261C); auricular and hindneck washed yellow, the auricular without chestnut; gr and med covs with narrow, whitish edging (Fig. 265); outer pp covs broad, truncate, fresh, and dusky with relatively distinct and broad, yellowish edging (Fig. 138), not contrasting in wear with the gr covs (Fig. 133F); outer rects (r4-r6) fresh, truncate (Fig. 139A), and dusky with a moderate amount of white (Fig. 262B-C). **Note: See HY/SY ♀.**

HY/SY ♂ (Aug-Jul): Cap grayish green with moderate, black streaking in Mar-Aug; upperparts and underparts washed brownish gray in Aug-Mar; feathers of the lower back with moderate, indistinct, blackish centers (Fig. 261B-C); auricular and hindneck washed yellowish, the auricular usually without chestnut (Aug-Mar), or with a restricted, chestnut patch (Mar-Aug); wing-cov and flight-feather criteria as in HY/SY ♀, except that the gr and med covs usually have indistinct, white edging (Fig. 265; the patterns sometimes can approach those of ♀♀), and the outer rects (r4-r6) average more white (Fig. 262B-D). **Note: See HY/SY ♀.**

AHY/ASY ♂ (Aug-Jul): Cap with heavy, black streaking in Mar-Aug; upperparts and underparts yellow in Aug-Mar; feathers of the lower back with large and distinct, black centers (Fig. 261D-E); auricular and hindneck yellow, the auricular with at least some chestnut (Aug-Mar), or with an extensive chestnut patch (Mar-Aug); wing-cov and flight-feather criteria as in AHY/ASY ♀, except that the gr and med covs have broad and distinct, white edging (Fig. 265), and the outer rects (r3-r6) average more white (Fig. 262C-E). **Note: See HY/SY ♀.**

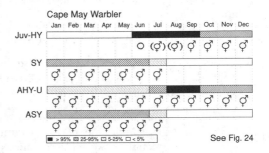

Hybrids reported—Blackpoll Warbler. See also Northern Waterthrush.

References—Stone (1896), Dwight (1900a), Ridgway (1902), Forbush (1929), Bent (1953), Roberts (1955), Robbins (1964), Wood (1969), Oberholser (1974), Sheppard & Klimkiewicz (1976), Parkes (1978, 1995c), Cramp & Perrins (1994b), Curson *et al.* (1994), Dunn & Garrett (1997), Pyle (1997c); M.C. Shieldcastle (*in litt.* to the BBL); PNR data, PRBO data.

BLACK-THROATED BLUE WARBLER
Dendroica caerulescens

BTBW
Species # 6540
Band size: 0-0A

Geographic variation—Subspecies taxonomy follows Mayr & Short (1970), who considered the species monotypic (synonymizing a previously recognized subspecies); see Ridgway (1902), Eifrig (1915), Oberholser (1917d), Monroe (1968), G.R. Graves *in* Holmes (1994). Birds

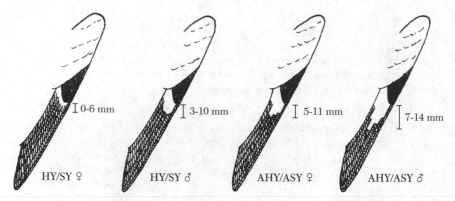

FIGURE 266. The extent and distinctness of the white patch at the base of the primaries by age and sex in Black-throated Blue Warbler.

breeding in montane W.Va-n.GA (*"cairnsi"*) average darker than northern birds, with more black in the upperparts of ♂♂ and bluer wing edging in HY/SY ♂♂, but this difference is broadly clinal.

Molt—PB: HY partial (Jun-Aug), AHY complete (Jul-Sep); PA absent-limited (Jan-May). The PBs occur on the summer grounds. The 1st PB (which largely can complete before fledging) includes all med covs, 8 to 10 (~90%) inner gr covs and rarely (in ~3% of birds) 1-2 terts, but no rects. The PA, if present, is limited to the body plumage, no wing covs or flight feathers being replaced; limited body-feather replacement may also occur in Oct-May, as in certain other warblers.

Skull—Pneumaticization completes in HY/SY from 15 Oct through Jan.

Age/Sex—Juv (Jun-Aug) is like HY/SY ♀ (see **Sex**), but the plumage is heavily washed with brownish; juv ♀=♂, although the distinctive sex-specific plumage of ♂ often is visible before fledging. CP/BP (Apr-Aug). ♀ wg(n100) 58-63, tl(n32) 46-52; ♂ wg(n100) 61-68, tl(n60) 48-54.

HY/SY ♀ (Aug-Jul): Body plumage greenish; molt limits occasionally occur among the gr covs (Fig. 133**D-E**; see **Molt**), the retained outermost covs worn and brown, contrasting with the fresher and greenish-dusky, replaced inner covs; outer greater alula and outer pp covs narrow, tapered, relatively abraded, and brownish with indistinct, narrow, or no green edging (Fig. 138), contrasting with the slightly fresher gr covs (Fig. 134); whitish patch at the base of the pp dingy and extending 0-6 mm from the pp covs (Fig. 266); rects relatively abraded, tapered (Fig. 139**A**), and dusky brown with dull green edging (without bluish); outer rect (r6) with little or no whitish (less than Fig. 262**A**). **Note: Sexing (by body plumage) should be performed before ageing; a few ♀♀ can be difficult to age. Bilateral gynandromorphism (*e.g.*, right side ♀-plumaged, left side ♂-plumaged) has been reported (see Patten 1993, Graves *et al.* 1996).**

AHY/ASY ♀ (Aug-Jul): Body plumage greenish; wing covs, terts, and ss uniformly adult (Fig. 133**F**) and dusky with green edging (sometimes tinged blue); greater alula and outer pp covs broad, truncate, relatively fresh, and dusky with relatively distinct and broad, green edging (Fig. 138), not contrasting markedly in color or wear with the gr covs (Fig. 133**F**); whitish at the base of the pp distinct and extending 3-10 mm from the pp covs (Fig. 266); outer rects (r5-r6) relatively fresh, truncate (Fig. 139**A**), and dusky with the greenish edging sometimes tinged bluish, and with little to a moderate amount of indistinct whitish (see Fig. 262**A-B**). **Note: See HY/SY ♀.**

HY/SY ♂ (Aug-Jul): Body plumage blue, black, and white, the feathers of the upperparts with green tipping; molt limits as in HY/SY ♀, the terts, greater alula, and outer pp covs brownish with indistinct, narrow, or no green edging (Fig. 138), contrasting with the slightly fresher, blackish, and blue-edged gr covs (Fig. 134); whitish at the base of the pp moderately distinct and extending 5-11 mm from the pp covs (Fig. 266); outer rects (r4-r6) relatively abraded, tapered (Fig. 139A), and dusky brown with a moderate amount of indistinct whitish (see Fig. 262B-D). **Note: See HY/SY ♀. HY/SY ♂♂ of darker southern birds (see Geographic variation) show little or no distinctive green edging to the back feathers and wing covs; on these use skull condition (see Skull), pp-cov, pp, and rect criteria.**

AHY/ASY ♂ (Aug-Jul): Body plumage blue, black, and white, the feathers of the upperparts without green; gr covs, terts, greater alula, and outer pp covs uniformly broad, truncate, relatively fresh, and black with relatively distinct and broad, blue edging (Figs. 133F & 138); white at the base of the pp distinct and extending 7-14 mm from the pp covs (Fig. 266); outer rects (r3-r6) truncate (Fig. 139A), fresh, and black with a moderate amount of distinct white (Fig. 262C-E). **Note: See HY/SY ♀ and HY/SY ♂.**

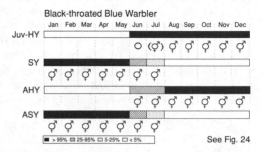

Black-throated Blue Warbler

See Fig. 24

Hybrids reported—Nashville Warbler.

References—Stone (1896), Dwight (1900a), Ridgway (1902), Forbush (1929), Bent (1953), Roberts (1955), Robbins (1964), Hubbard (1965b), Wood (1969), Oberholser (1974), Sheppard & Klimkiewicz (1976), Parkes (1979), CWS & USFWS (1991), Holmes *et al.* (1992), Cramp & Perrins (1994b), Curson *et al.* (1994), Holmes (1994), Graves *et al.* (1996), Dunn & Garrett (1997), Graves (1997), Pyle (1997c); G.R. Mayfield, C. Miller, C.S. Robbins, T. Smith (*in litt.* to the BBL); G.R. Graves, G.E. Wallace (pers. comm.); IBP (MAPS) data, PNR data, PRBO data.

YELLOW-RUMPED WARBLER
Dendroica coronata

See below
Band size: 0-1C-0A

Audubon's Warbler (AUWA)	Species # 6560
Unidentified Yellow-rumped Warbler (UYRW)	Species # 6556
Myrtle Warbler (MYWA)	Species # 6550

Species—HY from HY ♀ Cape May Warbler by longer tl (53-65; see **Geographic variation**); plumage without a greenish tinge; auricular without yellow; rump patch more distinct and brighter yellow.

Geographic variation—Well marked between subspecies groups and ranges fairly well defined, but moderate and clinal within groups. Subspecies taxonomy follows Hubbard (1970b); see also Ridgway (1902), Swarth (1904a, 1922), Taylor (1911), Oberholser (1921b, 1938, 1974), Griscom (1932), Brodkorb (1934), van Rossem (1936c, 1945a), Mailliard (1937), Twomey (1942), Wetmore (1943), Alexander (1945), Packard (1945), Moore (1946b), Rand (1946, 1948b), Godfrey (1951c, 1986), Miller (1955a), Phillips (1959b), Todd (1963), Phillips *et al.* (1964), Sutton (1967), Monroe (1968), Hubbard (1969), Mayr & Short (1970), Kaufman (1979c, 1990a), Barrowclough (1980), Phillips & Chase (1982), Behle (1985), Cramp & Perrins (1994b), Curson *et al.* (1994), Dunn & Garrett (in press). Two other subspecies of the

Audubon's Subspecies Group occur in Mex-C.Am. In the following, subspecies identifications (to subspecies group) of HY/SYs are best made while concurrently synthesizing information on age, sex, and plumage wear. Intergrades between the two subspecies groups are fairly regular, and sometimes can be identified as such by intermediate characters. These have alpha code **UYRW** (see above).

Audubon's (*D.c. auduboni*) Group. Face plain (Fig. 267); throat often with yellow.

D.c. auduboni (br & wint montane c.BC-sw.Sask to s.CA-w.TX; vag to MA-FL): **Audubon's Warbler.** Large; eye line and supercilium absent or indistinct, and auricular grayish brown (HY/SY ♀) to blue (AHY/ASY ♂), and not well defined (Fig. 267); rects with more white by age and sex (Fig. 262**C-F**; see **Age/Sex**); throat of AHY/ASYs and most HY/SY ♂♂ with yellow; breast streaking relatively indistinct. ♀ wg(n100) 68-78, tl(n27) 54-60; ♂ wg(n100) 71-83, tl(n37) 56-65. Birds breeding east of c.BC-sc.CA ("*memorabilis*") average larger and have the head and breast blacker (with less whitish mottling) in AHY/ASY ♂♂, but differences are slight and broadly clinal. Birds of montane s.AZ-s.NM average slightly larger and with more extensive black to the underparts, but differences represent slight intergradation with *nigrifrons* of nw.Mex; look also for possible vagrants of the blacker *nigrifrons* in this area.

Myrtle (*D.c. coronata*) Group. Face marked (Fig. 267); throat without yellow.

D.c. coronata (br AK-n.BC to NFL-MA, wint sw.OR-s.CA to ME-FL): **Myrtle Warbler.** Small; eye line and supercilium distinct, and auricular grayish (HY/SY ♀) to dusky black (AHY/ASY ♂), and well defined (Fig. 267); rects with less white by age and sex (Fig. 262**B-E**; see **Age/Sex**); throat without yellow (rarely a few feathers tinged yellow when fresh); breast streaking relatively distinct. ♀ wg(n100) 65-75, tl(n14) 53-58; ♂ wg(n100) 70-78, tl(n27) 54-60. Birds breeding in AK to sw.NWT-n.BC ("*hooveri*") average marginally larger, blacker underparts in ♂♂, and grayer (rather than browner) upperparts in HY/SYs and ♀♀, but differences are slight and broadly clinal.

Molt—PB: HY partial (Jun-Sep), AHY complete (Jul-Sep); PA partial (Dec-May). The PBs occur on the summer grounds. The 1st PB usually includes all med and gr covs (rarely the outer 1-3 coverts can be retained) and often the greater alula, but no terts or rects. The 1st PA includes 0 (~8%) to 9 inner gr covs, but no terts or rects. The adult PA includes 0 (~6%) to 10 (~18%) inner gr covs, but no terts or rects. The PAs may average slightly more extensive in Audubon's Warblers and ♂♂ than in Myrtle Warblers and ♀♀, and may involve continuous, limited replacement of the body feathers on the winter grounds, from Oct-May, as in certain other warblers.

Skull—Pneumaticization completes in HY/SY from 15 Oct through Jan in Myrtle Warbler, and 15 Sep through Jan in Audubon's Warbler. Look for windows (> 2 mm; Fig. 11**D**) on the top of the skull in some SYs through Feb.

Age/Sex—Juv (May-Aug) has underparts with heavy, dusky streaking; juv ♀ = ♂, although sexing of some birds may be possible by the amount of white in the rects, as in HY/SYs (see below), and (occasional?) juvs of Audubon's Warbler with yellow in the throat can be sexed ♂. CP/BP: Myrtle (May-Aug), Audubon's (Apr-Aug). See **Geographic variation** for measurements within each subspecies group.

Audubon's

Myrtle

FIGURE 267. The facial pattern by subspecies in Yellow-rumped Warbler. Intergrades, with intermediate features, can be identified, with experience.

Basic Plumage (Aug-Mar)

HY/SY ♀ (Aug-Mar): Upperparts without gray; back feathers usually with narrow and indistinct, dusky centers (Figs. 261A-B & 268A), the uppertail covs edged brown (without bluish gray); auricular brownish without black mottling; lesser covs edged brown; gr covs brown with buff corners; outer pp covs narrow, tapered, somewhat abraded, and brown with indistinct, narrow, or no pale buffy-brown edging (Fig. 138A), contrasting

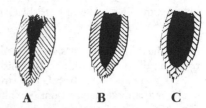

FIGURE 268. Variation in the centers to the uppertail coverts, by age and sex (see text), in Yellow-rumped Warbler. The color of the edging also varies, from brown or grayish-brown in ♀♀ to brownish blue or blue in ♂♂.

with the slightly fresher gr covs (Fig. 134); outer rects (r4-r6) relatively abraded, somewhat tapered (Fig. 139A), and dusky brown with a relatively small amount of white by subspecies group (Fig. 262C-D in Audubon's, Fig. 262B-C in Myrtle). **Note: The plumages of this species are variable and complex such that (except for sexing in spring) all criteria should coincide, and subspecies information should be synthesized, before reliable determinations are made; many intermediates cannot be reliably aged or sexed. Note that the flight feathers of ♀♀ average slightly browner than those of ♂♂, in both age groups. There is also more overlap in rect shape by age (Fig. 139A) in this species than in the other *Dendroica* warblers, but this still can be helpful with extremes, in combination with wear, and/or with experience by the handler.**

AHY/ASY ♀ (Aug-Mar): Upperparts usually tinged bluish gray; black centers to the back feathers and uppertail covs small and moderately indistinct (Figs. 261B-D & 268A-B), the uppertail covs edged brown or brown mixed with bluish gray; auricular grayish, without black mottling; lesser covs usually edged brown; gr covs dusky with a whitish fringe; outer pp covs broad, truncate, relatively fresh, and dusky with relatively distinct and broad, grayish edging (Fig. 138B), not contrasting in wear with the gr covs (Fig. 133F); outer rects (r3-r6) fresh, somewhat truncate (Fig. 139A), and dusky with a moderate amount of white by subspecies group (Fig. 262D-F in Audubon's, Fig. 262C-D in Myrtle). **Note: See HY/SY ♀.**

HY/SY ♂ (Aug-Mar): Upperparts usually tinged or washed bluish gray; black centers to the back feathers and uppertail covs small and moderately indistinct (Figs. 261B-D & 268A-B), the uppertail covs with mixed bluish and brown (usually) to bluish edging; auricular brownish, without black mottling; lesser covs usually edged bluish gray; gr covs brownish with buff corners; pp-cov and rect criteria as in HY/SY ♀, except that the outer rects (r3-r6) average duskier and with more white by subspecies group (Fig. 262D-F in Audubon's, Fig. 262B-D in Myrtle). **Note: See HY/SY ♀.**

AHY/ASY ♂ (Aug-Mar): Upperparts blue, heavily washed grayish; back feathers and uppertail covs with large black centers (Figs. 261D-E & 268C), the uppertail covs with bluish edging; auricular often mottled blackish; lesser covs edged bluish gray; gr covs blackish with a white fringe; pp-cov and rect criteria as in AHY/ASY ♀, except that the feather base color is blackish and the outer rects (r2-r6) average more white by subspecies group (Fig. 262F in Audubon's, Fig. 262D-E in Myrtle). **Note: See HY/SY ♀.**

Alternate Plumage (Mar-Jul)

SY ♀ (Mar-Jul): Upperparts and auricular brownish, sometimes tinged gray; outer pp covs narrow, tapered, abraded, and brown with little or no pale edging (Fig. 138C); outer rects (r4-r6) relatively abraded, somewhat tapered (Fig. 139A), and brownish with a relatively small amount of white by subspecies group (Fig. 262C-D in Audubon's, Fig. 262B-C in Myrtle);

breast with indistinct to distinct, black streaking but without a complete black band. **Note: See HY/SY ♀, above.**

ASY ♀ (Mar-Jul): Upperparts and auricular brownish with a gray wash; outer pp covs broad, truncate, relatively fresh, and brownish dusky, usually with distinct, grayish edging (Fig. 138**D**); outer rects (r3-r6) relatively fresh, somewhat truncate (Fig. 139**A**), and brownish dusky with a moderate amount of white by subspecies group (Fig. 262**D-F** in Audubon's, Fig. 262**C-D** in Myrtle); breast with distinct, black streaking but without a complete black band. **Note: See HY/SY ♀, above.**

SY ♂ (Mar-Jul): Upperparts bluish gray, often tinged brownish; auricular black (Myrtle), or dark bluish gray (Audubon's), sometimes tinged brownish; wing-cov and flight-feather criteria as in SY ♀, except that the outer rects (r3-r6) average duskier and with more white by subspecies group (Fig. 262**D-F** in Audubon's, Fig. 262**B-D** in Myrtle); breast with a wide, complete or nearly complete, black band. **Note: See HY/SY ♀, above.**

ASY ♂ (Mar-Jul): Upperparts bluish gray; auricular black (Myrtle), or dark bluish gray (Audubon's); molt-limit, wing-cov, and flight-feather criteria as in ASY ♀, except that the outer rects (r2-r6) average blacker and with more white by subspecies group (Fig. 262**F** in Audubon's, Fig. 262**D-E** in Myrtle); breast with a wide, complete black band. **Note: See HY/SY ♀, above.**

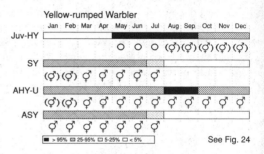

Hybrids reported—Northern Parula, Grace's Warbler, Pine Warbler, Bay-breasted Warbler. Possibly Townsend's Warbler.

References—Stone (1896), Dwight (1900a), Ridgway (1902), Forbush (1929), Dickey & van Rossem (1938), Graber & Graber (1951), Bent (1953), Roberts (1955), Robbins (1964), Yarbrough & Johnston (1965), Hubbard (1969, 1970b, 1980), Wood (1969), Fisk (1970, 1973c), Oberholser (1974), Sheppard & Klimkiewicz (1976), Banks & Baird (1978), Kaufman (1979c), Prescott (1981), Parkes (1985b, 1988a), Phillips (1986), Bledsoe (1988), Yunick (1989), Graves (1993), Curson *et al.* (1994), Dunn & Garrett (1997), Pyle (1997c); D. Beimborn, C.S. Robbins, F.S. Schaeffer, R.B.H. Smith (*in litt.* to the BBL); K. Burk, K. Burton, P.H. Homann, J. Statz, B. Walker (pers. comm.); IBP (MAPS) data, PNR data, PRBO data.

BLACK-THROATED GRAY WARBLER
Dendroica nigrescens

BTYW
Species # 6650
Band size: 0A-0

Geographic variation—Weak and largely based on size. Subspecies taxonomy follows Morrison (1990); see also Oberholser (1930a, 1974), van Rossem (1945a), Parkes (1953b), Phillips *et al.* (1964), Mayr & Short (1970), Morrison (1982), Behle (1985), Curson *et al.* (1994), Dunn & Garrett (in press). No other subspecies occur.

D.n. nigrescens (br coastal sw.BC-wc.CA, wint sw.CA): Averages small; upperparts often tinged brownish when fresh; white patches in the rects average smaller (white on the inner web of r5 extending 27-39 mm from the tip). ♀ wg(n83) 56-62, tl(n21) 45-51; ♂ wg(n100) 58-65, tl(n35) 46-53.

D.n. halseii (br interior s.BC-sc.CA to WY-sw.TX): Averages large; upperparts gray with little or no brownish when fresh; white patches in the rects average larger (white on the inner web of r5 extending 33-52 mm from the tip). ♀ wg(n15) 59-66, tl(n10) 48-54; ♂ wg(n17) 61-68, tl(n15) 49-56.

Molt—PB: HY partial (May-Aug), AHY complete (Jul-Aug); PA limited (Jan-Apr). The PBs occur on the summer grounds. The 1st PB usually includes all med and gr covs and often the greater alula, but no terts or rects. The PAs are limited to feathers of the head, and may be continuous from Oct-Apr, as in certain other warblers.

Skull—Pneumaticization completes in HY from 1 Oct through Dec.

Age/Sex—Juv (May-Aug) is similar to HY/SY ♀ (see below), but has considerably browner upperparts; juv ♀ = ♂, although some birds (of known subspecies) perhaps can be sexed by the amount of white in the rects, as in HY/SYs (see below). CP/BP (Apr-Aug). ♀ wg(n100) 56-66, tl(n49) 45-54; ♂ wg(n100) 58-69, tl(n70) 46-56; see **Geographic variation**.

HY/SY ♀ (Aug-Jul): Crown and back feathers gray with indistinct, narrow, dusky centers (Fig. 261**B**); auricular dull dusky gray with blackish mottling in Mar-Jul; white tips to the med covs with small shaft streaks (Fig. 270**B**); outer pp covs narrow, tapered, relatively abraded, and brownish with indistinct, narrow, or no grayish-brown edging (Fig. 138), contrasting with the slightly fresher, blackish, and white-tipped gr covs (Fig. 134); outer rects (r3-r6) relatively abraded, tapered (Fig. 139**A**), and dusky brown with a relatively small amount of white (Fig. 262**D-E** by subspecies; see **Geographic variation**); chin and throat white with little or no black (Aug-Mar), or chin white and throat mottled white and black (Mar-Jul; Fig. 269); streaking on the flanks narrow and indistinct. **Note: Most birds should be reliably aged and sexed, although a few ♀♀ can be hard to age, especially in spring.**

AHY/ASY ♀ (Aug-Jul): Crown mixed gray and black; back feathers with moderately large and fairly distinct, black centers (Fig. 261**C-E**); auricular gray to blackish; white tips to the med covs with small or no shaft streaks (Fig. 270**B-C**); outer pp covs broad, truncate, relatively fresh, and dusky or blackish, with relatively distinct and broad, gray edging (Fig. 138), not contrasting markedly in color or wear with the gr covs (Fig. 133**F**); outer rects (r3-r6) relatively fresh, truncate (Fig. 139**A**), and dusky with a moderate amount of white (Fig. 262**E-F** by subspecies; see **Geographic variation**); chin primarily white and throat mixed black and white (Fig. 269); streaking on the flanks moderately narrow and indistinct. **Note: See HY/SY ♀.**

HY/SY ♂ (Aug-Jul): Crown and auricular mixed gray and black (Aug-Mar), or mostly to entirely black (Mar-Jul); back feathers with moderately large and fairly distinct, black centers (Fig. 261**C-D**); white tips to the med covs usually without shaft streaks (Fig. 270**C**); pp-cov and rect criteria as in HY/SY ♀, except that the outer rects (r3-r6) average more white (Fig. 262**E-F** or more by subspecies; see **Geographic variation**); chin primarily white and throat mixed black and white (Aug-Mar), or chin and throat black (Fig. 269), often with some whitish or dusky mottling (Mar-Jul); streaking on the flanks moderately wide and distinct. **Note: See HY/SY ♀.**

AHY/ASY ♂ (Aug-Jul): Crown, auricular, chin, and throat black (Fig. 269), the feathers tipped gray in Aug-Dec; back feathers with large and distinct, black centers (Fig. 261**D-F**); pp-cov and rect criteria as in AHY/ASY ♀, except that the

♀ (Mar-Aug) ♂ (Mar-Aug)

FIGURE 269. The distinctness of the throat patch by sex in AHY/ASY and alternate-plumaged (Mar-Aug) Black-throated Gray Warblers.

outer rects (r2-r6) average more white (Fig. 262F or more depending on the subspecies; see **Geographic variation**); streaking on the flanks wide and distinct. **Note: See HY/SY ♀.**

Hybrids reported—Townsend's Warbler.

References—Ridgway (1902), Bent (1953), Robbins (1964), Oberholser (1974), Morrison (1982), Curson *et al.* (1994), Rohwer (1994), Dunn & Garrett (1997), Pyle (1997c); IBP (MAPS) data, PRBO data.

Black-throated Gray Warbler

See Fig. 24

TOWNSEND'S WARBLER
Dendroica townsendi

TOWA
Species # 6680
Band size: 0A-0

Species—From Hermit, Black-throated Green, and Golden-cheeked warblers by upperparts olive-green with fairly distinct and large, blackish to black centers to the feathers by age/sex class (Fig. 261**B-E**; see **Age/Sex**); well-defined auricular patch present; sides of the breast with streaking; lower belly and vent without yellow. Beware that juv Hermit Warbler can have a fairly well-defined auricular patch; juv Townsend's is separated by having a distinct, yellowish supercilium and a lack of yellow on the forecrown. Also, beware of hybrids with Hermit Warbler, which can show any combination of traits between the two species.

Geographic variation—No subspecies are recognized. Birds breeding in the Queen Charlotte Is, BC (and possibly north to coastal se.AK) and wintering to coastal c.CA average slightly shorter wg (59-67; see **Age/Sex**) and longer bills (nares to tip 6.5-7.3) than those breeding elsewhere in N.Am and wintering in Mex (wg 62-70, bill nares to tip 6.4-7.2); however, differences (as now known) are too slight to warrant subspecies recognition. See Grinnell (1905a), Morrison (1983).

Molt—PB: HY partial (Jun-Aug), AHY complete (Jul-Sep); PA limited (Jan-May). The PBs occur primarily on the summer grounds. The 1st PB usually includes all med and gr covs and often the greater alula, but no terts or rects. The 1st PA occasionally (in ~15% of birds) includes 1-2 inner gr covs but no med covs. Otherwise, the PAs are limited primarily to the head and upperparts and may be continuous from Oct-May, as in certain other warblers.

Skull—Pneumaticization completes in HY from 15 Oct through Dec.

Age/Sex—Juv (Jun-Aug) has the head and upperparts strongly washed brownish; juv ♀=♂, although some birds perhaps can be sexed by the amount of white in the rects, as in HY/SYs (see below). CP/BP (May-Aug). ♀ wg(n100) 59-68, tl(n100) 45-52; ♂ wg(n100) 62-70, tl(n100) 47-53; see **Geographic variation**.

HY/SY ♀ (Aug-Jul): Crown and auricular primarily olive (Aug-Mar), or olive with slight blackish mottling (Mar-Jul); back feathers with small and indistinct, black centers (Fig. 261**B-C**); med covs usually with wide, black streaks through the white tips (Fig. 270**A**); outer pp covs narrow, tapered, relatively abraded (Fig. 138), and brownish, contrasting with the slightly fresher and black-centered gr covs (Fig. 134); outer rects (r4-r6) relatively abraded, tapered (Fig. 139**A**), and dusky brown with a relatively small amount of white (Fig. 262**B-C**); chin and throat primarily yellow, the throat lightly mottled blackish in Mar-Jul. **Note: The amount of white in the outer rects (r4-r6) may vary more in coastal populations than in mountain** populations (see Geographic variation); more study is needed. Reliable ageing and sexing of hybrids with Hermit Warbler are possible using most of these criteria (see Jackson *et al.* 1992). Most birds should be reliably aged and sexed, although a few ♀♀ can be hard to age, especially in spring.

A   B   C

FIGURE 270. Variation in the pattern of the median coverts, by age and sex (see text), in certain *Dendroica* warblers.

AHY/ASY ♀ (Aug-Jul): Crown and auricular mottled dull blackish and olive; back feathers with fairly distinct, moderately large black centers (Fig. 261C-E); med covs with narrow, black streaks through the white tips, or (occasionally) without black streaks (Fig. 270B-C); outer pp covs broad, truncate, relatively fresh (Fig. 138), and dusky blackish, not contrasting markedly in color or wear with the gr covs; outer rects (r4-r6) relatively fresh, truncate (Fig. 139A), and dusky with little to a moderate amount of white (Fig. 262B-D); chin usually yellow; throat mottled black and yellow. **Note: See HY/SY ♀.**

HY/SY ♂ (Aug-Jul): Crown and auricular mottled dull blackish and olive (Aug-Mar), or primarily blackish (Mar-Jul); back feathers with fairly distinct, moderately large black centers (Fig. 261C-D); med covs usually with narrow, black streaks through the white tips (Fig. 270B); pp-cov and rect criteria as in HY/SY ♀, except that the outer rects (r4-r6) average more white (Fig. 262BD; the area of white on r4 0-100 sq mm); chin usually yellow and throat mottled black and yellow (Aug-Mar), or chin and throat entirely or primarily black, often with light yellow mottling (Mar-Jul). **Note: See HY/SY ♀.**

AHY/ASY ♂ (Aug-Jul): Crown, auricular, chin, and throat black, the feathers with narrow, yellow or green edging in Aug-Dec; back feathers with large and distinct, black centers (Fig. 261D-E); med covs uniformly bright white proximally, or with indistinct, black streaks on a few covs only (Fig. 270B-C); pp-cov and rect criteria as in AHY/ASY ♀, except that the outer rects (r3-r6) average more white (Fig. 262D-E; the area of white on r4 60-250 sq mm). **Note: See HY/SY ♀.**

Hybrids reported—Black-throated Gray Warbler, Hermit Warbler Black-throated Green Warbler. Possibly Yellow-rumped (Myrtle) Warbler. Hybrids with Hermit Warbler have alpha code **THWH** and **Species # 6686**.

Townsend's Warbler

[figure: seasonal bar chart by age/sex class — Juv-HY, SY, AHY, ASY with months Jan–Dec; legend: ■ > 95% ▨ 25-95% ▦ 5-25% □ < 5%. See Fig. 24]

References—Ridgway (1902), Brooks (1934), Jewett (1944b), Bent (1953), Phillips (1959b, 1986), Robbins (1964), Oberholser (1974), Morrison (1983), Morrison & Hardy (1983), Parkes (1988b), Jackson *et al.* (1992), Curson *et al.* (1994), Rohwer (1994), Dunn & Garrett (1997), Pyle (1997c); J. Dierschke, A.R. Phillips (pers. comm.); IBP (MAPS) data, PRBO data.

HERMIT WARBLER
Dendroica occidentalis

HEWA
Species # 6690
Band size: 0A

Species—From Townsend's, Black-throated Green, and Golden-cheeked warblers in all plumages by upperparts grayish to olive, without strong greenish tones, and with moderately large and distinct, dusky to black feather centers by age/sex class (Fig. 261B-F; see **Age/Sex**);

well-defined auricular patch lacking (non-juvs; see below); distinct eye line lacking; underparts without strong yellow coloration; streaking to the sides of the breast and flanks indistinct or lacking. Beware that juvs can have a fairly well-defined auricular patch; these are separated from Townsend's Warblers by the lack of a distinct supercilium and the presence of yellow on the forecrown. Also, beware of hybrids with Townsend's Warbler, which can show any combination of traits between the two species. HY/SY ♀♀ from Olive Warbler by shorter wing (59-71; see **Age/Sex**); reduced p10 absent; white at the base of the pp lacking; tail squarer (r6 − r1 ≤ 3.5 mm).

Geographic variation—No subspecies are recognized. See Morrison (1982).

Molt—PB: HY partial (Jun-Aug), AHY complete (Jun-Aug); PA limited (Jan-Apr). The PBs occur on the summer grounds. The 1st PB usually includes all med and gr covs and often the greater alula, but no terts or rects. The 1st PA sometimes (in ~30% of birds) includes 1-3 inner gr covs but no med covs. The PAs are otherwise limited primarily to the feathers of the head and upperparts, and may be continuous from Oct-Apr, as in certain other warblers.

Skull—Pneumaticization completes in HY from 1 Oct through Dec.

Age/Sex—Juv (Jun-Aug) resembles HY/SY ♀ (see below), but has upperparts washed brownish, underparts buff, face with little or no yellow, and (often) a well-defined, brownish auricular patch; juv ♀ = ♂, although some birds perhaps can be sexed by the amount of white in the outer rects (r4-r6), as in HY/SYs (see below). CP/BP (Apr-Aug). ♀ wg(n100) 59-67, tl(n21) 45-51; ♂ wg(n100) 62-71, tl(n35) 48-53.

HY/SY ♀ (Aug-Jul): Forehead and auricular extensively (Aug-Mar), or lightly (Mar-Jul) washed olive; back feathers and uppertail covs with very indistinct or no dusky centers (Fig. 261A-B); white tipping to the med covs with black triangular centers (Fig. 270A); outer pp covs narrow, tapered, relatively abraded, and brownish, usually without pale edging (Fig. 138), contrasting with the slightly fresher gr covs (Fig. 134); outer rects (r4-r6) relatively abraded, tapered (Fig. 139A), and dusky brown with a relatively small amount of white (Fig. 262B-C); chin and throat buffy white with very little or no black mottling (Aug-Mar), or chin and throat mottled yellow and black (Mar-Jul). **Note: Some overlap can occur with HY/SY ♂ in Aug-Mar; the amount of black in the back feathers and uppertail covs seems the most reliable criterion; compare with the pattern of white in the outer rects (r4-r6) and wg. Most birds should be reliably aged, although a few ♀♀ can be difficult to separate, especially in spring. Reliable ageing and sexing of hybrids with Townsend's Warbler are possible using most of these criteria (see Jackson *et al.* 1992).**

AHY/ASY ♀ (Aug-Jul): Forehead and auricular yellowish with an indistinct olive wash in Aug-Mar; back feathers and uppertail covs with relatively distinct, small blackish centers (Fig. 261C-D); white tipping to the med covs usually with moderately thin, black shaft streaks (occasionally all white; Fig. 270B-C); outer pp covs broad, truncate, relatively fresh, and blackish with narrow, gray edging (Fig. 138), not contrasting in wear with the gr covs (Fig. 133F); outer rects (r4-r6) relatively fresh, truncate (Fig. 139A), and dusky with a moderate amount of white (Fig. 262C-D); chin buffy white or yellowish with black mottling in Mar-Aug; throat black with buff mottling. **Note: See HY/SY ♀.**

HY/SY ♂ (Aug-Jul): Forehead and auricular yellow with an indistinct, olive wash in Aug-Mar; back feathers and uppertail covs with relatively distinct and moderately large, blackish centers (Fig. 261C-E); white tipping to the med covs usually with moderately thin, black shaft streaks (Fig. 270B); pp-cov and rect criteria as in HY/SY ♀, except that the outer rects (r4-r6) average more white (Fig. 262C-D; the area of the white patch in r4 0-55 sq mm); chin buffy white or yellowish and throat buffy, usually with noticeable black mottling (Aug-Mar), or chin and throat black, sometimes with light, yellow mottling (Mar-Jul). **Note: See HY/SY ♀.**

AHY/ASY ♂ (Aug-Jul): Forehead and auricular primarily yellow with little or no blackish or olive; back feathers and uppertail covs with large black centers (Fig. 261**D-F**); med covs uniformly pure white proximally, or with indistinct streaks on a few covs only (Fig. 270**B-C**); pp-cov and rect criteria as in AHY/ASY ♀, except that the outer rects (r3-r6) average more white (Fig. 262**D-E**; the area of the white patch on r4 45-225 sq mm); chin and throat black with thin, yellowish or whitish tips in Aug-Dec. **Note: See HY/SY ♀.**

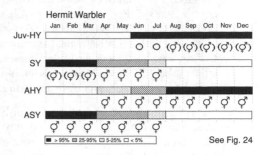

Hybrids reported—Townsend's Warbler, hybrids with which have alpha code **THWH** and **Species # 6686**.

References—Ridgway (1902), Jewett (1944b), Bent (1953), Phillips (1959b, 1986), Robbins (1964), Oberholser (1974), Morrison (1982), Morrison & Hardy (1983), Parkes (1988b), Jackson *et al.* (1992), Curson *et al.* (1994), Dunn & Garrett (1997), Pyle (1997c); J.R. King, A.R. Phillips (pers. comm.); IBP (MAPS) data, PRBO data.

BLACK-THROATED GREEN WARBLER

Dendroica virens

BTNW
Species # 6670
Band size: 0A-0

Species—From Townsend's, Hermit, and Golden-cheeked warblers by upperparts green, without or with much smaller, dusky to blackish centers to the feathers by age/sex class (Fig. 261**A-C**; see **Age/Sex**); distinct auricular patch and eye line lacking; vent with a yellow patch; black mottling and streaking to the sides of the breast and flanks distinct.

Geographic variation—Weak, but ranges well defined. Subspecies taxonomy follows Morse (1993); see also Bangs (1918), Monroe (1968), Mayr & Short (1970), Oberholser (1974), Curson *et al.* (1994), Dunn & Garrett (in press). No other subspecies occur.

> *D.v. virens* (br throughout most of the range in N.Am): Averages large; bill long (exp culmen 8.9-10.5); upperparts medium-bright olive with a yellow tinge; black throat of ♂♂ extensive, usually extending uniformly to the flanks. ♀ wg(n40) 54-64, tl(n10) 45-49; ♂ wg(n41) 60-68, tl(n10) 47-51.
>
> *D.v. waynei* (br coastal se.VA-e.SC): Averages small; bill short (exp culmen 8.1-8.9); upperparts medium-dull olive with little or no yellow; black throat of ♂♂ reduced, usually not extending uniformly to the flanks. ♀ wg(n10) 52-61, tl(n10) 43-47; ♂ wg(n10) 57-65, tl(n10) 45-49.

Molt—PB: HY partial (Jun-Aug); AHY complete (Jul-Sep); PA limited (Jan-May). The PBs occur on the summer grounds. The 1st PB usually includes all med and gr covs and often the greater alula, but no terts or rects. The PAs sometimes (~31% in SYs and ~23% in ASYs) include 1-3 inner gr covs but no med covs. Otherwise, the PAs are limited primarily to the head and upperparts and may be continuous from Oct-May, as in certain other warblers.

Skull—Pneumaticization completes in HY from 1 Oct (as early as 15 Sep in *D.v. waynei*; see **Geographic variation**) through Dec.

Age/Sex—Juv (Jun-Aug) resembles HY/SY ♀ (see below), but has upperparts washed brownish, underparts buff, and yellow in the face reduced; juv ♀=♂, although some birds perhaps can be sexed by the amount of white in the outer rects (r4-r6), as in HY/SYs (see below). CP/BP (Apr-Aug). ♀ wg(n60) 52-64, tl(n20) 43-49; ♂ wg(n61) 57-68, tl(n20) 45-51; see **Geographic variation**.

HY/SY ♀ (Aug-Jul): Upperparts brownish olive, the feathers without dusky centers (Fig. 261**A**); med covs with thick, black shaft streaks (Fig. 270**A**); outer pp covs narrow, tapered, relatively abraded (Fig. 138), and brownish, contrasting with the slightly fresher and black-centered gr covs (Fig. 134); outer rects (r4-r6) relatively abraded, tapered (Fig. 139**A**), and dusky brown with a relatively small amount of white (Fig. 262**B-C**); chin and throat whitish with little or no black mottling; upper breast whitish (Aug-Mar), or yellowish with light, black mottling (Mar-Jul). **Note: Most birds should be reliably aged and sexed, although a few ♀♀ can be hard to age, especially in spring.**

AHY/ASY ♀ (Aug-Jul): Back feathers greenish olive without dusky, or with indistinct, dusky centers (Fig. 261**A-B**); med covs with thin or thick, black shaft streaks (Fig. 270**A-B**); outer pp covs broad, truncate, relatively fresh (Fig. 138), and dusky, not contrasting markedly in color or wear with the gr covs; outer rects (r4-r6) relatively fresh, truncate (Fig. 139**A**), and dusky with a moderate amount of white (Fig. 262**C-D**); chin whitish to yellow, without black mottling; lower throat and upper breast with indistinct, black mottling, often concealed in Aug-Dec. **Note: See HY/SY ♀.**

HY/SY ♂ (Aug-Jul): Back feathers greenish olive, without dusky or with indistinct, dusky centers (Fig. 261**A-B**); med covs often with thin or (sometimes) thick, black shaft streaks (Fig. 270**A-B**); pp-cov and rect criteria as in HY/SY ♀, except that the outer rects (r4-r6) average more white (Fig. 262**C-D**); chin usually yellow, without black mottling (Aug-Mar), or black, often with light, yellow mottling (Mar-Jul); lower throat and upper breast black with extensive yellow mottling in Aug-Mar. **Note: See HY/SY ♀.**

AHY/ASY ♂ (Aug-Jul): Back feathers green with small but distinct, black centers (Fig. 261**C**); med covs usually without black shaft streaks (Fig. 270**C**); pp-cov and rect criteria as in AHY/ASY ♀, except that the outer rects (r3-r6) average more white (Fig. 262**D-F**); chin, throat, and upper breast extensively black with narrow, yellow tipping in Aug-Mar. **Note: See HY/SY ♀.**

Hybrids reported—Townsend's Warbler. Possibly Black-and-white Warbler.

References—Stone (1896), Dwight (1900a), Ridgway (1902), Forbush (1929), Bent (1953), Roberts (1955), Robbins (1964), Wood (1969), Oberholser (1974), Sheppard & Klimkiewicz (1976), Morse (1993), Curson *et al.* (1994), Rohwer (1994), Dunn & Garrett (1997), Pyle (1997c); G.A. Hall, J.S. Weske (*in litt.* to the BBL); IBP (MAPS) data, PNR data, PRBO data.

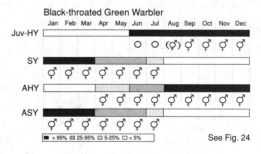

See Fig. 24

GOLDEN-CHEEKED WARBLER
Dendroica chrysoparia

GCWA
Species # 6660
Band size: 0A

Species—From Townsend's, Hermit, and Black-throated Green warblers by upperparts olive with large and distinct, blackish centers to feathers by age/sex class (Fig. 261**B-F**; see **Age/Sex**); distinct auricular patch lacking; distinct, black or blackish eye line present in all plumages;

underparts (including the vent area) without yellow. Beware of hybrids between Townsend's and Hermit warblers (which see), that might resemble this species.

Geographic variation—No subspecies are recognized.

Molt—PB: HY partial (Jun-Aug), AHY complete (Jun-Aug); PA limited (Jan-Apr). The PBs occur on the summer grounds. The 1st PB usually includes all med and gr covs and often the greater alula, but no terts or rects. The PAs sometimes (~50% in SYs and ~33% in ASYs) include 1-4 inner gr covs but no med covs. The PAs are otherwise limited to the body and may be continuous on the winter grounds, from Oct-Apr, as in certain other warblers.

Skull—Pneumaticization completes in HY from 1 Sep through Nov.

Age/Sex—Juv (Jun-Aug) has upperparts washed brownish and underparts buff; juv ♀ = ♂, although some birds perhaps can be sexed by the amount of white in the outer rects (r4-r6), as in HY/SYs (see below). CP/BP (Apr-Aug). ♀ wg(n35) 58-65, tl(n8) 46-52; ♂ wg(n32) 61-69, tl(n12) 49-55.

HY/SY ♀ (Aug-Jul): Crown and eye line olive with indistinct, dusky streaking (Aug-Mar), or with blackish flecking (Mar-Jul); back feathers and uppertail covs with indistinct dusky centers (Fig. 261**B-C**); white tipping to the med covs with black triangular centers (Fig. 270**A**); outer pp covs narrow, tapered, relatively abraded, and brownish with indistinct, narrow, or no pale grayish-brown edging (Fig. 138), contrasting with the slightly fresher and black-centered gr covs (Fig. 134); outer rects (r4-r6) relatively abraded, tapered (Fig. 139**A**), and dusky brown with a relatively small amount of white (Fig. 262**B-C**); chin and throat whitish to yellow, with little or no (Aug-Mar), or a moderate amount of (Mar-Jul) black mottling. **Note: Some overlap can occur with HY/SY ♂; the amount of black in the back feathers and uppertail covs seems to be the most reliable criterion; compare with measurements and the pattern of white in the outer rects (r4-r6). Most birds should be reliably aged, although a few ♀♀ can be difficult to separate, especially in spring.**

AHY/ASY ♀ (Aug-Jul): Crown and eye line olive with blackish flecking; back feathers and uppertail covs with relatively distinct, blackish centers (Fig. 261**C-D**); white tipping to the med covs usually with moderately thin, black shaft streaks (occasionally all white; Fig. 270**B-C**); outer pp covs broad, truncate, relatively fresh, and dusky with distinct, grayish edging (Fig. 138), not contrasting markedly in color or wear with the gr covs; outer rects (r4-r6) relatively fresh, truncate (Fig. 139**A**), and dusky with a moderate amount of white (Fig. 262**C-D**); chin yellowish with black mottling (Aug-Mar), or black with yellow mottling (Mar-Jul); throat black with yellow mottling. **Note: See HY/SY ♀.**

HY/SY ♂ (Aug-Jul): Crown and eye line olive with blackish mottling (Aug-Mar), or black with light, olive mottling (Mar-Jul); back feathers and uppertail covs with relatively distinct, moderately large, blackish centers (Fig. 261**C-E**), becoming primarily black by spring; white tipping to the med covs usually with moderately thin, black shaft streaks (Fig. 270**B**); pp-cov and rect criteria as in HY/SY ♀, except that the outer rects (r4-r6) average more white (Fig. 262**C-D**); chin buffy white or yellowish (Aug-Mar), or black with light, yellow mottling (Mar-Jul); throat buff, usually with noticeable black mottling (AugMar), or black (Mar-Jul). **Note: See HY/SY ♀.**

AHY/ASY ♂ (Aug-Jul): Forehead and eye line primarily black, with little or no olive mottling; back feathers and uppertail covs with large black centers (Fig. 261**E-F**), becoming black by spring; white tips of the med covs without shaft streaks, or (sometimes) with indistinct streaks on a few covs only (Fig. 270**B-C**); pp-cov and rect criteria as in AHY/ASY ♀, except that the outer rects (r3-r6) average more white (Fig. 262**E**); chin and throat black with thin, whitish tips in Aug-Dec. **Note: See HY/SY ♀.**

References—Ridgway (1902), Bent (1953), Phillips (1959b), Oberholser (1974), Curson *et al.* (1994), Dunn & Garrett (1997), Pyle (1997c); IBP (MAPS) data.

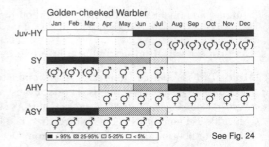

See Fig. 24

BLACKBURNIAN WARBLER
Dendroica fusca

BLBW
Species # 6620
Band size: 0-0A

Geographic variation—No subspecies are recognized.

Molt—PB: HY partial (Jun-Sep), AHY complete (Jun-Sep); PA partial (Oct-May). The PBs occur on the summer grounds. The 1st PB usually includes all med and gr covs and often the greater alula, but no terts or rects. The 1st PA includes 6 to 10 (~61%) inner gr covs and sometimes (in ~22% of birds) 1-2 terts, but no rects. The adult PA includes 9 to 10 (~90%) inner gr covs and sometimes (in ~30% of birds) 1-2 terts, but no rects. The PAs appear to involve continuous, limited replacement of body feathers on the winter grounds.

Skull—Pneumaticization completes in HY from 15 Oct through Dec.

Age/Sex—Juv (Jun-Aug) resembles HY/SY ♀ (see below), but is washed brownish, has buff wing bars, and has little or no orange in the face; juv ♀=♂, although some birds perhaps can be sexed by the amount of white in the outer rects (r4-r6), as in HY/SYs (see below). CP/BP (May-Aug). ♀ wg(n55) 63-71, tl(n30) 42-48; ♂ wg(n60) 65-73, tl(n42) 44-50.

Basic Plumage (Aug-Mar)

HY/SY ♀ (Aug-Mar): Nape, auricular patch, and shoulder dull olive-brown; inner gr covs with moderate, white edging (Fig. 271**A**) forming (with the med covs) two wing bars; outer pp covs narrow, tapered, somewhat abraded (Fig. 138**A**), and brownish, contrasting with the slightly fresher and dusky-centered gr covs (Fig. 134); outer rects (r4-r6) relatively abraded, tapered (Fig. 139**A**), and dusky brown with a relatively small amount of white (Fig. 262**B-C**). **Note: All birds should be reliably sexed and most reliably aged; the amount of white in the outer rects (r4-r6) is relatively useful in this species.**

AHY/ASY ♀ (Aug-Mar): Nape, auricular patch, and shoulder grayish olive to dusky brown; inner gr covs with moderately narrow, white edging (Fig. 271**A-B**) forming (with the med covs) two wing bars; outer pp covs broad, truncate, relatively fresh (Fig. 138**B**), and dusky brown, not contrasting markedly in color or wear with the gr covs; outer rects (r3-r6) fresh, truncate (Fig. 139**A**), and dusky with a moderate amount of white (Fig. 262**D-E**). **Note: See HY/SY ♀.**

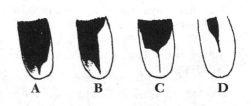

FIGURE 271. Variation in the amount of white on the outer greater coverts, by age and sex (see text), in Blackburnian Warbler.

HY/SY ♂ (Aug-Mar): Nape and auricular patch mixed black and brown; shoulder patch dull black; inner gr covs edged with moderately narrow, white edging (Fig. 271A-B); pp-cov and rect criteria as in HY/SY ♀, except that the outer rects (r3-r6) average more white (Fig. 262C-E). **Note: See HY/SY ♀.**

AHY/ASY ♂ (Aug-Mar): Nape, auricular, and shoulder black, the feathers edged yellowish; inner gr covs broadly edged white (Fig. 271C) forming (with the med covs) a wing patch; pp-cov and rect criteria as in AHY/ASY ♀, except that the outer rects (r3-r6) average more white (Fig. 262E-F or more). **Note: See HY/SY ♀.**

Alternate Plumage (Mar-Aug)

SY ♀ (Mar-Aug): Nape, auricular patch, and shoulder olive-gray; supercilium and throat yellowish; molt limits sometimes occur among the gr covs (Fig. 133C-E; see **Molt**), the inner covs with moderately narrow, white edging (Fig. 271A-B), contrasting with the retained outer covs (if present) brownish with the white-tipping usually worn off; outer pp covs narrow, tapered, abraded (Fig. 138C), and brown, contrasting markedly with the replaced, dusky-centered gr covs; outer rects (r4-r6) relatively abraded, tapered (Fig. 139A), and brownish with a relatively small amount of white (Fig. 262B-C). **Note: See HY/SY ♀, above.**

ASY ♀ (Mar-Aug): Nape, auricular patch, and shoulder olive-gray to gray; supercilium and throat yellowish, sometimes tinged orange; molt limits only occasionally occur among the gr covs (Fig. 133D-E; see **Molt**), most or all gr covs with moderately broad, white edging (Fig. 271B); outer pp covs broad, truncate, relatively fresh (Fig. 138D), and brownish dusky, contrasting only moderately in color and wear with the gr covs; outer rects (r3-r6) relatively fresh, truncate (Fig. 139A), and brownish dusky with a moderate amount of white (Fig. 262D-E). **Note: See HY/SY ♀, above.**

SY ♂ (Mar-Aug): Nape, auricular patch, and shoulder black, sometimes slightly mottled brownish; supercilium and throat bright orange, sometimes tinged yellowish; molt-limit, wing-cov, and flight-feather criteria as in SY ♀, except that the replaced, inner gr covs are primarily white (Fig. 271C-D), the brownish pp covs contrast more distinctly with the back color, and the outer rects (r3-r6) average more white (Fig. 262C-E). **Note: See HY/SY ♀, above.**

ASY ♂ (Mar-Aug): Nape, auricular patch, and shoulder black; supercilium and throat bright orange; molt-limit, wing-cov, and flight-feather criteria as in ASY ♀, except that inner gr covs are primarily white (Fig. 271D), the pp covs are uniform in color with the back, and the outer rects (r3-r6) average more white (Fig. 262E-F or more). **Note: See HY/SY ♀, above.**

Hybrids reported—Black-and-white Warbler. Also, observed paired with Bay-breasted Warbler.

Blackburnian Warbler

References—Stone (1896), Dwight (1900a), Ridgway (1902), Todd & Carriker (1922), Forbush (1929), Bent (1953), Roberts (1955), Robbins (1964), Wood (1969), Oberholser (1974), Sheppard & Klimkiewicz (1976), Harley & Jones (1983), Bledsoe (1988), Cramp & Perrins (1994b), Curson *et al.* (1994), Morse (1994), Dunn & Garrett (1997), Pyle (1997c); IBP (MAPS) data, PRBO data.

YELLOW-THROATED WARBLER
Dendroica dominica

YTWA
Species # 6630
Band size: 0A-0

Geographic variation—Moderately well marked and ranges fairly well defined. Subspecies taxonomy follows G.H. Lowery & B.L. Monroe *in* Paynter (1968), as modified by the indications of Browning (1978) and Stevenson (1982); see also Ridgway (1902), Sutton (1951b), Parkes (1953c), Ficken *et al.* (1968), Oberholser (1974), Browning (1990), Jaramillo (1993), Curson *et al.* (1994), Hall (1996), Dunn & Garrett (in press). One other subspecies occurs in the Bahama Is.

D.d. albilora (br se.NE-e.TX to montane WV-nc.GA, wint s.TX): Bill short (exp culmen 10.1-12.7) and supraloral area primarily white (Fig. 272; some yellow often is present near the eye). Birds breeding north and east of TX-MS ("*axantha*") average smaller-billed, but this difference is too slight to warrant subspecies recognition.

D.d. dominica (br & wint coastal s.NJ-s.FL): Bill long (exp culmen 11.4-17.0) and supraloral area primarily to entirely yellow (Fig. 272). Birds of coastal se.AL-w.FL ("*stoddardi*") have bills averaging larger and more slender than birds of VA-GA, but these essentially are inseparable from birds of NJ-MD, which also are larger-billed. Birds of the Bahama Is (*flavescens*), possible vagrants to FL, have facial features less distinct, the white patch on the neck reduced, and the sides of the breast and belly washed yellow.

Molt—PB: HY partial (May-Aug), AHY complete (Jun-Sep); PA absent. The PBs occur on the summer grounds. The 1st PB usually includes all med and gr covs and often the greater alula, but no terts or rects. A very limited PA may occur in Oct-Apr, as in other warblers.

Skull—Pneumaticization completes in HY from 1 Sep through Nov.

Age/Sex—Juv (Apr-Aug) has grayish to olive-brown upperparts with indistinct, dusky streaking, and buffy wing bars and underparts; juv ♀ = ♂, although some birds perhaps can be sexed by the amount of white in the outer rects (r4-r6), as in HY/SYs (see below). CP/BP (Mar-Jul). ♀ wg(n49) 59-69, tl(n39) 46-52; ♂ wg(n75) 61-72, tl(n73) 48-54.

HY/SY ♀ (Aug-Jul): Crown with light, black streaking (Fig. 273A); upperparts with a moderate brown wash; auricular washed dull brownish black; outer pp covs narrow, tapered, relatively abraded (Fig. 138), and dusky brown, contrasting with the slightly fresher and blackish-centered gr covs (Fig. 134); outer rects (r4-r6) relatively abraded, tapered (Fig. 139A), and dusky brown with a relatively small amount of white (Fig. 262**B-C**); flank streaking moderately narrow and indistinct. **Note: All criteria should coincide before birds are reliably aged and/or sexed. Many intermediates and birds with conflicting characters may occur.**

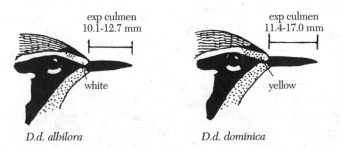

exp culmen
10.1-12.7 mm
white
D.d. albilora

exp culmen
11.4-17.0 mm
yellow
D.d. dominica

FIGURE 272. The bill size and head color by subspecies in Yellow-throated Warbler. Note that the amount of yellow in the supraloral region comes close to overlapping in these two subspecies.

AHY/ASY ♀ (Aug-Jul): Crown with light to moderate, black streaking (Fig. 273**A-B**); upperparts lightly washed brown; auricular dull black; outer pp covs broad, truncate, relatively fresh (Fig. 138), and blackish to dusky, not contrasting markedly in color or wear with the gr covs; outer rects (r4-r6) relatively fresh, truncate (Fig. 139**A**), and dusky with a moderate amount of white (Fig. 262**C-D**); flank streaking moderately narrow and indistinct. **Note: See HY/SY ♀.**

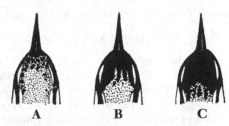

FIGURE 273. Variation in the crown streaking, by age and sex (see text), in spring Yellow-throated Warblers. Note that the crowns in all age/sex groups are more heavily veiled with grayish in the fall.

HY/SY ♂ (Aug-Jul): Crown with moderate to heavy, black streaking (Fig. 273**B-C**); upperparts lightly washed brown; auricular blackish to black; pp-cov and rect criteria as in HY/SY ♀, except that the outer rects (r4-r6) average more white (Fig. 262**C-D**); flank streaking wide and moderately distinct. **Note: See HY/SY ♀.**

AHY/ASY ♂ (Aug-Jul): Crown with heavy, black streaking (Fig. 273**C**); upperparts with a slight or no brown wash; auricular black; pp-cov and rect criteria as in AHY/ASY ♀, except that the outer rects (r3-r6) average more white (Fig. 262**D-E**); flank streaking wide and distinct. **Note: See HY/SY ♀.**

Hybrids reported—Northern Parula (resulting in "Sutton's Warbler", alpha code **SUWA, Species # 6634**).

References—Stone (1896), Dwight (1900a), Ridgway (1902), Forbush (1929), Haller (1940), Bent (1953), Wood (1969), Oberholser (1974), Sheppard & Klimkiewicz (1976), Curson *et al.* (1994), Hall (1996), Dunn & Garrett (1997), Pyle (1997c); C.H. Blake (*in litt.* to the BBL).

GRACE'S WARBLER
Dendroica graciae

GRWA
Species # 6640
Band size: 0A

Geographic variation—Moderately weak and clinal where most ranges meet. Subspecies taxonomy follows G.H. Lowery & B.L. Monroe *in* Paynter (1968); see Ridgway (1902), Griscom (1935), Brodkorb (1940), Phillips & Webster (1961), Webster (1961), Curson *et al.* (1994), Dunn & Garrett (in press). Three other subspecies occur in Mex-C.Am.

D.g. graciae (br throughout the range in N.Am): From subspecies of Mex-C.Am by larger size (wg 61-70, tl 44-53; see **Sex**, *vs* wg 54-68, tl 41-49 in the other subspecies); bill slender (depth at tip of nares 2.4-3.0, *vs* 2.6-3.4 in the other subspecies); upperparts with a heavier brownish wash when fresh; supercilium (posterior to the eye) white, without (*vs* with) yellow; throat and breast yellow, without (*vs* sometimes with) an orange tinge; lower underparts buffier when fresh.

Molt—PB: HY partial (May-Aug), AHY complete (Jul-Sep); PA absent-limited(?). The PBs occur on the summer grounds. The 1st PB usually includes all med and gr covs and often the greater alula, but no terts or rects. The PAs, if present, may involve continuous, limited replacement of body feathers on the winter grounds, from Oct-Apr, as in certain other warblers.

Skull—Pneumaticization completes in HY from 15 Sep through Nov.

Age/Sex—Juv (Apr-Aug) has grayish to olive-brown upperparts with indistinct, dusky streaking, and buffier and indistinctly spotted underparts; juv ♀=♂, although occasional birds perhaps can be sexed by the amount of white in the outer rects (r4-r6), as in HY/SYs (see below). CP/BP (Apr-Aug). ♀ wg(n30) 61-67, tl(n24) 44-51; ♂ wg(n100) 63-70, tl(n100) 46-53; measurements refer to *D.g. graciae* only; see **Geographic variation**.

HY/SY ♀ (Aug-Jul): Upperparts heavily washed brownish when fresh; back feathers usually without darker centers (Fig. 261**A**); outer pp covs narrow, tapered, relatively abraded (Fig. 138), and brownish, contrasting with the slightly fresher and blackish-centered gr covs (Fig. 134); outer rects (r4-r6) relatively abraded, tapered (Fig. 139**A**), and dusky brown with a relatively small amount of white (Fig. 262**B-C**); flank streaking narrow and indistinct. **Note: All criteria should coincide before birds are reliably aged and/or sexed. Many intermediates and birds with conflicting characters may occur.**

AHY/ASY ♀ (Aug-Jul): Upperparts with a moderate brownish wash when fresh; back feathers with small and indistinct, blackish centers (Fig. 261**B-C**); outer pp covs broad, truncate, relatively fresh (Fig. 138), and dusky gray, not contrasting markedly in color or wear with the gr covs; outer rects (r4-r6) relatively fresh, truncate (Fig. 139**A**), and dusky with a moderate amount of white (Fig. 262**C-D**); flank streaking moderately narrow and indistinct. **Note: See HY/SY ♀.**

HY/SY ♂ (Aug-Jul): Upperparts with a moderate brownish wash when fresh; back feathers with small and distinct, blackish to black centers (Fig. 261**C-D**); pp-cov and rect criteria as in HY/SY ♀, except that the outer rects (r4-r6) average slightly more white (Fig. 262**C-D**); flank streaking wide and moderately distinct. **Note: See HY/SY ♀.**

AHY/ASY ♂ (Aug-Jul): Upperparts with a slight brownish tinge when fresh; back feathers with large and distinct, black centers (Fig. 261**D-E**); pp-cov and rect criteria as in AHY/ASY ♀, except that the outer rects (r3-r6) average more white (Fig. 262**D-E**); flank streaking wide and distinct. **Note: See HY/SY ♀.**

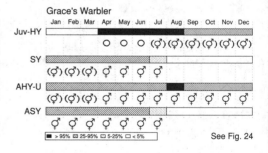

Grace's Warbler

Hybrids reported—Yellow-rumped (Audubon's) Warbler.

References—Ridgway (1902), Swarth (1904a), Bent (1953), Webster (1961), Oberholser (1974), Phillips (1986), Bledsoe (1988), Parkes (1988a), Curson *et al.* (1994), Dunn & Garrett (1997), Pyle (1997c).

PINE WARBLER
Dendroica pinus

PIWA
Species # 6710
Band size: 0-0A

Species—From Bay-breasted and Blackpoll warblers by wing morphology (longest p – longest s 16-22 mm); longest rect – longest undertail cov 20-25 mm; upperparts washed brown in HY/SYs and ♀♀, the feathers of the back without any black or dusky centers (Fig. 261A); eye line short and indistinct; auricular contrasting distinctly with the throat, but indistinctly with the nape; pp tips without white; wing edging dingy whitish; white patch on the outer rect larger (from the tip of the feather on the inner web 20-32 mm; see **Age/Sex**); undertail covs white; legs and soles of the feet blackish, without bluish gray. From HY/SY ♀ Prairie Warbler by longer wg (65-78; see **Age/Sex**); lower belly and undertail covs white.

Geographic variation—Weak and clinal between subspecies of N.Am. Subspecies taxonomy follows G.H. Lowery & B.L. Monroe *in* Paynter (1968); see Ridgway (1902), Maynard (1906), Howell (1930), Curson *et al.* (1994), Stevenson & Anderson (1994), Dunn & Garrett (in press). Two other subspecies occur in the W.Indies.

D.p. pinus (br & wint throughout most of the range in N.Am): Bill short (exp culmen 9.7-11.4); upperparts medium-bright olive to brownish olive; streaking on the sides more extensive by age/sex.

D.p. florida (res c-s.FL): Bill long (exp culmen 10.3-12.2); upperparts medium-dull olive to brownish olive; streaking on the sides reduced by age/sex.

Molt—PB: HY partial (May-Aug), AHY complete (Jun-Sep); PA absent. The PBs occur on the summer grounds. The 1st PB usually includes all med and gr covs and often the greater alula, but no terts or rects. Reports that the 1st PB can include some or all rects probably were incorrect.

Skull—Pneumaticization completes in HY from 1 Oct (as early as 15 Sep in populations south of VA-MO) through Nov.

Age/Sex—Juv (Apr-Jul) has completely brown upperparts, buffy underparts without yellow, and buffy wing bars; juv ♀ = ♂. CP/BP (Mar-Aug). ♀ wg(n40) 65-74, tl(n20) 46-52; ♂ wg(n43) 68-78, tl(n20) 50-56.

HY/SY ♀ (Aug-Jul): Upperparts brownish with little or no green; outer pp covs narrow, tapered, relatively abraded (Fig. 138), and brown, contrasting with the slightly fresher and dusky-centered gr covs; outer rects (r4-r6) relatively abraded, tapered (Fig. 139A), and dusky brown; breast buff, lightly washed yellow; belly and vent buff. **Note: There can be some overlap between this and HY/SY ♂; compare with wg, and leave intermediates unsexed if uncertain. Ageing and sexing criteria are broadly clinal in this species, and some intermediates cannot be reliably aged and/or sexed. In all age/sex classes, birds have a heavier brownish and buff wash in fall than in spring. See also AHY/ASY ♂.**

AHY/ASY ♀ (Aug-Jul): Back dull greenish; outer pp covs broad, truncate, relatively fresh (Fig. 138), and brownish dusky, not contrasting markedly in color or wear with the gr covs (Fig. 133F); outer rects (r4-r6) relatively fresh, truncate (Fig. 139A), and dusky; breast greenish-yellow; belly and vent white, often washed lightly with buff. **Note: See HY/SY ♀ and AHY/ASY ♂.**

HY/SY ♂ (Aug-Jul): Back primarily brownish, often with an olive wash (wearing to greenish in spring); pp-cov and rect criteria as in HY/SY ♀; breast yellow with a buff wash; belly and vent washed buff, becoming whitish by spring. **Note: See HY/SY ♀ and AHY/ASY ♂.**

AHY/ASY ♂ (Aug-Jul): Back olive with a slight brownish wash (fall) to greenish with a slight or no brownish wash (spring); pp-cov and rect criteria as in AHY/ASY ♀, except that the outer rects (r4-r6) average slightly more white (see below); breast bright yellow with a slight or no buff wash; belly and vent white. **Note: See HY/SY ♀. Also, the amount of white in the outer rects (r4-r6) average slightly more white in AHY/ASY ♂♂ (Fig. 262B-C) than in the other age/sex groups (Fig. 262A-B), but this is not as helpful for ageing or sexing as in other *Dendroica* warblers.**

Hybrids reported—Yellow-rumped (Myrtle) Warbler.

References—Stone (1896), Dwight (1900a), Ridgway (1902), Forbush (1929), Norris (1952), Bent (1953), Roberts (1955), Dennis (1958), Robbins (1964), Ficken *et al.* (1968), Wood (1969), Oberholser (1974), Phillips (1974), Sheppard & Klimkiewicz (1976), Whitney (1983), Kaufman (1990a), Pyle & McCaskie (1992), Curson *et al.* (1994), Dunn & Garrett (1997), Pyle (1997c); F.M. Weston (*in litt.* to the BBL). IBP (MAPS) data.

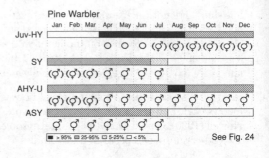

KIRTLAND'S WARBLER
Dendroica kirtlandii

KIWA
Species # 6700
Band size: 1C

Geographic variation—No subspecies are recognized.

Molt—PB: HY partial (Jun-Sep), AHY complete (Jun-Oct); PA limited-partial? (Jan-May). The PBs occur primarily on the summer grounds, but can complete on migration or the winter grounds. The 1st PB usually includes all med and gr covs and often the greater alula, but no terts or rects. The PAs may involve continuous, limited replacement of body feathers on the winter grounds, from Oct-May, as in certain other warblers.

Skull—Pneumaticization completes in HY from 1 Oct through Nov.

Age/Sex—Juv (Jun-Aug) has completely brown upperparts, buff wing bars, and distinct, black speckling on the throat and chin; juv ♀ = ♂. CP/BP (May-Aug); a reported BP in a ♂ probably should be regarded as anomalous. ♀ wg(n55) 64-71, tl(n34) 51-59; ♂ wg(n100) 68-75, tl(n88) 53-63.

HY/SY ♀ (Aug-Jul): Forecrown and lores brownish gray; upperparts primarily brown (Aug-Mar) to brownish gray (Mar-Aug); outer pp covs narrow, tapered, relatively abraded, and brownish with indistinct, narrow, or no grayish-brown edging (Fig. 138), contrasting with the slightly fresher and dusky-centered gr covs (Fig. 134); outer rects (r5-r6) relatively abraded, tapered (Fig. 139**A**), and dusky brown with a small amount of white (Fig. 262**A-B**); underparts pale yellow with a buff wash in Aug-Mar; flank streaking dusky, and indistinct (Aug-Mar) to moderately distinct (Mar-Jul). **Note: Plumage criteria for ageing are most useful in basic plumage. In alternate plumage (Mar-Aug) use covert contrast and rect criteria to age, and body plumage criteria to sex.**

AHY/ASY ♀ (Aug-Jul): Forecrown and lores primarily gray; upperparts grayish with a moderate (Aug-Mar) to light (Mar-Jul), brown wash; outer pp covs broad, truncate, relatively fresh, and dusky with relatively distinct and broad, grayish edging (Fig. 138), not contrasting markedly in color or wear with the gr covs (Fig. 133**F**); outer rects (r4-r6) relatively fresh, truncate (Fig. 139**A**), and dusky with a moderate amount of white (Fig. 262**B-C**); underparts moderately bright yellow; flank streaking blackish, and indistinct (Aug-Mar) to distinct (Mar-Jul). **Note: See HY/SY ♀.**

HY/SY ♂ (Aug-Jul): Forecrown and lores blackish; upperparts grayish with a moderate (Aug-Mar) to light (Mar-Jul), brown wash; pp-cov and rect criteria as in HY/SY ♀, except that the outer rects (r4-r6) average more white (Fig. 262**B-C**); underparts moderately bright yellow; flank streaking blackish, and indistinct (Aug-Mar) to moderately distinct (Mar-Jul). **Note: See HY/SY ♀.**

AHY/ASY ♂ (Aug-Jul): Forecrown and lores black; upperparts grayish blue with a slight brown wash when fresh; pp-cov and rect criteria as in AHY/ASY ♀, except that the outer rects (r4-r6) average slightly more white (Fig. 262**C-D**); underparts relatively bright yellow; flank streaking black and distinct. **Note: See HY/SY ♀.**

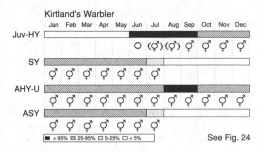

Kirtland's Warbler

See Fig. 24

References—Ridgway (1902), Wood (1904), J. Van Tyne *in* Bent (1953), Roberts (1955), Mayfield (1960, 1992), Goodman (1982), Sykes *et al.* (1989, 1993), Curson *et al.* (1994), Dunn & Garrett (1997), Pyle (1997c).

PRAIRIE WARBLER
Dendroica discolor

PRAW
Species # 6730
Band size: 0A-0

Species—HY/SY ♀ from Pine Warbler by shorter wg (49-61; see **Age/Sex**); lower belly and undertail covs yellow.

Geographic variation—Moderate and ranges well defined. Subspecies taxonomy follows G.H. Lowery & B.L. Monroe *in* Paynter (1968); see Ridgway (1902), Howell (1930), Hubbard & Banks (1970), Curson *et al.* (1994), Dunn & Garrett (in press). No other subspecies occur.

  D.d. discolor (br & wint throughout most of the range in N.Am): Upperparts olive with a yellow tinge and extensive chestnut streaks by age/sex (see **Age/Sex**); underparts deep yellow with black streaking relatively distinct by age/sex (see **Age/Sex**).
  D.d. paludicola (="*collinsi*"; res coastal s.FL): Upperparts grayish olive with the chestnut streaks reduced by age/sex (see **Age/Sex**); underparts pale yellow with black streaking relatively indistinct by age/sex (see **Age/Sex**).

Molt—PB: HY partial (Jun-Aug), AHY complete (May-Aug); PA limited (Oct-Apr). The PBs occur primarily on the summer grounds. The 1st PB usually includes all med and gr covs and often the greater alula, but no terts or rects. The PAs involve continuous, limited replacement of head feathers on the winter grounds.

Skull—Pneumaticization completes in HY from 15 Sep through Dec.

Age/Sex—Juv (Jun-Aug) has brownish-washed upperparts and buffy wing bars; juv ♀=♂, although some birds perhaps can be sexed by the amount of white in the rects, as in HY/SYs (see below). CP/BP (Apr-Aug). ♀ wg(n100) 49-57, tl(n20) 42-50; ♂ wg(n100) 52-61, tl(n36) 45-52.

HY/SY ♀ (Aug-Jul): Back feathers with little or no chestnut (Fig. 261**A-B**); eye line dusky and quite indistinct (Aug-Mar), or dull blackish (Mar-Jul); auricular largely grayish to whitish (Aug-Mar), or dull olive, often with a dusky and indistinct, crescent-shaped cheek patch (Mar-Jul); outer pp covs narrow, tapered, relatively abraded, and brownish with indistinct, narrow, or no yellow edging (Fig. 138), contrasting with the slightly fresher and dusky-centered gr covs (Fig. 134); outer rects (r4-r6) relatively abraded, tapered (Fig. 139**A**), and dusky brown with a relatively small amount of white (Fig. 262**B-C**); flank streaking very indistinct. **Note: The amount of chestnut in the back feathers, as indicated for each age/sex group, refer to the widespread nominate subspecies; these amounts in *D. d. paludicola* average less within each age/sex group. A few intermediate HY/SYs will occur in Aug-Mar which are not reliably sexed.**

AHY/ASY ♀ (Aug-Jul): Back feathers usually with indistinct, chestnut streaks (Fig. 261**B-C**); eye line dusky to dull black; auricular dull olive, often with an indistinct, dusky, crescent-shaped cheek patch; outer pp covs broad, truncate, relatively fresh, and dusky with relatively distinct and broad, yellow edging (Fig. 138), not contrasting markedly in color or wear with the gr covs (Fig. 133**F**); outer rects (r4-r6) relatively fresh, truncate (Fig. 139**A**), and dusky with a moderate amount of white (Fig. 262**C-D**); flank streaking narrow and indistinct. **Note: See HY/SY ♀.**

HY/SY ♂ (Aug-Jul): Back feathers with moderately large to large chestnut centers (Fig. 261**C-D**); eye line relatively distinct and blackish to black; auricular primarily grayish to whitish (Aug-Mar), or olive, often tinged gray (Mar-Jul), and with the crescent-shaped cheek patch blackish and fairly distinct; pp-cov and rect criteria as in HY/SY ♀, except that the outer rects (r4-r6) average more white (Fig. 262**C-D**); flank streaking wide and moderately indistinct to moderately distinct. **Note: See HY/SY ♀.**

AHY/ASY ♂ (Aug-Jul): Back feathers with large and distinct, chestnut centers (Fig. 261**D-E**); eye line distinct and black; auricular bright olive, without gray, and with the crescent-shaped cheek patch distinct and black (mottled yellow in Aug-Dec); pp-cov and rect criteria as in AHY/ASY ♀, except that the outer rects (r3-r6) average more white (Fig. 262**D-E**); flank streaking broad and distinct. **Note: See HY/SY ♀.**

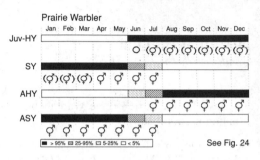

References—Stone (1896), Dwight (1900a), Ridgway (1902), Forbush (1929), Dickey & van Rossem (1938), Bent (1953), Robbins (1964), Nolan & Mumford (1965), Sutton (1967), Wood (1969), Oberholser (1974), Sheppard & Klimkiewicz (1976), Nolan (1978), Curson *et al.* (1994), Dunn & Garrett (1997), Pyle (1997c); V. Nolan (*in litt.* to the BBL); G.E. Wallace (pers. comm.); IBP (MAPS) data, PRBO data.

PALM WARBLER   See below
Dendroica palmarum   Band size: 0-0A

   Western Palm Warbler (WPWA)   Species # 6720
   Yellow Palm Warbler (YPWA)   Species # 6729

Geographic variation—Moderately well marked and ranges fairly well defined, although intergrades occur. Subspecies taxonomy follows G.H. Lowery & B.L. Monroe *in* Paynter (1968); see Ridgway (1902), Rand (1944b), Oberholser (1974), Johnston (1976), Godfrey (1986), Curson *et al.* (1994), Dunn & Garrett (in press). No other subspecies occur. Both subspecies average yellower in spring than in fall.

D.p. palmarum (br sw.NWT-Alb to Ont-MI, wint coastal MD-FL-TX, mig coastal CA): **Western Palm Warbler.** Averages small; crown averages duller and with less chestnut by age/sex/season (Table 8); back grayish, sometimes tinged olive; malar area, flanks, and center of the belly whitish (sometimes tinged yellow when fresh), contrasting with the yellow throat and undertail covs. ♀ wg(n30) 57-64, tl(n28) 47-53; ♂ wg(n30) 60-67, tl(n29) 49-55.

D.p. hypochrysea (br Que to s.NFL-NH, wint coastal MD-FL-LA): **Yellow Palm Warbler.** Averages large; crown averages brighter and with more chestnut by age/sex/season (Table 8); back brownish with an olive wash; malar area, flanks, and center of the belly yellow, not contrasting markedly with the yellow throat and undertail covs. ♀ wg(n30) 61-68, tl(n28) 51-56; ♂ wg(n30) 63-71, tl(n29) 53-59.

Table 8. Chestnut crown patch measurements in Palm Warbler by subspecies, plumage, age and, sex. Basic plumage occurs in Aug-Mar and alternate plumage occurs in Mar-Aug. Data is from museum specimen measurements of at least 10 individuals of each class. More study is needed. See Fig. 281 for measurement methods.

Subspecies	Plumage	HY/SY ♀	AHY/ASY ♀	HY/SY ♂	AHY/ASY ♂
Western Palm Warbler	Basic	0-0	0-4	0-3	2-8
D.p. palmarum	Alternate	11-14	13-16	12-16	14-19
Yellow Palm Warbler	Basic	0-0	0-5	0-4	3-10
D.p. hypochrysea	Alternate	12-15	14-18	13-18	16-21

Molt—PB: HY partial (Jun-Sep), AHY complete (Jul-Sep); PA limited (Jan-Apr). The PBs occur on the summer grounds. The 1st PB usually includes all med and gr covs and often the greater alula, but no terts or rects. The PA is limited to feathers of the head, and may be continuous from Oct-Apr, as in certain other warblers.

Skull—Pneumaticization completes in HY from 15 Oct through Dec.

Age—Juv (Jun-Aug) has upperparts and underparts grayish with dusky streaking, and buffy wing bars; juv ♀ = ♂.

HY/SY (Aug-Jul): Crown often without chestnut in Aug-Mar, or with a relatively small (by subspecies and sex) chestnut patch in Mar-Jul (Table 8); outer pp covs narrow, tapered, somewhat abraded (Fig. 138), and brownish, contrasting with the slightly fresher and dusky-centered gr covs (Fig. 134); outer rects (r5-r6) relatively abraded, somewhat tapered (Fig. 139A), and dusky brown with a medium-small amount of white (Fig. 262A-B). **Note: Plumage criteria in this species are very subtle; 50% or more of birds are not reliably aged after completion of pneumaticization.**

AHY/ASY (Aug-Jul): Crown often with chestnut feathers in Aug-Mar, or with a relatively large (by subspecies and sex) chestnut patch in Mar-Jul (Table 8); outer pp covs broad, truncate, relatively fresh (Fig. 138), and brownish dusky, not contrasting markedly in color or wear with the gr covs (Fig. 133F); outer rects (r4-r6) relatively fresh, truncate (Fig. 139A), and dusky with a medium-large amount of white (Fig. 262B-C). **Note: See HY/SY ♀.**

Sex—CP/BP (May-Aug). See **Geographic variation** for measurements. Only a few ♂♂ can be sexed by plumage, including known HY/SYs in Aug-Mar with one or more chestnut feathers in the crown, and AHY/ASYs in Mar-Jul with extensive chestnut in the crown (see Table 8); a few other extremes (of known age) are possibly sexed by crown plumage (Table 8) but more study is needed to confirm this. Otherwise, ♂♂ average brighter than ♀♀, especially in Mar-Jul, and average more white in the outer rects (r4-r6) by age (see **Age**) but no reliable criteria are currently known for sexing most individuals (by plumage) in the hand.

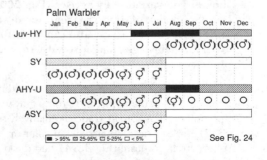

References—Stone (1896), Dwight (1900a), Ridgway (1902), Forbush (1929), Bent (1953), Roberts (1955), Goodpasture (1963), Robbins (1964), Wood (1969), Oberholser (1974), Johnston (1976), Sheppard & Klimkiewicz (1976), Curson *et al.* (1994), Wilson (1996), Dunn & Garrett (1997), Pyle (1997c); R.M. Patterson, J. Statz (*in litt.* to the BBL); PRBO data.

BAY-BREASTED WARBLER
Dendroica castanea

BBWA
Species # 6600
Band size: 0-1C-0A

Species—Basic-plumaged birds (without distinct, chestnut on the sides) from Pine Warbler by upperparts olive to yellow-olive, usually with distinct, dusky or black centers to the feathers (Fig. 274); eye line long and fairly distinct; auricular contrasting indistinctly with the throat but distinctly with the nape; pp tips with white when fresh; wing edging brighter whitish; white patch of the outer rect smaller (from the tip of the feather on the inner web 14-23 mm; see also **Age/Sex**); undertail covs tinged buff; legs and soles of the feet bluish gray. From Blackpoll Warbler by undertail cov, leg and foot color (as above); p6 usually at least slightly emarginated; p8 > p9 by 1-2 mm; p8 – p7 1-2 mm; longest p – longest s 14-23 mm; longest rect – longest undertail cov 16-26 mm.

Geographic variation—No subspecies are recognized.

Molt—PB: HY partial (Jun-Aug), AHY complete (Jun-Aug); PA partial (Jan-May). The PBs occur on the summer grounds. The 1st PB usually includes all med and gr covs and often the greater alula, but no terts or rects. The 1st PA includes most lesser and med covs and 3 to 10 (~29%) inner gr covs, but no terts or rects. The adult PA includes some to most lesser and med covs and 8 to 10 (~89%) inner gr covs, but no terts or rects. The PAs may involve continuous, limited replacement of body feathers on the winter grounds, from Oct-May, as in certain other warblers.

Skull—Pneumaticization completes in HY from 15 Oct through Dec.

Age/Sex—Juv (Jun-Aug) has grayish-olive upperparts, buffy wing bars, and dusky spotting on the underparts; juv ♀ = ♂. CP/BP (May-Aug). ♀ wg(n100) 67-74, tl(n20) 46-53; ♂ wg(n100) 70-78, tl(n20) 48-57.

Basic Plumage (Aug-Mar)

HY/SY ♀ (Aug-Mar): Crown, throat, and flanks without chestnut; back feathers with indistinct, dusky centers (Fig. 274); rump primarily green; gr covs dusky, usually with yellowish-white tips; outer pp covs narrow, tapered, somewhat abraded, and brownish dusky with little or no grayish-brown edging (Fig. 138A), contrasting with the slightly fresher and dusky-centered gr covs (Fig. 134); outer rects (r4-r6) relatively abraded, tapered (Fig. 139A), and dusky brown; flanks without chestnut. **Note: The amount of white in the rects shows some variation by age/sex (Fig. 262A-C), as in other *Dendroica* warblers, but the usefulness of this criterion seems to be obscured by individual variation. Differences in rect shape also can be difficult to use. Intermediates will occur which are not reliably aged and/or sexed; extreme caution is required, especially with basic-plumaged birds.**

AHY/ASY ♀ (Aug-Mar): Crown and throat without chestnut feathers; back feathers with indistinct, blackish centers (Fig. 274); rump gray with little or no green; gr covs usually with white tips; outer pp covs broad, truncate, relatively fresh, and dusky with narrow, gray edging (Fig. 138B), not contrasting markedly in color or wear with the gr covs (Fig. 133F); outer rects (r4-r6) fresh, truncate (Fig. 139A), and dusky; flanks usually with some indistinct chestnut. **Note: See HY/SY ♀.**

HY/SY ♂ (Aug-Mar): Crown and throat occasionally with some chestnut feathers; back feathers with small but distinct, blackish centers (Fig. 274); rump grayish with a green wash; pp-cov and rect criteria as in HY/SY ♀; flanks sometimes with some indistinct chestnut. **Note: See HY/SY ♀.**

AHY/ASY ♂ (Aug-Mar): Crown and throat with some chestnut feathers; back feathers with large and distinct, black centers (Fig. 274); rump gray with little or no green; pp-cov and rect criteria as in AHY/ASY ♀; flanks with a moderate amount of chestnut. **Note: See HY/SY ♀.**

Alternate Plumage (Mar-Aug)

SY ♀ (Mar-Aug): Forehead green with black streaking; auricular dusky with an olive wash; crown and nape grayish olive with indistinct, black and chestnut streaking; molt limits usually occur among the gr covs (Fig. 133**B-E**; see **Molt**), 1-7 retained, first-basic, outer covs worn and brownish with little or no tipping, contrasting moderately with the fresher, dusky and white-tipped, recently replaced, inner covs; outer pp covs narrow, tapered, abraded, and brown without gray edging (Fig. 138**C**); outer rects (r4-r6) relatively abraded, tapered (Fig. 139**A**), and brownish; chestnut on the breast and flanks indistinct, reduced, and mixed with buff. **Note: See HY/SY ♀, above.**

ASY ♀ (Mar-Aug): Forehead black with green streaking; auricular dusky; crown and nape grayish olive with distinct, black and chestnut streaking; molt limits occasionally occur among the gr covs (Fig. 133**D-E**; see **Molt**), the 1-2 retained, adult, outer covs brownish dusky, contrasting slightly (in wear only) with the recently replaced, inner covs; outer pp covs broad, truncate, relatively fresh, and brownish dusky, often with gray edging (Fig. 138**D**); outer rects (r4-r6) fresh, truncate (Fig. 139**A**), and brownish dusky; chestnut on the breast and flanks moderately indistinct. **Note: See HY/SY ♀, above.**

SY ♂ (Mar-Aug): Forehead, lores, and auricular blackish, sometimes (especially lores) washed buff; forecrown dusky, contrasting indistinctly with the pale chestnut and unstreaked crown and nape; molt-limit, wing-cov, and flight-feather criteria as in SY ♀; chestnut on the breast and flanks extensive and moderately distinct. **Note: See HY/SY ♀, above.**

ASY ♂ (Mar-Aug): Forehead, lores, and auricular black, usually without buff; forecrown black, contrasting distinctly with the deep chestnut and unstreaked crown and nape; molt-limit, wing-cov, and flight-feather criteria as in ASY ♀; chestnut on the breast and flanks extensive and distinct. **Note: See HY/SY ♀, above.**

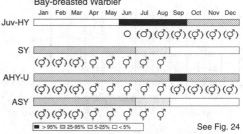

Bay-breasted Warbler

See Fig. 24

Hybrids reported—Yellow-rumped (Myrtle) Warbler, Blackpoll Warbler. Also, observed paired with Blackburnian Warbler.

References—Stone (1896), Dwight (1900a), Ridgway (1902), Forbush (1929), Brodkorb (1934), Bent (1953), Blake (1954a), Roberts (1955), Robbins (1964), Howard (1968), Wood (1969), Oberholser (1974), Sheppard & Klimkiewicz (1976), Banks & Baird (1978), Harley & Jones (1983), Stiles & Campos (1983), Whitney (1983), Kaufman (1990a), Curson *et al.* (1994), Williams (1996b), Dunn & Garrett (1997), Pyle (1997c); D.V. Howard, M.C. Shieldcastle (*in litt.* to the BBL); J. Curson (pers. comm.); PNR data.

BLACKPOLL WARBLER
Dendroica striata

BLPW
Species # 6610
Band size: 0-1C-0A

Species—Basic-plumaged birds from Bay-breasted Warbler (which see for separation from Pine Warbler) by longest p – longest s 20-26 mm; p6 not emarginated; p9 > p8 by 0-2 mm;

p8 – p7 2-3 mm; longest rect – longest undertail cov 12-15 mm; flanks and undertail covs white (without chestnut), often tinged lemon-yellow; soles of the feet (and often all or part of the legs) yellowish.

Geographic variation—Subspecies taxonomy follows G.H. Lowery & B.L. Monroe *in* Paynter (1968), who considered the species monotypic (synonymizing a previously recognized subspecies); see Burleigh & Peters (1948), Parkes (1954), Oberholser (1974). Birds breeding west of Ont ("*D.s. lurida*") may average slightly larger and duller, but differences, if present, are too weak for subspecies recognition.

Molt—PB: HY partial (Jul-Aug), AHY complete (Jul-Aug); PA partial (Feb-May). The PBs occur on the summer grounds. The 1st PB usually includes all med and gr covs, often the greater alula, and sometimes (in ~25% of birds) 1-3 terts, but no rects. The PAs include 5 to 10 (~26%) inner gr covs and 1-3 terts, but no rects; SYs average slightly fewer feathers replaced than ASYs. The PAs may possibly involve continuous, limited replacement of body feathers on the winter grounds, from Oct-May, as in certain other warblers, but most PA molting appears to occur in Feb-May in this species.

Skull—Pneumaticization completes in HY from 15 Oct through Dec.

Age/Sex—Juv (Jun-Aug) has upperparts grayish brown with black mottling, and underparts heavily mottled brownish; juv ♀ = ♂. CP/BP (May-Aug). ♀ wg(n100) 67-75, tl(n44) 45-51; ♂ wg(n100) 71-78, tl(n53) 47-54.

Basic Plumage (Aug-Mar)

HY/SY ♀♂ (Aug-Mar): Back feathers with no or small and indistinct, dark centers (Fig. 274); rump olive to grayish olive; outer pp covs narrow, tapered, somewhat abraded (Fig. 138**A**), and dusky, contrasting with the slightly fresher and blackish-centered gr covs (Fig. 134); 1-3 terts sometimes contrastingly fresh (Fig. 133**D-E**; this contrast can be subtle); outer rects (r4-r6) relatively abraded, tapered (Fig. 139**A**), and dusky brown; throat without blackish; upper breast and flanks with indistinct, dusky streaking. **Note: The amount of white in the rects shows some variation by age/sex (Fig. 262B-C), as in other *Dendroica* warblers, but differences are slight and obscured by individual variation. Differences in rect shape also can be difficult to use. HY/SY ♀♀ average duller and yellower on the belly than HY/SY ♂♂, and average smaller dusky centers to the back feathers (Fig. 274), but individuals are not separated reliably, except, perhaps, extremes in combination with measurements. Intermediates will also occur which are not reliably aged; extreme caution is required.**

AHY/ASY ♀ (Aug-Mar): Back feathers with small and indistinct, blackish centers (Fig. 274); rump grayish; outer pp covs broad, truncate, relatively fresh (Fig. 138**B**), and blackish, not contrasting markedly in color or wear with the gr covs (Fig. 133**F**); terts uniform in color and wear with the middle ss (s4-s6; Fig. 133**F**); outer rects (r4-r6) fresh, truncate (Fig. 139**A**), and dusky; throat without blackish; upper breast and flanks with moderately distinct, black-

HY/SY ♀   AHY/ASY ♀   HY/SY ♂   AHY/ASY ♂

FIGURE 274. Variation in the pattern of dusky or black in the back feathers, by age and sex, in Bay-breasted and Blackpoll warblers.

ish streaking; belly heavily washed yellow, without white. **Note: See HY/SY ♀. Some over-lap can occur with AHY/ASY ♂; combine with measurements.**

AHY/ASY ♂ (Aug-Mar): Back feathers with large black centers (Fig. 274); rump grayish; pp-cov and rect criteria as in AHY/ASY ♀; throat often with black spotting; upper breast and flanks with distinct, black streaking; belly white, or primarily white with some yellow wash. **Note: See HY/SY ♀ and AHY/ASY ♀.**

Alternate Plumage (Mar-Aug)

SY ♀ (Mar-Aug): Crown and nape grayish olive to olive, with indistinct, black streaking; contrast between crown and auricular indistinct or lacking; outer pp covs narrow, tapered, abraded (Fig. 138C), and brownish dusky, contrasting markedly with the recently replaced, first-alternate gr covs (see **Molt**); outer rects relatively abraded, tapered (Fig. 139A), and brownish; underparts white with a yellow tinge or wash. **Note: See HY/SY ♀, above. In Mar-Aug, both SYs and ASYs can show contrasts between replaced and retained gr covs (Fig. 133C-E; see Molt).**

ASY ♀ (Mar-Aug): Crown and nape grayish to grayish olive, with distinct, black streaking; contrast between crown and auricular indistinct or lacking; outer pp covs broad, truncate, relatively fresh (Fig. 138D), and dusky, contrasting only moderately with the recently replaced gr covs (see **Molt**); outer rects (r4-r6) fresh, truncate (Fig. 139A), and brownish dusky; underparts white, sometimes tinged yellow. **Note: See HY/SY ♀ (above) and SY ♀.**

SY ♂ (Mar-Aug): Crown and nape black, without streaking, and sometimes with slight olive mottling, contrasting moderately with the white auricular; pp-cov and rect criteria as in SY ♀; underparts white. **Note: See HY/SY ♀ (above) and SY ♀.**

ASY ♂ (Mar-Aug): Crown and nape black, without streaking, contrasting sharply with the white auricular; pp-cov and rect criteria as in ASY ♀; underparts white. **Note: See HY/SY ♀ (above) and SY ♀.**

Hybrids reported—Cape May Warbler, Bay-breasted Warbler. Probably Northern Waterthrush (which see).

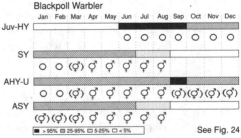

Note: In Oct-Dec, some AHYs can be sexed but birds of unknown age should be left unsexed.

References—Stone (1896), Dwight (1900a), Ridgway (1902), Preble (1908), Todd & Carriker (1922), Forbush (1929), Brodkorb (1934), A.O. Gross *in* Bent (1953), Blake (1954a), Roberts (1955), Nisbet *et al.* (1963), Robbins (1964), Short & Robbins (1967), Howard (1968), Wood (1969), Oberholser (1974), Sheppard & Klimkiewicz (1976), Parkes (1978, 1995c), Stiles & Campos (1983), Whitney (1983), Kaufman (1990a), Cramp & Perrins (1994b), Curson *et al.* (1994), Hertzel & Hertzel (1995), Dunn & Garrett (1997), Pyle (1997c); E.H. Dunn, D.J.T. Hussell, K.C. Parkes (*in litt.* to the BBL); IBP (MAPS) data, PRBO data.

CERULEAN WARBLER
Dendroica cerulea

CERW
Species # 6580
Band size: 0A-0

Species—HY/SY ♀ from other warblers by tl short (38-47); wing bars distinct and whitish.

Geographic variation—No subspecies are recognized.

Molt—PB: HY partial (Jun-Aug), AHY complete (Jun-Aug); PA partial (Jan-May). The PBs occur on the summer grounds. The 1st PB usually includes all med and gr covs and often the greater alula, but no terts or rects. The PAs include no gr covs but often (in ~62% of birds) 1-3 terts, and occasionally (in ~6% of birds) 1-2 central rects (r1); the 1st PA averages slightly more terts and rects replaced than the adult PA. The PAs may involve continuous, limited replacement of body feathers on the winter grounds, from Oct-May, as in certain other warblers.

Skull—Pneumaticization completes in HY from 1 Oct through Dec.

Age/Sex—Juv (Jun-Aug) has brownish-gray upperparts, a pale median crown stripe, and entirely white underparts; juv ♀ = ♂, although some birds can be sexed by the color of the wing and tail edging, as in HY/SYs (see below). CP/BP (May-Aug). Measurements are useful: ♀ wg(n37) 58-66, tl(n20) 38-43; ♂ wg(n35) 61-70, tl(n35) 41-47.

Basic Plumage (Aug-Mar)

HY/SY ♀ (Aug-Mar): Upperparts olive with little or no blue; back feathers without blackish streaks (Fig. 261A); greater alula (usually) and the outer pp covs narrow, tapered, somewhat abraded, and brown with thin or no dull green edging (Fig. 138A), contrasting with the slightly fresher, dusky-centered, and blue-green-edged, replaced gr covs (Fig. 134); outer rects (r4-r6) relatively abraded, tapered (Fig. 139A), and dusky brown with relatively little white (Fig. 262B-C); streaking on the flanks very obscure. **Note: Rect shape shows more overlap in this species than in most other *Dendroica*, but amount of white in the rects is quite useful for ageing and sexing. Most birds should be reliably aged and sexed by the combination of skull condition, measurements, and plumage.**

AHY/ASY ♀ (Aug-Mar): Upperparts greenish with a distinct, blue wash (especially on rump); back feathers without blackish streaking (Fig. 261A); greater alula and outer pp covs broad, truncate, relatively fresh, and dusky with relatively distinct and broad, blue-green edging (Fig. 138B), not contrasting markedly in color or wear with the gr covs; outer rects (r3-r6) fresh, truncate (Fig. 139A), and dusky with a moderate amount of white (Fig. 262C-E); underparts washed yellowish; flanks with indistinct, black streaking. **Note: See HY/SY ♀.**

HY/SY ♂ (Aug-Mar): Upperparts greenish with a distinct, blue wash (especially on rump); back feathers often with indistinct, blackish streaks (Fig. 261A-B); greater alula (usually) and outer pp covs narrow, tapered, somewhat abraded, and dusky brown with relatively narrow, greenish-gray edging (Fig. 138A), contrasting with the slightly fresher, blackish-centered, and greenish-blue-edged gr covs (Fig. 134); outer rects (r3-r6) relatively abraded, tapered (Fig. 139A), and dusky brown with a moderate amount of white (Fig. 262C-E); underparts primarily white, the throat tinged yellow; flanks with indistinct, black streaking. **Note: See HY/SY ♀.**

AHY/ASY ♂ (Aug-Mar): Upperparts largely blue; back feathers with distinct, black centers (Fig. 261C-D); pp-cov and rect criteria as in AHY/ASY ♀, except that the alula and flight feathers are blackish with blue edging, and the outer rects (r3-r6) average more white (Fig. 262D-F); flanks and sides of the upper breast with distinct, black streaking. **Note: See HY/SY ♀.**

Alternate Plumage (Mar-Aug)

SY ♀ (Mar-Aug): Yellow supercilium moderately distinct; upperparts grayish with a green wash; flight feathers relatively worn, the edging (if present) greenish yellow; outer pp covs narrow, tapered, abraded, and brown (Fig. 138C); outer rects (r4-r6) relatively abraded, tapered (Fig. 139A), and brownish with relatively little white (Fig. 262B-C). **Note: See HY/SY ♀, above. Both SYs and ASYs can show 1-3 contrastingly fresh terts (Fig. 133D-E) and (occasionally) central rects (r1; see Molt).**

ASY ♀ (Mar-Aug): Yellow supercilium distinct; upperparts grayish with a green tinge; flight feathers edged bluish green; outer pp covs broad, truncate, relatively fresh, and brownish dusky, usually with distinct, bluish-green edging (Fig. 138**B**); outer rects (r3-r6) fresh, truncate (Fig. 139**A**), and brownish dusky with a moderate amount of white (Fig. 262**C-E**). **Note: See HY/SY ♀(above) and SY ♀.**

SY ♂ (Mar-Aug): Supercilium absent; upperparts blue, sometimes slightly mottled greenish; flight feathers relatively worn, the edging (if present) grayish green; pp-cov and rect criteria as in SY ♀ except that the outer rects (r3-r6) average more white (Fig. 262**C-E**). **Note: See HY/SY ♀ (above) and SY ♀.**

ASY ♂ (Mar-Aug): Supercilium absent; upperparts blue; flight-feather criteria as in ASY ♀, except that all feathers are blackish with blue edging, and the outer rects (r3-r6) average more white (Fig. 262**D-F**). **Note: See HY/SY ♀ (above) and SY ♀.**

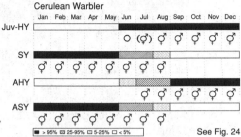

Hybrids reported—Black-and-white Warbler.

References—Stone (1896), Dwight (1900a), Ridgway (1902), Forbush (1929), Bent (1953), Roberts (1955), Robbins (1964), Sutton (1967), Wood (1969), Oberholser (1974), Sheppard & Klimkiewicz (1976), Parkes (1978), Curson *et al.* (1994), Dunn & Garrett (1997), Pyle (1997c); IBP (MAPS) data.

BLACK-AND-WHITE WARBLER
Mniotilta varia

BAWW
Species # 6360
Band size: 0-0A-1C

Geographic variation—No subspecies are recognized. Western birds and birds of the southern Appalachian Mts may average slightly longer winged than northeastern birds (see Noble 1919, Burleigh & Peters 1948, Cramp & Perrins 1994b).

Molt—PB: HY partial (Jun-Aug), AHY complete (May-Aug); PA partial (Oct-Apr). The PBs occur on the summer grounds. The 1st PB includes all med and gr covs, but no terts or rects; a pseudolimit (see p. 207) occurs in both age groups, the terts being blacker than the middle ss (s4-s6), appearing to be more recently replaced. Southern breeding birds commence molt earlier than northern breeding birds. The PAs include no gr covs, usually (in ~82% of birds) 1-3 terts, and sometimes (in ~22% of birds) 1-2 central rects (r1); SYs and ASYs replace similar numbers of feathers.

Skull—Pneumaticization completes in HY/SY from 1 Oct. Look for windows (> 2 mm; Fig. 11**D**) on the top of the skull in some SYs through Apr.

Age/Sex—Juv (Jun-Aug) resembles HY/SY ♀ (see below), but has upperparts washed brownish and underparts buffier, with dusky spots or streaking; juv ♀ = ♂, although some birds perhaps can be sexed by the amount of white in the outer rects, as in HY/SYs (see below). CP/BP (Apr-Jul). ♀ wg(n100) 59-69, tl(n25) 43-50; ♂ wg(n100) 63-74, tl(n53) 45-52; see **Geographic variation**.

HY/SY ♀ (Aug-Jul): Auricular buffy whitish (Aug-Mar), or grayish, sometimes tinged buff (Mar-Jul); outer pp covs narrow, tapered, somewhat abraded, and brownish with little or no pale edging (Fig. 138), contrasting with the slightly fresher and dusky-centered gr covs (Fig. 134);

outer rects (r5-r6) relatively abraded, tapered (Fig. 139A), and dusky brown with a relatively small amount of white (Fig. 262A); chin and throat whitish; flanks washed pinkish-buff, with very indistinct and dusky streaking. **Note: Occasional intermediates (particularly ♀♀) will be difficult to age but most birds should be reliably sexed. In Mar-Jul both SYs and ASYs can show 1-3 contrastingly fresh terts and, occasionally, central rects (r1; see Molt).**

AHY/ASY ♀ (Aug-Jul): Auricular grayish or whitish, the feathers washed buff in Aug-Mar; outer pp covs broad, truncate, relatively fresh, and dusky with distinct but thin, gray edging (Fig. 138), not contrasting markedly in color or wear with the gr covs (Fig. 133F); outer rects (r5-r6) fresh, truncate (Fig. 139A), and dusky with little to a moderate amount of white (Fig. 262A-B); flanks tinged pinkish-buff, with indistinct and dusky streaking; chin and throat white. **Note: See HY/SY ♀.**

HY/SY ♂ (Aug-Jul): Auricular grayish to whitish (Aug-Mar), or blackish, often lightly mottled whitish (Mar-Jul); wing-cov and rect criteria as in HY/SY ♀, except that the replaced gr covs are blacker (thus, the contrast with the pp covs is greater), and the outer rects (r5-r6) average slightly more white (Fig. 262A-B); flanks whitish with fairly bold, blackish streaking, often blurred but distinct; chin and throat whitish (Aug-Mar), or blackish, often mottled white (Mar-Jul). **Note: See HY/SY ♀.**

AHY/ASY ♂ (Aug-Jul): Auricular, chin, and throat black or blackish, the feathers with whitish tips in Aug-Dec; wing-cov and rect criteria as in AHY/ASY ♀, except that all feather centers are black, and the outer rects (r4-r6) average slightly more white (Fig. 262B-C); flanks white with bold, black streaking. **Note: See HY/SY ♀.**

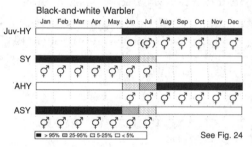

Hybrids reported—Blackburnian Warbler, Cerulean Warbler.

References—Stone (1896), Dwight (1900a), Ridgway (1902), Todd & Carriker (1922), Forbush (1929), Bent (1953), Roberts (1955), Robbins (1964), Sutton (1967), Wood (1969), Oberholser (1974), Sheppard & Klimkiewicz (1976), Parkes (1978), Bledsoe (1988), CWS & USFWS (1991), Cramp & Perrins (1994b), Curson *et al.* (1994), Kricher (1995), Dunn & Garrett (1997), Pyle (1997c); K.C. Parkes, C.S. Robbins, R.P. Yunick (*in litt.* to the BBL); H. Smith, B. Walker, G.E. Wallace (pers. comm.); IBP (MAPS) data, PNR data, PRBO data.

AMERICAN REDSTART
Setophaga ruticilla

AMRE
Species # 6870
Band size: 0A-0

Geographic variation—Subspecies taxonomy follows G.H. Lowery & B.L. Monroe *in* Paynter (1968), who considered the species monotypic (synonymizing a previously recognized subspecies); see Oberholser (1938, 1974), Wetmore (1940, 1949), Burleigh & Peters (1948), Mengel (1965), Monroe (1968), Mayr & Short (1970), Rohwer *et al.* (1983), Godfrey (1986), Cramp & Perrins (1994b). Northern and western breeding birds ("*S.r. tricolora*") may average slightly less yellow or orange in the wing, and have ♀♀ and HY/SYs with duller upperparts, but differences are weak and obscured by individual variation. ♂♂ of western birds also may average less body-feather replacement during the 1st PB and 1st PA than ♂♂ of eastern birds.

Molt—PB: HY partial (Jun-Sep), AHY complete (Jun-Aug); PA absent-limited (Oct-Apr). The PBs occur on the summer grounds. The 1st PB (which largely can complete before fledging) usually includes all med and gr covs and often the greater alula, but no terts or rects. The 1st PA occasionally (in ~11% of birds) can include 1-3 inner gr covs, but no terts or rects. The adult PA, if present, does not include wing covs. The PAs involve continuous, limited replacement of body feathers on the winter grounds, more extensive in HY/SY ♂♂ than in the other age/sex groups.

Skull—Pneumaticization completes in HY/SY from 15 Oct through Dec.

Age/Sex—Juv (Jun-Sep) has brownish upperparts, grayish underparts, and two whitish-yellow wing bars; extremes perhaps can be sexed by the amount of yellow in r3, as in HY/SYs (see below). CP/BP (May-Aug). ♀ wg(n40) 55-66, tl(n30) 52-61; ♂ wg(n100) 58-69, tl(n20) 49-58.

HY/SY ♀ (Aug-Jul): Upperparts and throat without black mottling; terts brown with little or no olive edging; outer pp covs narrow, tapered, relatively abraded (Fig. 138), and pale brown with buff tips when fresh, contrasting with the slightly fresher gr covs (Fig. 134); rects relatively abraded and washed brownish; yellow patch on r3 reduced and washed dusky (Fig. 275A-B), occasionally lacking; patches at the sides of the breast lemon-yellow, not contrasting markedly in color with the underwing covs; rump pale gray, not contrasting distinctly in color with the back. **Note: HY/SYs in Aug-Mar, without the black feathering of ♂♂, should be sexed with caution; the rump/back plumage appears to be the best criterion for sexing. Rect shape (Fig. 139A) in this species is subtle and variable, but can be useful with extremes.**

AHY/ASY ♀ (Aug-Jul): Upperparts and throat without black mottling; terts dusky brown, usually edged olive; outer pp covs broad, truncate, relatively fresh (Fig. 138), and dusky brown, not contrasting in wear with the gr covs (Fig. 133F); rects relatively fresh and dusky; r3 usually with a large patch of yellow (Fig. 275B-C); patches at the sides of the breast lemon-yellow to orange-yellow, not contrasting markedly in color with the underwing covs. **Note: See HY/SY ♀ and HY/SY ♂. Also, beware that very old females with some black body feathering occasionally can occur.**

HY/SY ♂ (Sep-Aug): Upperparts and throat with no (Aug-Apr) to some (Sep-Aug) black mottling, especially about the lores, throat, and breast (occasionally including 1-3 inner gr covs); pp-cov and rect criteria as in HY/SY ♀, except that the amount of yellow in r3 averages more extensive (Fig. 275B-C); patches at the sides of the breast orangish yellow to salmon colored, often contrasting with the yellow underwing covs; rump dark gray, contrasting distinctly with the paler gray back. **Note: See HY/SY ♀ and AHY/ASY ♀. Beware of occasional SY ♂♂ in Apr-Jun that can lack black feathering.**

AHY/ASY ♂ (Sep-Aug): Upperparts, throat and breast black; flight feathers black and orange.

Hybrids reported—Northern Parula. Possibly Nashville Warbler.

References—Stone (1896), Dwight (1900a), Ridgway (1902), Forbush (1929), Petrides (1943), Burleigh (1944), A.O. Gross *in* Bent (1953), Roberts (1955), Ficken (1964), Robbins (1964), Wood (1969), Gray (1973),

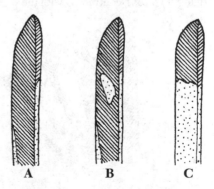

A   B   C

FIGURE 275. Variation in the amount of yellow in r3, by age and sex (see text), in American Redstart.

Foy (1974a, 1974b), Oberholser (1974), Sheppard & Klimkiewicz (1976), Rohwer *et al.* (1983), Arendt (1987), Spellman *et al.* (1987), Parkes (1988b), CWS & USFWS (1991), Lefebvre *et al.* (1992), Marra *et al.* (1993), Cramp & Perrins (1994b), Curson *et al.* (1994), Sibley (1994), Dunn & Garrett (1997), Pyle (1997c), Sherry & Holmes (1997); E.J. Fisk (*in litt.* to the BBL); P.P. Marra, G.E. Wallace (pers. comm.); PRBO data.

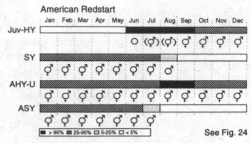

See Fig. 24

Note: In Mar-Jul all ♂♂ should be aged SY or ASY but some ♀♀ should be aged AHY.

PROTHONOTARY WARBLER
Protonotaria citrea

PROW
Species # 6370
Band size: 0

Geographic variation—No subspecies are recognized. Northern birds average slightly larger than southern birds; *e.g.*, birds of MI average wg 69.0 in ♀♀ and 73.9 mm in ♂♂, whereas birds of TN average 67.5 in ♀♀ and 70.9 in ♂♂ (L.H. Walkinshaw *in litt.* to the BBL).

Molt—PB: HY partial (May-Dec), AHY complete (May-Aug); PA absent. The 1st PB appears to start on the summer grounds and complete on the winter grounds; possibly a presupplemental molt (see p. 16) occurs (more study is needed). The adult PB occurs on the summer grounds. The 1st PB usually includes all med and gr covs, but not the greater alula, terts, or rects.

Skull—Pneumaticization completes in HY from 1 Oct (as early as 15 Sep in birds of FL) through Nov.

Age/Sex—Juv (May-Jul) has brownish-olive upperparts, grayish-olive underparts, and two olive wing bars; juvs can be sexed by the amount of white in the rects, as in HY/SYs (see below). CP/BP (Apr-Aug). ♀ wg(n100) 63-72, tl(n20) 41-49; ♂ wg(n100) 66-76, tl(n20) 43-50; see **Geographic variation**.

HY/SY ♀ (Aug-Jul): Crown and nape greenish, blending with the color of the back (Fig. 259); terts relatively worn and brownish with little or no bluish; greater alula and outer pp covs narrow, tapered, relatively abraded, and brownish with indistinct, narrow, or no bluish-gray edging (Fig. 138), contrasting with the slightly fresher and dusky-centered gr covs (Fig. 134);

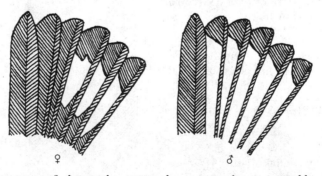

♀   ♂

FIGURE 276. The amount of white in the rectrices by sex in Prothonotary Warbler. Note that some ♀♀ can have a bit of white on r2 and/or r3.

outer rects relatively abraded, tapered (Fig. 139**A**), and dusky brown; distinct, white patches occur on the outer 2-3 rects (r4-r6) only (Fig. 276). **Note: All birds should be easily sexed and most reliably aged; it is best to sex birds before ageing. In addition, HY/SYs average slightly reduced and less distinctly defined white in the rects than AHY/ASYs and this might prove useful in ageing; more study is needed.**

AHY/ASY ♀ (Aug-Jul): Crown and nape greenish yellow, contrasting slightly with the greenish back (Fig. 259); terts relatively fresh and bluish; greater alula and outer pp covs broad, truncate, relatively fresh, and dusky with relatively distinct and broad, bluish or whitish edging (Fig. 138), not contrasting markedly in color or wear with the gr covs (Fig. 133**F**); outer rects relatively fresh, truncate (Fig. 139**A**), and dusky; distinct, white patches occur on the outer 2-3 rects (r4-r6) only (Fig. 276; r2-r3 can have small and/or indistinct patches). **Note: See HY/SY ♀.**

HY/SY ♂ (Aug-Jul): Crown and nape yellow with a greenish wash, contrasting moderately with the greenish back (Fig. 259); wing-cov and flight-feather criteria as in HY/SY ♀, except that r2-r6 with distinct, white patches (Fig. 276). **Note: See HY/SY ♀.**

AHY/ASY ♂ (Aug-Jul): Crown and nape bright yellow, contrasting sharply with the greenish back (Fig. 259); wing-cov and flight-feather criteria as in AHY/ASY ♀, except that r2-r6 with distinct, white patches (Fig. 276). **Note: See HY/SY ♀.**

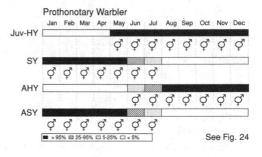

References—Dwight (1900a), Ridgway (1902), Forbush (1929), Bent (1953), Roberts (1955), Robbins (1964), Sutton (1967), Wood (1969), Oberholser (1974), Sheppard & Klimkiewicz (1976), Kowalski (1986), Lefebvre *et al.* (1992), Pyle & McCaskie (1992), Curson *et al.* (1994), Dunn & Garrett (1997), Pyle (1997c); L.H. Walkinshaw (*in litt.* to the BBL); B. Walker (pers. comm.); IBP (MAPS) data.

WORM-EATING WARBLER
Helmitheros vermivorus

WEWA
Species # 6390
Band size: 1C-0

Geographic variation—No subspecies are recognized.

Molt—PB: HY partial (Jun-Aug), AHY complete (Jul-Aug); PA absent. The PBs occur on the summer grounds. The 1st PB usually includes all med and gr covs, but not the greater alula, terts, or rects.

Skull—Pneumaticization completes in HY from 1 Oct through Dec.

Age—Juv (Jun-Jul) has duskier head markings and generally is buffier, with two cinnamon wing bars; juv ♀ = ♂.

HY/SY (Aug-Jul): Terts with rusty tips (usually wearing off in Nov-Mar); outer pp covs narrow, tapered, relatively abraded, pale brown with buff tips when fresh, and with little or no olive edging (Fig. 138), contrasting with the slightly fresher gr covs (Fig. 134); outer rects relatively abraded and tapered (Fig. 139**A**). **Note: Intermediates will occur, especially in spring, which are not reliably aged.**

AHY/ASY (Aug-Jul): Terts without rusty tips; outer pp covs broad, truncate, relatively fresh, and dusky brown, without buff tips, and usually with distinct but narrow, olive edging (Fig. 138), not contrasting in wear with the gr covs (Fig. 133F); outer rects relatively fresh and truncate (Fig. 139A). **Note: See HY/SY.**

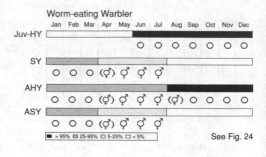

Worm-eating Warbler

Sex—♀ = ♂ by plumage. CP/BP (Apr-Aug). ♀ wg(n100) 62-72, tl(n10) 44-48; ♂ wg(n100) 66-75, tl(n10) 46-51.

References—Dwight (1900a), Ridgway (1902), Forbush (1929), Bent (1953), Robbins (1964), Wood (1969), Oberholser (1974), Curson *et al.* (1994), Dunn & Garrett (1997), Pyle (1997c); G.E. Wallace (pers. comm.); IBP (MAPS) data, PNR data.

SWAINSON'S WARBLER
Limnothlypis swainsonii

SWWA
Species # 6380
Band size: 1C

Geographic variation—Subspecies taxonomy follows G.H. Lowery & B.L. Monroe *in* Paynter (1968), who considered the species monotypic (synonymizing a previously recognized subspecies); see Meanley & Bond (1950), Monroe (1968), Brown & Dickson (1994). Breeding birds of montane WV-n.GA (*"L.s. alta"*) may average duller upperparts and whiter (less yellow) underparts than coastal and lowland breeding birds, but differences are slight and obscured by individual variation.

Molt—PB: HY partial (May-Aug), AHY complete (Jun-Aug); PA absent. The PBs occur on the summer grounds. The 1st PB usually includes all med and gr covs, but not the greater alula, terts, or rects.

Skull—Pneumaticization completes in HY from 1 Oct through Dec.

Age—Juv (May-Jul) usually lacks a supercilium (sometimes it is present but is indistinct and very short) and has buffy wing bars; juv ♀ = ♂.

HY/SY (Aug-Jul): Outer pp covs narrow, tapered, relatively abraded (Fig. 138), and medium-pale brown, sometimes with indistinct, buff tips when fresh, and contrasting with the slightly fresher gr covs (Fig. 134); outer rects relatively abraded and tapered (Fig. 139A). **Note: Plumage distinctions can be difficult to infer; many intermediates cannot be reliably aged.**

AHY/ASY (Aug-Jul): Outer pp covs broad, truncate, relatively fresh (Fig. 138), and medium-dark brown, without buff tips, and not contrasting in wear with the gr covs (Fig. 133F); outer rects relatively fresh and truncate (Fig. 139A). **Note: See HY/SY.**

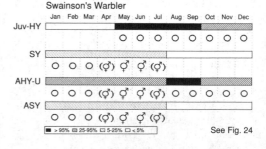

Swainson's Warbler

Sex—♀ = ♂ by plumage. CP/BP (Apr-Jul). ♀ wg(n42) 64-73, tl(n20) 43-51; ♂ wg(n62) 66-76, tl(n20) 44-51.

References—Dwight (1900a), Ridgway (1902), Bent (1953), Meanley (1971), Oberholser (1974), Brown & Dickson (1994), Curson *et al.* (1994), Dunn & Garrett (1997), Pyle (1997c); IBP (MAPS) data, PNR data.

OVENBIRD
Seiurus aurocapillus

OVEN
Species # 6740
Band size: 1C-1-0

Geographic variation—Moderately weak and clinal where ranges meet. Subspecies taxonomy follows G.H. Lowery & B.L. Monroe *in* Paynter (1968); see Batchelder (1918), Miller (1942), Burleigh & Duvall (1952), Monroe (1968), Oberholser (1974), Ramos & Warner (1980), Wetmore *et al.* (1984), Godfrey (1986), Curson *et al.* (1994), Dunn & Garrett (in press). No other subspecies occur.

> *S.a. cinereus* (br s.Alb to CO-NE): Upperparts dull grayish olive; auricular dull tawny olive.
> *S.a. aurocapillus* (br e.BC to NS-GA): Crown stripe medium-pale brownish orange; upperparts bright brownish olive with a greenish tinge; auricular bright tawny olive. Birds breeding in montane WV to n.AL-w.SC ("*canivirens*") may average grayer upperparts, but this difference is weak and broadly clinal.
> *S.a. furvior* (br Nfl): Crown stripe medium-dark brownish; upperparts deep brownish olive; auricular deep tawny.

Molt—PB: HY partial (Jun-Aug), AHY complete (Jun-Aug); PA absent-limited (Jan-Mar). The PBs occur on the summer grounds. The 1st PB usually includes all med and gr covs, but not the greater alula, terts, or rects; reports of regular tert and rect replacement in this species need confirmation. The PAs are limited to feathers of the head, and may be continuous from Oct-Apr, as in certain other warblers.

Skull—Pneumaticization completes in HY/SY from 1 Nov. Look for windows (> 2 mm; Fig. 11**D**) on the top of the skull in some SYs through summer.

Age—Juv (Jun-Aug) lacks a prominent head pattern (they can have an indistinct supercilium), has feathers of the upperparts and breast edged cinnamon, and has two rusty wing bars; juv ♀ = ♂.

> HY/SY (Aug-Jul): Terts and wing covs with narrow, rusty tipping when fresh (through Oct-May or later); outer pp covs narrow, tapered, relatively abraded, pale brown with rusty tips when fresh, and with little or no olive edging (Fig. 138), contrasting with the slightly fresher gr covs (Fig. 134); outer rects relatively abraded, tapered (Fig. 139**A**), and sometimes with pale edging but usually without pale spots. **Note: Intermediates, especially in spring/summer, may not be reliably aged.**

> AHY/ASY (Aug-Jul): Terts and wing covs without rusty tips; outer pp covs broad, truncate, relatively fresh, and dusky brown, without rusty tips, and usually with narrow, olive edging (Fig. 138), not contrasting in wear with the gr covs (Fig. 133**F**); outer rects relatively fresh and truncate (Fig. 139**A**); edges of the outer rects whitish when fresh, occasionally (on about 5% of AHY/ASYs) with indistinct, pale spots extending > 1 mm onto the inner webs. **Note: See HY/SY.**

Sex—♀ = ♂ by plumage, although occasional birds with a pale patch in the outer rects (see **Age**) possibly can be sexed ♂♂, in combination with wg; more study is needed. CP/BP (Apr-Aug). ♀ wg(n100) 67-78, tl(n28) 48-55; ♂ wg(n100) 70-81, tl(n33) 51-57.

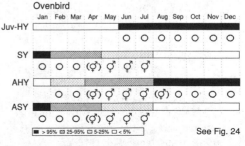

Ovenbird

See Fig. 24

References—Stone (1896), Dwight (1900a), Ridgway (1902), Forbush (1929), Bent (1953), Roberts (1955), Eaton (1957b), Robbins (1964), Short & Robbins (1967), Wood (1969), Taylor (1972, 1973), Oberholser (1974), Sheppard & Klimkiewicz (1976), Crawford (1978), CWS & USFWS (1991), Cramp & Perrins (1994b), Curson *et al.* (1994), Van Horn & Donovan (1994), Donovan & Stanley (1995), Dunn & Garrett (1997), Pyle (1997c); E.J. Fisk, C.S. Robbins (*in litt.* to the BBL); G.E. Wallace (pers. comm.); IBP (MAPS) data, PNR data, PRBO data.

NORTHERN WATERTHRUSH
Seiurus noveboracensis

NOWA
Species # 6750
Band size: 1C-0

Species—Larger and whiter northwestern birds (see **Geographic variation**) from Louisiana Waterthrush by shorter wg (67-82; see **Sex**); wg – tl 22-29 mm; bill shorter (nares to tip 9.0-10.7), supercilium usually yellowish and tapering behind the eye, and chin and throat usually with distinct and narrow, black streaking (Fig. 277); flanks and underparts uniformly yellowish or whitish in coloration; undertail covs with regularly patterned, dusky bases (Fig. 277).

Geographic variation—Subspecies taxonomy follows Behle (1985), who considered the species monotypic (synonymizing three previously recognized subspecies); see also Ridgway (1902), McCabe & Miller (1933), Taverner & Sutton (1934), Burleigh & Peters (1948), Eaton (1957a, 1995), Todd (1963), Phillips *et al.* (1964), Monroe (1968), Oberholser (1974), Ramos & Warner (1980), Godfrey (1986), Cramp & Perrins (1994b), Curson *et al.* (1994), Dunn & Garrett (in press). Birds breeding in BC-sw.Alb ("*S.n. limnaeus*") are slightly smaller with grayer upperparts; birds breeding in AK to w.Que-MI ("*notabilis*") are slightly larger and have grayer upperparts and whiter underparts; and birds breeding in Nfl ("*uliginosus*") may be longerwinged and shorter-billed, and have more dusky-olive upperparts and yellower underparts; but in all cases differences are broadly clinal and obscured by substantial individual variation.

Molt—PB: HY partial (Jun-Sep), AHY complete (Jun-Aug); PA limited (Oct-Apr). The PBs occur on the summer grounds. The 1st PB usually includes all med and gr covs, but not the greater alula, terts, or rects; reports of regular tert and rect replacement in this species need confirmation. The PAs are limited to feathers of the body and involve continuous, limited replacement on the winter grounds.

Skull—Pneumaticization completes in HY/SY from 1 Nov. Look for windows (> 2 mm; Fig. 11**D**) on the top of the skull in some SYs through summer.

Age—Juv (Jun-Jul) has the feathers of the upperparts tipped cinnamon, distinct, buffy wing bars, and buffy-washed underparts with dusky streaking; juv ♀ = ♂.

HY/SY (Aug-Jul): Terts and wing covs with narrow, rusty tipping when fresh (Aug-Dec, at least); outer pp covs narrow, tapered, relatively abraded (Fig. 138), and brown with rusty tipping when fresh, contrasting with the slightly fresher gr covs (Fig. 134); outer rects relatively abraded and tapered (Fig. 139**A**), often without pale edging, and usually without pale spots. **Note: Many intermediates, especially in spring/summer, may not be reliably aged.**

AHY/ASY (Aug-Jul): Terts and wing covs without rusty tipping; outer pp covs broad, truncate, relatively fresh (Fig. 138), and dark olive-brown, without rusty tips, and not contrasting in wear with the gr covs (Fig. 133**F**); outer rects relatively fresh and truncate (Fig. 139**A**); edges of the outer rects occasionally (on about 8% of AHY/ASYs; ♂♂ only?) with indistinct, whitish spots, extending > 1 mm onto the inner webs. **Note: See HY/SY.**

Sex—♀ = ♂ by plumage, although birds with some whitish in the outer rects (see **Age**) possibly can be sexed ♂♂, in combination with wg; more study is needed. CP/BP (Apr-

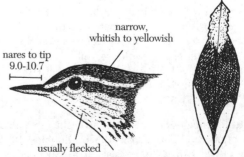

nares to tip
9.0-10.7

narrow,
whitish to yellowish

usually flecked

FIGURE 277. The bill size, head plumage, and undertail covert pattern in Northern Waterthrush.

Aug). ♀ wg(n100) 67-78, tl(n30) 46-55; ♂ wg(n100) 71-82, tl(n45) 48-57; see **Geographic variation**.

Hybrids reported—*Dendroica* species, probably Blackpoll Warbler but possibly Cape May Warbler.

References—Stone (1896), Dwight (1900a), Ridgway (1902), Forbush (1929), Bent (1953), Roberts (1955), Eaton (1957a, 1957b, 1995), Robbins (1964), Short & Robbins (1967), Wood (1969), Binford (1971), Collins & Binford (1974), Oberholser (1974), Sheppard & Klimkiewicz (1976), Wallace (1976), Parkes (1978, 1995c), Kaufman (1990a), CWS & USFWS (1991), Lefebvre *et al.* (1992), Winker *et al.* (1992), Curson (1993), Cramp & Perrins (1994b), Curson *et al.* (1994), Dunn & Garrett (1997), Pyle (1997c); D. Brewer, S.W. Eaton (*in litt.* to the BBL); B. Walker (pers. comm.); IBP (MAPS) data, PNR data, PRBO data.

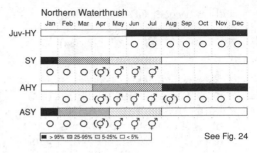

LOUISIANA WATERTHRUSH
Seiurus motacilla

LOWA
Species # 6760
Band size: 1C-1

Species—From Northern Waterthrush (which see) by longer wg (72-87; see **Sex**); wg – tl 26-34 mm; bill longer (nares to tip 10.2-12.2), supercilium white, broad, and usually extending to the nape, and chin and throat usually without streaking (Fig. 278); flanks and undertail covs buff, contrasting with the white underparts; largest undertail covs with irregular and restricted, pale gray patches (Fig. 278).

Geographic variation—No subspecies are recognized. Eastern birds average slightly larger than western birds (see Eaton 1958).

Molt—PB: HY partial (May-Aug), AHY complete (Jun-Aug); PA absent-limited(?). The PBs occur on the summer grounds. The 1st PB usually includes all med and gr covs, but not the greater alula, terts, or rects; reports that some or all rects are occasionally replaced need confirmation. The PAs, if present, are limited to the body feathers and may be continuous from Oct-Apr, as in Northern Waterthrush.

Skull—Pneumaticization completes in HY/SY from 1 Oct. Look for windows (> 2 mm; Fig. 11D) on the top of the skull in some SYs through Jun.

Age—Juvs (May-Jul) have a more prominent supercilium, and the pp covs of adults are dark brown with a slight or no olive tinge; otherwise the ageing criteria of Northern Waterthrush apply to this species. It is possible that HY/SYs also average more flecking to the throat, but more study is needed.

Sex—♀ = ♂ by plumage, although birds with some white in the outer rects (see Northern Waterthrush) possibly can be sexed ♂♂, in combination with measurements; more

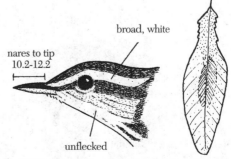

FIGURE 278. The bill size, head plumage, and undertail covert pattern in Louisiana Waterthrush.

study is needed. CP/BP (Mar-Aug). Measurements are somewhat useful: ♀ wg(n63) 72-83, tl(n20) 45-53; ♂ wg(n84) 77-87, tl(n20) 48-56; see **Geographic variation**.

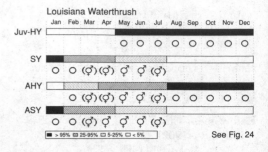

Louisiana Waterthrush

References—Dwight (1900a), Ridgway (1902), Forbush (1929), Bent (1953), Roberts (1955), Eaton (1957b, 1958), Robbins (1964), Short & Robbins (1967), Sutton (1967), Wood (1969), Binford (1971), Collins & Binford (1974), Schaeffer (1974), Oberholser (1974), Sheppard & Klimkiewicz (1976), Wallace (1976), Kaufman (1990a), CWS & USFWS (1991), Curson (1993), Curson *et al.* (1994), Robinson (1995), Dunn & Garrett (1997), Pyle (1997c); D. Brewer, S.W. Eaton (*in litt.* to the BBL); IBP (MAPS) data, PNR data.

KENTUCKY WARBLER
Oporornis formosus

KEWA
Species # 6770
Band size: 1C-1

Geographic variation—Subspecies taxonomy follows Browning (1990), who considered the species monotypic (synonymizing a previously recognized subspecies); see also Oberholser (1974), Browning (1978). Birds breeding north of n.MO-VA (*"O.f. umbraticus"*) average slightly larger than southern birds, but this difference is too weak for subspecies recognition, and the supposed paler coloration of northern birds probably was based on relative specimen wear.

Molt—PB: HY partial (May-Aug), AHY complete (Jun-Aug); PA limited (Jan-May). The PBs occur on the summer grounds. The 1st PB (which can be largely completed before fledging) usually includes all med and gr covs, but not the greater alula, terts, or rects. The PAs are limited to feathers of the head, may be continuous from Oct-Apr (as in certain other warblers), and possibly average more extensive in SYs than ASYs.

Skull—Pneumaticization completes in HY/SY from 1 Oct through Jan.

Age/Sex—Juv (May-Jul) lacks black on the crown and face and has brownish upperparts and brownish-yellow plumage; juv ♀ = ♂. CP/BP (Apr-Jul). ♀ wg(n100) 60-70, tl(n20) 45-51; ♂ wg(n100) 64-75, tl(n25) 47-53.

HY/SY ♀ (Aug-Jul): Crown dusky with an extensive olive-brown wash (Aug-Mar), or dull black

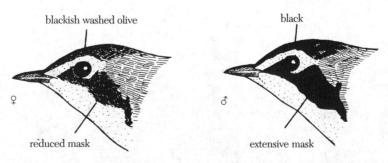

FIGURE 279. The head plumage by sex in Kentucky Warbler. Note that HY/SY ♂♂ can show intermediate characters.

with a brown wash (Mar-Jul); face mask (see Fig. 279) dusky or olive and restricted (Aug-Mar), or moderately restricted (Mar-Jul); outer pp covs narrow, tapered, relatively abraded, and dull brown with little or no greenish edging (Fig. 138), contrasting with the slightly fresher, duskier, and yellow-edged gr covs (Fig. 134); outer rects relatively abraded and tapered (Fig. 139A). **Note: A few intermediates will occur which cannot be reliably aged and/or sexed; combine all criteria (including measurements) for accurate determinations of most birds.**

AHY/ASY ♀ (Aug-Jul): Crown dull black, the feathers tipped gray (with little or no brown) in Aug-Dec; face mask blackish and restricted (Fig. 279); outer pp covs broad, truncate, relatively fresh, and dusky brown with relatively distinct and broad, greenish edging (Fig. 138), not contrasting markedly in color or wear with the gr covs (Fig. 133F); outer rects relatively fresh and truncate (Fig. 139A). **Note: See HY/SY ♀.**

HY/SY ♂ (Aug-Jul): Crown blackish, the feathers tipped dusky brown (Aug-Mar), or black, lightly suffused olive (Mar-Jul); face mask (see Fig. 279) dull black, suffused with greenish, and moderately reduced (Aug-Mar), or blackish, moderately distinct, and extensive (Mar-Jul); wing-cov and rect criteria as in HY/SY ♀. **Note: See HY/SY ♀.**

AHY/ASY ♂ (Aug-Jul): Crown black, the feathers tipped gray (with little or no brown); face mask black, distinct, and extensive (Fig. 279); wing-cov and rect criteria as in AHY/ASY ♀. **Note: See HY/SY ♀.**

Kentucky Warbler

Hybrids reported—Blue-winged Warbler. Possibly Mourning Warbler.

See Fig. 24

References—Stone (1896), Dwight (1900a), Ridgway (1902), Forbush (1929), McCamey (1950), Bent (1953), Goodpasture (1963), Robbins (1964), Wood (1969), Oberholser (1974), Graves (1988), Millard (1988), Parkes (1988a, 1989b), Pyle & McCaskie (1992), Curson *et al.* (1994), Dunn & Garrett (1997), Pyle (1997c); IBP (MAPS) data, PNR data, PRBO data.

CONNECTICUT WARBLER
Oporornis agilis

CONW
Species # 6780
Band size: 1C-1

Species—From dull Nashville Warblers by much larger size (wg 63-75, tl 42-54; see **Age/Sex**); belly and vent uniformly yellow; legs fleshy pink. From Mourning and MacGillivray's warblers by larger size (see above); wg(flat) – tl 19-27 mm; p9 > p6 by at least 3.5 mm; eye ring full and distinct (occasionally with small and abrupt breaks); lores and breast of alternate-plumaged ♂♂ without distinct and extensive black; HY/SYs and ♀♀ with the throat buffy or dingy whitish, usually without yellow, and the breast band with a broad, uninterrupted, dingy brownish wash.

Geographic variation—No subspecies are recognized.

Molt—PB: HY partial (Jun-Aug), AHY complete (Jun-Aug); PA limited (Jan-May). The PBs occur on the summer grounds. The 1st PB (which can be largely completed before fledging) usually includes all med and gr covs, but not the greater alula, terts, or rects. The PAs are limited to feathers of the head, may be continuous from Oct-Apr, as in certain other warblers, and possibly average more extensive in SY ♂♂ than in ♀♀ and ASYs.

Skull—Pneumaticization completes in HY from 1 Nov through Dec.

Age/Sex—Juv (Jun-Aug) has the entire plumage washed brownish; juv ♀ = ♂. CP/BP (May-Jul). ♀ wg(n100) 63-73, tl(n72) 42-51; ♂ wg(n100) 65-75, tl(n100) 44-54.

HY/SY ♀ (Aug-Jul): Forecrown and upper breast olive-brown (Aug-Mar), or olive-gray with a buff tinge (Mar-Jul); eye ring buff to buffy white and relatively thin; outer pp covs narrow, tapered, relatively abraded, and dull brown with indistinct, narrow, or no olive edging (Fig. 138), contrasting with the slightly fresher and dusky-centered gr covs (Fig. 134); outer rects relatively abraded and tapered (Fig. 139A); throat buffy white, sometimes tinged yellow. **Note: Many intermediates between this and HY/SY ♂ can occur in Aug-Mar; combine all sexing criteria, including measurements. Some intermediates also will occur that are not reliably aged.**

AHY/ASY ♀ (Aug-Jul): Forecrown, throat, and upper breast olive-gray (Aug-Mar), or pale grayish (Mar-Jul); eye ring white and relatively thick; outer pp covs broad, truncate, relatively fresh, and dusky with relatively distinct and broad, olive edging (Fig. 138), not contrasting markedly in color or wear with the gr covs (Fig. 133F); outer rects relatively fresh and truncate (Fig. 139A); throat whitish. **Note: See HY/SY ♀.**

HY/SY ♂ (Aug-Jul): Forecrown and upper breast brownish gray (Aug-Mar), or slate gray (Mar-Jul); eye ring buff to buffy white and relatively thin; pp-cov and rect criteria as in HY/SY ♀; throat pale whitish (Aug-Mar), or pale slate (Mar-Jul). **Note: See HY/SY ♀.**

AHY/ASY ♂ (Aug-Jul): Forecrown, throat, and upper breast slate gray, the feathers tipped olive (crown), or pale gray (throat), when fresh; eye ring white and relatively thick; pp-cov and rect criteria as in AHY/ASY ♀. **Note: See HY/SY ♀.**

Connecticut Warbler

Jan Feb Mar Apr May Jun Jul Aug Sep Oct Nov Dec

Juv-HY   ○ ○ (♂)(♀)(♀)(♀)(♀)

SY   (♀)(♀)(♀) ♂ ♂ ♂ ♂

AHY-U   (♀)(♀)(♀) ♂ ♂ ♂ ♂ ♂ ♂ ♂ ♂ ♂

ASY   ♂ ♂ ♂ ♂ ♂ ♂ ♂

■ > 95% ▨ 25-95% ▢ 5-25% ☐ < 5%   See Fig. 24

Hybrids reported—Possibly Mourning Warbler.

References—Stone (1896), Dwight (1900a), Ridgway (1902), Forbush (1929), Kilgore & Breckenridge (1929), Bent (1953), Roberts (1955), Blake (1956), Robbins (1964), Lanyon & Bull (1967), Sutton (1967), Wood (1969), Oberholser (1974), Sheppard & Klimkiewicz (1976), Gustafson (1988), Pyle & Henderson (1990), Curson (1992), Curson *et al.* (1994), Dunn & Garrett (1997), Pyle (1997c).

MOURNING WARBLER
Oporornis philadelphia

MOWA
Species # 6790
Band size: 0-1C-1

Species—From the eastern subspecies of Orange-crowned Warbler by much larger size (wg 54-65, tl 43-53; see **Age/Sex**); undertail covs and belly uniformly yellow; legs fleshy pink. From Connecticut Warbler by smaller size (see above); wg(flat) – tl 9-18 mm; p9 < p6 or, rarely, > p6 by 0-3 mm; eye ring absent or with a few whitish feathers (alternate-plumaged ♂♂) to partial (rarely complete) and thin, with tapered breaks (Fig. 280); throat strongly yellow (first-basic plumage) to white or gray, often with yellow flecking (AHY/ASY ♀♀); breast band grayish to brownish gray, usually interrupted in the center by the pale throat coloration; AHY/ASY ♂ with the lores and the area directly above the bill gray, occasionally with slight blackish mottling, and the chin usually gray, without whitish. From MacGillivray's Warbler by wg(flat) – tl 9-18 mm, eye ring, lore, and underpart plumage (as above); tl shorter (43-53; see **Age/Sex**). A few HY/SYs in basic plumage may not be separable from MacGillivray's by wg(flat) – tl (those with 9-12, possibly to 14 mm); compare with plumage and tail length. More study is needed on wg – tl measurements of live birds, as opposed to specimens. Some ♂♂ in alternate plumage (probably SYs only) can have white eye arcs, as in MacGillivray's Warbler (although the arcs are not as distinct); on these use wg(flat) – tl and the presence of distinct black in the lores and breast. Also, beware of variants (common in this species) and (probably) hybrids.

Geographic variation—No subspecies are recognized. See Pitocchelli (1992).

Molt—PB: HY partial (Jun-Aug), AHY complete (Jun-Aug); PA limited (Jan-May). The PBs occur primarily on the summer grounds. The 1st PB (which can be largely completed before fledging) usually includes all med and gr covs, but not the greater alula, terts, or rects. The 1st PA includes 0 (~62%) to 3 inner gr covs but no terts or rects, and the adult PA usually includes no gr covs, terts, or rects. The PAs possibly can involve continuous, limited replacement of body feathers on the winter grounds, from Oct-Apr, as in certain other warblers, and they appear to be more extensive in SYs than ASYs.

Skull—Pneumaticization completes in HY from 15 Oct through Dec.

Age/Sex—Juv (Jun-Aug) has the entire plumage washed brownish; juv ♀ = ♂. CP/BP (May-Aug). ♀ wg(n100) 54-63, tl(n54) 43-51; ♂ wg(n100) 57-65, tl(n100) 45-53.

Basic Plumage (Aug-Mar)

HY/SY ♀ (Aug-Mar): Head olive to brownish olive; partial to nearly complete eye ring yellowish; outer pp covs narrow, tapered, relatively abraded, and brownish with indistinct, narrow, or no olive edging (Fig. 138A), and often with indistinct, buffy-yellow tips when fresh, contrasting with the slightly fresher, duskier, and olive-edged gr covs (Fig. 134); outer rects relatively abraded and tapered (Fig. 139A); throat and upper breast buffy yellow to yellow, without gray or concealed black mottling; sides of the upper breast with indistinct, brownish-olive patches, sometimes nearly complete across the center. **Note: HY/SYs without black mottling in the breast are not necessarily ♀♀ and many of these are best left unsexed; combine all sexing criteria, including measurements.**

AHY/ASY ♀ (Aug-Mar): Head pale gray; partial eye ring absent or, if present, white to grayish white, sometimes nearly complete; outer pp covs broad, truncate, relatively fresh, and dusky brown with relatively distinct and broad, olive edging (Fig. 138**B**), without buffy-yellow tips, and not contrasting markedly in color or wear with the gr covs (Fig. 133**F**); outer rects relatively fresh and truncate (Fig. 139A); throat and center of the upper breast white or gray, often with yellow flecking or a yellow wash; breast band variable, usually restricted to the sides.

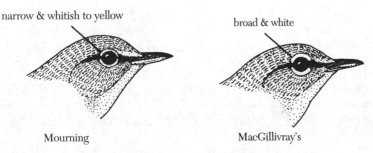

narrow & whitish to yellow   broad & white

Mourning   MacGillivray's

FIGURE 280. The eye ring features in Mourning and MacGillivray's warblers.

HY/SY ♂ (Aug-Mar): Head olive to grayish olive; partial to nearly complete eye ring yellowish white; pp-cov and rect criteria as in HY/SY ♀; throat and upper breast yellow to pale gray with a yellow wash, often with concealed blackish centers to some feathers; sides of the upper breast with brownish-gray patches and often some concealed black mottling, sometimes nearly complete across the center. **Note: See HY/SY ♀.**

AHY/ASY ♂ (Aug-Mar): Head and throat dark slate; eye ring absent; pp-cov and rect criteria as in AHY/ASY ♀; breast gray with a black patch or mottling.

Alternate Plumage (Mar-Aug)

SY ♀ (Mar-Aug): Head pale gray to brownish gray; whitish eye ring usually present, narrow, and broken; molt limits sometimes occur among the gr covs (see **Molt**; Fig. 133**B**), the inner 1-3 feathers contrastingly fresh (this can be subtle); outer pp covs narrow, tapered, abraded, and brown, usually without olive edging (Fig. 138**C**); outer rects relatively abraded, tapered (Fig. 139**A**), and brownish with dull olive edging; throat whitish, sometimes tinged yellow. **Note: Some intermediates will occur, especially ♀♀, that are not reliably aged.**

ASY ♀ (Mar-Aug): Head pale gray; whitish eye ring often present (sometimes absent), narrow, and broken; inner gr covs usually uniform in color and wear (Fig. 133**F**; although some med and lesser covs may be contrastingly fresh); outer pp covs broad, truncate, relatively fresh and brownish dusky, usually with distinct but narrow, olive edging (Fig. 138**D**); outer rects relatively fresh, truncate (Fig. 139**A**), and brownish dusky with brightish olive edging; throat white to pale grayish. **Note: See SY ♀.**

SY ♂ (Mar-Aug): Head and throat medium-pale slate gray; eye ring absent or with a few white feathers; molt-limit, wing-cov, and flight-feather criteria as in SY ♀; throat usually slate, contrasting with the blackish mottling of the breast patch. **Note: See SY ♀. Also, the presence of white feathering around the eye or a thin, whitish eye ring may be a reliable indicator of SY ♂, but more study is needed.**

ASY ♂ (Mar-Aug): Head and throat medium-dark slate; eye ring absent (possibly occasionally with a few white feathers; see SY ♂); molt-limit, wing-cov, and flight-feather criteria as in ASY ♀; throat and breast patch full and black. **Note: See SY ♀ and SY ♂.**

Hybrids reported—Common Yellowthroat, Canada Warbler. Probably MacGillivray's Warbler. Possibly Kentucky and Connecticut warblers. See also Blue-winged Warbler.

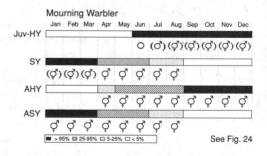

References—Stone (1896), Dwight (1900a), Ridgway (1902), Todd & Carriker (1922), Forbush (1929), Dickey & van Rossem (1938), Bent (1953), Roberts (1955), Blake (1956), Cox (1960, 1973), Robbins (1964), Lanyon & Bull (1967), Sutton (1967), Wood (1969), Oberholser (1974), Phillips (1975a, 1986), Patti & Meyers (1976), Sheppard & Klimkiewicz (1976), Beimborn (1977), Parkes (1978, 1988a), Hall (1979), Kowalski (1983), Bledsoe (1988), Graves (1988), Gustafson (1988), Millard (1988), Pitocchelli (1990, 1992, 1993), Pyle & Henderson (1990), Pyle & McCaskie (1992), Curson (1992), Binford & DeSante (1993), Curson *et al.* (1994), Dunn & Garrett (1997), Pyle (1997c); A.R. Phillips (pers. comm.); IBP (MAPS) data, PNR data, PRBO data.

MACGILLIVRAY'S WARBLER
Oporornis tolmiei

MGWA
Species # 6800
Band size: 1C-1-0

Species—From Mourning Warbler (which see for separation from Connecticut Warbler) by tl longer (47-63; see **Geographic variation** & **Age/Sex**); wg(flat) – tl 2-12 mm (rarely or anomalously to 14 mm); partial eye ring wide, abruptly broken, and white in all plumages (Fig. 280); throat dingy white to grayish (HY/SYs and ♀♀), occasionally washed dingy yellowish (HY/SY ♀♀); breast band grayish to brownish gray and usually complete across the center; AHY/ASY ♂♂ with the lores and the area above the eye black or primarily blackish and the chin usually whitish. Note that a few HY/SYs in basic plumage can be difficult to separate from Mourning Warbler. Beware also of alternate-plumaged ♂♂ Mourning Warblers with white in the eye ring and, probably, hybrids. See Mourning Warbler.

Geographic variation—Weak and clinal where ranges meet. Subspecies taxonomy follows Behle (1985); see also Phillips (1947a), Rand (1948b), Dickinson (1953), Blake (1958), Phillips *et al.* (1964), Sutton (1967), Monroe (1968), Oberholser (1974), Monson & Phillips (1981), Dunn & Garrett (in press). No other subspecies occur.

> *O.t. tolmiei* (br se.AK to OR-SD and CA): Tl relatively short, thus wg(flat) – tl averages longer (4-12 mm); belly medium-bright yellow; olive wash on the flanks reduced. Tl: ♀(n25) 47-55, ♂(n30) 49-57. Breeding birds of interior s.BC-se.CA (*"intermedia"*) may average slightly duller and breeding birds of se.BC-c.ID to SD (*"austinsmithi"*) may average shorter-tailed and duller, but differences are slight and obscured by individual variation.
>
> *O.t. monticola* (br NV-s.WY to AZ-NM): Tl relatively long, thus wg(flat) – tl averages shorter (1-7 mm); belly medium-dull yellow; olive wash on the flanks extensive. Tl: ♀(n10) 53-59, ♂(n15) 55-63.

Molt—PB: HY partial (Jun-Aug), AHY complete (Jul-Aug); PA limited-partial (Jan-May). The PBs occur on the summer grounds. The 1st PB (which can be largely completed before fledging) usually includes all med and gr covs, but not the greater alula, terts, or rects. The 1st PA includes 0 (~60%) to 3 inner gr covs but no terts or rects, and the adult PA usually includes no gr covs, terts, or rects. The PAs may involve continuous, limited replacement of body feathers on the winter grounds, from Oct-Apr, as in certain other warblers, and they appear to be more extensive in SYs than ASYs.

Skull—Pneumaticization completes in HY from 1 Oct through Dec.

Age/Sex—Juv (Jun-Aug) has the entire plumage washed brownish and cinnamon wing bars; juv ♀=♂. CP/BP (Apr-Aug). ♀ wg(n100) 52-61, tl(n100) 47-59; ♂ wg(n100) 54-64, tl(n100) 49-63; see **Geographic variation**.

Basic Plumage (Aug-Mar)

HY/SY ♀ (Aug-Mar): Head olive to brownish olive, blending or contrasting only slightly with the back color; outer pp covs narrow, tapered, relatively abraded, and brownish with indistinct, narrow, or no olive edging (Fig. 138A), often with indistinct, yellowish tips when fresh, and contrasting with the slightly fresher and dusky-centered gr covs (Fig. 134); outer rects tapered and relatively abraded (Fig. 139A); throat and upper breast buffy gray to dingy yellowish, without concealed black feathers or mottling. **Note: HY/SYs without black mottling in the breast are not necessarily ♀♀ and many of these are best left unsexed; combine all sexing criteria, including measurements.**

AHY/ASY ♀ (Aug-Mar): Head gray, lightly washed olive when fresh, and contrasting moderately with the greener back; outer pp covs broad, truncate, relatively fresh, and dusky with relatively broad, olive edging (Fig. 138B), without yellowish tips, and not contrasting markedly in color or wear with the gr covs (Fig. 133**F**); rects uniformly adult, relatively fresh, and truncate (Fig. 139**A**); throat and breast gray, without black feathers or mottling. **Note: See HY/SY ♀.**

HY/SY ♂ (Aug-Mar): Head grayish, lightly washed pale brownish or olive, contrasting moderately with the greener back; pp-cov and rect criteria as in HY/SY ♀; throat and upper breast gray, often with concealed blackish centers to some feathers. **Note: See HY/SY ♀.**

AHY/ASY ♂ (Aug-Mar): Head and throat dark slate; pp-cov and rect criteria as in AHY/ASY ♀; center of the breast with distinct, black mottling.

Alternate Plumage (Mar-Aug)

SY ♀ (Mar-Aug): Head pale gray to brownish gray; molt limits sometimes occur among the gr covs (Fig. 133**B**; see **Molt**), the inner 1-3 feathers contrastingly fresh (this can be subtle); outer pp covs narrow, tapered, abraded, and brown, usually without olive edging (Fig. 138**C**); outer rects relatively abraded, tapered (Fig. 139**A**), and brownish; throat pale grayish, often tinged buffy. **Note: Some intermediates will occur, especially ♀♀, that are not reliably aged.**

ASY ♀ (Mar-Aug): Head pale gray; inner gr covs usually uniform in color and wear (Fig. 133**F**, although there may be contrasts among the med and lesser covs); outer pp covs broad, truncate, relatively fresh, and dusky brown with olive edging (Fig. 138**D**); outer rects relatively fresh, truncate (Fig. 139**A**), and brownish dusky; throat pale grayish. **Note: See SY ♀.**

SY ♂ (Mar-Aug): Head and throat medium-pale slate gray; molt-limit, wing-cov, and rect criteria as in SY ♀; breast primarily gray, with black mottling. **Note: See SY ♀.**

ASY ♂ (Mar-Aug): Head and throat medium-dark slate; molt-limit, wing-cov, and flight-feather criteria as in ASY ♀; breast primarily black with gray mottling. **Note: See SY ♀.**

Hybrids reported—Probably Mourning Warbler.

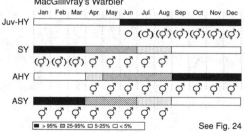

References—Ridgway (1902), Dickey & van Rossem (1938), Phillips (1947a, 1975a), Bent (1953), Lanyon & Bull (1967), Cox (1973), Oberholser (1974), Patti & Meyers (1976), Sheppard & Klimkiewicz (1976), Beimborn (1977), Parkes (1978), Hall (1979), Kowalski (1983), Pitocchelli (1990, 1995), Pyle & Henderson (1990), Curson (1992), Binford & DeSante (1993), Curson et al. (1994), Dunn & Garrett (1997), Pyle (1997c); A.R. Phillips (pers. comm.); IBP (MAPS) data, PRBO data.

COMMON YELLOWTHROAT
Geothlypis trichas

COYE
Species # 6810
Band size: 0-1C-0A

Species— ♀♀ from the other plain warblers (including HY/SY *Oporornis* warblers) by short wg (47-58) but relatively long tl (43-58); rects uniformly olive-yellow (without distinct, white or yellow patches); legs pale flesh to horn. ♀♀ from Gray-crowned Yellowthroat by smaller average size (see above); wg ≥ tl; bill thinner (depth at tip of nares 1.9-3.3); culmen straight or weakly decurved; crown, eye ring, and lores uniformly buffy brown to olive-brown, without gray, whitish, or dusky coloration; lower mandible primarily blackish. Bahama Yellowthroat (*G. rostrata*; alpha code **BAYE**, **Species # 9145**), a possible vagrant to s.FL, is larger (wg 57-66, tl 53-62), with a much longer bill (exp culmen 14.5-17.5; *vs* 9.0-12.8 in Common Yellowthroat), crown washed gray, ♂♂ with a more extensive black mask, and underparts more extensively yellow than eastern subspecies of Common Yellowthroat (see **Geographic variation**).

Geographic variation—Variably moderate to well marked, but clinal where ranges meet, differences are obscured by fairly substantial individual variation, and the nomenclature is complicated by divergent interpretations. Subspecies taxonomy follows G.H. Lowery & B.L. Monroe *in* Paynter (1968), as modified by the indications of Monson & Phillips (1981) and Rea (1983); see also Ridgway (1902), Chapman (1907b), Swarth (1912b, 1929), Grinnell (1914a), Oberholser (1917d, 1948, 1974), Schussler (1918), van Rossem (1930e, 1941c), Van Tyne (1933), Burleigh (1934), Braund & McCullagh (1940), Behle & Aldrich (1947), Behle (1950b, 1985), Godfrey (1950, 1986), Parkes (1954), Phillips (1959b, 1961a), Todd (1963), Phillips *et al.* (1964), Kaufman (1979d), Wetmore *et al.* (1984), Cramp & Perrins (1994b), Curson *et al.* (1994), Dunn & Garrett (in press). Three other subspecies occur in Mex. The following is largely based on AHY/ASY ♂♂; ♀♀ and HYs show similar differences (apart from the color of the mask border), but generally are duller and more difficult, if not impossible, to distinguish.

Pacific Coastal (*G.t. arizela*) Group. Small; moderately dark; dull.

G.t. arizela (br & wint coastal se.AK-c.CA): Medium small; bill medium in length (exp culmen 9.4-12.0); p9 – p4 -1 to 4 mm; mask border of ♂♂ white; upperparts medium-dull and moderately dark olive; flanks washed pale olive; ♀ wg(n100) 48-56, tl(n10) 46-53; ♂ wg(n100) 51-58, tl(n89) 48-56.

G.t. sinuosa (br San Francisco Bay area, wint coastal CA): Small; bill medium short (exp culmen 9.0-12.0); p9 – p4 -3 to 2 mm; mask border of ♂♂ creamy white with a grayish tinge; upperparts medium-dark brownish green; flanks washed dark olive. ♀ wg(n10) 47-53, tl(n10) 43-50; ♂ wg(n26) 50-56, tl(n25) 45-53.

Western (*G.t. occidentalis*) Group. Large; moderately pale; bright.

G.t. yukonicola (br s.Yuk-n.BC, wint TX): Medium large; bill medium short (exp culmen 9.9-11.5); p9 – p4 0-4 mm; mask border of ♂♂ white with a grayish tinge; upperparts grayish olive; flanks washed grayish olive. ♀ wg(n3) 51-55, tl(n3) 45-52; ♂ wg(n10) 54-59, tl(n10) 47-55.

G.t. campicola (br BC-se.WA to w.Ont-MN, wint s.AZ-s.TX): Variable in size; tl relatively short; bill medium short (exp culmen 9.1-12.1); p9 – p4 -1 to 3 mm; mask border of ♂♂ white with a grayish tinge; upperparts medium-dull olive with a grayish tinge; flanks washed grayish brown; vent whitish. ♀ wg(n100) 48-56, tl(n10) 43-53; ♂ wg(n100) 51-59, tl(n100) 45-55. Local variation may account for the synonymized names "*alberticola*" (reportedly darker and shorter-tailed birds breeding in Alb-s.Sask), "*coloradonicola*" in part (see *occidentalis*), and "*minnesoticola*" in part (reportedly paler birds of Man-w.Ont to NE-n.IL), but differences, if present, are weak and probably temporally unstable.

G.t. occidentalis (br e.OR-e.CA to CO-ne.TX): Medium large; bill medium in length (exp culmen 9.4-12.3); p9 – p4 -4 to 2 mm; mask border of ♂♂ white; upperparts pale olive with a grayish-yellow wash; flanks tinged medium-pale buffy olive; vent whitish. ♀ wg(n10) 50-57, tl(n10) 46-55; ♂ wg(n100) 52-60, tl(n100) 48-58. Local variation may account for the synonymized names "*californicola*" (typical birds breeding in e.CA), "*idahonicola*" (reportedly greener and larger birds breeding in e.OR-s.ID to n.UT), "*oregonicola*" (reportedly shorter-tailed birds breeding in c.OR-n.NV), "*utahicola*" (birds fitting the above description breeding in c.UT-w.WY), and "*coloradonicola*" (reportedly smaller and paler birds breeding from ND to c.NM-w.TX), but differences, if present, are weak, obscured by individual variation, and probably temporally unstable.

G.t. scirpicola (res s.CA to sw.UT-sw.AZ): Medium large; bill medium long (exp culmen 9.6-12.5); p9 – p4 0-5 mm; mask border of ♂♂ creamy white; upperparts medium-bright greenish olive; flanks washed medium brownish olive; vent whitish with a yellow tinge. ♀ wg(n10) 50-57, tl(n10) 47-58; ♂ wg(n70) 52-60, tl(n69) 49-60. Birds breeding in desert sw.UT to se.CA-s.AZ ("*arizonicola*") may average yellower underparts, but differences, if present, are weak and obscured by individual variation.

G.t. chryseola (br & wint se.AZ-sw.TX): Large; bill medium long (exp culmen 10.5-12.4); p9 – p4 0-4 mm; mask border of ♂♂ whitish, usually tinged yellow; upperparts dull olive with a yellow tinge; flanks yellow with a brown tinge; vent yellow, sometimes tinged whitish. ♀ wg(n10) 51-58, tl(n10) 48-55; ♂ wg(n43) 53-61, tl(n41) 50-57.

Eastern (*G.t. trichas*) Group. Intermediate in size and plumage.

G.t. insperata (res s.TX): Medium small; bill medium long (exp culmen 10.7-12.2); p9 – p4 -4 to 1 mm; mask border of ♂♂ whitish; upperparts medium-pale greenish olive; flanks washed grayish olive. ♀ wg(n10) 50-55, tl(n10) 46-52; ♂ wg(n10) 52-57, tl(n10) 48-53.

G.t. trichas (br e.Ont-Nfl to e.TX-ec.VA, wint s.TX-FL): Variable in size; bill medium short (exp culmen 9.1-12.1); p9 – p4 0-5 mm; mask border of ♂♂ grayish white; upperparts fairly bright greenish olive; flanks washed grayish olive to brownish olive. ♀ wg(n100) 46-56, tl(n35) 42-50; ♂ wg(n100) 50-60, tl(n100) 44-54. Birds breeding north of NE to w.NC-NJ ("*brachidactylus*") average larger and brighter, and birds breeding on Anticosti I, Que ("*pelagitis*") may average slightly smaller and duller, but differences are slight and almost completely obscured by individual variation. Local variation also may account for several other synonymized names: "*minnesoticola*" in part (see *campicola*), "*ontarionicola*" (reportedly larger and brighter birds breeding in w.Ont), "*ohionicola*" (reportedly larger and yellower birds breeding in MI-w.PA to n.GA), "*roscoe*" (reportedly smaller and grayer birds breeding in e.TX to AR-LA), "*marilandica*" (reportedly grayish-olive birds breeding in e.PA-NJ to VA), "*quebecicola*" (reportedly longer-tailed and duller birds breeding in Que-Nfl), and "*novascoticola*" (reportedly larger and browner birds breeding in NS), but in all cases variation, if present, slight, obscured by individual variation, and possibly temporally unstable.

G.t. typhicola (br & wint AL to se.VA-interior sc.GA): Medium large but tl relatively short; bill short (exp culmen 9.0-11.6); p9 – p4 -2 to 3 mm; mask border of ♂♂ pale grayish; upperparts medium-bright olive with a brownish tinge; flanks washed brownish olive. ♀ wg(n19) 48-55, tl(n10) 46-52; ♂ wg(n32) 50-57, tl(n10) 48-55.

G.t. ignota (res coastal LA-FL-SC): Small but tl relatively long; bill long (exp culmen 9.9-12.8); p9 – p4 -3 to 2 mm; mask border of ♂♂ grayish; upperparts dark olive with a brown wash; flanks washed dark tawny olive. ♀ wg(n14) 48-54, tl(n14) 47-53; ♂ wg(n18) 50-57, tl(n18) 49-56.

Molt—PB: HY partial-incomplete (Jun-Sep), AHY complete (Jun-Sep); PA absent-partial (Nov-Apr). The PBs occur on the summer grounds. The 1st PB (which is completed soon after fledging) includes all med and gr covs, sometimes (in ~50% of birds) the greater alula, sometimes (in ~37% of birds) 1-3 terts, and sometimes (in ~36% of birds) 1-2 central rects (r1). Also, the 1st PB sometimes (in ~21-50% of HYs) can be eccentric (see p. 208 and Fig. 136), with the outermost 3-5 pp, the innermost 3-5 ss, and 2-12 rects, but no pp covs replaced. The extent of the 1st PB likely varies geographically (*e.g.*, more feathers may be replaced on average in southern subspecies); more study is needed. The 1st PA includes 0 (~52%) to 3 inner gr covs, but no terts or rects. The adult PA typically includes no gr covs, terts, or rects. The PA occurs to a greater extent in HY/SY ♂♂ than in the other age/sex groups.

Skull—Pneumaticization completes in HY/SY from 1 Oct (as early as 1 Sep in CA subspecies) through Jan.

Age/Sex—Juv (May-Aug) is washed brownish and has two buffy-cinnamon wing bars; juv ♀ = ♂. CP/BP (Mar-Aug). ♀ wg(n100) 47-58, tl(n100) 43-58; ♂ wg(n100) 50-61, tl(n100) 44-60; see **Geographic variation**.

HY/SY ♀♂ (Aug-Jul): Forehead, lores, and auricular brown to buffy brown; inner 1-3 gr covs sometimes contrastingly fresh in Feb-Jul (Fig. 133**B**; see **Molt**); 3-5 outermost pp and 1-5 innermost ss sometimes replaced (see **Molt**), contrasting with the older inner pp and outer ss (Fig. 136**A**); outer pp covs narrow, tapered, relatively abraded (Fig. 138), and brownish-olive, contrasting with the slightly fresher and dusky-olive gr covs (Fig. 134); outer rects usually relatively abraded and tapered (Fig. 139**A**), the central rects (r1, and occasionally other rects) sometimes replaced, contrastingly fresh and truncate; throat and upper breast buff to buffy yellow. **Note: Those HY/SYs that replace all rects also should replace outer pp and terts, and can be aged by contrasts there, although these contrasts can be subtle. In Aug-Mar, birds without blackish in the lores or auriculars should not be sexed ♀, as apparently a** small proportion of ♂♂ can lack blackish after the 1st PB. More study is needed: HY/SY ♂♂ without black may be more prevalent in eastern than in western populations. By Mar-Jul all ♀♀ can be sexed and some HY/SY ♀♀ can be aged, but many are difficult if not impossible to distinquish from AHY/ASY ♀♀ due to extreme plumage wear.

AHY/ASY ♀ (Aug-Jul): Forehead, lores, and auricular brown to olive-brown; gr covs, outer pp, terts, and middle ss (s4-s6) uniformly adult (Fig. 133F); outer pp covs broad, truncate, relatively fresh (Fig. 138), and dusky with an olive wash, not contrasting markedly in color or wear with the gr covs; rects uniformly adult, relatively fresh, and truncate (Fig. 139A); throat and upper breast buffy yellow to yellow. **Note: See HY/SY ♀.**

HY/SY ♂ (Aug-Jul): Forehead, lores, and auricular uniformly brown to brown with blackish mottling (Aug-Feb), or black, sometimes lightly mottled buff (Feb-Jul); eye ring buff (Aug-Feb), or mixed buff and black (Aug-Jul; occasionally all black in Mar-Jul); molt-limit, wing-cov, and flight-feather criteria as in HY/SY ♀. **Note: See HY/SY ♀.**

AHY/ASY ♂ (Aug-Jul): Forehead, lores and auricular completely black (sometimes lightly mottled buff, when fresh in fall); eye ring usually black (occasionally partially buff); molt-limit, wing-cov and flight-feather criteria as in AHY/ASY ♀.

Common Yellowthroat
See Fig. 24

Hybrids reported—Mourning Warbler.

References—Stone (1896), Dwight (1900a), Ridgway (1902), Forbush (1929), Dickey & van Rossem (1938), Behle (1950b), Stewart (1952), A.O. Gross *in* Bent (1953), Roberts (1955), Robbins (1964), Wood (1969), Ewert & Lanyon (1970), Fisk (1972), Oberholser (1974), Sheppard & Klimkiewicz (1976), Taylor (1976), Bledsoe (1988), Parkes (1988a), Francis & Wood (1989), CWS & USFWS (1991), Cramp & Perrins (1994b), Curson *et al.* (1994), Dunn & Garrett (1997), Pyle (1997c); C.H. Blake, M.E. Doscher, R.P. Yunick (*in litt.* to the BBL); J. Dierschke (pers. comm.); IBP (MAPS) data, PNR data, PRBO data.

GRAY-CROWNED YELLOWTHROAT
Geothlypis poliocephala

GCYE
Species # 6821
Band size: 1-1C

Species—♀♀ from Common Yellowthroat (which see for separation from other warblers) by larger average size (wg 51-55, tl 55-63; see **Age/Sex**); wg < tl; bill thicker (depth at tip of nares 3.2-4.2); culmen strongly decurved; sides of the crown often washed grayish; lores usually dusky to blackish; thin, white, partial eye ring usually present (see **Geographic variation**); lower mandible with an extensive pale area. From Yellow-breasted Chat by much smaller size (see above); face without distinct, white marks; undertail covs yellow.

Geographic variation—Weak to moderate and clinal where ranges meet. Subspecies taxonomy follows G.H. Lowery & B.L. Monroe *in* Paynter (1968); see Ridgway (1902), Wetmore (1943, 1944), Curson *et al.* (1994), Dunn & Garrett (in press). Five other subspecies occur in Mex-C.Am.

G.p. ralphi (former res, vag to s.TX): From subspecies of Mex-C.Am by blackish of the lores not or only thinly meeting across the forehead; ♂ with the crown pale blue-gray when fresh (*vs* olive to olive-gray in the other subspecies); upperparts pale grayish olive (*vs* darker grayish olive or olive); vent with little or no yellow (*vs* tinged yellow in the other subspecies).

Molt—Not well studied, but apparently as follows in most birds: PB HY partial (May-Sep), AHY complete (Jun-Sep), PA absent-limited (Nov-Apr). The 1st PB usually includes all med and gr covs, but not the greater alula, terts, or rects. Some birds may possibly replace more feathers, as in Common Yellowthroat; more study is needed. The PA, if present, may be limited to the head and probably is more extensive in HY/SY ♂♂ than in the other age/sex groups.

Skull—Pneumaticization completes in HY from 1 Sep through Dec.

Age—Juv (May-Aug) is brownish yellow, lacks dusky or black in the lores, and has two buffy-lemon wing bars; juv ♀ = ♂.

HY/SY (Aug-Jul): Outer pp covs narrow, tapered, relatively abraded (Fig. 138), and brownish with a slight or no olive tinge, contrasting with the slightly fresher and dusky-olive gr covs (Fig. 134); outer rects relatively abraded and tapered (Fig. 139A); yellow of the underparts tinged buff when fresh.

AHY/ASY (Aug-Jul): Outer pp covs broad, truncate, relatively fresh (Fig. 138), and dusky with an olive wash, not contrasting markedly in color or wear with the gr covs (Fig. 133F); outer rects relatively fresh and truncate (Fig. 139A); yellow of the underparts not tinged buff.

Sex—CP/BP (Mar-Aug). ♀ wg(n6) 51-55, tl(n6) 55-63; ♂ wg(n10) 55-62, tl(n10) 56-67; includes *G.p. ralphi* only (see **Geographic variation**).

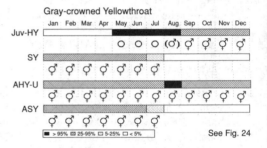

♀: Crown olive-brown with little to a moderate amount of gray wash to the sides; lores dusky to blackish.

♂: Crown gray with an olive-brown wash when fresh; lores black.

References—Ridgway (1902), Dickey & van Rossem (1938), Bent (1953), Eisenmann (1962b), Oberholser (1974), Curson *et al.* (1994), Howell & Webb (1995), Dunn & Garrett (1997), Pyle (1997c).

HOODED WARBLER
Wilsonia citrina

HOWA
Species # 6840
Band size: 0-1C

Species—HY/SY ♀ from Bachman's Warbler by tl longer (47-54); crown without gray; eye ring lacking. From the other yellow warblers by the combination of medium large size (see **Age/Sex**); wing bars lacking but outer rects with distinct, white patches; rictal bristles long.

Geographic variation—No subspecies are recognized.

Molt—PB: HY partial (May-Aug), AHY complete (Jun-Aug); PA absent. The PBs occur on the summer grounds. The 1st PB (which completes shortly after fledging) usually includes all med and gr covs, but usually not the greater alula, terts, or rects; rarely the outermost gr cov can be retained. Reports that some or all flight feathers can be replaced during the 1st PB require confirmation.

Skull—Pneumaticization completes in HY from 1 Oct through Dec.

Age/Sex—Juv (May-Aug) has the entire plumage washed buff or brownish with two buffy wing bars; juv ♀ = ♂. CP/BP (Apr-Aug). ♀ wg(n100) 58-67, tl(n20) 47-56; ♂ wg(n100) 63-71, tl(n20) 50-59.

HY/SY ♀ (Aug-Jul): Crown, nape, chin, throat, and upper breast usually without black mottling (occasionally, one to a few black feathers may be present); outer pp covs narrow, tapered, relatively abraded (Fig. 138), and moderately pale brown with little or no olive, contrasting with the slightly fresher, dusky-centered, and olive-washed gr covs (Fig. 134); outer rects relatively abraded, tapered (Fig. 139A), and pale brown. **Note: The amount of white in the outer rects (r4-r6) shows a slight amount of variation by age/sex (Fig. 262C-D but with more white in r5-r6), as in *Dendroica* warblers, but differences are slight and obscured by individual variation. Differences in rect shape also can be difficult to use; however, most birds should be reliably aged and sexed.**

AHY/ASY ♀ (Aug-Jul): Crown, nape, chin, throat, and upper breast with some black mottling, from a moderate amount of mottling to almost fully black (as in ♂♂), but the chin always has at least some yellowish; outer pp covs broad, truncate, relatively fresh, and dusky brown with the outer webs washed olive (Fig. 138), not contrasting markedly in color or wear with the gr covs (Fig. 133F); outer rects relatively fresh, truncate (Fig. 139A), and dusky brown. **Note: See HY/SY ♀.**

HY/SY ♂ (Aug-Jul): Crown, nape, chin, throat, and upper breast black, the feathers often (Aug-Dec), or sometimes (Jan-Jul) with narrow, yellow edging; pp-cov and rect criteria as in HY/SY ♀. **Note: See HY/SY ♀. ♂♂ can be especially difficult to age after completion of skull pneumaticization.**

AHY/ASY ♂ (Aug-Jul): Crown, nape, chin, throat, and upper breast black, with little (Aug-Dec) or no yellow mottling; pp-cov and rect criteria as in AHY/ASY ♀. **Note: See HY/SY ♀ and HY/SY ♂.**

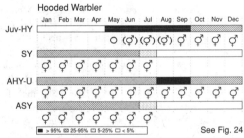

Hooded Warbler

Hybrids reported—A reported hybrid with Canada Warbler likely refers to a variant Hooded Warbler.

See Fig. 24

References—Palmer (1894), Stone (1896), Dwight (1900a), Ridgway (1902), Forbush (1929), Bent (1953), Wood (1969), Oberholser (1974), Walters & Lamm (1980), Lynch *et al.* (1985), Morton (1989), Cramp & Perrins (1994b), Curson *et al.* (1994), Evans Odgen & Stutchbury (1994), Stutchbury (1994), Stutchbury & Howlett (1995), Dunn & Garrett (1997), Pyle (1997c); E. Elias (pers. comm.); IBP (MAPS) data, PNR data, PRBO data.

WILSON'S WARBLER
Wilsonia pusilla

WIWA
Species # 6850
Band size: 0A-0

Species—HY/SY ♀ (without black in the cap) from the other yellow warblers by small size (wg 46-57, tl 44-50; see **Age/Sex**); supercilium and auricular fairly well defined; distinct wing bars lacking; outer rects without distinct whitish or yellow patches.

Geographic variation—Moderate and ranges fairly well defined. Subspecies taxonomy follows G.H. Lowery & B.L. Monroe *in* Paynter (1968); see Ridgway (1902), Phillips *et al.* (1964), Oberholser (1974), Wetmore *et al.* (1984), Behle (1985), Godfrey (1986), Cramp & Perrins (1994b), Curson *et al.* (1994), Dunn & Garrett (in press). No other subspecies occur.

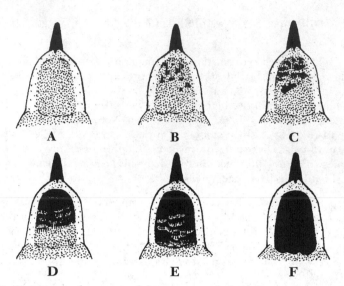

FIGURE 281. Variation in the extent of the crown patch, by subspecies, age, and sex, in Wilson's Warbler; see text and Table 9. The crown patch measurement is the length along the median axis of the crown, between the anterior and posterior points of the crown patch coloration, these points not necessarily being along the median axis.

W.p. chryseola (br coastal sw.BC-sw.CA): Medium small; forehead bright yellow with an orange tinge; underparts bright yellow; cap (especially of ♀♀) with more black by age/sex (Table 9 and Fig. 281**C-F**); upperparts bright yellowish. ♀ wg(n100) 49-56, tl(n10) 45-50; ♂ wg(n100) 52-60, tl(n24) 45-52.

W.p. pileolata (br AK-n.Alb to e.CA-c.NM): Medium large; forehead and underparts bright yellow without an orange tinge; cap (especially of ♀♀) with a moderate amount of black by age/sex (Table 9 and Fig. 281**A-F**); upperparts bright greenish yellow. ♀ wg(n100) 52-58, tl(n17) 46-51; ♂ wg(n100) 54-62, tl(n36) 47-53.

W.p. pusilla (br e.Alb-Nfl to n.MN-NS): Small; forehead and underparts dull yellow with an olive tinge; cap (especially of ♀♀) with less black by age/sex (Table 9 and Fig. 281**A-E**); upperparts dull yellowish olive. ♀ wg(n51) 46-55, tl(n24) 44-49; ♂ wg(n100) 50-58, tl(n45) 45-50.

Molt—PB: HY partial (May-Jul), AHY complete (Jun-Aug); PA absent-limited (Jan-May). The PBs occur on the summer grounds. The 1st PB (which is often well underway before fledging) usually includes all med and gr covs, but not the greater alula, terts, or rects. The PA, if present, is limited to feathers of the head, and may be continuous from Oct-Apr, as in certain other warblers.

Skull—Pneumaticization completes in HY from 15 Oct (as early as 15 Sep in *W.p. chryseola*) through Nov.

Age/Sex—Juv (May-Aug) has the entire plumage washed brownish or buff with yellow lores and two buffy-yellow wing bars; juv ♀ = ♂. CP/BP (Apr-Aug). ♀ wg(n100) 46-58, tl(n51) 44-51; ♂ wg(n100) 50-62, tl(n64) 45-53; see **Geographic variation**.

TABLE 9. The amount of black in the caps of Wilson's Warblers by subspecies, age, and sex. Note that % green refers to the entire area of crown (that which is black in Fig. 281**F**). See the text for differences in the cap length by age in ♂♂.

| Subspecies | HY/SY ♀ | | AHY/ASY ♀ | | ♂♂ |
	length	% green	length	% green	length
W.p. chryseola	7-10	60-90	9-15	25-55	14-19
W.p. pileolata	0-9	85-100	7-13	35-60	13-18
W.p. pusilla	0-5	90-100	5-12	50-85	12-17

HY/SY ♀ (Aug-Jul): Black cap absent or reduced by subspecies (Fig. 281**A-C** [to **D** in some ♀♀ of northwestern populations] & Table 9); outer pp covs narrow, tapered, relatively abraded, and brownish with indistinct, narrow, or no olive edging (Fig. 138), contrasting with the slightly fresher, dusky, and olive-edged gr covs (Fig. 134); outer rects relatively abraded, tapered (Fig. 139**A**), and brownish. **Note: Intermediates occur that are difficult to age.**

AHY/ASY ♀ (Aug-Jul): Black cap reduced to moderately extensive by subspecies (Fig. 281**B-D** [to **E** in some birds of northwestern populations] & Table 9); outer pp covs broad, truncate, relatively fresh, and dusky with relatively distinct and broad, olive edging (Fig. 138), not contrasting markedly in color or wear with the gr covs (Fig. 133**F**); outer rects relatively fresh, truncate (Fig. 139**A**), and dusky. **Note: See HY/SY ♀.**

HY/SY ♂ (Aug-Jul): Black cap shiny, 12-16 mm (Fig. 281**D-E** & Table 9), sometimes slightly (< 5%) mottled greenish; pp-cov and rect criteria as in HY/SY ♀. **Note: See HY/SY ♀.**

AHY/ASY ♂ (Aug-Jul): Black cap shiny, 14-19 mm (Fig. 281**E-F** & Table 9), without green; pp-cov and rect criteria as in AHY/ASY ♀. **Note: See HY/SY ♀.**

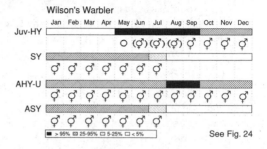

References—Stone (1896), Dwight (1900a), Ridgway (1902), Forbush (1929), W.M. Tyler *in* Bent (1953), Roberts (1955), Wood (1969), Stewart (1972a, 1972c), Oberholser (1974), Sheppard & Klimkiewicz (1976), McNicholl (1977), CWS & USFWS (1991), Cramp & Perrins (1994b), Curson *et al.* (1994), Dunn & Garrett (1997), Pyle (1997c); J. Curson, J.R. King, E. Ruhlen (pers. comm.); IBP (MAPS) data, PNR data, PRBO data.

CANADA WARBLER
Wilsonia canadensis

CAWA
Species # 6860
Band size: 0-0A

Geographic variation—No subspecies are recognized.

Molt—PB: HY partial (Jun-Aug), AHY complete (Jun-Aug); PA limited-partial (Jan-May). The PBs occur on the summer grounds. The 1st PB (which largely can be completed before fledging) usually includes all med and gr covs, but not the greater alula, terts, or rects. The 1st PA includes 0 (~70%) to 3 inner gr covs, but no terts or rects. The adult PA usually includes no gr covs, terts, or rects. The PAs may involve continuous, limited replacement of body feathers on the winter grounds, from Oct-Apr, as in certain other warblers.

Skull—Pneumaticization completes in HY from 15 Oct through Dec.

Age/Sex—Juv (Jun-Jul) has upperparts and underparts heavily washed brown, and buffy wing bars; juv ♀ = ♂. CP/BP (May-Jul). ♀ wg(n100) 57-67, tl(n20) 46-54; ♂ wg(n100) 61-70, tl(n46) 50-57.

HY/SY ♀ (Aug-Jul): Forehead, crown, and auricular greenish, without black flecking (Aug-Mar), or gray with a greenish tinge, rarely flecked with black (Mar-Jul); outer pp covs narrow, tapered, somewhat abraded (Fig. 138), and brownish, contrasting with the slightly fresher and grayer gr covs (Fig. 134) and back; outer rects relatively abraded, tapered (Fig. 139**A**), and dusky brown; streaking on the upper breast very indistinct and olive (Aug-Mar), or indistinct and grayish olive to dusky (Mar-Jul). **Note: Use caution; flight-feather differences and contrasts can be very subtle and many intermediates cannot be reliably aged and/or sexed (compare with wg).**

AHY/ASY ♀ (Aug-Jul): Forehead, crown, and auricular grayish with a greenish tinge (Aug-Mar), or gray, often flecked black (Mar-Jul); outer pp covs broad, truncate, relatively fresh (Fig. 138), and dusky, not contrasting markedly in color or wear with the gr covs and back; outer rects relatively fresh, truncate (Fig. 139A), and dusky; streaking on the upper breast moderately indistinct and grayish olive to dusky (Aug-Mar), or dusky to blackish (Mar-Jul). **Note: See HY/SY ♀.**

HY/SY ♂ (Aug-Jul): Forehead grayish with a greenish tinge, often flecked black (Aug-Mar), or black to primarily black, the feathers often edged gray (Mar-Jul); back bluish, often tinged greenish; pp-cov and rect criteria as in HY/SY ♀; upper breast with narrow, distinct, and dusky (Aug-Mar), or blackish (Mar-Jul), streaking and spots. **Note: See HY/SY ♀.**

AHY/ASY ♂ (Aug-Jul): Forehead bluish with black flecking; back bluish with a slight or no greenish wash; pp-cov and rect criteria as in AHY/ASY ♀; upper breast with wide, distinct, black streaks and spot. **Note: See HY/SY ♀.**

Hybrids reported—Mourning Warbler. A reported hybrid with Hooded Warbler likely refers to a variant Hooded.

Canada Warbler

See Fig. 24

References—Stone (1896), Dwight (1900a), Ridgway (1902), Forbush (1929), Bent (1953), Roberts (1955), Wood (1969), Oberholser (1974), Riggins & Riggins (1977), Rappole (1983), Phillips (1986), Bledsoe (1988), Parkes (1988a), Curson *et al.* (1994), Dunn & Garrett (1997), Pyle (1997c); J.S. Weske (*in litt.* to the BBL); IBP (MAPS) data, PNR data.

RED-FACED WARBLER
Cardellina rubrifrons

RFWA
Species # 6900
Band size: 0A

Geographic variation—Subspecies taxonomy follows G.H. Lowery & B.L. Monroe *in* Paynter (1968), who considered the species monotypic (synonymizing a previously recognized subspecies); see Griscom (1930c), Monroe (1968). Northern birds may have red of the faces averaging more orange and underparts averaging grayer than southern birds ("*C.r. belli*"), but differences, if present, are broadly clinal and largely obscured by individual variation.

Molt—PB: HY partial (Jun-Aug), AHY complete (Jun-Aug); PA absent. The PBs probably occur on the summer grounds. The 1st PB usually includes all med and gr covs, but not the greater alula, terts, or rects.

Skull—Pneumaticization completes in HY from 1 Oct through Dec.

Age—Juv (Jun-Jul) is washed brownish overall, with dull pinkish orange in the face and breast; juv ♀ = ♂.

HY/SY (Aug-Jul): Outer pp covs narrow, tapered, relatively abraded, and brownish with little or no grayish edging (Fig. 138), contrasting with the slightly fresher and dusky-centered gr covs (Fig. 134); outer rects relatively abraded, somewhat tapered (Fig. 139A), and dusky brown. **Note: Flight-feather differences and contrasts are subtle, and many intermediates can be impossible to age reliably.**

AHY/ASY (Aug-Jul): Outer pp covs broad, truncate, relatively fresh, and dusky, usually with thin, gray edging (Fig. 138), and not contrasting markedly in color or wear with the gr covs (Fig. 133F); outer rects relatively fresh, somewhat truncate (Fig. 139A), and dusky. **Note: See HY/SY.**

Sex—CP/BP (Apr-Jul). ♀ wg(n65) 62-69, tl(n20) 55-61; ♂ wg(n65) 65-72, tl(n20) 57-63. ♀♀ average duller and with more orange in the face than ♂♂, allowing sexing of mated pairs and some single birds (with previous experience); however, this difference likely varies by age and possibly by geography (see above); thus, most birds probably should not be sexed without direct comparison or extensive previous experience.

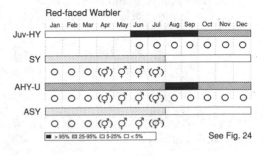

References—Ridgway (1902), Swarth (1904a), Bent (1953), Curson *et al.* (1994), Martin & Barber (1995), Dunn & Garrett (1997), Pyle (1997c); T. Martin (pers. comm.).

PAINTED REDSTART
Myioborus pictus

PARE
Species # 6880
Band size: 0A

Geographic variation—Moderate and ranges well defined. Subspecies taxonomy follows G.H. Lowery & B.L. Monroe *in* Paynter (1968); see Ridgway (1902), Curson *et al.* (1994). One other subspecies occurs in Mex-C.Am.

M.p. pictus (br & wint throughout the range in N.Am): From *guatemalae* of Mex-C.Am by larger size (see **Sex**, *vs* wg 62-71, tl 56-65 in *guatemalae*); gr covs and terts with distinct, white edging (*vs* no or indistinct, grayish-white edging) r4 primarily white (*vs* primarily blackish in *guatemalae*).

Molt—PB: HY partial (May-Sep), AHY complete (Jun-Sep); PA absent. The PBs occur primarily on the summer grounds. The 1st PB usually includes all med and gr covs, but not the greater alula, terts, or rects; beware of pseudolimits (see p. 207) among s6-s8, that cause the terts to appear newer.

Skull—Pneumaticization completes in HY from 1 Sep through Dec.

Age—Juv (May-Sep) has dull black upperparts and buff-tinged wing edging, and lacks red on the belly; juv ♀ = ♂.

HY/SY (Aug-Jul): Outer pp covs narrow, tapered, relatively abraded, and brownish black with indistinct, narrow, or no grayish-brown edging (Fig. 138); rects relatively abraded (see Fig. 139A) and brownish black to brown. **Note: Rect shape seems unhelpful, and molt limits are subtle; many intermediates can be impossible to age reliably. Note that flight-feather color varies as much by season (becoming browner in spring in both SYs and ASYs) as it does by age.**

AHY/ASY (Aug-Jul): Outer pp covs broad, truncate, relatively fresh, and black with relatively distinct and broad, white to grayish edging (Fig. 138); rects relatively fresh (see Fig. 139**A**) and black to brownish black. **Note: See HY/SY.**

Sex— ♀ = ♂ by plumage. CP/BP (Mar-Aug). ♀ wg(n30) 66-71, tl(n20) 59-65; ♂ wg(n30) 68-75, tl(n20) 61-68; includes *M.p. pictus* only (see **Geographic variation**). Some mated pairs can be sexed, with ♀♀ having slightly more orange-tinged belly than ♂♂, but this is not reliably with single birds and without extensive experience.

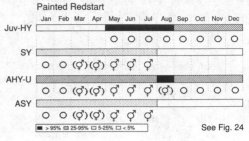

References—Ridgway (1902), Swarth (1904a), Bent (1953), Parkes (1961), Oberholser (1974), Curson *et al.* (1994), Dunn & Garrett (1997), Pyle (1997c).

RUFOUS-CAPPED WARBLER
Basileuterus rufifrons

RCWA
Species # 6921
Band size: 1

Geographic variation—Moderate and ranges well defined. Subspecies taxonomy follows G.H. Lowery & B.L. Monroe *in* Paynter (1968); see Ridgway (1902), Todd (1929), Dickey & van Rossem (1938), Monroe (1968), Curson *et al.* (1994), Dunn & Garrett (in press). Three to six other subspecies occur in Mex-S.Am, depending on the species taxonomy.

  B.r. caudatus (vag to se.AZ): Tl usually > wg; upperparts pale grayish olive; face cinnamon-rufous; yellow of the breast usually extends to the pp covs of the closed wing; flanks washed tawny and gray.
  B.r. jouyi (br vag to s-sw.TX): Tl usually < wg; upperparts medium olive with a grayish tinge; face rufous; yellow of the breast usually does not extend to the pp covs of the closed wing; flanks washed grayish brown.

Molt—PB: HY partial (May-Sep), AHY complete (Jun-Sep); PA absent-limited. The PBs occur primarily on the summer grounds. The 1st PB usually includes all med and gr covs, but not the greater alula, terts, or rects. The PAs, if regular, are limited to a few feathers of the head and throat.

Skull—Pneumaticization completes in HY from 1 Sep through Dec.

Age—Juv (May-Sep) has brownish-olive upperparts, brownish throat and breast, and distinct, buffy-cinnamon wing bars; juv ♀ = ♂.

  HY/SY (Aug-Jul): Outer pp covs narrow, tapered, relatively abraded, and brownish with little or no olive edging (Fig. 138), contrasting with the slightly fresher and dusky-olive gr covs (Fig. 134); outer rects relatively abraded, tapered (Fig. 139**A**), and washed brown. **Note: Intermediates can be difficult to age.**

  AHY/ASY (Aug-Jul): Outer pp covs broad, truncate, relatively fresh, and dusky with relatively distinct and broad, olive edging (Fig. 138), not contrasting markedly in color or wear with the gr covs (Fig. 133**F**); outer rects relatively fresh, truncate (Fig. 139**A**), and dusky. **Note: See HY/SY.**

Sex—CP/BP (Mar-Aug). ♀ wg(n5) 46-54, tl(n5) 50-59; ♂ wg(n15) 48-57, tl(n15) 52-61; includes the subspecies of N.Am only (see **Geographic variation**). ♀♀ average slightly duller and with more olive-tinged caps than ♂♂, but this likely varies by age (and possibly by subspecies) so this probably is not useful for sexing, except, perhaps, with mated pairs. More study is needed.

References—Ridgway (1902), Dickey & van Rossem (1938), Oberholser (1974), Curson *et al.* (1994), Dunn & Garrett (1997), Pyle (1997c).

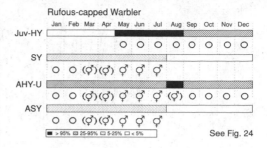

Rufous-capped Warbler

See Fig. 24

YELLOW-BREASTED CHAT
Icteria virens

YBCH
Species # 6830
Band size: 1B-1A

Species—Dull ♀♀ from Gray-crowned Yellowthroat by much larger size (wg 69-82, tl 69-82; see **Sex**); face with distinct, whitish marks; undertail covs white.

Geographic variation—Moderately weak and somewhat clinal where ranges meet. Subspecies taxonomy follows G.H. Lowery & B.L. Monroe *in* Paynter (1968); see Ridgway (1902), van Rossem (1939c), Phillips *et al.* (1964), Sutton (1967), Oberholser (1974), Phillips (1975a), Browning (1978, 1990), Rea (1983), Godfrey (1986), Curson *et al.* (1994), Dunn & Garrett (in press). No other subspecies occur.

  I.v. auricollis (br s.BC-s.Sask to s.CA-w.TX; vag to GA): Large; wg usually ≤ tl; upperparts dull grayish olive; white submoustachial stripe wide (2.0-3.5 mm) and long, usually extending behind the eye; breast medium-bright yellow with an orange tinge. ♀ wg(n100) 71-82, tl(n10) 72-82; ♂ wg(n100) 74-85, tl(n24) 75-86. Birds of the Pacific coast (*"longicauda"*) may average greener upperparts and browner (less gray-brown) flanks, but differences are slight and broadly clinal.
  I.v. virens (br e.SD-NH to e.TX-n.FL): Small; wg usually ≥ tl; upperparts bright greenish olive; white submoustachial stripe narrow (0-2.5 mm) and short, usually not extending behind the eye; breast medium-dull yellow with a slight or no orange tinge. ♀ wg(n100) 69-79, tl(n10) 69-76; ♂ wg(n100) 71-81, tl(n17) 71-81. Birds of ec-s.TX (*"danotia"*) may average larger and grayer, but differences are slight and probably result from intergradation with *auricollis*.

Molt—PS/PB: HY incomplete (May-Sep), AHY complete (Jul-Oct); PA absent. The PBs occur on the summer grounds. A presupplemental molt (see p. 16) may occur prior to the 1st PB; more study is needed. The 1st PB is eccentric (see p. 208 and Fig. 136), with all gr covs, the outermost 3-7 pp, the innermost 3-6 ss, and occasionally (in ~10% of birds) 1-2 central rects (r1), but no pp covs replaced. The occurrence of a complete or (possibly) no replacement of pp by some birds during the 1st PB requires confirmation.

Skull—Pneumaticization completes in HY/SY from 1 Oct. Look for windows (> 2 mm; see Fig. 11**D**) in the rear of the skull in some SYs through Jun.

Age—Juv (May-Aug) has duller grayish-olive or brownish-olive upperparts, no yellow on the underparts, and dusky spotting on the throat and upper breast; juv ♀ = ♂.

  HY/SY (Sep-Aug): The innermost 3-5 ss (including the terts) and the outermost 3-6 (usually 5) pp replaced, relatively fresh and green, contrasting slightly with the older and more faded outer ss and inner pp (Fig. 136**A**), the distance between the adjacent pp of these two feather groups 3-7 mm (Fig. 282); outer pp covs narrow, tapered, relatively abraded, and brownish with indistinct, relatively narrow, and dull greenish edging (Fig. 138), contrasting with the slightly fresher and duskier gr covs (Fig. 134); central rects (r1) occasionally replaced, contrastingly fresh;

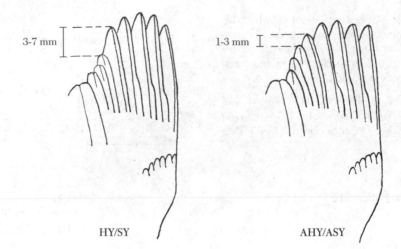

FIGURE 282. The wing morphology by age in Yellow-breasted Chat. The difference results from the eccentric replacement pattern (see p. 208) during the first prebasic molt, and the measurement refers to the largest distance between primary tips, among p2-p7. In HY/SYs, this distance occurs between the replaced and the retained primaries. A formula such as this is to be looked for in other species of passerines with eccentric molts.

outer rects relatively abraded and tapered (Fig. 139**B**). **Note: Beware of occasional HY/SYs that possibly may have replaced no or all pp (and ss?; see Molt); use pp-cov and rect criteria to age these. See also Sex for slight mouth-color differences by age.**

AHY/ASY (Sep-Aug): Wing covs and flight feathers uniformly adult (Fig. 133**F**) and dusky with distinct, greenish edging, the maximum distance between adjacent pp of p3 – p7 1-3 mm (Fig. 282); outer pp covs broad, truncate, relatively fresh, and dusky with relatively distinct and broad, greenish edging (Fig. 138), not contrasting markedly in color or wear with the gr covs (Fig. 133**F**); rects uniformly adult, the outer rects relatively fresh and truncate (Fig. 139**B**). **Note: See HY/SY.**

Sex—CP/BP (Apr-Aug). ♀ wg(n100) 69-82, tl(n20) 69-82; ♂ wg(n100) 71-85, tl(n41) 71-86.

♀: Lores dark gray; bill brown or blackish brown in Mar-Aug; mouth pinkish (HY/SY) to dark gray (AHY) in Mar-Aug. **Note: Some intermediates can occur. Compare with age; these likely are HY/SY ♂♂ or AHY/ASY ♀♀. More study is needed on bill color during Sep-Mar; that of AHY/ASY ♂ may be blacker than those of ♀♀ and HY/SY ♂♂.**

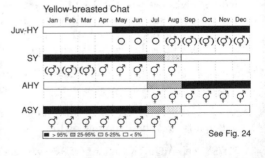

♂: Lores black or blackish; bill blackish to black in Mar-Aug; mouth grayish pink (HY/SY) to black (AHY) in Mar-Aug (possibly longer). **Note: See ♀.**

References—Stone (1896), Dwight (1900a), Ridgway (1902), Forbush (1929), Bent (1953), Dennis (1958, 1967), Blake (1962b), Wood (1969), Oberholser (1974), Phillips (1974b), Sheppard & Klimkiewicz (1976), Curson *et al.* (1994), Thompson & Leu (1994), Dunn & Garrett (1997), Pyle (1997c); M. San Miguel, A.R. Phillips, J.M. Sheppard (*in litt.* to the BBL); K. Burton (pers. comm.); IBP (MAPS) data, PNR data, PRBO data.

TANAGERS

THRAUPIDAE

Five species. Family characters include fairly robust postures, bright plumage, and conical bills. Tanagers have 9 visible primaries, 9 secondaries, and 12 rectrices. The first prebasic molt is partial, including some or all greater coverts, but no tertials or rectrices. In three species partial prealternate molts occur, which include some or all greater coverts, and often the tertials and central rectrices. Plumage varies by age and sex, but sequences differ among the five species of North America; the color of replaced feathers depends more on the season than the age/sex group. Breeding characters are reliable for sexing in spring and summer, and males average larger than females. The combination of these criteria should allow age and sex determinations of most birds in both basic and alternate plumages.

HEPATIC TANAGER
Piranga flava

HETA
Species # 6090
Band size: 1A

Species—From the other tanagers of N.Am by the combination of large size (wg 93-109, tl 75-88; see **Age/Sex**); bill medium small (nares to tip 11.4-13.3); p7 > p6 by < 2 mm and p6 ≥ p9; wing bars indistinct or lacking; auricular and flanks gray or strongly washed grayish (both sexes); bill blackish or bluish; edge of the upper mandible usually with a distinct tooth (Fig. 283). Juv from juv Summer Tanager by bill color and a grayish-tan rump.

Geographic variation—Moderate and ranges well defined within N.Am. Subspecies taxonomy follows R.W. Storer *in* Paynter (1970); see Ridgway (1902), Bangs (1907), Oberholser (1919g, 1930a, 1974), Zimmer (1929), van Rossem (1931a, 1942d), Griscom (1934a), Sutton & Phillips (1942), Phillips (1966e). Thirteen other subspecies occur in C.Am-S.Am.

   P.f. hepatica (br & wint se.CA to nw.NM-s.AZ): Averages large; upperparts medium-pale, dull, red or yellow, with a grayish tinge; gray of the auricular and flanks extensive. ♀ wg(n34) 94-104, tl(n15) 76-86; ♂ wg(n45) 98-109, tl(n17) 78-88. Birds of N.Am (*"zimmeri"*) average paler and grayer than birds of Mex, but differences, if present, are weak and obscured by individual variation; also, the subspecific designation possibly was based on specimens with different degrees of wear.
   P.f. dextra (br s.CO to sc.NW-w.TX): Averages small; upperparts dark, brightish, red or yellow, without a grayish tinge; gray of the auricular and flanks reduced. ♀ wg(n10) 93-101, tl(n10) 73-81; ♂ wg(n12) 96-105, tl(n10) 75-84. Birds of N.Am (*"oreophasma"*) average larger than those of Mex, but differences are broadly clinal.

Molt—PB: HY partial (Jul-Oct), AHY complete (Jun-Oct); PA absent-limited (Jan-Mar). The PBs occur on the summer grounds. The 1st PB usually includes all med and gr covs, but no terts or rects. The PA may regularly include a few body feathers throughout the winter, and perhaps is more extensive in HY/SY ♂♂, but more study is needed. Look for a few birds to retain (or suspend during migration) middle ss (among s4-s6) during the adult PBs; this likely happens more often with SYs than with older birds. Feathers adventitiously replaced in spring-summer (of all age/sex groups) are green or yellow; see AHY/ASY ♂ (below).

Skull—Pneumaticization completes in HY/SY from 1 Nov through Jan. Check for windows (> 3 mm; Fig. 11**D**) on SYs through spring.

Age/Sex—Juv (Jun-Aug) is dull yellow with a dusky-brownish wash, has a grayish-tan rump, and has dusky or blackish streaking over much of the body plumage; juv ♀ = ♂. CP/BP (May-Aug). ♀ wg(n44) 93-104, tl(n20) 75-86; ♂ wg(n57) 96-109, tl(n22) 76-88; see **Geographic variation.**

HY/SY ♀♂ (Sep-Aug): Plumage grayish and yellow, without any red feathers; outer pp covs narrow, tapered, relatively abraded (Fig. 138), and brown, contrasting with the slightly fresher and dusky-centered gr covs (Fig. 134); outer rects tapered (Fig. 139**B**), brownish, and relatively abraded; throat and undertail covs without an orange tinge. **Note: HY/SYs probably are not reliably sexed ♀♀ (except by measurements or CP/BP), although it is possible that HY/SYs without red feathers in Mar-Jul can be assumed to be ♀♀; more study is needed. Also, among ♀♀ and HY/SYs, many intermediates can be difficult or impossible to age reliably.**

AHY/ASY ♀ (Sep-Aug): Plumage grayish yellow and yellow, usually without any markedly contrasting, red feathers; outer pp covs broad, truncate, relatively fresh (Fig. 138), and dusky, not contrasting markedly in color or wear with the gr covs (Fig. 133**F**); outer rects truncate (Fig. 139**B**), dusky, and relatively fresh; throat and undertail covs often lightly tinged orange. **Note: See HY/SY ♀ and HY/SY ♂.**

HY/SY ♂ (Nov-Oct): Plumage, pp-cov, and rect criteria as in HY/SY ♀, but body (especially head area) with one or more reddish feathers or patches, which contrast markedly with the surrounding plumage; throat and undertail covs sometimes tinged orange. **Note: See HY/SY ♀. Plumage change in ♂♂ of this species is quite complicated and also may vary geographically (see Zimmer 1929). Also, beware of some AHY/ASY ♀♀ (probably ASY/ATYs) that can show a few reddish feathers; confirm age before sexing these birds. See also AHY/ASY ♂.**

AHY/ASY ♂ (Oct-Sep): Plumage entirely reddish, or reddish with a few scattered green or yellow feathers; pp-cov and rect criteria as in AHY/ASY ♀. **Note: See HY/SY ♂. Feathers adventitiously replaced in Apr-Jun (exact date span needs to be defined), of all age/sex groups including AHY/ASY ♂♂, are green or yellow rather than red; thus, AHY/ASYs with a few green or yellow feathers or patches are not necessarily SY/TYs, as has previously been reported. Additionally, feathers replaced early during the adult PB (e.g., the innermost 1-2 pp in late Jun) often can be tinged orange or yellowish.**

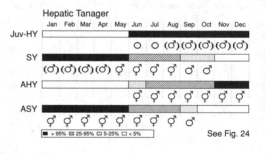

References—Ridgway (1902), Swarth (1904a), Zimmer (1929), Dickey & van Rossem (1938), Bent (1958), Eisenmann (1969), Rea (1972b), Oberholser (1974), CWS & USFWS (1991), Pyle (1997c); E.J. Fisk, M.K. Klimkiewicz (*in litt.* to the BBL).

SUMMER TANAGER
Piranga rubra

SUTA
Species # 6100
Band size: 1A-1B

Species—From the other tanagers of N.Am by medium-large size (wg 86-107, tl 63-88; see **Geographic variation**); bill large (Fig. 283; nares to tip 12.2-16.8, depth at tip of nares 7.6-9.7; see **Geographic variation**); p7 > p6 by ≥ 3 mm; p9 ≥ p6; plumage (including the wings) of HY/SYs and ♀♀ uniformly yellow, brownish yellow, or orange-yellow, with a slight or no olive tinge; wing bars (if present) indistinct; pp and ss without distinct white on the inner web; auricular and flanks uniform in coloration with the surrounding plumage, or with a slight brownish wash; underwing covs uniformly yellow to orangish; bill pinkish tan (juv) to whitish-horn (occasionally smudged dusky); edge of the upper mandible usually without a distinct tooth (Fig. 283). Juv from juv Hepatic Tanager by bill color and a rich cinnamon-buff rump.

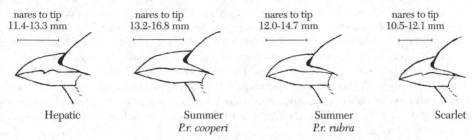

nares to tip 11.4-13.3 mm	nares to tip 13.2-16.8 mm	nares to tip 12.0-14.7 mm	nares to tip 10.5-12.1 mm
Hepatic	Summer *P.r. cooperi*	Summer *P.r. rubra*	Scarlet

FIGURE 283. The bill size and tooth character in Hepatic, Summer, and Scarlet tanagers. Note that Western Tanager has an indistinct tooth, similar to that of Scarlet Tanager in size.

Geographic variation—Variably weak to well marked and ranges fairly well defined. Subspecies taxonomy follows Monson & Phillips (1981); see also Ridgway (1902), van Rossem (1938e), Phillips *et al.* (1964), Phillips (1966e), Eisenmann (1969), Rea (1970b, 1972b, 1983), Oberholser (1974), Browning (1990), Cramp & Perrins (1994b). No other subspecies occur.

> **P.r. cooperi** (br s.CA-sw.UT to sw.TX): Large; tl long; bill large (Fig. 283; exp culmen 17.8-20.3, nares to tip 13.2-16.8, depth at tip of nares 8.5-9.7); longest p – longest s 17-25 mm; plumage bright and pale, the ♂♂ vermilion, the juvs pale yellow washed brownish, and the HYs and ♀♀ pale, bright yellow; AHY/ASY ♀♀ average less reddish or orange coloration (see **Age/Sex**). ♀ wg(n26) 93-102, tl(n26) 75-84; ♂ wg(n69) 96-107, tl(n68) 77-88. Birds of desert s.NV to se.CA-sw.AZ ("*hueyi*") may average larger-billed, paler, and grayer, but differences are too slight for subspecific recognition.
>
> **P.r. ochracea** (br ec.AZ, Mohave Co): Size, bill size, and plumage as in *cooperi* (perhaps averaging slightly smaller), except that juvs are brownish and gray, with little or no yellowish, HY/SY ♂♂ and ♀♀ average brighter greenish yellow, and AHY/ASY ♂♂ average darker red.
>
> **P.r. rubra** (br se.NE-cw.TX to DE-FL; vag to CA-MN-NS): Small; tl short; bill small (Fig. 283; exp culmen 16.5-19.3, nares to tip 12.0-14.7, depth at tip of nares 7.6-9.2); longest p – longest s 17-25 mm; plumage dull and dark, the ♂♂ moderately dark red, and the HYs and ♀♀ dark, dull brownish yellow; AHY/ASY ♀♀ average more reddish or orange coloration (see **Age/Sex**). ♀ wg(n68) 86-98, tl(n41) 63-74; ♂ wg(n91) 91-101, tl(n43) 66-77.

Molt—PB: HY partial (Jul-Sep), AHY complete (Jun-Sep); PA: SY partial-incomplete (Nov-Apr), ASY limited-partial (Jan-Apr). The PBs occur on the summer grounds. The 1st PB includes all med covs, 8 to 10 (~95%) inner gr covs and sometimes (in ~35% of birds) 1-2 terts, but no rects. The 1st PA includes 0 (~21%) to 4 inner gr covs, often (in ~64% of birds) 1-3 terts, occasionally (in ~7% of birds) s6 and/or s5, and 0 (~50%) to all 12 (~21%) rects; most molting appears to occur in Feb-Mar. The adult PA includes 0 (~78%) to 3 inner gr covs and occasionally (in ~17% of birds) 1-2 terts, but no rects. The PAs are highly variable, but usually are more extensive in HY/SY ♂♂ than in the other age/sex groups. Feathers adventitiously replaced by all age/sex groups in summer are yellow; see AHY/ASY ♂ (below).

Skull—Pneumaticization completes in HY/SY from 1 Oct through Jan. Check for windows (> 3 mm; Fig. 11**D**) on SYs through spring.

Age/Sex—Juv (May-Aug) resembles HY/SY ♀♀, but is washed brownish (see **Geographic variation**) and has distinctly pale wing bars, buffy underparts, and dusky streaking throughout; juv ♀ = ♂. CP/BP (Mar-Aug). See **Geographic variation** for measurements, which vary more by subspecies than by sex.

> HY/SY ♀ (Aug-Jul): Body plumage (including the undertail covs) yellowish olive to brownish yellow, without red feathers, and usually without orange (sometimes a slight orange tinge in *P.r. rubra* in Mar-Jul); 1-2 terts sometimes replaced during the 1st PB, contrast-

ing with the older middle ss (s4-s6) in Aug-Mar (Fig. 133**D**); outer pp covs narrow, tapered, relatively abraded, and pale brown with indistinct, narrow, or no buffy-yellow edging (Fig. 138), contrasting with the slightly fresher, duskier, and yellow-edged gr covs (Fig. 134); central (r1) and other rects sometimes replaced at the 1st PA, contrastingly fresh in Mar-Jul; outer rects usually tapered (Fig. 139**B**) and relatively abraded. **Note: Reliable sexing of HY/SYs in Aug-Mar requires some experience and comparison with measurements by subspecies. Also, note that HY/SYs average more gr covs and terts replaced during the PAs than AHY/ASYs, and this can be of further assistance in age-ing during Mar-Jul.**

AHY/ASY ♀ (Aug-Jul): Body plumage primarily yellowish, often washed orange or reddish (especially on the throat and undertail covs and more so in *P.r. rubra* than in the other sub-species), the red and yellow not contrasting markedly; terts and middle ss (s4-s6) uniformly adult in Aug-Mar (Fig. 133**F**); outer pp covs broad, truncate, relatively fresh, and dark brown with relatively distinct and broad, yellow edging (Fig. 138), not contrasting markedly in color or wear with the gr covs (Fig. 133**F**); rects uniformly adult, truncate (Fig. 139**B**), and rela-tively fresh. **Note: Rare AHY/ASY ♀♀ can approach complete red coloration; more study is needed on the occurrence of this. See also HY/SY ♀ and HY/SY ♂.**

HY/SY ♂ (Sep-Aug): Body plumage varies from rich yellow or brownish yellow, sometimes with scattered reddish feathers in Sep-Feb, to variably mixed yellow and red (can be pri-marily yellow or primarily red), the red and yellow contrasting markedly in Mar-Aug; undertail covs rich yellow to orangish; molt-limit, wing-cov, and flight-feather criteria as in HY/SY ♀, except that the replaced terts and rects are edged orange or red. **Note: See HY/SY ♀. Beware of possible overlap with some AHY/ASY ♀♀; it usually is best to con-firm age before sexing. Also, beware of AHY/ASY ♂♂ (which see) with scattered yellow feathers.**

AHY/ASY ♂ (Sep-Aug): Body plumage entirely red, or red with a few scattered yellow feath-ers; molt-limit, wing-cov, and flight-feather criteria as in AHY/ASY ♀, except that all flight feathers are edged red. **Note: See AHY/ASY ♀. Feathers adventitiously replaced in Apr-Jun (exact date span needs to be determined), of all age/sex groups including AHY/ASY ♂♂, are yellow rather than red; thus, AHY/ASYs with a few yellow feathers or patches are not HY/SYs or SY/TYs. Additionally, feathers replaced early during the adult PB (*e.g.*, the inner-most 1-2 pp in late Jun) often can be tinged orange.**

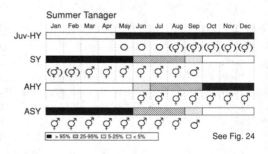

Hybrids reported—Scarlet Tanager.

References—Dwight (1900a), Ridgway (1902), Swarth (1904a), Todd & Carriker (1922), Forbush (1929), Fitch & Fitch (1955), Roberts (1955), Bent (1958), Phillips *et al.* (1964), Blake (1965b), Parkes (1967), Eisenmann (1969), Wood (1969), Rea (1970b, 1972a, 1972b), Davis (1971, 1972), Teulings (1973), Oberholser (1974), Phillips (1975a), Kaufman (1988b), CWS & USFWS (1991), Cramp & Perrins (1994b), Robinson (1996), Pyle (1997c); E.J. Fisk, K.C. Parkes (*in litt.* to the BBL); B. Walker (pers. comm.); IBP (MAPS) data.

SCARLET TANAGER
Piranga olivacea

SCTA
Species # 6080
Band size: 1B

Species—From the other tanagers of N.Am by small size (wg 86-101, tl 62-72; see **Age/Sex**), bill small (Fig. 283; nares to tip 10.5-12.1, depth at tip of nares 7.3-8.2); p9 > p6; ♀♀ and HY ♂♂ with the upperparts (including the nape) yellowish olive, blending into the paler rump; wings dusky green (♀♀) to blackish (♂♂); pp and ss usually with distinct white on the inner web; wing bars absent; underwing covs whitish with a dusky or black bar on the leading edge; bill horn colored; edge of the upper mandible usually with a distinct tooth (Fig. 283). Rare HY/SY ♀♀ can show narrow but distinct, yellowish wing bars, as in Western Tanager, but these can be identified by the color of the back and underwing covs.

Geographic variation—No subspecies are recognized.

Molt—PB: HY partial (Jul-Sep), AHY complete (Jul-Sep); PA: SY incomplete (Jan-May), ASY partial (Feb-May). The PBs occur on the summer grounds. The 1st PB usually includes all med covs and 0 (~5%) to 10 (~29%) inner gr covs, but no terts or rects. The 1st PA includes 7 to 10 (~60%) inner gr covs, 1-3 terts (rarely s6 or s6-s5, as well), and 3 to all 12 (~84%) rects. The adult PA includes 8 to 10 (~80%) inner gr covs, occasionally (in ~5% of birds) 1 or more terts, and occasionally (in ~5% of birds) 1-2 central rects (r1). Feathers adventitiously replaced by all age/sex groups in summer can be yellow; see **Age/Sex**.

Skull—Pneumaticization completes in HY/SY from 1 Nov. Look for windows (> 3 mm; see Fig. 11**D**) in the rear of the skull in some SYs through Aug.

Age/Sex—Juv (Jun-Aug) is like HY/SY ♀♀, but is washed grayish and has distinctly paler wing bars, dusky-streaked plumage, and a grayish iris; juv ♀ = ♂, although some birds possibly are sexed by the color of the flight feathers, paler brown in ♀♀, and darker, grayish brown in ♂♂. CP/BP (May-Sep). ♀ wg(n100) 86-96, tl(n26) 62-70; ♂ wg(n100) 90-101, tl(n38) 63-72.

Basic Plumage (Aug-Mar)

HY/SY ♀ (Aug-Mar): Body plumage dull or dusky olive; molt limits often occur among the med and gr covs (Fig. 133**A-E**; see **Molt**), the retained outer covs relatively abraded and grayish brown with yellow tips, contrasting with the fresher, duskier, and olive-edged, replaced inner covs; outer pp covs narrow, tapered, relatively abraded, pale brown with dull greenish edging (Fig. 138**A**), and (sometimes) with yellow tipping, contrasting with the slightly fresher, replaced gr covs; outer rects tapered (Fig. 139**B**) and relatively abraded; iris grayish to grayish brown (through Nov at least).

AHY/ASY ♀ (Aug-Mar): Body plumage moderately bright yellowish green; wing covs uniformly adult (Fig. 133**F**) and dusky with olive edging; outer pp covs broad, truncate, relatively fresh, and dusky brown with green edging (Fig. 138**B**), not contrasting in color or wear with the gr covs (Fig. 133**F**); outer rects truncate (Fig. 139**B**) and relatively fresh; iris blackish brown.

HY/SY ♂ (Aug-Mar): Body plumage moderately bright olive-green; head without blackish eye-brows; molt-limit, wing-cov, flight-feather, and iris-color criteria as in HY/SY ♀, except that the replaced lesser, med, and/or gr covs are black, contrasting markedly with the retained, juvenal gr covs and/or pp covs and flight feathers.

AHY/ASY ♂ (Aug-Mar): Body plumage brightish olive-green, occasionally with the breast and/or rump tinged orange, or the underparts with one or more red feathers; blackish eye-brows sometimes present; wing covs and flight feathers uniformly black; rects truncate (Fig. 139**B**) and relatively fresh; iris blackish brown.

Alternate Plumage (Mar-Sep)

SY ♀ (Mar-Jul): Body plumage yellowish green without an orange tinge; molt limits sometimes occur among the gr covs (Fig. 133**C-E**; see **Molt**), the retained outer covs either juvenal and brown with abraded yellow tips, or first basic and brownish dusky with dull green edging, contrasting with the fresher, dusky, and green-edged, recently replaced, inner covs (see also Fig. 135); 1-3 terts replaced and dusky, contrasting with the brown ss and pp (Fig. 133**D-E**); outer pp covs narrow, tapered, abraded, and brown with little or no green edging (Fig. 138**C**); rects fresh and dusky, occasionally with 1-9 brown, retained feathers. **Note: Some ♀♀ may be difficult to age.**

ASY ♀ (Mar-Jul): Body plumage yellowish green, occasionally with areas tinged orange; molt limits occasionally occur among the gr covs (Fig. 133**D-E**; see **Molt**), the 1-2 retained, adult, outer covs brownish dusky with green edging, contrasting slightly (in wear only) with the recently replaced, inner covs (*cf.* Fig. 135); terts and middle ss (s4-s6) usually uniform in wear; outer pp covs broad, truncate, relatively fresh, and dusky, usually with greenish edging (Fig. 138**D**); rects usually uniformly brownish dusky (1-2 central rects rarely slightly fresher). **Note: See SY ♀.**

SY ♂ (Mar-Sep): Body plumage red or mixed red and green; molt limits sometimes occur among the gr covs (Fig. 133**C-E**; see **Molt**), the retained outer covs either juvenal and brown with abraded yellow tips, or first basic and brownish black, contrasting with the black, recently replaced, inner covs (see Fig. 135); 1-3 terts (occasionally s6) replaced, black, contrasting markedly with the brown ss and pp (Fig. 133**D-E**); outer pp covs narrow, tapered, abraded, and brown with little or no green edging (Fig. 138**C**); rects fresh and black, occasionally with 1-9 brown, retained feathers. **Note: See ASY ♂.**

ASY ♂ (Mar-Sep): Body plumage red or primarily red; flight feathers and wing covs fairly uniformly black (the outermost 1-2 gr covs sometimes brownish black); rects usually uniformly blackish. **Note: Feathers adventitiously replaced in Apr-Jun (exact date span needs to be defined), of all age/sex groups including ASY ♂♂, are yellow rather than red; thus, ASYs with a few yellow feathers or patches are not SYs or TYs. Also, ASYs occasionally can show red or orange feathers or tips among the black wing covs; perhaps these were replaced in Apr-Jun, as well(?). More study is needed.**

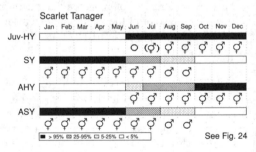

Hybrids reported—Summer Tanager, Western Tanager.

References—Stone (1896), Dwight (1900a), Ridgway (1902), Forbush (1929), Tordoff (1950), Roberts (1955), Bent (1958), Mengel (1963), Blake (1965b), Wood (1969), Davis (1971, 1972), Oberholser (1974), Phillips (1975a), Sheppard & Klimkiewicz (1976), Kaufman (1988b), Parkes (1988d), CWS & USFWS (1991), Cramp & Perrins (1994b), Pyle (1997c); R.C. Leberman, C.S. Robbins, J.S. Weske (*in litt.* to the BBL); B. Walker (pers. comm.); IBP (MAPS) data, PNR data.

WESTERN TANAGER
Piranga ludoviciana

WETA
Species # 6070
Band size: 1B

Species—HY/SYs and ♀♀ from the other tanagers of N.Am by small size (wg 85-97, tl 64-73; see **Age/Sex**); upperparts grayish green, often contrasting distinctly with the paler yellowish rump and nape; wing bars distinct, usually yellowish (can be narrow and whitish in some worn birds);

underwing covs bright to pale yellowish; edge of the upper mandible with an indistinct to distinct tooth (see Fig. 283).

Geographic variation—Subspecies taxonomy follows Browning (1990), who considered the species monotypic (synonymizing a previously recognized subspecies); see also Oberholser (1974), Browning (1978), Rea (1983). Birds breeding east of s.BC-se.AZ (*"P.l. zephyrica"*) average slightly larger and may average slightly paler, but differences are slight and obscured by substantial individual variation.

Molt—PB: HY partial (Jul-Aug), AHY complete (Jul-Aug); PA: SY partial-incomplete (Feb-Apr), ASY limited-partial (Feb-Apr). The PBs occur on the summer grounds. The 1st PB includes no to all lesser and med covs and 0 (~88%) to 1 inner gr cov, but no terts or rects. The 1st PA includes no to some (occasionally all) med covs, 0 (~5%) to 10 (~25%) inner gr covs, often (in ~75% of birds) 1-2 terts, and occasionally (in ~15% of birds) the central (r1) or more rects (but not all). The adult PA includes 0 (~88%) to 3 inner gr covs, but no terts or rects.

Skull—Pneumaticization completes in HY/SY from 1 Nov. Some SYs retain windows (> 3 mm; Fig. 11**D**) through spring.

Age/Sex—Juv (Jun-Aug) is like ♀♀, but is washed dusky and has distinct streaking to the underparts; juv ♀ = ♂. CP/BP (Apr-Aug). ♀ wg(n30) 85-97, tl(n20) 64-73; ♂ wg(n100) 88-101, tl(n87) 66-75; see **Geographic variation**.

Basic Plumage (Aug-Mar)

HY/SY ♀ (Aug-Mar): Head without red; med covs brown with moderately thin, white edges (Fig. 284); outer pp covs narrow, tapered, relatively abraded (Fig. 138**A**), and pale brown; rump dull yellow, uniform or nearly uniform in color with the back; outer rects tapered (Fig. 139**B**), washed brownish, and relatively abraded; throat dull yellow. **Note: Some intermediates can occur which are not reliably sexed. See also HY/SY ♂.**

AHY/ASY ♀ (Aug-Mar): Head without red; med covs dusky with yellow tips (Fig. 284); outer pp covs broad, truncate, relatively fresh (Fig. 138), and dark brown; rump moderately bright yellow, not contrasting markedly with the back; outer rects truncate (Fig. 139**B**), dusky, and fresh; throat moderately bright yellow. **Note: See HY/SY ♀ and HY/SY ♂.**

HY/SY ♂ (Aug-Mar): Head without red; med covs brown with moderately extensive, whitish to whitish-yellow tips (Fig. 284); pp-cov and rect criteria as in HY/SY ♀; rump brightish yellow, usually contrasting distinctly with the greener back; throat brightish yellow. **Note: Some overlap in plumage occurs with ♀♀; for reliable separation combine plumage brightness with age and wg.**

AHY/ASY ♂ (Aug-Mar): Head with varying amounts of red; med covs primarily bright yellow (Fig. 284); flight feathers (including the pp covs and rects) uniformly black; rects truncate (Fig. 139**B**).

First-basic ♀ Alternate & adult-basic ♀ First-basic ♂ Alternate & adult-basic ♂

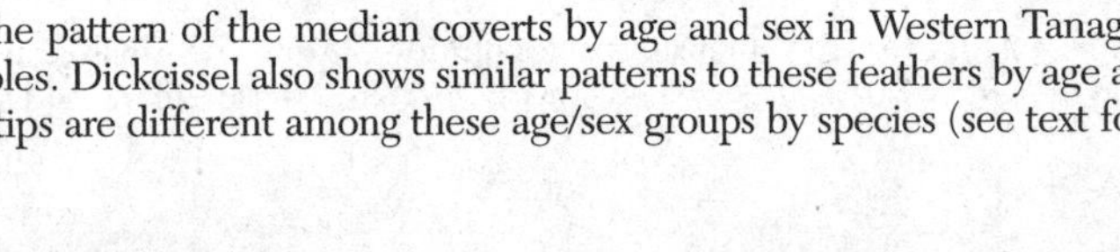

FIGURE 284. The pattern of the median coverts by age and sex in Western Tanager and Baltimore and Bullock's orioles. Dickcissel also shows similar patterns to these feathers by age and sex. Note that the colors of the tips are different among these age/sex groups by species (see text for each).

Alternate Plumage (Mar-Aug)

SY ♀ (Mar-Aug): Head without red; back olive; molt limits often occur among the med and gr covs (Fig. 133**A-E**; see **Molt**), the retained juvenal covs worn and brownish with whitish edging, contrasting markedly with the fresher, dusky, and yellow-tipped (lesser and med covs; Fig. 284), or pale yellow-edged (gr covs), recently replaced, inner covs; 1-2 terts often replaced and dusky, contrasting with the brown ss and pp (Fig. 133**D**); outer pp covs narrow, tapered, abraded (Fig. 138**C**), and brown; central (r1) or other rects occasionally replaced, contrastingly fresh and dusky; outer rects tapered (Fig. 139**B**), relatively abraded, and brownish. **Note: Some ♀♀ may be difficult to age.**

ASY ♀ (Mar-Aug): Head without red, or with a slight reddish wash; back dusky olive; med covs usually uniformly dusky with yellow tips (Fig. 284); gr covs often uniformly adult (Fig. 133**F**; see **Molt**) and dusky with yellowish edging, occasionally contrasting slightly (in wear only) with the 1-3 replaced inner covs; terts, ss, and pp uniformly dusky (Fig. 133**F**); outer pp covs broad, truncate, relatively fresh (Fig. 138**D**), and dusky; rects uniformly adult, the outer rects truncate (Fig. 139**B**) and brownish dusky. **Note: See SY ♀.**

SY ♂ (Mar-Aug): Head red or primarily red; back black, often slightly mottled olive; molt-limit and wing-cov criteria as in SY ♀, except that the replaced med covs are primarily yellow (Fig. 284; occasionally all med covs can be replaced) and the replaced lesser and gr covs are black; 1-2 terts often replaced, black, contrasting markedly with the brown ss and pp (Fig. 133**D**); outer pp covs narrow, tapered, abraded (Fig. 138**C**), and brown, contrasting with the blacker lesser covs; central (r1) or other rects occasionally replaced, contrastingly fresh and black; outer rects tapered (Fig. 139**B**), relatively abraded, and brownish.

ASY ♂ (Mar-Aug): Head bright red; back black; med covs usually uniformly yellow (Fig. 284); molt-limit, pp-cov, and rect criteria as in ASY ♀, except that the flight feathers and wing covs are uniformly black (the innermost 1-3 gr covs sometimes being slightly fresher).

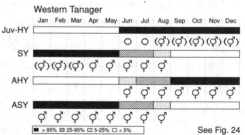

Hybrids reported—Scarlet Tanager.

References—Dwight (1900a), Ridgway (1902), Forbush (1929), Dickey & van Rossem (1938), Tordoff (1950), Roberts (1955), Bent (1958), Mengel (1963), Davis (1971, 1972), Sheppard & Collins (1971a), Oberholser (1974), Kaufman (1988b), CWS & USFWS (1991), Pyle (1997c); C.T. Collins, D.F. DeSante, M.K. Klimkiewicz, J.M. Sheppard (*in litt.* to the BBL); J.R. King (pers. comm.), IBP (MAPS) data, PRBO data.

FLAME-COLORED TANAGER
Piranga bidentata

FCTA
Species # 6071
Band size: 1A

Geographic variation—Moderately well marked and ranges well defined. Subspecies taxonomy follows R.W. Storer *in* Paynter (1970); see Ridgway (1902), LeFebvre & Warner (1959), Howell & Webb (1995). Three other subspecies occur in Mex-C.Am.

P.b. bidentata (br se.AZ): From the other subspecies of Mex-C.Am by bill small (exp culmen 15.1-17.7, bill width at tip of nares 8.7-9.8); back washed grayish (less olive); head, throat, and breast of AHY/ASY

♂♂ orange (*vs* red in the other subspecies); breast of ♀♀ bright yellow (*vs* washed dusky or orange in the other subspecies); white spots on the outer rects (r5-r6) average larger by age/sex.

Molt—Not well studied, but possibly as follows: PB HY partial (May-Aug), AHY complete (Jun-Oct); PA absent. The 1st PB appears to include all med and gr covs, but few terts or rects; some terts (at least) can be replaced in some birds. Also, look for a partial or incomplete PAs, as in the other tanagers. More study is needed.

Skull—Pneumaticization completes in HY/SY from 15 Oct through Jan. Check for windows (> 3 mm; Fig. 11**D**) on SYs through spring.

Age/Sex—Juv (Apr-Aug) is brownish above, dull yellow below, and has dusky streaking over much of the body plumage; juv ♀ = ♂. CP/BP (May-Aug). ♀ wg(n30) 89-100, tl(n15) 73-82; ♂ wg(n31) 91-104, tl(n20) 76-85.

HY/SY ♀♂ (Aug-Jul): Head and underparts dull yellow to olive-yellow, without an orange wash; streaks on the back dusky and indistinct; outer pp covs narrow, tapered, relatively abraded (Fig. 138), and brownish, contrasting with the slightly fresher and dusky-centered gr covs (Fig. 134); outer rects (r4-r6) tapered (Fig. 139**B**), washed brownish, relatively abraded, and with reduced white spots; throat and undertail covs without an orange tinge. **Note: Some HY/SYs in the above plumage may be ♂♂ and thus not reliably sexed ♀♀; more study is needed. In addition, look for molt limits to assist with ageing, as in the other tanagers of N.Am. Also, the amount of white in the rects appears to vary, as in *Dendroica* warblers (see Fig. 262), and thus is useful in ageing and sexing (see p. 459), although this also varies by subspecies (see Geographic variation). More study is needed.**

AHY/ASY ♀ (Aug-Jul): Head and underparts brightish yellow, sometimes variably washed orange; streaks on the back blackish and moderately distinct; outer pp covs broad, truncate, relatively fresh (Fig. 138), and dusky, not contrasting markedly in color or wear with the gr covs (Fig. 133**F**); outer rects (r4-r6) truncate (Fig. 139**B**), dusky, relatively fresh, and with moderate white spots. **Note: See HY/SY ♀♂ and HY/SY ♂.**

HY/SY ♂ (Aug-Jul): Head and underparts brightish yellow, often variably washed orange; streaks on the back blackish and moderately distinct; pp-cov and rect criteria as in HY/SY ♀, except that the white spots in the outer rects (r4-r6) average larger. **Note: See HY/SY ♀♂. Beware that there is likely some overlap with ♀♀ of both age groups.**

AHY/ASY ♂ (Aug-Jul): Head and underparts bright orange to reddish; streaks on the back black and distinct; pp-cov and rect criteria as in AHY/ASY ♀, except that the white spots in the outer rects (r4-r6) average larger. **Note: See HY/SY ♀♂.**

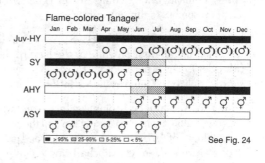

References—Ridgway (1902), Dickey & van Rossem (1938), LeFebvre & Warner (1959), Howell & Webb (1995).

TOWHEES, SPARROWS, AND LONGSPURS   *EMBERIZIDAE*

Forty-nine species. Family characters include generally subdued plumages, thick, seed-eating bills, and short wings. Emberizines have 9 visible primaries, 9 secondaries, and 12 rectrices (13 have been noted in aberrant Dark-eyed Juncos). The first prebasic molts are variable, but generally are partial to incomplete in extent. The prealternate molts usually are partial, although they can be incomplete in certain species. In many species the first prebasic molt includes all wing coverts, but not the tertials and/or the central rectrices, whereas in some species it can be eccentric, including the outer primaries, inner secondaries and the rectrices. One species has an eccentric prealternate molt. Plumage characters also are variable, ages being similar and sexes being alike in most of the species. Breeding condition characters are reliable for sexing and males average moderately larger than females.

WHITE-COLLARED SEEDEATER

Sporophila torqueola

WCSE
Species # 6020
Band size: 0

Geographic variation—Well marked (in ♂♂), but complicated by age-related plumage variation; ranges are fairly well defined. Subspecies taxonomy follows Paynter (1970); see Ridgway (1901), Oberholser (1974), Howell & Webb (1995). One to three other subspecies occur in Mex-C.Am, depending on the species taxonomy.

> *S.t. sharpei* (former res s.TX): From the other subspecies of Mex-C.Am by smaller average size (see **Sex**, *vs* wg 50-60, tl 42-50 in the other subspecies); alternate-plumaged ♂♂ with the upperparts mixed grayish and black, the rump whitish (*vs* white or cinnamon in the other subspecies), and the blackish breast collar broken; ♀♀ and HY/SY ♂♂ with two prominent, whitish wing bars.

Molt—Not well described, but apparently as follows: PB HY partial-incomplete (Jun-Oct), AHY complete (Jun-Sep); PA limited-partial (Feb-Apr). The 1st PB is variable, including no to all med covs, 0 (~10%) to 10 (~20%) inner gr covs, often (in ~70% of birds) 1-3 terts, and 0 (~30%) to all 12 (~70%) rects. The PAs include few if any gr covs and usually no terts or rects. This species could breed year round, and thus may show wider variation in the extents and timing of the molts than is indicated here; more study is needed.

Skull—Pneumaticization completes in HY/SY from 15 Aug. Look for windows (> 2 mm; Fig. 11**D**) on some SYs through spring.

Age/Sex—Juv (Apr-Sep) is like HY/SY ♀, but has loosely textured plumage; juvs can be sexed by the color and amount of white at the base of the outer pp, as in HY/SYs (see below). CP/BP (Mar-Sep). ♀ wg(n30) 45-52, tl(n20) 37-45; ♂ wg(n30) 48-56, tl(n20) 39-47; includes *S.t. sharpei* only (see **Geographic variation**).

HY/SY ♀ (Aug-Jul): Body plumage brown and whitish, without dusky or black; bases of outer pp brown without white extending beyond the pp covs (if present, at least 3 mm < longest pp cov); molt limits often occur among the med and gr covs (Fig. 133**A-E**; see **Molt**), the retained outer covs worn and brown with buff tips, contrasting with the fresher, dusky-brown, and white-tipped, replaced inner covs; 1-3 terts often replaced, contrasting with the older middle ss (s4-s6; Fig. 133**D-E**); outer pp covs narrow, tapered, relatively abraded (Fig. 138), and pale brown with indistinct, buff tips when fresh; outer rects sometimes tapered, relatively abraded (Fig. 139**A**), and pale brown. **Note: Plumage criteria are reliable for sexing but possible year-round breeding may complicate ageing and age-code assignment. More study is needed.**

AHY/ASY ♀ (Aug-Jul): Body plumage brown and whitish, without dusky or black; bases of outer pp dark brown with an indistinct white area seldom extending beyond the pp covs (at most, 2 mm > longest pp cov); wing covs, terts, and middle ss (s4-s6) uniformly adult (Fig. 133F) and dusky brown; outer pp covs broad, truncate, relatively fresh (Fig. 138), and dusky brown without buff tips; outer rects truncate, relatively fresh (Fig. 139A), and dusky brown. **Note: See HY/SY ♀.**

HY/SY ♂ (Aug-Jul): Body plumage brown and whitish, without dusky or black (Aug-Mar), or mixed grayish and buff, often with some blackish feather centers on the upperparts and breast (Mar-Jul); bases of outer pp dusky with a distinct, white patch, extending 2-6 mm beyond the pp covs; wing-cov and flight-feather criteria as in HY/SY ♀, except that the replaced gr covs and terts are blackish, contrasting markedly with the retained, juvenal gr covs, pp covs, and pp; rects variable (see **Molt**), from uniformly brown and tapered (Fig. 139A), to uniformly blackish with gray tips. **Note: See HY/SY ♀.**

AHY/ASY ♂ (Aug-Jul): Body plumage brown and whitish, often with concealed blackish feathers, especially in the crown, back, and breast (Aug-Mar), or grayish and white, with black in the head, back, and breast (Mar-Jul); bases of pp blackish with a distinct, white patch extending 5-10 mm beyond the pp covs; wing covs, terts, and middle ss (s4-s6) uniformly adult (Fig. 133F) and blackish; outer pp covs broad, truncate, relatively fresh (Fig. 138) and blackish, not contrasting with the pp or the centers of the gr covs (Fig. 133F); outer rects uniformly truncate (Fig. 139A) and blackish with gray tips. **Note: See HY/SY ♀.**

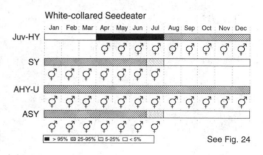

References—Ridgway (1901), Bent *et al.* (1968), Oberholser (1974), Howell & Webb (1995), Rising (1996a), Eitnier (1997), Pyle (1997c).

OLIVE SPARROW
Arremonops rufivirgatus

OLSP
Species # 5860
Band Size: 1-1B

Species—From dull Green-tailed Towhees by much smaller size (wg 58-68, tl 57-70; see **Sex**); crown without reddish feathers.

Geographic variation—Weak to moderate and most ranges well defined. Subspecies taxonomy follows Paynter (1970); see Ridgway (1901), Todd (1923), Sutton & Burleigh (1941), Monroe (1963), Byers *et al.* (1995), Howell & Webb (1995). Seven other subspecies occur in Mex.

A.r. rufivirgatus (res s.TX): From the subspecies of Mex by bill thinner (depth at tip of nares 5.6-6.5), and fairly uniformly dark horn (*vs* bicolored, blackish and flesh in the subspecies of Mex); lateral crown stripes duller brownish and less distinct; upperparts duller olive-green; underparts washed dull (*vs* rich) buff.

Molt—PB: HY partial (Jun-Oct), AHY complete (May-Sep); PA absent. The 1st PB usually includes all med and gr covs, but no terts or rects.

Skull—Pneumaticization completes in HY/SY from 15 Sep through Feb.

Age—Juv (Apr-Aug) has brown-washed and dusky-streaked upperparts, dusky-streaked underparts, lacks crown stripes, and has pale brown wing bars; juv ♀=♂. A supplemental plumage (see p. 16), similar to juvenal plumage but without streaking, may occur in this species; more study is needed.

HY/SY (Sep-Aug): Outer pp covs narrow, tapered, relatively abraded, and brown with indistinct, narrow, or no green edging (Fig. 138), and with buff tips when fresh, contrasting with the slightly fresher, dusky-centered, and green-edged, replaced gr covs (Fig. 134); outer pp and rects relatively abraded. **Note: Intermediates will be difficult to age; the rect shape is rounded in both age groups and thus is unhelpful in ageing.**

AHY/ASY (Sep-Aug): Outer pp covs broad, truncate, relatively fresh, and dusky with relatively distinct, broad, green edging (Fig. 138), without buff tipping, and not contrasting markedly in color or wear with the gr covs (Fig. 133**F**); outer pp and rects relatively fresh. **Note: See HY/SY.**

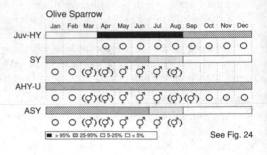

Sex—♀=♂ by plumage. CP/BP (Mar-Sep). Measurements are useful: ♀ wg(n55) 58-65, tl(n28) 57-65; ♂ wg(n67) 62-68, tl(n35) 59-70.

References—Ridgway (1901), O. Austin Jr. *in* Bent *et al.* (1968), Oberholser (1974), Foster (1975), Byers *et al.* (1995), Rising (1996a), Pyle (1997c).

GREEN-TAILED TOWHEE
Pipilo chlorurus

GTTO
Species # 5900
Band size: 1B-1A

Species—Dull individuals from Olive Sparrow by much larger size (wg 70-85, tl 74-89; see **Sex**); crown with at least some dull reddish feathering.

Geographic variation—Subspecies taxonomy follows Paynter (1970), who considered the species monotypic (synonymizing a previously recognized subspecies); see Oberholser (1932, 1974). Breeding birds of c.OR to e.CA-w.NV ("*P.c. zapolius*") may average grayer than others, but differences, if present, are slight and broadly clinal.

Molt—PB: HY partial (Jul-Oct), AHY complete (Jul-Sep); PA absent-limited (Feb-May). The PBs occur on the summer grounds. The 1st PB includes all med covs and 9 to 10 (~91%) inner gr covs, but no terts or rects. The PAs, if present, are primarily restricted to the head and crown.

Skull—Pneumaticization completes in HY/SY from 15 Nov. Some SYs can retain windows (> 3 mm; Fig. 11**D**) through spring/summer.

Age—Juv (Jun-Aug) is primarily brownish with distinct streaking to the upperparts and upper breast; juv ♀ = ♂.

HY/SY (Sep-Aug): Rufous of the head sometimes restricted to the forecrown and often with heavy (Sep-Mar), or a moderate amount (Mar-Aug), of buff or grayish mottling; outer pp covs narrow, tapered, relatively abraded, and brown with indistinct, narrow, or no dull green edging (Fig. 138), contrasting with the slightly fresher, duskier, and brighter green, replaced gr covs (Fig. 134); outer rects tapered (Fig. 139**B**) and relatively abraded. **Note: Crown color is variable in HY/SYs (see also Sex) and can show some overlap with AHY/ASYs, especially with ♂♂ in Mar-Aug. Intermediates can be difficult to age.**

AHY/ASY (Sep-Aug): Rufous of the head extensive (to the nape), with light, grayish mottling in

Aug-Dec only; outer pp covs broad, truncate, relatively fresh, and dusky with relatively distinct and broad, bright green edging (Fig. 138), not contrasting markedly in color or wear with the gr covs (Fig. 133**F**); outer rects truncate (Fig. 139**B**) and relatively fresh. **Note: See HY/SY ♀.**

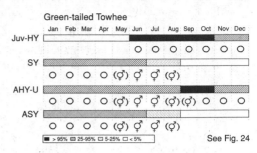

Green-tailed Towhee

See Fig. 24

Sex—CP/BP (May-Sep). ♀ wg(n45) 70-80, tl(n20) 74-85; ♂ wg(n47) 74-85, tl(n20) 78-89. No reliable plumage criteria are known, although ♀♀ average duller than ♂♂, especially in the crown; compare with measurements and age.

Hybrids reported—Spotted Towhee.

References—Ridgway (1901), Parkes (1957b), R.A. Norris *in* Bent *et al.* (1968), Davis (1974a), Oberholser (1974), Morton (1991), Sibley (1994), Byers *et al.* (1995), Rising (1996a), Pyle (1997c); IBP (MAPS) data, PRBO data.

EASTERN TOWHEE
Pipilo erythrophthalmus

EATO
Species # 5870
Band size: ♀ 1A-2, ♂ 2-1A

Species—From Spotted Towhee by tl averages shorter (79-101; see **Geographic variation** & **Age/Sex**); scapulars, med covs, and gr covs without white tipping (*cf.* Fig. 285); pp with white extending > pp covs; ♀♀ with the head and upperparts warm brown to reddish brown. Birds not identified to species ("Unknown Rufous-sided Towhees"), including hybrids, have alpha code **URST** and **Species # 5876**.

Geographic variation—Moderately weak and clinal where ranges meet. Subspecies taxonomy follows Paynter (1970); see Ridgway (1901), Howell (1913, 1932), Worthington & Todd (1926), Oberholser (1938, 1974), Koelz (1939), Wetmore (1941), Dickinson (1952), Sibley & West (1959), Sutton (1967) Byers *et al.* (1995), Grenlaw (1996a), Rising (1996a). No other subspecies occur.

   P.e. erythrophthalmus (br Man-sw.ME to ne.OK-ec.VA, wint to s.TX-s.FL): Wg of ♂ long; bill small (exp culmen 12.9-15.2); white patches in the rects extensive (27-53 mm long on r6); iris of AHY bright red. ♀ wg(n100) 76-86, tl(n100) 80-91; ♂ wg(n100) 81-94, tl(n100) 86-100.

   P.e. canaster (br LA-sw.TN to c.SC-nw.FL, wint to e.SC-c.FL): Wg medium long; bill large (exp culmen 14.2-16.7); white patches in the rects moderate in size (19-41 mm long on r6); iris of AHY orange-red to yellowish. ♀ wg(n45) 77-86, tl(n45) 84-96; ♂ wg(n100) 80-91, tl(n100) 87-101. Birds of se.LA (*"leptoleucus"*) may average slightly smaller, with less white in the rects, but differences, if present, are slight.

   P.e. rileyi (br & wint se.AL-se.VA to n.FL): Wg medium in length; bill large (exp culmen 13.8-16.0); white patches in the rects moderately reduced (18-35 mm long on r6); iris of AHY orange to light yellowish. ♀ wg(n57) 75-84, tl(n35) 82-93; ♂ wg(n100) 80-90, tl(n100) 88-98.

   P.e. alleni (res peninsular FL): Wg short; bill large (exp culmen 13.8-16.0); white patches in the rects reduced (7-24 mm long on r6); iris of AHY brownish yellow to white. ♀ wg(n55) 71-79, tl(n37) 78-89; ♂ wg(n100) 74-84, tl(n100) 85-99.

Molt—PB: HY partial-incomplete (Jul-Oct), AHY complete (Jun-Sep); PA absent-limited (Feb-Apr). The PBs occur on the breeding grounds. The 1st PB usually includes all med and gr covs (occasionally the outermost gr cov can be retained), often (in ~65% of birds) 1-3 terts, and 0 (~65%) to all 12 (~15%) rects. Southern subspecies may average slightly more terts and rects replaced than northern subspecies. The PAs sometimes include some throat feathers.

Skull—Pneumaticization completes in HY/SY from 1 Nov. Look for windows (> 3 mm; Fig. 11**D**) on the top of the skull in some SYs through May.

Age/Sex—Juv (Jun-Aug) has buffy to brown body plumage, with distinct dark streaking throughout; juvs can be sexed by the color of the flight feathers, as in HY/SYs (see below). ♀ wg(n100) 72-87, tl(n100) 79-96; ♂ wg(n100) 75-94, tl(n100) 86-101; see **Geographic variation**.

HY/SY ♀ (Aug-Jul): Upperparts, head, and throat brown; 1-3 terts often replaced (see **Molt**) and dark brownish with white edging, contrasting with the older, pale brownish, and buff-edged middle ss (s4-s6; Fig. 133**D-E**); outer pp covs narrow, tapered, relatively abraded, and brown with little or no pale edging (Fig. 138), contrasting with the slightly fresher and dark-centered, replaced gr covs (Fig. 134); some or all rects tapered (Fig. 139**C**), pale brown, and relatively abraded, or occasionally all rects dark brown and truncate; iris gray-brown to dull red or dull whitish (through Nov, possibly through spring on some SYs; see **Geographic variation**). **Note: Beware of HY/SYs that replace all rects; these also replace terts (usually all 3) and can be aged by contrasts there and between the pp covs and gr covs. In addition, the white spot on r4 varies by age and sex, but more study is needed on the usefulness of this within each subspecies (see Geographic variation).**

AHY/ASY ♀ (Aug-Jul): Upperparts, head, and throat brown; terts and ss uniformly adult (Fig. 133**F**) and dark brownish with white edging; outer pp covs broad, truncate, relatively fresh, and dark brown, often with rusty edging (Fig. 138), not contrasting markedly in color or wear with the gr covs (Fig. 133**F**); rects uniformly truncate (Fig. 139**C**), relatively fresh, and dark brown; iris bright red to white (see **Geographic variation**). **Note: See HY/SY ♀.**

HY/SY ♂ (Sep-Aug): Upperparts, head, and throat blackish to black; molt-limit, flight-feather and iris-color criteria as in HY/SY ♀, except that the retained juvenal pp covs and flight feathers are blackish and the replaced gr covs, terts, and rects are black. **Note: See HY/SY ♀.**

AHY/ASY ♂ (Sep-Aug): Upperparts, head, and throat glossy black; molt-limit, flight-feather and iris-color criteria as in AHY/ASY ♀, except that the wing feathers and rects are uniformly glossy black. **Note: See HY/SY ♀.**

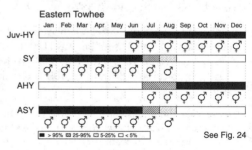

Hybrids reported—Spotted Towhee.

References—Stone (1896), Dwight (1900a), Ridgway (1901), Forbush (1929), Sutton (1935a), Nichols (1953a), Roberts (1955), J.C. Dickinson Jr. *in* Bent *et al.* (1968), Wood (1969), Oberholser (1974), Cramp & Perrins (1994b), Byers *et al.* (1995), Greenlaw (1996a), Rising (1996a), Pyle (1997c); C.S. Robbins (*in litt.* to the BBL); IBP (MAPS) data, PNR data.

SPOTTED TOWHEE
Pipilo maculatus

SPTO
Species # 5880
Band size: 1A-2

Species—From Eastern Towhee by tl averages longer (79-112; see **Geographic variation** & **Age/Sex**); scapulars, med covs, and gr covs with white tipping (Fig. 285; see **Geographic variation**); pp without white extending > pp covs; ♀ with the head and upperparts grayish brown to blackish slate. Birds not identified to species ("Unknown Rufous-sided Towhees"), includ-ing hybrids, have alpha code **URST** and **Species # 5876**.

Geographic variation—Weak to moderate and clinal where ranges meet. Subspecies taxonomy follows Paynter (1970); see Ridgway (1901), Swarth (1905, 1913b), Grinnell (1911b), van Rossem (1934a), Van Tyne & Sutton (1937), Twomey (1942), Sibley (1950, 1954), Miller (1955a), Sibley & West (1959, 1964), Phillips *et al.* (1964), Sutton (1967), Oberholser (1974), D.M. Power (1980), Behle (1985), Godfrey (1986), Byers *et al.* (1995) Greenlaw (1996b), Rising (1996a). Ten other extant subspecies occur in Mex-C.Am.

Coastal (*P.m. oregonus*) Group. Dark; white spots and patches reduced.

P.m. oregonus (br coastal sw.BC-sw.OR, wint to cw.CA): Tl short; feet small (hind toe with claw 16.5-20.0); head, back, and rump dark slaty brown in ♀♀ and uniformly glossy black in ♂♂; white spots of the wing covs and scapulars quite reduced (Fig. 285A); white patches in the rects reduced (12-25 mm long on r6). ♀ wg(n24) 76-86, tl(n18) 84-96; ♂ wg(n44) 78-88, tl(n31) 88-100.

P.m. falcifer (res coastal nw-wc.CA, Del Norte-Santa Cruz Cos.): Tl medium short; feet medium large (hind toe with claw 18.2-22.0); head, back, and rump dark brown to slaty brown in ♀♀ and uniformly glossy black in ♂♂; white spots of the wing covs and scapulars moderately reduced (Fig. 285A-B); white patches in the rects reduced (16-25 mm long on r6). ♀ wg(n91) 73-85, tl(n15) 87-97; ♂ wg(n100) 77-90, tl(n25) 88-101.

P.m. megalonyx (res coastal wc-sw.CA, Monterey-San Diego Cos & Santa Cruz I): Tl medium in length; feet large (hind toe with claw 18.4-23.0); head, back, and rump dull slaty in ♀♀ and uniformly glossy blackish in ♂♂; white spots of the wing covs and scapulars variable (Fig. 285A-C); white patches in the rects moder-ately reduced (18-30 mm long on r6). ♀ wg(n38) 74-87, tl(n17) 85-96; ♂ wg(n74) 78-90, tl(n26) 92-102.

P.m. clementae (res Santa Rosa, Santa Catalina & San Clemente Is, CA): Tl medium short; feet very large (hind toe with claw 18.6-24.0); head and back dark brown to slaty brown in ♀♀ and black in ♂♂; rump washed grayish; white spots of the wing covs and scapulars moderately extensive (Fig. 285B-C); white patches in the rects moderately reduced (17-27 mm long on r6). ♀ wg(n13) 78-84, tl(n13) 86-96; ♂ wg(n23) 81-90, tl(n23) 89-102.

Interior (*P.m. maculatus*) Group. Pale; white spots and patches extensive.

P.m. falcinellus (res interior s.OR-sc.CA): Tl medium short; feet medium in size (hind toe with claw 17.0-20.5); head and back dark brown to slaty brown in ♀♀ and medium black in ♂♂; rump tinged grayish; white spots of the wing covs and scapulars moderate in size (Fig. 285B); white patches in the rects mod-erate in size (19-34 mm long on r6). ♀ wg(n20) 75-85, tl(n16) 85-96; ♂ wg(n61) 79-89, tl(n24) 90-100.

P.m. curtatus (br interior s.BC-n.ID to ec.CA-c.NV, wint to s.CA-s.AZ): Tl medium short; feet medium small (hind toe with claw 17.2-19.3); head, back, and rump dark slaty brown in ♀♀ and uniformly blackish in ♂♂; white spots of the wing covs and scapulars moderate in size (Fig. 285B); white patches in the rects moder-ate in size (22-35 mm long on r6). ♀ wg(n28) 77-87, tl(n19) 86-96; ♂ wg(n40) 80-90, tl(n26) 90-101.

P.m. montanus (br se.CA-s.AZ to c.CO, wint to sw.TX): Tl long; feet medium small (hind toe with claw 17.0-19.0); head, back, and rump blackish slate in ♀♀ and uniformly blackish in ♂♂; white spots of the wing covs and scapulars moderately extensive (Fig. 285B-C); white patches in the rects moderately extensive (25-40 mm long on r6). ♀ wg(n22) 80-88, tl(n27) 91-105; ♂ wg(n43) 84-94, tl(n44) 96-112.

P.m. arcticus (br s.Alb-ND to ne.CO-NE, wint to sw.NM-s.TX; vag to FL): Tl medium in length; feet small (hind toe with claw moder-ately short 16.5-20.0); head and back slaty brown in ♀♀ and grayish black in ♂♂; rump tinged olive; white spots of the wing covs and scapulars moderate in size (Fig. 285B); white patches in rects moderately extensive (27-42 mm long on r6). ♀ wg(n30) 78-88, tl(n36) 84-99; ♂ wg(n43) 81-92, tl(n60) 89-104.

P.m. gaigei (br & wint se.NM-w.TX): Tl medi-um long; ♀ with head and back slaty and rump ashy gray; ♂ with upperparts black; white spots of the wing covs and scapulars

A   B   C

FIGURE 285. Variation in the amount of white on the largest scapular, by subspecies (see text), in Spotted Towhee. Note that Eastern Towhee shows no white on this feather.

moderate in size (Fig. 285**B**); white patches in the rects moderately extensive (25-40 mm long on r6). ♀ wg(n11) 79-87, tl(n11) 90-102; ♂ wg(n16) 84-91, tl(n16) 96-108.

Molt—PB: HY partial-incomplete (Jul-Oct), AHY complete (Jun-Sep); PA absent-limited (Feb-Apr). The PBs occur on the breeding grounds. The 1st PB usually includes all med and gr covs (occasionally the outermost gr cov can be retained), often (in ~78% of birds) 1-3 terts, and 0 (~63%) to all 12 (~27%) rects. Southern subspecies average slightly more terts and rects replaced than northern subspecies. The PAs sometimes include some throat feathers.

Skull—Pneumaticization completes in HY/SY from 1 Nov. Look for windows (> 3 mm; Fig. 11**D**) on the top of the skull in some SYs through spring.

Age/Sex—Juv (May-Aug) has buffy to brown body plumage, with distinct, dark streaking throughout; juvs of some subspecies of the Interior Subspecies Group can be sexed by the color of the flight feathers, as in HY/SYs (see below). CP/BP (Mar-Sep). ♀ wg(n100) 73-88, tl(n100) 79-105; ♂ wg(n100) 77-93, tl(n100) 86-112; see **Geographic variation**.

HY/SY ♀ (Aug-Jul): Upperparts, head, and throat grayish brown to dull blackish gray (see **Geographic variation**); 1-3 terts often replaced (see **Molt**), dark brownish or slaty with white edging, contrasting with the older and buff-edged middle ss (s4-s6; Fig. 133**D-E**); outer pp covs narrow, tapered, relatively abraded, and brownish with little or no pale edging (Fig. 138), contrasting with the slightly fresher and dark-centered, replaced gr covs (Fig. 134); some or all rects tapered (Fig. 139**C**), brown, and relatively abraded, or (sometimes) all rects dark brown to slaty and truncate; iris gray-brown to dull red (through Nov, possibly through spring on some SYs). **Note: Beware of HY/SYs that replace all rects; these also replace terts (usually all 3) and can be aged by contrasts there and between the pp covs and gr covs. In addition, the white spot on r4 varies by age and sex, but more study is needed on the usefulness of this within each subspecies (see Geographic variation). Among HY/SYs, the sexes of certain interior subspecies (notably *P.m. montanus* and *gaigei*) may be difficult or impossible to separate, especially without experience; compare with age, as HY/SYs average duller black than AHY/ASYs within each sex.**

AHY/ASY ♀ (Aug-Jul): Upperparts, head, and throat dark grayish brown to blackish (see **Geographic variation**); terts and ss uniformly adult (Fig. 133**F**) and dark grayish brown to blackish, with white edging; outer pp covs broad, truncate, relatively fresh, and dark grayish brown to blackish, often with rusty edging (Fig. 138), not contrasting markedly in color or wear with the gr covs (Fig. 133**F**); rects uniformly truncate (Fig. 139**C**), relatively fresh, and dark grayish brown to slaty; iris bright red. **Note: See HY/SY ♀.**

HY/SY ♂ (Sep-Aug): Upperparts, head, and throat blackish to black; molt-limit, flight-feather, and iris-color criteria as in HY/SY ♀, except that the retained juvenal pp covs and flight feathers are dusky to blackish and the replaced gr covs, terts, and rects are blackish to black (see **Geographic variation**). **Note: See HY/SY ♀.**

AHY/ASY ♂ (Sep-Aug): Upperparts, head, and throat glossy blackish to black (see **Geographic variation**); molt-limit, flight-feather and iris-color criteria as in AHY/ASY ♀, except that the feathers are uniformly glossy blackish to black. **Note: See HY/SY ♀.**

Hybrids reported—Green-tailed Towhee, Eastern Towhee, Collared Towhee (*P. torquatus*).

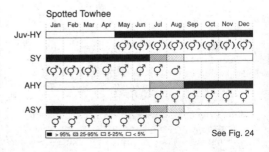

Spotted Towhee

See Fig. 24

References—Ridgway (1901), C.G. Sibley (1954), Sibley & West (1964), J. Davis (1957, 1958, 1961, 1974b), O.L. Austin Jr. *in* Bent *et al.* (1968), Oberholser (1974), D. Sibley (1994), Byers *et al.* (1995), Greenlaw (1996), Rising (1996a), Pyle (1997c); S.M. Russell (*in litt.* to the BBL); IBP (MAPS) data, PRBO data.

CALIFORNIA TOWHEE
Pipilo crissalis

CALT
Species # 5911
Band size: 2-1A

Species—From Canyon Towhee by tl longer (96-119; see **Geographic variation** & **Sex**); p9 ≥ ss; crown, upperparts, and underparts fairly uniformly medium-dark grayish-brown, contrasting with the darker, reddish-brown lores; eye ring fairly distinct below the eye but indistinct or lacking above the eye; malar region and throat (including the center of the throat) with indistinct, dusky markings, not coalescing to a patch on the central breast; legs dark reddish pink; juvs with a cinnamon tinge to the feather edging and a brownish belly, not markedly paler than the remainder of the underparts. From Abert's Towhee by grayish-brown coloration; face without dusky or blackish; lower throat with dusky streaks; bill dark.

Geographic variation—Moderately weak and clinal where ranges meet. Subspecies taxonomy follows Paynter (1970); see Ridgway (1901), Grinnell (1912), Swarth (1918c), Oberholser (1919i), Grinnell & Swarth (1926c), van Rossem (1935b), Grinnell & Behle (1937b), Davis (1951b), Byers *et al.* (1995), Rising (1996a). Two other subspecies occur in Baja CA.

P.c. bullatus (res s.OR-n.CA): Large; bill large (nares to tip 9.9-11.9, depth at tip of nares 8.0-8.9); coloration dark grayish brown. ♀ wg(n11) 92-100, tl(n11) 104-112; ♂ wg(n20) 97-104, tl(n24) 107-118.

P.c. petulans (res coastal nw-wc.CA, Humboldt-Santa Cruz Cos): Medium in size; bill medium large (nares to tip 9.8-11.6, depth at tip of nares 7.6-8.8); coloration medium grayish brown with a tawny tinge. ♀ wg(n66) 87-99, tl(n34) 104-113; ♂ wg(n74) 90-103, tl(n57) 106-115.

P.c. crissalis (res coastal wc-sw.CA, Monterey-Ventura Cos): Medium small; bill medium small (nares to tip 9.5-11.0, depth at tip of nares 7.4-8.6); coloration pale grayish brown. ♀ wg(n64) 84-95, tl(n47) 102-114; ♂ wg(n77) 89-101, tl(n63) 105-118.

P.c. senicula (res coastal sw.CA, Los Angeles-San Diego Cos): Small; bill small (nares to tip 9.2-11.1, depth at tip of nares 7.1-8.6); coloration dark brown with a grayish tinge. ♀ wg(n100) 82-92, tl(n81) 96-107; ♂ wg(n100) 85-97, tl(n93) 100-113.

P.c. carolae (res interior c.CA, Humboldt-Kern Cos): Large; bill large (nares to tip 9.8-12.0, depth at tip of nares 7.9-9.2); tarsus long (26.6-30.5); coloration medium brown with a gray tinge. ♀ wg(n67) 88-97, tl(n57) 103-113; ♂ wg(n100) 95-107, tl(n100) 106-119. Birds of w.Kern Co. ("*kernensis*") may average grayer, especially on the nape, but differences are too slight for subspecific recognition.

P.c. eremophilus (res se.CA, Inyo-Kern Cos): Medium in size; bill medium in size (nares to tip 9.9-11.0, depth at tip of nares 7.9-8.4); tarsus short (26.4-28.3); coloration pale grayish brown. ♀ wg(n10) 91-100, tl(n10) 102-108; ♂ wg(n10) 96-103, tl(n10) 105-114.

Molt—PB: HY partial-incomplete (Jun-Nov), AHY complete (Jun-Oct); PA absent. The 1st PB usually includes all med and gr covs, sometimes (in ~29% of birds) 1-3 terts, and 0 (~79%) to all 12 (~6%) rects.

Skull—Pneumaticization completes in HY/SY from 1 Sep. Some SYs can retain windows (> 3 mm; Fig. 11**D**) through spring, but these can be difficult to see through the skin.

Age—Juv (Apr-Aug) is pale brownish with indistinct streaking in the underparts; juv ♀ = ♂.

HY/SY (Aug-Jul): 1-3 terts sometimes replaced, contrasting with the older middle ss (s4-s6; Fig. 133**D-E**); outer pp covs narrow, tapered, relatively abraded (Fig. 138), and pale brown with indistinct, buff tips when fresh, contrasting with the slightly fresher and darker, replaced gr covs (Fig. 134); some or all rects tapered (Fig. 139**C**) and relatively abraded, or all rects occasionally truncate. **Note: Beware of occasional HY/SYs that have replaced all of the rects; these usually have also replaced at least one tert and often can be aged by this and the pp covs. The above criteria can be subtle, especially in Feb-Jul when the feathers can become worn; many intermediates will not be reliably aged.**

AHY/ASY (Aug-Jul): Terts and ss uniformly adult (Fig. 133**F**); outer pp covs broad, truncate, relatively fresh (Fig. 138), and dark grayish brown without buff tips, not contrasting markedly in color or wear with the gr covs (Fig. 133**F**); rects uniformly truncate (Fig. 139**C**) and relatively fresh. **Note: See HY/SY.**

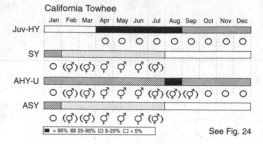

Sex—♀ = ♂ by plumage. CP/BP (Feb-Sep). Measurements are useful within subspecies: ♀ wg(n100) 82-100, tl(n100) 96-114; ♂ wg(n100) 85-107, tl(n100) 100-119; see **Geographic variation**.

References—Ridgway (1901), Davis (1951b, 1974c), Parkes (1957b), H.E. Childs Jr. *in* Bent *et al.* (1968), Rea (1983), Zimmer (1988), Byers *et al.* (1995), Rising (1996a), Pyle (1997c); IBP (MAPS) data, PRBO data.

CANYON TOWHEE
Pipilo fuscus

CANT
Species # 5910
Band size: 2-1A

Species—From California Towhee (which see for separation from Abert's Towhee) by tl shorter (90-111; see **Geographic variation & Sex**); p9 < ss; crown medium-dark brown with a rufous tinge, contrasting with the pale gray-brown lores, back, and underparts; eye ring fairly distinct and full; malar region and throat (but not the center of the throat) with indistinct to distinct, dusky markings, coalescing to a patch on the central breast; legs pale brownish with a pink tinge; juvs with a buff tinge to the feather edging and a whitish belly, paler than the remainder of the underparts.

Geographic variation—Weak and clinal where ranges meet. Subspecies taxonomy follows Paynter (1970); see Ridgway (1901), van Rossem (1934c, 1934e, 1946b), Oberholser (1937b, 1974), Phillips *et al.* (1964), Browning (1978, 1990), Monson & Phillips (1981), Rea (1983), Byers *et al.* (1995), Rising (1996a). Seven other subspecies occur in Mex.

P.f. mesoleucus (res AZ-w.TX, El Paso-Culberson Cos): Small; tl relatively long; bill averages large (nares to tip 9.7-11.9, depth at tip of nares 8.2-9.6); crown heavily washed rufous; upperparts dark grayish brown. ♀ wg(n77) 86-95, tl(n59) 95-106; ♂ wg(n100) 92-99, tl(n100) 99-111. Birds of wc.AZ (Yuma-Maricopa Cos; "*relictus*") may average darker, but differences are slight and this population possibly is too restricted for subspecies recognition. Suggested three-letter subspecies code (see p. 30-31): "mso".

P.f. mesatus (res s.CO-ne.NM to w.OK): Large; tl relatively short; bill averages short and moderately stout (nares to tip 9.7-10.6, depth at tip of nares 8.2-9.3); crown dull brownish with a rufous tinge; upperparts pale grayish brown with a tawny tinge. ♀ wg(n10) 92-99, tl(n10) 98-107; ♂ wg(n10) 96-104, tl(n10) 100-111. Suggested three-letter subspecies code (see p. 30-31): "msa".

P.f. texanus (res c-sw.TX): Small; tl relatively short; bill averages long and thin (nares to tip 9.7-11.9, depth at tip of nares 8.0-9.2); crown dull brownish with little or no rufous; upperparts medium-dark grayish brown with a tawny tinge. ♀ wg(n20) 87-95, tl(n19) 90-99; ♂ wg(n39) 91-99, tl(n34) 94-105. Birds of sw.TX (*"aimophilus"*) may average slightly paler, but differences are obscured by individual variation and represent intergradation with *mesoleucus*.

Molt—PB: HY partial-incomplete (Jun-Nov), AHY complete (Jun-Oct); PA absent. The 1st PB usually includes all med and gr covs, occasionally (in ~17% of birds) 1-2 terts, and occasionally (in ~17% of birds) 1-4 central rects (r1-r2).

Skull—Pneumaticization completes in HY/SY from 1 Sep. Some SYs can retain windows (> 3 mm; Fig. 11**D**) through spring, but these can be difficult to see through the skin.

Age—Ageing is difficult and parallels that of California Towhee, which see.

Sex—♀=♂ by plumage. CP/BP (Feb-Sep). Measurements are somewhat useful within subspecies: ♀ wg(n100) 86-99, tl(n100) 90-107; ♂ wg(n100) 91-104, tl(n100) 94-111; see **Geographic variation**.

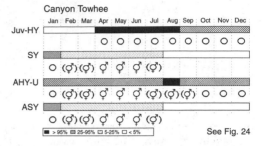

References—Ridgway (1901), Davis (1951b, 1974c), Parkes (1957b), J.T. Marshall Jr. & R.R. Johnson *in* Bent *et al.* (1968), Oberholser (1974), Rea (1983), Zimmer (1988), Byers *et al.* (1995), Johnson & Haight (1996), Rising (1996a), Pyle (1997c).

ABERT'S TOWHEE
Pipilo aberti

ABTO
Species # 5920
Band size: 1A-2

Species—From California Towhee (which see for separation from Canyon Towhee) by coloration brown with a reddish to grayish tinge (see **Geographic variation**); face with a distinct, dusky to black patch; lower throat without dusky streaks; bill pale.

Geographic variation—Weak and clinal where ranges meet. Subspecies taxonomy follows the AOU (1957) as supported by Hubbard (1972b) and Browning (1990); see also van Rossem (1946a), Davis (1951b), Phillips (1962), Phillips *et al.* (1964), Rea (1983), Behle (1985), Byers *et al.* (1995). No other subspecies occur.

P.a. dumeticolus (res sw.UT to se.CA-sw.AZ): Upperparts pale brown with a reddish tinge; underparts tinged cinnamon.
P.a. aberti (= *"vorhiesi"*; res s.AZ-sw.NM): Upperparts medium-pale brown with a grayish tinge; underparts tinged pinkish.

Molt—PB: HY partial (Jun-Nov), AHY complete (Jun-Nov); PA absent. The 1st PB usually includes all med and gr covs and occasionally (in ~15% of birds) 1-2 terts, but no rects. Reports that the 1st PB can include rects and pp require verification.

Skull—Pneumaticization completes in HY/SY from 1 Sep. Some SYs can retain windows (> 3 mm; Fig. 11**D**) through spring, but these can be difficult to see through the skin.

Age—Ageing criteria parallel those of California Towhee (which see), except that all juvenal rects typically are retained by HY/SYs, providing the best ageing criterion.

Sex—♀=♂ by plumage. CP/BP (Feb-Sep). Measurements are somewhat useful: ♀ wg(n100) 82-92, tl(n100) 102-114; ♂ wg(n100) 87-97, tl(n100) 109-121.

References—Ridgway (1901), Davis (1951b, 1974d), W.R. Dawson *in* Bent *et al.* (1968), Zimmer (1988), Tweit & Finch (1994), Byers *et al.* (1995), Rising (1996a), Pyle (1997c).

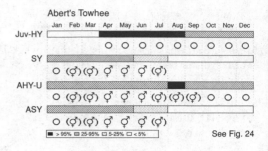

BACHMAN'S SPARROW
Aimophila aestivalis

BACS
Species # 5750
Band size: 1C

Species—From Botteri's Sparrow and Cassin's Sparrow (which see for separation from other sparrows) by shorter wg (54-65; see **Sex**); tl – wg 0-7 mm; wing morphology medium in length (p9 – p3 -3 to 3 mm, longest p – longest s 6-11 mm); bill medium in depth (at tip of nares 5.0-5.7); upperparts moderately dark gray to rufous with an orange tinge, the back feathers usually (see **Geographic variation**) with distinct, black shaft streaks, forming well-defined, broad, black streaking; uppertail covs with shaft streaks but without an anchor-shaped pattern (Fig. 286); terts edged buff to grayish rufous when fresh; outer rect (r6) with buffy-whitish tips measuring 5-6 mm (Fig. 286); central rects (r1) with indistinct, dusky barring and without shaft streaks; supercilium distinct; upper breast grayish buff to rich buff, contrasting with the whitish belly.

Geographic variation—Moderate, but somewhat clinal where ranges meet. Subspecies taxonomy follows Paynter (1970); see Ridgway (1901), Oberholser (1938), Wetmore (1939), Byers *et al.* (1995), Rising (1996a). No other subspecies occur.

A.a. illinoensis (br & wint e.TX to s.IN-nw.FL): Upperparts pale reddish with a pale grayish-brown wash; dark centers to the back feathers indistinct or absent; breast washed buff to buffy orange.

A.a. bachmani (br s.OH-NC to MS-c.SC, wint to n.FL): Upperparts medium-dark reddish with a grayish-brown tinge; black centers to the back feathers large and distinct; breast washed buff, often tinged orange.

A.a. aestivalis (br coastal se.SC-c.FL, wint to s.FL): Upperparts medium-dark reddish with a grayish wash; black centers to the back feathers moderately large and distinct; breast washed buff to grayish buff.

Molt—PS/PB: HY complete (Jul-Dec), AHY complete (Jun-Nov); PA partial (Feb-Jul). A presupplemental molt (see p. 16) occurs in most or all HYs, with the body plumage being replaced

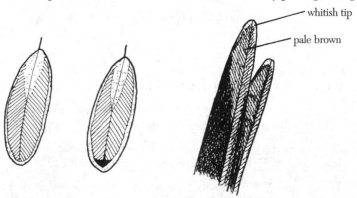

FIGURE 286. The patterns of the uppertail coverts (left) and outer rectrices (r5-r6) in Bachman's Sparrow.

once on the summer grounds in Jun-Sep and again (during the 1st PB) on the summer and/or winter grounds with the flight feathers in Sep-Dec. The adult PB occurs primarily on the winter grounds, although it can commence on the summer grounds. The presupplemental molt usually includes all med and gr covs, occasionally (in ~7% of birds) 1-2 terts and occasionally (in ~7% of birds) 1-2 central rects (r1). Look for some pp covs and middle ss (among s3-s6) possibly to be retained during the otherwise complete 1st PB. The PAs sometimes (~21-41%) include 1-3 terts and occasionally can include 1-2 central rects (r1), but otherwise are limited to body feathers, primarily on the head and throat. Limited replacement of body feathers occurs almost continuously in this species, the timing of individuals dependent on the timing of breeding.

Skull—Pneumaticization completes in HY/SY from 1 Oct through Jan.

Age—Juv (May-Sep) has blackish streaking on the breast and crown; juv ♀ = ♂.

HY/SY (Jul-Mar): Breast with one or more distinct, blackish spots. **Note: Most HY/SYs cannot be aged by plumage after Nov; only occasional birds show one or more breast spots through Mar. See also U/AHY.**

U/AHY (Nov-Oct): Breast without blackish spots. **Note: Look for occasional AHYs in Jan-Sep or later with retained middle ss (among s4-s6) and/or pp covs, probably indicating SY. More study is needed.**

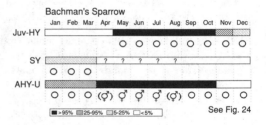

Bachman's Sparrow

Sex—♀ = ♂ by plumage. CP/BP (Apr-Aug). ♀ wg(n47) 54-63, tl(n23) 56-64; ♂ wg(n50) 56-65, tl(n56) 60-67.

References—Ridgway (1901), F.M. Weston *in* Bent *et al.* (1968), Oberholser (1974), Wolf (1977), Landing & Patti (1986), Willoughby (1986), Dunning (1993b), Thompson & Leu (1994), Byers *et al.* (1995), Rising (1996a), Pyle (1997c).

BOTTERI'S SPARROW
Aimophila botterii

BOSP
Species # 5760
Band size: 1C

Species—From Bachman's Sparrow and Cassin's Sparrow (which see for separation from other sparrows) by longer wg (59-71; see **Geographic variation** & **Sex**); tl – wg -7 to 0 mm; wing morphology short (p9 – p3 -3 to 3 mm, longest p – longest s 4-9 mm); bill stout (depth at tip of nares 5.3-5.9); upperparts brownish gray to buffy rufous, the back feathers with distinct, blackish shaft streaks forming well-defined, narrow, black streaking on the back; uppertail covs with broad shaft streaks but without an anchor-shaped pattern (Fig. 287); wing bars absent to indistinct and buff; terts edged buff to rufous when fresh; outer rect (r6) with slightly paler, indistinct, brown tips measuring 10-15 mm (Fig. 287); central rects (r1) without shaft streaks, and with indistinct, dusky barring; supercilium indistinct; upper breast buff, contrasting indistinctly with the whitish belly; flanks without dusky flank streaks.

Geographic variation—Moderately well marked and ranges fairly well defined. Subspecies taxonomy follows Paynter (1970); see Ridgway (1901), Phillips (1943), Webster (1959b), Byers *et al* (1995). Seven other subspecies occur in Mex-C.Am.

A.b. arizonae (br se.AZ): Wg averages short; upperparts medium-dark reddish to reddish brown; breast medium-dark grayish buff. ♀ wg(n20) 59-66, tl(n21) 56-66; ♂ wg(n100) 61-69, tl(n76) 59-71.

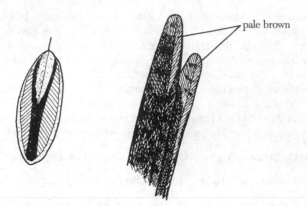

FIGURE 287. The patterns of the uppertail coverts (left) and outer rectrices (r5-r6) in Botteri's Sparrow.

A.b. texana (br s.TX): Wg averages long; upperparts medium-pale grayish brown with a reddish tinge; breast pale grayish buff to whitish. ♀ wg(n10) 62-68, tl(n10) 56-65; ♂ wg(n72) 64-71, tl(n72) 58-68.

Molt—Not well known, but apparently similar to that of the other *Aimophila* sparrows: PS/PB HY complete? (Jun-Dec), AHY complete (Jun-Nov); PA partial (Feb-Apr). The PBs probably occur primarily on the winter grounds. The 1st PB may be eccentric (see p. 208 and Fig. 136) in some individuals; more study is needed. The PAs often (in ~63% of birds) include 1-3 terts and occasionally (in ~11% of birds) include 1-2 central rects (r1; rarely more?), but few if any wing covs. Limited year-round replacement of body feathers likely occurs, as in the other *Aimophila* sparrows.

Skull—Pneumaticization completes in HY/SY from 1 Oct through Jan.

Age—Juv (May-Sep) has blackish streaking on the breast and crown; juv ♀ = ♂.

HY/SY (Jul-Mar): Breast with one or more distinct, blackish spots. **Note: Most HY/SYs cannot be aged by plumage after Nov; only occasional birds show one or more breast spots through Mar. Also, look for retained feathers suggesting an eccentric 1st PB (Fig. 136) which would also be indicative of HY/SYs through Aug or later.**

U/AHY (Nov-Oct): Breast without blackish spots. **Note: See HY/SY.**

Sex—♀ = ♂ by plumage. CP/BP (Mar-Aug). ♀ wg(n40) 59-68, tl(n31) 56-66; ♂ wg(n100) 61-71, tl(n100) 58-71; see **Geographic variation**.

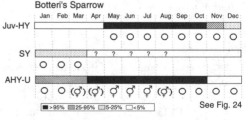

See Fig. 24

References—Ridgway (1901), Webster (1959b), G. Monson *in* Bent *et al.* (1968), Oberholser (1974), Wolf (1977), Bowers & Dunning (1986), Landing & Patti (1986), Kaufman (1989, 1990a), Byers *et al.* (1995), Rising (1996a), Webb & Bock (1996), Pyle (1997c).

CASSIN'S SPARROW
Aimophila cassinii

CASP
Species # 5780
Band size: 1C

Species—From Bachman's and Botteri's sparrows by wg medium in length (56-68; see **Sex**); tl – wg 0-8 mm; wing morphology long (p9 – p3 3-7 mm, longest p – longest s 8-13 mm); bill slen-

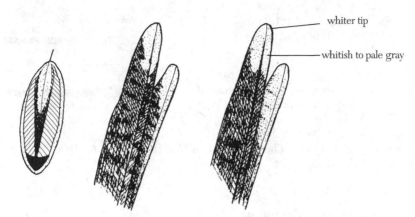

whiter tip

whitish to pale gray

FIGURE 288. The patterns of the uppertail coverts (left) and outer rectrices (r5-r6) in Cassin's Sparrow.

der (depth at tip of nares 4.5-5.3); upperparts pale brownish gray to rufous, without an orange tinge, the back feathers without distinct, black shaft streaks but with irregular, terminal, round or anchor-shaped spots; uppertail covs with black, anchor-shaped patterns (Fig. 288); whitish wing bars indistinct to distinct; terts edged whitish when fresh; outer rect (r6) usually with the pale grayish measuring > 15 mm from the tips and contrasting with the white on the terminal 2-5 mm (Fig. 288); central rects (r1) variable, with central shaft streaks and distinct, dusky barring in some birds (typical of grayer individuals), or without shaft streaks, and with indistinct, dusky barring in others (typical of rufous-washed individuals); supercilium distinct; upper breast grayish, sometimes with a slight buffy wash, not contrasting markedly with the color of the belly; flanks with dusky shaft streaks. Juv from juv Rufous-crowned Sparrow by crown and back uniform in color, grayish or reddish. From Brewer's Sparrow (which see for separation from the other *Spizella* sparrows) by longer tl (60-72; see **Sex**) and bill (exp culmen 10.6-12.0); tail graduated (r1 – r6 8-13 mm); central rects (r1) with irregular shaft streaks; outer rect (r6) tipped white (Fig. 288).

Geographic variation—No subspecies are recognized.

Molt—PS/PB: HY complete (Jul-Nov), AHY complete (Aug-Oct); PA partial (Feb-Jul). A presupplemental molt (see p. 16) occurs in most or all HYs, with the body plumage replaced once on the summer grounds in Jun-Sep and again (during the 1st PB) on the summer and/or winter grounds with the flight feathers in Sep-Nov. The adult PB occurs on the summer grounds. The presupplemental molt includes some to all wing covs, occasionally (in ~7% of birds) 1-3 terts, and occasionally (in ~7% of birds) 1-2 central rects (r1). The PAs occasionally (in ~17% of birds) include 1-3 terts and occasionally (in ~8% of birds) 1-2 central rects (r1), but few if any wing covs. Some replacement of body feathers occurs almost continuously in this species, the timing of individuals dependent on the timing of breeding.

Skull—Pneumaticization completes in HY/SY from 15 Sep through Feb.

Age—Juv (May-Sep) has blackish streaking on the breast and crown; juv ♀ = ♂.

HY/SY (Jul-Mar): Breast with one or more distinct, blackish spots. **Note: Most HY/SYs cannot be aged by plumage after Nov; only occasional birds show one or more breast spots through Mar. See also U/AHY.**

U/AHY (Oct-Sep): Breast without blackish spots. **Note: Look for occasional AHYs in Jan-Sep or later with retained middle ss (among s4-s6) and/or pp covs, probably indicating SY. More study is needed.**

Sex— ♀ = ♂ by plumage. CP/BP (Apr-Sep). ♀ wg(n30) 56-65, tl(n20) 60-70; ♂ wg(n30) 59-68, tl(n20) 62-72.

References—Ridgway (1901), Swarth (1929), F.C. Williams & A.L. LaSassier *in* Bent *et al.* (1968), Oberholser (1974), Wolf (1977), Bowers & Dunning (1986), Landing & Patti (1986), Willoughby (1986), Kaufman (1989, 1990a), Thompson & Leu (1994), Byers et al. (1995), Rising (1996a), Pyle (1997c); PRBO data.

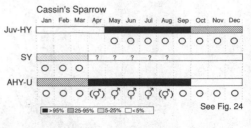

Cassin's Sparrow

See Fig. 24

RUFOUS-WINGED SPARROW
Aimophila carpalis

RWSP
Species # 5790
Band size: 0

Species—Non-juvs from the other *Aimophila* and *Spizella* sparrows by the presence of rufous in the lesser covs. Juvs from these sparrows by crown rufous with gray streaking, contrasting with the brown back; back feathers with buff fringes and without streaks; underparts whitish to white.

Geographic variation—Weak and clinal where ranges meet. Subspecies taxonomy follows Paynter (1970); see Moore (1932, 1946c), van Rossem (1945a), Phillips (1966e), Byers *et al.* (1995). Two other subspecies occur in Mex.

> **A.c. carpalis** (res s.AZ): From subspecies of Mex by larger size (see **Sex**, *vs* wg 54-61, tl 53-62 in subspecies of Mex); coloration paler, grayer.

Molt—PB: HY partial-incomplete (Aug-Nov), AHY complete (Sep-Nov); PA partial-incomplete (May-Jun). The 1st PB usually includes all med covs, 8 to 10 (~90%) inner gr covs, 2-3 terts, occasionally (in ~20% of birds) s6, and 0 (~40%) to all 12 (~10%) rects. Look also for the innermost 1-3 pp (among p1-p3) to occasionally be replaced. The 1st PA includes 0 (~13%) to 10 (~13%) inner gr covs, 1-3 terts, occasionally (in ~13% of birds) s5 and/or s6, and 2 to all 12 (~38%) rects. The adult PA includes 2-9 inner gr covs, 2-3 terts, and 2 to all 12 (~25%) rects. Molts in this species show interannual variation depending on the timing of the breeding season.

Skull—Completion of pneumaticization in HY/SYs varies according to breeding season conditions. The skull can complete as early as 1 Oct in wet years. In dry (normal) years, completion occurs from 15 Nov through Feb.

Age—Juv (Jun-Nov) is browner overall and has distinct spotting or streaking on the breast; juv ♀ = ♂.

> HY/SY (Sep-Aug): 2-3 terts and sometimes s6 replaced during the PB, contrasting with the older middle ss (s4-s6) in Sep-May (Fig. 133**E**); outer pp covs narrow, tapered, relatively abraded, and brown with indistinct, narrow, or no pale grayish-brown edging (Fig. 138), contrasting with the slightly fresher and dusky-centered, replaced gr covs (Fig. 134); central (r1) and other rects sometimes replaced, contrastingly fresh in Sep-May; outer rects often tapered (Fig. 139**B**) and relatively abraded. **Note: Some HY/SYs replace all rects at the PB or the PA and are not reliably aged by rect shape and wear. Note also that both SYs and ASYs can show mixed generations of gr covs, terts, and rects in May-Aug. The pp-cov criteria are the best to use at this time.**

> AHY/ASY (Sep-Aug): Terts and middle ss (s4-s6) uniformly adult in Sep-May (Fig. 133**F**); outer pp covs broad, truncate, relatively fresh, and dusky brown with relatively distinct, gray

edging (Fig. 138), not contrasting in wear with the gr covs in Sep-May; rects uniformly adult in Sep-May, truncate (Fig. 139**B**), and relatively fresh. **Note: See HY/SY.**

Sex—♀ = ♂ by plumage. CP/BP (Apr-Nov; timing variable). ♀ wg(n39) 55-62, tl(n20) 60-66; ♂ wg(n42) 58-67, tl(n20) 62-68.

Rufous-winged Sparrow

See Fig. 24

References—Ridgway (1901), A.R. Phillips in Bent *et al.* (1968), van Rossem (1945a), Moore (1946c), Phillips (1951), Wolf (1977), Byers *et al.* (1995), Rising (1996a), Pyle (1997c).

RUFOUS-CROWNED SPARROW
Aimophila ruficeps

RCSP
Species # 5800
Band size: 1

Species—Juv from juv Rufous-winged Sparrow by back feathers without a buff fringe and with dusky streaks; underparts tan to pale brownish.

Geographic variation—Moderate to well marked, but clinal where most ranges meet. Subspecies taxonomy follows Paynter (1970), as modified by Monson & Phillips (1981); see also Todd (1922), Dickey & van Rossem (1923), van Rossem (1934a, 1946b, 1947a), Burleigh & Lowery (1939), Miller (1955a), Phillips *et al.* (1964), Phillips (1966e), Hubbard & Crossin (1974), Oberholser (1974), Hubbard (1975), Rea (1983), Byers *et al.* (1995), Rising (1996a). Six other subspecies occur in Mex.

Pacific Coastal (*A.r. ruficeps*) Group. Small; upperparts reddish.
A.r. ruficeps (res c-s.CA): Small; bill small (nares to tip 6.7-8.2, width at tip of nares 3.7-4.1, depth at tip of nares 4.8-5.6); upperparts chestnut with medium-dark buff streaking; underparts creamy brown. ♀ wg(n10) 53-60, tl(n10) 56-66; ♂ wg(n17) 55-62, tl(n17) 58-68.
A.r. obscura (res Channel Is, CA): Small, bill medium in size (nares to tip 7.1-8.7, width at tip of nares 4.0-4.5, depth at tip of nares 5.1-6.0); upperparts dull chestnut with buffy-gray streaking; underparts pale brownish. ♀ wg(n5) 55-60, tl(n5) 55-61; ♂ wg(n7) 57-62, tl(n7) 58-64.
A.r. canescens (res sw.CA): Medium small; bill small (nares to tip 6.7-8.2, width at tip of nares 4.0-4.4, depth at tip of nares 4.9-5.6); upperparts rufous-brown with grayish-buff streaking; underparts brown with a grayish wash. ♀ wg(n10) 54-63, tl(n6) 59-67; ♂ wg(n26) 57-65, tl(n21) 64-70.

Southwest Desert (*A.r. scottii*) Group. Large; upperparts brownish.
A.r. scottii (res AZ-w.TX to se.CO-w.OK): Large; bill medium in size (nares to tip 7.3-8.9, width at tip of nares 4.1-4.6, depth at tip of nares 5.1-5.9); upperparts gray with an extensive, reddish-brown wash; underparts pale brown with a gray tinge. ♀ wg(n61) 57-68, tl(n43) 63-72; ♂ wg(n100) 60-74, tl(n100) 65-76. Birds of wc.AZ (Yuma-Maricopa Cos; "*rupicola*") may average darker, and birds of se.NM-w.TX ("*tenuirostra*") may average paler and narrower-billed, but differences are slight, obscured by individual variation, and (for "*tenuirostra*") represent intergradation with *eremoeca*.
A.r. eremoeca (br & wint c.OK-sw.TX): Medium large; bill large (nares to tip 7.8-9.7, width at tip of nares 4.3-5.0, depth at tip of nares 5.4-6.3); upperparts brownish gray with sparse, brown streaking; underparts pale brown. ♀ wg(n56) 56-67, tl(n32) 60-70; ♂ wg(n100) 60-70, tl(n100) 63-73.

Molt—PB: HY partial-incomplete (Jun-Nov), AHY complete (Jun-Nov); PA absent-limited. The 1st PB usually includes all med and gr covs, 2-3 terts, sometimes (in ~24% of birds) s5 and/or s6, and 0 (~35%) to all 12 (~41%) rects. The 1st PB occasionally (in ~18% of birds) can be eccentric (see p. 208 and Fig. 136), with the innermost 4-5 ss, the outermost 4-5 pp, and occasionally (in

~12% of birds) the outermost 1-3 pp covs replaced. More study is needed on the range of variation in eccentric molts; the extent of the 1st PB varies with the timing and conditions of the breeding season, as with Rufous-winged Sparrow. The 1st PA sometimes includes a few head feathers; a more extensive PA may occur in some subspecies of Mex. More study is needed.

Skull—Pneumaticization completes in HY/SY from 1 Oct. Windows (> 2 mm; Fig. 11**D**) can persist in many birds through the spring/summer.

Age—Juv (May-Oct) lacks a solid rufous crown, has streaking in the upper breast, and has a rufous-tinged tail; juv ♀ = ♂.

HY/SY (Sep-Aug): Most or all outer pp covs (see **Molt**) narrow, tapered, relatively abraded, and pale brown with indistinct, narrow, or no pale grayish-brown edging (Fig. 138), contrasting with the slightly fresher and dusky-centered gr covs (Fig. 134); molt limits occur among the flight feathers, the innermost 1-5 ss, no or the outermost 4-5 pp, the outermost 0-3 pp covs, and/or some or all rects dark brown with reddish edging, contrasting with the paler brown and more abraded, outer ss, inner pp, most or all pp covs (Fig. 136**A**), and some or all rects; retained outer rects tapered (Fig. 139**B**). **Note: Most birds should be reliably aged, although some intermediates among the Southwest Desert Subspecies Group (see Geographic variation) can be difficult.**

AHY/ASY (Sep-Aug): Outer pp covs broad, truncate, relatively fresh, and dusky brown with relatively distinct and broad, rufous edging (Fig. 138), not contrasting in wear with the gr covs (Fig. 133**F**); terts, ss, pp, and rects uniformly adult (Fig. 133**F**); rects uniformly truncate (Fig. 139**B**) and relatively fresh. **Note: See HY/SY.**

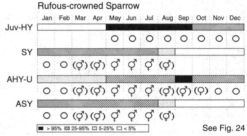

Rufous-crowned Sparrow

See Fig. 24

Sex—♀ = ♂ by plumage. CP/BP (Mar-Oct). ♀ wg(n100) 54-68, tl(n100) 56-72; ♂ wg(n100) 55-74, tl(n100) 58-76; see **Geographic variation**.

References—Ridgway (1901), A.R. Phillips & H.L. Cogswell *in* Bent *et al.* (1968), Oberholser (1974), Hubbard (1975), Wolf (1977), Byers *et al.* (1995), Rising (1996a), Pyle (1997c); IBP (MAPS) data, PRBO data.

FIVE-STRIPED SPARROW

Aimophila quinquestriata

FSSP
Species # 5742
Band size: 1B

Geographic variation—Moderate and breeding ranges well defined. Subspecies taxonomy follows Paynter (1970); see van Rossem (1934a), Phillips & Phillips (1993), Byers *et al.* (1995). One other subspecies occurs in Mex.

A.q. septentrionalis (br s.AZ): Larger than nominate subspecies of Mex (see **Sex**, *vs* wg 61-68, tl 59-65 in the nominate subspecies); upperparts medium (*vs* dark) grayish brown; breast spot averages smaller.

Molt—Not well studied, but probably as follows: PS/PB HY partial-incomplete (Sep-Dec), AHY complete (Aug-Nov); PA limited (Mar-Jun). A presupplemental molt (see p. 16) probably occurs. The PBs may commence on the summer grounds but appear to occur mostly on the winter grounds. The 1st PS/PB includes 9 to 10 (~83%) inner gr covs, 2-3 terts, occasionally (in ~17% of birds) s6, and 0 (~33%) to all 12 (~33%) rects. Look for some birds to replace pp, probably in an eccentric molting pattern (see p. 208 and Fig. 136). The 1st PA appears to be limited to body feathers, not including any wing covs or flight feathers.

Skull—Pneumaticization completes in HY/SY from 1 Oct through Jan.

Age—Juv (May-Nov) is streaked dusky throughout and has distinct, buffy wing bars; juv ♀ = ♂.

HY/SY (Aug-Jul): Supercilium indistinct, malar area pale grayish, and belly washed yellow in Aug-Oct; 2-3 terts (and occasionally s6) replaced, contrasting with the older middle ss (s4-s6; Fig. 133**E**) in Oct-Jul; outer pp covs narrow, tapered, relatively abraded, and brown with indistinct, narrow, or no pale brownish edging (Fig. 138); some or all rects tapered (Fig. 139**B**), or all rects sometimes truncate.

AHY/ASY (Aug-Jul): Supercilium distinct, malar area blackish, and belly white; terts and middle ss (s4-s6) uniformly adult (Fig. 133**F**); outer pp covs broad, truncate, relatively fresh, and dusky gray with relatively distinct and broad, brown edging (Fig. 138); rects uniformly adult, truncate (Fig. 139**B**), and relatively fresh.

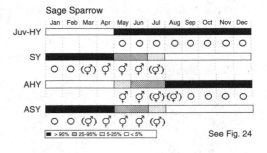

Sex—♀ = ♂ by plumage. CP/BP (Mar-Sep). ♀ wg(n23) 63-72, tl(n23) 60-69; ♂ wg(n57) 67-76, tl(n64) 63-73; includes *A.q. septentrionalis* only (see **Geographic variation**).

References—Ridgway (1901), Phillips (1961b), Wolf (1977), Mills *et al.* (1979), Groschupf (1992), Phillips & Phillips (1993), Byers *et al.* (1995), Howell & Webb (1995), Rising (1996a), Pyle (1997c).

AMERICAN TREE SPARROW
Spizella arborea

ATSP
Species # 5590
Band size: 0-1C

Species—From the other species of *Spizella* by larger size (wg 67-82, tl 60-74; see **Sex**); breast spot present; lower mandible yellow.

Geographic variation—Weak and probably clinal where ranges meet. Subspecies taxonomy follows Paynter (1970); see Ridgway (1901), Oberholser (1974), Byers *et al.* (1995). No other subspecies occur.

S.a. ochracea (br AK-nw.BC to c.NWT, wint BC-ND to n.TX): Large; coloration pale; nape pale gray to grayish-brown; outer rect (r6) edged whitish to white. ♀ wg(n10) 71-80, tl(n10) 65-72; ♂ wg(n10) 73-82, tl(n10) 67-74.

S.a. arborea (br e.NWT-Lab, wint MN-e.OK to NS-NC; vag to NV): Small; coloration dark; nape medium-dark gray; outer rect (r6) edged pale grayish to buffy white. ♀ wg(n10) 67-77, tl(n10) 60-69; ♂ wg(n10) 70-78, tl(n10) 63-70.

Molt—PB: HY partial (Aug-Oct), AHY complete (Jul-Sep); PA limited (Feb-May). The PBs occur primarily on the summer grounds. The 1st PB usually includes all med and gr covs, 1-3 terts, and sometimes (in ~36% of birds) 1-2 central rects (r1). The PAs are primarily limited to body feathers, although 1-2 terts and/or central rects (r1) rarely can be replaced; more study is needed.

Skull—Pneumaticization completes in HY/SY from 15 Nov through Jan.

Age—Juv (Jul-Oct) has streaking on the crown, nape, and upper breast (juv ♀ = ♂); hints of streaking can remain on some birds through Oct.

HY/SY (Sep-Aug): 1-3 terts replaced, edged whitish to buffy white, contrasting with the older and buff-edged, middle ss (s4-s6; Fig. 133**D-E**); outer pp covs narrow, tapered, relatively abraded, and pale brown with indistinct, narrow, or no buff edging (Fig. 138), contrasting with the slightly fresher gr covs (Fig. 134); central rects (r1) sometimes replaced, contrastingly fresh; outer rects somewhat tapered (Fig. 139**B**) and relatively abraded. **Note: Contrastingly fresh terts and rects rarely occur in both SYs and ASYs in Apr-Aug (see Molt); use pp-cov criteria on these. Most birds should be reliably aged. In addition, HY/SYs average duller than AHY/ASYs, especially in the crown, but overlap occurs and this also varies by sex (see Sex).**

AHY/ASY (Sep-Aug): Terts and middle ss (s4-s6) uniformly adult (Fig. 133**F**), edged whitish to buffy white; outer pp covs broad, truncate, relatively fresh, and dusky brown with relatively distinct and broad, rufous to pale rufous edging (Fig. 138), not contrasting in wear with the gr covs (Fig. 133**F**); rects uniformly adult, somewhat truncate (Fig. 139**B**), and relatively fresh. **Note: See HY/SY.**

Sex—CP/BP (May-Sep). ♀ wg(n100) 67-80, tl(n55) 60-72; ♂ wg(n100) 70-82, tl(n66) 63-74; see **Geographic variation**. Some AHY/ASY ♂♂ and HY/SY ♀♀ possibly can be reliably sexed by brightness or amount of buff veiling in the crown plumage, but overlap occurs in most birds (see Age and Heydweiller 1936). Otherwise, no reliable plumage criteria are known.

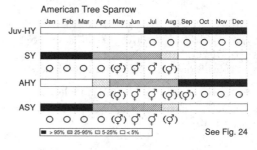

References—Stone (1896), Dwight (1900a), Ridgway (1901), Forbush (1929), Nice (1932), Heydweiller (1936), Baumgartner (1938), Roberts (1955), A.M. Baumgartner *in* Bent *et al.* (1968), Wood (1969), Oberholser (1974), Sheppard & Klimkiewicz (1976), Ketterson & Nolan (1986), Willoughby (1991), Naugler (1993), Byers *et al.* (1995), Rising (1996a), Pyle (1997c); IBP (MAPS) data, PRBO data.

CHIPPING SPARROW
Spizella passerina

CHSP
Species # 5600
Band size: 0-1C

Species—Juv from juv Rufous-winged Sparrow by crown and back uniformly rufous and brown, the feathers of the back with narrow, dusky centers. From American Tree Sparrow by smaller size (wg 62-77, tl 51-66; see **Geographic variation** & **Sex**); breast spot absent; lower mandible without yellow. Basic-plumaged birds (especially paler individuals; see **Geographic variation**) from Clay-colored and Brewer's sparrows by larger size (see above); wg – tl 7-16 mm; bill long (exp culmen 8.0-9.3); crown often with one or more rufous feathers; gray nape collar indistinct, contrasting with the brown crown and back, but not contrasting markedly in color with the breast (Fig. 289); rump gray (non-juvs), contrasting with the brown back; partial eye ring white and broken in front of and behind the eye (Fig. 289); dusky eye line more distinct than the malar stripe, and usually extending to the lores (Fig. 289); juvs (plumage often held through Nov; see **Molt**) with heavier black streaking and the lower mandible dusky pinkish, dull horn, or blackish. Juv from juv Field Sparrow by longer and relatively more slender bill (nares to tip

6.2-8.1, depth at tip of nares 4.1-4.6); streaking on the breast and (especially) the crown relatively distinct and heavy.

Geographic variation—Weak, clinal where ranges meet, and differences are obscured by substantial individual variation. Subspecies taxonomy follows Paynter (1970), as modified by Behle (1985); see also Ridgway (1901), Grinnell (1927c), Jewett *et al.* (1953), Oberholser (1955, 1974), Phillips *et al.* (1964), Sutton (1967), Hubbard & Crossin (1974), Monson & Phillips (1981), Rea (1983), Unitt (1984), Byers *et al.* (1995). Four other subspecies occur in Mex-C.Am.

   S.p. stridula (br coastal sw.BC-s.CA): Medium small; tl relatively long; coloration medium in hue; back feather edging medium brown with a rufous wash. ♀ wg(n100) 62-72, tl(n10) 51-61; ♂ wg(n100) 64-74, tl(n10) 54-64.

   S.p. arizonae (br & wint s.AK-w.Ont to s.CA-sw.TX): Medium large; coloration pale; back feather edging pale brown with a rufous tinge. ♀ wg(n100) 64-74, tl(n24) 54-63; ♂ wg(n100) 66-77, tl(n23) 56-66. Birds of AK-w.Ont to NM (*"boreophila"*) may average darker and grayer, but differences are slight and almost completely obscured by individual variation.

   S.p. passerina (br & wint c.Ont-s.TX to Nfl-FL): Medium small; tl relatively short; coloration dark; back feather edging rufous. ♀ wg(n100) 62-71, tl(n10) 53-61; ♂ wg(n100) 66-74, tl(n10) 54-62.

Molt—PB: HY partial-incomplete (Jul-Nov), AHY complete (Jul-Oct); PA limited (Mar-Apr). The 1st PB can occur on the summer grounds, the winter grounds, or both; a higher percentage of western birds (*S.p. stridula* and *arizonae*) than eastern birds (*S.p. passerina*) can retain the juvenal plumage for migration. The adult PB occurs primarily on the summer grounds. The 1st PB includes all med and gr covs, usually (in ~94% of birds) 1-3 terts, occasionally (in ~6% of birds) s6, and sometimes (~27-32%) 1-2 central rects (r1). The PAs primarily are limited to head feathers, and they can be continuous, essentially throughout the year.

Skull—Pneumaticization completes in HY/SY from 1 Oct through Jan.

Age—Juv (May-Nov) lacks rufous in the crown and has distinct streaking on the breast and flanks; juv ♀ = ♂. Some juvenal streaking possibly is evident on some HY/SYs through Jan.

   HY/SY (Sep-Aug): Crown primarily brown with little or no rufous (Sep-Apr), or rufous, usually with a few to many distinct, black streaks (Apr-Aug); 1-3 terts (and occasionally s6) usually replaced, contrasting with the older middle ss (s4-s6; Fig. 133**D-E**); outer pp covs narrow, tapered, relatively abraded, and pale brown with indistinct, narrow, or no buffy-gray edging (Fig. 138), contrasting with the slightly fresher and darker-centered gr covs (Fig. 134); central rects (r1) occasionally replaced and contrastingly fresh; outer rects somewhat tapered (Fig. 139**B**) and relatively abraded; juvenal breast streaks often retained through Sep (occasionally through Jan?).

   AHY/ASY (Sep-Aug): Crown brown with a few to many rufous feathers (Sep-Apr), or rufous with few or no black streaks (Apr-Aug); terts and middle ss (s4-s6) uniformly adult (Fig. 133**F**); outer pp covs broad, truncate, relatively fresh, and dusky brown with relatively distinct and broad, rufous to pale rufous edging (Fig. 138), not contrasting markedly in color or wear with the gr covs (Fig. 133**F**); rects uniformly adult, truncate (Fig. 139**B**), and relatively fresh; breast without streaks.

Sex—CP/BP (Mar-Sep). ♀ wg(n100) 62-74, tl(n44) 51-63; ♂ wg(n100) 64-77, tl(n43) 54-66; see **Geographic variation**. No reliable plumage criteria are known, although ♀♀ average duller than ♂♂, especially in the crown; compare with age and wg.

Hybrids reported—Clay-colored Sparrow, Brewer's Sparrow.

References—Stone (1896), Dwight (1900a), Ridgway (1901), Forbush (1929), Sutton (1935a, 1937), Storer (1954), Roberts (1955), Phillips *et al.* (1964), W.D. Stull *in* Bent *et al.* (1968), Wood (1969), Oberholser (1974), Simon (1977), Bunn (1985), Fix (1988), Kaufman (1990a), Willoughby (1989, 1991), Byers *et al.* (1995), Pyle & Howell (1996), Rising (1996a), Pyle (1997c); O.M. Root (*in litt.* to the BBL); J. Church (pers. comm.); IBP (MAPS) data, PNR data, PRBO data.

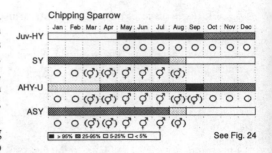

CLAY-COLORED SPARROW

Spizella pallida

CCSP
Species # 5610
Band size: 0

Species—From Chipping Sparrow (which see for separation from other sparrows) by smaller size (wg 56-67, tl 53-63; see **Sex**); wg – tl 0-6 mm; crown usually without rufous-tinged feathers; gray nape collar distinct, contrasting with the brown crown, back, and breast (Fig. 289); rump brown, not contrasting in color with the back; dusky eye line less distinct than the malar stripe and usually not extending to the lores (Fig. 289); juv (plumage usually lost by Sep) with sparser streaking. From Brewer's Sparrow by longer bill (exp culmen 7.8-9.3); shorter wg ÷

FIGURE 289. The head patterns in Chipping (a dull individual), Clay-colored, and Brewer's sparrows. Figure from Pyle and Howell (1996). See Figure 2 for feather tract terminology.

exp culmen (6.6-7.9 mm); crown with a fairly distinct to distinct median stripe; gray nape collar distinct and usually unstreaked (except at the base of the head stripes; Fig. 289); tips of the wing covs usually without dusky shaft streaks (Fig. 290**B-D**); rump with indistinct or no streaking; supercilium buffy and distinct, the eye ring less distinct below the eye than above the eye, and the malar stripes moderately distinct (Fig. 289); auricular and breast usually rich buff (when fresh, especially in HY/SYs). Some birds with intermediate characters can be difficult to separate from Brewer's Sparrow; these are often pale, immature Clay-colored Sparrows.

Geographic variation—No subspecies are recognized.

Molt—PB: HY partial (Jul-Dec), AHY complete (Jul-Sep); PA partial (Mar-May). The PBs commence on the breeding grounds, with some HYs and occasional AHYs completing the molt on the winter grounds. The 1st PB usually includes all med and gr covs, often (in ~68% of birds) 1-3 terts, and often (in ~73% of birds) 1-2 central rects (r1). During the adult PB, a few flight feathers occasionally can be retained until the winter grounds (and possibly the next summer?), especially middle ss (among s3-s6). The 1st PA includes 0 (~23%) to 5 inner gr covs, usually (in ~85% of birds) 1-3 terts, and sometimes (in ~31% of birds) 1-2 central rects (r1). The adult PA includes 0 (~33%) to 4 inner gr covs, usually (in ~83% of birds) 1-3 terts, and sometimes (in ~25% of birds) 1-2 central rects (r1).

Skull—Pneumaticization completes in HY/SY from 1 Nov through Jan.

Age—Juv (Jul-Sep) has blackish streaking on the breast and flanks, and the gr covs tipped buff (Fig. 290**A**); juv ♀ = ♂.

HY/SY (Sep-Aug): 1-3 terts often replaced, contrasting with the older middle ss (s4-s6) in Sep-Mar (Fig. 133**D-E**), or if all juvenal terts are retained, these are relatively worn and edged buff; outer pp covs narrow, tapered, relatively abraded, and pale brown with indistinct, narrow, or no pale buff edging (Fig. 138), contrasting with the slightly fresher and darker-centered gr covs (Fig. 134); central rects (r1) sometimes replaced and contrastingly fresh in Sep-Mar; outer rects tapered (Fig.139**B**) and relatively abraded. **Note: The retention of some juvenal streaking and/or one or more juvenal gr covs (Fig. 290A) can be used to age occasional HY/SYs through fall and even (rarely) through the 2nd PB. Note that both SYs and ASYs can show contrastingly fresh terts and central rects (r1) in Apr-Aug. In addition, HY/SYs (Aug-Apr) average buffier on the breast than AHY/ASYs, and this can be useful on birds in fresh plumage. Most birds are reliably aged, although some intermediates can occur in Apr-Aug.**

AHY/ASY (Sep-Aug): Terts and middle ss (s4-s6) uniformly adult in Sep-Mar (Fig. 133**F**) and edged whitish; outer pp covs broad, truncate, relatively fresh, and dusky brown with relatively distinct and broad, pale rufous edging (Fig. 138), not contrasting markedly in color or wear with the gr covs (Fig. 133**F**); rects uniformly adult in Sep-Mar; outer rects truncate (Fig. 139**B**) and relatively fresh. **Note: See HY/SY. Occasional AHY/ASYs retain middle ss (among s3-s5) through Oct and probably until the next PB, but distinguishing retained juvenal feathers on SY/TYs from retained adult feathers on ASY/ATYs (see Fig. 25) probably is too difficult; more study is needed.**

Sex—♀ = ♂ by plumage. CP/BP (May-Aug). ♀ wg(n100) 56-62, tl(n28) 53-60; ♂ wg(n100) 59-67, tl(n28) 55-63. In May-Aug the supercilium may average whiter on ASY ♂♂ and buffier on ♀♀ and SYs, but more study is needed to determine the use of this in sexing.

Hybrids reported—Chipping Sparrow, Brewer's Sparrow. Interspecific nesting reported with Field Sparrow.

References—Ridgway (1901), Walkinshaw (1944), Storer (1954), Roberts (1955), O.M. Root *in* Bent *et al.* (1968), Wood (1969), Oberholser (1974), Simon (1977), Knapton (1978), Brooks (1980), Bunn (1985), Forster (1985), Fix (1988), Kaufman (1990a), Willoughby (1991), Byers *et al.* (1995), Pyle & Howell (1996), Rising (1996a), Pyle (1997c); O.M. Root (*in litt.* to the BBL); IBP (MAPS) data, PRBO data.

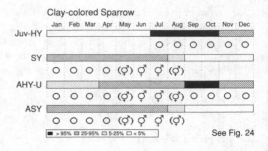

BREWER'S SPARROW
Spizella breweri

BRSP
Species # 5620
Band size: 0-1C-0A

Species—From Cassin's Sparrow (which see for separation from the other *Aimophila* sparrows) by shorter tl (54-69; see **Sex**) and bill (exp culmen 7.3-8.3); tail squared (r1 – r6 1-4 mm); central (r1) and outer (r6) rects brown without shaft streaks or white tips. From Clay-colored Sparrow (which see for separation from Chipping Sparrow) by shorter bill (exp culmen 7.3-8.3); wg ÷ exp culmen (7.4-9.3 mm) longer; crown with indistinct or no median crown stripe; gray nape collar indistinct, not contrasting markedly with the crown, back, and breast, and usually with dusky streaking throughout (Fig. 289); tips of the wing covs usually with pointed shaft streaks (Fig. 290**C-E**); rump with indistinct to distinct streaking; supercilium pale grayish white and indistinct, the eye ring uniformly full above and below the eye, and the malar stripes absent to indistinct (Fig. 289); auricular and breast pale grayish brown. **Note: Birds with intermediate characters may pertain to *S.b. taverneri* (see Geographic variation), which approaches Clay-colored Sparrow more closely in appearance.**

Geographic variation—Moderate and breeding ranges well defined. Subspecies taxonomy follows Paynter (1970); see Swarth & Brooks (1925), Grinnell *et al.* (1930), Phillips *et al.* (1964), Oberholser (1974), Rea (1983), Byers *et al.* (1995), Pyle & Howell (1996), Rising (1996a). No other subspecies occur.

S.b. taverneri (br montane s.AK-s.Yuk to n.Alb, wint s.CA-NM): Bill averages smaller (exp culmen 7.0-8.2); black streaking of the nape and back relatively heavy, facial features moderately distinct and eye ring dingy white (Fig. 289); breast dark gray, contrasting with the paler belly.

S.b. breweri (br & wint throughout most of the range in N.Am): Bill averages larger (exp culmen 7.3-8.3); black streaking of the nape and back relatively narrow, facial features indistinct and eye ring bright white (Fig. 289); breast pale gray, not contrasting with the belly.

Molt—PB: HY partial (Jul-Oct), AHY complete (Jul-Oct); PA limited-partial (Feb-May). The PBs commence on the breeding grounds, with some HYs and occasional AHYs completing the molt on the winter grounds. The 1st PB usually includes all med and gr covs, usually (in ~90% of birds) 1-3 terts, and occasionally (in ~20% of birds) 1-2 central rects (r1). During the adult PB, a few flight feathers occasionally (in ~8% of birds) can be retained until the winter grounds (and possibly the next summer?), especial-

A   B   C   D   E

FIGURE 290. The pattern to the median and greater coverts by species and age in Clay-colored and Brewer's sparrows. See text for details. Juvs of both species have coverts as in illustration **A**. From Pyle and Howell (1996).

ly middle ss (among s3-s6). The 1st PA includes 0 (~30%) to 5 inner gr covs, usually (in ~90% of birds) 1-3 terts, and occasionally (in ~5% of birds) s6, but usually no rects. The adult PA includes 0 (~50%) to 4 inner gr covs and often (in ~75% of birds) 1-3 terts, but usually no rects.

Skull—Pneumaticization completes in HY/SY from 15 Oct through Jan.

Age—Juv (Jun-Sep) has indistinct streaking on the breast and flanks and buff-tipped gr covs (Fig. 290**A**); juv ♀ = ♂.

HY/SY (Sep-Aug): 1-3 terts usually replaced, contrasting with the older middle ss (s4-s6) in Sep-Mar (Fig. 133**D-E**), or if all juvenal terts are retained, these are relatively worn and edged buff; outer pp covs narrow, tapered, relatively abraded, and pale brown with indistinct, narrow, or no buff edging (Fig. 138), contrasting with the slightly fresher and darker-centered gr covs (Fig. 134); central rects (r1) occasionally replaced and contrastingly fresh; outer rects tapered (Fig. 139**B**) and relatively abraded. **Note: The retention of some juvenal streaking and/or one or more juvenal gr covs (Fig. 290A) can be used to age occasional HY/SYs through fall and even (rarely) through the 2nd PB. Note that both SYs and ASYs show contrastingly fresh terts (and rarely 1-2 central rects?) in Apr-Aug. Most birds are reliably aged, although some intermediates can occur in Apr-Aug.**

AHY/ASY (Sep-Aug): Terts and middle ss (s4-s6) uniformly adult (Fig. 133**F**) and edged whitish; outer pp covs broad, truncate, relatively fresh, and dusky brown with relatively distinct and broad, whitish edging (Fig. 138), not contrasting markedly in color or wear with the gr covs (Fig. 133**F**); rects uniformly adult, truncate (Fig. 139**B**), and relatively fresh. **Note: See HY/SY. Occasional AHY/ASYs retain middle ss (among s3-s5) through Oct and probably until the next PB, but distinguishing retained juvenal feathers on SY/TYs from retained adult feathers on ASY/ATYs (see Fig. 25) probably is too difficult; more study is needed.**

Sex—♀ = ♂ by plumage. CP/BP (Apr-Aug). ♀ wg(n81) 56-64, tl(n32) 54-64; ♂ wg(n80) 59-69, tl(n26) 59-69.

Hybrids reported—Chipping Sparrow, Clay-colored Sparrow.

Brewer's Sparrow

See Fig. 24

References—Ridgway (1901), Grinnell (1914a), Forbush (1929), R.T. Paine *in* Bent *et al.* (1968), Oberholser (1974), Simon (1977), Bunn (1985), Kaufman (1990a), Willoughby (1991), Byers *et al.* (1995), Pyle & Howell (1996), Rising (1996a), Pyle (1997c); S.C. Mery, R.T. Paine (*in litt.* to the BBL); IBP (MAPS) data, PRBO data.

FIELD SPARROW
Spizella pusilla

FISP
Species # 5630
Band size: 0-1C

Species—Juv from the other species of *Spizella* by no or very indistinct streaking to the crown and breast; bill pinker. From Worthen's Sparrow (*S. wortheni*), a possible vagrant to N.Am, by longer average tl (55-74; see **Geographic variation** & **Sex**, *vs* 57-64 in Worthen's Sparrow); shorter wg – tl (-3 to 5 mm, *vs* 3-10 mm); brownish crown extends to the bill (*vs* separated by gray forecrown); distinct, white wing bars present (*vs* absent or indistinct and brownish if present); chest usually washed brownish (*vs* grayish); legs flesh pink (*vs* dark or blackish in Worthen's Sparrow).

Geographic variation—Well marked, but clinal where ranges meet. Subspecies taxonomy follows Paynter (1970); see Ridgway (1901), Wetmore (1939), Sutton (1967), Oberholser (1974), Browning (1978, 1990), Byers *et al.* (1995). No other subspecies occur.

> *S.p. arenacea* (br MT-ND to se.CO-OK, wint to TX-s.MS): Large; tl long; crown with an indistinct median crown stripe; back streaks indistinct and dusky; face and chest fairly uniformly grayish brown. ♀ wg(n14) 59-66, tl(n14) 62-67; ♂ wg(n33) 64-72, tl(n31) 65-74. Birds breeding in se.SD-NE (*"perissura"*) may average darker and redder, but differences are due to intergradation with *pusilla*.
> *S.p. pusilla* (br MN-s.ME to e.TX-n.FL, wint to s.TX-s.FL): Small; tl short; crown with a narrow, distinct, and gray median crown stripe; back streaks distinct and blackish; face with an indistinct to distinct, brownish auricular, contrasting with the grayish-brown chest. ♀ wg(n100) 56-64, tl(n100) 55-63; ♂ wg(n100) 61-69, tl(n100) 59-67. Birds breeding in e.KS-w.AR to e.TX (*"vernonia"*) may average paler and grayer, but differences are due to intergradation with *arenacea*.

Molt—PS/PB: HY partial-incomplete (Jul-Nov), AHY complete (Jul-Oct); PA limited (Mar-Jun). A limited presupplemental molt (see p.16) may occur in Jul, especially on the back. The PBs can commence on the summer grounds and complete on either the summer or the winter grounds. The 1st PB includes all med and gr covs, the innermost 2-7 ss, and 0 (~21%) to all 12 (~42%) rects. The 1st PB also often (~53-57%) is eccentric (see p. 208 and Fig. 136), with the outermost 3-7 pp but no outer pp covs usually replaced. Some wild birds may retain 1-3 inner pp (and possibly middle ss among s3-s6) during the adult PB, as reported for birds in captivity; more study is needed. The PAs are limited to some feathers on the face and throat and can occur throughout the summer.

Skull—Pneumaticization completes in HY/SY from 1 Nov (as early as 15 Oct in extreme southern populations) through Jan.

Age—Juv (May-Oct) usually has indistinct streaking on the breast and flanks; juv ♀ = ♂.

> HY/SY (Aug-Jul): Outer pp covs narrow, faded, abraded, and brown with indistinct or no pale buff edging (Fig. 138), contrasting with the slightly fresher and dusky-centered gr covs (Fig. 134); the innermost 2-7 ss and (often) the outermost 3-7 pp replaced, contrastingly fresh and dark (Fig. 136**A-B**); some or all rects tapered (Fig. 139**B**) and abraded, sometimes the rects uniformly truncate.

> AHY/ASY (Aug-Jul): Outer pp covs broad, truncate, relatively fresh, and dark brown with relatively distinct and broad, pale rufous edging (Fig. 138), not contrasting markedly in color or wear with the gr covs (Fig. 133**F**); ss and pp uniformly adult (Fig. 133**F**) and dark brown; rects uniformly adult, truncate (Fig. 139**B**), and relatively fresh.

Sex—CP/BP (Apr-Aug). ♀ wg(n100) 56-66, tl(n100) 55-67; ♂ wg(n100) 61-72, tl(n100) 59-74; see **Geographic variation**. ♂♂ average brighter and darker than ♀♀, and some extremes (both sexes) can be sexed, with experience (compare with wg and age). Otherwise, no reliable plumage criteria are known.

Hybrids reported—Vesper Sparrow. Interspecific nesting reported with Clay-colored Sparrow.

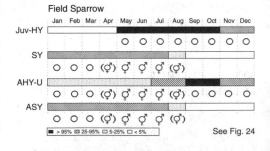

References—Stone (1896), Dwight (1900a), Ridgway (1901), Doolittle (1929), Forbush (1929), Sutton (1935a), Roberts (1955), L.H. Walkinshaw *in* Bent *et al.* (1968), Wood (1969), Oberholser (1974), Brooks (1980), Schneider (1981), Willoughby (1989, 1991), Carey *et al.* (1994), Suthers (1994), Byers *et al.* (1995), Howell & Webb (1995), Rising (1996a), Pyle (1997c); C.H. Blake, O.M. Root (*in litt.* to the BBL); IBP (MAPS) data, PNR data.

BLACK-CHINNED SPARROW
Spizella atrogularis

BCSP
Species # 5650
Band size: 0-1C

Geographic variation—Weak and somewhat clinal where ranges meet. Subspecies taxonomy follows Paynter (1970), as modified by Monson & Phillips (1981); see also Ridgway (1901), Grinnell & Swarth (1926d), Miller (1929), van Rossem (1935c), Phillips *et al.* (1964), Byers *et al.* (1995). One other subspecies occurs in Mex.

> **S.a. caurina** (br coastal c.CA, Marin-San Benito Cos): Plumage dark; head, breast, and rump with little or no brown wash; back rufous-brown.
> **S.a. cana** (br & wint ec-sw.CA to sw.TX): Plumage pale; head, breast, and rump often tinged or washed buffy brown; back cinnamon-brown.

Molt—PB: HY partial (Jul-Oct), AHY complete (Aug-Nov); PA partial (Feb-Jul). The 1st PB occurs on the summer grounds whereas the adult PB can begin on the summer grounds and complete on the winter grounds. The 1st PB usually includes all med and gr covs, but no terts or rects. The 1st PA includes 0 (~46%) to 5 inner gr covs, sometimes (in ~29% of birds) 1-3 terts, and occasionally (in ~8% of birds) 1-2 central rects (r1). The adult PA includes 0 (~60%) to 4 inner gr covs and occasionally (in ~10% of birds) 1-2 terts, but no rects.

Skull—Pneumaticization completes in HY/SY from 1 Nov through Jan.

Age/Sex—Juv (Jun-Aug) lacks any black or dark gray in the throat, has more distinct and buffier wing bars, and has faint streaking to the underparts; juv ♀ = ♂. CP/BP (Apr-Aug). ♀ wg(n100) 56-66, tl(n77) 58-70; ♂ wg(n100) 59-68, tl(n100) 61-74.

Basic Plumage (Sep-Apr)

HY/SY ♀♂ (Sep-Apr): Outer pp covs narrow, tapered, relatively abraded, and pale brown with indistinct, relatively narrow, buff edging (Fig. 138), contrasting with the slightly fresher and darker-centered gr covs (Fig. 134); outer rects tapered (Fig. 139**B**) and relatively abraded; chin and throat pale buffy gray, sometimes with 1-2 dusky feathers (Fig. 291**A-B**). **Note: Very dull HY/SYs probably are ♀♀, and HY/SYs showing a few dusky feathers in the throat probably are ♂♂ (more study is needed). Otherwise, no criteria are known to separate the sexes of HY/SYs in basic plumage. A few intermediates may be difficult to separate from AHY/ASY ♀.**

AHY/ASY ♀ (Sep-Apr): Outer pp covs broad, truncate, relatively fresh, and dark brown with relatively distinct, broad, pale rufous edging (Fig. 138), not contrasting markedly in color or wear with the gr covs (Fig. 133**F**); outer rects truncate (Fig. 139**B**) and relatively fresh; chin and throat dusky gray, sometimes with one or more dark gray feathers (Fig. 291**A-B**). **Note: See HY/SY ♀♂.**

AHY/ASY ♂ (Aug-Mar): Pp-cov and rect criteria as in AHY/ASY ♀; chin and (often) throat substantially dark grayish to blackish, contrasting with the paler gray breast (Fig. 291**B-C**).

A   B   C   D   E

FIGURE 291. Variation in the throat pattern by age, sex, and season (see text) in Black-chinned Sparrow. Note that the darker feathers can be either dusky (usually **B-C**) or black (**D-E**).

Alternate Plumage (Apr-Sep)

SY ♀ (Apr-Sep): Crown pale gray, usually washed brownish; outer pp covs narrow, tapered, abraded, and pale brown with little or no pale edging (Fig. 138); 1-2 central rects (r1) occasionally contrastingly fresh; outer rects tapered (Fig. 139**B**), relatively abraded, and brownish; chin and throat with few or no restricted, dark gray feathers (Fig. 291A-C), contrasting indistinctly with the lighter gray upper breast. **Note: Both SYs and ASYs can show contrasting gr covs and terts in Apr-Sep, but SYs average more feathers replaced (see Molt) and this can be of use in ageing some birds. Intermediates can occur that are not reliably aged.**

ASY ♀ (Apr-Sep): Crown pale gray, sometimes tinged brownish; outer pp covs broad, truncate, relatively fresh, and dark brown, usually with distinct, pale rufous edging (Fig. 138); rects uniformly truncate (Fig. 139**B**) and brownish dusky; chin and throat with a dark gray patch (Fig. 291**B-C**), contrasting indistinctly with the lighter gray upper breast. **Note: See SY ♀.**

SY ♂ (Apr-Sep): Crown dusky gray, sometimes tinged brownish; pp-cov and rect criteria as in SY ♀; chin and throat patch extensively blackish, sometimes mottled grayish (Fig. 291**D-E**), contrasting fairly sharply with the gray upper breast. **Note: See SY ♀.**

ASY ♂ (Apr-Sep): Crown dark dusky gray, without brownish; pp-cov and rect criteria as in ASY ♀; chin and throat patch extensively black, contrasting sharply with the gray upper breast (Fig. 291**E**). **Note: See SY ♀.**

Black-chinned Sparrow

	Jan	Feb	Mar	Apr	May	Jun	Jul	Aug	Sep	Oct	Nov	Dec
Juv-HY							O	O	O	O	O	O
SY												
	O	(♂)	(♂)	(♀)	♂	♂	♂	♂	♂			
AHY-U												
	O	(♂)	(♀)	♂	♂	♂	♂	♂	♂	♂	♂	♂
ASY												
	♂	♂	♂	♂	♂	♂	♂	♂	♀			

■ > 95% ▨ 25-95% ▥ 5-25% ☐ < 5%   See Fig. 24

Note: In Nov-Dec, AHYs can be sexed but birds of unknown age should be left unsexed.

References—Ridgway (1901), J.D. Newman *in* Bent *et al.* (1968), Oberholser (1974), Willoughby (1991), Byers *et al.* (1995), Rising (1996a), Pyle (1997c), Tenney (1997).

VESPER SPARROW
Pooecetes gramineus

VESP
Species # 5400
Band size: 1B-1

Species—From other sparrows by the combination of medium-large size (wg 71-92, tl 51-69; see **Geographic variation** and **Sex**); lesser covs with substantial chestnut in most plumages (but see Juv, below); outer web of the outer rect (r6) mostly or entirely white; outer web of r5 with a white tip; rects pointed (see Fig. 3X00).

Geographic variation—Moderately well marked, but clinal where ranges meet. Subspecies taxonomy follows Paynter (1970), as modified by Browning (1990); see also Ridgway (1901), Oberholser (1932, 1974), Braund & Aldrich (1941), Miller (1941a), Jewett *et al.* (1953), Phillips (1964), Phillips *et al.* (1964), Browning (1979a), Rea (1983), Behle (1985), Byers *et al.* (1995), Rising (1996a). No other subspecies occur.

P.g. affinis (br coastal w.WA-w.OR, wint sw.CA-NM): Small; tl relatively short; bill medium slender (depth at tip of nares 5.4-6.3); upperparts medium-dark grayish brown; underparts white with a buff tinge. ♀ wg(n10) 71-77, tl(n10) 51-59; ♂ wg(n10) 73-81, tl(n10) 52-62.

P.g. confinis (br BC-e.CA to w.Ont-NE, wint to se.CA-s.TX; vag to FL): Large; tl relatively long; bill slender (depth at tip of nares 5.2-6.1); upperparts pale grayish brown; underparts creamy. ♀ wg(n59) 75-84, tl(n24) 58-67; ♂ wg(n64) 78-87, tl(n21) 62-70. Birds of e.WA-se.CA ("*definitus*") average darker but differences represent intergradation with *affinis*.

P.g. altus (br s.UT-n.AZ to s.CO-n.NM): Large; tl relatively long; bill stout (depth at tip of nares 5.8-6.7); upperparts medium-dark grayish brown; underparts whitish. ♀ wg(n4) 76-85, tl(n4) 57-65; ♂ wg(n10) 82-92, tl(n10) 59-69.

P.g. gramineus (br n.MN-PEI to MO-VA, wint to s.TX-FL): Medium in size; tl relatively long; bill medium stout (depth at tip of nares 5.7-6.6); upperparts pale grayish; underparts white. ♀ wg(n16) 73-81, tl(n16) 55-63; ♂ wg(n24) 76-85, tl(n24) 59-66. Birds of ec.Ont-c.MI (*"polius"*) may average grayer, but differences, if present, are too slight for subspecies recognition.

Molt—PB: HY partial (Jul-Oct), AHY complete (Jul-Nov); PA absent. The PBs occur on the summer grounds. The 1st PB usually includes all med and gr covs, but no terts or rects; it is unlikely that p9 normally can be replaced, as previously reported. Beware of a slight pseudolimit (see p. 207) at s6-s8 that causes terts to appear more recently replaced.

Skull—Pneumaticization completes in HY/SY from 15 Nov through Feb.

Age—Juv (Jun-Sep) is like HY/SY, but is drabber brown, has wider and buffier wing bars, and has little or no chestnut in the lesser covs; juv ♀ = ♂.

HY/SY (Aug-Jul): Outer pp covs relatively abraded and brownish with pale brown edging (Fig. 138); terts brownish with buffy-brown edging, wearing off by Mar-Jul; outer rects tapered, pointed (Fig. 3X00), and relatively abraded. **Note: In addition, HY/SYs average duller chestnut in the lesser covs than AHY/ASYs, but overlap occurs and this varies with sex, as well. Many intermediates cannot be reliably aged.**

AHY/ASY (Aug-Jul): Outer pp covs relatively fresh and dark brown with grayish (sometimes tinged rufous) edging (Fig. 138); terts blackish with grayish or rufous-washed edging usually present in Mar-Jul; outer rects relatively truncate (Fig. 3X00) and fresh. **Note: See HY/SY.**

Sex—♀ = ♂ by plumage. CP/BP (Apr-Sep). ♀ wg(n88) 72-84, tl(n43) 52-67; ♂ wg(n95) 74-87, tl(n52) 53-70; see **Geographic variation**.

Vesper Sparrow

Hybrids reported—Field Sparrow.

References—Stone (1896), Dwight (1900a), Ridgway (1901), Doolittle (1929), Forbush (1929), Sutton (1935a, 1941c), Salt (1954), Roberts (1955), A.J. Berger *in* Bent *et al.* (1968), Wood (1969), Oberholser (1974), Yunick (1984), Byers *et al.* (1995), Rising (1996a), Pyle (1997c); T. Leukering (pers. comm.); IBP (MAPS) data, PNR data, PRBO data.

LARK SPARROW
Chondestes grammacus

LASP
Species # 5520
Band size: 1B

Geographic variation—Moderately weak, clinal where ranges meet, and differences are obscured by individual variation. Subspecies taxonomy follows Paynter (1970); see Ridgway (1901), Oberholser (1932, 1974), van Rossem (1934a, 1945a), Burleigh (1972), Browning (1978, 1990), Byers *et al.* (1995). No other subspecies occur.

C.g. strigatus (br BC-Man to CA-w.TX, wint CA-FL): Plumage pale; crown and face markings medium-pale rufous; dusky streaks on the upperparts narrow (1-3 mm wide). Birds of s.OR (*"actitus"*) may average larger and paler, but differences, if present, are slight and obscured by individual variation. Birds of

NE-TX (*"quillini"*) may average smaller and darker, but differences are slight and due to intergradation with *grammacus*.

C.g. grammacus (br MN-e.TX to PA-GA, wint se.TX-FL): Plumage dark; crown and face markings medium-dark rufous; blackish streaks on the upperparts broad (2-4 mm wide).

Molt—PS/PB: HY partial-incomplete (Jun-Nov), AHY complete (Jun-Oct); PA absent-limited (Feb-Apr). A presupplemental molt (see p. 16) occurs, with the body plumage replaced once in Jun-Aug on the summer grounds, and again with the flight feathers (during the 1st PB) in Aug-Nov on the summer and/or winter grounds. The adult PB occurs primarily on the summer grounds. The extent of the PS and 1st PB (combined) is quite variable, typically including all med and gr covs, usually (in ~87% of birds) 1-3 terts, often (in ~72% of birds) 1-6 outer ss (molting in typical sequence from s1 to s6), usually (in ~78% of birds) 1-9 inner pp (molting in typical sequence from p1 to p9), sometimes (in ~34% of birds) 1-3 outer pp covs (in those birds that replace all pp), and 0 (~19%) to all 12 (~66%) rects. Approximately 44% of HYs replace all pp, ss and rects, but retain at least the inner 7 pp covs. Occasionally (in ~8% of birds) 1-3 middle ss (among s4-s6) can be retained during the adult PB. The PAs are limited primarily to feathers of the head.

Skull—Pneumaticization completes in HY/SY from 1 Dec (as early as 1 Nov in populations of CA) through Feb; look for windows (> 2 mm; Fig. 11**D**) on some SYs in spring.

Age—Juv (May-Sep) has underparts with heavy streaking; juv ♀ = ♂; Most birds should be reliably aged by the following.

HY/SY (Sep-Aug): Most or all outer pp covs narrow, tapered, relatively abraded, and pale brown with indistinct, narrow, or no buff edging (Fig. 138) but with buff tips when fresh, contrasting with the slightly fresher and darker gr-covs (Fig. 134) and sometimes contrasting with 1-3 replaced, outer pp covs (Fig. 136**C**); molt limits often occur among the ss and pp (see **Molt**), the terts, outer ss, and/or inner pp dark brown, contrasting with the paler brown and abraded middle ss (often among s3-s6) and outer pp (Fig. 137); some or all rects juvenal, tapered (Fig. 139**B**), and with relatively broad, black shaft streaks, or rects often uniformly truncate. **Note: Some HY/SYs can have a near-complete 1st PB; on these look for retained juvenal pp covs (at least the inner 7 feathers) and one or more ss (among s3-s6), the last feathers to be replaced. In addition, head plumage averages duller in HY/SYs than AHY/ASYs, but much overlap seems to occur. Look also for one to a few black streaks on the breast in some HYs in supplemental plumage (Aug-Oct) and occasional SYs through Aug. See also AHY/ASY.**

AHY/ASY (Sep-Aug): Outer pp covs uniformly broad, truncate, relatively fresh, and dark brown with relatively distinct, pale brown edging (Fig. 138) but no pale tips, not contrasting markedly in color or wear with the gr covs (Fig. 133**F**); ss and pp uniformly adult (Fig. 133**F**) and dark brown; rects uniformly adult, relatively fresh, truncate (Fig. 139**B**), and with thin or no black shaft streaks. **Note: See HY/SY. Occasional AHY/ASYs retain middle ss (among s3-s5) through Oct and probably until the next PB, but distinguishing retained juvenal feathers on SY/TYs from retained adult feathers on ASY/ATYs (see Fig. 25) probably is too difficult; more study is needed. These AHY/ASYs have adult pp covs and thus should not be confused with HY/SYs that have near-complete molts (see HY/SY).**

Sex—♀ = ♂ by plumage. CP/BP (Apr-Sep). Measurements are fairly useful: ♀ wg(n34) 79-88, tl(n34) 61-71; ♂ wg(n56) 82-95, tl(n56) 65-78.

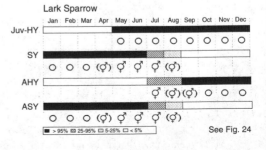

References—Dwight (1900a), Ridgway (1901), Forbush (1929), Roberts (1955), Sutton (1967), D.H. Baepler *in* Bent *et al.* (1968), Oberholser (1974), Byers *et al.* (1995), Rising (1996a), Pyle (1997c); PRBO data.

BLACK-THROATED SPARROW

Amphispiza bilineata

BTSP
Species # 5730
Band size: 1C

Species—Juv from juv Sage Sparrow by distinct supercilium, extending > 5 mm behind the eye (Fig. 292); crown without streaks.

Geographic variation—Moderate, but clinal where ranges meet. Subspecies taxonomy follows Paynter (1970); see Ridgway (1901), Grinnell (1927a), van Rossem (1930f, 1934a), Burleigh & Lowery (1939), Miller (1954, 1955a), Phillips *et al.* (1964), Oberholser (1974), Browning (1978, 1990), Byers *et al.* (1995). Six other subspecies occur in Mex.

A.b. deserticola (br & wint ne-sw.CA to sw.WY-sw.NM): Large; back pale reddish brown; white spot on r6 small (3-10 mm). ♀ wg(n10) 60-66, tl(n10) 57-63; ♂ wg(n27) 63-70, tl(n27) 59-67.

A.b. opuntia (br & wint se.CO-w.OK to se.NM-sw.TX): Large; back medium-pale gray with a brown tinge; white spot on r6 small (5-12 mm). ♀ wg(n10) 61-68, tl(n10) 54-63; ♂ wg(n19) 64-70, tl(n10) 61-67. Birds of sw.TX ("*dapolia*") may average smaller and darker, but differences are the result of intergradation with other subspecies.

A.b. bilineata (res c-s.TX): Small; back medium-dark grayish brown; white spot on r6 large (12-16 mm). ♀ wg(n10) 55-64, tl(n10) 53-61; ♂ wg(n16) 60-67, tl(n10) 56-64.

Molt—PB: HY incomplete (Jun-Nov), AHY complete (Jun-Sep); PA absent. A presupplemental molt (see p. 16) may occur in this species; more study is needed. The 1st PB can commence on the summer grounds but probably completes on the winter grounds; the adult PB occurs on the summer grounds. The 1st PB is eccentric (see p. 208 and Fig. 136), including all med covs, gr covs, and rects, the innermost 2-5 ss, and the outermost 3-6 pp, but no pp covs.

Skull—Pneumaticization completes in HY/SY from 15 Nov through Feb.

Age—Juv (Apr-Sep) has distinct, buffy wing bars, a white throat, and distinct, black streaking to the breast and back; juv ♀ = ♂.

HY/SY (Sep-Aug): Some or all scapulars brown with black shaft streaks (through Nov, sometimes later); outer pp covs narrow, tapered, relatively abraded, and pale brown with indistinct, narrow, or no buff edging (Fig. 138), contrasting with the slightly fresher and dusky-centered gr covs (Fig. 134); the innermost 2-5 ss and the outermost 3-6 pp replaced, dusky, contrasting with the browner and more abraded outer ss and inner pp (Fig. 136**A-B**); throat and chin without black, or mixed black and white; upper breast with distinct, blackish

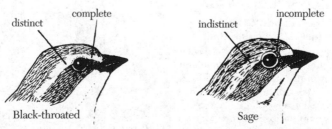

FIGURE 292. The head plumage in juvenile (or supplemental-plumaged?) Black-throated and Sage sparrows.

streaking (through Nov). **Note: A few intermediates can occur, but most birds should be reliably aged. Also, look for some HY/SYs to retain some streaking on the breast through at least winter.**

AHY/ASY (Sep-Aug): Scapulars brownish gray to gray, without shaft streaks; outer pp covs broad, truncate, relatively fresh, and brownish gray with relatively distinct and broad, whitish edging (Fig. 138), not contrasting markedly in color or wear with the gr covs (Fig. 133**F**); pp and ss uniformly adult (Fig. 133**F**) and dusky; throat, chin, and upper breast black with little or no white mottling. **Note: See HY/SY.**

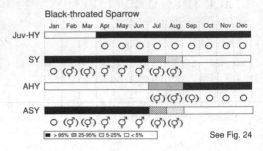

Sex—♀ = ♂ by plumage. CP/BP (Feb-Sep). ♀ wg(n48) 55-68, tl(n19) 54-63; ♂ wg(n92) 60-70, tl(n43) 57-67; see **Geographic variation**.

References—Ridgway (1901), Banks (1963), R.C. Banks *in* Bent *et al.* (1968), Oberholser (1974), Byers *et al.* (1995), Rising (1996a), Pyle (1997c).

SAGE SPARROW
Amphispiza belli

SAGS
Species # 5740
Band size: 1

Species—Juv From juv Black-throated Sparrow by less distinct supercilium, extending < 5 mm behind the eye (Fig. 292); crown with dusky streaks.

Geographic variation—Moderate to well marked and most ranges are well defined. Subspecies taxonomy follows Paynter (1970), as modified by Behle (1985); see also Ridgway (1901), Grinnell (1905b), van Rossem (1932b), Oberholser (1946, 1974), Jewett *et al.* (1953), Phillips *et al.* (1964), Burleigh (1972), Johnson & Marten (1992), Byers *et al.* (1995), Rising (1996a). One other subspecies occurs in Baja CA.

Coastal (*A.b. belli*) Group. Small; dark brownish; malar streak distinct.

A.b. belli (res coastal cw-sw.CA): Small; bill small (exp culmen 7.8-9.8); head and back uniformly dark brownish with indistinct, dusky streaking; malar stripe distinct, blackish, and usually complete to the bill. ♀ wg(n35) 58-67, tl(n25) 58-67; ♂ wg(n44) 61-70, tl(n29) 61-71.

A.b. clementeae (res San Clemente I, CA): Small; bill large (exp culmen 9.1-10.9); plumage as in *belli*. ♀ wg(n10) 60-67, tl(n10) 58-68; ♂ wg(n10) 63-71, tl(n10) 62-71.

Interior (*A.b. nevadensis*) Group. Large; pale grayish; malar streak indistinct.

A.b. canescens (br c.CA to sc.CA-w.NV, wint to w.AZ): Medium in size; head medium gray, contrasting with the medium-brownish back, the latter with very indistinct, dusky streaking; malar stripe moderately distinct, blackish, and usually not complete to the bill. ♀ wg(n10) 64-68, tl(n10) 63-71; ♂ wg(n10) 69-73, tl(n10) 67-75.

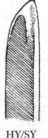 

HY/SY   AHY/ASY

FIGURE 293. The shape and pattern of white on the outer rectrix (r6) in Sage Sparrow. There is some variation within each age group.

A.b. campicola (br e.WA-e.OR to ID, wint se.CA-AZ?): Large; head and back uniformly medium gray-ish with indistinct, dusky streaking; malar stripe moderately indistinct and not complete to the bill. ♀ wg(n10) 72-79, tl(n10) 68-74; ♂ wg(n10) 75-82, tl(n10) 70-77.

A.b. nevadensis (br interior e.CA to s.WY-n.NM, wint to se.CA-sw.TX): Medium large; head grayish, contrasting with the pale grayish-brown to brown back, the latter with moderately distinct, blackish streaking; malar stripe lacking to indistinct, dusky, and not complete to the bill. ♀ wg(n15) 71-78, tl(n15) 64-72; ♂ wg(n18) 75-81, tl(n17) 69-75.

Molt—PB: HY partial-incomplete (Jul-Oct), AHY complete (Jun-Sep); PA absent. The PBs occur on the summer grounds. The 1st PB usually includes all med and gr covs, 2-3 terts, and occasionally (in ~14% of birds) s5 and/or s6, but no pp, pp covs, or rects.

Skull—Pneumaticization completes in HY/SY from 15 Oct through Jan.

Age—Juv (May-Aug) has distinct, buffy wing bars, a brownish crown with black streaking, and the upper breast with heavy streaking; juv ♀ = ♂.

HY/SY (Aug-Jul): 2-3 terts (and often s5 and/or s6) replaced, contrasting with the older middle ss (s4-s6; Fig. 133E); outer pp covs narrow, tapered, relatively abraded, and pale brown with indistinct, narrow, or no buff edging (Fig. 138), contrasting with the slightly fresher gr covs (Fig. 134); outer rects tapered and relatively abraded, with reduced or no buffy-white tips (Fig. 293). **Note: Most birds should be reliably aged, although rapid wear of the flight feathers can cause some intermediates in May-Jul.**

Five-striped Sparrow

AHY/ASY (Aug-Jul): Terts and middle ss (s4-s6) uniformly adult (Fig. 133F); outer pp covs broad, truncate, relatively fresh, and dusky brown with relatively distinct and broad, pale brown edging (Fig. 138), not contrasting in wear with the gr covs (Fig. 133F); outer rects truncate and relatively fresh, with distinct, white tips (Fig. 293). **Note: See HY/SY.**

Sex—♀ = ♂ by plumage. CP/BP (Mar-Aug). ♀ wg(n70) 58-79, tl(n60) 58-74; ♂ wg(n88) 61-82, tl(n73) 61-77; see **Geographic variation**.

References—Ridgway (1901), A.H. Miller *in* Bent *et al.* (1968), Oberholser (1974), Byers *et al.* (1995), Rising (1996a), Pyle (1997c); IBP (MAPS) data.

LARK BUNTING
Calamospiza melanocorys

LARB
Species # 6050
Band size: 1A

Geographic variation—No subspecies are recognized.

Molt—PB: HY incomplete (Jul-Sep), AHY complete (Jul-Sep); PA partial-incomplete (Jan-Apr). The PBs begin on the summer grounds and complete at stopover sites or on the winter grounds. The 1st PB is eccentric (see p. 208 and Fig. 136), including the innermost 1-6 ss, the outermost 2-5 (usually 4) pp, often (in ~58% of birds) the outermost (reduced) pp cov, and all 12 rects; most or all med and gr covs apparently are retained (more study is needed). The 1st PA includes all gr covs, 1-3 terts/ss among s5-s9, and sometimes (in ~25% of birds) 1-2 central rects (r1). The 1st PB/PA may be continuous through winter; inner ss replaced during the 1st PA often are in sequence to those replaced at the 1st PB (*e.g.*, if s7-s9 are replaced at the PB, s6-s5 can be replaced at the PA). More study is needed. The adult PA includes no gr covs, 1-3 terts, sometimes (in ~25% of birds) s6 and/or s5, and sometimes (in ~30% of birds) 1-2 central rects (r1).

Skull—Pneumaticization completes in HY/SY from 15 Nov through Feb.

Age/Sex—Juv (Jul-Aug) is like ♀♀ but is buffier, has bolder spotting on the upperparts, and has well-marked streaking on the underparts; some juvs possibly are sexed by the color and pattern of white in the rects (Fig. 294). CP/BP (May-Sep). ♀ wg(n30) 79-87, tl(n20) 59-70; ♂ wg(n30) 84-92, tl(n20) 63-74.

HY/SY ♀ (Aug-Jul): Body plumage (including the chin) entirely brown and whitish, without black feathers; most or all outer pp covs narrow, tapered, relatively abraded, and pale brown with indistinct, narrow, or no buff edging (Fig. 138), often (see **Molt**) contrasting with the darker brown outermost (reduced) pp cov and, in Mar-Jul, contrasting with the slightly fresher and darker brown gr covs (Fig. 134); the innermost 1-6 ss and the outermost 2-5 pp replaced (see **Molt**), dark brown, contrasting with the older, paler and more abraded outer ss and inner pp (Fig. 136A). **Note: Plumage criteria should separate the sexes; however, some intermediate ♀♀ may not be reliably aged. In Mar-Jul, ♀♀ of both age groups can have contrasting terts and/or s6 (see Molt), but the pp and pp-cov criteria are reliable during this time. Also, the pattern among the inner ss noted under HY/SY ♂ (which see) is present in ♀♀, as well, but color contrasts are not as pronounced.**

Juvenal ♀   Juvenal ♂

FIGURE 294. The pattern of white in the outer rectrix (r6) by sex in juvenile Lark Buntings.

AHY/ASY ♀ (Aug-Jul): Body plumage entirely brown and whitish, without black feathers (the chin can have slight black mottling in Mar-Jul); outer pp covs uniformly broad, truncate, relatively fresh, and dark brown with relatively distinct and broad, pale brown edging (Fig. 138), not contrasting markedly in color or wear with the gr covs (Fig. 133F); terts and middle ss (s4-s6) uniformly adult (Fig. 133F) in Aug-Mar, dark brown with rusty edges; outer pp uniformly adult and dark brown. **Note: See HY/SY ♀.**

HY/SY ♂ (Aug-Jul): Body plumage brown and whitish, usually mixed with black feathers, the chin primarily whitish (Aug-Mar), or body plumage primarily black with some brownish mottling (Mar-Jul); most or all outer pp covs narrow, tapered, relatively abraded, and pale brown with indistinct, narrow, or no buff edging (Fig. 138), often (see **Molt**) contrasting with the blacker outermost (reduced) pp cov and, in Mar-Jul, contrasting with the slightly fresher and blacker gr covs (Fig. 134); 1-6 inner ss replaced (see **Molt**) dark brown (s7-s9), or blackish (s4-s6), contrasting with the pale brown and buff-edged, retained outer ss, and 2-5 outer pp replaced, blackish, contrasting with the older, brown and more abraded inner pp (Fig. 136A). **Note: See HY/SY ♀. Also, beware that AHY/ASY ♂♂ have brown terts, s6, and sometimes s5 during Aug-Mar, and can retain some of these (often s5-s7; see Molt) during Mar-Jul; these should not be confused with the contrasting patterns of HY/SY ♂♂, as described above.**

AHY/ASY ♂ (Aug-Jul): Body plumage grayish brown and whitish, with heavy, black mottling, the chin primarily blackish (Aug-Mar), or body plumage primarily to entirely black (Mar-Jul); outer pp covs uniformly broad, truncate, relatively fresh (Fig. 138), and black, not contrasting in color or wear with the gr covs (Fig. 133**F**); inner ss (among s6-s9, sometimes s5) brown with rusty edges in Aug-Mar, contrasting with the black outer ss; outer pp uniformly adult and black. **Note: See HY/SY ♀ and HY/SY ♂.**

References—Dwight (1900a), Ridgway (1901), Forbush (1929), Roberts (1955), H.E. Baumgarten *in* Bent *et al.* (1968), Oberholser (1974), Byers *et al.* (1995), Rising (1996a), Pyle (1997c); J. Curson (pers. comm.); PRBO data.

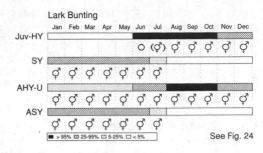

SAVANNAH SPARROW
Passerculus sandwichensis

SAVS
Species # 5420
Band size: 1C

Belding's Savannah Sparrow (BSSP)	Species # 5430
Large-billed Sparrow (LBSP)	Species # 5440
Ipswich Sparrow (IPSP)	Species # 5410

Species—From Baird's Sparrow by longer average wing morphology (p9 – p5 2-7 mm); median crown stripe whitish; supercilium usually with yellow; eye line complete behind the eye; posterior corners of the auricular not distinctly set apart from the eye line and subauricular stripe; back without conspicuous pale streaks. Juv from juvs of the other *Ammodramus* sparrows by the combination of measurements (wg 50-81, tl 41-62, if full grown; see **Geographic variation &**

Sex); upperparts streaked, without scales; malar stripe distinct. Juv from juv Vesper, Lincoln's, Song and most other sparrows of N.Am by the combination of long wing morphology (Fig. 295; p9 – p5 2-7 mm); tl short (41-62 if full grown; see **Geographic variation & Sex**) and squared (longest r – r6 0-3 mm); bill thin (depth at tip of nares 4.3-6.7, excluding *P.s. rostratus*; see **Geographic variation**); supercilium, face, and/or belly usually with some buffy yellow; lesser covs without chestnut; rects extremely tapered (Fig. 297); r5 without white.

Geographic variation—Variably weak to well marked, but largely clinal where most ranges meet, and differences are obscured by slight plumage dichromatism (pale and dark grayish-brown plumages). Subspecies taxonomy follows Paynter (1970); see Howe (1901), Ridgway (1901), Grinnell (1910c,

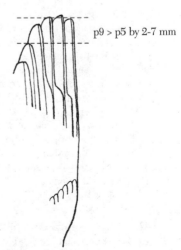

p9 > p5 by 2-7 mm

FIGURE 295. The wing morphology of Savannah Sparrow. See Figure 10 for measurement techniques.

1939), Swarth (1911, 1922, 1933, 1934b), Bishop (1915), Figgins (1918), Oberholser (1919j, 1930a, 1974), Huey (1930), van Rossem (1930f, 1931a, 1947c), Taverner (1932), Peters & Griscom (1938), Wetmore (1939, 1940), Aldrich (1940), Camras (1940), Duvall (1943), Norris & Hight (1957), Dickerman & Parkes (1960), Todd (1963), Phillips *et al.* (1964), Hubbard (1974), Sutton (1980), Behle (1985), Godfrey (1986), Rising (1987, 1988, 1996a), Zink *et al.* (1991), Wright & Rising (1993), Byers *et al.* (1995), Freeman-Gallant (1996). Seven other subspecies occur in Mex-C.Am.

Pacific Coastal (*P.s. alaudinus*) Group. Medium small; dark; bill variable in size.

P.s. crassus (br coastal se.AK, wint to coastal CA): Medium large; bill medium short and stout (exp culmen 10.0-11.2, depth at tip of nares 5.2-6.1); upperparts medium-dark brown with blackish-brown streaking; yellow of the supercilium and auricular deep; streaking to the underparts moderately heavy and dusky brown. ♀ wg(n10) 66-73, tl(n10) 47-54; ♂ wg(n51) 69-76, tl(n41) 50-57.

P.s. brooksi (br coastal sw.BC-nw.CA, wint to coastal sw.CA): Small; bill small (exp culmen 9.1-10.6, depth at tip of nares 4.5-5.4); upperparts medium-pale brownish gray with blackish streaking; yellow of the supercilium moderately pale; streaking to the underparts heavy and blackish. ♀ wg(n16) 59-67, tl(n10) 43-50; ♂ wg(n81) 62-70, tl(n63) 46-53.

P.s. alaudinus (res coastal c.CA, Humboldt-San Luis Obispo Cos): Small; bill medium long and slender (exp culmen 9.7-11.7, depth at tip of nares 4.6-5.8); upperparts medium brownish gray with blackish-brown streaking; yellow of the supercilium moderately deep; streaking to the underparts moderately heavy and dusky. ♀ wg(n15) 60-68, tl(n10) 42-49; ♂ wg(n55) 63-71, tl(n38) 44-52.

P.s. beldingi (res coastal sw.CA, Santa Barbara-San Diego Cos): **Belding's Savannah Sparrow.** Small; bill long (exp culmen 11.1-12.7, depth at tip of nares 5.3-6.6); culmen straight; upperparts medium brownish olive with blackish-brown streaking; yellow of the supercilium and auricular deep; streaking to the underparts moderately heavy and black. ♀ wg(n35) 59-67, tl(n35) 41-47; ♂ wg(n100) 62-70, tl(n69) 43-51.

Large-billed (*P.s. rostratus*) Group. Pale; very large-billed; culmen decurved.

P.s. rostratus (br ne.Mex, wint to coastal wc.CA): **Large-billed Savannah Sparrow.** Medium in size; bill very large (exp culmen 12.4-14.1, depth at tip of nares 6.7-8.2), the culmen decurved; upperparts pale grayish brown with reduced, indistinct, brownish streaking; supercilium whitish to very pale yellow; streaking to the underparts moderate, brownish, and indistinct. ♀ wg(n18) 62-69, tl(n18) 46-52; ♂ wg(n20) 66-74, tl(n20) 49-55.

Western (*P.s. sandwichensis*) Group. Large; medium-pale; bill variable in size.

P.s. sandwichensis (br e.Aleutian Is to w.AK; wint coastal sw.BC-wc.CA): Large; bill large (exp culmen 10.8-12.8, depth at tip of nares 5.7-6.7); upperparts medium brown with blackish-brown streaking; supercilium deep yellow; streaking to the underparts sparse and blackish brown. ♀ wg(n38) 68-77, tl(n13) 47-53; ♂ wg(n100) 71-80, tl(n67) 49-58.

P.s. anthinus (br nw.AK-w.NWT to c.BC-nw.Man, wint to sw.CA-s.TX): Medium large; bill medium small (exp culmen 9.6-11.2, depth at tip of nares 4.4-5.7); upperparts medium brown with dark brown streaks; yellow of the supercilium moderately deep; streaking to the underparts moderately heavy and dark brownish. ♀ wg(n28) 64-73, tl(n18) 47-55; ♂ wg(n100) 67-78, tl(n100) 51-59.

P.s. nevadensis (br interior BC-e.CA to c.Man-n.AZ, wint to sw.CA-SC): Medium in size; bill medium long and slender (exp culmen 9.6-11.6, depth at tip of nares 4.3-5.5); upperparts medium-dark brownish gray with black streaking; supercilium creamy white to pale yellow; streaking to the underparts moderate, blackish brown, and indistinct. ♀ wg(n10) 62-71, tl(n10) 45-54; ♂ wg(n100) 66-75, tl(n100) 48-57. Birds of e.Alb-c.Man ("*campestris*"), show no differences from the other birds of this subspecies.

P.s. rufofuscus (br c.AZ-c.NM): Medium in size; bill medium in size (exp culmen 10.0-11.6, depth at tip of nares 4.8-5.9); upperparts medium-dark brownish gray with blackish streaking; supercilium deep yellow; streaking to the underparts moderately heavy and blackish. ♀ wg(n6) 63-68, tl(n6) 41-47; ♂ wg(n8) 65-73, tl(n8) 45-53.

Eastern (*P.s. savanna*) Group. Medium small; dark; small-billed.

P.s. oblitus (br e.Man to MN-MI, wint OK-TX to GA): Medium in size; tl relatively long; bill small (exp culmen 9.4-10.4, depth at tip of nares 5.0-5.9); upperparts dark brownish with blackish-brown streaking; supercilium deep yellow; streaking to the underparts moderately sparse and black. ♀ wg(n10) 63-72, tl(n10) 46-55; ♂ wg(n100) 66-74, tl(n100) 49-59.

P.s. mediogriseus (br n.Ont-w.Que to IL-NJ, wint KS-e.TX to FL): Medium in size; bill medium large (exp culmen 9.9-11.9, depth at tip of nares 5.2-6.3); upperparts medium-dark brown with blackish-brown streaking; supercilium creamy to deep greenish yellow; streaking to the underparts moderately heavy and blackish brown. ♀ wg(n40) 63-72, tl(n40) 43-54; ♂ wg(n100) 66-75, tl(n100) 46-57.

P.s. labradorius (br e.Que-Nfl, wint se.TX to MD-FL): Medium in size; tl relatively short; bill small (exp culmen 9.4-10.9, depth at tip of nares 4.9-6.0); upperparts dark brown with dusky-blackish streaking; supercilium deep yellow; streaking to the underparts moderately heavy and blackish. ♀ wg(n12) 64-71, tl(n10) 45-53; ♂ wg(n100) 66-74, tl(n70) 48-56. Birds wintering on St. James I, SC, supposedly smaller and buffier, were mistakenly thought to be breeding there and named (*"bradburyi"*).

P.s. savanna (br NS-PEI, wint coastal MA-FL): Medium in size; bill medium small (exp culmen 9.6-11.1, depth at tip of nares 4.9-6.0); upperparts medium brown with blackish-brown streaking; supercilium pale to medium yellow; streaking to the underparts moderately sparse and dusky brownish. ♀ wg(n65) 62-69, tl(n32) 46-54; ♂ wg(n100) 65-74, tl(n100) 49-57.

Ipswich (*P.s. princeps*) Group. Large; pale; large-billed.

P.s. princeps (br Cape Sable Is, NS; wint coastal MA-FL): **Ipswich Sparrow.** Large; bill medium long and stout (exp culmen 10.1-11.5, depth at tip of nares 5.3-6.1); upperparts pale gray with indistinct, brown streaking; supercilium whitish or with some pale yellow; streaking to the underparts sparse and brown. ♀ wg(n87) 66-76, tl(n73) 49-58; ♂ wg(n92) 71-81, tl(n80) 53-62.

Molt—PB: HY partial (Jul-Sep), AHY complete (Jul-Sep); PA limited-incomplete (Feb-Apr). The PBs occur on the summer grounds; reported suspension of the molt over migration requires confirmation. The 1st PB usually includes all med and gr covs and usually (in ~78% of birds) 1-3 terts, but no rects. The Pacific Coastal subspecies (see **Geographic variation**) average slightly more feathers replaced at the 1st PB than the other subspecies. The PA includes no gr covs, sometimes (in ~42% of birds) 1-3 terts, and sometimes (in ~42% of birds) 1-2 central rects (r1; rarely up to 4 rects). The 1st and adult PAs are similar in extent.

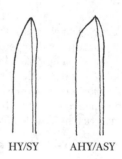

HY/SY   AHY/ASY

FIGURE 296. The shape of the outer rectrices (r4-r6) by age in Vesper, Savannah, and Baird's sparrows.

Skull—Pneumaticization completes in HY/SY from 15 Nov through Jan.

Age—Juv (Jun-Aug) resembles adults, but has more distinct, pale wing bars; juv ♀ = ♂.

HY/SY (Aug-Jul): 1-3 terts often replaced, contrasting with the older middle ss (s4-s6) in Aug-Mar (Fig. 133**D-E**, although beware of pseudolimits in AHY/ASYs, as well); outer pp covs narrow, tapered, relatively abraded (Fig. 138), and brown; outer rects extremely tapered (Fig. 297) and relatively abraded. **Note: Both age groups can show contrastingly fresh terts and central rects (r1) in Mar-Jul (see Molt). Some intermediates occur that are not reliably aged.**

AHY/ASY (Aug-Jul): Terts and middle ss (s4-s6) uniformly adult in Aug-Mar (Fig. 133**F**, but beware of pseudolimits; see p. 207); outer pp covs broad, truncate, relatively fresh (Fig. 138), and dusky brown; outer rects somewhat truncate (Fig. 297), relatively fresh. **Note: See HY/SY.**

Sex—♀ = ♂ by plumage. CP/BP (Apr-Aug). ♀ wg(n100) 50-77, tl(n100) 41-58; ♂ wg(n100) 62-81, tl(n100) 43-62; measurements are useful within populations, but highly variable among subspecies (see **Geographic variation**). See also Wheelwright *et al.* (1994) for a discriminant function analysis, based on live birds, using wg and weight, that separated the sexes in 94% of juvs in NB.

Hybrids reported—Grasshopper Sparrow.

References—Stone (1896), Dwight (1900a), Ridgway (1901), Forbush (1929), Sutton (1935a), Peters & Griscom (1938), Roberts (1955), J.J. Elliot, J. Baird, W. Taber, & R.F. Johnston *in* Bent *et al.* (1968), Dickerman (1968), Wood (1969), Hubbard (1974), Oberholser (1974), Sheppard & Klimkiewicz (1976), Weatherhead (1980), Broyd (1985), Yunick (1990), Pyle & Sibley (1992), Wheelwright & Rising (1993), Cramp & Perrins (1994b), Wheelwright *et al.* (1994), Byers *et al.* (1995), Rising (1996a), Pyle (1997c); J.J. Elliott, H.W. Kale II (*in litt.* to the BBL); J.L. Dunn, L.M. Krajcirik (pers. comm.); IBP (MAPS) data, PNR data, PRBO data.

Savannah Sparrow

See Fig. 24

BAIRD'S SPARROW

Ammodramus bairdii

BAIS
Species # 5450
Band size: 1C

Species—From Savannah Sparrow by shorter average wing morphology (p9 – p5 1-4 mm); median crown stripe and supercilium uniformly buffy ochre; back with conspicuous pale streaks; eye line usually broken behind the eye; dark patches at the posterior corners of the auricular isolated or distinctly larger than the eye line and subauricular stripe. Juv from juvs of the other *Ammodramus* sparrows by the combination of measurements, medium wing morphology, and squared tail (Table 10); median crown stripe indistinct or lacking; malar stripe distinct; auricular rich buff, with a pattern as described above.

Geographic variation—No subspecies are recognized.

Molt—PB: HY partial (Jul-Nov), AHY complete (Aug-Nov); PA limited-partial (Feb-Apr). The 1st PB can occur on the summer grounds, the winter grounds, or be suspended over migration; adult PBs occur primarily on the winter grounds. The 1st PB usually includes all med and gr covs, 2-3 terts, and usually (in ~78% of birds) 1-2 central rects (r1). The PAs include 0 (~43%) to 5 inner gr covs, sometimes (in ~30% of birds) 1-3 terts, and occasionally (in ~17% of birds) 1-2 central rects (r1). The 1st and adult PAs are similar in extent.

Skull—Pneumaticization completes in HY/SY from 15 Nov through Feb.

Age—Juv (Jul-Sep) has more heavily streaked underparts and dark back feathers with buff edging, giving a scaled appearance (*vs* a more streaked appearance after the 1st PB); juv ♀ = ♂.

Juv-HY/SY (Sep-Aug): Flight feathers relatively fresh and not molting in Sep-Oct but relatively abraded in Nov-Aug; 2-3 terts replaced, contrasting with the older middle ss (s4-s6) in Nov-Mar (Fig. 133E, but beware of a pseudolimit in AHY/ASYs); outer pp covs narrow, tapered, relatively abraded, and brown with indistinct, buffy-rufous edging (Fig. 138); cental rects (r1) occasionally replaced, contrastingly fresh; outer rects extremely tapered (Fig. 297), relatively abraded. **Note: Both age groups sometimes can show contrastingly fresh terts and central rects (r1) in Mar-Aug.**

AHY/ASY (Sep-Aug): Flight feathers relatively worn and/or molting in Aug-Oct but relatively fresh in Nov-Jul; terts and middle ss (s4-s6) uniformly adult in Sep-Mar (Fig. 133F), but beware of a pseudolimit; see p. 207); outer pp covs broad, truncate, relatively fresh, and dusky brown with relatively distinct, rufous edging (Fig. 138); rects uniformly adult in Sep-Mar; outer rects somewhat truncate (Fig. 297), relatively fresh. **Note: See Juv-HY/SY.**

Sex— ♀ = ♂ by plumage. CP/BP (May-Sep). ♀ wg(n30) 65-72, tl(n20) 45-54; ♂ wg(n30) 67-75, tl(n20) 49-57.

References—Ridgway (1901), Roberts (1955), J. Lane *in* Bent *et al.* (1968), Oberholser (1974), Pyle & Sibley (1992), McLaren (1994), Byers *et al.* (1995), Rising (1996a), Pyle (1997c); J.L. Dunn (pers. comm.).

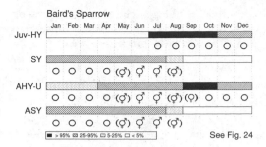

Baird's Sparrow

See Fig. 24

GRASSHOPPER SPARROW
Ammodramus savannarum

GRSP
Species # 5460
Band size: 1C-1

Florida Grasshopper Sparrow (FGSP)   Species # 5464

Species—Juv from juvs of the other *Ammodramus* sparrows by the combination of measurements, long wing morphology, and somewhat graduated tail (Table 10); median crown stripe distinct; malar stripe lacking; auricular buff with a large dark patch at the rear but with a poorly defined eye line and subauricular stripe.

Geographic variation—Moderately well marked and breeding ranges fairly well defined. Subspecies taxonomy follows Paynter (1970); see Ridgway (1901), Mearns (1902), Oberholser (1942, 1974), Phillips *et al.* (1964), Sutton (1967), Byers *et al.* (1995), Rising (1996a). Seven other subspecies occur in the W.Indies and Mex-S.Am.

> **A.s. perpallidus** (br s.BC-sw.CA to w.Ont-nc.TX, wint to s.CA-FL): Medium small; bill small (exp culmen 10.0-11.6, depth at tip of nares 5.2-5.9); upper back dull gray with reddish-brown streaks; breast dull buffy brown. ♀ wg(n25) 56-64, tl(n10) 43-50; ♂ wg(n77) 58-66, tl(n12) 45-52.
>
> **A.s. ammolegus** (br & wint se.AZ): Large; bill long and slender (exp culmen 11.0-12.5, depth at tip of nares 5.4-6.1); upper back pale gray with reddish streaks; breast medium-bright tawny. ♀ wg(n10) 59-65, tl(n10) 43-48; ♂ wg(n10) 62-68, tl(n10) 45-52.
>
> **A.s. pratensis** (br WS-ME to ne.TX-n.GA, wint to s.TX-FL): Small; bill medium in size and stout (exp culmen 10.5-12.2, depth at tip of nares 5.7-6.3); upper back bright gray with reddish-brown streaks; breast bright tawny. ♀ wg(n14) 55-63, tl(n12) 39-48; ♂ wg(n67) 58-65, tl(n20) 42-50.
>
> **A.s. floridanus** (res c.FL): **Florida Grasshopper Sparrow.** Small; bill large and stout (exp culmen 10.9-12.5, depth at tip of nares 5.9-6.5); upper back dull brown with blackish streaks; breast pale buffy whitish. ♀ wg(n23) 55-61, tl(n10) 41-49; ♂ wg(n60) 58-64, tl(n10) 44-51.

Molt—PS/PB: HY incomplete-complete (Jul-Nov), AHY complete (Jul-Sep); PA absent-limited (Feb-Apr). A limited presupplemental molt (see p. 16) of at least some back feathers may occur in some or all juvs. The 1st PB can occur on the summer grounds, the winter grounds, or be suspended over migration; adult PBs probably occur primarily on the summer grounds. Up to 3 middle ss (among s4-s6) occasionally (in ~14% of birds, of both age groups) can be retained during the 1st PB; this probably is rare or anomalous during the adult PB. More study is needed. The PAs are limited to body feathers and include no wing covs, terts or rects.

Skull—Pneumaticization completes in HY/SY from 1 Nov (as early as 1 Oct in birds of CA and FL) through Feb.

Age—Juv (May-Aug) has distinct streaking on the upper breast; look for occasional streaks on some HYs on migration or on the winter grounds through Nov; juv ♀ = ♂.

HY/SY (Oct-Sep): 1-3 middle ss (among s4-s6) retained, faded and worn, contrasting markedly with the fresher, adjacent ss. **Note: Only a small proportion of HY/SYs (~20-**

30%) can be aged by plumage. Beware of a pseudolimit (see p. 207) between the dark s7 and the pale s6, which can cause s6 to appear older when it is not; confirm retained feathers with contrasts in wear.

U/AHY (Oct-Sep): Middle ss (s4-s6) uniform, showing no marked contrasts in color or wear; if anything, s4-s6 fresher than s7-s9. **Note: See HY/SY and Skull.**

Sex—♀ = ♂ by plumage. CP/BP (Apr-Sep). ♀ wg(n100) 55-65, tl(n41) 39-50; ♂ wg(n100) 58-68, tl(n44) 42-52; see **Geographic variation**. See also Delany *et al.* (1994) for a discriminant function analysis, using wg and weight of live birds in FL (*A.s. floridanus*), that correctly distinguished 87.7% of the sexes.

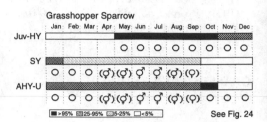

Hybrids reported—Savannah Sparrow.

References—Stone (1896), Dwight (1900a), Ridgway (1901), Forbush (1929), Sutton (1935a, 1936), Roberts (1955), R.L. Smith *in* Bent *et al.* (1968), Dickerman (1968), Wood (1969), Oberholser (1974), Pyle & Sibley (1992), Delany *et al.* (1994), McLaren (1994), Byers *et al.* (1995), Rising (1996a), Vickery (1996), Pyle (1997c); R.L. Smith (*in litt.* to the BBL); IBP (MAPS) data, PRBO data.

HENSLOW'S SPARROW
Ammodramus henslowii

HESP
Species # 5470
Band size: 0-1C

Species—Juv from juvs of the other *Ammodramus* sparrows by the combination of measurements, moderately short wing morphology, and graduated tail (Table 10); median crown stripe indistinct; malar stripe indistinct or lacking; auricular olive; eye line broken behind the eye; dark patches at the posterior corners of the auricular isolated or distinctly larger than the eye line and subauricular stripe.

Geographic variation—Moderate, but differences are obscured by individual variation. Subspecies taxonomy follows Paynter (1970), as confirmed by Browning (1990); see also Ridgway (1901), Brewster (1918), Hyde (1939), Arnold (1983), Byers *et al.* (1995). No other subspecies occur.

A.h. henslowii (br e.SD-s.Ont to e.TX-w.WV, wint TX to SC-FL; vag to MA): Bill small and thin (exp culmen 10.1-12.2, depth at tip of nares 5.7-6.4); upperparts average paler. Birds of se.TX ("*houstonensis*") may average duller and darker, but differences, if present, are largely obscured by individual variation.

TABLE 10. Measurements of *Ammodramus* sparrows for separation of juveniles. Juveniles of Baird's, Grasshopper, and Le Conte's sparrows can be found on migration.

	Baird's	Grasshopper	Henslow's	Le Conte's	Sharp-tailed[1]	Seaside
Wing	65-75	55-68	47-56	48-56	51-62	53-66
Tail	45-57	39-52	43-53	44-56	42-56	47-59
Tarsus	20-22	19-21	15-17.5	17-19	19-23	21-24
Exp culmen	9.4-12.7	10.7-12.4	10.2-14.0	8.4-11.2	9.4-13.0	11.9-15.0
P9 – p5	1-4	3-8	-1 to 4	-1 to 4	-3 to 3	-4 to -9
Longest r – r6	1-4	2-7	6-14	9-15	6-11	6-11

[1] Includes both Saltmarsh and Nelson's sharp-tailed sparrows.

A.h. susurrans (br NY-NH to e.WV-NC, wint coastal SC-FL): Bill large and stout (exp culmen 11.7-13.8, depth at tip of nares 6.3-7.1); upperparts average darker.

Molt—PS/PB: HY partial-complete? (Jul-Oct), AHY complete (Jul-Sep); PA limited (Feb-Apr). The PBs occur primarily on the summer grounds. A limited presupplemental molt (see p. 16) of at least some back feathers may occur in some or all juvs. The 1st PB usually includes all med and gr covs, 2-5 inner ss, and 0 (~28%) to all 12 (~22%) rects. It also occasionally (in ~17% of birds) can be eccentric (see p. 208 and Fig. 136), with the outermost 4-5 pp and (in ~11% of birds) the outermost 1-3 pp covs replaced. The 1st PB may possibly be complete in some birds; more study is needed. The PAs are limited to body feathers and include no wing covs, terts, or rects.

Skull—Pneumaticization completes in HY/SY from 15 Nov through Feb.

Age—Juv (Jun-Oct) has buff edging to the scapulars, lacks a malar stripe, and has the breast olive without black streaking; juv ♀ = ♂.

HY/SY (Sep-Aug): Most or all outer pp covs narrow, tapered, relatively abraded, and brownish with indistinct, narrow, or no pale brown edging (Fig. 138), contrasting with the slightly fresher and dusky-centered gr covs (Fig. 134) and, occasionally (see **Molt**), with the darker brown, outer 1-3 pp covs (Fig. 136**B-C**); the innermost 2-5 ss replaced (see **Molt**), contrasting with the older outer ss (Figs. 133**E** & 136**A**), but beware of a pseudolimit between s8 and s6 in AHY/ASYs); the outermost 4-5 pp occasionally replaced (see **Molt**), contrasting with the older inner pp (Fig. 136**A**); some or all rects relatively abraded, or sometimes all rects replaced and fresh. **Note: Rect shape is not useful in this species, as they are acutely pointed in both age groups. See also U/AHY.**

U/AHY (Oct-Sep): Outer pp covs uniformly broad, truncate, relatively fresh, and dusky brown with distinct, relatively broad, tawny edging (Fig. 138), not contrasting markedly in color or wear with the gr covs (Fig. 133**F**); ss and pp uniformly adult (Fig. 133**F**), but beware of a pseudolimit between s8 and s6; see p. 207); rects uniform in wear and relatively fresh. **Note: See HY/SY. It is possible that U/AHYs showing uniformly adult feathers can be aged AHY/ASY (Sep-Aug), but more study is needed on the possible occurrence of complete 1st PBs. Look for at least some inner pp covs to be retained by all HY/SYs.**

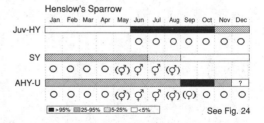

Henslow's Sparrow

Sex—♀ = ♂ by plumage. CP/BP (May-Sep). ♀ wg(n30) 47-54, tl(n23) 43-51; ♂ wg(n30) 50-56, tl(n34) 45-53.

See Fig. 24

References—Stone (1896), Dwight (1900a), Ridgway (1901), Forbush (1929), Sutton (1935a), Hyde (1939), Roberts (1955), J.W. Graber *in* Bent *et al.* (1968), Wood (1969), Oberholser (1974), Pyle & Sibley (1992), McLaren (1994), Byers *et al.* (1995), Rising (1996a), Pyle (1997c).

LE CONTE'S SPARROW
Ammodramus leconteii

LCSP
Species # 5480
Band size: 1C-1

Species—Juv from juvs of the other *Ammodramus* sparrows by the combination of measurements, moderately short wing morphology, and graduated tail (Table 10); median crown stripe indistinct to distinct; malar stripe lacking; auricular buffy; eye line widening posteriorly and fairly complete behind the eye; subauricular stripe indistinct or absent.

Geographic variation—No subspecies are recognized. See Murray (1969).

Molt—PB: HY partial-incomplete (Aug-Dec), AHY complete (Jul-Sep); PA partial (Mar-May). The 1st PB can occur on the summer grounds or the winter grounds; adult PBs occur primarily on the summer grounds. The 1st PB usually includes all med and gr covs, 2-3 terts, and occasionally (in ~20% of birds) s6, but no rects. The 1st PA includes 1-5 inner gr covs, 2-3 terts, and sometimes (in ~30% of birds) 1-2 central rects (r1). The adult PA includes 3 to 10 (~8%) inner gr covs, 2-3 terts, and often (in ~67% of birds) 1-2 central rects (r1).

Skull—Pneumaticization completes in HY/SY from 15 Nov through Jan.

Age—Juv (Jul-Nov) lacks rich orange tones in the head and breast and has distinct and fine streaking across the upper breast (this plumage can be retained through the fall migration); juv ♀ = ♂.

Juv-HY/SY (Aug-Jul): Buffy head and streaks on the central breast (of juvenal plumage) often retained through Oct; 2-3 terts and occasionally (in ~20% of birds) s6 replaced, contrasting with the older middle ss (s4-s6) in Sep-Mar (Fig. 133E), but beware of a pseudolimit at s7-s6 in AHY/ASYs); outer pp covs narrow, tapered, relatively abraded, and pale brown with indistinct, narrow, or no buff edging (Fig. 138); rects relatively abraded. **Note: Rect shape is not useful in this species, as rects of both age groups are acutely pointed. Both age groups also can show contrastingly fresh terts and central rects (r1) in Mar-Jul (see Molt); thus, the pp covs and relative wear of the flight feathers are the only means of ageing spring birds. Intermediates can occur that are difficult to age.**

AHY/ASY (Aug-Jul): Head with orange, and central breast unstreaked in Aug-Oct; terts and middle ss (s4-s6) uniformly adult in Aug-Mar (Fig. 133F), but beware of a pseudolimit at s6-s7 (see p. 207); outer pp covs broad, truncate, relatively fresh, and dusky brown with relatively distinct and broad, tawny edging (Fig. 138); rects relatively fresh. **Note: See Juv-HY/SY.**

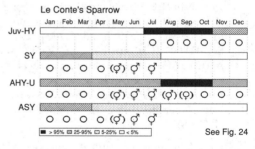

Le Conte's Sparrow

Sex—♀ = ♂ by plumage. CP/BP (May-Sep). ♀ wg(n60) 48-54, tl(n20) 44-53; ♂ wg(n100) 50-56, tl(n20) 47-56.

Hybrids reported—Nelson's Sharp-tailed Sparrow.

References—Ridgway (1901), Tordoff & Mengel (1951), Roberts (1955), Dickerman (1962), L.H. Walkinshaw *in* Bent *et al.* (1968), Murray (1968, 1969), Oberholser (1974), Pyle & Sibley (1992), McLaren (1994), Byers *et al.* (1995), Lowther (1996), Rising (1996a), Pyle (1997c); PRBO data.

SALTMARSH SHARP-TAILED SPARROW
Ammodramus caudacutus

SSTS
Species # 5490
Band size: 1-1B

Species—Juv from juvs of most other *Ammodramus* sparrows by the combination of measurements, short wing morphology, and fairly graduated tail (Table 10); median crown stripe and malar stripe indistinct or lacking; auricular brownish; eye line uniform in width and fairly complete behind the eye; subauricular stripe abbreviated or absent. From Nelson's Sharp-tailed Sparrow, with caution, by the combination of the long bill (nares to tip 8.3-10.1); longest p –

longest s 0-7 mm; malar stripe blackish and usually distinct; throat white, contrasting markedly with the orange to buffy submoustachial stripe; breast whitish to buffy, not contrasting sharply with the color of the belly, and with distinct, blackish streaks. Note that Nelson's Sharp-tailed Sparrow (which see) has both duller and brighter subspecies than Saltmarsh Sharp-tailed Sparrows. Most of these features are good for the separation of juvs, as well. See also differences in the PA molt for further identification clues. Beware of occasional hybrids between dull Nelson's and Saltmarsh sharp-tailed sparrows. Sharp-tailed sparrows not identified to species can be recorded with alpha code **STSP** and **Species # 5499**.

Geographic variation—Weak, clinal where ranges meet, and differences are obscured by individual variation. Subspecies taxonomy follows Greenlaw (1993); see also Bishop (1901), Ridgway (1901), Oberholser (1931), Todd (1938, 1942, 1963), Montagna (1940, 1942), Beecher (1955), Murray (1969), Parkes (1992b), Rising & Avise (1993), Greenlaw & Rising (1994), Byers *et al.* (1995), Sibley (1996). No other subspecies occur.

A.c. *caudacutus* (br coastal se.ME-n.NJ, wint to coastal FL): Bill large (nares to tip 8.8-10.1); upperparts dark grayish brown with moderately dull grayish-white streaking; supercilium bright buffy orange.
A.c. *diversus* (br coastal s.NJ-NC, wint to coastal LA-FL): Bill medium large (nares to tip 8.3-9.9); upperparts dark brownish with dull buff streaking; supercilium dark buffy orange.

Molt—PB: HY partial-incomplete (Aug-Oct), AHY complete (Aug-Oct); PA incomplete (Mar-Apr). The PBs occur on the summer grounds. The 1st PB usually includes all med and gr covs, 2-3 terts, sometimes (in ~21% of birds) s6, and 0 (~57%) to all 12 (~14%) rects. PAs occur primarily on the winter grounds but can complete on the summer grounds. The PAs include 5 to 10 (~11%) inner gr covs, 1-3 terts, occasionally (in ~18% of birds) s6, and all 12 rects; the 1st and adult PAs are similar in extent.

Skull—Pneumaticization completes in HY/SY from 15 Nov through Feb.

Age—Juv (Jul-Sep) has brownish-washed upperparts, buffy underparts, and large black centers to the back feathers; juv ♀ = ♂.

HY/SY (Aug-Jul): 2-3 terts and sometimes s6 replaced, contrasting with the older middle ss (s4-s6) in Aug-Mar (Fig. 133**E**); outer pp covs narrow, tapered, relatively abraded, and pale brown with indistinct, narrow, or no pale edging (Fig. 138), contrasting (slightly in Aug-Mar and markedly in Mar-Jul) with the fresher and dusky-centered gr covs (Fig. 134); some or all rects juvenal and relatively abraded, or all rects occasionally (Aug-Mar), or usually (Mar-Jul), uniformly fresh. **Note: Rect shape is acutely pointed in both age groups and thus is of little or no use in ageing. Both SYs and ASYs can show inner gr covs and terts contrasting with the other wing feathers in Mar-Jul (see Molt); at this time the condition of the pp covs is the only reliable means of ageing. In addition, HY/SYs may average heavier streaking to the underparts than AHY/ASYs; more study is needed.**

AHY/ASY (Aug-Jul): Terts and middle ss (s4-s6) uniformly adult in Aug-Mar (Fig. 133**F**); outer pp covs broad, truncate, relatively fresh, and dusky with relatively distinct and broad, tawny edging (Fig. 138), not contrasting markedly in color or wear with the gr covs (Fig. 133**F**); rects uniformly adult and relatively fresh in Aug-Mar. **Note: See HY/SY.**

Sex—♀ = ♂ by plumage. CP/BP (May-Sep). ♀ wg(n100) 52-60, tl(n100) 42-51; ♂ wg(n100) 54-62, tl(n100) 45-55.

Hybrids reported—Nelson's Sharp-tailed Sparrow, Seaside Sparrow.

References—Stone (1896), Dwight (1900a), Ridgway (1901), Forbush (1929), Tordoff & Mengel (1951), Roberts (1955), N.P. Hill *in* Bent *et al.* (1968), Murray (1969), Wood (1969),

Parkes (1992b), Pyle & Sibley (1992), Greenlaw & Rising (1994), McLaren (1994), Byers *et al.* (1995), Rising (1996a), Sibley (1996), Pyle (1997c); N.P. Hill, B. Sharp (*in litt.* to the BBL).

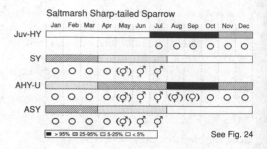

See Fig. 24

NELSON'S SHARP-TAILED SPARROW
Ammodramus nelsoni

NSTS
Species # 5491
Band size: 1-1B

Species—From Saltmarsh Sharp-tailed Sparrow (which see for the separation of the other *Ammodramus* sparrows), with caution, by the combination of the short bill (nares to tip 7.8-9.4; see **Geographic variation**); longest p – longest s 5-12 mm; malar stripe absent or dusky and (usually) indistinct; throat whitish to buffy, usually not contrasting markedly with the dull grayish-orange to buffy-orange submoustachial stripe; breast bright to dull buffy-orange, with indistinct, dusky streaks (occasionally blackish and distinct in *A.n. nelsoni*; see **Geographic variation**), and usually contrasting markedly with the white belly. Note that *A.n. nelsoni* is generally brighter than Saltmarsh Sharp-tailed Sparrow whereas *A.n. subvirgatus* is duller than both *nelsoni* and Saltmarsh (see **Geographic variation**). Those birds showing the most distinct breast streaks also show the greatest contrast between the breast and belly color. Most of these features are good for the separation of juvs, as well. See also differences in the PA molt for further identification clues. Beware of occasional hybrids between *subvirgatus* and Saltmarsh Sharp-tailed Sparrows. Sharp-tailed sparrows not identified to species can be recorded with alpha code **STSP** and **Species # 5499**.

Geographic variation—Moderately well marked and ranges well defined. Subspecies taxonomy follows Greenlaw (1993); see also Ridgway (1901), Todd (1938, 1942, 1963), Montagna (1940, 1942), Peters (1942), Beecher (1955), Murray (1969), Oberholser (1974), Parkes (1992b), Rising & Avise (1993), Greenlaw & Rising (1994), Byers *et al.* (1995), Rising (1996a), Sibley (1996). No other subspecies occur.

A.n. nelsoni (br ne.BC-sw.NWT to s.Man-ne.SD, wint coastal CA and TX-FL-SC): Bill averages short (nares to tip 7.8-9.0); p9 – p5 -3 to 0 mm; upperparts dark grayish brown with bright whitish streaks; supercilium bright orange; breast bright buffy orange.

A.n. alterus (br ne.Ont-cw.Que, wint coastal LA-FL-NY): Bill averages short (nares to tip 7.8-8.8); p9 – p5 -1 to 3 mm; upperparts medium-pale brownish with dull whitish streaks; supercilium dull orange; breast dull buffy orange.

A.n. subvirgatus (br coastal s.Que-NS-ce.ME, wint coastal NY-FL): Bill averages long (nares to tip 8.0-9.4); p9 – p5 -3 to 1 mm; upperparts dull grayish olive with grayish streaking; supercilium dull grayish buff; breast dull buffy.

Molt—PB: HY partial (Aug-Oct), AHY complete (Aug-Oct); PA incomplete (Mar-Apr). The PBs occur on the summer grounds. The 1st PB usually includes all med and gr covs and 1-3 terts, but no rects. PAs occur primarily on the winter grounds but can complete on the summer grounds. The PAs are eccentric (see p. 208 and Fig. 136), including 6 to 10 (~54%) inner gr covs, the innermost 3-6 ss, the outermost 3-6 pp, occasionally (in ~17% of birds) the outermost (reduced) pp cov, and all 12 rects; the 1st and adult PAs are similar in extent.

Skull—Pneumaticization completes in HY/SY from 15 Nov through Feb.

Age—Juv (Jul-Sep) has upperparts washed orange or brownish, underparts buffy-orange (including the belly), and back feathers with large black centers; juv ♀ = ♂.

HY/SY (Aug-Jul): 1-3 terts replaced, contrasting with the older middle ss (s4-s6) in Aug-Mar (Fig. 133**E**); outer pp covs narrow, tapered, relatively abraded, and pale brown with indistinct, narrow, or no pale edging (Fig. 138), contrasting (slightly in Aug-Mar and markedly in Mar-Jul) with the fresher and dusky-centered gr covs (Fig. 134); outer rects relatively abraded in Aug-Mar. **Note: Both SYs and ASYs can show an eccentric replacement pattern (Fig. 136A) in Mar-Jul; at this time the condition of the pp covs is the only reliable means of ageing. Rect shape is acutely pointed in both age groups and is of little or no use in ageing. In addition, HY/SYs can average heavier streaking to the underparts than AHY/ASYs; more study is needed.**

AHY/ASY (Aug-Jul): Terts and middle ss (s4-s6) uniformly adult in Aug-Mar (Fig. 133**F**); outer pp covs broad, truncate, relatively fresh, and dusky with relatively distinct and broad, tawny edging (Fig. 138), not contrasting markedly in color or wear with the gr covs (Fig. 133**F**); rects relatively fresh in Aug-Mar. **Note: See HY/SY.**

Sex—♀ = ♂ by plumage. CP/BP (May-Sep). ♀ wg(n100) 52-60, tl(n100) 43-52; ♂ wg(n100) 54-62, tl(n100) 46-56. ♂♂ reportedly average heavier ventral streaking than ♀♀, but substantial individual variation in plumage probably precludes reliable sexing; more study is needed.

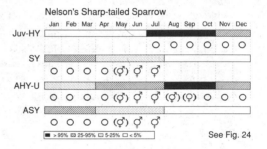

Nelson's Sharp-tailed Sparrow

Hybrids reported—Saltmarsh Sharp-tailed Sparrow, Le Conte's Sparrow.

See Fig. 24

References—Stone (1896), Dwight (1900a), Ridgway (1901), Forbush (1929), Montagna (1940), Tordoff & Mengel (1951), Roberts (1955), Dickerman (1962), N.P. Hill *in* Bent *et al.* (1968), Murray (1968, 1969), Wood (1969), Oberholser (1974), Parkes (1992b), Pyle & Sibley (1992), Greenlaw & Rising (1994), McLaren (1994), Byers *et al.* (1995), Rising (1996a), Sibley (1996), Pyle (1997c); N.P. Hill, B. Sharp (*in litt.* to the BBL).

SEASIDE SPARROW
Ammodramus maritimus

SESP
Species # 5500
Band size: 1B

Dusky Seaside Sparrow (DSSP)   Species # 5510
Cape Sable Seaside Sparrow (CSSS)   Species # 5511

Species—Juv from juv Sharp-tailed Sparrow (which see for separation from the other *Ammodramus* sparrows) by larger measurements (especially bill) and shorter wing morphology (Table 10); median crown stripe lacking; malar stripe and subauricular stripe present but indistinct.

Geographic variation—Variably weak to well marked and ranges well defined, but differences are confused by plumage dichromatism (grayish and buffy plumages) in most subspecies. Subspecies taxonomy follows Paynter (1970), as modified by M.V. McDonald *in* Stevenson & Anderson (1994); see also Ridgway (1901), Howell (1919), Griscom & Nichols (1920), Oberholser (1931b, 1974), Tomkins (1937, 1941), Griscom (1944, 1948a), Beecher (1955), Murray (1969), Hubbard & Banks (1970), Funderburg & Quay (1983), Kale (1983), Post & Greenlaw (1994), Byers *et al.* (1995), Rising (1996a), Pyle (1997c). No other subspecies occur. See also **Molt**.

Gulf of Mexico (*A.m. sennetti*) Group. Bright; buffy; distinctly streaked.

A.m. sennetti (br & wint coastal se.TX): Upperparts grayish olive with distinct, blackish streaks; breast pale buffy with moderately distinct, blackish streaking.

A.m. fisheri (br & wint coastal e.TX-nw.FL): Upperparts olive-brown with moderately heavy, blackish streaking; breast rich to pale buffy, with moderately indistinct to distinct, blackish streaking. Birds of AL-MS ("*howelli*") may average duller and paler, but differences are primarily due to plumage dichromatism rather then subspecies variation.

A.m. peninsulae (res coastal n-sw.FL): Upperparts dark olive to grayish-olive with distinct, brownish-black streaks; breast buffy gray to whitish, with moderately distinct, black streaking. Birds of coastal n.FL ("*juncicola*") may average grayer upperparts and more distinct streaking to the underparts, but differences are weak and obscured by individual variation.

Atlantic (*A.m. maritimus*) Group. Dull; grayish; indistinctly streaked.

A.m. maritimus (br coastal MA-ne.NC, wint to coastal nw.FL): Upperparts medium olive-gray with very indistinct or no brownish streaks; breast grayish to buffy gray, with indistinct, dusky streaking.

A.m. macgillivraii (res coastal ec.NC-ne.FL): Upperparts buffy gray to gray, with indistinct, brownish-black streaks; breast grayish buff to whitish, with moderately distinct, dusky streaking. Birds of se.SC-GA ("*waynei*") may average paler, but differences probably are due to plumage dichromatism rather than subspecies variation. Birds of ne.FL ("*shannoni*" and/or "*pelonota*") may average darker and less distinctly streaked, but differences are weak and obscured by individual variation.

Dusky (*A.m. nigrescens*) Group. Blackish.

A.m. nigrescens (former res coastal ce.FL): **Dusky Seaside Sparrow.** Upperparts blackish with indistinct, brownish-gray streaks; breast white with distinct, heavy, blackish streaking.

Cape Sable (*A.m. mirabilis*) Group. Bright olive.

A.m. mirabilis (res coastal s.FL): **Cape Sable Seaside Sparrow.** Upperparts olive with distinct, brownish streaks; breast white with distinct, brownish-black streaking.

Molt—PB: HY partial-incomplete (Jul-Dec), AHY complete (Jul-Sep); PA absent-partial (Mar-Apr). In migratory subspecies, the 1st PB can begin on the summer grounds and complete (including most or all flight feathers) on the winter grounds; adult PBs occur on the summer grounds. Look for a presupplemental molt (see p. 16) possibly to occur in this species. The molts appear to differ between subspecies groups (see **Geographic variation**), as follows: in the Gulf of Mexico, Atlantic, and (possibly) the Cape Sable subspecies groups, the 1st PB is eccentric (see p. 208 and Fig. 136), including all med and gr covs, the innermost 2-6 ss, 0 (~13%) or the outermost 5-6 pp, sometimes (in ~50% of birds) the outermost 1-2 pp covs, and all 12 rects. The PAs include 0 (~44%) to 5 inner gr covs and sometimes (in ~33% of birds) 1-3 terts, but no rects. In the Dusky Seaside Sparrow no molt limits are apparent on specimens in basic or alternate plumage, indicating that the 1st PB can be partial, involving all gr covs, but no terts or rects (or possibly complete), and that the PAs involve no wing covs or flight feathers. It is possible that some of the other southern subspecies (*e.g.*, Cape Sable Sparrow) may show replacement patterns more extensive or varying from that described above; more study is needed.

Skull—Pneumaticization completes in HY/SY from 15 Nov (as early as 15 Oct in southern populations) through Feb.

Age—Juv (May-Aug) generally is much buffier and has distinct streaking on the crown, breast, and flanks; juv ♀ = ♂. The following probably applies to most subspecies of this species (see **Molt**). No plumage criteria are known to age Dusky Seaside Sparrow (see **Molt**).

HY/SY (Aug-Jul): Most or all (see **Molt**) outer pp covs narrow, tapered, relatively abraded, and pale brown with indistinct, narrow, or no pale edging (Fig. 138), contrasting with the slightly fresher and darker-centered gr covs (Fig. 134); flight feathers juvenal, relatively worn, and tapered in Aug-Oct (on migration), molting in Sep-Dec (on the winter grounds), or showing eccentric replacement patterns (Fig. 136A) in Jan-Jul, with the innermost 2-6 ss, usually (in ~87% of birds) the outermost 5-6 pp, and sometimes (in ~50% of birds) the outermost 1-2 pp covs replaced and fresh, contrasting with the older and more worn, outer ss and inner pp. **Note: Both age groups sometimes can show 1-3 replaced terts in Mar-Jul (see Molt). See above regarding ageing of subspecies, especially Dusky Seaside Sparrow.**

AHY/ASY (Aug-Jul): Outer pp covs broad, truncate, relatively fresh, and dark brown with relatively distinct and broad, olive edging (Fig. 138), not contrasting markedly in color or wear with the centers of the gr covs (Fig. 133F); terts and middle ss (s4-s6) uniformly adult (Fig. 133F) in Aug-Mar; pp and pp covs uniformly adult, relatively fresh, and truncate in Aug-Oct (on migration). **Note: See HY/SY.**

Sex—♀ = ♂ by plumage. CP/BP (Apr-Aug). ♀ wg(n100) 53-62, tl(n100) 47-57; ♂ wg(n100) 55-66, tl(n100) 50-59.

Hybrids reported—Saltmarsh Sharp-tailed Sparrow.

Seaside Sparrow

	Jan	Feb	Mar	Apr	May	Jun	Jul	Aug	Sep	Oct	Nov	Dec
Juv-HY												
SY					○	○	○	○	○	○	○	○
AHY-U				○	○	○ (♀)	♂	♂	♂			
ASY	○	○	○	(♀)	♂	♂	♂	♂ (♀)	○	○	○	○
	○	○	○	(♀)	♂	♂	♂					

■ > 95% ▨ 25-95% ▱ 5-25% ▢ < 5%   See Fig. 24

References—Stone (1896), Dwight (1900a), Ridgway (1901), Forbush (1929), G.E. Woolfenden, C.H. Trost, & L.A. Stimson *in* Bent *et al.* (1968), Murray (1968), Wood (1969), Oberholser (1974), Werner & Woolfenden (1983), Pyle & Sibley (1992), McLaren (1994), Post & Greenlaw (1994), Byers *et al.* (1995), Rising (1996a), Sibley (1996), Pyle (1997c); E.J. Fisk, B. Sharp, C.H. Trost, G.E. Woolfenden (*in litt.* to the BBL).

FOX SPARROW
Passerella iliaca

FOSP
Species # 5850
Band size: 1A-1B

Species—From large Alaskan Song Sparrows by generally larger size (wg 73-92, tl 62-91; see **Geographic variation & Sex**); upperparts without streaking (western subspecies groups); malar streak indistinct or absent; spotting to the underparts heaviest on the upper breast.

Geographic variation—Well marked between subspecies groups, but moderately weak and clinal among subspecies within groups. Subspecies taxonomy follows Paynter (1970), as modified by Unitt (1984) and Browning (1990); see also Ridgway (1901, 1906), Grinnell (1902a, 1910a), Riley (1911), Mailliard (1912, 1918), Grinnell & Storer (1917), Swarth (1918d, 1920, 1922), Linsdale (1928), van Rossem (1933, 1934b), Cushing (1938), Aldrich (1943b), Oberholser (1946, 1974), Webster (1950, 1983), Behle & Selander (1951), Todd (1963), Phillips *et al.* (1964), Zink (1983, 1986, 1994), Behle (1985), Godfrey (1986), Burns (1993), Byers *et al.* (1995), Rising & Beadle (1995), Rising (1996a). No other subspecies occur. Note that museum specimens become redder with age.

Coastal Northwest Sooty (*P.i. unalaschcensis*) Group. Sooty brownish; wg > tl.

P.i. unalaschcensis (br e.Aleutian Is to w.AK, wint coastal sw.BC-sw.CA): Medium in size; bill medium large (exp culmen 11.6-13.4, depth at tip of nares 6.9-8.0); crown and back uniformly dull, dark brown with a gray wash; breast and belly spots heavy and brownish gray. ♀ wg(n16) 75-83, tl(n10) 68-75; ♂ wg(n23) 78-86, tl(n12) 73-79.

P.i. ridgwayi (= *"insularis"*; br Kodiak Is, AK; wint coastal w.WA-sw.CA): Medium in size; bill large (exp culmen 11.9-13.7, depth at tip of nares 7.0-8.0); crown and back uniformly bright, medium-dark brown with a reddish tinge; breast and belly spots heavy and brown. ♀ wg(n10) 77-83, tl(n10) 66-74; ♂ wg(n19) 80-87, tl(n19) 71-78.

P.i. sinuosa (br coastal sc.AK, wint coastal sw.BC-sw.CA): Medium small; bill medium large (exp culmen 11.2-13.4, depth at tip of nares 7.3-8.2); crown and back uniformly dull brown with a grayish-red tinge;

breast and belly spots moderately heavy and brownish. ♀ wg(n10) 75-81, tl(n10) 66-73; ♂ wg(n10) 78-84, tl(n10) 68-76.

P.i. annectens (br coastal sc-se.AK, wint coastal w.WA-sw.CA): Medium small; bill medium in size and stout (exp culmen 10.8-12.7, depth at tip of nares 6.8-7.8); crown and back uniformly brightish, medium brown with a reddish tinge; breast and belly spots moderately heavy and brown. ♀ wg(n10) 73-81, tl(n10) 66-72; ♂ wg(n33) 78-86, tl(n33) 67-75.

P.i. townsendi (br coastal se.AK-Queen Charlotte Is, BC; wint to coastal wc.CA): Small; tl relatively long; bill medium in size and slender (exp culmen 10.4-13.0, depth at tip of nares 6.4-7.8); crown and back uniformly brightish, dark brown with a reddish wash; breast and belly spots heavy and brown with a reddish wash. ♀ wg(n10) 73-82, tl(n10) 65-74; ♂ wg(n90) 76-85, tl(n89) 67-77.

P.i. chilcatensis (br coastal s.AK-cw.BC, wint coastal w.OR-wc.CA): Small; tl relatively short; bill medium large and relatively slender (exp culmen 10.9-13.3, depth at tip of nares 6.3-7.5); crown and back uniformly sooty brown with a reddish wash; breast and belly spots heavy and sooty brown with a reddish wash. ♀ wg(n10) 73-82, tl(n10) 62-71; ♂ wg(n51) 76-85, tl(n49) 65-74.

P.i. fuliginosa (br coastal cw.BC-nw.WA, wint to coastal wc.CA): Medium small; bill medium in size and slender (exp culmen 10.8-13.1, depth at tip of nares 6.3-7.5); crown and back uniformly, dark sooty brown with a reddish tinge; breast and belly spots heavy and sooty brown with a reddish tinge. ♀ wg(n10) 75-82, tl(n10) 67-75; ♂ wg(n14) 78-86, tl(n14) 70-80.

Western Thick-billed (*P.i. megarhyncha*) Group. Grayish; wg ≤ tl.

P.i. megarhyncha (br montane sc.OR-c.CA, wint c-s.CA): Medium in size; bill large (exp culmen 11.2-13.8, depth at tip of nares 8.0-9.9); crown and back uniformly, medium brownish gray; breast and belly spots sparse and dark brown. ♀ wg(n32) 75-84, tl(n14) 75-85; ♂ wg(n93) 78-87, tl(n60) 79-90. Birds breeding in sc.OR-nc.CA ("*fulva*") may average darker and smaller-billed, and birds breeding in interior ec.CA ("*monoensis*") average paler and smaller-billed, but in both cases differences are too slight to warrant subspecies distinctions. Birds breeding in c.CA ("*mariposae*") may average paler and grayer than birds of sw.OR-nc.CA, but differences are slight and/or this designation was based on comparisons of birds collected at different seasons.

P.i. brevicauda (br coastal nw.CA, wint coastal cw-sw.CA): Medium in size; bill very large and relatively narrow (exp culmen 13.3-15.4, depth at tip of nares 9.7-11.8, width at tip of nares 7.5-8.5); crown and back uniformly dark grayish brown; breast and belly spots sparse and dark brown. ♀ wg(n10) 76-83, tl(n10) 76-84; ♂ wg(n10) 79-87, tl(n10) 79-89.

P.i. stephensi (br montane sc.CA, wint coastal sw.CA): Medium large; bill very large and relatively wide (exp culmen 13.2-16.0, depth at tip of nares 10.2-11.9, width at tip of nares 8.3-10.0); crown and back uniformly, medium-dark gray; breast and belly spots sparse and dark brown. ♀ wg(n43) 76-85, tl(n10) 78-87; ♂ wg(n82) 79-89, tl(n37) 81-91.

Western Slate-colored (*P.i. schistacea*) Group. Grayish; wg ≤ tl.

P.i. olivacea (br interior sc.BC-e.WA, wint interior c-sc.CA): Medium small; bill medium small (exp culmen 10.4-12.4, depth at tip of nares 6.7-7.7); crown and back uniformly, medium grayish olive with a reddish tinge; breast and belly spots moderate in size and brown. ♀ wg(n10) 75-82, tl(n10) 72-80; ♂ wg(n10) 79-85, tl(n10) 75-83.

P.i. schistacea (br se.BC-sc.Alb to e.OR-c.CO, wint interior nc-sc.CA to sw.TX): Medium small; bill medium small and relatively slender (exp culmen 10.5-12.4, depth at tip of nares 6.3-7.4); crown and back uniformly, medium brownish gray; breast and belly spots moderately heavy and dusky brown. ♀ wg(n34) 73-83, tl(n10) 74-79; ♂ wg(n46) 78-86, tl(n29) 77-84.

P.i. swarthi (br se.ID-se.UT, wint AZ-NM?): Medium small; bill medium in length and slender (exp culmen 10.4-13.0, depth at tip of nares 5.3-7.0); crown and back uniformly, medium-dark gray; breast and belly spots heavy and brown. ♀ wg(n10) 74-83, tl(n10) 74-81; ♂ wg(n32) 78-87, tl(n32) 77-86.

P.i. canescens (br montane e.CA-ec.NV, wint s.CA-s.AZ): Small; bill small and stout (exp culmen 9.9-12.2, depth at tip of nares 7.5-8.4); crown and back uniformly pale gray; breast and belly spots moderately sparse and dusky brown. ♀ wg(n10) 74-80, tl(n10) 72-82; ♂ wg(n36) 77-84, tl(n36) 76-86.

Northern Red (*P.i. iliaca*) Group. Reddish; wg > tl.

P.i. altivagans (br interior BC-sw.Alb, wint CA-s.AZ): Medium large; bill medium small (exp culmen 10.9-12.5, depth at tip of nares 6.4-7.5); crown and back dark, dull grayish chestnut with indistinct, brown streaks; breast spots moderately heavy, indistinct, and dull reddish brown. ♀ wg(n10) 76-86, tl(n10) 65-75; ♂ wg(n26) 79-89, tl(n26) 68-78. An intermediate form, this subspecies may belong with the Western Slate-colored Group.

P.i. zaboria (br interior AK-c.Alb to s.NWT-Man, wint s.CA & IA-s.TX to GA): Large; bill medium small (exp culmen 10.4-12.5, depth at tip of nares 6.7-7.6); crown and back dark brownish gray with reduced, dull chestnut streaks; breast spots moderately sparse, distinct, and dull reddish brown. ♀ wg(n19) 80-87, tl(n10) 65-73; ♂ wg(n74) 84-92, tl(n63) 68-77.

P.i. iliaca (br ne.Man-Ont to Nfl, wint MI-MS to NH-n.FL): Large; bill medium small (exp culmen 10.6-12.4, depth at tip of nares 6.7-7.5); crown and back medium gray with extensive, bright chestnut streaks; breast and belly spots heavy, distinct, and bright reddish brown. ♀ wg(n10) 82-87, tl(n10) 63-70; ♂ wg(n10) 85-91, tl(n10) 67-75.

Molt—PB: HY partial (Jul-Sep), AHY complete (Jul-Sep); PA absent-limited (Mar-Apr). The PBs occur on the summer grounds. The 1st PB usually includes all med and gr covs (rarely 1-2 outer gr covs can be retained), but no terts or rects. The PAs, when present, are limited to a few head feathers.

Skull—Pneumaticization completes in HY/SY from 1 Dec. Look for windows (> 2 mm; Fig. 11**D**) on the top of the skull in some SYs through summer and (rarely) into fall.

Age—Juv (Jun-Aug) is similar to adults, but averages duller on the upperparts and has a buff wash to the underparts; juv ♀ = ♂.

HY/SY (Aug-Jul): Outer pp covs somewhat narrow, tapered, and brown with indistinct or no pale brown edging (Fig. 138), contrasting with the slightly fresher gr covs (Fig. 134); outer rects tapered (Fig. 139**B**) and relatively abraded. **Note: Many intermediates occur that are difficult to age.**

AHY/ASY (Aug-Jul): Outer pp covs somewhat broad, truncate, and dusky brownwith relatively distinct, rufous to gray edging (Fig. 138), not contrasting in wear with the gr covs (Fig. 133**F**); outer rects truncate (Fig. 133**F**), relatively fresh. **Note: See HY/SY.**

Sex—♀ = ♂ by plumage. CP/BP (Apr-Aug). ♀ wg(n100) 73-87, tl(n100) 62-87; ♂ wg(n100) 76-92, tl(n100) 65-91; see **Geographic variation**.

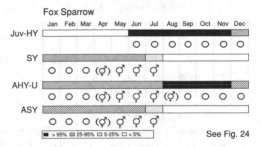

See Fig. 24

References—Stone (1896), Dwight (1900a), Ridgway (1901), Forbush (1929), Roberts (1955), O.L. Austin Jr. & S.M. Terrill *in* Bent *et al.* (1968), Wood (1969), Stewart (1972a), Oberholser (1974), Byers *et al.* (1995), Rising (1996a), Pyle (1997c); IBP (MAPS) data, PNR data, PRBO data.

SONG SPARROW
Melospiza melodia

SOSP
Species # 5810
Band size: 1B-1

Species—All races from Savannah Sparrow by stouter bill (depth at tip of nares 5.1-8.0; see **Geographic variation**); wing morphology shorter (Fig. 297; p5 > p9 by 4-12 mm); tl longer (52-84; see **Geographic variation**) and graduated (longest r – r6 7-14 mm); supercilium, face and belly (juvs) without yellow; rects not pointed (compare Figs. 139**B** and 297). Larger subspecies of AK (see **Geographic variation**) from Fox Sparrow by upperparts streaked dusky or reddish; malar streak distinct; streaking to the underparts heaviest on the flanks. Juv from juv Lincoln's and Swamp sparrows by longer average tl (52-84; see **Geographic variation** & **Sex**); shorter wing morphology (Fig. 297; longest p ≈ p7 and/or p6, and p5 > p9 by 4-12 mm); bill stout (depth at tip of nares 5.1-8.0, width at tip of nares 4.1-6.1); crown primarily brown with relatively indistinct streaks, and with the median crown stripe absent or present; malar stripe distinct and wide; throat primarily unstreaked; breast with heavy streaks; roof of the mouth (upper mandible lining) yellow to yellowish white.

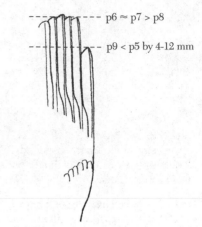

Geographic variation—Highly variable: very well marked between extreme forms, but generally weak and clinal among subspecies within groups. Subspecies taxonomy follows Paynter (1970); see Grinnell (1901, 1909a, 1910a, 1911c, 1928e), McGregor (1901), Ridgway (1901), Fisher (1902), Grinnell & Daggett (1903), Oberholser (1911c, 1974), Riley (1911), Bangs (1912),

FIGURE 297. The wing morphology of Song Sparrow. See Figure 10 for measurement techniques.

Swarth (1912b, 1922, 1923), Thayer & Bangs (1914), Brooks (1919), Todd (1924, 1930, 1963), van Rossem (1924, 1945a), Worthington & Todd (1926), Fargo (1932), Cumming (1933), Wetmore (1936, 1937), Marshall & Behle (1942), Phillips (1943), Munro & Cowan (1947), Twomey (1947), Behle (1948, 1985), Marshall (1948a, 1948b), Webster (1950), Gabrielson & Lincoln (1951b), Dickinson (1953), Parkes (1954), Dickerman (1963), Phillips *et al.* (1964), Mengel (1965), Hubbard & Banks (1970), Browning (1978, 1979a, 1990), Aldrich (1984), Godfrey (1986), Paulson (1992), Cramp & Perrins (1994b), Byers *et al.* (1995), Rising (1996a), Pyle (1997c). Ten other subspecies occur in Mex. Note that plumage coloration becomes browner or blacker (less red) with seasonal wear. See also **Molt**.

Alaskan Island (*M.m. insignis*) Group. Very large; grayish with reddish streaking.

M.m. maxima (res Attu to Atka Is, AK): Very large; bill extremely large (exp culmen 14.9-17.5, depth at tip of nares 7.1-8.0); upper back grayish brown with light, reddish-brown streaking; lower back with indistinct, dusky-brown streaking; underparts grayish white with rusty streaks. ♀ wg(n19) 76-83, tl(n19) 71-80; ♂ wg(n26) 79-87, tl(n26) 74-83. Suggested three-letter subspecies code (see p. 30-31): "mxm".

M.m. sanaka (res e.Aleutian Is-w.AK): Very large; bill very large (exp culmen 14.0-15.8, depth at tip of nares 6.5-7.5); upper back medium-dark grayish brown with indistinct, reddish-brown streaking; lower back with indistinct, dusky-brown streaking; underparts grayish white with diffuse, rusty streaks. ♀ wg(n18) 77-85, tl(n18) 72-80; ♂ wg(n28) 80-89, tl(n28) 76-84. Birds of the Semidi Is ("*semidiensis*") average browner and smaller-billed, but differences are too slight for subspecies recognition.

M.m. amaka (res Amak I, w.AK): Very large; bill very large (exp culmen 14.0-15.5, depth at tip of nares 6.6-7.6); upper back grayish brown with heavy, reddish-brown streaking; lower back with indistinct, dusky-brown streaking; underparts grayish white with diffuse, broad, rufous streaks. ♀ wg(n2) 77-82, tl(n2) 76-80; ♂ wg(n4) 81-85, tl(n4) 78-83.

M.m. insignis (res coastal sc.AK-Kodiak Is, AK): Very large; bill very long and relatively slender (exp culmen 14.3-16.0, depth at tip of nares 5.8-6.9); upper back dark sooty brown; lower back with indistinct or no dusky-brown streaking; underparts grayish white with diffuse, brown to reddish-brown streaks. ♀ wg(n10) 74-82, tl(n10) 71-80; ♂ wg(n10) 78-86, tl(n10) 74-83.

Northwest Coastal Pacific (*M.m. rufina*) Group. Large; sooty to rusty.

M.m. kenaiensis (br coastal sc.AK, wint to coastal WA): Large; bill large (exp culmen 13.2-14.3, depth at tip of nares 6.0-6.8); upper back dark gray with sooty-brown streaking; lower back with indistinct, blackish-brown streaking; underparts grayish white with diffuse, dark brown streaks. ♀ wg(n10) 71-79, tl(n10) 60-70; ♂ wg(n10) 73-81, tl(n10) 63-72.

M.m. caurina (br coastal sc-se.AK, wint to coastal nw.CA): Large; bill long and relatively slender (exp culmen 12.0-13.8, depth at tip of nares 5.4-6.3); upper back medium-dark gray with reddish-brown streaking; lower back with indistinct, blackish-brown streaking; underparts grayish white with diffuse, dark reddish-brown streaks. ♀ wg(n10) 66-71, tl(n10) 62-69; ♂ wg(n20) 69-75, tl(n20) 64-72.

M.m. rufina (br se.AK Is-Queen Charlotte Is, BC; wint to coastal sw.WA; vag to AZ): Large; bill medium in size (exp culmen 11.3-13.1, depth at tip of nares 5.5-6.8); upper back dark gray with dark brownish streaking; lower back with indistinct, blackish streaking; underparts whitish with diffuse, dark rufous-brown streaks. ♀ wg(n18) 63-72, tl(n16) 60-70; ♂ wg(n38) 66-76, tl(n33) 62-74. Birds of the Queen Charlotte Is (*"kwaisa"*) may average grayer (less ruddy), but difference, if present, are slight.

M.m. inexpectata (br coastal se.AK-s.Yuk to interior c.BC-sw.Alb, wint s.BC-OR): Medium in size; bill medium small (exp culmen 10.8-12.4, depth at tip of nares 5.2-6.2); upper back dark rufous with gray streaking; lower back with moderately indistinct, blackish streaking; underparts grayish white with diffuse, rufous streaks. ♀ wg(n10) 58-66, tl(n10) 54-63; ♂ wg(n10) 60-67, tl(n10) 56-64.

M.m. morphna (br coastal sw.BC-cw.OR, wint to coastal cw.CA; vag to UT): Medium large; bill long and relatively slender (exp culmen 11.9-13.7, depth at tip of nares 5.5-6.4); upper back reddish brown with dusky streaking; lower back with moderately indistinct, blackish streaking; underparts whitish with diffuse, rusty streaks. ♀ wg(n100) 60-69, tl(n13) 58-67; ♂ wg(n100) 63-73, tl(n54) 61-71. Birds breeding in cw.OR (*"phaea"*) average slightly smaller and browner, but differences are weak and due to intergradation with *cleonensis*.

California Mainland (*M.m. gouldii*) Group. Small; brownish olive.

M.m. cleonensis (res coastal sw.OR-nw.CA): Medium small; bill medium small (exp culmen 10.5-12.7, depth at tip of nares 5.3-6.3); upper back dark olive-brown with chestnut streaking; lower back with moderately distinct, blackish streaking; underparts whitish with moderately distinct, dark rusty streaks. ♀ wg(n100) 53-62, tl(n10) 53-61; ♂ wg(n100) 56-65, tl(n20) 57-63. Suggested three-letter subspecies code (see p. 30-31): "cln".

M.m. gouldii (res coastal cw.CA, Mendocino-San Mateo Cos): Small; bill small (exp culmen 10.1-12.1, depth at tip of nares 5.5-6.3); upper back dark grayish brown to reddish brown, with blackish streaking; lower back with distinct, blackish-brown streaking; underparts whitish with dark brown streaks. ♀ wg(n100) 53-61, tl(n10) 51-61; ♂ wg(n100) 57-64, tl(n10) 55-65. Birds of San Francisco-San Mateo Cos (*"santaecrucis"*) average paler and grayer, but differences are slight and due to intergradation with *cooperi*.

M.m. samuelis (res n.San Francisco Bay, CA): Small; bill medium small (exp culmen 10.9-12.7, depth at tip of nares 5.4-6.5); upper back brown to olive-brown, with chestnut streaking; lower back with distinct, blackish streaking; underparts white to yellowish-buff, with distinct, moderately sparse, dusky streaks. ♀ wg(n26) 54-60, tl(n11) 52-60; ♂ wg(n48) 57-64, tl(n22) 54-62.

M.m. pusillula (res s.San Francisco Bay, CA): Small; bill small (exp culmen 10.0-11.6, depth at tip of nares 5.1-6.0); upper back medium olive-gray with blackish-brown streaking; lower back with distinct, blackish-brown streaking; underparts yellowish-buff with distinct, heavy, blackish streaks. ♀ wg(n25) 53-59, tl(n10) 52-59; ♂ wg(n27) 57-62, tl(n10) 54-61.

M.m. maxillaris (res Suisun Bay, wc.CA): Medium small; bill large (exp culmen 11.9-14.2, depth at tip of nares 6.2-7.4); upper back dark brown with blackish streaking; lower back with distinct, broad, blackish streaking; underparts white with distinct, broad, blackish streaking or spotting. ♀ wg(n20) 57-62, tl(n10) 57-62; ♂ wg(n20) 61-66, tl(n10) 59-65. Suggested three-letter subspecies code (see p. 30-31): "mxl".

M.m. mailliardi (res interior wc.CA, Glenn-Stanislaus Cos): Medium small; bill medium in size (exp culmen 11.6-13.6, depth at tip of nares 6.0-7.1); upper back dark brown with indistinct, sooty streaking; lower back with moderately distinct, blackish-brown streaking; underparts white with distinct, blackish streaks. ♀ wg(n10) 57-64, tl(n10) 57-63; ♂ wg(n10) 60-67, tl(n10) 58-66.

M.m. heermanni (res interior c.CA, Merced-Kern Cos): Medium in size; bill medium large (exp culmen 11.5-13.4, depth at tip of nares 6.1-7.2); upper back medium grayish brown with dark reddish-brown streaking; lower back with moderately distinct, blackish-brown streaking; underparts white with distinct, blackish streaks. ♀ wg(n52) 59-68, tl(n10) 57-66; ♂ wg(n48) 63-72, tl(n17) 60-70.

M.m. cooperi (res coastal cw-sw.CA, Santa Cruz-San Diego Cos): Medium small; bill medium in size (exp culmen 11.0-13.3, depth at tip of nares 6.4-7.3); upper back medium grayish olive with dark brown streaking; lower back with distinct, blackish-brown streaking; underparts white with distinct, broad, blackish-brown streaks. ♀ wg(n59) 54-63, tl(n10) 57-63; ♂ wg(n100) 56-66, tl(n47) 58-67.

California Island (*M.m. clementae*) Group. Medium small; pale grayish to brownish.

M.m. micronyx (res San Miguel I, CA): Medium small; bill medium small (exp culmen 11.5-12.5, depth at tip of nares 5.8-6.5); hind claw short (6.2-7.9 mm); upper back gray with dark brown streaking; lower back with distinct, dark brown streaking; underparts white with distinct, moderately dense, dusky streaks. ♀ wg(n10) 55-61, tl(n10) 57-64; ♂ wg(n12) 60-65, tl(n12) 60-67.

M.m. clementae (res Santa Rosa to San Clemente Is, CA): Medium in size; bill medium in size (exp culmen 11.5-12.6, depth at tip of nares 5.8-6.7); hind claw long (7.2-9.8 mm); upper back pale brownish gray with dark brown streaking; lower back with moderately distinct, blackish-brown streaking; underparts white with distinct, sparse, black streaks. ♀ wg(n10) 58-64, tl(n10) 58-65; ♂ wg(n30) 61-67, tl(n30) 60-68. Birds of the Coronado Is (*coronatorum*), within sight of CA, are browner with a smaller bill (exp culmen 10.7-12.1) and smaller feet. Suggested three-letter subspecies code (see p. 30-31): "clm".

M.m. graminea (former res Santa Barbara I, CA): Small; bill small (exp culmen 11.7-12.4, depth at tip of nares 5.5-6.4); upper back pale olive-gray with brown streaking; lower back with moderately indistinct, blackish-brown streaking; underparts white with distinct, sparse, blackish streaks. ♀ wg(n10) 53-60, tl(n10) 50-59; ♂ wg(n23) 57-63, tl(n23) 53-61.

Interior Western (*M.m. montana*) Group. Medium in size; pale brownish to reddish.

M.m. merrilli (br interior s.BC-sw.Alb to e.WA-nw.MT, wint to s.CA-NM): Medium in size; bill medium in size (exp culmen 11.3-13.0, depth at tip of nares 5.8-6.7); upper back medium grayish brown with indistinct, dusky streaking; lower back with indistinct, dark brown streaking; underparts whitish with distinct, dark dusky-reddish streaks. ♀ wg(n63) 60-68, tl(n10) 61-70; ♂ wg(n66) 63-73, tl(n11) 64-72.

M.m. fisherella (br interior e.OR-sw.ID to n.CA-w.NV, wint to s.CA-s.AZ): Medium in size; bill medium small (exp culmen 11.1-12.7, depth at tip of nares 5.7-6.8); upper back medium gray with brown streaking; lower back with moderately distinct, blackish streaking; underparts white with heavy, moderately distinct, dark brown streaks. ♀ wg(n59) 59-68, tl(n10) 61-69; ♂ wg(n92) 61-71, tl(n10) 63-71.

M.m. montana (br montane ne.OR-c.MT to e.AZ-n.NM, wint to se.CA-w.TX): Medium large; bill medium large (exp culmen 10.7-13.7, depth at tip of nares 6.0-7.2); upper back medium-pale grayish with reddish streaking; lower back with moderately distinct, reddish-brown and blackish streaking; underparts whitish with moderately distinct, reddish-brown to brown streaks. ♀ wg(n30) 62-69, tl(n30) 63-72; ♂ wg(n36) 65-73, tl(n36) 65-75.

M.m. fallax (br & wint se.NV-sw.UT to AZ): Medium large; bill medium in size (exp culmen 11.3-13.1, depth at tip of nares 5.9-6.8); upper back medium-pale grayish with reddish-brown streaking; lower back with moderately distinct, reddish-brown and blackish streaking; underparts whitish with indistinct, reddish-brown streaks. ♀ wg(n24) 61-69, tl(n24) 62-70; ♂ wg(n52) 64-72, tl(n52) 65-76. Birds of sw.UT ("*virginis*") may average paler and browner, but this difference is slight and due to intergradation with *saltonis* and *montana*. The name "*bendirei*" for birds of c-se.AZ was mistakenly applied to migrants of *saltonis* in fresh plumage.

M.m. saltonis (br desert s.CA-s.NV to sw.AZ, wint to se.AZ): Medium small; bill medium short but relatively stout (exp culmen 11.1-12.8, depth at tip of nares 6.0-7.2); upper back pale grayish with reddish-brown streaking; lower back with moderately distinct, reddish (with little or no blackish) streaking; underparts white with indistinct and sparse, reddish streaks. ♀ wg(n24) 58-65, tl(n24) 59-68; ♂ wg(n24) 62-68, tl(n24) 64-73.

Eastern (*M.m. melodia*) Group. Medium in size; brownish.

M.m. juddi (br ne.BC-s.NWT to e.MT-MI, wint to AZ-FL): Medium in size; bill medium short but relatively stout (exp culmen 10.3-12.6, depth at tip of nares 6.5-7.5); upper back medium-pale brown with dark brownish streaking; lower back with distinct, black streaking; underparts white with distinct, black streaks. ♀ wg(n39) 59-68, tl(n36) 62-71; ♂ wg(n89) 62-72, tl(n87) 65-74. Birds breeding in se.Man-w.KY ("*beata*") may average shorter-winged (wg < tl, *vs* wg ≈ tl in other *juddi*) and darker, but differences, if present, are very slight and obscured by individual variation.

M.m. euphonia (br n.WI-w.NY to MO-SC, wint to TX-GA): Medium in size; bill medium small and relatively slender (exp culmen 10.3-12.6, depth at tip of nares 6.1-7.0); upper back medium-dark grayish with reddish-brown streaking; lower back with moderately distinct, blackish streaking; underparts white with distinct, blackish-brown streaks. ♀ wg(n100) 57-65, tl(n10) 60-69; ♂ wg(n100) 62-70, tl(n10) 64-72. Birds breeding in se.Ont-KY ("*melanchra*") may average darker, but differences, if present, are weak and obscured by individual variation.

M.m. melodia (br e.Ont to Nfl-VA, wint to e.TX-FL): Medium in size; bill medium large (exp culmen 11.4-13.2, depth at tip of nares 6.3-7.2); upper back medium brownish gray with reddish streaking; lower back with distinct, blackish streaking; underparts white with distinct, dusky-brown streaks. ♀ wg(n100) 57-68, tl(n100) 56-68; ♂ wg(n100) 61-72, tl(n100) 61-71. Birds breeding in NS ("*acadia*") may average darker and birds breeding in e.MA-NJ ("*callima*") may average paler, grayer, and smaller-billed, but differences, if present, are weak and obscured by individual variation.

M.m. atlantica (br coastal NY-NC, wint to coastal GA): Medium in size; bill large (exp culmen 11.9-13.8, depth at tip of nares 7.0-7.9); upper back medium brownish gray with reddish streaking; lower back with moderately distinct, blackish-brown streaking; underparts white with moderately distinct, dusky-brown streaks. ♀ wg(n28) 58-66, tl(n27) 57-67; ♂ wg(n41) 61-70, tl(n36) 61-71. The name "*rossignolii*" for presumably redder birds of Hog I, VA, was applied with insufficient material and comparison only with *juddi*.

Molt—PB: HY partial-incomplete (Jul-Nov), AHY complete (Jul-Oct); PA absent. In migratory subspecies, the PBs occur primarily on the breeding grounds. The 1st PB is variable, including all gr and med covs, the innermost 1-6 ss, and 0 (~16%) to all 12 (~74%) rects. Also, the 1st PB sometimes (in ~49% of birds) can be eccentric (see p. 208 and Fig. 136), with the outermost 1-7 pp but no pp covs replaced. Occasionally (in ~12% of birds with eccentric replacement patterns), the outermost 1-3 ss (among s1-s3) and the innermost 1-3 pp (among p1-p3) also can be replaced (see Fig. 136**D**), and probably all pp and ss rarely can be replaced in a small proportion of individuals. Higher proportions of birds with eccentric replacement patterns occur among the California and Eastern subspecies groups (see **Geographic variation**), whereas few if any birds among the Alaska and Pacific Northwest subspecies groups replace pp. More study is needed on variation in the 1st PB of this species.

Skull—Pneumaticization completes in HY/SY from 1 Nov (as early as 1 Oct in the subspecies groups of CA; see **Geographic variation**). Look for windows (> 2 mm; Fig. 11**D**) on the top of the skull in some SYs through summer and (rarely) fall.

Age—Juv (Apr-Sep) generally is drabber and buffier than adults, with diffuse streaking to the face and underparts, has less distinct facial and median crown stripe features, and lacks rusty tones to the crown and back; juv ♀ = ♂.

HY/SY (Aug-Jul): Outer pp covs narrow, tapered, relatively abraded, and brown with indistinct, narrow, or no pale gray-brown edging (Fig. 138), contrasting with the slightly fresher and dusky-centered gr covs (Fig. 134); the innermost 1-6 ss (also, occasionally one or more of s1-s3) replaced, contrasting with the more abraded outer or middle ss (among s1-s6 or s4-s6), and the outermost 1-7 pp (also occasionally p1 and/or p2) sometimes replaced, contrasting with the more worn inner or middle pp (Figs. 136**A-D**); rects usually uniformly truncate but sometimes uniformly tapered (Fig. 139**B**) or mixed tapered and truncate; iris olive to gray-brown (through Dec-Mar). **Note: See Molt for geographic variation in the extent of the 1st PB, hence, molt-limit criteria. Molt limits among the flight feathers of HY/SYs can be hard to detect; thus, many intermediates occur that are not reliably aged. Also, occasional HY/SYs may have replaced all pp, ss, and rects; these will be hard to distinguish from AHY/ASYs. The condition of the pp covs should be reliable for ageing all birds, although it often is hard to judge without experience.**

AHY/ASY (Aug-Jul): Outer pp covs broad, truncate, relatively fresh, and dusky brown with relatively distinct and broad, reddish-brown edging (Fig. 138), not contrasting markedly in color or wear with the uniformly adult, gr covs, ss, and pp (Fig. 133**F**); rects uniformly truncate (Fig. 139**B**); iris chestnut-brown. **Note: See HY/SY.**

Sex—♀ = ♂ by plumage. CP/BP (Feb-Sep). See **Geographic variation** for measurements, which vary substantially more by geography than by sex.

Hybrids reported—White-crowned Sparrow.

References—Stone (1896), Dwight (1900a), Ridgway (1901), Forbush (1929), Nice (1932, 1937, 1943), Sutton (1935a), Marshall (1948b), Wetherbee (1951), Roberts (1955), Dickerman (1961), V. Nolan Jr., M.M. Nice, R.F. Johnston, & R.W. Dickerman *in* Bent *et al.* (1968), Wood (1969), Oberholser (1974), Sheppard & Klimkiewicz (1976), Smith & Zach (1979), Dhondt & Smith (1980), Aldrich (1984), Rimmer (1986), Hamel & Wagner (1990), Righter (1990),

Yunick (1990), CWS & USFWS (1991), Suthers (1994), Byers *et al.* (1995), Rising (1996a), Pyle (1997c); B.A. Addelson, R.F. Johnston, C.M. Weise (*in litt.* to the BBL); R.G. McKinney (pers. comm.); IBP (MAPS) data, PNR data, PRBO data.

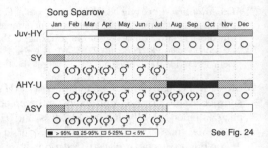

LINCOLN'S SPARROW
Melospiza lincolnii

LISP
Species # 5830
Band size: 1C-0

Species—Juv from juv Savannah Sparrow by shorter wing morphology (Fig. 298; p9 – p5 - 2 to 2 mm); supercilium, face, and belly without yellow; rects not extremely tapered (compare Figs. 139**B** and 297). Juv from juv Song and Swamp sparrows by shorter average tl (48-61; see **Geographic variation & Sex**); longer wing morphology (Fig. 298; p8 > p7 > p6 or p8 ≈ p7 > p6, p5 – p9 -2 to 2 mm); bill slender (depth at tip of nares 5.6-7.0, width at tip of nares 3.5-4.1); crown buffy brown to brown, with distinct, black streaking; malar stripe indistinct and narrow; throat distinctly streaked; breast with fine streaks; roof of the mouth (upper mandible lining) gray to grayish white.

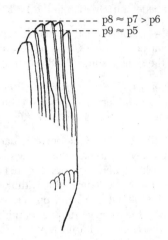

p8 ≈ p7 > p6
p9 ≈ p5

FIGURE 298. The wing morphology of Lincoln's Sparrow. See Figure 10 for measurement techniques.

Geographic variation—Weak, clinal where ranges meet, and differences are obscured by slight dichromatism (grayish and brownish plumages) and individual variation. Subspecies taxonomy follows Paynter (1970); see Grinnell (1914a), Miller & McCabe (1935), Wetmore (1943), Phillips (1959a), Phillips *et al.* (1964), Sutton (1967), Oberholser (1974), Behle (1985), Byers *et al.* (1995). No other subspecies occur.

M.l. gracilis (br coastal se.AK to sw.BC, wint c-s.CA to w.AZ): Small; upperparts grayish brown with a buff tinge and broad, blackish streaking. ♀ wg(n14) 54-60, tl(n10) 48-55; ♂ wg(n12) 56-62, tl(n10) 50-57.

M.l. alticola (br montane e.OR-w.MT to CA-n.NM, wint to s.CA-sw.TX): Large; upperparts brown to medium-pale brown with a grayish tinge and narrow, blackish streaking. ♀ wg(n100) 57-65, tl(n34) 51-58; ♂ wg(n100) 60-69, tl(n73) 54-61.

M.l. lincolnii (br w.AK-e.WA to Nfl-ME, wint CA to NC-FL): Medium in size; upperparts brown to medium brown with a reddish tinge and narrow, blackish streaking. ♀ wg(n100) 56-63, tl(n10) 48-56; ♂ wg(n100) 58-66, tl(n53) 50-59.

Molt—PB: HY partial (Jul-Aug), AHY complete (Jul-Aug); PA limited-partial (Feb-Apr). The PBs occur on the summer grounds. The 1st PB usually includes all med and gr covs, occasionally (in ~5% of birds) 1-2 terts, and sometimes (in ~30% of birds) 1-2 central rects (r1). The PAs include no gr covs or rects but, occasionally (in ~7% of birds), 1-2 terts.

Skull—Pneumaticization completes in HY/SY from 15 Nov. Look for windows (> 2 mm; Fig. 11**D**) on the top of the skull in some SYs through summer and (rarely) fall.

Age—Juv (Jun-Aug) has the crown and supercilium buffier brown, and generally is drabber and more coarsely streaked than adults; juv ♀ = ♂.

HY/SY (Aug-Jul): Outer pp covs narrow, tapered, relatively abraded and brown with indistinct, narrow, or no pale brown edging (Fig. 138), contrasting with the slightly fresher and dusky-centered gr covs (Fig. 134); 1-2 terts occasionally contrastingly fresh (Fig. 133**D**, but beware of pseudolimits in AHY/ASYs); central rects (r1) sometimes contrastingly fresh; outer rects tapered and relatively abraded (Fig. 139**A**). **Note: Many intermediates can be difficult to age.**

AHY/ASY (Aug-Jul): Outer pp covs broad, truncate, relatively fresh, and dusky brown with relatively distinct and broad, pale brown edging (Fig. 138), not contrasting markedly in color or wear with the gr covs (Fig. 133**F**); terts and middle ss (s4-s6) uniform in wear in Aug-Mar (Fig. 133**F**, although beware of pseudolimits between blacker terts and brown ss; see p. 207); rects uniformly truncate and relatively fresh (Fig 139**A**). **Note: See HY/SY.**

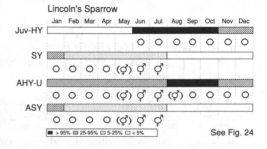

Sex—♀ = ♂ by plumage. CP/BP (May-Aug). ♀ wg(n100) 54-65, tl(n100) 48-58; ♂ wg(n100) 56-69, tl(n100) 50-61; see **Geographic variation**.

References—Dwight (1900a), Ridgway (1901), Forbush (1929), Roberts (1955), J.M. Speirs & D.H. Speirs *in* Bent *et al.* (1968), Wood (1969), Oberholser (1974), Rimmer (1986), Righter (1990), Yunick (1990), Ammon (1995), Byers *et al.* (1995), Rising (1996a), Pyle (1997c); L.M. Krajcirik (pers. comm.); IBP (MAPS) data, PNR data, PRBO data.

SWAMP SPARROW
Melospiza georgiana

SWSP
Species # 5840
Band size: 1C-1

Species—Juv from juv Song and Lincoln's sparrows by short wing morphology (Fig. 299; p8 ≈ p7 ≈ p6, p5 – p9 2-9 mm); tl medium in length (51-64; see **Sex**); bill moderately slender (depth at tip of nares 5.5-7.0, width at tip of nares 3.8-4.4); crown primarily black, sometimes with heavy, olive streaking, and without a median crown stripe; malar stripe indistinct and narrow; throat unstreaked; breast with fine streaks; roof of the mouth (upper mandible lining) yellow to yellowish white.

Geographic variation—Moderate, but broadly clinal where the ranges of the two northern subspecies meet. Subspecies taxonomy follows Paynter (1970), as modified by Greenberg & Droege (1990); see also

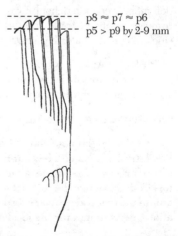

p8 ≈ p7 ≈ p6
p5 > p9 by 2-9 mm

FIGURE 299. The wing morphology of Swamp Sparrow. See Figure 10 for measurement techniques.

Oberholser (1938, 1974), Wetmore (1940), Griscom (1948b), Godfrey (1949, 1986), Bond & Stewart (1951), Todd (1963), Sutton (1967), Behle (1985), Byers *et al.* (1995). No other subspecies occur.

M.g. ericrypta (br sw.NWT-ec.BC to Nfl-Que, wint to CA-FL): Bill small (nares to tip 7.7-8.6, depth at tip of nares 4.7-5.4, width at tip of nares 3.7-4.3); crown in alternate plumage medium-pale rufous with little or no black streaking by sex (see **Sex**); upper back medium-pale brown; flanks bright, medium-pale brown with a slight reddish tinge.

M.g. georgiana (br e.SD-MO to NB-WV & n.NJ, wint to TX-FL; vag to AZ): Bill small (nares to tip 7.7-8.6, depth at tip of nares 4.8-5.5, width at tip of nares 3.7-4.3); crown in alternate plumage dark rufous with little or no black streaking by sex (see **Sex**); upper back medium grayish brown; flanks dark brown with a buffy-rufous tinge.

M.g. nigrescens (br coastal s.NJ-MD, wint grounds unknown): Bill large (nares to tip 8.2-9.2, depth at tip of nares 5.3-6.1, width at tip of nares 4.2-4.9); crown in alternate plumage dull rufous with moderately heavy, black streaking by sex (see **Sex**); upper back dark brownish gray; flanks grayish olive with little or no reddish.

Molt—PB: HY partial (Jul-Oct), AHY complete (Jul-Oct); PA limited (Feb-Apr). The PBs occur on the summer grounds. The 1st PB usually includes all med and gr covs, often (in ~54% of birds) 1-3 terts, and occasionally (in ~8% of birds) 1-2 central rects (r1). The PAs are limited primarily to feathers of the head.

Skull—Pneumaticization completes in HY/SY from 15 Nov. Look for windows (> 2 mm; see Fig. 11**D**) at the rear of the skull in some SYs through May.

Age—Juv (Jun-Aug) lacks a distinct median crown stripe and has distinct streaking to the underparts; juv ♀ = ♂.

HY/SY (Aug-Jul): Nape and supercilium buff to brownish gray; crown with a limited amount or no rufous in Aug-Mar; 1-3 terts often replaced, contrasting with the older middle ss (s4-s6; Fig. 133**D-E**, although beware of pseudolimits in AHY/ASYs); outer pp covs narrow, tapered, relatively abraded, and pale brown with indistinct, narrow, or no buffy-brown edging (Fig. 138); central rects (r1) occasionally replaced, contrastingly fresh; outer rects tapered (Fig. 139**B**) and relatively abraded. **Note: Most birds should be reliably aged; compare with sexing criteria (see Sex) on intermediates.**

AHY/ASY (Aug-Jul): Nape and supercilium gray or primarily gray; crown with substantial rufous in Aug-Mar; terts and middle ss (s4-s6) uniformly adult (Fig. 133**F**, although beware of a pseudolimit between the richer brown terts and the more faded brown s5-s6); outer pp covs broad, truncate, relatively fresh, and dusky brown with relatively distinct and broad, rufous edging (Fig. 138); rects uniformly adult, truncate (Fig. 139**B**), and relatively fresh. **Note: See HY/SY.**

Sex—CP/BP (Apr-Aug). ♀ wg(n100) 52-63, tl(n30) 51-60; ♂ wg(n100) 55-65, tl(n30) 55-64. No reliable plumage criteria are known for sexing basic-plumaged birds (in Aug-Mar), although ♂♂ average more rufous in the crowns than ♀♀; some extreme AHY/ASY ♂♂ may be sexed, with experience.

Alternate Plumage (Mar-Aug)

AHY ♀ (Mar-Aug): Crown brownish without rufous, to rufous, usually with > 15% brown or black streaking. **Note: A few intermediates (with the crown 50-85% rufous) are not reliably sexed by crown plumage alone and should be sexed by breeding characters or left unsexed; these may be ASY ♀♀ or SY ♂♂ (more study is needed). Also, these criteria pertain to the two widespread subspecies (*M.g. ericrypta* and *georgiana*; see Geographic variation); percentages for the local *nigrescens* average lower and are in need of more study.**

AHY ♂ (Mar-Aug): Crown entirely rufous, to rufous with < 50% brown or black streaking. **Note: See AHY ♀.**

References—Stone (1896), Dwight (1900a), Ridgway (1901), Forbush (1929), Sutton (1935a), Roberts (1955), D.K. Wetherbee *in* Bent *et al.* (1968), Wood (1969), Oberholser (1974), Riggins & Riggins (1974), Sheppard & Klimkiewicz (1976), Rimmer (1986), Greenberg (1988), Greenberg & Droege (1990), Hamel & Wagner (1990), Righter (1990), Yunick (1990), Byers *et al.* (1995), Rising (1996a), Mowbray (1997), Pyle (1997c); R.P. Yunick (*in litt.* to the BBL); IBP (MAPS) data, PNR data, PRBO data.

Swamp Sparrow

See Fig. 24

WHITE-THROATED SPARROW
Zonotrichia albicollis

WTSP
Species # 5580
Band size: 1B

Geographic variation—No subspecies are recognized.

Molt—PB: HY partial (Jul-Sep), AHY complete (Jul-Sep); PA limited (Mar-May). The PBs occur on the summer grounds. The 1st PB usually includes all med and gr covs, but no terts or rects. The PAs are limited to body feathers, primarily in the head region. Beware of pseudolimits (see p. 207) between the richer brown terts and inner gr covs, and the duller brown middle ss (s4-s6) and outer gr covs, which causes the inner feathers to appear more recently replaced.

Skull—Pneumaticization completes in HY/SY from 15 Nov. Some SYs can show windows (> 2 mm; Fig. 11**D**) on the top of the skull into summer and (rarely) fall. The timing of completion has been shown to vary interannually (see Wiley & Piper 1992).

Age—Juv (Jun-Aug) has considerable blackish streaking on the upper breast and flanks, and a gray-brown iris; juv ♀ = ♂, although juv ♀♀ may average duller yellow in the lores than juv ♂♂.

HY/SY (Aug-Jul): Outer pp covs narrow, tapered, relatively abraded, and brown with indistinct, narrow, or no pale brown edging (Fig. 138), contrasting with the slightly fresher and dusky-centered gr covs (Fig. 134); outer rects tapered (Fig. 139**B**) and relatively abraded; central breast sometimes (Aug-Mar), or occasionally (Mar-Jul), with distinct streaking; iris gray-brown to brown (through Feb). **Note: In addition, variation in the head plumage by age and sex occurs, but is complicated by plumage dichromatism (bright and dull plumages) and individual variation. In all plumages, but especially basic (Aug-Mar), AHY/ASYs and ♂♂ generally have bolder black and white head patterns, brighter and more yellow on the lores, whiter throats, and grayer and less streaked breasts than HY/SYs and ♀♀. With experience and comparison with the other age/sex criteria, plumage can prove useful for ageing some known-sex birds and vice versa. But this should not be attempted without a full understanding of the dichromatic plumage variations exhibited. For more information, see Lowther (1961), Vardy (1971), Kuenzel & Helms (1974), Atkinson & Ralph (1980), Rising & Shields (1980), Watt (1986), and Piper & Wiley (1989a).**

AHY/ASY (Aug-Jul): Outer pp covs broad, truncate, relatively fresh, and dusky brown with relatively distinct and broad, pale rufous edging (Fig. 138); rects uniformly adult, truncate (Fig. 139**B**), and relatively fresh; central breast usually without distinct streaking; iris reddish brown. **Note: See HY/SY concerning plumage dichromatism.**

Sex—CP/BP (May-Aug). ♀ wg(n100) 64-72, tl(n20) 67-75; ♂ wg(n100) 69-78, tl(n20) 70-78. ♀♀ average duller and more streaked than ♂♂, especially in the head plumage, but differences probably are not reliable for sexing without experience and an understanding of the plumage dichromatism in this species (see HY/SY, above). See also Schlinger & Adler (1990) for a multiple logistic regression, using wg and color of the crown stripes, that separated 87% of birds (primarily specimens) to sex.

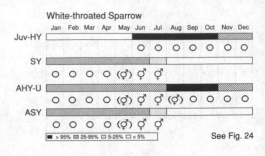

White-throated Sparrow

Hybrids reported—Golden-crowned Sparrow, Harris's Sparrow, Dark-eyed Junco. A reported hybrid with White-crowned Sparrow probably was based on an anomalous White-crowned Sparrow.

References—Stone (1896), Dwight (1900a), Ridgway (1901), Forbush (1929), Law (1929), Nice (1932), Odum (1949), Wolfson (1952), Snyder (1954), Roberts (1955), Sibley (1956), Abbott (1959), Lowther (1961), Short & Simon (1965), J.K. Lowther *in Bent et al.* (1968), Mellancamp (1969), Wood (1969), Banks (1970a), Vardy (1971), Kuenzel & Helms (1974), Oberholser (1974), Sheppard & Klimkiewicz (1976), Yunick (1977a), Payne (1979), Atkinson & Ralph (1980), Rising & Shields (1980), Blem (1981b), Prescott (1986), Watt (1986), Piper & Wiley (1989a, 1989b, 1991), Brewer (1990), Schlinger & Adler (1990), Yunick (1990), CWS & USFWS (1991), Wiley & Piper (1992), Parkes (1993), Cramp & Perrins (1994b), Falls & Kopachena (1994), Jung *et al.* (1994), Byers *et al.* (1995), Rising (1996a), Pyle (1997c); D.H. Baldwin, J.K. Lowther (*in litt.* to the BBL); IBP (MAPS) data, PNR data, PRBO data.

HARRIS' SPARROW
Zonotrichia querula

HASP
Species # 5530
Band size: 1A

Geographic variation—No subspecies are recognized.

Molt— PB: HY partial (Jul-Oct), AHY complete (Jul-Oct); PA limited-partial (Mar-May). The PBs occur on the summer grounds. The 1st PB usually includes all med and gr covs, but no terts or rects. Beware of pseudolimits (see p. 207) between the richer brown terts and inner gr covs, and the duller brown middle ss (s4-s6) and gr covs, which causes the inner feathers to appear more recently replaced. The 1st PA includes 0 (~80%) to 2 inner gr covs, 2-3 terts, and usually (in ~87% of birds) 1-2 central rects (r1). The adult PA typically includes 0 (~80%) to 2 inner gr covs, all 3 terts, and the 2 central rects (r1).

Skull—Pneumaticization completes in HY/SY from 15 Nov through Feb.

Age—Juv (Jul-Aug) has fine, dusky streaking on the underparts; juv ♀ = ♂.

HY/SY (Sep-Aug): Crown primarily brown, with black scalloping (Sep-Apr), or primarily black, with the lores and the supercilium in front of the eye buffy brownish and the chin and throat white or predominantly white (Apr-Aug); outer pp covs narrow, tapered, relatively abraded, and brown with indistinct or no pale edging (Fig. 138), contrasting with the slightly fresher gr covs (Fig. 134); outer rects tapered (Fig. 139**B**) and relatively abraded. **Note: A few intermediates will be difficult to age in May-Aug when plumage becomes worn.**

AHY/ASY (Sep-Aug): Crown primarily black (with some brown or whitish streaking in Sep-Mar) or entirely black, the lores and the supercilium in front of the eye black or blackish, and the chin and throat with light to heavy, black mottling (occasionally all white, in some ♀♀ only?); outer pp covs broad, truncate, relatively fresh, and dusky brown with relatively distinct, pale edging (Fig. 138), not contrasting in wear with the gr covs in Sep-Mar (Fig. 133**F**); outer rects truncate (Fig. 139**B**) and relatively fresh. **Note: See HY/SY.**

Sex—CP/BP (May-Sep). Measurements are useful: ♀ wg(n100) 76-85, tl(n20) 75-83; ♂ wg(n100) 82-91, tl(n20) 78-88. ♀♀ average less black in the throat and head than ♂♂, especially in basic plumage (Aug-Apr), but too much variation apparently exists for reliable sexing by plumage alone. It is possible that birds can be reliably sexed by a formula including wg and amount of black in the plumage, but details need to be worked out. Otherwise, no plumage criteria are known for sexing.

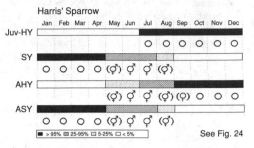

Harris' Sparrow

Hybrids reported—White-throated Sparrow, White-crowned Sparrow.

See Fig. 24

References—Ridgway (1901), Forbush (1929), Law (1929), Swenk & Stevens (1929), Harkins (1937), Roberts (1955), Woolfenden (1955), A.M. Baumgartner *in* Bent *et al.* (1968), Rohwer (1973), Oberholser (1974), Rohwer & Rohwer (1978), Payne (1979), Rohwer *et al.* (1981), deGraw & Kern (1990), Norment & Shackleton (1993), Byers *et al.* (1995), Norment (1995), Rising (1996a), Pyle (1997c); S. Fretwell, M.V. Jones, S.A. Rohwer, J.M. Sheppard (*in litt.* to the BBL); C. Norment (pers. comm.); PRBO data.

WHITE-CROWNED SPARROW
Zonotrichia leucophrys

WCSP
Species # 5540
Band size: 1B

Gambel's White-crowned Sparrow (GWCS)	Species # 5550
Puget Sound White-crowned Sparrow (PSWS)	Species # 5547
Nuttall's White-crowned Sparrow (NWCS)	Species # 5560
Mountain White-crowned Sparrow (MWCS)	Species # 5546
Eastern White-crowned Sparrow (EWCS)	Species # 5541

Species—Juv from juv Golden-crowned Sparrow by forehead without yellow; well-defined, dark brown lateral crown stripes present.

Geographic variation—Moderately well marked and most ranges are well defined. Subspecies taxonomy follows Paynter (1970); see also Ridgway (1901), Grinnell (1928c), Swenk (1930b), Oberholser (1932, 1974), Taverner & Sutton (1934), Miller (1941a), Rand (1948a, 1948b), Todd (1948, 1953, 1963), Banks (1964), Phillips *et al.* (1964), Godfrey (1965, 1986), Browning (1974, 1978, 1979a, 1990), Mewaldt (1977), Rea (1983), Behle (1985), Corbin & Wilkie (1988), Lein & Corbin (1990), Byers *et al.* (1995), Dunn *et al.* (1995), Rising (1996a), Pyle (1997a, 1997c). No other subspecies occur. Note that the established taxonomy, where *leucophrys* (*vs* "*nigrilora*") refers to the eastern birds and *gambelii* to the northwestern birds is followed here, even though the reverse probably is correct; see Todd (1948, 1953, 1963), Wetmore (1953), Banks (1964), Phillips *et al.* (1964), Monson & Phillips (1981), Rea (1983) and Dunn *et al.* (1995). In the following, "lean weight" refers to the total weight minus fat deposits in gms. To calculate lean weight, subtract 0 to 8 gms from the total weight for no to substantial (bulging from the furculum) fat present, respectively. See also **Molt**.

Z.l. gambelii (br AK-BC to NWT-n.Man, wint to CA-TX; vag to MA-FL): **Gambel's White-crowned Sparrow.** Large; bill small (nares to tip 7.0-8.3); wing morphology long (p5 – p9 -5 to 3 mm); upperparts medium-dark grayish brown and reddish; upper lores pale grayish brown (HY) to white (AHY), not contrasting with the supercilium; auricular of HY moderately distinct and grayish-brown; bend of the wing pale grayish, sometimes tinged yellow; underwing covs silvery gray; breast pale, bright brownish (HY) to gray (AHY); bill pinkish to tawny. ♀ wg(n100) 69-79, tl(n20) 64-73; ♂ wg(n100) 74-84, tl(n20) 67-76.

Z.l. pugetensis (br coastal sw.BC-nw.CA, wint to coastal sw.CA): **Puget Sound White-crowned Sparrow.** Small; bill small (nares to tip 7.0-8.3); wg ÷ lean weight (see above) > 2.6 (mm/gm); wing morphology short (p5 – p9 by -1 to 7 mm); crown of SY (Mar-Jul) black and white, with little or no brown; upperparts medium-dull brown and olive; upper lores pale grayish brown (HY) or white (AHY), not contrasting with the supercilium; auricular of HY indistinct and brownish-gray; bend of the wing yellowish and brown; underwing covs brown with a yellowish wash; breast medium-dull brownish (HY) to grayish brown (AHY); bill yellowish to orange-yellow. ♀ wg(n100) 64-72, tl(n10) 62-70; ♂ wg(n100) 67-75, tl(n10) 64-74.

Z.l. nuttalli (res coastal cw.CA, Sonoma-Santa Barbara Cos): **Nuttall's White-crowned Sparrow.** Small; bill large (nares to tip 7.4-8.8); wg ÷ lean weight (see above) ≤ 2.6 (mm/gm); wing morphology short (p5 – p9 2-9 mm); plumage and bill color similar to *pugetensis*, except that the crown of SY in Mar-Jul is mixed brown, black, and white (see **Age**). ♀ wg(n100) 63-71, tl(n20) 62-71; ♂ wg(n100) 67-75, tl(n20) 65-74.

Z.l. oriantha (br montane sw.Alb to e.CA-nw.NM, wint s.CA-sw.TX): **Mountain White-crowned Sparrow.** Large; tl relatively long; bill large (nares to tip 7.4-8.8); wing morphology medium long (p5 – p9 -4 to 3 mm); upperparts medium-pale brownish and reddish; upper lores dark gray to dark brown (HY) to black (AHY), contrasting with the pale gray or white supercilium; auricular of HY distinct and brown; breast medium-pale grayish with a brown wash; bill brownish pink. ♀ wg(n100) 69-78, tl(n12) 67-74; ♂ wg(n100) 73-82, tl(n10) 70-78. Birds breeding in ID-nw.WY ("*aphaea*") average darker, but differences are slight and broadly clinal; the possible placement of this population with *leucophrys* (Browning 1974, 1978, 1990) requires further study.

Z.l. leucophrys (= "*nigrilora*"; br n.Ont-Nfl, wint KS-TX to MD-FL; vag to AZ): **Eastern White-crowned Sparrow.** Large; tl relatively short; bill medium large (nares to tip 7.3-8.6); wing morphology medium long (p5 – p9 -3 to 5 mm); upperparts medium-dark grayish brown and reddish; upper lores dark gray to dark brown (HY) or black (AHY), contrasting with the pale gray or white supercilium; auricular of HY moderately distinct and brownish; breast medium-dark brown; bill pinkish. ♀ wg(n100) 70-80, tl(n12) 63-72; ♂ wg(n100) 73-83, tl(n24) 66-75.

Molt—PB: HY partial (Jul-Oct), AHY complete (Jul-Oct); PA partial (Jan-May). The PBs occur on the summer grounds; the adult PB begins earlier in ♂♂ than in ♀♀ and is more protracted in *Z.l. nuttalli* than in the other subspecies. The 1st PB usually includes all med and gr covs, sometimes (in ~34% of birds) 1-3 terts, and sometimes (in ~30% of birds) 1-2 central rects (r1). The PAs include 0 (~25%) to 8 inner gr covs, usually (in ~91% of birds) 1-3 terts, and often (in ~56% of birds) 1-2 central rects (r1). The 1st PA can complete on the summer grounds in the migratory species. The PAs are similar between the two age groups but differ in extent by geography. In *gambelii*, *oriantha*, and *leucophrys*, 3-7 gr covs and 2-3 terts are replaced and the central rects (r1) usually (in ~84% of birds) are replaced, whereas in *pugetensis* and, especially, *nuttalli*, fewer feathers are replaced on average: Typically, 0-3 gr covs and terts, and only occasionally (in ~17% of birds) the central rects (r1). Replacement of head feathers is also more restricted in *nuttalli* than in the other subspecies (see **Age**).

Skull—Pneumaticization completes in HY/SY from 15 Nov (as early as 15 Oct in *Z.l. nuttalli*) through Jan.

Age—Juv (May-Aug) has distinct, dusky streaking on the breast and crown; juv ♀ = ♂.

HY/SY (Sep-Aug): Crown stripes brown (Sep-Apr), or black and white (Apr-Aug; see below); 1-3 terts sometimes replaced, contrasting with the older middle ss in Sep-Mar (s4-s6; Fig. 133**D-E**, although beware of pseudolimits in AHY/ASYs); outer pp covs narrow, tapered, relatively abraded, and brown with indistinct, narrow, or no pale edging (Fig. 138), contrasting with the slightly fresher gr covs in Sep-Mar (Fig. 134); outer rects tapered (Fig. 139**B**) and relatively abraded. **Note: In Apr-Aug, SYs of *Z.l. nuttalli* show substantial brown in the hind crown (*vs* entirely black and white in ASYs) and can be reliably aged based on this feature. Occasional SYs of the other subspecies (more so in *pugetensis*) can show a few brown feathers in the hindcrown (especially in May during completion of the molt, and sometimes following migration) and also are reliably aged SY (although just one or two isolated brown feathers may indicate adventitious loss in either age group in May-Jun?; more study is needed). Also, note that both SYs and ASYs can show contrasting gr covs, terts, and rects in Apr-Aug (see Molt); the shape and condition of the pp covs and rects are the only ageing criteria (for subspecies other than *nuttalli*) at this time.**

AHY/ASY (Sep-Aug): Crown black and white, without brown feathers; terts and middle ss (s4-s6) uniformly adult in Sep-Apr (Fig. 133**F**, although beware of a pseudolimit between the richer brown terts and the more faded brown s5-s6); outer pp covs broad, truncate, relatively fresh, and dusky brown with relatively distinct and broad, pale edging (Fig. 138); outer rects truncate (Fig. 139**B**) and relatively fresh.
   Note: See HY/SY.

Sex—♀ = ♂ by plumage. CP/BP (Mar-Sep). ♀ wg(n100) 63-80, tl(n100) 62-74; ♂ wg(n100) 67-84, tl(n100) 64-78.

Hybrids reported—Song Sparrow, Golden-crowned Sparrow, Harris' Sparrow. Rufous-collared Sparrow (*Z. capensis*) in captivity. A reported hybrid with White-throated Sparrow probably was based on an anomalous White-crowned Sparrow.

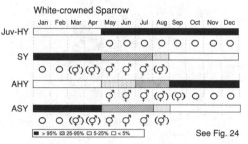

White-crowned Sparrow

See Fig. 24

Note: In May-Aug, all birds of the Nuttall's subspecies (*Z.l. nuttalli*) should be aged but only some birds of the other subspecies can be aged.

References—Stone (1896), Dwight (1900a), Ridgway (1901), Grinnell (1914a, 1928c), Swarth (1926a), Forbush (1929), Law (1929), Miller (1940), Blanchard (1941), Michener & Michener (1943), Norris (1954), Roberts (1955), Abbott (1959), Morton & Mewaldt (1960), Dickerman (1961), Banks (1964, 1970a), R.C. Clement & B.B. DeWolfe *in* Bent *et al.* (1968), Mewaldt *et al.* (1968), Morton *et al.* (1969), Wood (1969), Ralph & Pearson (1971), Mewaldt (1973, 1977), Morton & Welton (1973), Oberholser (1974), Sheppard & Klimkiewicz (1976), Mewaldt & King (1977, 1978a, 1978b, 1986), Payne (1979), Fugle & Rothstein (1985), Morton & Morton (1990), Morton (1992), Barrentine *et al.* (1993), Byers *et al.* (1995), Chilton *et al.* (1995), Dunn *et al.* (1995), Rising (1996a), Pyle (1997c); J. Church, E.J. Fisk, L.R. Mewaldt, S.H. Spofford (*in litt.* to the BBL); A. Jesse, A.R. Phillips (pers. comm.); IBP (MAPS) data, PNR data, PRBO data.

GOLDEN-CROWNED SPARROW
Zonotrichia atricapilla

GCSP
Species # 5570
Band size: 1B-1A

Species—Juv from juv White-crowned Sparrow by forehead usually with at least a faint yellow tinge; lateral crown stripes very indistinct or lacking.

Geographic variation—No subspecies are recognized.

Molt—PB: HY partial (Jul-Nov), AHY complete (Jul-Nov); PA partial (Feb-May). The PBs occur primarily on the summer grounds but can be suspended and completed on the winter grounds. The 1st PB usually includes all med and gr covs, but no terts or rects. Beware of pseudolimits (see

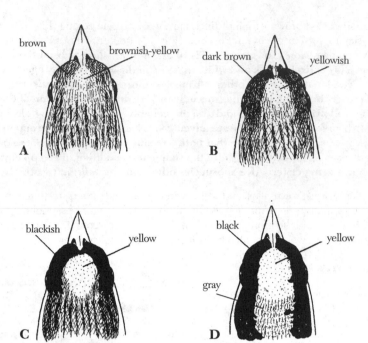

FIGURE 300. Variation in the head plumage by age and season (and to a lesser extent, sex) in Golden-crowned Sparrow. See text for details.

p. 207) between the richer brown terts and inner gr covs, and the duller brown middle ss (s4-s6) and gr covs, which causes the inner feathers to appear more recently replaced. The 1st PA includes 2-6 inner gr covs, 2-3 terts, and often (in ~56% of birds) 1-2 central rects (r1). The adult PA includes 2-4 inner gr covs, 1-3 terts, and occasionally (in ~20% of birds) 1-2 central rects (r1).

Skull—Pneumaticization completes in HY/SY from 15 Nov through Jan.

Age—Juv (Jul-Sep) has distinct streaking on the upper breast and flanks; juv ♀ = ♂.

HY/SY (Aug-Jul): Crown stripes entirely absent, or with a hint of light brown restricted to the area above the lores, in Aug-Apr (Fig. 300A); outer pp covs narrow, tapered, relatively abraded, and brown with indistinct or no pale edging (Fig. 138), contrasting with the slightly fresher gr covs (Fig. 134); outer rects tapered (Fig. 139B) and relatively abraded. **Note: There is some overlap in the crown plumage between the darkest HY/SYs and the lightest AHY/ASYs in Aug-Apr (Fig. 300B); in Apr-Jul the crowns are similar in both age groups (Fig. 300C-D), averaging slightly duller in SYs (see also Sex). Also, note that both SYs and ASYs can have contrastingly fresh terts and central rects (r1) in Apr-Jul, although the proportion of SYs that replace rects at the 1st PA is higher than that of ASYs (see Molt). A few intermediates will be difficult to age, especially in May-Jul when plumage becomes worn.**

AHY/ASY (Aug-Jul): Crown stripes usually with at least some black extending above the lores to at least the eye in Aug-Apr (Fig. 300C-D); outer pp covs broad, truncate, relatively fresh, and dusky brown with relatively distinct, pale edging (Fig. 138), not contrasting in wear with the gr covs (Fig. 133F); outer rects truncate (Fig. 139B) and relatively fresh. **Note: See HY/SY.**

Sex—CP/BP (May-Aug). ♀ wg(n100) 71-81, tl(n40) 70-80; ♂ wg(n100) 76-84, tl(n57) 74-83. In both basic and alternate plumages (see Age), the crown stripes of AHY/ASY ♀♀ average duller black, gray, and yellow than in AHY/ASY ♂♂, but substantial overlap precludes reliable sexing of individuals. Otherwise, no plumage criteria are known.

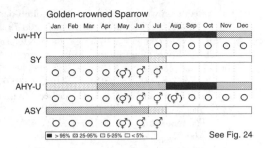

Hybrids reported—White-throated Sparrow, White-crowned Sparrow.

References—Ridgway (1901), Swarth (1926a), Forbush (1929), Law (1929), Mailliard (1932), Miller (1940), Sibley (1956), Morton & Mewaldt (1960), J.W. Kelly *in* Bent *et al.* (1968), Stewart (1972a, 1972b), Oberholser (1974), Payne (1979), Byers *et al.* (1995), Rising (1996a), Pyle (1997c); H.L. Cogswell (*in litt.* to the BBL); T. & J. Heindel (pers. comm.); IBP (MAPS) data, PRBO data.

DARK-EYED JUNCO
Junco hyemalis

See below
Band size: 0-1C-1

Oregon Junco (ORJU)	Species # 5671
Gray-headed Junco (GHJU)	Species # 5690
White-winged Junco (WWJU)	Species # 5660
Slate-colored Junco (SCJU)	Species # 5670
Unidentified Dark-eyed Junco (UDEJ)	Species # 5677

Species—Juv of *J.h. dorsalis* from juv Yellow-eyed Junco by terts and gr covs edged dull buffy brown, sometimes tinged cinnamon, and tipped whitish.

Geographic variation—Well marked, but broadly clinal and differences are obscured by age/sex-related and individual variation in plumage. Subspecies taxonomy follows Paynter (1970), as modified by Monson & Phillips (1981) and Browning (1990); see also Ridgway (1901), Swarth (1912b, 1922), Dwight (1918), van Rossem (1931b), Miller (1936, 1939a, 1941c, 1955a), Wetmore (1937), Twomey (1942), Dickinson (1953), Parkes (1954), Phillips (1959b, 1961a), Phillips *et al.* (1964), Bailey & Niedrach (1965), Sutton (1967), Short (1969a), Browning (1974), Oberholser (1974), D.M. Power (1980), Rea (1983), Unitt (1984), Behle (1985), Godfrey (1986), Kolb (1986), Mulvihill & Chandler (1991), Cramp & Perrins (1994b), Byers *et al.* (1995), Rising (1996a), Mulvihill & Winstead (1997). Two to three other subspecies occur in Baja CA, depending on the species taxonomy. In addition to the following, wing morphology (*e.g.*, longest p – p9) varies geographically and may provide a useful means of separating subspecies; more study is needed. See also differences in the 1st PB by subspecies.

Oregon (*J.h. oreganus*) Group. Small; head gray to black; back brown.
J.h. oreganus (br coastal se.AK-wc.BC, wint to coastal CA): **Oregon Junco.** Medium small; head (including the lores) medium gray (♀ and HYs) to black (AHY/ASY ♂); back and flanks bright, medium pinkish brown (♀ and HYs), to medium-dark reddish brown (AHY/ASY ♂). ♀ wg(n100) 67-75, tl(n45) 58-67; ♂ wg(n100) 71-79, tl(n84) 62-70.
J.h. simillimus (br coastal sw.BC-cw.OR, wint to CA-AZ): **Oregon Junco.** Medium small; head (including the lores) medium-pale gray (♀ and HYs) to slaty black (AHY/ASY ♂); back and flanks dull, medi-

um pinkish brown (♀ and HYs), to medium-dark brown with a reddish tinge (AHY/ASY ♂). ♀ wg(n100) 67-75, tl(n30) 58-67; ♂ wg(n100) 69-79, tl(n66) 63-71.

J.h. thurberi (br coastal sw.OR-nw.CA to wc.NV-coastal sw.CA, wint to NM): **Oregon Junco.** Medium small; head (including the lores) medium gray (♀ and HYs) to blackish (AHY ♂); back and flanks bright, pale pinkish brown (♀ and HYs), to medium-pale cinnamon-brown (AHY/ASY ♂). ♀ wg(n100) 68-76, tl(n45) 61-69; ♂ wg(n100) 72-80, tl(n100) 65-73.

J.h. pinosus (res coastal cw.CA, San Francisco-Monterey Cos): **Oregon Junco.** Small; head (including the lores) medium gray (♀ and HYs) to dark slate (AHY/ASY ♂); back and flanks pale cinnamon-brown (♀ and HYs) to medium reddish brown (AHY/ASY ♂). ♀ wg(n50) 65-73, tl(n46) 57-66; ♂ wg(n72) 69-75, tl(n67) 60-70.

J.h. shufeldti (= "*montanus*"; br interior c.BC-sw.Alb to ne.OR-MT, wint to CA-TX): **Oregon Junco.** Medium in size; head medium-dark gray (♀ and HYs) to dark slate (AHY/ASY ♂), the lores contrastingly dusky; back medium brown, tinged (♀ and HYs) to washed (AHY/ASY ♂) dull grayish cinnamon; flanks medium brown with a pinkish-cinnamon tinge. ♀ wg(n100) 70-78, tl(n56) 61-70; ♂ wg(n100) 74-84, tl(n100) 65-75. Birds of BC-OR ("*eumesus*") average paler, but differences are slight and due to intergradation with *simillimus*.

Pink-sided (*J.h. mearnsi*) Group. Large; head pale gray; back washed pinkish.

J.h. mearnsi (br se.Alb-sw.Sask to e.ID-nw.WY, wint to e.CA-sw.TX): **Oregon Junco.** Large; head medium-pale gray (♀ and HYs) to pale slate (AHY/ASY ♂), the lores contrastingly blackish; back medium brown, tinged (♀ and HYs) to washed (AHY/ASY ♂) pinkish; flanks pinkish. ♀ wg(n54) 73-81, tl(n53) 65-74; ♂ wg(n82) 77-86, tl(n81) 68-78.

Gray-headed (*J.h. caniceps*) Group. Medium large; back rufous.

J.h. caniceps (br s.ID-se.CA to s.WY-n.NM, wint to se.CA-sw.TX): **Gray-headed Junco.** Medium large; head and flanks medium-pale grayish, the lores contrastingly black; back bright rufous; bill whitish. ♀ wg(n93) 72-80, tl(n10) 64-74; ♂ wg(n100) 76-86, tl(n100) 68-79. Birds of se.CA-s.NV ("*mutabilis*") average darker and duller but differences are due to slight intergradation with *thurberi*.

J.h. dorsalis (br & wint nc.AZ-sw.TX): **Gray-headed Junco.** Large; head and flanks pale grayish, the lores contrastingly black; back bright rufous; bill dusky. ♀ wg(n50) 75-82, tl(n50) 69-77; ♂ wg(n100) 78-87, tl(n100) 72-82.

White-winged (*J.h. aikeni*) Group. Very large; gray with white wing bars.

J.h. aikeni (br se.MT-ne.WY to w.SD-nw.NE, wint to n.AZ-w.OK): **White-winged Junco.** Very large; head, back, and flanks pale gray with a brown wash (♀ and HYs) to gray (AHY/ASY ♂); distinct, white wing bars present; r4 primarily to entirely white. ♀ wg(n57) 78-88, tl(n40) 72-82; ♂ wg(n78) 82-92, tl(n58) 75-85.

Slate-colored (*J.h. hyemalis*) Group. Medium in size; slate; without white wing bars.

J.h. cismontanus (="*henshawi*"; br interior s.Yuk to c.BC-wc.Alb, wint to CA-TX; vag to MA-VA-LA): **Slate-colored Junco.** Medium in size; head (including the lores) medium-dark brownish slate (♀ and HYs) to slate (AHY/ASY ♂); back and flanks medium (♀ and HYs) to dark (AHY/ASY ♂) gray, with a brown tinge. ♀ wg(n40) 72-79, tl(n38) 62-69; ♂ wg(n46) 75-83, tl(n44) 66-74.

J.h. hyemalis (br nw.AK-c.Alb to Nfl-MA, wint to CA-n.FL): **Slate-colored Junco.** Medium in size; head, lores, back, and flanks dark grayish brown (♀ and HYs) to dark slate (AHY/ASY ♂); wings without distinct, white wing bars (a few white tips to the gr covs occasionally can occur); r4 primarily dusky; bill pale pinkish to whitish. ♀ wg(n100) 69-77, tl(n65) 61-70; ♂ wg(n100) 73-82, tl(n100) 64-74.

J.h. carolinensis (br montane e.WV-w.MD to n.GA-nw.SC, wint to c.MD-e.SC): **Slate-colored Junco.** Medium large; head, back, and flanks medium-pale brownish gray (♀ and HYs) to medium-pale slate (AHY/ASY ♂); wings without distinct, white wing bars; r4 primarily dusky; bill medium-dark grayish horn. ♀ wg(n66) 71-80, tl(n46) 65-73; ♂ wg(n100) 76-84, tl(n87) 68-77.

Molt—PB: HY partial (Jul-Oct), AHY complete (Jul-Oct); PA limited (Feb-Apr). The PBs occur primarily on the summer grounds. The 1st PB includes most to all med covs, 3 to 10 (~69%) inner gr covs, sometimes (in ~21% of birds) 1-2 (rarely 3) terts, and occasionally (in ~6% of birds) 1-2 central rects (r1). The extent of the 1st PB varies geographically: Southern subspecies (*e.g., J.h. caniceps, dorsalis,* and *carolinensis*) typically replace all 10 gr covs and 1-3 terts whereas subspecies to the north can replace fewer gr covs and only occasionally replace

1-2 terts (if so, often just s9). ♂♂ also may replace more feathers on average than ♀♀ replace; more study is needed. Up to 3 pp covs and 3 middle ss (among s4-s6) rarely can be retained during the adult PB; this likely occurs more often during the 2nd PB than during subsequent adult PBs (more study is needed). The PAs are limited to body feathers (primarily around the head), and include no wing covs or flight feathers.

Skull—Pneumaticization completes in HY/SY from 1 Nov (as early as 1 Oct in birds of the Oregon Subspecies Group; see **Geographic variation**). Some SYs can show windows (> 2 mm; Fig. 11**D**) on the top of the skull into summer and (rarely) fall.

Age/Sex—Juv (May-Sep) has plumage with distinct streaking; juv ♀ = ♂. CP/BP (Mar-Sep). See **Geographic variation** for measurements by sex within each subspecies group.

HY/SY ♀ (Aug-Jul): Head, throat, and upper breast relatively pale gray or pale blackish, with a moderately heavy to heavy brown wash depending on the subspecies (see **Geographic variation**), usually > 50% brown (Aug-Mar), or primarily dark gray with a slight brownish wash (Mar-Jul); molt limits sometimes occur among the med and gr covs (Fig. 133**B-E**; see **Molt**), the retained outer covs worn, brownish with buff corners, contrasting with the fresher and duskier, replaced inner covs, without buff corners; 1-3 terts sometimes replaced (especially in southern subspecies; see **Molt**), contrasting with the older middle ss (s4-s6; Fig. 133**D-E**), or if all juvenal terts are retained, these are relatively worn and brownish; outer pp covs narrow, tapered, relatively abraded, and brownish with indistinct, narrow, or no pale edging (Fig. 138), contrasting with the duskier and slightly fresher, replaced gr covs; outer rects somewhat tapered (Fig. 139**B**) and relatively abraded; iris grayish brown to brown (through Oct-Mar). **Note: By combining plumage with measurements by subspecies (see Geographic variation), many birds can be reliably aged and sexed. Differences in the shape of the rects can be very subtle, however, and many intermediates will occur (especially in the White-winged and Gray-headed subspecies groups) which cannot be reliably determined. The amount of white in the rects also varies by age and sex, less in HY/SY ♀♀ to more in AHY/ASY ♂♂ (see Miller 1941c, Wood 1951, Yunick 1972, Pyle et al. 1987, Cramp & Perrins 1994b, Byers et al. 1995), but differences appear to be obscured by too much individual and geographic variation for reliable use in ageing.**

AHY/ASY ♀ (Aug-Jul): Head, throat, and upper breast pale to medium gray or dull blackish, with a moderate amount to little brown wash depending on the subspecies (see **Geographic variation**), usually 25-50% brown (Aug-Mar), or slightly tinged brown (Mar-Jul); wing covs, terts, and middle ss (s4-s6) uniformly adult (Fig. 133**F**), dusky with brown (western subspecies) to gray (eastern subspecies) edging; outer pp covs broad, truncate, relatively fresh, and dusky brown with relatively distinct and broad, brown to gray edging (Fig. 138), not contrasting markedly in color or wear with the gr covs (Fig. 133**F**); outer rects truncate (Fig. 139**B**), relatively fresh; iris reddish brown to dark red. **Note: See HY/SY ♀.**

HY/SY ♂ (Aug-Jul): Head, throat, and upper breast pale to medium gray or dull blackish, with a moderate amount or no brown wash depending on the subspecies (see **Geographic variation**), usually 15-40% brown (Aug-Mar), or dark with little or no brownish wash (Mar-Jul); molt-limit, wing-cov, flight-feather, and iris-color criteria as in HY/SY ♀. **Note: See HY/SY ♀.**

AHY/ASY ♂ (Aug-Jul): Head, throat, and upper breast relatively dark gray or black depending on the subspecies (see **Geographic variation**), with little (Aug-Mar), or no (Mar-Jul), brownish wash; molt-limit, wing-cov, flight-feather, and iris-color criteria as in AHY/ASY ♀. **Note: See HY/SY ♀.**

Hybrids reported—White-throated Sparrow.

References—Dwight (1900a), Ridgway (1901), Forbush (1929), Nice (1932), Miller (1941c), Wood (1951), Snyder (1954), Roberts (1955), Blake (1962c, 1964, 1967), Short & Simon (1965), Dow (1966), N.R. Whitney Jr., S.W. Eaton, A. Sprunt Jr., J.H. Phelps Jr., & D.M. Thatcher *in* Bent *et al.* (1968), Wood (1969), Grant & Quay (1970), Yunick (1972, 1976b, 1977a, 1977b, 1981c, 1984), Oberholser (1974), Balph (1975), Ketterson & Nolan (1976, 1982, 1986), Brackbill (1977), Ryan (1978), Ketterson (1979), Prescott (1979), Kolb (1980), Blem (1981b), Nolan & Ketterson (1983, 1990), Mulvihill & Chandler (1990), Chandler & Mulvihill (1992), Cristol & Evers (1992), Nolan *et al.* (1992), Cramp & Perrins (1994b), Jung *et al.* (1994), Byers *et al.* (1995), Rising (1996a), Mulvihill & Winstead (1997), Pyle (1997c); J. Baird, C. Barrows, C.H. Blake, H. du Mont, E.J. Fisk, E.D. Ketterson, M. Killpack, D.E. Payne, M. Plymire, B.A. Sorrie, N.R. Whitney, R.B. Williams (*in litt.* to the BBL); J. Curson, R.S. Mulvihill, A.R. Phillips (pers. comm.); IBP (MAPS) data, PNR data, PRBO data, R.P. Yunick data.

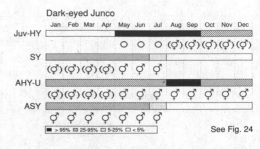

YELLOW-EYED JUNCO
Junco phaeonotus

YEJU
Species # 5700
Band size: 1C

Species—Juv from juv Dark-eyed Junco (subspecies *J.h. dorsalis*) by terts and gr covs edged and tipped bright rufous.

Geographic variation—Moderate, but clinal where ranges meet. Subspecies taxonomy follows Paynter (1970); see Ridgway (1901), Miller (1941c), Byers *et al.* (1995), Howell & Webb (1995). Four other subspecies occur in Mex-C.Am.

   J.p. palliatus (res se.AZ-sw.NM): From subspecies of Mex-C.Am by the combination of larger size (see **Age/Sex**, *vs* wg 64-74, tl 58-68 in the subspecies of Mex-C.Am); plumage paler; white of the rects more extensive (inner web of r6 usually all white, that of r5 usually > 50% white); belly grayish, not contrasting with the color of the flanks (*vs* whitish, often contrasting with the brownish flanks in the subspecies of Mex-C.Am).

Molt—PB: HY partial (Jul-Sep), AHY complete (Jul-Sep); PA limited (Feb-Apr). The 1st PB usually includes all med and gr covs and often (in ~53% of birds) 1-3 terts, but no rects; look for 1-2 central rects (r1) to be replaced in a small proportion of birds, as in Dark-eyed Junco. The PAs are limited to body feathers (primarily around the head), and include no wing covs or flight feathers.

Skull—Pneumaticization completes in HY/SY from 15 Oct through Jan.

Age/Sex—Juv (May-Sep) has plumage with heavy, dusky streaking; juv ♀ = ♂. CP/BP (Mar-Aug). ♀ wg(n100) 72-82, tl(n71) 68-77; ♂ wg(n100) 75-85, tl(n100) 70-79; measurements apply to *J.p. palliatus* only (see **Geographic variation**).

   HY/SY ♀ (Aug-Jul): Head, throat, and upper breast dull brownish-gray, often with one or more dusky streaks or spots in the crown; 1-3 terts often replaced, contrasting with the older middle ss (s4-s6; Fig. 133**D-E**), or if all juvenal terts are retained, these are relatively worn and edged dull brownish; outer pp covs narrow, tapered, relatively abraded, and brownish dusky with indistinct, narrow, or no brownish gray edging (Fig. 138), contrasting with the slightly fresher gr covs (Fig. 134); outer rects tapered (Fig. 139**B**) and relatively abraded; iris olive-gray to grayish yellow (through Oct-Mar). **Note: Look for slight variation by age/sex class in the amount of white in the rects, as in Dark-eyed Junco. Some intermediate HY/SYs may be difficult to sex in Aug-Apr.**

AHY/ASY ♀ (Aug-Jul): Head, throat, and upper breast medium-dull grayish, without dusky streaks or spots; terts and middle ss (s4-s6) uniformly adult (Fig. 133**F**), edged bright rufous; outer pp covs broad, truncate, relatively fresh, and dusky with relatively distinct and broad, gray edging (Fig. 138), not contrasting in wear with the gr covs (Fig. 133**F**); outer rects truncate (Fig. 139**B**) and relatively fresh; iris yellow to orange-yellow. **Note: See HY/SY ♀.**

HY/SY ♂ (Aug-Jul): Head, throat, and upper breast medium-dull grayish, often with one or more dusky streaks or spots; pp-cov, flight-feather, and iris criteria as in HY/SY ♀. **Note: See HY/SY ♀.**

AHY/ASY ♂ (Aug-Jul): Head, throat, and upper breast bright gray, without dusky streaks or spots; pp-cov, flight-feather, and iris criteria as in AHY/ASY ♀. **Note: See HY/SY ♀.**

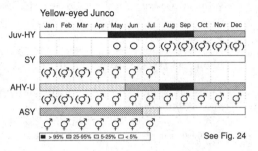

References—Ridgway (1901), Swarth (1904a), Miller (1941c), O.L. Austin Jr. *in* Bent *et al.* (1968), Lamm & Luepke (1982), Bowers & Dunning (1986), Byers *et al.* (1995), Rising (1996a), Pyle (1997c); J. Curson (pers. comm.).

McCOWN'S LONGSPUR
Calcarius mccownii

MCLO
Species # 5390
Band size: 1

Species— ♀♀ and HYs from the other longspurs by wg medium-large (80-94) but tl relatively short (44-57; see **Sex**); p7 – p6 3-6 mm; longest p – longest s 17-28 mm; bill large (exp culmen 10.6-13.2, depth at tip of nares 6.5-7.6) and pinkish (Aug-Mar), or black (Mar-Aug); med covs variably edged rufous (see Fig. 306); tail pattern with substantial white on r2-r6 (Fig. 301).

Geographic variation—No subspecies are recognized.

Molt—PB: HY partial (Jul-Sep), AHY complete (Jul-Sep); PA limited (Feb-Apr). The PBs occur on the summer grounds. The 1st PB usually includes all med and gr covs but no terts or rects. The PAs are limited to body feathers (primarily around the head and breast), and include no wing covs or flight feathers.

Skull—Pneumaticization completes in HY/SY from 1 Nov through Jan.

Age/Sex—Juv (Jun-Aug) has buff edging to

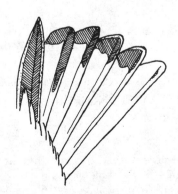

FIGURE 301. The pattern of white in the rectrices of McCown's Longspur.

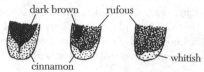

FIGURE 302. The pattern of the median coverts by age and sex in McCown's Longspur.

FIGURE 303. The pattern of the crown feathers by sex in basic-plumaged (Aug-Mar) McCown's Longspurs.

the back feathers and distinct streaking to the upper breast; juv ♀ = ♂. CP/BP (May-Aug). Wg is useful: ♀ wg(n30) 80-88, tl(n20) 44-52; ♂ wg(n30) 86-94, tl(n20) 47-57.

HY/SY ♀ (Aug-Jul): Crown and breast brown, with little or no black; crown feathers buffy brown with dark brown shaft streaks in Aug-Mar (Fig. 303); med covs dark brown with little to some cinnamon (Fig. 302); outer pp covs narrow, tapered, relatively abraded, and brown with indistinct, narrow, or no pale brown edging (Fig. 138), contrasting with the slightly fresher gr covs (Fig. 134); outer rects tapered (Fig. 139**B**) and relatively abraded. **Note: In addition, basic-plumaged HY/SYs average buffier than AHY/ASYs.**

AHY/ASY ♀ (Aug-Jul): Crown, breast, and med covs as in HY/SY ♀ (Figs. 302 & 303); outer pp covs broad, truncate, relatively fresh, and dusky with relatively distinct and broad, buffy white edging (Fig. 138), not contrasting in wear with the gr covs (Fig. 133**F**); outer rects truncate (Fig. 139**B**) and relatively fresh. **Note: See HY/SY ♀.**

HY/SY ♂ (Aug-Jul): Crown and breast brown with some black mottling (Aug-Mar), or black with some brown mottling (Mar-Jul); crown feathers blackish with white tips in Aug-Mar (Fig. 303); med covs largely rufous, often with some dark brown, and with cinnamon at the tip (Fig. 302); outer pp covs and rects as in HY/SY ♀. **Note: See HY/SY ♀.**

AHY/ASY ♂ (Aug-Jul): Crown and breast with brown mottling (Aug-Mar), or black (Mar-Jul); crown feathers black with white tipping in Aug-Mar (Fig. 303); med covs entirely or mostly rufous, with buffy or white at the tips (Fig. 302); outer pp covs and rects as in AHY/ASY ♀. **Note: See HY/SY ♀.**

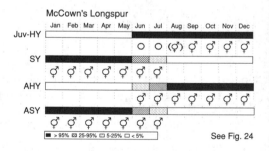

Hybrids reported—Chestnut-collared Longspur.

References—Ridgway (1901), Roberts (1955), Sibley & Pettingill (1955), H. Krause *in* Bent *et al.* (1968), Oberholser (1974), With (1994), Byers *et al.* (1995), Rising (1996a), Pyle (1997c).

LAPLAND LONGSPUR
Calcarius lapponicus

LALO
Species # 5360
Band size: 1B

Species—♀♀ and HYs from the other longspurs by large size (wg 82-101, tl 50-64; see **Age/Sex**); p7 – p6 5-8 mm; longest p – longest s 23-33 mm; bill medium large (exp culmen 10.1-12.4, depth at tip of nares 5.5-6.6) and brownish-pink (Aug-Mar), or yellowish (Mar-Aug); med covs edged dull whitish to buff; tail pattern with white restricted to r5-r6 (Fig. 304).

Geographic variation—Moderately weak and probably clinal where ranges meet. Subspecies taxonomy follows Cramp & Perrins (1994b); see also Ridgway (1901), Dement'ev & Gladkov (1954), Todd (1963), Oberholser (1974), Gibson (1986), Byers *et al.* (1995). Three other subspecies occur in Eurasia.

FIGURE 304. The pattern of white in the rectrices of Lapland Longspur.

C.l. coloratus (br vag to w.AK Is): Plumage dark; black streaking on back heavy; wing edging bright chestnut.

C.l. alascensis (br AK-nw.NWT, wint CA-TX): Plumage pale; black streaking on back sparse; wing edging grayish brown with a slight or no rufous tinge.

C.l. subcalcaratus (br nc.NWT-Man to n.Que-nw.Lab, wint TX-NC): Plumage medium dark; black streaking on back heavy; wing edging brownish with a rufous tinge.

Molt—PB: HY partial (Jul-Sep), AHY complete (Jul-Sep); PA limited (Mar-May). The PBs occur on the summer grounds. The 1st PB includes some to all med covs and 0 (~94%) to 2 inner gr covs, but no terts or rects. The PAs are limited to body feathers (primarily around the head and breast), and include no wing covs or flight feathers.

Skull—Pneumaticization completes in HY/SY from 15 Nov through Jan.

Age/Sex—Juv (Jul-Aug) has prominent streaking on the upper breast; juv ♀ = ♂. CP/BP (Jun-Aug). Measurements are useful: ♀ wg(n100) 82-94, tl(n67) 50-60; ♂ wg(n100) 88-101, tl(n58) 55-64.

HY/SY ♀ (Aug-Jul): Crown feathers with narrow (Aug-Mar), or broad (Mar-Jul), dusky shaft streaks (Fig. 305); nape buffy brownish with indistinct, dusky streaking; outer pp covs narrow, tapered, relatively abraded, and brownish dusky with indistinct, narrow, or no buffy-whitish edging (Fig. 138); outer rects tapered (Fig. 139**B**) and relatively abraded; upper breast with sparse, indistinct, dusky streaking (Aug-Mar), or light, blackish mottling (Mar-Jul); iris grayish brown to dull chestnut (through Feb-Jul). **Note: In addition, HY/SYs of both sexes average buffier underparts and have less rufous in the nape than AHY/ASYs. Intermediates can be difficult to age and/or sex; these are likely HY/SY ♂♂ or AHY/ASY ♀♀ so combine all criteria with measurements.**

AHY/ASY ♀ (Aug-Jul): Crown feathers with moderately broad (Aug-Mar), or broad (Mar-Jul), dusky shaft streaks (Fig. 305); nape brown with a rufous tinge and moderately distinct, blackish streaking; outer pp covs broad, truncate, relatively fresh, and dusky with relatively distinct and broad, grayish-white edging (Fig. 138); outer rects truncate (Fig. 139**B**) and relatively fresh; upper breast with moderately heavy, blackish streaking (Aug-Mar), or heavy, blackish mottling (Mar-Jul); iris rich chestnut. **Note: See HY/SY ♀.**

HY/SY ♂ (Aug-Jul): Crown feathers with moderately narrow, black shaft streaks (Aug-Mar; Fig. 305), or black, sometimes narrowly edged buff (Mar-Jul); nape brown with a rufous tinge and indistinct, dusky streaking (Aug-Mar), or medium-bright rufous, sometimes with indistinct, dusky streaking (Mar-Jul); pp-cov, rect, and iris-color criteria as in HY/SY ♀;

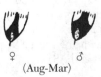

♀   ♂
(Aug-Mar)

FIGURE 305. The pattern of the crown feathers by sex in basic-plumaged (Aug-Mar) Lapland Longspurs.

upper breast with light, blackish mottling (Aug-Mar), or black, often with light, whitish mottling (Mar-Jul). **Note: See HY/SY ♀.**

AHY/ASY ♂ (Aug-Jul): Crown feathers with heavy, black shaft streaks (Aug-Mar; Fig. 305), or black, without buffy edging (Mar-Jul); nape dull rufous with indistinct, dusky mottling (Aug-Mar), or bright rufous, usually without dusky streaks (Mar-Jul); pp-cov, rect, and iris-color criteria as in AHY/ASY ♀, except that the edging to the pp covs is often mixed with pale rufous; upper breast with heavy, blackish mottling (Aug-Mar), or black, without whitish mottling (Mar-Jul). **Note: See HY/SY ♀.**

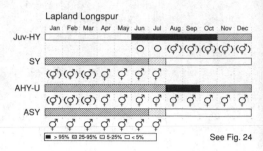

References—Stone (1896), Dwight (1900a), Ridgway (1901), Forbush (1929), Roberts (1955), F.S.L. Williamson *in* Bent *et al.* (1968), Davis (1969b), Wood (1969), Oberholser (1974), Francis *et al.* (1991), Svensson (1992), Jenni & Winkler (1994), Byers *et al.* (1995), Rising (1996a), Pyle (1997c).

SMITH'S LONGSPUR
Calcarius pictus

SMLO
Species # 5370
Band size: 1

Species— ♀♀ and HYs from the other longspurs by large wg (84-97) and relatively long tl (54-67; see **Age/Sex**); p7 – p6 1-5 mm; longest p – longest s 15-29 mm; bill medium small (exp culmen 9.7-11.7, depth at tip of nares 5.1-5.8) and brownish; med covs edged bright white (see Fig. 3X11); tail pattern with white restricted to r5-r6 (Fig. 306).

Geographic variation—Subspecies taxonomy follows Jehl (1968a), who considered the species monotypic (synonymizing two previously recognized subspecies); see also Kemsies (1961), E. Kemsies *in* Bent *et al.* (1968), Oberholser (1974), Browning (1990). Subspecies designations based on plumage differences, darker in birds breeding in AK ("*C.p. roweorum*") and more contrasting in birds breeding in n.Ont ("*mersi*"), were likely based on comparisons of variably worn specimens, although slight differences may be present.

Molt—PB: HY partial (Jul-Sep), AHY complete (Jul-Sep); PA limited-partial (Feb-Apr). The PBs probably occur on the summer grounds, although the 1st PB may be completed on the winter grounds; more study is needed. The 1st PB includes few if any med and gr covs and no terts or rects. The PAs include no to some med covs and 0 (~89%) to 2 inner gr covs, but no terts or rects; the extent of the PA appears to be similar in SYs and ASYs.

Skull—Pneumaticization completes in HY/SY from 15 Nov through Jan.

FIGURE 306. The pattern of white in the rectrices of Smith's Longspur.

Age/Sex—Juv (Jul-Aug) has distinct streaking on the upper breast; juv ♀=♂, although some juvs possibly are sexed by the color of the inner pp covs, as in HY/SYs (see below); more study is needed. CP/BP (May-Aug); the CP is relatively large due to a polygynandrous breeding system. ♀ wg(n100) 84-92, tl(n100) 54-63; ♂ wg(n100) 89-97, tl(n100) 57-67.

FIGURE 307. The pattern of the median coverts by sex in Smith's Longspur.

HY/SY ♀ (Aug-Jul): Crown and face buffy brownish; med covs narrowly edged buffy white (Fig. 307); outer pp covs narrow, tapered, relatively abraded, and brownish with indistinct, narrow, or no pale brown edging (Fig. 138); inner pp covs tipped buff (see Fig. 309); outer rects tapered (Fig. 139**B**) and relatively abraded. **Note: See AHY/ASY ♀.**

AHY/ASY ♀ (Aug-Jul): Crown and face brownish; med covs narrowly edged buffy white (Fig. 307); outer pp covs broad, truncate, relatively fresh, and dusky with relatively distinct and broad, grayish edging (Fig. 138); inner pp covs tipped grayish buff (see Fig. 309); outer rects truncate (Fig. 139**B**) and relatively fresh. **Note: Intermediates in basic plumage likely are HY/SY ♂♂ or AHY/ASY ♀♀; compare all plumage criteria with wg.**

HY/SY ♂ (Aug-Jul): Crown and face buffy ochre (Aug-Mar), or black and white, often tinged ochre (Mar-Jul); med covs broadly edged whitish (Fig. 307); pp cov and rect criteria as in HY/SY ♀, except that the inner pp covs are tipped buffy white (see Fig. 309). **Note: See AHY/ASY ♀. In addition, check the amount of the white in the lesser and med covs for possible ageing of ♂♂.**

AHY/ASY ♂ (Aug-Jul): Crown and face buffy ochre (Aug-Mar; occasionally with a veiled black and white pattern), or boldly black and white, without ochre (Mar-Jul); med covs broadly edged white (Fig. 307); pp-cov and rect criteria as in AHY/ASY ♀, except that the outer pp covs are edged whitish and the inner pp covs are tipped white (see Fig. 309). **Note: See AHY/ASY ♀ and HY/SY ♂.**

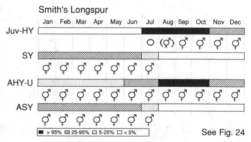

References—Ridgway (1901), Roberts (1955), E. Kemsies *in* Bent *et al.* (1968), Jehl (1968b), Oberholser (1974), Tomer (1982), Briskie (1993a, 1993b), Byers *et al.* (1995), Rising (1996a), Pyle (1997c).

CHESTNUT-COLLARED LONGSPUR
Calcarius ornatus

CCLO
Species # 5380
Band size: 1

Species—♀♀ and HYs from the other longspurs by smaller size (wg 76-91, tl 48-61; see **Sex**); p7 – p6 0-3 mm; longest p – longest s 12-22 mm; bill small (exp culmen 8.9-10.7, depth at tip of nares 4.8-5.7) and brownish-horn (Aug-Mar), or grayish (Mar-Aug); med covs edged whitish; tail pattern with extensive white on r4-r6 and reduced white on r2-r3 (Fig. 308).

Geographic variation—No subspecies are recognized.

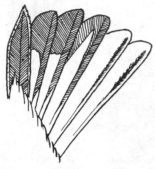

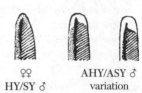

♀♀
HY/SY ♂

AHY/ASY ♂
variation

FIGURE 308. The pattern of white in the rectrices of Chestnut-collared Longspur.

FIGURE 309. The pattern of white on the inner primary coverts by age and sex in Chestnut-collared Longspur. Similar variation occurs in Smith's Longspur; more study is needed.

Molt—PB: HY partial (Jul-Sep), AHY complete (Jul-Sep); PA limited (Feb-Apr). The PBs occur on the summer grounds. The 1st PB includes few if any med and gr covs and no terts or rects. The PAs are limited to body feathers (primarily around the head and breast), and include no wing covs or flight feathers.

Skull—Pneumaticization completes in HY/SY from 1 Nov through Jan.

Age—Juv (Jul-Aug) has distinct streaking on the upper breast; juv ♀ = ♂.

HY/SY (Aug-Jul): Outer pp covs narrow, tapered, relatively abraded, and brownish with indistinct, narrow, or no pale edging (Fig. 138); inner pp covs without white (Fig. 309); outer rects tapered (Fig. 139**B**) and relatively abraded. **Note: In addition, HY/SYs (especially ♂♂) average duller than AHY/ASYs.**

AHY/ASY (Aug-Jul): Outer pp covs broad, truncate, relatively fresh, and dusky brown with relatively distinct and broad, pale edging (Fig. 138); inner pp covs without (♀♀), or with (♂♂), white (Fig. 309); outer rects truncate (Fig. 139**B**) and relatively fresh. **Note: See HY/SY.**

Sex—CP/BP (Apr-Aug). ♀ wg(n50) 76-85, tl(n20) 48-57; ♂ wg(n60) 81-91, tl(n20) 51-61.

♀: Crown, breast, nape, and med covs primarily buffy brown, occasionally with the scattered black and chestnut coloration of ♂♂ in Mar-Jul.

♂: Crown and breast brown with black mottling (Aug-Mar), or black or mixed black and chestnut (Mar-Jul); nape tinged (Aug-Mar), or fully (Mar-Jul), chestnut; med covs primarily white.

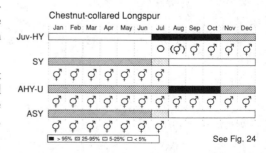

Hybrids reported—McCown's Longspur.

References—Dwight (1900a), Ridgway (1901), Forbush (1929), Harris (1944), Roberts (1955), Sibley & Pettingill (1955), G.M. Fairfield *in* Bent *et al.* (1968), Oberholser (1974), Byers *et al.* (1995), Rising (1996a), Hill & Gould (1997), Pyle (1997c).

SNOW BUNTING
Plectrophenax nivalis

SNBU
Species # 5340
Band size: 1A-1B

Species—From McKay's Bunting by back and rump buffy rufous, gray, or black, with little or no white (♂♂ in Mar-Aug and ♀♀), to whitish with extensive blackish streaking (AHY/ASY ♂♂ in Aug-Mar); outer pp with white usually not extending beyond the tips of the pp covs (Fig. 311); r3 primarily blackish or black (Fig. 310).

Geographic variation—Moderate, but clinal where ranges meet. Subspecies taxonomy follows Paynter (1970); see Ridgway (1901), Salomonsen (1931), Swarth (1934b), Dement'ev & Gladkov (1954), de Korte (1971), Cramp & Perrins (1994b), Byers *et al.* (1995), Lyon & Montgomerie (1995). Two other subspecies occur in Eurasia.

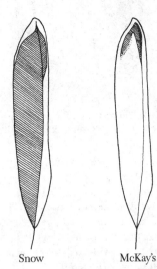

Snow   McKay's

FIGURE 310. The pattern of the third rectrix (r3) in Snow and McKay's buntings.

P.n. townsendi (br & wint w.AK Is): Large; bill long (exp culmen 10.9-13.7); body plumage white with a slight or no buff tinge. ♀ wg(n18) 101-112, tl(n12) 61-69; ♂ wg(n50) 108-120, tl(n22) 66-76.

P.n. nivalis (br & wint throughout most of the range in N.Am): Small (see **Age/Sex**); bill short (exp culmen 9.5-11.6); body plumage white with a buff tinge or wash.

Molt—PB: HY partial (Jul-Sep), AHY complete (Jul-Sep); PA absent. The PBs occur on the summer grounds. The 1st PB usually includes all med covs and apparently most or all gr covs, but no terts or rects. In European populations some outer gr covs can be retained and the terts can be replaced; look for this in occasional birds of N.Am, as well. Molt limits are difficult to detect in this species.

Skull—Pneumaticization completes in HY/SY from 15 Nov through Jan.

Age/Sex—Juv (Jul-Aug) has the head and breast dusky with blackish streaking; juv ♂ and ♀ are separated easily by the pattern of the ss, p9 (Fig. 311), and pp covs (Fig. 313), as in HY/SYs (see below). CP/BP (May-Aug). Measurements are useful: ♀ wg(n76) 95-107, tl(n20) 57-67; ♂ wg(n100) 103-116, tl(n36) 61-71 (nominate subspecies only; see **Geographic variation**).

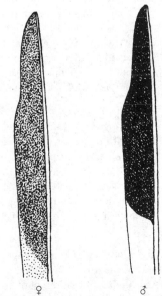

♀   ♂

FIGURE 311. The pattern of the outer primary (p9) by sex in Snow Bunting. Compare with Figure 314 for separation from McKay's Bunting.

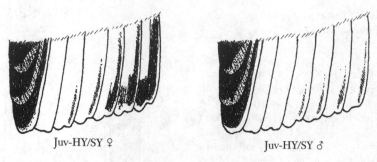

Juv-HY/SY ♀   Juv-HY/SY ♂

FIGURE 312. The pattern of the inner ss (s1-s4) by sex in Snow Bunting. This can be used to separate the sexes in all age groups, including juveniles.

HY/SY ♀ (Sep-Aug): Crown brown with heavy, blackish streaking (Sep-Mar), or dusky with distinct, dusky streaking (Mar-Aug); s1-s3 with substantial blackish (Fig. 312); outer gr covs blackish with white tips; outer pp covs narrow, tapered, relatively abraded (Fig. 138), and black with a moderate amount to little white edging (Fig. 313A-B); outer rects tapered (Fig. 139B) and relatively abraded; underwing pattern (including p9; Fig. 311) indistinctly defined, dusky brown and whitish. **Note: When combined with measurements, all birds should be reliably sexed (especially by underwing and p9 contrasts) and most birds should be reliably aged.**

AHY/ASY ♀ (Sep-Aug): Crown tan with light, blackish streaking (Sep-Mar), or grayish with indistinct, dusky streaking (Mar-Aug); outer gr covs blackish with white tips; s1-s3 with substantial blackish (Fig. 312); outer pp covs broad, truncate, relatively fresh (Fig. 138), and white with some to a moderate amount of black (Fig. 313B-D); outer rects truncate (Fig. 139B) and relatively fresh; underwing pattern (including p9; Fig. 311) indistinctly defined, dusky and whitish. **Note: See HY/SY ♀.**

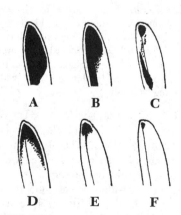

A   B   C

D   E   F

FIGURE 313. Variation in the pattern of the longest primary coverts pattern by age and sex (see text), in Snow Bunting.

HY/SY ♂ (Sep-Aug): Crown tan with dusky streaking (Sep-Mar), or white, sometimes with indistinct, dusky streaking (Mar-Aug); s1-s3 mostly or entirely white (Fig. 312); wing-cov and flight-feather criteria as in HY/SY ♀, except that the outer gr covs are white or primarily white, with black smudging, and the longest pp covs have less black (Fig. 313B-E); underwing pattern (including p9; Fig. 311) distinctly defined, blackish brown and white. **Note: See HY/SY ♀.**

AHY/ASY ♂ (Sep-Aug): Crown tan with little or no dusky streaking (Sep-Mar), or white, without dusky (Mar-Aug); s1-s3 white (Fig. 312); wing-cov and flight-feather criteria as in AHY/ASY ♀, except that the outer gr covs are white and the longest pp covs are entirely to primarily white (Fig. 313E-F); underwing pattern (including p9; Fig. 311) distinctly defined, black and white. **Note: See HY/SY ♀.**

Hybrids reported—McKay's Bunting. Yellowhammer (*Emberiza citrinella*) in captivity.

References—Stone (1896), Dwight (1900a), Ridgway (1901), Forbush (1929), Salomonsen (1931), Roberts (1955), D.F. Parmelee *in* Bent *et al.* (1968), Sealy (1969), Wood (1969), Green & Summers (1975), Svensson (1992), Cramp & Perrins (1994b), Byers *et al.* (1995), Lyon & Montgomerie (1995), Rising (1996a), Pyle (1997c); D. Brewer, R. Montgomerie (*in litt.* to the BBL).

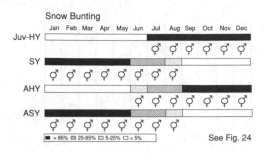

MCKAY'S BUNTING
Plectrophenax hyperboreus

MCBU
Species # 5350
Band size: 1B

Species—From Snow Bunting by back white or whitish tan, without black (AHY/ASY ♂♂), to primarily white with small black centers to the feathers (HY/SY ♀); rump without black; outer pp with white or whitish extending beyond the tips of the pp covs (Fig. 314); r3 primarily white (Fig. 310).

Geographic variation—No subspecies are recognized.

Molt—PB: HY partial (Jul-Sep), AHY complete (Jul-Sep); PA absent. The PBs occur on the summer grounds. The 1st PB usually includes all med and gr covs, but no terts or rects.

Skull—Pneumaticization completes in HY/SY from 15 Nov through Jan.

Age/Sex—Juv (Jul-Sep) has a dusky wash and streaking to the upper breast; juvs can be sexed by the combination of measurements and the patterns of p9 (Fig 314), the alula, and the pp covs (see Fig. 315), as in HY/SYs (see below). CP/BP (May-Aug). Measurements are useful: ♀ wg(n30) 99-115, tl(n20) 62-71; ♂ wg(n30) 106-122, tl(n13) 65-75.

HY/SY ♀ (Sep-Aug): Back feathers with large and distinct, black centers; outer pp (including p9) brownish black with a moderate amount of indistinct white at the bases (Fig. 314); outer pp covs narrow, tapered, relatively abraded (Fig. 138), and primarily blackish (Fig. 315); outer rects tapered (Fig. 139**B**) and relatively abraded. **Note: In comparison with measurements, all birds should be reliably sexed, but a few intermediates may not be reliably aged.**

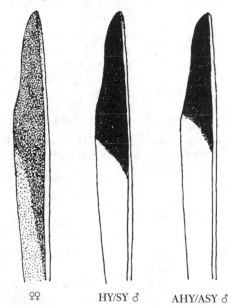

FIGURE 314. The pattern of the outer primary (p9), by sex and age, in McKay's Bunting. Compare with Figure 311 for separation from Snow Bunting.

HY/SY ♀   AHY/ASY ♀   HY/SY ♂   AHY/ASY ♂
              HY/SY ♂

FIGURE 315. The patterns of the longest primary covert and greater alula, by age and sex, in McKay's Bunting.

AHY/ASY ♀ (Sep-Aug): Back feathers with large and distinct, black centers; outer pp (including p9) blackish with a moderate amount of indistinct whitish at the bases (Fig. 314); outer pp covs broad, truncate, relatively fresh (Fig. 138), and primarily white (Fig. 315); outer rects truncate (Fig. 139**B**) and relatively fresh. **Note: See HY/SY ♀.**

HY/SY ♂ (Sep-Aug): Back feathers usually with small black centers; wing-cov and flight-feather criteria as in HY/SY ♀, except that the outer pp (including p9) blackish with a moderately large amount of distinct white at the bases (Fig. 314), and the pp covs primarily white with small black tipping (Fig. 315); alula tipped black (Fig. 315); most or all of r2-r6 with black (see Fig. 310). **Note: See HY/SY ♀.**

AHY/ASY ♂ (Sep-Aug): Back feathers with small black centers or lacking black entirely; wing-cov and flight-feather criteria as in AHY/ASY ♀ except that the outer pp (including p9) black with a large amount of distinct white at the bases (Fig. 314), and the pp covs usually are entirely white (*cf.* Fig. 315); alula usually white, without black tipping (Fig. 315); r2-r6 usually white (*cf.* Fig. 310). **Note: See HY/SY ♀.**

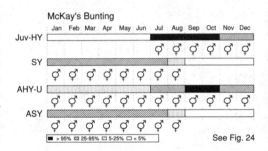

Hybrids reported—Snow Bunting.

References—Ridgway (1901), Swarth (1934b), I.N. Gabrielson *in* Bent *et al.* (1968), Sealy (1969), Byers *et al.* (1995), Lyon & Montgomerie (1995), Rising (1996a), Pyle (1997c).

CARDINALS, GROSBEAKS, AND ALLIES   *CARDINALIDAE*

Ten species. Family characters include bright and colorful male plumages and very robust, conical bills. Cardinals have 9 visible primaries, 9 secondaries, and 12 rectrices. The molts show substantial variation as to sequence and extent; most or all species have a presupplemental molt (see p. 16) and many species replace outer secondaries, primaries, and some or all rectrices during the first year. Plumage differs by age and sex, and males average larger than females. Most birds are reliably aged and sexed when all criteria are combined.

NORTHERN CARDINAL
Cardinalis cardinalis

NOCA
Species # 5930
Band size: 1A-2

Geographic variation—Weak to moderate and clinal where ranges meet. Subspecies taxonomy follows Paynter (1970), as modified by Stevenson & Anderson (1994); see Ridgway (1901), Bangs (1903), van Rossem (1933, 1934c), Huey (1940), Stevenson (1940), Banks (1963), Sutton (1967), Oberholser (1974), Browning (1990), Parkes (1997). Twelve other subspecies occur in Mex-C.Am.

*C.c. **superbus*** (res s.AZ-sw.NM): Large; tl – wg long (4-16 mm); crest long (longest crest feather 25-32 mm); bill medium large and stout (exp culmen 15.3-18.7, depth at tip of nares 12.9-14.7); upperparts and edges of the rects washed grayish; tawny-brown wash to the underparts of ♀♀ pale, usually extending to the belly; plumage of ♂♂ pale red. ♀ wg(n10) 95-102, tl(n10) 109-120; ♂ wg(n10) 98-105, tl(n10) 113-127.

*C.c. **canicaudus*** (res w.OK to se.NM-se.TX): Medium in size; tl – wg medium (0-8 mm); crest short (longest crest feather 20-27 mm); bill medium large (exp culmen 14.8-17.2, depth at tip of nares 11.9-13.5); upperparts and edges of the rects tinged to washed gray; brown wash to the underparts of ♀♀ rarely extends to the belly; plumage of ♂♂ medium red. ♀ wg(n78) 82-95, tl(n16) 95-109; ♂ wg(n100) 88-99, tl(n71) 98-111. Birds of w.OK-n.TX (*"planicola"*) may average slightly larger, larger-billed, and browner (less gray), but differences are slight and broadly clinal.

*C.c. **magnirostris*** (res. ec.TX-s.LA): Medium in size; tl – wg short (-4 to 4 mm); crest medium long (longest crest feather 23-30 mm); bill long (exp culmen 15.8-19.2, depth at tip of nares 12.3-14.3); upperparts and edges of the rects without a brownish or olive wash; brown wash to the underparts of ♀♀ deep, usually extending to the belly; plumage of ♂♂ deep red. ♀ wg(n15) 86-92, tl(n15) 90-99; ♂ wg(n17) 89-98, tl(n17) 95-106.

*C.c. **cardinalis*** (res se.ND-n.TX to NB-FL): Variably small; tl – wg medium (0-13 mm); crest short (longest crest feather 19-28 mm); bill medium small (exp culmen 13.5-16.3, depth at tip of nares 10.9-12.9); upperparts and edges of the rects washed brownish-olive; brown wash to the underparts of ♀♀ rarely extends to the belly; plumage of ♂♂ bright, medium to deep red. ♀ wg(n100) 84-96, tl(n59) 86-106; ♂ wg(n100) 87-98, tl(n42) 94-109. Birds of se.GA-s.FL (*"floridanus"*), average slightly smaller and darker, but differences are broadly clinal.

Molt—PS/PB: HY partial-complete (Jun-Nov), AHY complete (Aug-Oct); PA absent. A presupplemental molt (see p. 16) occurs in HYs, with the body plumage being replaced once in Jun-Sep and again (during the 1st PB) with the flight feathers in Jul-Nov (with some overlap due to individual variation in timing). It is unknown whether or not the PS can involve gr covs; more study is needed. The extent of the PS and 1st PB (combined) is variable, usually including all gr covs, but varying from no terts, pp, or rects (in ~72% of birds) to all flight feathers (probably in birds from southern populations only). Pp covs are replaced with the corresponding pp, although 1-2 covs occasionally can be retained during an otherwise complete molt (see Fig. 137**B**). Incomplete pp and ss replacement is not eccentric, but follows typical sequence (see p. 14 and Fig. 137), beginning with the innermost p (p1) and outermost s (s1, along with the terts), although sometimes s6 and s5 can be replaced before the outer ss (s2-s4). More study is needed on the proportion of birds (in the different subspecies) that have a complete 1st PB.

Skull—Pneumaticization completes in HY/SY from 15 Oct through Feb.

Age—Juv (Apr-Sep) is like HY/SY ♀♀, but has duller plumage, little or no red on the crest, a black or dusky bill, and a grayish iris; juv ♀ = ♂, although the presence of red on the crest and breast in juvs (or birds in supplemental plumage) might indicate ♂♂; more study is needed.

HY/SY (Sep-Aug): One to all outer pp covs narrow, tapered, relatively abraded (Figs. 137 & 138), and brown or brownish red, without dusky, contrasting with the brighter brown (♀) or red (♂) gr covs; molt limits usually (see **Molt**) occur among the flight feathers (Fig. 137), the middle ss (s5-s6 at least), outer pp, and some or all rects retained, pale brown, abraded, and tapered (Figs. 139**C** & 140**B**), contrasting with the fresher and dark brown (♀) or reddish (♂) terts, outer ss, inner pp, and/or some or all rects; bill or bill tip washed dusky (through Oct); iris gray to gray-brown (through Dec). **Note: Some HY/SYs (perhaps most in southern populations) can have a complete 1st PB and are not reliably aged by plumage; see AHY/ASY. On HY/SYs having undergone near-complete molt, look for retained juvenal pp covs and/or s5-s6, the last feathers to be replaced.**

U/AHY (Oct-Sep): Outer pp covs broad, truncate, relatively fresh (Fig. 138), and dull (♀) to brightish (♂) red, broadly washed dusky at the tip, and not markedly contrasting in color or wear with the gr covs (Fig. 133**F**); terts, ss, pp, and rects uniformly adult and truncate (Figs. 133**F**, 139**C**, & 140**B**); bill orange to red, without dusky; iris dark brown. **Note: It is likely that birds of northern populations (*e.g., C.c. cardinalis*; see Geographic variation) in this plumage can be reliably aged AHY/ASY, but more study is needed.**

Sex—CP/BP (Mar-Sep). ♀ wg(n100) 82-102, tl(n100) 86-121; ♂ wg(n100) 87-105, tl(n100) 94-127; see **Geographic variation**.

♀: Body plumage brown, except for a red crest. **Note: Beware of juv ♂♂; molting birds with incoming brown feathers in Aug-Nov can be sexed ♀, but those in Jun-Jul may be juv ♂♂ undergoing the presupplemental molt; more study is needed.**

♂: Body plumage partially (molting juvs or supplemental-plumaged HYs) or entirely bright red. **Note: See ♀.**

Hybrids reported—At least three other cardinal or finch species in captivity (see Gray 1958).

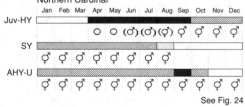

Northern Cardinal

See Fig. 24

References—Stone (1896), Dwight (1900a), Ridgway (1901), Forbush (1929), Swarth (1929), Sutton (1935a), Roberts (1955), Scott (1967), Bent *et al.* (1968), Wiseman (1968b, 1977), Wood (1969), Blake (1971), Oberholser (1974), Reese (1975), Sheppard & Klimkiewicz (1976), Yen (1989), CWS & USFWS (1991), Thompson & Leu (1994), Pyle (1997c); O.L. Austin, C.H. Blake, E.J. Fisk, S.M. Russell, J.S. Weske, A.J. Wiseman (*in litt.* to the BBL); C.W. Thompson, B. Walker (pers. comm.); IBP (MAPS) data.

PYRRHULOXIA
Cardinalis sinuatus

PYRR
Species # 5940
Band size: 1A

Geographic variation—Moderate and ranges fairly well defined. Subspecies taxonomy follows Paynter (1970); see Ridgway (1901), van Rossem (1933, 1934b), Amadon & Phillips (1947), Oberholser (1974). One other subspecies occurs in Mex.

C.s. fulvescens (res sc-se.AZ): Upperparts grayish brown; ♂♂ with little or no dusky in the face, and with the underparts orange-red and pale brownish.

C.s. sinuatus (res s.NM-se.TX): Upperparts dark brownish gray; ♂♂ with little to a moderate amount of dusky in the face, and with the underparts deep red and dark grayish. Birds of s.NM-w.TX (*"beckhami"*) may average longer-winged and smaller-billed, but differences are slight and probably broadly clinal.

Molt—PB: HY partial-incomplete (Jun-Nov), AHY complete (Jun-Oct); PA absent. A presupplemental molt possibly occurs, as in Northern Cardinal; more study is needed. The 1st PB includes all med and gr covs, often (in ~62% of birds) 1-3 terts, and often (in ~52% of birds) 1-2 central rects (r1). Also, the 1st PB sometimes (in ~38% of HYs) can be eccentric (see p. 208 and Fig. 136), with the outermost 2-7 pp, the innermost 3-6 ss, 6 to 12 (~74%) rects, and occasionally (in ~18% of birds) the outermost (reduced) pp cov replaced, in those birds showing eccentric molt.

Skull—Pneumaticization completes in HY/SY from 1 Oct through Jan.

Age—Juv (May-Sep) is like HY/SY ♀♀, but usually lacks red in the crest and has distinct, pale wing bars; juv ♀ = ♂, although the presence of some red on the crest and throat might indicate ♂; more study is needed.

HY/SY (Sep-Aug): Most or all outer pp covs (see **Molt**) narrow, tapered, relatively abraded (Fig. 138), and pale grayish brown with a red wash, contrasting with the slightly fresher gr covs; molt limits often occur among the flight feathers (Fig. 136**A-B**), the innermost 1-6 ss, no pp or the outermost 2-7 pp, and/or some or all rects, fresh, dark brown or reddish, and truncate, contrasting with the paler brown, more abraded, and tapered, retained ss, pp, and rects (Figs. 139**C** & 140**B**). **Note: A few birds can be difficult to age, especially worn ♀♀ in May-Jul.**

AHY/ASY (Sep-Aug): Outer pp covs broad, truncate, relatively fresh (Fig. 138), and red with a dusky wash at the tip, not contrasting with the gr covs in wear; terts, ss, pp, and rects uniformly adult (Fig. 133**F**), dark brownish or reddish, the pp and rects uniformly truncate (Figs. 139**C** & 140**B**). **Note: See HY/SY.**

Sex—CP/BP (Mar-Sep). ♀ wg(n30) 86-96, tl(n20) 89-104; ♂ wg(n30) 89-101, tl(n27) 94-110.

♀: Face, chin, and throat with little or no red.

♂: Face, chin, and throat red.

Pyrrhuloxia

	Jan	Feb	Mar	Apr	May	Jun	Jul	Aug	Sep	Oct	Nov	Dec
Juv-HY												
SY					○	○	(♂)	(♀)	♂	♂	♂	♂
	♂	♂	♂	♂	♂	♂	♂	♂				
AHY												
ASY							♂	♂	♂	♂	♂	♂ ♂ ♂
	♂	♂	♂	♂	♂	♂	♂	♂				

■ > 95%   ▨ 25-95%   ▨ 5-25%   □ < 5%   See Fig. 24

References—Ridgway (1901), A.H. Anderson *in* Bent *et al.* (1968), Oberholser (1974), Pyle (1997c).

ROSE-BREASTED GROSBEAK

Pheucticus ludovicianus

RBGR
Species # 5950
Band size: 1A-2

Species—♀♀ and HY ♂♂ from Black-headed Grosbeak (with caution) by supercilium white or whitish; underparts (especially throat and flanks) whitish, the breast buff (fresh) to whitish (worn), with thick, dusky streaking spanning across the center of the breast (Fig. 316); underwing covs pale lemon-yellow (most birds), salmon, mixed yellowish and pink (some AHY/ASY

♀♀), or pink (HY/SY ♂); bill primarily pinkish or whitish in Mar-Aug. **Note: Intermediate ♀♀ may be AHY/ASY Rose-breasted Grosbeaks or HY/SY Black-headed Grosbeaks; compare with age. Also, beware of hybrids between these two species.**

Geographic variation—No subspecies are recognized. Northern and eastern breeding birds (that migrate farther south) average slightly longer wings than birds breeding in ND-WI to KS (see Cook 1991).

Molt—PS(?)/PB: HY partial (Jul-Nov), AHY complete (Jul-Nov); PA: HY/SY partial-incomplete (Dec-May), ASY absent-limited (Jan-May). A presupplemental molt (see p. 16) probably occurs in HYs, with the body plumage being replaced once on the summer grounds in Jun-Sep and again (during the 1st PB) on the summer and/or winter grounds in Aug-Nov. The first molt on the summer grounds (PS and 1st PB combined) includes some to all med covs, 0 (~15%) to 10 (~8%) inner gr covs, occasionally (in ~8% of birds) s8 and occasionally (in ~8% of birds) 1-2 central rects (r1). Molt of HY/SYs on the winter grounds (1st PB and PA combined) includes no to some med covs, 8 to 10 (~91%) inner gr covs, 1-3 terts (rarely s6, as well), and 0 (~12%) to all 12 (~35-52%) rects. The replacement of the gr covs on the winter grounds possibly is protracted, from Sep-Apr. Replacement of the terts and rects appears to occur in Jan-Apr, along with the body plumage again(?), part of the 1st PA. The adult PB occurs primarily on the summer grounds, although 1-4 ss (among s3-s6) occasionally are retained until the winter grounds, and possibly one or more of these ss may rarely be retained until the next PB. More study is needed; it is possible that PAs do not occur, just protracted PBs.

Skull—Pneumaticization completes in HY/SY from 1 Nov through Feb. The Skull can be difficult to see through the skin.

Age/Sex—Juv (Jun-Jul) is like HY/SY ♀♀, but has feathers of the upperparts distinctly edged tawny, and cinnamon wing bars; juvs (and nestlings) are reliably sexed by the color of the underwing covs (yellow in ♀♀, pink or yellowish pink in ♂♂), bases of the pp sometimes washed blackish in ♂♂ (uniformly brown in ♀♀), and by the length of the white at the base of the pp, as in HY/SYs (see below). CP/BP (May-Sep); a partial BP (Fig. 22**B**) develops in some

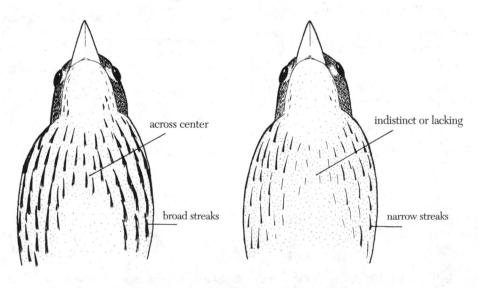

Rose-breasted   Black-headed

FIGURE 316. The underparts of ♀ Rose-breasted and Black-headed grosbeaks.

♂♂. ♀ wg(n100) 90-105, tl(n20) 66-75; ♂ wg(n100) 93-110, tl(n35) 69-79; see **Geographic variation**, and note that HY/SYs average much shorter measurements (especially SYs in spring).

HY/SY ♀ (Aug-Jul): Head and back streaked brown; molt limits usually occur among the med and gr covs in Aug-Mar (Fig. 133**A-E**; see **Molt**), the retained outer covs worn and pale brown, contrasting with the fresher and darker, replaced inner covs; 1-3 terts replaced in Jan-Apr, contrasting with the older middle ss (s4-s6) in Feb-Jul (Fig. 133**D-E**); outer pp covs narrow, tapered, relatively abraded (Fig. 138), and pale brown; white at the base of the pp extends -2 to 2 mm from the tip of the longest pp cov; outer rects juvenal and tapered (Fig. 139**C**) in Aug-Mar, and mixed tapered and truncate or completely truncate in Mar-Jul (see **Molt**); underwing covs lemon-yellow to pale salmon; underparts relatively buffy with indistinct, dusky streaks (through Mar); breast without pink. **Note: Most if not all birds should be reliably aged and sexed; a few ♀♀ can be difficult to age in May-Jul. HY/SY ♀♀ are easiest to separate by skull through Oct, by the gr cov contrasts in Aug-Mar (most to all HY/SYs), and by the tert and rect contrasts in Mar-Jul; those SYs that replace all rects at the 1st PA usually also replace three terts.**

AHY/ASY ♀ (Aug-Jul): Head and back streaked brown; wing covs, terts, and middle ss (s4-s6) uniformly adult (Fig. 133**F**) and dark brown, the terts more worn (due to exposure) than the middle ss in Mar-Jul (see Fig. 133**F**); outer pp covs broad, truncate, relatively fresh (Fig. 138), and dark brown; white at the base of the pp extends 0-4 mm from the tip of the longest pp cov; rects uniformly adult and truncate (Fig. 139**C**); underwing covs deep salmon or mixed yellow and pink (occasionally entirely pinkish); underparts relatively whitish with distinct, dusky streaks; breast without pink (occasionally one or two feathers can be pinkish). **Note: See HY/SY ♀.**

HY/SY ♂ (Sep-Aug): Head and back streaked brown (Sep-Mar), or blackish with brown mottling (Apr-Aug); molt-limit and wing-cov criteria as in HY/SY ♀, except that the replaced feathers are blackish to black (so the contrasts with the brown, retained feathers are distinct); white at the base of the pp extends 4-14 mm from the tip of the longest pp cov; rects brown and tapered (Fig. 139**C**) in Sep-Mar (sometimes with r1 contrastingly black), or mixed brown and black or entirely black (outer rects with white spots) and truncate in Mar-Aug; underwing covs pink; breast and throat brownish, usually with some pink (Sep-Mar), or pinkish, often with some brown mottling (Mar-Aug). **Note: See HY/SY ♀. Some SY/TYs can be distinguished through fall migration and possibly later by still retaining a few abraded brown juvenal outermost pp and/or ss (among s3-s6), which contrast markedly with the blacker and fresher, replaced ss and pp; see AHY/ASY ♂.**

AHY/ASY ♂ (Sep-Aug): Head and back black, heavily veiled brown in Sep-Dec; wing covs and flight feathers uniformly black (Fig. 133**F**); white at the base of the pp extends 14-24 mm from the tip of the longest pp cov; rects uniformly black and truncate (Fig. 139**C**); underwing covs pink; breast and throat with a substantial pink patch, veiled brownish in Sep-Dec. **Note: See HY/SY ♀. Occasional ASY/ATYs can be aged through fall and perhaps later by the retained adult outer pp and middle ss (among s3-s6) blackish, contrasting only moderately (in wear only) with the adjacent, replaced feathers; see HY/SY ♂.**

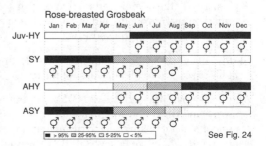

Hybrids reported—Black-headed Grosbeak.

References—Stone (1896), Dwight (1900a), Ridgway (1901), Forbush (1929), Swenk (1930a, 1936), Dickey & van Rossem (1938), Whittles (1938), Ivor (1944), Roberts (1955), West (1962), Smith (1966), Bent *et al.* (1968), Short (1969a), Wood (1969), Goodpasture (1972), Anderson & Daugherty (1974), Kroodsma (1974), Oberholser (1974), Sheppard & Klimkiewicz (1976), Cannell *et al.* (1983), Rising (1983a), Leberman (1984), Francis & Cooke (1990), CWS & USFWS (1991), Morlan (1991), Cramp & Perrins (1994b), Pyle (1997c); C.S. Robbins, C.E. Smith, R.P. Yunick (*in litt.* to the BBL); B. Walker (pers. comm.); IBP (MAPS) data, PRBO data.

BLACK-HEADED GROSBEAK
Pheucticus melanocephalus

BHGR
Species # 5960
Band size: 1A

Species—♀♀ and HY ♂♂ from Rose-breasted Grosbeak (with caution) by supercilium buff to buffy white; underparts (including the throat and flanks) with a heavy (fresh) to light (worn), tawny-buff wash, especially across the breast, and with the narrow, black streaking usually confined to the sides of the breast (Fig. 316); underwing covs deep yellow to brownish yellow or mustard colored; bill primarily dusky in Mar-Aug. **Note: Intermediates and hybrids occur; see Rose-breasted Grosbeak.**

Geographic variation—Weak and differences are obscured by substantial individual variation. Subspecies taxonomy follows Paynter (1970); see Ridgway (1901), Grinnell (1914a), Oberholser (1919h), Phillips *et al.* (1964). No other subspecies occur. More study is needed on variation in this species.

> **P.m. maculatus** (br coastal sw.BC-s.CA): Wg averages short; bill averages small (nares to tip 10.1-12.0); AHY/ASY ♂♂ with an indistinct to distinct, tawny supercilium. Wg: ♀(n100) 88-101, ♂(n100) 90-104; note that HY/SYs average smaller than AHY/ASYs, within the ranges.
>
> **P.m. melanocephalus** (br interior sc.BC-e.CA to ND-sw.TX): Wg averages long; bill averages large (nares to tip 10.9-12.7); AHY/ASY ♂♂ with an indistinct or no tawny supercilium. Wg: ♀(n100) 93-108, ♂(n100) 96-111; note that HY/SYs average smaller.

Molt—PS(?)/PB: HY partial (Jul-Nov), AHY complete (Jul-Oct); PA: HY/SY partial-incomplete (Dec-May), ASY absent-limited (Jan-May). A presupplemental molt (see p. 16) may occur in HYs, with the body plumage being replaced once on stopover and/or the winter grounds in Aug-Sep and again (during the 1st PB) on the winter grounds in Oct-Nov. The PS includes no to some med covs and 0 (~86%) to 2 inner gr covs, but no terts or rects. Molt of HY/SYs on the winter grounds (1st PB and PA combined) includes no to some med covs, usually all gr covs, occasionally (~8-13%) 1-3 terts, and 0 (~15%) to 12 (~8-12%) rects. The replacement of the gr covs possibly is protracted, from Sep-Apr. Replacement of the terts and rects appears to occur in Jan-Apr, along with the body plumage again(?), as part of the 1st PA. The adult PB occurs primarily on the summer grounds, although 1-4 ss (among s3-s6) occasionally can be retained until the winter grounds, and rarely until the next PB. More study is needed; it is possible that no PAs occur, just protracted PBs.

Skull—Pneumaticization completes in HY/SY from 1 Oct through Jan. The skull can be very difficult to see due to the thickness of the skin.

Age/Sex—Juv (May-Jul) is like HY/SY ♀♀, but has feathers of the upperparts distinctly edged tawny, and cinnamon wing bars; juv ♀=♂, although some juvs can be sexed by ♀ having a greater amount of streaking to the underparts, and by the length of the white at the base of the pp, as in HY/SYs (see below). CP/BP (Apr-Aug); some ♂♂ can develop a partial BP (Fig. 22**B**).

♀ wg(n100) 88-108, tl(n100) 73-85; ♂ wg(n100) 90-111, tl(n100) 75-87; see **Geographic variation**, and note that HY/SYs average much shorter measurements than AHY/ASYs (especially SYs in spring).

HY/SY ♀ (Aug-Jul): Crown and back streaked brown; face dark brown; rump brown, usually with some streaking, not contrasting markedly with the back; molt limits sometimes to usually occur among the med and gr covs in Aug-Mar (Fig. 133A-E; see **Molt**), the retained outer covs worn and pale brown, contrasting with the fresher and darker, replaced inner covs; 1-3 terts occasionally replaced in Jan-Apr, contrasting with the older middle ss (s4-s6) in Feb-Jul (Fig. 133**D**); outer pp covs narrow, tapered, relatively abraded (Fig. 138), and pale brown; white at the base of the pp extends -5 to 2 mm from the tip of the longest pp cov; outer rects tapered (Fig. 139**C**) in Aug-Mar, or mixed tapered and truncate or completely truncate in Mar-Jul; breast deep buff with a larger number of more prominent dusky streaks (found sometimes across the center of the breast, especially in Aug-Mar). **Note: All birds should easily be sexed and ♂♂ should readily be aged, but some ♀♀ can be difficult to age, especially in May-Jul. HY/SY ♀♀ are easiest to age by skull through Oct, by gr cov contrasts in Nov-Mar (see Molt), and by tert and rect contrasts in Mar-Jul; those SYs that replace all rects usually also replace all three terts.**

AHY/ASY ♀ (Aug-Jul): Crown and back streaked brown; face dark brown; rump brown, usually with some streaking, not contrasting markedly with the back; wing covs, terts, and middle ss (s4-s6) uniformly adult (Fig. 133**F**) and dark brown, the terts more worn (due to exposure) than the middle ss in Mar-Jul (see Fig. 133**F**); outer pp covs broad, truncate, relatively fresh (Fig. 138), and dark brown; white at the base of the pp extends 0-6 mm from the tip of the longest pp cov; rects uniformly adult and truncate (Fig. 139**C**); breast pale buffy with narrow, dusky streaks, usually restricted to the sides of the underparts. **Note: See HY/SY ♀.**

HY/SY ♂ (Sep-Aug): Crown, face and back streaked brown (Sep-Mar), or blackish with brown mottling (Apr-Aug); rump tawny (Sep-Mar), or cinnamon (Apr-Aug), and unstreaked or lightly spotted, contrasting with the brown-streaked back in Sep-Mar; molt limits as in HY/SY ♀, except that the replaced feathers are blackish brown to blackish (so contrasts with the brown, retained feathers are distinct); white at the base of the pp extends 4-9 mm from the tip of the longest pp cov; rects brown and tapered (Fig. 139**C**) in Aug-Mar, or mixed brown and black or entirely black (outer rects with white spots) and truncate in Mar-Aug; breast with a moderate tawny wash (Sep-Mar), or dull tawny cinnamon (Mar-Aug). **Note: See HY/SY ♀. Some SY/TYs can be distinguished through fall migration and possibly later by retaining a few abraded brown juvenal outermost pp and/or middle ss (among s3-s6), which contrast markedly with the blackish-brown and fresher, replaced ss and pp; see AHY/ASY ♂.**

AHY/ASY ♂ (Sep-Aug): Crown, face, and back black, heavily veiled brownish in Sep-Dec; rump cinnamon and unstreaked, contrasting markedly with the brown-streaked back; wing covs and flight feathers uniformly black; white at the base of the pp extends 11-19 mm from the tip of the longest pp cov; rects uniformly truncate (Fig. 139**C**); breast strongly washed tawny (Sep-Mar), or rich tawny cinnamon (Mar-Aug). **Note: See HY/SY ♀. A few ASY/ATYs can be aged through fall and perhaps later by having the retained adult outermost pp and 1-4 middle ss (among s3-s6) blackish, contrasting only moderately with the adjacent, replaced feathers; see HY/SY ♂.**

Hybrids reported—Rose-breasted Grosbeak.

References—Ridgway (1901), Swarth (1904a), Swenk (1930a, 1936), Michener & Michener

(1951), West (1962), Bent *et al.* (1968), Short (1969a), Sheppard & Collins (1971b), Anderson & Daugherty (1974), Kroodsma (1974), Oberholser (1974), Rising (1983a), Hill (1987, 1988a, 1988b, 1994, 1995), CWS & USFWS (1991), Morlan (1991), Pyle (1997c); D.F. DeSante (*in litt.* to the BBL); W. Richardson (pers. comm.); IBP (MAPS) data, PRBO data.

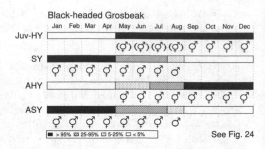

See Fig. 24

BLUE GROSBEAK
Guiraca caerulea

BLGR
Species # 5970
Band size: 1B

Species—From all bunting species by larger size (wg 79-99, tl 57-79; see **Geographic variation** & **Age/Sex**); wing bars distinct and deep buff to tawny.

Geographic variation—Moderate, but clinal where ranges meet, and differences are obscured by substantial individual variation. Subspecies taxonomy follows Paynter (1970); see Ridgway (1901), Grinnell (1911a), Dwight & Griscom (1927), van Rossem (1945a), Storer & Zimmerman (1959), Phillips *et al.* (1964), Sutton (1967), Oberholser (1974), Browning (1978, 1990). Two other subspecies occur in Mex-C.Am.

G.c. salicaria (br c.CA-wc.NV to s.CA-sw.AZ): Medium in size; bill small (nares to tip 9.5-12.4, depth at tip of nares 9.8-11.6); upperparts of ♀♀ and HY ♂♂ medium-pale brown, with the rump tinged grayish; plumage of AHY/ASY ♂♂ medium blue. ♀ wg(n10) 82-91, tl(n10) 62-71; ♂ wg(n23) 86-97, tl(n23) 66-74.

G.c. interfusa (br NV-ec.CA to c.SD-w.TX): Medium in size; bill medium in size (nares to tip 10.6-13.8, depth at tip of nares 10.8-12.0); upperparts of ♀♀ and HY ♂♂ pale brown, with the rump washed grayish; plumage of AHY/ASY ♂♂ medium-pale blue. ♀ wg(n10) 82-90, tl(n10) 62-71; ♂ wg(n53) 86-94, tl(n52) 66-75.

G.c. eurhyncha (br & wint nc.Mex; vag to sw.TX): Large; bill large (nares to tip 11.7-13.7, depth at tip of nares 11.9-13.2); upperparts of ♀♀ and HY ♂♂ medium-dark brown, with the rump tinged bluish gray; plumage of AHY/ASY ♂♂ dark purplish blue. ♀ wg(n10) 87-95, tl(n10) 66-75; ♂ wg(n31) 91-99, tl(n31) 70-79.

G.c. caerulea (br se.SD-s.TX to NJ-n.FL): Small; bill medium in size (nares to tip 10.8-13.4, depth at tip of nares 10.9-12.1); upperparts of ♀♀ and HY ♂♂ (including the rump) medium-dark brown; plumage of AHY/ASY ♂♂ medium-dark blue. ♀ wg(n47) 79-86, tl(n20) 57-67; ♂ wg(n89) 81-92, tl(n47) 62-72. Birds of se.SD-s.TX (*"mesophila"*) may average paler and larger, but differences are slight and represent intergradation with *interfusa*.

Molt—PS/PB: HY incomplete (Jun-Dec), AHY complete (Aug-Nov); PA: SY limited-partial (Dec-Apr), ASY absent. A presupplemental molt (see p. 16) occurs in HYs, with the body plumage being replaced once on the summer grounds in Jun-Sep and again (during the 1st PB) on the winter grounds in Sep-Dec. The adult PB occurs primarily on the winter grounds. The PS includes some to all med covs and 0 (~11%) to 5 inner gr covs, but no terts or rects. The 1st PB is eccentric (see p. 208 and Fig. 136), including no to some med covs, 3 to 10 (~67%) inner gr covs, 3-8 inner ss, usually (in ~88% of birds) 3-7 outer pp, often (in ~67% of birds) 1-5 outer pp covs, and 0 (~11%) to all 12 (~70%) rects. Some birds showing the eccentric replacement pattern can also replace the outermost 1-3 ss (among s1-s3) and the innermost 1-3 pp (among p1-p3; see Fig. 136**D**), and complete replacement of the pp and ss has been reported (in up to 54% of birds). The 1st PA is limited primarily to the body plumage, with occasional birds (~19%) replacing 1-2 inner gr covs. Some AHY/ASYs (~23%, including both SY/TYs and ASY/ATYs) appear to retain pp covs or middle ss (among s3-s6) during the adult PBs; more study is needed on the incidence of feather retention and its use in ageing (see **Age/Sex**).

Skull—Pneumaticization completes in HY/SY from 1 Oct through Jan. The skull may be difficult to see through the skin.

Age/Sex—Juv (May-Aug) is like HY/SY, but has heavier streaking on the grayer upperparts, and indistinct, dusky streaking on the buffier underparts; juv ♀ = ♂, although some juv ♂♂ can be sexed by the presence of slight blue edges to the rects (see HY ♀ ♂, below). CP/BP (Apr-Aug). Measurements are useful within subspecies (see **Geographic variation**): ♀ wg(n77) 79-95, tl(n50) 57-75; ♂ wg(n100) 81-99, tl(n100) 62-79.

Supplemental Plumages (Aug-Oct)

HY ♀♂ (Aug-Oct): Body plumage entirely brown; molt limits usually occur among the med and gr covs (Fig. 133**A-C**; see **Molt**), the retained outer covs worn and brown with buff tips, contrasting with the fresher, dusky, and tawny-edged, replaced inner covs; flight feathers uniformly fresh; outer pp covs narrow, tapered, and brown without blue edging (Fig. 138**A**); outer rects tapered (Fig. 139**C**) and relatively abraded. **Note: Most HYs in supplemental plumage are not reliably sexed by plumage alone, although some birds with slight blue edges to the bases of the rects might be reliably sexed ♂, with experience and in combination with measurements (see above and Geographic variation). Actively molting HYs in Sep-Oct with incoming brown body feathers in the head and breast can be reliably sexed ♀, and those with incoming blue body feathers can be sexed ♂.**

Basic and Alternate Plumages (Oct-Sep)

HY/SY ♀ (Sep-Aug): Body plumage entirely brown, often with a few blue feathers in the lesser covs or rump in Mar-Sep; molt limits occur among the wing covs and flight feathers (Figs. 133**B-E** & 136**A-D**); most or all pp covs retained, the inner feathers (at least) narrow, faded, brown, and abraded (Fig. 138), often (see **Molt**) contrasting with 1-5, darker brown, and (sometimes) bluish-tinged, replaced outermost covs (Fig. 136**B-D**); the outermost 3-8 pp (sometimes all pp) and the innermost 3-8 ss replaced, contrastingly dark brown (Fig. 136); all or some juvenal rects sometimes retained, contrastingly faded, brown, and tapered (Fig. 139**C**). **Note: By May-Sep most HY/SYs (especially ♀♀) will be difficult to age, although those with replaced outer pp covs are readily aged through the adult PB. See also AHY/ASY ♀♀.**

AHY/ASY ♀ (Sep-Aug): Body plumage brown, with a few to many blue feathers in the lesser covs and rump; pp covs uniformly broad, truncate, relatively fresh, and dark brown, sometimes tinged or edged pale bluish (Fig. 138); gr covs, ss, and pp uniformly adult (Fig. 133**F**) and dark brown; rects uniformly adult, dark brown, truncate (Fig. 139**C**), and relatively fresh. **Note: See HY/SY ♀. Beware of HY/SY ♀♀ that may have a complete molt during the 1st PB and thus would be impossible to age by molt limits; use color of the body feathers on these. Most HY/SYs should have retained at least a few inner pp covs and middle ss (among s2-s6); but beware of AHY/ASYs retaining ss; see AHY/ASY ♂. More study is needed.**

HY/SY ♂ (Oct-Sep): Body plumage brown with scattered, distinct, blue feathers, often becoming heavily mottled with blue on the head and breast in Mar-Sep; molt-limit, wing-cov and flight-feather criteria as in HY/SY ♀, except that the replaced pp covs, pp, and ss are dusky with bluish edging, contrasting markedly with the brown, retained juvenal feathers. **Note: See HY/SY ♀, AHY/ASY ♀, and AHY/ASY ♂.**

AHY/ASY ♂ (Oct-Sep): Body plumage entirely blue, the feathers tipped brownish in Aug-Dec; wing covs and flight feathers uniformly adult (Fig. 133F) and dull black with blue edging; rects uniformly truncate (Fig. 139C). **Note: Some AHY/ASYs (see Molt) can show a few retained flight feathers, especially among the pp covs and middle ss (among s3-s6). AHY/ASYs with retained blackish adult feathers probably can be aged ASY/ATY. Those with retained brown juvenal feathers likely are SY/TYs, but could be HY/SYs with a near-complete molt (see AHY/ASY ♀). On these check the relative wear of the retained feathers; juvenal feathers on SY/TYs should be extremely faded and abraded whereas those of HY/SYs would be relatively fresh. More study is needed.**

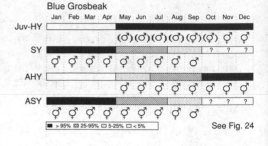

Hybrids reported—Possibly with Dickcissel (which see).

References—Dwight (1900a), Ridgway (1901), Forbush (1929), Dickey & van Rossem (1938), Bent *et al.* (1968), Blake (1969), Oberholser (1974), Phillips (1974), Ingold (1993), Cramp & Perrins (1994b), Sibley (1994), Thompson & Leu (1994), Pyle (1997c); D. Cimprich (pers. comm.); IBP (MAPS) data, PRBO data.

LAZULI BUNTING
Passerina amoena

LAZB
Species # 5990
Band size: 1-1C

Species— ♀♀ and HY ♂♂ from Indigo Bunting by larger size (wg 64-73, tl 48-56; see **Age/Sex**); back brownish, usually contrasting slightly with the grayer rump; edges of the terts and gr covs distinctly paler, forming distinct wing bars; throat indistinctly pale buffy; breast often tinged buffy cinnamon, without olive. Beware of fresh, adult basic-plumaged ♀♀ which can lack distinct, pale wing bars and be difficult to separate from adult ♀ Indigo Buntings; measurements and (usually) the presence of a tawny wash on the breast are the best criteria on these. Juvs may be inseparable by plumage. From ♀ Varied Bunting by larger size (see above); culmen straighter; wing morphology longer (p9 > p5; Fig. 317); wing bars average more distinct; terts distinctly edged pale.

Geographic variation—No subspecies are recognized.

Molt—PS/PB: HY incomplete (Jun-Nov), AHY complete (Aug-Oct); PA limited (Feb-May). A presupplemental molt (see p. 16) occurs in some or all HYs, with the body plumage being replaced once on the summer grounds in Jun-Sep and again (during the 1st PB) on the winter grounds with the flight feathers in Sep-Nov. The adult PB begins on the summer grounds, but most molting occurs during migration

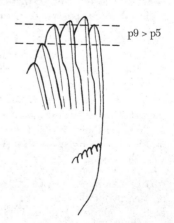

FIGURE 317. The wing morphology in Lazuli and Indigo buntings. Beware of migrants still growing p9.

or on the winter grounds. The presupplemental molt includes few if any med and gr covs and no terts or rects. The 1st PB is eccentric (see p. 208 and Fig. 136), with all gr covs, the outermost 4-8 pp, the innermost 3-6 ss, the outermost 0 (~19%) to 5 pp covs, and the rects replaced. Occasional birds also can replace the innermost 1-3 pp (among p1-p3) and the outermost 1-3 ss (among s1-s3). The PA occurs primarily on the winter grounds, and is limited to body feathers, mostly on the head, throat, and breast; it likely is more extensive in SY ♂♂ than in the other age/sex groups.

Skull—Pneumaticization completes in HY/SY from 15 Oct (as early as 1 Sep in birds of CA) through Jan. Some SYs probably retain windows (> 2 mm; Fig. 11**D**) through summer/fall.

Age/Sex—Juv (May-Aug) resembles HY/SY ♀♂ (see below), but has feathers of the upperparts edged pale brown and relatively heavy streaking to the underparts; juv ♀ = ♂, although check for blue-tinged bases to the rects, possibly indicating ♂♂ (see HY/SY ♀♂, below). CP/BP (Mar-Aug). Measurements are useful: ♀ wg(n100) 64-73, tl(n54) 48-56; ♂ wg(n100) 67-77, tl(100) 50-58.

Supplemental Plumage (Aug-Oct)

HY ♀♂ (Aug-Oct): Body plumage entirely brownish; most or all wing covs (see **Molt**) and flight feathers uniformly fresh and brownish with pale buff edging; outer pp covs narrow, tapered, and brown without greenish edging (Fig. 138); outer rects tapered (Fig. 139**A**). **Note: For HYs in supplemental plumage, the sexes are not separated reliably by plumage alone, although blue-tinged rects may be a reliable indicator of ♂♂; more study is needed. Actively molting HYs in Sep-Oct with incoming brown body feathers can be reliably sexed ♀, and those with incoming blue or orange body feathers can be reliably sexed ♂.**

Basic and Alternate Plumages (Oct-Sep)

HY/SY ♀ (Sep-Aug): Body plumage primarily or entirely brown; most or all pp covs retained, the inner feathers narrow, faded, brown and abraded (Fig. 138), often (see **Molt**) contrasting with the darker brown and greenish-tinged, outer 1-5 covs (see Fig. 136**B-C**); the outermost 4-8 pp and the innermost 3-6 ss replaced, fresh, and dark brown with greenish edging, contrasting with the paler brown inner pp and outer ss (Fig. 136**A-B**), sometimes with the innermost pp and the outermost ss replaced as well (Fig. 136**D**). **Note: Some ♀♀ can be difficult to age, especially in summer when plumage becomes quite worn.**

AHY/ASY ♀ (Sep-Aug): Body plumage primarily brown, with a few to many bluish-green feathers in the lesser covs and/or rump only; outer pp covs uniformly broad, truncate, relatively fresh, and dark brown, often with indistinct, bluish-green edging (Fig. 138); outer pp and inner ss uniformly adult (Fig. 133**F**) and dark brown. **Note: See HY/SY ♀.**

HY/SY ♂ (Oct-Sep): Body plumage brownish, with distinct, blue (throat) or orange (belly), feathers, from a scattering (Oct-Mar), to largely blue and orange, with some brown or white mottling in the upperparts and throat (Mar-Sep); molt limits as in HY/SY ♀, except that the replaced outer pp covs, outer pp, and inner ss are dusky with bluish edging, contrasting more distinctly with the retained, brown, juvenal feathers.

AHY/ASY ♂ (Oct-Sep): Body plumage largely blue and orange, the feathers tipped brownish in Oct-Dec; wing covs and flight feathers uniformly dull black with blue edging.

Hybrids reported—Indigo Bunting. Hybrid Indigo X Lazuli buntings (ILBH) are given species # 5986.

References—Ridgway (1901), Breckenridge (1930), Sibley & Short (1959), M.M. Erickson *in* Bent *et al.* (1968), Short (1969a), Sheppard (1972a), Oberholser (1974), Emlen *et al.* (1975), Kroodsma (1975), Rising (1983a), Young (1989, 1991), Cramp & Perrins (1994b), Thompson & Leu (1994), Howell & Webb (1995), Greene *et al.* (1996), Pyle (1997c); IBP (MAPS) data, PRBO data.

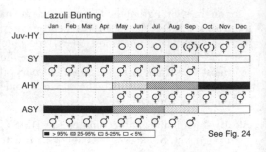

INDIGO BUNTING

Passerina cyanea

INBU
Species # 5980
Band size: 1C-1

Species—From Blue Grosbeak by smaller size (wg 59-72, tl 45-54; see **Age/Sex**). ♀♀ and HY ♂♂ from Lazuli Bunting by smaller size (wg 59-68, tl 45-51); upperparts (including the rump) usually uniformly brownish; edges of the terts and gr covs indistinctly paler, usually not forming distinct wing bars; throat distinctly whitish or pale buffy; breast brownish or gray, without cinnamon, and often mottled with olive. Measurements and lack of a tawny wash on the breast are the best criteria for separating fresh, adult basic-plumaged ♀♀, which can be difficult to identify (see Lazuli Bunting). Juvs may be inseparable by plumage. From ♀ Varied Bunting by culmen straighter; wing morphology longer (p9 > p5; Fig. 317); terts distinctly edged pale; breast usually with streaks.

Geographic variation—No subspecies are recognized.

Molt—PS/PB: HY incomplete (Jun-Dec), AHY complete (Aug-Oct); PA partial-incomplete (Jan-May). A presupplemental molt (see p. 16) occurs in some or all HYs, with the body plumage being replaced once on the summer grounds in Jun-Oct and again (during the 1st PB) on the winter grounds with the flight feathers in Oct-Dec. The adult PB begins on the summer grounds, but most molting occurs during migration or on the winter grounds. The presupplemental molt occasionally includes the innermost gr cov, but no terts or rects. The 1st PB is eccentric (see p. 208 and Fig. 136), with all gr covs, the outermost 2-7 pp, the innermost 2-5 ss, the outermost 0 (~52%) to 2 pp covs, and the rects replaced. The 1st PA occurs primarily on the winter grounds, but often completes on the summer grounds. It includes 0 (~13%) to 9 inner gr covs and sometimes (in ~50% of birds) 1-3 terts and/or s6, but no rects. The adult PA includes 5 to 10 (~41%) inner gr covs, often (in ~59% of birds) 1-3 terts, and occasionally (in ~11% of birds) 1-4 central rects (r1).

Skull—Pneumaticization completes in HY/SY from 15 Oct. Windows (> 2 mm; Fig. 11**D**) occur on the top of the skull of some SYs through summer and (rarely) fall.

Age/Sex—Juv (May-Aug) resembles HY/SY (see below), but has feathers of the upperparts edged pale gray, and heavier streaking to the underparts; juv ♀ = ♂, although check for blue-tinged bases to the rects, or darker rects, possibly indicating ♂♂ (see HY ♀♂, below). CP/BP (Apr-Aug). Measurements are useful: ♀ wg(n100) 59-68, tl(n35) 45-51; ♂ wg(n100) 63-72, tl(n60) 47-54.

Supplemental Plumage (Aug-Oct)

HY ♀♂ (Aug-Oct): Body plumage entirely brownish; some or all med and gr covs (see **Molt**) with pale buff edging; flight feathers uniformly fresh; outer pp covs narrow, tapered, somewhat abraded (Fig. 138), and brown; outer rects tapered (Fig. 139A). **Note: In supplemental plumage the sexes are not separated reliably by plumage alone, although blue-tinged or darker rects may be a reliable indicator of ♂♂; more study is needed. Actively molting HYs in Sep-Oct, with incoming brown body feathers in the head and breast, can be reliably sexed ♀, and those with incoming blue body feathers can be sexed ♂.**

Basic and Alternate Plumages (Oct-Sep)

HY/SY ♀ (Sep-Aug): Body plumage (including the feather centers) entirely dull brown, sometimes with a few greenish feathers in the lesser covs and/or rump in Mar-Aug; most or all (see **Molt**) outer pp covs narrow, tapered, somewhat abraded, and brown without bluish edging (Fig. 138); the outermost 2-7 pp, the innermost 2-5 ss, and sometimes the outermost 1-2 pp covs dark brown, often edged greenish blue, contrasting with the paler brown, retained inner pp, outer ss, and most or all pp covs (Fig. 136A-B). **Note: Both SYs and ASYs can have mixed generations of gr covs and terts in Mar-Aug (see Molt). Some ♀♀ can be difficult to age, especially in summer when plumage becomes quite worn.**

AHY/ASY ♀ (Sep-Aug): Body plumage primarily or entirely rich brown (Aug-Feb), with a few to many bluish feathers in the lesser covs and/or rump in Mar-Aug; outer pp covs uniformly broad, truncate, relatively fresh, and dark brown, usually with pale bluish edging (Fig. 138); pp and ss uniformly adult (Fig. 133F) and dark brown, often with pale bluish edging. **Note: See HY/SY ♀.**

HY/SY ♂ (Oct-Sep): Body plumage dull brown, except for some body feather centers (especially on the breast) bluish in Oct-Mar, or plumage with a variable amount of distinct, blue feathers in Mar-Sep, from a scattering to largely blue with some brown mottling; molt limits as in HY/SY ♀, except that the outer pp, inner ss, and (sometimes) the outer pp covs are dusky with bluish edging, contrasting markedly with the retained, brown, juvenal feathers. **Note: See HY/SY ♀.**

AHY/ASY ♂ (Oct-Sep): Body plumage rich brown, with blue mottling in the lesser covs and rump in Oct-Mar, or entirely blue in Apr-Sep, with little or no brown mottling; molt limits as in AHY/ASY ♀, except that the ss, pp, and pp covs are uniformly dull black with bright blue edging. **Note: See HY/SY ♀. The adult-basic terts and gr covs are brown with tawny edging. These can sometimes be retained during Apr-Sep, contrasting distinctly with the replaced, blue feathers.**

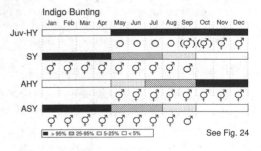

Hybrids reported—Lazuli Bunting, Painted Bunting. Orange-breasted Bunting (*P. leclancherii*) and Island (Common) Canary (*Serinus canaria*) in captivity.

References—Stone (1896), Dwight (1900a, 1900b), Ridgway (1901), Forbush (1929), Breckenridge (1930), Braun (1935), Sutton (1935a), Dickey & van Rossem (1938), Roberts (1955), Sibley & Short (1959), Blake (1965c, 1969), Emlen (1967), D.W. Johnston (1967), W. Taber & D.W. Johnston *in* Bent *et al.* (1968), Johnston & Downer (1968), Short (1969a), Wood (1969), Oberholser (1974), Taylor (1974), Emlen *et al.* (1975), Kroodsma (1975), Sheppard & Klimkiewicz (1976), Payne (1982, 1992), Hamel *et al.* (1983), Rising (1983a), Rohwer (1986), Quay (1987), Payne & Payne (1989), Young (1989, 1991), Mulvihill (1993), Cramp & Perrins (1994b), Thompson & Leu (1994), Howell & Webb (1995), Pyle (1997c); R.B. Payne, F.G. Stiles (*in litt.* to the BBL); B. Walker (pers. comm.); IBP (MAPS) data, PNR data, PRBO data.

VARIED BUNTING
Passerina versicolor

VABU
Species # 6000
Band size: 1C

Species— ♀♀ and HY/SY ♂♂ from Lazuli and Indigo buntings by the combination of small size (wg 58-70, tl 47-57; see **Age/Sex**); culmen more strongly decurved; wing morphology shorter (p9 < p5; Fig. 318); wing bars and pale edging on the terts lacking completely, or very indistinct (except in juvs); breast without streaks.

Geographic variation—Moderate and ranges fairly well defined. Subspecies taxonomy follows Paynter (1970), as modified by Monson & Phillips (1981); see also Ridgway (1901), Griscom (1930c), van Rossem (1931a, 1934d). Two other subspecies occur in Mex-C.Am.

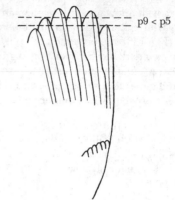

FIGURE 318. The wing morphology in Varied Bunting.

P.v. pulchra (br & wint s.AZ-sw.NM): Plumage of HYs and ♀♀ brown, often tinged reddish; AHY/ASY ♂♂ with the nape bright red, the throat purple with little or no red tinge, and the rump purplish blue. HYs and ♀♀ of birds of N.Am ("*dickeyae*") average more reddish brown than those of s.Baja CA, but differences are slight and obscured by individual variation.

P.v. versicolor (br & wint se.NM-s.TX; vag to AZ): Plumage of HYs and ♀♀ grayish brown; AHY/ASY ♂♂ with the nape medium-dull red, the throat reddish purple to maroon, and the rump pale blue with little or no purple tinge.

Molt—PS/PB: HY incomplete (Jun-Nov), AHY complete (Jun-Oct); PA absent. A presupplemental molt (see p. 16) probably occurs in some or all HYs, with the body plumage being replaced once on the summer grounds in Jun-Sep, and again (during the 1st PB) on the winter grounds, with the flight feathers in Sep-Nov. The adult PB begins on the summer grounds, but most molting occurs during migration or on the winter grounds. The presupplemental molt includes few if any med and gr covs and no terts or rects. The 1st PB is eccentric (see p. 208 and Fig. 136), with all gr covs, the outermost 4-8 pp, the innermost 3-6 ss, the outermost 0 (~71%) to 3 pp covs, and the rects replaced. Occasional birds also can replace the innermost 1-3 pp (among p1-p3) and the outermost 1-3 ss (among s1-s3).

Skull—Pneumaticization completes in HY/SY from 15 Sep through Jan. Some SYs probably retain windows (> 2 mm; Fig. 11**D**) through spring.

Age/Sex—Juv (May-Aug) is like HY/SY ♀, but has distinct, buffy wing bars; juv ♀ = ♂. CP/BP (Mar-Aug). ♀ wg(n35) 58-66, tl(n20) 47-54; ♂ wg(n46) 63-72, tl(n43) 50-57.

HY/SY ♀♂ (Sep-Aug): Body plumage entirely brownish; flight feathers uniformly fresh in Sep-Oct; most or all pp covs narrow, faded, relatively abraded (Fig. 138), and brown, often (see **Molt**) contrasting with the darker brown, 1-3 replaced outer covs (Fig. 136**B-C**) in Nov-Aug; the outermost 4-8 pp and the innermost 2-6 ss replaced, fresh, and dark brown, contrasting with the paler brown inner pp and outer ss (Fig. 136**A-B**) in Nov-Aug, sometimes with the inner 1-3 pp and outer 1-3 ss also contrastingly fresh (Fig. 136**D**); rects uniformly tapered (Sep-Oct), or uniformly truncate (Nov-Aug). **Note: For birds in both supplemental (Sep-Oct) and first-basic (Nov-Aug) plumages, unless there are some purple or red body feathers present (see HY/SY ♂), the sexes are not separated reliably by plumage alone,** although for HY/SYs in brown plumage, rects tinged dusky or bluish may be a reliable indicator of ♂♂ (but beware that AHY/ASY ♀♀ also can have dusky-bluish rects); more study is needed. SYs can be sexed by CP/BP in Mar-Aug. Some intermediates can occur that are not reliably aged, especially ♀-plumaged birds in May-Jul, when plumage can become quite worn.

AHY/ASY ♀ (Sep-Aug): Body plumage brown, the rump sometimes tinged greenish; outer pp covs uniformly broad, truncate, relatively fresh (Fig. 138), and dark brown; outer pp and inner ss uniformly adult (Fig. 133F) and dark brown. **Note: See HY/SY ♀♂.**

HY/SY ♂ (Nov-Oct): Plumage, molt-limit, and flight-feather criteria as in HY/SY ♀♂ (above), but one to a few (adventitiously replaced) purple or red body feathers present in Nov-Jun, or plumage becoming purple and red (from brown) in Jun-Oct during the 2nd PB. **Note: HY/SY ♂♂ also average slightly duskier rects than HY/SY ♀♀, and some ♂♂ may have the head and throat tinged peach, but more study is needed on sexing HY/SYs; see HY/SY ♀♂.**

AHY/ASY ♂ (Oct-Sep): Body plumage entirely purple and red, the feathers edged brown in Oct-Mar; molt-limit, wing-cov and flight-feather criteria as in AHY/ASY ♀, except that the flight feathers are uniformly dusky blackish with dark bluish edging.

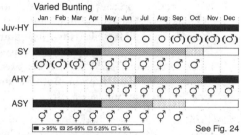

Hybrids reported—Painted Bunting.

References—Ridgway (1901), Storer (1961), L.R. Wolfe *in* Bent *et al.* (1968), Oberholser (1974), Phillips & Holmgren (1980), Howell & Webb (1995), Pyle (1997c).

PAINTED BUNTING
Passerina ciris

PABU
Species # 6010
Band size: 1C

Geographic variation—Subspecies taxonomy follows the recommendation of Thompson (1991a) to consider the species monotypic (synonymizing a previously recognized subspecies); see also Mearns (1911), Blake (1950), Storer (1951), Sutton (1967), Oberholser (1974), Wetmore *et al.* (1984), Thompson (1992). Birds of sc.KS to se.NM-s.TX (*"P.c. pallidior"*), or west of longitude 94° W, average larger and paler, but differences are broadly clinal and obscured by substantial individual variation.

Molt—PS/PB: HY incomplete (Jun-Nov), AHY complete (Aug-Oct); PA limited-partial (Dec-May). A presupplemental molt (see p. 16) occurs in some or all HYs, with the body plumage being replaced once on the summer grounds or on migration in Jun-Oct and again (during the 1st PB), on the summer or the winter grounds (with the flight feathers) in Sep-Nov. The presupplemental molt, 1st PB, and adult PB of western birds (see **Geographic variation**) occur primarily on migration and the winter grounds, whereas those of eastern birds occur on the summer grounds. The presupplemental molt includes few if any med and gr covs and no terts or rects. The 1st PB is eccentric (see p. 208 and Fig. 136), with all gr covs, the outermost 3-7 pp, the innermost 2-5 ss, the outermost 0 (~60%) to 4 pp covs, and the rects replaced. The 1st PA includes 0 (~30%) to 7 inner gr covs and sometimes (in ~30% of birds) 1-3 terts, but no rects. The adult PA includes 6 to 10 (~56%) inner gr covs and sometimes (in ~30% of birds) 1-

3 terts, but no rects. In ♂♂ of both age groups, feathers (including the terts and gr covs) replaced during the PA can be either green or colored (red or blue). This may relate to timing, as in the tanagers (which see); more study is needed.

Skull—Pneumaticization completes in HY/SY from 1 Nov. Some SYs retain windows (> 2 mm; Fig. 11**D**) through spring/summer.

Age/Sex—Juv (May-Jul) has nearly uniformly brownish-olive plumage and brown flight feathers; juv ♀ = ♂. CP/BP (Mar-Sep). ♀ wg(n100) 61-73, tl(n100) 48-57; ♂ wg(n100) 63-78, tl(n100) 52-60.

HY/SY ♀♂ (Sep-Aug): Body plumage entirely dull (Aug-Sep) to brightish (Oct-Aug) green and yellow; flight feathers uniformly juvenal in Sep-Oct; most or all (see **Molt**) outer pp covs narrow, tapered, somewhat abraded, and brown with little or no green edging (Fig. 138); the outermost 3-7 pp, the innermost 2-5 ss, and sometimes the outermost 1-4 pp covs replaced in Oct-Nov, dark brown with green edging, contrasting with the retained inner pp, outer ss, and most or all pp covs pale brownish without green edging (Fig. 136**A-B**); rects uniformly tapered (Sep-Oct) to uniformly truncate (Nov-Aug). **Note: For birds in both supplemental (Sep-Oct) and first-basic (Nov-Aug) plumages, unless there are some red or blue body feathers present (see HY/SY ♂), the sexes usually are not separated reliably by plumage alone; occasional HY/SY ♀♀ can be sexed by duller plumage in Oct-Jul, and SYs can be sexed by CP/BP in Mar-Sep. Both SYs and ASYs can have mixed generations of gr covs and terts in Mar-Sep (see Molt).**

AHY/ASY ♀ (Oct-Sep): Body plumage entirely green, occasionally with a few red and/or blue feathers of AHY/ASY ♂♂; outer pp covs broad, truncate, relatively fresh, and dusky with relatively distinct and broad, green edging (Fig. 138); outer pp and inner ss uniformly adult (Fig. 133**F**) and dark brown with green edging. **Note: See HY/SY ♀♂.**

HY/SY ♂ (Nov-Oct): Plumage, molt-limit, and flight-feather criteria as in HY/SY ♀♂ (above), but body plumage averages brighter, and one to a few blue or red body feathers sometimes are present in Nov-Jun (~43% of SYs in Apr-Jun), or are incoming during the 2nd PB in Jun-Oct. **Note: See HY/SY ♀. Note that in ♂♂ of any age, feathers adventitiously replaced in Jan-Jun can be green rather than blue or red (see also AHY/ASY ♂).**

AHY/ASY ♂ (Oct-Sep): Head entirely blue and underparts entirely red, the feathers edged greenish when fresh; outer pp covs broad, truncate, relatively fresh, and dusky blue with rusty edging (Fig. 138). **Note: See HY/SY ♀. In western populations, some molting ASY ♂♂, with old red and/or blue feathers remaining, may be distinguished through Oct or later. The replaced flight feathers and gr covs in Mar-Aug can be either green or dusky blue, with rusty edging; often the innermost 1-2 pp and 1-3 terts replaced in Aug are green. More study is needed.**

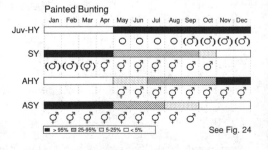

Painted Bunting

See Fig. 24

Hybrids reported—Indigo Bunting, Varied Bunting. Island (Common) Canary in captivity.

References—Dwight (1900a), Ridgway (1901), Storer (1951, 1961), Phillips *et al.* (1964), A. Sprunt Jr. *in* Bent *et al.* (1968), Fisk (1974), Oberholser (1974), Taylor (1974), Tipton & Tipton (1978), Thompson (1991a, 1991b, 1992), Young (1991), Thompson & Leu (1994), Pyle (1997c); E.J. Fisk (*in litt.* to the BBL); C.W. Thompson (pers. comm.); IBP (MAPS) data.

DICKCISSEL
Spiza americana

DICK
Species # 6040
Band size: 1B

Geographic variation—No subspecies are recognized.

Molt—PB: HY partial (Jul-Oct), AHY complete (Jun-Oct); PA limited (Dec-Apr). The PBs commence on the summer grounds but can complete on migration or on the winter grounds; it is possible that molt on the summer grounds is a presupplemental molt (see p. 16); more study is needed. The 1st PB includes all med and gr covs, sometimes (in ~35% of birds) 1-3 terts, and occasionally (in ~10% of birds) 1-2 central rects (r1). The PA may occur continuously from Oct-Apr and occasionally can include a few med covs.

Skull—Pneumaticization completes in HY/SY from 1 Nov. Some SYs retain windows (> 2 mm; Fig. 11**D**) through spring.

Age/Sex—Juv (May-Aug) is similar to HY/SY ♀, but has buffier underparts and two distinct, pale wing bars; juv ♀=♂, although most juvs can be sexed by wg (see below). CP/BP (Apr-Aug). Measurements are very useful for sexing: ♀ wg(n100) 69-78, tl(n22) 49-55; ♂ wg(n100) 77-86, tl(n24) 54-62.

HY/SY ♀ (Sep-Aug): Wg 69-76; supercilium and breast usually without yellow (through Mar); lesser covs brown or brown mixed with some rufous; med covs brown with narrow, buff tipping (see Fig. 284; occasionally some replaced inner covs can be fresher and tipped pale rufous in Mar-Aug); 1-3 terts sometimes replaced, contrasting with the older middle ss (s4-s6; Fig. 133**D-E**); outer pp covs narrow, tapered, relatively abraded, and pale brown with little or no pale edging (Fig. 138); central rects (r1) occasionally replaced, contrastingly fresh; outer rects tapered, pointed (Fig. 319), and relatively abraded; upper breast without black. **Note: Combine with measurements for reliable separation from HY/SY ♂♂ in Sep-Mar.**

AHY/ASY ♀ (Sep-Aug): Wg 71-78; supercilium and breast usually with some yellow; lesser covs primarily rufous; med covs brown with pale rufous tips (see Fig. 284); terts and middle ss (s4-s6) uniformly adult (Fig. 133**F**); outer pp covs broad, truncate, relatively fresh, and dusky brown, usually with narrow, pale rufous edging (Fig. 138); rects uniformly adult, relatively truncate (Fig. 319), and relatively fresh; upper breast without black.

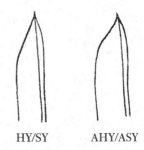

HY/SY   AHY/ASY

FIGURE 319. The shape of the outer rectrices (r4-r6) by age in Dickcissel.

HY/SY ♂ (Sep-Aug): Wg 77-84; supercilium and breast usually with some yellow in Sep-Mar; lesser covs brown or brown mixed with some rufous; med covs brown with moderately broad, rusty-buff tipping (see Fig. 284; occasionally some replaced inner covs may have broad, rufous tips in Mar-Aug); molt-limit and flight-feather criteria as in HY/SY ♀; upper breast with little or no black (Sep-Mar), or with a moderate amount of black, mottled with whitish (Mar-Aug). **Note: Combine with measurements for reliable separation from HY/SY ♀♀ in Sep-Mar.**

AHY/ASY ♂ (Sep-Aug): Wg 79-86; supercilium and breast with yellow; lesser covs rufous; med covs with broad, rufous tips (see Fig. 284); molt-limit, wing-cov and flight-feather criteria as in AHY/ASY ♀; upper breast with substantial black (can be obscured by yellow feather tips in fall).

Hybrids reported—Possibly with Blue Grosbeak, although this reported hybrid may refer to a melanistic Dickcissel.

References—Dwight (1900a), Ridgway (1901), Gross (1921), Forbush (1929), Roberts (1955), Zimmerman (1965), ffrench (1967), A.O. Gross *in* Bent *et al.* (1968), Wood (1969), Oberholser (1974), Sibley (1994), Pyle (1997c); A.O. Gross (*in litt.* to the BBL); IBP (MAPS) data, PRBO data.

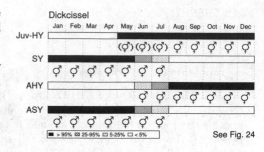

See Fig. 24

BLACKBIRDS AND ORIOLES

ICTERIDAE

Twenty-two species. Family characters include generally slender and often decurved bills, long tails, strong legs, and lack of rictal bristles. Blackbirds and orioles have 9 visible primaries, 9 secondaries, and 12 rectrices (occasionally 13 in meadowlarks). The first prebasic molt is variable, being complete or almost complete in most of the blackbirds and partial to incomplete in most of the orioles. More study is needed on the retention patterns of the juvenal underwing coverts in blackbirds and other birds showing complete or near-complete first prebasic molts; it is possible that pale feathers may actually be those of first basic rather than of juvenal plumage. The timing and locality of the prebasic molts in the orioles is variable, and certain species undergo eccentric replacement patterns in some or all individuals. Most species show plumage differences by age and sex and, in some species, molt limits and the shape of the rectrices are reliable ageing criteria. Wing and tail lengths also are very useful if not entirely reliable for sexing, there being little or no overlap between the smaller females and the larger males. Breeding condition characters are reliable for sexing all icterids in spring/summer, except for female cowbirds, which do not develop brood patches.

BOBOLINK
Dolichonyx oryzivorus

BOBO
Species # 4940
Band size: ♀ 1B, ♂ 1A

Geographic variation—No subspecies are recognized. Western birds average larger than eastern birds (Ridgway 1902, Behle 1985), but differences are completely clinal and too slight to warrant subspecies recognition.

Molt—PB: HY partial (Jul-Oct), AHY complete (Jul-Oct); PA complete (Jan-Jun). The PBs occur on the summer grounds or can be suspended, completing on the winter grounds. Likewise, PAs can complete on the summer grounds. The 1st PB (prior to migration) includes all med covs, 8 to 10 (~89%) inner gr covs and occasionally (in ~5% of birds) 1-2 terts, but no rects. It is possible that more feathers are replaced by HYs on the winter grounds; however, the occurrence of occasional replacement of the outer pp or other flight feathers before or after the migration requires confirmation. Occasional AHYs (~8%) can retain middle ss (among s4-s6) and rarely the outermost 1-2 pp (p8-p9) for migration and (probably) until the PA; more study is needed. Some birds (SYs only?) rarely can retain middle ss during the PAs, but in the great majority of birds this molt is complete.

Skull—Pneumaticization completes in HY/SY from 1 Nov into Jan.

Age—Juv (Jul-Aug) has indistinct spotting on the throat and upper breast and lacks streaking on the flanks; juv ♀ = ♂ by plumage, but see measurements under **Sex**. The following is reliable in basic plumage only. No reliable criteria are known to age alternate-plumaged (Apr-Jul) birds, although look for brown-tipped pp covs on SY ♂♂, *vs* uniformly black covs on ASY ♂♂, and occasional retained middle ss (among s3-s6) on both sexes (see **Molt**), that may indicate SY; more study is needed.

Basic Plumage (Aug-Apr)

HY/SY (Aug-Apr): Molt limits occasionally occur among the gr covs (Fig. 133**D-E**; see **Molt**), 1-2 retained outer covs worn and brown with buff tips, contrasting with the fresher, duskier, and yellowish-edged, replaced inner covs; 1-2 terts occasionally replaced, contrasting with the older middle ss (s4-s6; Fig. 133**D-E**); outer pp covs narrow, tapered, somewhat abraded (Fig. 138**A**), and dusky brown with buff edging; outer rects tapered, sharply pointed (Fig. 320), and relatively abraded; breast and flanks without distinct, black markings. **Note: In addition,**

HY/SYs average buffier upperparts and edges to the terts and richer yellow underparts than AHY/ASYs. Some ♀♀ can be difficult to age.

AHY/ASY (Aug-Apr): Wing covs, terts, and middle ss (s4-s6) uniformly adult (Fig. 133**F**); outer pp covs broad, truncate, relatively fresh (Fig. 138**B**), and dusky with grayish edging; outer rects truncate, bluntly pointed (Fig. 320), and relatively fresh; ♂♂ with the breast and/or throat feathers usually with distinct, black centers, and the flanks with distinct, black streaks. **Note: See HY/SY.**

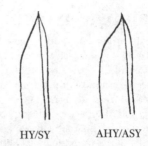

FIGURE 320. The shape of the outer rectrices (r4-r6) by age in basic-plumaged (Aug-Mar) Bobolinks.

Sex—CP/BP (May-Aug). Measurements are useful: ♀ wg(n100) 82-93, tl(n100) 55-66; ♂ wg(n100) 91-105, tl(n100) 63-75; see **Geographic variation**.

♀: Wg < 91 and/or tl < 63; crown, head, flight feathers and underparts brown, without black or blackish feathers. **Note: The small percentage of birds with wg 91-93 and tl 63-66 can be sexed in combination with age, as these will be AHY/ASY ♀♀ or HY/SY ♂♂. See also ♂.**

♂: Wg > 93 and/or tl > 66; underparts sometimes with one or more black-centered feathers (AHY/ASYs, Aug-Mar), or crown, underparts and flight feathers entirely or partially black (Apr-Jul). **Note: See ♀. Also, beware of a few old ♀♀ that may obtain a few black feathers in Apr-Jul.**

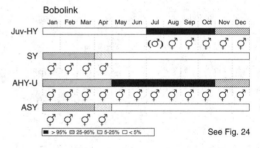

References—Stone (1896), Dwight (1900a), Ridgway (1902), Forbush (1927), Jones (1930), Parkes (1952b), Roberts (1955), Bent (1958), Meanley (1967), Wood (1969), Oberholser (1974), Sheppard & Klimkiewicz (1976), Bollinger & Gavin (1989), Cramp & Perrins (1994b), Martin & Gavin (1995), Pyle (1997c); B. Meanley (*in litt.* to the BBL); PRBO data.

RED-WINGED BLACKBIRD
Agelaius phoeniceus

RWBL
Species # 4980
Band size: ♀ 1A, ♂ 2

Species—From the corresponding plumages of Tricolored Blackbird by p9 usually ≤ p6 (Fig. 321; p9 − p6 -6 to 1 mm); tail graduated (longest r − r6 4-12 mm when fresh, to 0 mm when worn); bill relatively short and stout (see Table 11, especially the ratio of the bill length ÷ depth); ♀♀ sooty to pale grayish, with the nape and/or central back feathers often with chestnut edging, the chin and throat often with a peach or pinkish wash, and the undertail covs usually without pale gray edging; AHY/ASY ♂ with dull black plumage, and outer med covs black or buffy whitish to yellow, often mixed with black (Fig. 322**A-E**). Tawny-shouldered Blackbird (*A. humeralis*), a vagrant to FL, is smaller (♀ wg 92-98, tl 69-75; ♂ wg 99-107, tl 74-84) and has pale cinnamon-rufous in the lesser covs of all age/sex groups.

TABLE 11. Bill measurements of Red-winged and Tricolored Blackbirds.

		exp culmen	depth at tip of nares	exp culmen ÷ depth
Red-winged Blackbird[1]	♀	15.3-22.0	6.5-10.4	1.94-2.51
	♂	18.2-26.5	7.4-12.5	1.98-2.55
Red-winged Blackbird[2]	♀	17.5-19.9	7.4-10.0	1.99-2.37
	♂	19.5-23.0	8.1-12.3	2.04-2.35
Tricolored Blackbird	♀	17.5-19.9	6.2-7.9	2.41-3.00
	♂	19.5-23.0	7.1-8.9	2.44-3.02

[1] See **Geographic variation**.
[2] Random sample of 30 birds (of each sex) that have bill lengths within the range of Tricolored Blackbird.

Geographic variation—Moderate to well marked, but broadly clinal and differences are obscured by substantial individual variation, probably the result of frequent mixing. Subspecies taxonomy follows E.R. Blake *in* Paynter (1968), as modified by the suggestions of Howe *et al.* (1977) and Browning (1990); see also Ridgway (1902), Oberholser (1907, 1918e, 1919k, 1974), J.W. Mailliard (1910), Grinnell (1914b), J. Mailliard (1915), van Rossem (1926, 1942c), Howell & van Rossem (1928), Swarth (1929), Bishop (1938), Taverner (1939), Behle (1940, 1948, 1985), Twomey (1942), Snyder & Lapworth (1953), Todd (1963), Phillips *et al.* (1964), Mengel (1965), Power (1969, 1970a, 1970b), Browning (1974, 1978), Dickerman (1974), Rea (1983), James *et al.* (1984), Godfrey (1986), Gavin *et al.* (1991), Stevenson &

p9 usually ≤ p6

FIGURE 321. The wing morphology of Red-winged Blackbird.

Anderson (1994). Eight other subspecies occur in Mex-C.Am. In the following, the plumages of HY/SY ♂♂ should be intermediate between those of ♀♀ and AHY/ASY ♂♂, averaging duskier than the former and averaging more black in the med and gr covs (by subspecies) than the latter (see Fig. 322). Except in the Coastal Western Subspecies Group (see below) ♀♀ are similar in plumage (and likely inseparable), showing substantial intrasubspecific variation. Note also that juv-HY/SYs average shorter bill lengths (through the first spring) and slightly shorter wg and tl (through the 2nd PB) than AHY/ASYs.

Coastal Western (*A.p. californicus*) Group. Medium in size; ♀♀ dark; med covs of ♂♂ black or with black.

A.p. mailliardorum (res coastal cw.CA, Mendocino-Monterey Cos): Medium large; tl relatively short; bill small (exp culmen ♀ 15.4-18.3, ♂ 18.5-22.5; depth at tip of nares ♀ 6.7-7.7, ♂ 7.4-8.8); ♀♀ with the underparts sooty with narrow, grayish streaks; AHY/ASY ♂♂ with the tips of the outer med covs deep tawny with substantial black, to entirely black (Fig. 322**D-E**). ♀ wg(n16) 99-110, tl(n10) 70-77; ♂ wg(n15) 116-131, tl(n15) 82-92.

A.p. californicus (br & wint c.CA, Tehama-e.Los Angeles Cos): Medium in size; bill medium in size (exp culmen ♀ 15.3-17.5, ♂ 18.5-21.2; depth at tip of nares ♀ 7.4-8.8, ♂ 8.3-10.1); ♀♀ with the underparts variable, from medium-dark gray with indistinct streaks, to sooty with narrow, grayish streaks throughout; AHY/ASY ♂♂ with the tips of the outer med covs deep tawny with substantial black, to entirely black (Fig. 322**D-E**). ♀ wg(n14) 100-108, tl(n14) 69-78; ♂ wg(n34) 120-130, tl(n34) 86-98.

FIGURE 322. Variation in the pattern of the eighth median covert (third from the outside) by sub-species in AHY/ASY ♂♂ Red-winged Blackbirds. Note that HY/SY ♂♂ average more black by sub-species, but that subspecific differences are similar. See **Geographic variation** for details.

A.p. aciculatus (br & wint sc.CA, c.Kern Co): Medium large; bill very long (exp culmen ♀ 18.4-22.0, ♂ 22.1-26.5; depth at tip of nares ♀ 7.7-9.3, ♂ 8.6-11.3); ♀♀ with the underparts sooty with narrow, gray-ish streaks; AHY/ASY ♂♂ with the tips of the outer med covs tawny with a narrow, black terminus (Fig. 322**B**). ♀ wg(n19) 102-108, tl(n19) 73-81; ♂ wg(n22) 123-132, tl(n22) 90-100.

A.p. neutralis (res coastal sw.CA, San Luis Obispo-San Diego Cos): Medium large; bill medium in size (exp culmen ♀ 16.0-18.6, ♂ 19.1-23.2; depth at tip of nares ♀ 8.7-10.4, ♂ 9.6-11.0); ♀♀ with the under-parts medium-dark gray with indistinct, dusky streaks; AHY/ASY ♂♂ with the tips of the outer med covs tawny with a moderate amount of black (Fig. 322**B-C**). ♀ wg(n29) 96-105, tl(n10) 71-80; ♂ wg(n26) 121-131, tl(n26) 88-99.

Interior Western (*A.p. sonoriensis*) Group. Large; ♀♀ pale; outer med covs of ♂♂ with little or no black.

A.p. caurinus (br coastal sw.BC-nw.CA, wint to s.CA): Medium in size; bill long and relatively slender (exp culmen ♀ 16.6-19.6, ♂ 19.5-24.7; depth at tip of nares ♀ 6.5-8.4, ♂ 7.8-9.8); ♀♀ with the under-parts medium-dark gray with indistinct streaks; AHY/ASY ♂♂ with the tips of the outer med covs deep tawny and yellow, occasionally with light, black mottling (Fig. 322**A-B**). ♀ wg(n24) 98-107, tl(n17) 73-83; ♂ wg(n20) 117-127, tl(n20) 86-97.

A.p. sonoriensis (br & wint desert se.CA-s.NV to se.AZ): Medium large; bill long and relatively slender (exp culmen ♀ 16.3-18.8, ♂ 20.1-24.0; depth at tip of nares ♀ 6.8-8.2, ♂ 7.5-10.0); ♀♀ with the under-parts pale gray with indistinct streaks; AHY/ASY ♂♂ with the tips of the outer med covs tawny with light, black mottling on at least some feathers (Fig. 322**B**). ♀ wg(n48) 99-111, tl(n23) 73-85; ♂ wg(n73) 121-131, tl(n73) 87-100. Birds of s.NV to se.CA-sw.AZ ("*thermophilus*") may average larger and brown-er (♀♀), but differences, if present, are very slight and obscured by individual variation.

A.p. nevadensis (br interior s.BC to e.CA-sw.UT, wint to sw.CA-s.AZ): Large; bill long (exp culmen ♀ 18.4-21.9, ♂ 22.8-25.4; depth at tip of nares ♀ 6.8-9.1, ♂ 7.8-10.2); ♀♀ with the underparts pale gray with indistinct streaks; AHY/ASY ♂♂ with the tips of the outer med covs medium tawny-buff, sometimes streaked black (Fig. 322**A-B**). ♀ wg(n33) 95-109, tl(n24) 72-83; ♂ wg(n45) 115-133, tl(n38) 88-102.

A.p. zasterius (br ID-w.MT to w.WY, wint to UT-TX): Large; bill medium long and relatively slender (exp culmen ♀ 15.9-18.6, ♂ 20.6-23.9; depth at tip of nares ♀ 6.7-8.6, ♂ 7.9-9.8); AHY/ASY ♂♂ with the tips of the outer med covs medium tawny-buff, without black (Fig. 322**A**). ♀ wg(n10) 101-111, tl(n10) 72-82; ♂ wg(n10) 123-135, tl(n10) 88-102.

A.p. stereus (br e.MT-ND to c.CO, wint to AZ-w.TX): Large; bill medium small (exp culmen ♀ 15.5-18.6, ♂ 18.7-22.4; depth at tip of nares ♀ 7.2-9.2, ♂ 8.4-10.4); AHY/ASY ♂♂ with the tips of the outer med covs medium tawny-buff, without black (Fig. 322**A**). ♀ wg(n10) 100-107, tl(n10) 73-82; ♂ wg(n10) 122-132, tl(n10) 90-104.

A.p. fortis (br SD-n.AZ to w.KS-n.TX, wint to s.AZ-n.FL): Large; bill medium in size (exp culmen ♀ 15.4-17.7, ♂ 18.2-23.5; depth at tip of nares ♀ 8.1-10.0, ♂ 9.7-12.5); AHY/ASY ♂♂ with the tips of the outer med covs deep tawny, without black (Fig. 322**A**). ♀ wg(n80) 96-109, tl(n74) 69-83; ♂ wg(n100) 118-133, tl(n100) 89-105. Birds breeding in n-e.UT ("*utahensis*") may average smaller-billed, and birds breeding in n.AZ-n.NM ("*heterus*") may average paler (♀♀) and shorter-billed, but, in both cases, dif-ferences represent slight intergradation with other subspecies.

Mexican (*A.p. nelsoni*) Group. Small; ♀♀ pale; outer med covs of ♂♂ with some black.

A.p. megapotamus (res s.TX): Small; bill small (exp culmen ♀ 16.1-18.7, ♂ 19.3-22.2; depth at tip of nares ♀ 6.6-7.9, ♂ 7.4-9.4); AHY/ASY ♂♂ with the tips of the outer med covs tawny, usually streaked black (Fig. 322**B**). ♀ wg(n37) 88-101, tl(n37) 64-75; ♂ wg(n40) 112-120, tl(n40) 84-95.

Eastern (*A.p. phoeniceus*) Group. Medium small, ♀♀ pale, outer med covs of ♂♂ without black.

A.p. arctolegus (br s.NWT-se.BC to ne.Ont-IA, wint to e.AZ-OH to LA): Medium in size; bill relatively large (exp culmen ♀ 15.7-18.5, ♂ 19.6-23.2; depth at tip of nares ♀ 7.4-9.9, ♂ 9.5-11.7); AHY/ASY ♂♂ with the tips of the outer med covs tawny-buff, without black (Fig. 322A). ♀ wg(n60) 97-108, tl(n48) 70-80; ♂ wg(n84) 120-130, tl(n84) 85-98.

A.p. littoralis (br & wint coastal se.TX-nw.FL): Medium small; bill relatively large (exp culmen ♀ 17.0-21.1, ♂ 21.7-25.6; depth at tip of nares ♀ 7.4-8.9, ♂ 8.6-10.4); AHY/ASY ♂♂ with the tips of the outer med covs pale buff to medium tawny-buff, without black (Fig. 322A). ♀ wg(n24) 90-98, tl(n24) 67-74; ♂ wg(n15) 110-119, tl(n15) 84-93.

A.p. phoeniceus (br WI-PEI to ne.TX-FL, wint to s.TX-FL): Medium small; bill relatively long and slender (exp culmen ♀ 16.8-19.5, ♂ 19.9-22.6; depth at tip of nares ♀ 7.3-8.6, ♂ 8.1-9.8); AHY/ASY ♂♂ with the tips of the outer med covs medium buff to tawny-buff, without black (Fig. 322A). ♀ wg(n100) 88-104, tl(n100) 66-78; ♂ wg(n100) 108-127, tl(n100) 80-97. Birds of se.GA-c.FL ("*mearnsi*") and birds of s.FL ("*floridanus*") average slightly smaller, larger billed and darker (♀♀), but differences probably are too broadly clinal to warrant subspecies recognition; more study is needed on the possible validity of "*floridanus*".

Molt—PB: HY incomplete-complete (Jul-Nov), AHY complete (Jun-Sep); PA: SY limited-partial (Mar-Jun), ASY absent-limited (Mar-May). The PBs occur on the summer grounds. The 1st PB includes all flight feathers, except that occasionally (in ~6% of birds) 1-5 middle ss (among s1-s6) can be retained, and all body plumage, except possibly some to most gr underwing covs (see Family account). Reports that the juvenal terts can be retained during the 1st PB likely are in error. The PAs include some or all body feathers but no gr covs or flight feathers.

Skull—Pneumaticization completes in HY/SY from 15 Dec (as early as 15 Oct in the Coastal Pacific Subspecies Group; see **Geographic variation**). Some SYs retain windows (> 4 mm; Fig. 11**D**) and larger apneumaticized areas at the rear of the skull through at least summer. Birds with smaller windows (< 5 mm; see Fig. 186) cannot be reliably aged by skull; compare with the other ageing criteria. Also, skull can be difficult to see through the skin.

Age/Sex—Juv (May-Sep) is like HY/SY ♀♀, but is paler buff overall; juv ♀ = ♂, but measurements are reliable for sexing juvs, if fully grown (see below). CP/BP (Mar-Aug); note that many SY ♂♂ may not breed or develop CPs. ♀ wg(n100) 88-111, tl(n100) 64-85; ♂ wg(n100) 108-135, tl(n100) 80-105; see **Geographic variation**.

HY/SY ♀ (Aug-Jul): Wg < 110 and/or tl < 84 (see **Geographic variation** for small proportions of exceptions in the 1-2 larger subspecies); body plumage primarily streaked black, brown, buff, and/or whitish; lesser covs blackish with buffy-orange or orangish tips (with little or no rusty);

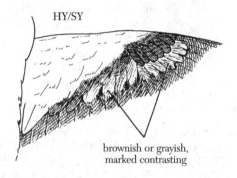

HY/SY

brownish or grayish, marked contrasting

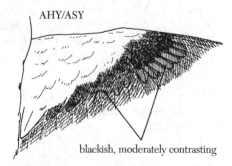

AHY/ASY

blackish, moderately contrasting

FIGURE 323. Contrasts among the underwing coverts by age in blackbirds and cowbirds. It is unknown if the more worn feathers of HY/SYs are retained juvenal feathers or replaced 1st basic feathers. Also, some HY/SYs may show reduced contrasts resembling those of AHY/ASYs. More study is needed.

chin usually whitish with a slight or no peach to reddish wash; some or all gr underwing covs often pale brownish, contrasting markedly with the adjacent, darker brown feathers (Fig. 323). **Note: Much variation occurs with plumage of HY/SYs; however, plumage combined with measurements will lead to reliable age/sex determinations of most birds. In addition, a small proportion of birds (see Molt) retain 1-5 middle juvenal ss (among s1-s6); if feathers are contrastingly brown and worn, this pattern indicates HY/SY.**

AHY/ASY ♀ (Aug-Jul): Measurements and overall body plumage as in HY/SY ♀; lesser covs variably mixed bright orange, or rusty and blackish, forming an indistinct shoulder patch; chin often washed with peach or pinkish; gr underwing covs blackish brown, with little or no contrast between adjacent feathers (Fig. 323). **Note: See HY/SY ♀.**

HY/SY ♂ (Aug-Jul): Wg > 110 and/or tl > 83 (see **Geographic variation** for small proportions of exceptions in the 1-2 smaller subspecies); body plumage varies from blackish with heavy, white or buff streaking or mottling, especially on the upperparts (Aug-Apr), to almost entirely black with some brown mottling (May-Jul); lesser covs orangish, or orange-red and yellow, many feathers mixed with variable amounts of blackish; some or all gr underwing covs often pale brownish or grayish, contrasting markedly with the adjacent, blacker feathers (Fig. 323). **Note: See HY/SY ♀.**

AHY/ASY ♂ (Aug-Jul): Measurements as in HY/SY ♂; body plumage entirely black (feathers edged brown in Aug-Mar), without whitish or buff streaking or mottling; lesser covs bright red, or red and yellow, the feathers with little or no blackish; gr underwing covs blackish, with little or no contrast between adjacent feathers (Fig. 323).

Red-winged Blackbird

See Fig. 24

Hybrids reported—Great-tailed Grackle.

References—Stone (1896), Dwight (1900a), Ridgway (1902), Mailliard (1910), Lincoln (1919), van Rossem (1926), Forbush (1927), Packard (1936), Dickey & van Rossem (1938), Wright & Wright (1944), Nero (1954, 1960, 1984), Roberts (1955), Bent (1958), Selander & Giller (1960), Meanley (1964, 1967), Dunson (1965), Payne (1969), Wood (1969), Meanley & Bond (1970), Power (1970a), Oberholser (1974), DeHaven (1975a, 1975b), Holcomb (1975), Sheppard & Klimkiewicz (1976), Crawford (1977), Miskimen (1980a, 1980b), Blank & Nolan (1983), Greenwood et al. (1983), Linz et al. (1983), Linz (1986), Linz & Linz (1987), Yasukawa & Searcy (1995), Johnsen et al. (1996); H.W. Kale (in litt. to the BBL); IBP (MAPS) data, PNR data, PRBO data.

TRICOLORED BLACKBIRD

Agelaius tricolor

TRBL
Species # 5000
Band size: 2

Species—From the corresponding plumages of Red-winged Blackbird by p9 usually ≥ p6 (Fig. 324; p9 – p6 -1 to 6 mm); tail squared (longest r – r6 0-4 mm); bill relatively long and slender (see Table 11, especially the ratio of the bill length ÷ depth); ♀♀ primarily dark sooty, the nape and/or central back feathers without chestnut edging, the chin and throat whitish, rarely with a faint pinkish or peach wash, and the undertail covs usually with distinct, pale gray edging; AHY/ASY ♂ with glossy black plumage and outer med covs buffy whitish (Aug-Feb) to white (Feb-Jul), without black (Fig. 322A).

Geographic variation—No subspecies are recognized.

Molt—PB: HY incomplete-complete (Jul-Oct), AHY complete (Jun-Sep); PA: SY limited-partial (Jan-May), ASY absent-limited (Jan-Apr). The 1st PB usually includes all flight feathers, except possibly some to all gr underwing covs (see Family account); look for a few middle ss (among s3-s6) to be retained in occasional birds, as in Red-winged Blackbird. Reports that the juvenal terts can be retained during the 1st PB likely are in error. This species occasionally attempts breeding in the fall. Although successful fledgings from such attempts may be rare, the first PB of such fledglings may not coincide with those of summer breeders; it is possible that some or all of these birds may retain flight feathers until the 2nd PB. The 1st PA includes some or all lesser covs but no gr covs or flight feathers.

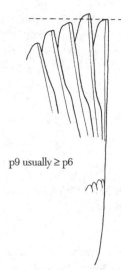

p9 usually ≥ p6

FIGURE 324. The wing morphology of Tricolored Blackbird.

Skull—Completion of pneumaticization in HY/SY is quite variable due to a protracted nesting season. HY/SYs of spring clutches complete as early as 15 Oct in southern populations, and 1 Dec in northern populations. Windows (> 4 mm; see Figs. 11**D** & 186) can persist up to a year after hatching. Caution and consideration of the plumage should be used when ageing by skull, especially in summer and fall (see Red-winged Blackbird). Note also that the skull can be difficult to see through the skin.

Age/Sex—Juv (Apr-Aug) is like HY/SY ♀♀, but generally is much paler gray and buff; juv ♀ = ♂, but measurements are reliable when birds are fully grown (see below). CP/BP (Mar-Sep). ♀ wg(n30) 101-110, tl(n20) 71-80; ♂ wg(n30) 115-127, tl(n20) 83-94.

HY/SY ♀ (Aug-Jul): Wg < 112 and/or tl < 81; body plumage primarily blackish with distinct, grayish streaks; throat whitish; lesser covs blackish with little or no reddish brown; some or all gr underwing covs often pale brownish, contrasting markedly with the adjacent, dark brown feathers (Fig. 323). **Note: Some ♀♀ may not be reliably aged. Beware of occasional offspring of fall breeding (see Molt), which may show irregular plumage.**

AHY/ASY ♀ (Aug-Jul): Measurements and body plumage as in HY/SY ♀; lesser covs with substantial reddish-brown tipping, forming a small but distinct shoulder patch; gr underwing covs blackish brown, with little or no contrast between adjacent feathers (Fig. 323). **Note: See HY/SY ♀.**

HY/SY ♂ (Aug-Jul): Wg > 112 and/or tl > 81; body plumage varies from blackish with substantial grayish mottling (Aug-Mar), to almost entirely dull black (Apr-Jul); lesser and med covs brownish red or pale buffy orange, some feathers often mixed with variable amounts of blackish (Aug-Mar only); outer gr covs mottled black; some or all gr underwing covs often brownish or grayish, contrasting markedly with the adjacent, black feathers (Fig. 323). **Note: See HY/SY ♀.**

AHY/ASY ♂ (Aug-Jul): Measurements as in HY/SY ♂; body plumage black with light gray feather edging (Aug-Mar), or uniformly glossy black (Apr-Jul); lesser covs uniformly red, the feathers with little or no blackish; outer gr covs with little or no black; gr underwing covs blackish, with little or no contrast between adjacent feathers (Fig. 323). **Note: See HY/SY ♀.**

References—Ridgway (1902), Mailliard (1910), Bent (1958), Orians (1963), Payne (1969), DeHaven *et al.* (1974), DeHaven (1975a, 1975b); W. Hamilton (pers. comm.).

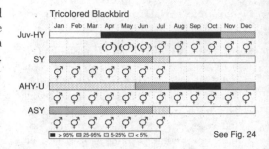

EASTERN MEADOWLARK
Sturnella magna

EAME
Species # 5010
Band size: ♀ 2-3, ♂ 3

Species—From Western Meadowlark with caution; this is one of the most difficult in-hand species identification problems. Wg ÷ tarsus smaller (♀ 2.65-2.94, ♂ 2.71-2.99); Eastern Subspecies Group (see **Geographic variation**) with the crown stripes black to blackish and the upperparts dark brown with a reddish tinge; auricular of the Southwestern Subspecies Group usually whitish to pale brown, contrasting with the blackish postocular streak; malar region usually whitish, such that the yellow of the lores and throat are not continuous, and the height of yellow above the submalar apterium (bare space between feather tracts) is small (Fig. 325; ♀ usually has no yellow above the apterium and ♂ has maximum vertical extent of yellow 1.0-5.5 mm, but use caution in Aug-Jan when yellow can be obscured by whitish or buff feather tipping); rects (especially r3) with an extensive amount of white, and the shaft streaks on r4-r6 relatively narrow (Fig. 326A-C). Intermediates can be impossible to identify in the hand, although

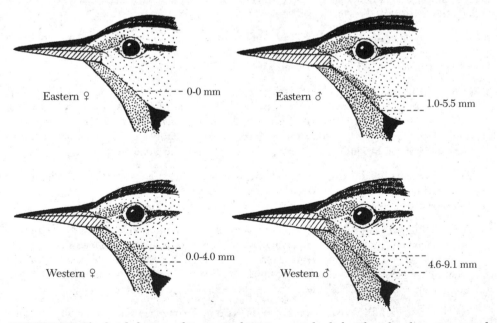

FIGURE 325. The facial plumage of Eastern and Western meadowlarks. The submalar apterium, indicating the space between feather tracts, is highlighted. The maximum vertical extent of yellow above the submalar apterium (as indicated), by sex, is one of the best means of separating the two species in the hand.

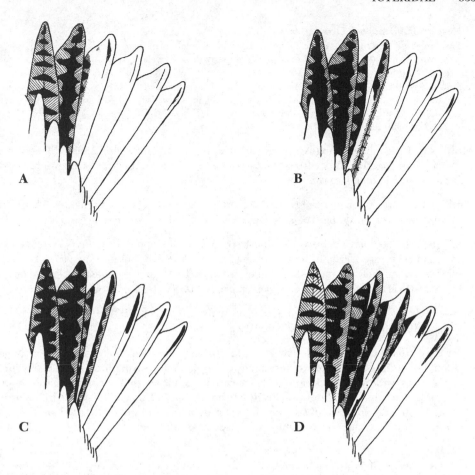

FIGURE 326. Variation in the color pattern of the rectrices in Eastern and Western meadowlarks. See text for details.

normally overlapping subspecies (see **Geographic variation**) usually are separable; the maximum extent of yellow above the submalar apterium (Fig. 325) is the best identifying feature. Birds of the paler Southwestern Subspecies Group (see **Geographic variation**), which are closest to Western Meadowlark in coloration of the upperparts and malar area, also average paler faces and more white on r3 (Fig. 326**A**).

Geographic variation—Moderately well marked between subspecies groups, but moderately weak and somewhat clinal within groups. Subspecies taxonomy follows Lanyon (1995); see also Ridgway (1902), Oberholser (1930a, 1974), Wetmore (1939, 1940), Lanyon (1962, 1966), Mengel (1965), Sutton (1967), Short (1968b), Rohwer (1972, 1976). Thirteen other subspecies occur in the W.Indies and Mex-S.Am.

Southwestern (*S.m. lilianae*) Group. Pale.

S.m. lilianae (br & wint c-se.AZ to sw.TX): Large; tl relatively short; feathers of the upperparts pale brown with buff edging; auricular whitish; underparts medium-deep yellow; white in the rects extensive (Fig. 325**A**). ♀ wg(n10) 105-116, tl(n10) 62-70; ♂ wg(n20) 116-125, tl(n10) 68-75.

S.m. hoopesi (res s.TX): Medium in size; feathers of the upperparts dark brown with buff edging; auricular washed pale brown; underparts deep yellow with an orange tinge; white in the rects variably extensive (Fig. 325**A-B**). ♀ wg(n27) 100-112, tl(n27) 62-71; ♂ wg(n47) 112-124, tl(n47) 71-79.

Eastern (*S.m. magna*) Group. Dark.

S.m. argutula (br & wint se.KS-se.TX to NC-FL): Small; feathers of the upperparts black with reddish-brown edging; auricular washed dark brown; underparts deep yellow; white in the rects moderately extensive (Fig. 325**B**). ♀ wg(n32) 96-109, tl(n28) 59-70; ♂ wg(n57) 109-120, tl(n36) 66-78.

S.m. magna (br MN-NB to n.TX-VA, wint to s.TX-n.FL): Large; tl relatively long; feathers of the upperparts blackish with medium-dark reddish-brown edging; auricular washed dark brown; underparts medium yellow; white in the rects relatively restricted (Fig. 325**B-C**). ♀ wg(n35) 104-115, tl(n28) 64-74; ♂ wg(n59) 115-130, tl(n47) 74-88.

Molt—PB: HY complete (Aug-Nov), AHY complete (Aug-Oct); PA absent. The PBs occur on the summer grounds. Birds of the Southwestern Subspecies Group (see **Geographic variation**) can extend molt into late Nov.

Skull—Pneumaticization completes in HY/SY from 1 Nov. Windows (> 4 mm; Fig. 11**D**) occur in some SYs through spring. The skull generally is difficult to see through the skin.

Age—Juv (May-Sep) has a buffy-whitish throat, streaking on the upper breast (in place of the black "V"), and buffy-edged flight feathers (through Oct-Nov); juv ♀ = ♂, but measurements are reliable for sexing juvs, if fully grown (see **Sex**). Otherwise, no reliable plumage criteria are known for ageing, although HY/SYs average paler and buffier than AHY/ASYs, sex for sex (see **Sex**). See also **Skull**.

Sex—♀ = ♂ by plumage. CP/BP (Mar-Sep). ♀ wg(n100) 96-116, tl(n100) 59-74; ♂ wg(n100) 109-130, tl(n100) 66-88; see **Geographic variation**.

♀: Wg < 109 and/or tl < 66; yellow in the face usually does not extend above the submalar apterium (Fig. 325). **Note: Measurements are reliable for sexing most birds; a few intermediates (with wg 109-116 and tl 66-74) can occur, although if the subspecies is known (see Geographic variation) practically all birds should be reliably sexed by measurements. In addition, within seasons, ♀♀ average paler and duller than ♂♂ on the head and breast, but some overlap may occur (see also Age). See ♂.**

♂: Wg > 116 and/or tl > 74; yellow in the face usually extends 1.0-5.5 mm above the submalar apterium (Fig. 325). **Note: See ♀. Also, beware that the yellow of the face can be obscured or partially obscured by whitish or buff feather tips in Aug-Jan.**

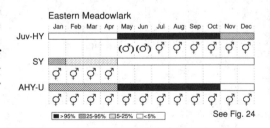

Hybrids reported—Western Meadowlark.

References—Stone (1896), Chapman (1900), Dwight (1900a), Ridgway (1902), Forbush (1927), Swarth (1929), Roberts (1955), Lanyon (1957, 1962, 1966, 1994, 1995), A.O. Gross *in* Bent (1958), Monroe (1959), Szijj (1963, 1966), Wood (1969), Rohwer (1972, 1976), Oberholser (1974), DeBenedictis (1976), Sheppard & Klimkiewicz (1976), Hubbard (1983), Wilson (1983), Zimmer (1984); M. Baumgartner, J.A. Jackson, S.A. Rohwer, J.M. Sheppard (*in litt.* to the BBL); J.L. Dunn, D.A. Sibley (pers. comm.); IBP (MAPS) data.

WESTERN MEADOWLARK

Sturnella neglecta

WEME
Species # 5011
Band size: ♀ 2-3, ♂ 3

Species—From Eastern Meadowlark (which see), with caution. Wg ÷ tarsus larger (♀ 2.89-3.22, ♂ 2.94-3.32); crown stripes dark brown to blackish; upperparts pale to moderately dark, brown with a grayish tinge; auricular brownish, not contrasting with the dark brownish postocular streak; yellow of the lores and throat often continuous, and the maximum height of yellow above the submalar apterium is larger (Fig. 325; ♀ has a maximum vertical extent of yellow 0.0-4.0 mm, usually with at least a spot, and ♂ has a maximum vertical extent of 4.6-9.1 mm, but use caution in Aug-Jan when yellow can be obscured by whitish or buff feather tipping); rects (especially r3) with a reduced amount of white, and the shaft streaks on r4-r6 relatively broad (Fig. 326**B-D**). Intermediates may be impossible to identify in the hand, although normally overlapping subspecies (see **Geographic variation** and Eastern Meadowlark) usually are separable.

Geographic variation—Weak and clinal where ranges meet. Subspecies taxonomy follows Rea (1983); see also Rathbun (1917), Phillips *et al.* (1964), Short (1968b), Oberholser (1974), Lanyon (1994). No other subspecies occur.

> *S.n. confluenta* (br coastal sw.BC-sw.CA, wint to w.AZ): Feathers of the upperparts blackish with brown edging; terts and central rects (r1) usually with moderately distinct, blackish shaft streaks (see Fig. 326**B**); breast deep yellow.
>
> *S.n. neglecta* (br interior s.BC-se.CA to s.Ont-nw.LA, wint to sw.CA-MS): Feathers of the upperparts dark brown with medium-pale buffy-brown edging; terts and central rects (r1) usually with weak or no blackish shaft streaks (see Fig. 326**D**); breast medium-pale yellow.

Molt—PB: HY complete (Aug-Nov), AHY complete (Aug-Oct); PA absent. The PBs occur on the summer grounds.

Skull—Pneumaticization completes in HY/SY from 15 Nov (as early as 1 Nov in birds of CA). Windows (> 4 mm; Fig. 11**D**) can occur in some SYs through summer, but the skull generally is difficult to see through the skin.

Age—No reliable plumage criteria are known after the 1st PB, juvs (Apr-Sep) and ageing through Oct-Nov as in Eastern Meadowlark.

Sex—♀ = ♂ by plumage. CP/BP (Feb-Sep). ♀ wg(n100) 105-117, tl(n77) 60-73; ♂ wg(n100) 117-132, tl(n88) 71-83.

> ♀: Wg < 118 and/or tl < 72; yellow in the face reduced, usually extending 0.0-4.0 mm above the submalar apterium (Fig. 325). **Note: Measurements should be reliable for sexing almost all birds; a few intermediates (wg 117 and tl 72-73) may occur. Also, the plumage of ♀♀ averages duller and buffier than that of ♂♂ (see Eastern Meadowlark). See ♂.**

> ♂: Wg > 116 and/or tl > 73. yellow in the face extensive, usually extending 4.6-9.1 mm above the submalar apterium (Fig. 325). **Note: See ♀. Also, beware that the yellow of the face can be obscured or partially obscured by whitish or buff feather tips in Aug-Jan.**

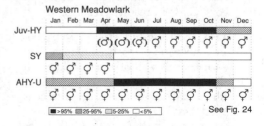

Hybrids reported—Eastern Meadowlark.

References—Chapman (1900), Ridgway (1902), Swarth (1929), Roberts (1955), Lanyon (1957, 1962, 1966, 1994, 1995), Bent (1958), Monroe (1959), Szijj (1963, 1966), Rohwer (1972, 1976), Oberholser (1974), DeBenedictis (1976), Hubbard (1983), Wilson (1983), Zimmer (1984); S.A. Rohwer (*in litt.* to the BBL); J.L. Dunn, D.A. Sibley (pers. comm.); PRBO data.

YELLOW-HEADED BLACKBIRD
Xanthocephalus xanthocephalus

YHBL
Species # 4970
Band size: ♀ 1A, ♂ 2

Geographic variation—No subspecies are recognized. See Cramp & Perrins (1994b) and Twedt & Bleier (1994).

Molt—PB: HY partial (Jul-Sep), AHY complete (Jun-Aug); PA absent-limited? (Jan-Apr). The PBs occur on the summer grounds. The 1st PB usually includes all med and gr covs but no terts or rects. The adult PB appears to commence earlier in SYs than in ASYs. More study is need-ed on the occurrence and extent of the PAs; if they do occur they probably are more extensive in SY ♂ than in the other age/sex classes.

Skull—Pneumaticization completes in HY/SY from 15 Nov through Feb. Some SYs probably retain windows (> 4 mm; Fig. 11**D**) through spring.

Age/Sex—Juv (Jun-Aug) has a buffy-yellow head (extent as in AHY/ASY ♂), a dark auricular, and whitish buff wing bars and throat; juv ♀ = ♂, but measurements are reliable for sexing juvs, if fully grown (see HY/SY ♀ and ♂, below; see also Fig. 327). CP/BP (Apr-Aug). ♀ wg(n100) 105-125, tl(n100) 72-90; ♂ wg(n100) 126-150, tl(n100) 90-112; measurements vary substan-tially by age, as well as by sex (see below).

HY/SY ♀ (Aug-Jul): Wg 105-119, tl 72-83; yellow of the head and breast usually mottled brown; outer pp covs narrow, tapered, relatively abraded (Fig. 138), and often with reduced, white tipping when fresh (Fig. 327); outer rects tapered (Fig. 139**C**) and relatively abraded.

AHY/ASY ♀ (Aug-Jul): Wg 110-125, tl 77-90; yellow of the head and breast with little or no brown mottling; outer pp covs broad, truncate, and relatively fresh (Fig. 138), without white tipping (Fig. 327); outer rects truncate (Fig. 139**C**) and relatively fresh.

HY/SY ♂ (Aug-Jul): Wg 126-137, tl 88-104; body plumage blackish brown; crown and auricular primarily brown, some-times with yellow mottling (Aug-Mar); head dingy yellow with heavy (Aug-Mar), or light (Mar-Jul), brownish mottling; pp cov and rect criteria as in HY/SY ♀, except that the white tipping of the pp covs averages broader (Fig. 327).

AHY/ASY ♂ (Aug-Jul): Wg 135-150, tl 96-112; body plumage black; crown and auricular yellow; head bright yellow with slight (Aug-Mar), or no (Mar-Jul), black-ish mottling; pp-cov and rect criteria as in AHY/ASY ♀, except that the pp covs are primarily white with black bases (Fig. 327).

HY/SY ♀   AHY/ASY ♀   HY/SY ♂   AHY/ASY ♂

FIGURE 327. The pattern of the outer primary coverts by age and sex in Yellow-headed Blackbird.

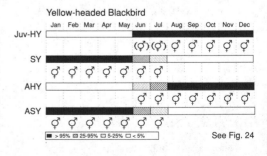

See Fig. 24

References—Ridgway (1902), Forbush (1929), Fautin (1941), Roberts (1955), Bent (1958), Oberholser (1974), Crawford (1977), Crawford & Hohman (1978), Searcy (1979), Ortega & Cruz (1992a), Cramp & Perrins (1994b), Twedt & Crawford (1995), Pyle (1997c); R.D. Crawford (*in litt.* to the BBL); PRBO data.

RUSTY BLACKBIRD
Euphagus carolinus

RUBL
Species # 5090
Band size: 2

Species—HY/SY in fall from Brewer's Blackbird by tl shorter (77-96; see **Sex**); bill thinner (depth at tip of nares ♀ 5.7-6.6, ♂ 6.0-6.9); terts edged rusty; iris of ♀♀ dark to light yellowish.

Geographic variation—Subspecies taxonomy follows Mayr & Short (1970), who considered the species monotypic (synonymizing a previously recognized subspecies); see Burleigh & Peters (1948), Parkes (1954), Todd (1963). Birds breeding in Nfl-NS ("*E.c. nigrans*") may average darker and with a bluer (*vs* greener) gloss, but differences, if present, are weak and obscured by individual variation.

Molt—PB: HY incomplete-complete (Jul-Sep), AHY complete (Jul-Sep); PA absent. The PBs occur on the summer grounds. Most (if not all) HYs possibly retain some underwing covs during the 1st PB (see Family account); otherwise all feathers typically are replaced, although look for retention of 1-3 middle ss (among s3-s6) in occasional HYs, as occurs in other blackbirds.

Skull—Pneumaticization completes in HY/SY from 1 Nov. Look for windows (> 4 mm; Fig. 11**D**) on the top and/or rear of the skull in some SYs through summer and (rarely) fall.

Age—Juv (Jun-Aug) has distinct, buffy wing bars; juv ♀ = ♂, but measurements are reliable for sexing juvs, if fully grown (see **Sex**).

HY/SY (Aug-Jul): Body plumage with heavy (Aug-Mar), to moderate (Mar-Jul), rusty edging; some or all gr underwing covs often pale brownish (♀) or grayish (♂), contrasting with the adjacent, gray (♀) or blackish (♂) feathers (Fig. 323). **Note: See U/AHY.**

U/AHY (Oct-Sep): Body plumage with a moderate amount of rusty edging in Aug-Mar, to little or none in Mar-Jul; gr underwing covs dark gray (♀) or blackish (♂), with little or no contrast between adjacent feathers (Fig. 323). **Note: It is possible that birds in this plumage can be reliably aged AHY/ASY (Aug-Jul) but more study is needed; look also for differences in the color of the pp, as in Brown-headed Cowbird.**

Sex—CP/BP (Apr-Aug). ♀ wg(n100) 101-112; tl(n20) 77-87, ♂ wg(n100) 112-123, tl(n20) 86-96.

♀: Wg < 112 and/or tl < 87; body plumage (including the rump) gray or grayish brown, without glossy black.

♂: Wg > 112 and/or tl > 87; body plumage with substantial dull to glossy black; rump black.

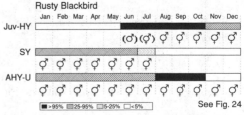

Rusty Blackbird

See Fig. 24

References—Stone (1896), Dwight (1900a), Ridgway (1902), Forbush (1927), Roberts (1955), Bent (1958), Meanley (1967), Wood (1969), Oberholser (1974), Sheppard & Klimkiewicz (1976), Avery (1995); B.L. Monroe, K.C. Parkes (*in litt.* to the BBL); R.G. McKinney (pers. comm.).

BREWER'S BLACKBIRD
Euphagus cyanocephalus

BRBL
Species # 5100
Band size: 2

Species—In fall some HY/SYs resemble Rusty Blackbird; these are separated by tl longer (92-118; see **Geographic variation** & **Sex**); bill thicker (depth at tip of nares ♀ 6.3-7.5, ♂ 6.7-7.9); terts not edged rusty; iris of ♀♀ dark.

Geographic variation—Weak, broadly clinal, and differences are obscured by individual and seasonal variation. Subspecies taxonomy follows Rea (1983); see also Grinnell (1920), Oberholser (1932, 1974), Jewett *et al.* (1953), Phillips *et al.* (1964), Browning (1978), Unitt (1984). No other subspecies occur. Note that subspecies boundaries are in need of critical definition. Plumage in ♂♂ shows little or no geographic variation; unless distinguished by measurements they cannot be identified to subspecies.

> ***E.c. minusculus*** (br & wint coastal sw.OR-CA): Small; ♀♀ medium-dark gray, the feathers with broad, rufous-brown edging when fresh. ♀ wg(n10) 111-118, tl(n10) 92-102; ♂ wg(n10) 121-131, tl(n10) 102-111.
>
> ***E.c. brewsteri*** (br sw.NWT-n.OR to WI, wint to CA-GA): Large; ♀♀ dark gray to blackish, the feathers with narrow, brown edging when fresh. ♀ wg(n10) 115-126, tl(n10) 94-105; ♂ wg(n10) 126-137, tl(n10) 105-118.
>
> ***E.c. cyanocephalus*** (br e.OR-se.CA to s.WY-n.NM, wint to s.CA-s.TX): Large; ♀♀ pale gray, the feathers with pale brownish-rufous edging when fresh. ♀ wg(n10) 115-123, tl(n10) 94-102; ♂ wg(n10) 126-135, tl(n10) 105-115. Birds of the Great Basin ("*aliastus*") average darker, but differences are obscured by individual variation and due to intergradation with *brewsteri.*

Molt—PB: HY incomplete-complete (Jul-Sep), AHY complete (Jul-Aug); PA absent-limited? (Mar-May). The PBs occur on the summer grounds. Most if not all HYs probably retain some underwing covs during the 1st PB (see Family account); otherwise all feathers typically are replaced, although look for retention of 1-3 middle ss (among s3-s6) in occasional HYs, as with other blackbirds. Reports that the juvenal terts can be retained during the 1st PB likely are in error. The PA may include some head feathers in some birds (SY ♂♂ only?); more study is needed.

Skull—Pneumaticization completes in HY/SY from 15 Nov (as early as 15 Oct in *E.c. minusculus*; see **Geographic variation**). Look for windows (> 4 mm; Fig. 11**D**) through spring in some SYs.

Age—Juv (Jun-Aug) resembles HY/SY ♀♀, but flight feathers are brownish, without gloss; juv ♀ = ♂, but measurements are reliable for sexing most juvs, if fully grown (see **Geographic variation** & **Sex**).

HY/SY (Aug-Jul): Body plumage with moderate to heavy, brownish tipping in Aug-Mar; some or all gr underwing covs often pale brownish (♀) or grayish (♂), contrasting with the adjacent, gray (♀) or blackish (♂) feathers (Fig. 323). **Note: See U/AHY.**

U/AHY (Oct-Sep): Body plumage with light to moderate, brownish tipping in Aug-Mar; gr underwing covs dark gray (♀) or blackish (♂), with little or no contrast between adjacent feathers (Fig. 323). **Note: It is possible that birds in this plumage can be reliably aged AHY/ASY (Aug-Jul) but more study is needed; look also for differences in the color of the pp, as in Brown-headed Cowbird.**

Sex—CP/BP (Mar-Aug). Measurements are useful for sexing many birds, especially those of known subspecies (see **Geographic variation**): ♀ wg(n100) 111-126, tl(n30) 92-105; ♂ wg(n100) 121-137, tl(n30) 102-118.

> ♀: Body plumage (including the rump) gray or grayish, with a brown wash, and without black

or glossy black, the plumage becoming duskier by spring.

♂: Body plumage entirely or with substantial, dull to glossy black; rump black.

References—Ridgway (1902), Roberts (1955), L. Williams *in* Bent (1958), Selander & Giller (1960), Meanley (1967), Sutton (1967), Wood (1969), Oberholser (1974), Sheppard & Klimkiewicz (1976); IBP (MAPS) data, PRBO data.

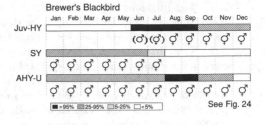

Brewer's Blackbird

See Fig. 24

COMMON GRACKLE
Quiscalus quiscula

COGR
Species # 5110
Band size: 3-3B

Species—From Boat-tailed Grackle (which see for separation from Great-tailed Grackle) by smaller size by sex, especially shorter tl (see **Sex**); wing morphology shorter (p9 < p8 ≈ p7); tail squarer (r1 – r6: ♀ 22-37 mm, ♂ 30-48 mm); ♀♀ dull black; ♂♂ glossy green to purplish; iris of AHY yellow.

Geographic variation—Moderately well marked, but broadly clinal between adjacent forms. Subspecies taxonomy follows E.R. Blake *in* Paynter (1968); see Ridgway (1902), Oberholser (1919l, 1974), Chapman (1935a, 1935b, 1936, 1939a, 1939b, 1940), Wetmore (1939), Huntington (1952), Yang & Selander (1968), Godfrey (1986), Cramp & Perrins (1994b). No other subspecies occur. The following plumage descriptions refer to both sexes, although note that the colors of ♂♂ are brighter than those of ♀♀ (see **Sex**).

> *Q.q. versicolor* (br sw.NWT-n.NM to Nfl-sw.LA, wint to s.TX-GA): Large; bill stout (depth at tip of nares ♀ 9.0-11.0, ♂ 10.2-12.0); body plumage uniformly bronze to glossy olive; wing covs, pp, and rects tinged purplish. ♀ wg(n100) 118-132, tl(n10) 105-125; ♂ wg(n100) 130-149, tl(n10) 130-148.

> *Q.q. stonei* (br c.LA to CT-w.NC, wint to NS & n.FL): Large; bill medium in depth (at tip of nares ♀ 8.4-10.5, ♂ 9.6-11.6); body plumage somewhat variably, bluish bronze (anterior) to greenish bronze (posterior), with a purple tinge; wing covs, pp, and rects greenish with diffuse bluish-purple barring. ♀ wg(n49) 119-135, tl(n10) 102-122; ♂ wg(n51) 133-150, tl(n10) 127-144.

> *Q.q. quiscula* (res e.LA to se.VA-FL): Small; bill slender (depth at tip of nares ♀ 7.8-10.1, ♂ 9.1-11.1); body plumage variably bluish (anterior) to greenish (posterior), with a purple tinge; wing covs, pp, and rects purple with diffuse greenish barring. ♀ wg(n10) 115-129, tl(n10) 97-113; ♂ wg(n10) 128-140, tl(n10) 116-128.

Molt—PB: HY incomplete-complete (Jul-Oct), AHY complete (Jul-Oct); PA absent-limited (Mar-May). The PBs occur primarily on the summer grounds. Some underwing covs possibly are retained during the 1st PB (see Family account); rarely (in ~4% of birds) 1-3 juvenal middle ss (among s3-s6), and perhaps p10, also can be retained. Otherwise, all feathers are replaced; reports that the juvenal terts can be retained during the 1st PB likely are in error. The PA may be limited to the head and breast feathers in SY ♂♂ only; more study is needed.

Skull—Pneumaticization completes in HY/SY from 15 Dec. Look for windows (> 5 mm; see Fig. 11**D**) at the rear of the skull in some SYs through summer and (rarely) fall. The skull can be difficult to see through the skin.

Age—Juv (Jun-Sep) has dull brown body plumage and flight feathers; juv ♀ averages browner than juv ♂, and the wg is reliable for sexing juvs of known subspecies, if fully grown (see **Geographic variation**).

HY/SY (Aug-Jul): Some or all gr underwing covs often pale brownish (♀) or grayish (♂), contrasting with the gray (♀) or blackish (♂), adjacent feathers (Fig. 323); rects (first basic) somewhat tapered (see Fig. 139C); iris brownish to brownish yellow, through Oct-Feb. **Note: In addition, HY/SYs average shorter wg and tl than AHY/ASYs, within each sex and subspecies (see Geographic variation), generally having measurements in the lower half of the respective ranges, *vs* the upper half in AHY/ASYs. Also, look for HY/SYs to rarely retain 1-3 juvenal middle ss (among s3-s6) and/or the outermost p (see Molt), and for HY/SYs of both sexes to average duller in plumage than AHY/ASYs (but this is complicated by sex-specific variation; see Sex). Occasional birds (especially ♀♀ and those resembling AHY/ASY in spring) may be difficult or impossible to age.**

AHY (Jan-Dec): Gr underwing covs dark gray (♀) or blackish (♂), with little or no contrast between adjacent feathers (Fig. 323); rects truncate (Fig. 139C); iris yellow. **Note: See HY/SY. It is possible that birds in this plumage can be reliably aged AHY/ASY (Aug-Jul) but more study is needed; look also for differences in the color of the pp, as in Brown-headed Cowbird.**

Sex—CP/BP (Mar-Aug); note that many ♂♂ (non-breeders?) do not develop CPs. Measurements are reliable for sexing within subspecies (see **Geographic variation**): ♀ wg(n100) 115-135, tl(n100) 97-125; ♂ wg(n100) 128-150, tl(n100) 116-148; see **Geographic variation**.

♀: Wg shorter by subspecies (see **Geographic variation**); gloss of head dull; back brownish, with little gloss; belly brown with little or no gloss. **Note: Some HY/SY ♂♂ can approach some AHY/ASY ♀♀ in plumage; combine with measurements (by subspecies) and age for accurate sexing.**

♂: Wg longer by subspecies (see **Geographic variation**); gloss of head bright; back blackish brown, moderately to substantially glossy; belly blackish brown, slightly to moderately glossy. **Note: See ♀.**

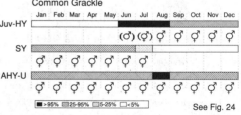

Common Grackle

See Fig. 24

References—Stone (1896), Dwight (1900a), Ridgway (1902), Forbush (1927), Gillespie & Gillespie (1932), Snyder (1937), Wood (1945), Roberts (1955), A.C. Bent & A.O. Gross *in* Bent (1958), Selander & Giller (1960), Meanley (1967), Wood (1969), Oberholser (1974), Sheppard & Klimkiewicz (1976), Cramp & Perrins (1994b), Hunt (1994), Peer & Bollinger (1997); J.J. Flora, P.B. Hamel, F.E. Ludwig (*in litt.* to the BBL); IBP (MAPS) data, PNR data.

BOAT-TAILED GRACKLE
Quiscalus major

BTGR
Species # 5130
Band size: ♀ 3, ♂ 4

Species—From Great-tailed Grackle by smaller wg and relatively shorter tl (see **Geographic variation** & **Sex**); wing morphology longer (usually p9 ≥ p8 ≥ p7); tail less graduated (r1 − r6: ♀ 31-49 mm, ♂ 46-76 mm); ♀♀ with an indistinct or no supercilium (not contrasting markedly with the darker crown) and upperparts medium-pale brown; gloss of ♂♂ tinged greenish blue to bluish; juvs with little or no indistinct streaking on the underparts; iris yellow to brown or brownish yellow, depending on the subspecies (see **Geographic variation**). From Common Grackle by larger size by sex, especially longer tl (see **Geographic variation** & **Sex**); ♀♀ brownish; ♂♂ uniformly black with a glossy-bluish tinge; iris color of AHY variable (see above). Synthesize information on geographic variation (which see) in each species of grackle before concluding the identification process.

Geographic variation—Moderate and ranges fairly well defined. Subspecies taxonomy follows Stevenson (1978); see also Harper (1934), Sprunt (1934), Lowery (1938), Selander & Giller (1961), Browning (1990), Post (1994). No other subspecies occur. Note that juv-HY/SYs have more brown in the iris through Dec and average smaller than AHY/ASYs, through the 2nd PB (see **Age**).

Q.m. major (br & wint coastal e.TX-LA): Small; tl relatively long (tl ÷ wg ♀ 0.82-0.96, ♂ 0.91-1.07); ♀ averages medium-pale brown; iris of AHY primarily brown with some yellow mottling or a yellow ring. ♀ wg(n33) 127-146, tl(n33) 109-132; ♂ wg(n55) 164-188, tl(n55) 158-191.

Q.m. alabamensis (br & wint coastal MS-nw.FL): Medium small; tl relatively long (tl ÷ wg ♀ 0.83-0.94, ♂ 0.88-1.01); ♀ averages medium-dark brown; iris of AHY primarily yellow with some brown mottling or a brown ring. ♀ wg(n16) 130-143, tl(n16) 110-133; ♂ wg(n16) 167-189, tl(n16) 154-180.

Q.m. westoni (br & wint nc-s.FL): Medium large; tl relatively short (tl ÷ wg ♀ 0.81-0.93, ♂ 0.87-0.99); ♀ averages medium-pale brown; iris of AHY brown, usually without yellow. ♀ wg(n40) 131-147, tl(n40) 108-131; ♂ wg(n47) 173-187, tl(n47) 154-182.

Q.m. torreyi (br coastal NY-ne.FL, wint to s.FL): Large; tl relatively short (tl ÷ wg ♀ 0.78-0.90, ♂ 0.82-0.98); ♀ averages medium-dark brown; iris of AHY yellow with little or no brown. ♀ wg(n39) 133-150, tl(n39) 109-143; ♂ wg(n47) 174-194, tl(n47) 147-184.

Molt—PB: HY incomplete-complete (Jul-Oct), AHY complete (Jul-Oct); PA absent-limited (Mar-Apr). Some or all underwing covs possibly are retained during the 1st PB (see Family account); occasionally (in ~15% of birds) 1-3 juvenal middle ss (among s3-s6), and perhaps p10, also can be retained. Otherwise, all feathers are replaced. The PA, if present, may be confined to SY ♂♂ only.

Skull—Pneumaticization completes in SY from 1 Jan through Jun. The skull can be difficult to see through the skin.

Age—Juv (May-Aug) resembles HY/SY ♀♀, but is paler and has a more distinct supercilium; juv ♀ averages browner than juv ♂, and the wg is reliable for sexing juvs and nestlings (see Bancroft 1984) of known subspecies, if fully grown (see **Geographic variation & Sex**).

HY/SY (Aug-Jul): Plumage brown with a buff wash (♀), or dull black with little to a moderate amount of gloss (♂); some or all gr underwing covs often pale brownish (♀) or grayish (♂), contrasting with the gray (♀) or blackish (♂), adjacent feathers (Fig. 323); rects (first basic) somewhat tapered (see Fig. 139**C**); iris brownish to brownish yellow, becoming yellow in some subspecies (see **Geographic variation**) in Oct-Feb. **Note: In addition, HY/SYs average substantially shorter wg and tl than AHY/ASYs, within each sex and subspecies (see Geographic variation), generally having measurements in the lower half of the respective ranges, *vs* the upper half in AHY/ASYs. Also, look for occasional HY/SYs to retain 1-3 juvenal middle ss (among s3-s6) and/or the outermost p (see Molt). Occasional birds (especially ♀♀ and those resembling AHY/ASY in spring) can be difficult or impossible to age; look also for differences in the color of the pp, as in Brownheaded Cowbird.**

AHY/ASY (Aug-Jul): Plumage dark brown (♀) or glossy black (♂); gr underwing covs dark gray (♀) or blackish (♂), with little or no contrast between adjacent feathers (Fig. 323); rects truncate (Fig. 139**C**); iris yellow or brown (see **Geographic variation**). **Note: See HY/SY.**

Sex—CP/BP (Feb-Aug). ♀ wg(n100) 127-150, tl(n100) 108-143; ♂ wg(n100) 164194, tl(n100) 147-191; see **Geographic variation**.

♀: Wg < 155; body plumage brownish or dusky olive, without black feathers.

♂: Wg > 155; body plumage dull to glossy black.

Hybrids reported—Great-tailed Grackle.

References—Stone (1896), Dwight (1900a), Ridgway (1902), Forbush (1927), McIlhenny (1937), Lowery (1938), A. Sprunt Jr. *in* Bent (1958), Selander (1958), Selander & Giller (1961), Meanley (1967), Wood (1969), Oberholser (1974), Pratt (1974, 1991), Bancroft (1984), Post *et al.* (1996).

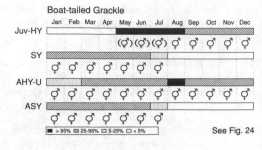

GREAT-TAILED GRACKLE
Quiscalus mexicanus

GTGR
Species # 5120
Band size: ♀ 3, ♂ 4

Species—From Boat-tailed Grackle (which see for separation from Common Grackle) by larger wg and relatively longer tl (see **Geographic variation & Sex**); wing morphology shorter (p9 < p8 < p7); tail more graduated (r1 – r6: ♀ 50-80 mm, ♂ 75-100 mm); ♀♀ with a distinct supercilium (contrasting with the darker crown) and upperparts dark olive-brown with a dusky wash; gloss of ♂♂ tinged purplish; juvs with indistinct but obvious streaking on the underparts; iris whitish to bright yellow (or dark brown to brownish yellow in juv-HY/SYs through Aug-Feb). Synthesize geographic variation (which see) in each species of grackle before concluding the identification process.

Geographic variation—Moderately well marked, but clinal where ranges meet. Subspecies taxonomy follows E.R. Blake *in* Paynter (1968); see Ridgway (1902), Griscom (1932), van Rossem (1934a, 1945a), Lowery (1938), Phillips (1950b), Selander & Giller (1961), Phillips *et al.* (1964), Dickerman & Phillips (1966), Oberholser (1974). Four other subspecies occur in Mex-S.Am.

> *Q.m. nelsoni* (br & wint desert se.CA-s.NV to sw.AZ): Small; bill slender (depth at tip of nares ♀ 8.8-10.2, ♂ 11.3-12.3); underparts of ♀♀ pale brown with a buff wash; iris whitish to pale yellow. ♀ wg(n12) 124-140, tl(n12) 117-134; ♂ wg(n10) 160-178, tl(n10) 143-185.

> *Q.m. monsoni* (br & wint s.UT-s.CO to sc.AZ-sw.TX): Medium large; tl relatively long; bill moderately slender (depth at tip of nares ♀ 9.6-10.6, ♂ 11.8-12.9); underparts of ♀♀ brownish gray; iris whitish to pale yellow. ♀ wg(n10) 140-152, tl(n10) 141-165; ♂ wg(n10) 174-192, tl(n10) 180-225.

> *Q.m. mexicanus* (br & wint nc.MX, vag to s.TX): Large; bill stout (depth at tip of nares ♀ 10.6-11.6, ♂ 12.7-14.0); underparts of ♀♀ dark brown with a dusky wash; iris pale to bright yellow. ♀ wg(n60) 142-158, tl(n60) 141-161; ♂ wg(n50) 189-206, tl(n50) 203-229.

> *Q.m. prosopidicola* (br & wint s.NE to s.TX-LA): Medium large; tl relatively short; bill moderately slender (depth at tip of nares ♀ 9.6-10.6, ♂ 11.7-12.9); underparts of ♀♀ medium-pale brown with an olive tinge; iris pale to bright yellow. ♀ wg(n82) 137-150, tl(n82) 130-149; ♂ wg(n100) 172-197, tl(n100) 181-214.

Molt—PB: HY incomplete-complete (Jun-Oct), AHY complete (Jul-Oct); PA absent-limited (Mar-Apr). Some or all underwing covs possibly are retained during the 1st PB (see Family account), and occasionally (in ~8% of birds) 1-3 juvenal middle ss (among s3-s6) and the p10 also can be retained. Otherwise, all feathers typically are replaced; reports that the juvenal terts can be retained during the 1st PB likely are in error. The PA, if present, may be confined to SY ♂♂ only.

Skull—Pneumaticization completes in SY from 1 Feb through Aug. The skull can be difficult to see through the skin.

Age—Juv (May-Aug) is like HY/SY ♀♀, but has indistinct streaking to the underparts and a dark iris; juv ♀ averages browner than juv ♂, and the wg is reliable for sexing juvs, if fully grown (see **Geographic variation & Sex**).

HY/SY (Aug-Jul): Plumage brown with a buff wash (♀), or dull black with little to a moderate amount of gloss (♂); some or all gr underwing covs often pale brownish (♀) or grayish (♂), contrasting with the gray (♀) or blackish (♂), adjacent feathers (Fig. 323); rects (first basic) somewhat tapered (see Fig. 139C); iris brownish to brownish yellow (through Oct-Feb). **Note: In addition, HY/SYs average substantially shorter wg and tl than AHY/ASYs, within each sex and subspecies (see Geographic variation), generally having measurements in the lower half of the respective ranges, vs the upper half in AHY/ASYs. Also, look for occasional HY/SYs to retain 1-3 juvenal middle ss (among s3-s6) and/or the outermost p (see Molt). Some birds (especially ♀♀ and those resembling AHY/ASY in spring) can be difficult or impossible to age; look also for differences in the color of the pp, as in Brown-headed Cowbird.**

AHY/ASY (Aug-Jul): Plumage dark brown (♀) or glossy black (♂); gr underwing covs dark gray (♀) or blackish (♂), with little or no contrast between adjacent feathers (Fig. 323); rects truncate (Fig. 139C); iris whitish to bright yellow, without brown mottling. **Note: See HY/SY.**

Sex—CP/BP (Mar-Aug). ♀ wg(n100) 124-158, tl(n100) 117-165; ♂ wg(n100) 160-206, tl(n100) 143-229; see **Geographic variation**.

♀: Wg < 159; body plumage brownish or dusky olive, without black feathers.

♂: Wg > 159; body plumage dull to glossy black.

Hybrids reported—Red-winged Blackbird, Boat-tailed Grackle.

Great-tailed Grackle

See Fig. 24

References—Ridgway (1902), Dickey & van Rossem (1938), Lowery (1938), Phillips (1950b), A.F. Skutch *in* Bent (1958), Selander (1958), Selander & Giller (1961), Oberholser (1974), Pratt (1974, 1991).

SHINY COWBIRD
Molothrus bonariensis

SHCO
Species #4961
Band size: 2

Species— ♀♀ of the subspecies of N.Am (*M.b. minimus*) from ♀♀ Brown-headed Cowbird (which see for separation from Bronzed Cowbird) and other blackbirds by small wg (82-90) but relatively long tl (61-70); bill long and slender (Fig. 328; exp culmen 15.7-17.3, depth at tip of nares 6.5-7.9; exp culmen ÷ depth 1.99-2.41); p7-p9 moderately sinuate (Fig. 329); wing morphology short (Fig. 328; p9 usually < p6; p9 – p6 -10 to 3 mm); ♀♀ medium-dark brown, often with an indistinct, pale supercilium; ♂♂ uniformly glossy purplish black, without a brown head; iris dark brown.

Geographic variation—Subspecies of N.Am markedly differentiated, perhaps to the species level. Subspecies taxonomy follows Blake *in* Paynter (1968); see Friedmann (1927, 1929). Six other subspecies occur in C-S.Am.

M.b. minimus (br & wint throughout range in N.Am): From the other subspecies by much smaller size (see **Sex**, *vs* wg > 90 in ♀♀ and > 100 in ♂♂ of all other subspecies); juv ♀ dark blackish (*vs* brown), similar in color to the juv ♂ (*vs* much paler in the other subspecies); adult ♀ with the forehead and crown darker grayish brown, and the back with more distinct, dusky streaks.

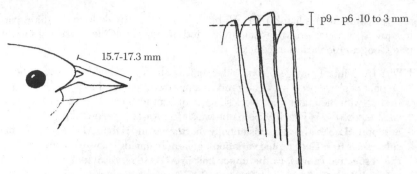

FIGURE 328. The bill shape and size and wing morphology in Shiny Cowbird.

Molt—PB: HY incomplete-complete (Jul-Oct?), AHY complete (Jul-Oct?); PA absent. The PBs probably occur primarily on the summer grounds. Some underwing covs probably are retained during the 1st PB (see Family account), and usually (~80% of birds reported in tropical America) some juvenal flight feathers (probably among s2-s6, the rects, and perhaps p10) also are retained. More study is needed, especially in the populations of N.Am, where molting strategies may have diverged from those of tropical populations.

Skull—Pneumaticization completes in HY/SY from 1 Dec. Check for windows (> 4 mm; Fig. 11**D**) in some SYs through summer.

Age—Juv (May-Aug) is similar to HY/SY ♀♀, but the wing covs are edged buffy brown, creating two buffy wing bars, and the underparts are indistinctly streaked; juv ♀ = ♂, although juv ♀♀ average slightly paler than ♂♂ (see **Geographic variation**), and wg can be used to sex juvs, if fully grown (see **Sex**); look also for juv ♂♂ to average darker underwing covs than juv ♀♀, as in Brown-headed Cowbird.

HY/SY (Aug-Jul): One or more juvenal flight feathers often retained (see **Molt**), contrastingly pale, and abraded; some or all gr underwing covs often pale brownish (♀) or grayish (♂), contrasting markedly with the adjacent, darker feathers (Fig. 323). **Note: Some intermediates (especially ♀♀ and birds resembling AHY/ASY) may be difficult or impossible to age. More study is needed (see Molt).**

U/AHY (Sep-Aug): Flight feathers uniformly adult, dark, and fresh; gr underwing covs gray (♀) or blackish (♂), showing little or no contrast with the adjacent feathers (Fig. 323). **Note: See HY/SY. It is possible that birds in this plumage can be reliably aged AHY/ASY (Aug-Jul) but more study is needed; look also for differences in the color of the pp, as in Brown-headed Cowbird.**

Sex—CP (Mar-Aug), BP does not develop in this species. ♀ wg(n20) 82-90, tl(n20) 61-70; ♂ wg(n20) 92-101, tl(n20) 71-79; measurements pertain to the subspecies of N.Am (*M.b. minimus*) only; see **Geographic variation**.

♀: Wg < 91 and tl < 71; body plumage brownish gray. **Note: Measurements pertain to *M.b. minimus* only. Beware of juv ♂♂ in Jun-Aug, before black feathers begin to emerge; compare with wg.**

♂: Wg > 90 and tl > 70; body plumage entirely or partially black. **Note: See ♀.**

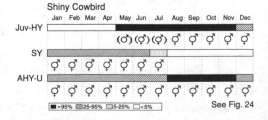

References—Friedmann (1929), Wetmore *et al.* (1984), Smith & Sprunt (1987).

BRONZED COWBIRD
Molothrus aeneus

BROC
Species # 4960
Band size: ♀ 1A, ♂ 2

Species— ♀♀ from Brown-headed Cowbird (which see for separation from Shiny Cowbird) by larger wg (97-109) and relatively longer tl (64-77); bill large (Fig. 330; exp culmen 17.7-21.2; depth at tip of nares 9.1-10.7; exp culmen ÷ depth 1.64-2.25); p7-p9 sinuate (Fig. 329); wing morphology medium in length (Fig 330; p9 – p6 -6 to 5 mm); plumage dark gray or dull black; feathers of the neck somewhat thick and hairlike, forming a neck ruff; iris of non-juvs dull to bright red.

Geographic variation—Well marked (♀♀ plumages) and ranges well defined. Subspecies taxonomy follows E.R. Blake *in* Paynter (1968); see Ridgway (1902), Friedmann (1927, 1929), van Rossem (1933, 1934b), Parkes & Blake (1965). Two other subspecies occur in Mex-S.Am.

> ***M.a. loyei*** (=*"milleri"*; br & wint se.CA-sw.NM): Medium large; tl relatively long; ♀ dark gray to brownish gray; ♂ with the rump washed violet, contrasting with the greenish-bronze back. ♀ wg(n20) 100-109, tl(n20) 69-77; ♂ wg(n20) 115-124, tl(n20) 81-89.
>
> ***M.a. aeneus*** (br & wint s.TX): Medium small; tl relatively short; ♀ brownish black to dull black; ♂ with the back and rump uniformly greenish bronze. ♀ wg(n20) 97-107, tl(n20) 64-74; ♂ wg(n20) 111-121, tl(n20) 75-84.

Molt—PB: HY incomplete-complete (Jul-Oct), AHY complete (Jul-Oct); PA absent-limited (Feb-Mar). The PBs occur primarily on the summer grounds. Some or all underwing covs possibly are retained in most HYs during the 1st PB (see Family account). Otherwise, all feathers typically are replaced during the 1st PB, although look for 1-3 middle ss rarely to be retained, as in other blackbirds. The PA is confined to the body, primarily the neck, and usually occurs in SY ♂♂ only.

Skull—Pneumaticization completes in HY/SY from 15 Nov. Check for windows (> 4 mm; Fig. 11**D**) in some spring SYs.

Age/Sex—Juv (May-Sep) is uniformly brownish to brownish gray, with indistinct streaks

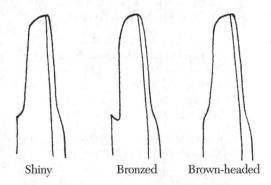

Shiny   Bronzed   Brown-headed

FIGURE 329. The shape of p8 in Shiny, Bronzed, and Brown-headed cowbirds.

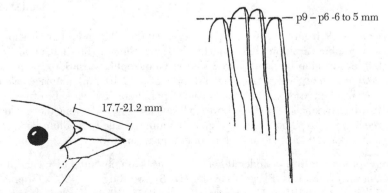

p9 – p6 -6 to 5 mm

17.7-21.2 mm

FIGURE 330. The bill shape and size and wing morphology in Bronzed Cowbird.

(*M.a. loyei*), or uniformly brownish black (*aeneus*); juv ♀ averages browner than juv ♂, and measurements are reliable for sexing juvs, if fully grown (see below and **Geographic variation**). CP (Mar-Jul); BP does not occur in this species. ♀ wg(n40) 97-109, tl(n40) 64-77; ♂ wg(n40) 111-124, tl(n40) 75-89; see **Geographic variation**.

HY/SY ♀ (Aug-Jul): Wg < 110 and/or tl < 75; body plumage brownish gray (*loyei*) or dull black with little or no gloss (*aeneus*); some or all gr underwing covs often pale brownish gray, contrasting with the adjacent, darker gray or blackish feathers (Fig. 323). **Note: Beware of juv ♂♂ (of both subspecies) and HY/SY ♂ *M.a. aeneus* that can resemble ♀♀ in plumage; always combine with measurements (see Geographic variation) for reliable sexing. Also, some HY/SYs (especially ♀♀) may replace all underwing covs (or show little or no contrast among these feathers), and would be difficult if not impossible to age; more study is needed.**

U/AHY ♀ (Sep-Aug): Wg < 110 and/or tl < 75; body plumage gray (*loyei*) or dull black with a glossy-bronze tinge (*aeneus*); gr underwing covs dark gray to blackish, with little or no contrast between adjacent feathers (Fig. 323). **Note: See HY/SY ♀. It is possible that birds in this plumage can be reliably aged AHY/ASY (Aug-Jul) but more study is needed; look also for differences in the color of the pp, as in Brown-headed Cowbird.**

HY/SY ♂ (Aug-Jul): Wg > 110 and/or tl > 77; body plumage often mixed gray or dull black, and glossy black with a bronze tinge; some or all gr underwing covs often grayish, contrasting with the adjacent, blackish feathers (Fig. 323). **Note: See HY/SY ♀.**

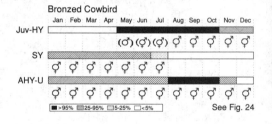

U/AHY ♂ (Sep-Aug): Wg > 110 and/or tl > 77; body plumage uniformly black with a glossy-bronze wash; gr underwing covs blackish with little or no contrast between adjacent feathers (Fig. 323). **Note: See HY/SY ♀ and U/AHY ♀.**

References—Ridgway (1902), Friedmann (1929), Dickey & van Rossem (1938), Bent (1958), Oberholser (1974), Lowther (1995).

BROWN-HEADED COWBIRD
Molothrus ater

BHCO
Species # 4950
Band size: ♀ 1B, ♂ 1A

Species—♀♀ from Shiny Cowbird by larger wg (85-104) and relatively shorter tl (57-73; see **Geographic variation**); bill stout (Fig. 331; exp culmen 12.7-16.0, depth at tip of nares 6.3-9.6; exp culmen ÷ depth 1.48-2.13; see **Geographic variation**); p7-p9 not sinuate (Fig. 329); wing morphology long (Fig. 331; p9 > p6 by 2-10 mm); plumage pale to medium-dark brown, often with an indistinct, pale supercilium; iris dark brown. ♀♀ from Bronzed Cowbird by smaller size (see above); bill smaller (Fig. 331); wing morphology long (Fig 331; see above); p7-p9 not sinuate (Fig. 329); plumage pale to medium-dark brown; feathers of the neck not thick and hairlike; iris of non-juvs dark brown.

Geographic variation—Moderate, but differences are obscured by recent mixing. Subspecies taxonomy follows E.R. Blake *in* Paynter (1968); see Ridgway (1902), Grinnell (1909b, 1914a, 1934b), Bishop (1910), Oberholser (1917d, 1938, 1974), Dickey & van Rossem (1922),

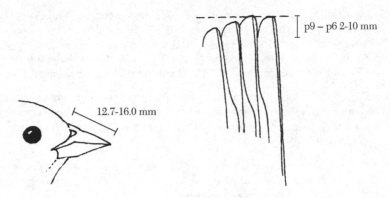

FIGURE 331. The bill shape and size and wing morphology in Brown-headed Cowbird.

Friedmann (1927, 1929), Willett (1933), Miller (1935), Dickerman & Phillips (1954), Todd (1963), Phillips *et al.* (1964), Hubbard & Crossin (1974), Rothstein (1978), Behle (1985), Godfrey (1986), Fleischer & Rothstein (1988), Ortega & Cruz (1992b). No other subspecies occur.

M.a. obscurus (br & wint w-s.CA-sw.LA): Small; bill small (nares to tip ♀ 8.6-9.8, ♂ 9.7-11.9; depth at tip of nares ♀ 6.3-7.5, ♂ 6.7-8.4; width at tip of nares ♀ 4.1-5.0, ♂ 4.6-6.1); culmen straight; ♀♀ medium-pale grayish brown; gape of nestlings and juvs yellow. ♀ wg(n100) 85-95, tl(n15) 57-67; ♂ wg(n100) 96-105, tl(n27) 63-73. Birds of c-s.CA ("*californicus*") average larger and possibly darker (♀♀), but differences are slight and obscured by individual variation.

M.a. artemisiae (br se.AK-ne.CA to w.Ont-n.NM, wint to CA-LA): Large; bill long and relatively slender (nares to tip ♀ 9.5-11.3, ♂ 11.3-13.2; depth at tip of nares ♀ 7.5-8.9, ♂ 8.0-9.7; width at tip of nares ♀ 5.1-6.0, ♂ 5.5-6.9); culmen straight; ♀♀ medium-pale brownish with a gray tinge; gape of nestlings and juvs whitish. ♀ wg(n100) 96-104, tl(n10) 63-73; ♂ wg(n100) 107-118, tl(n11) 71-79. Birds in the northeastern portion of the range ("*dwighti*") may average larger and browner (♀♀), but differences, if present, are slight and obscured by individual variation.

M.a. ater (br se.CO-TX to Nfl-n.FL, wint to AZ-s.FL; vag to s.CA): Medium large; bill medium in length and relatively stout (nares to tip ♀ 9.3-11.1, ♂ 10.4-12.6; depth at tip of nares ♀ 7.3-8.4, ♂ 8.2-9.6, width at tip of nares ♀ 5.0-6.2, ♂ 5.4-6.6); culmen decurved; ♀ dark brown; gape of nestlings and juvs whitish. ♀ wg(n60) 92-103, tl(n15) 61-71; ♂ wg(n74) 104-114, tl(n26) 67-78. Birds of NM-n.LA ("*buphilus*") may average thicker-billed and paler (♀), but differences are slight and due to intergradation with *artemisiae*.

Molt—PB: HY incomplete-complete (Jul-Oct); AHY complete (Jul-Oct); PA absent-limited (Feb-May). The PBs occur primarily on the summer grounds. The 1st PB is rarely complete, with a varying number of underwing covs possibly retained (see Family account). Otherwise, all feathers typically are replaced during the 1st PB; look for some flight feathers to rarely be retained, as in other blackbirds. Reports that the juvenal terts can be retained during the 1st PB are likely in error. The PA, primarily involving head feathers, may be more extensive in HY/SY ♂♂ and in *M.a. obscurus* than in other birds.

Skull—Pneumaticization completes in HY/SY from 1 Dec. Look for windows (> 4 mm; see Fig. 11**D**) in the rear of the skull on some SYs through Jun.

Age—Juv (May-Aug) is similar to HY/SY ♀♀, but the body feathers and wing covs are edged buff, creating two buffy wing bars; juv ♂♂ average darker underwing covs than juv ♀♀, which is useful, and wg can be used to sex juvs of known subspecies, if fully grown (see **Geographic variation & Sex**).

HY/SY (Aug-Jul): Body plumage pale gray (♀), or brown (head) and dull glossy black (♂); inner pp and tips to pp washed brownish, contrasting with the darker and grayer (♀) or blacker (♂) ss; some or all gr underwing covs often pale brownish (♀) or grayish (♂), contrasting markedly with the adjacent, darker feathers (Fig. 323). **Note: Some intermediates (especially ♀♀ and birds resembling AHY/ASY) can be difficult or impossible to age.**

AHY/ASY (Aug-Jul): Body plumage dark gray (♀), or brown and bright glossy black (♂); inner pp and tips to pp without a brownish wash, not contrasting in color with the ss; gr underwing covs gray (♀) or blackish (♂), showing little or no contrast between adjacent feathers (Fig. 323). **Note: See HY/SY.**

Sex—CP (Mar-Aug): BP does not develop in this species. Wg is reliable for sexing birds of known subspecies (see **Geographic variation**): ♀ wg(n100) 85-104, tl(n40) 57-73; ♂ wg(n100) 96-118, tl(n63) 63-79; see **Geographic variation**.

♀: Wg shorter by subspecies (see **Geographic variation**); body plumage entirely brownish. **Note: Beware of juv ♂♂ in Jun-Aug, before black feathers begin to emerge; compare with wg and subspecies (see Geographic variation).**

♂: Wg larger by subspecies (see **Geographic variation**); body plumage entirely or partially black with a brown head. **Note: See ♀.**

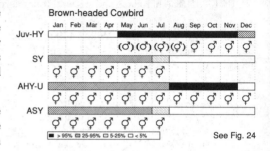

References—Stone (1896), Dwight (1900a), Ridgway (1902), Forbush (1927), Friedmann (1929), Stanley (1941), Roberts (1955), Baird (1958), Bent (1958), Selander & Giller (1960), Meanley (1967), Wood (1969, 1970), Oberholser (1974), Hill (1976), CWS & USFWS (1991), Ortega & Cruz (1992b), Lowther (1993), Ortega *et al.* (1996); R.A. Hill, R.C. Leberman, R.A. Montgomery (*in litt.* to the BBL); IBP (MAPS) data, PNR data, PRBO data.

ORCHARD ORIOLE
Icterus spurius

OROR
Species # 5060
Band size: 1B

Species— ♀♀ and HY/SY ♂♂ from Hooded and Scott's orioles by smaller size, especially the relatively short tl (wg 69-83, tl 59-76; see **Age/Sex**); wing morphology long (p9 ≥ p5 by 0-6 mm); bill short, relatively stout, and only moderately decurved (exp culmen 13.8-16.9, depth at tip of nares 4.2-5.2; Fig. 332); back greenish with a gray-brown wash and little or no blackish mottling; tail relatively square (r1 – r6 8-15 mm when fresh). Beware especially of juv ♀♀ Hooded Oriole (which see), which can be similar to Orchard Oriole in size and (especially) bill length when not fully grown. ♀♀ and HY/SY ♂♂ from Baltimore Oriole (which see for separation from Bullock's Oriole) by smaller size (see above); bill smaller (Fig. 332; see above); underparts uniformly greenish yellow; back without dusky mottling.

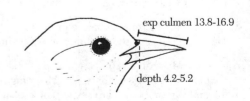

FIGURE 332. The bill shape and size in Orchard Oriole.

Geographic variation—Moderate (in ♂♂), but clinal where ranges meet. Subspecies taxonomy follows E.R. Blake *in* Paynter (1968); see Chapman (1911), Sclater (1939), Wetmore (1943), Amadon & Phillips (1947), Graber & Graber (1954), Dickerman & Warner (1962), Sutton (1967), Hubbard & Crossin (1974), Oberholser (1974). One other subspecies occurs in Mex. Between the following, ♀♀ are difficult if not impossible to separate.

I.s. spurius (br throughout range in N.Am): Averages larger (see **Age/Sex**); ♀♀ and HY/SY ♂♂ average darker yellowish; rump and belly of AHY/ASY ♂ chestnut. Birds of s.Tx ("*affinis*" or "*capensis*") average smaller and paler but differences are very slight and possibly due to intergradation toward *fuertesi*.

I.s. fuertesi (br coastal ne.Mex; vag to s.TX): Averages smaller; ♀♀ and HY/SY ♂♂ average paler yellowish; rump and belly of AHY/ASY ♂ ochre. ♀ wg(n11) 67-75, tl(n10) 61-68; ♂ wg(n13) 71-79, tl(n10) 63-71.

Molt—PB: HY incomplete (Sep-Nov), AHY complete (Aug-Oct); PA absent-limited (Jan-Apr). The PBs occur primarily on the winter grounds. The presupplemental molt (see p. 16) possibly occurs. The 1st PB is eccentric (see p. 208 and Fig. 136), with all gr covs, the innermost 3-6 ss, the outermost 5-7 pp, the outermost 0 (~19%) to 5 pp covs, and 0 (~16%) to all 12 (47%) rects typically replaced. Rarely (~3-5%) the 1st PB can be complete, perhaps in ♂♂ only. The PAs are limited to body feathers and occur more extensively in SY ♂♂ than in the other age/sex groups; this may involve a continuous overwinter molt beginning in Nov (at the completion of the PB), as in some other passerines (more study is needed).

Skull—Pneumaticization completes in HY/SY from 1 Nov. Look for windows (> 3 mm; see Fig. 11**D**) at the rear of the skull in some SYs through May.

Age/Sex—Juv (Jun-Oct) is like HY/SY ♀♀, but has buffy wing bars and tert edgings, and has fresher feathers at that time of the year; juv ♀ = ♂, but most juvs are reliably sexed by wg (see Juv-HY ♀♂), if fully grown. CP/BP (Apr-Sep). Wg is useful: ♀ wg(n100) 69-79, tl(n100) 59-72; ♂ wg(n100) 73-83, tl(n100) 62-76; includes nominate birds only (see **Geographic variation**).

Juv-HY ♀♂ (Jul-Oct): Body plumage greenish yellow and brownish, without chestnut or black feathers; flight feathers (especially rects) fresh; throat without black. **Note: Juv-HY ♀♀ and ♂♂ (before they reach the winter grounds) are usually similar in plumage, but almost all birds can be separated by wg: juv-HY ♀♀ ≤ 74 mm and juv-HY ♂♂ ≥ 74 mm. Also, some black feathering can occur on the throats of occasional HY ♂♂ before or during migration. In both sexes, SYs in Aug are separated from HYs by extremely worn flight feathers (*vs* fresh in HYs), and SY ♂♂ during this time have an extensive black patch in the throat.**

HY/SY ♀ (Sep-Aug): Body plumage greenish yellow and brownish, without chestnut or black feathers; most or all (see **Molt**) outer pp covs narrow, tapered, somewhat abraded, and brown with little or no olive edging (Fig. 138); the outermost 5-7 pp, the innermost 3-6 ss, and often the outermost 1-5 pp covs dark dusky brown, contrasting with the paler brownish, retained inner pp, outer ss, and most or all pp covs (Fig. 136**A-B**); rects tapered (Fig. 138**B**) and yellow-green with a brownish tinge, mixed tapered and truncate, or uniformly truncate and washed dusky. **Note: Beware of juv-HY ♂♂ in Oct (possibly later) that have not yet acquired black in the throat; see Juv-HY ♀♂. Occasional ♀♀ can be difficult to age.**

AHY/ASY ♀ (Sep-Aug): Body plumage greenish yellow with few or no chestnut or black feathers (a few chestnut and black feathers can be present on ASY/ATYs); outer pp covs broad, truncate, relatively fresh, and dusky brown with relatively distinct, narrow, olive edging (Fig. 138); pp, ss, and pp covs uniformly adult (Fig. 133**F**) and dusky brown; rects uniformly adult, truncate (Fig. 139**B**), greenish with a dusky or sooty wash, and relatively fresh (especially in May-Sep). **Note: See HY/SY ♀. Also, bilateral gynandromorphism (*e.g.*, left side ♀-plumaged, right side ♂-plumaged) has been reported (see Scharf & Kren 1996).**

HY/SY ♂ (Oct-2nd Oct): Body plumage primarily greenish, with one or more black feathers present in the throat, and one or more chestnut feathers often present on the rump and/or belly, becoming fully black and chestnut by their 2nd Oct; flight-feather and pp-cov criteria as in HY/SY ♀, except that the replaced pp covs are blackish and the replaced pp and rects are green with a sooty wash and blackish shaft streaks.

AHY/ASY ♂ (Oct-Sep): Body plumage black and chestnut, without greenish (feathers can be edged greenish in Oct-Mar); pp covs and flight feathers uniformly blackish.

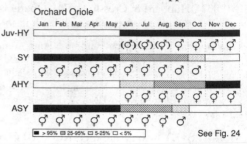

Orchard Oriole

See Fig. 24

References—Stone (1896), Dwight (1900a), Ridgway (1902), Todd & Carriker (1922), Forbush (1927), Dickey & van Rossem (1938), Bent (1958), Wood (1969), Oberholser (1974), Sheppard & Klimkiewicz (1976), Kaufman (1987b), Lehman (1988), Enstrom (1992a, 1992b), Howell & Webb (1995), Scharf & Kren (1996), Pyle (1997c); B. Walker (pers. comm.); IBP (MAPS) data, PNR data, PRBO data.

HOODED ORIOLE
Icterus cucullatus

HOOR
Species # 5050
Band size: 1A-1B

Species— ♀♀ and HY/SY ♂♂ from Orchard (which see for separation from Baltimore), Streak-backed, and Scott's orioles by medium size, and relatively long tl (wg 76-88, tl 73-94; see **Geographic variation & Sex**); wing morphology short (p9 < p5 by 3-9 mm); bill long, slender, and strongly decurved (Fig. 333; exp culmen 14.9-20.4, depth at tip of nares 4.4-5.8; see **Geographic variation**); back brownish gray, often tinged greenish, with little or no blackish streaking or mottling; tail graduated (r1 – r6 15-22 mm when fresh). Beware especially of juv ♀♀, which can be similar to Orchard Oriole in size and (especially) bill length when not fully grown (including the migratory period). From corresponding plumages of Altamira Oriole by much smaller size (see above); bill thinner (Fig. 333; depth at tip of nares < 6 mm); lesser covs brownish (♀♀) to black and white (AHY/ASY ♂♂), without orange; outer pp without distinct white at bases.

Geographic variation—Moderate and ranges fairly well defined. Subspecies taxonomy follows E.R. Blake *in* Paynter (1968); see Ridgway (1902), Grinnell (1927a), van Rossem (1945a), Sutton (1948c), Phillips (1962), Phillips *et al.* (1964), Oberholser (1974). Two other sub-species occur in Mex-C.Am.

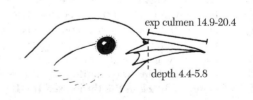

FIGURE 333. The bill shape and size in Hooded Oriole.

I.c. nelsoni (br & wint CA-sw.TX): Large; bill long (exp culmen 17.7-20.4); plumage (including the flanks) of ♀♀ medium yellow; head plumage of AHY/ASY ♂♂ yellow with a slight or no orange tinge. ♀ wg(n10) 76-85, tl(n10) 73-84; ♂ wg(n20) 84-93, tl(n20) 82-95. Birds of c-sw.CA ("*californicus*") may average greener, but differences, if present, are slight and broadly clinal.

I.c. cucullatus (br sc.TX, Terrell-Maverick Cos): Medium in size; bill medium in size (exp culmen 15.4-18.2); plumage of ♀♀ medium-dark yellow with an orange tinge or wash and contrastingly gray flanks; head plumage of AHY/ASY ♂♂ orange. ♀ wg(n10) 75-84, tl(n10) 75-83; ♂ wg(n10) 82-91, tl(n10) 84-94.

I.c. sennetti (br s.TX): Small; bill small and stout (exp culmen 14.9-18.0); plumage (including the flanks) of ♀♀ pale yellow; head plumage of AHY/ASY ♂♂ orange-yellow; ♀ wg(n7) 74-83, tl(n7) 80-89; ♂ wg(n10) 80-89, tl(n10) 84-97.

Molt—PB: HY partial-incomplete (Jul-Nov), AHY complete (Aug-Oct); PA absent-limited (Jan-Apr). A presupplemental molt (see p. 16) possibly occurs. The 1st PB can commence on the summer grounds, but occurs primarily on the winter grounds; more study is needed. The adult PB occurs primarily on the winter grounds. The 1st PB typically includes all gr covs and usually (in ~83% of birds) is eccentric (see p. 208 and Fig. 136), with the innermost 3-5 ss, the outermost 4-7 pp, the outermost 0 (~45%) to 3 pp covs, and 0 (~79%) to all 12 (3%) rects replaced. The 1st PB of *I.c. nelsoni* (see **Geographic variation**) appears to average more extensive than that of the eastern and southern subspecies. The PAs are limited to body feathers and probably occur more extensively in SY ♂♂ than in the other age/sex groups; this may involve a continuous overwinter molt beginning in November (at the completion of the PB), as in some other passerines (more study is needed).

Skull—Pneumaticization completes in HY/SY from 1 Nov. Look for windows (> 3 mm; Fig. 11**D**) in the skull of some SYs through spring.

Age/Sex—Juv (May-Aug) is like HY/SY ♀ in plumage coloration, but has buffier wing bars and fresher feathers at this time of year; juv ♀ = ♂, although some juvs of known subspecies can be sexed by measurements (see **Geographic variation** and Juv-HY ♀♂, below), if fully grown. CP/BP (Mar-Sep). ♀ wg(n42) 74-85, tl(n42) 76-91; ♂ wg(n74) 80-93, tl(n74) 82-100; see **Geographic variation**.

Juv-HY ♀♂ (Jul-Oct): Body plumage greenish yellow and brownish, without black feathers in the face or throat; flight feathers (especially rects) fresh. **Note: Juv-HY ♀♀ and ♂♂ (before they reach the winter grounds) usually are similar in plumage but generally can be separated by wg, if the subspecies is known (see Geographic variation; the wings of juvs usually will fall within the lower half of the ranges, sex for sex). Also, some black feathering can occur on the throats of occasional HY ♂♂ before or during migration; more study is needed. In both sexes, SYs in Aug are separated from HYs by extremely worn flight feathers, and SY ♂♂ during this time have extensive black in the throat, at least.**

HY/SY ♀ (Oct-Aug): Body plumage greenish yellow and brownish, without black feathers in the back, face, or throat; most or all (see **Molt**) outer pp covs narrow, tapered, somewhat abraded, and brown with little or no olive edging (Fig. 138); the outermost 4-7 pp (occasionally no pp), the innermost 3-5 ss, and often the outermost 1-3 pp covs dark dusky brown, contrasting with the paler brownish, retained inner pp, outer ss, and most or all pp covs (Fig. 136**A-B**); most or all rects tapered (Fig. 139**B**) and brownish yellow, sometimes mixed tapered and truncate. **Note: Beware of juv-HY ♂♂ in Oct or later (through Mar?) that have not yet acquired black in the throat; see Juv-HY ♀♂. Occasional ♀♀ can be difficult to age.**

AHY/ASY ♀ (Sep-Aug): Body plumage medium-bright greenish yellow, without black feathers in the back, face, throat, and/or breast (a few dusky feathers might be present on ASY/ATYs); outer pp covs broad, truncate, relatively fresh, and dusky brown with relatively distinct, narrow, olive edging (Fig. 138); pp, ss, and pp covs uniformly adult (Fig. 133**F**) and dusky brown; rects uniformly adult, truncate (Fig. 139**B**), greenish with a dusky or sooty wash, and relatively fresh (especially in May-Sep). **Note: See HY/SY ♀.**

HY/SY ♂ (Nov-Oct): Body plumage dull greenish yellow with a brownish tinge; back, face, and throat mottled blackish or black; flight-feather and pp-cov criteria as in HY/SY ♀, except that the replaced pp covs are blackish and the replaced pp and rects are green with a sooty wash and blackish shaft streaks. **Note: More study is needed on when HY/SY ♂♂ acquire black in the throat; see HY/SY ♀.**

AHY/ASY ♂ (Oct-Sep): Body plumage bright greenish yellow to orangish, with the back, face and throat fully black (feathers can be edged greenish in Oct-Mar); pp covs and flight feathers blackish. **Note: Look for some SY/TY ♂♂ to possibly be aged by having more restricted black around the face (not encircling the eye) and rects black with green mottling (vs all black with green edging when fresh, in AHY/ASY); more study is needed.**

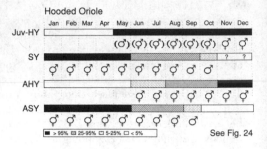

Hybrids reported—Bullock's Oriole in captivity.

References—Brewster (1902), Ridgway (1902), van Rossem (1945a), Bent (1958), Oberholser (1974), Kaufman (1987b), Lehman (1988), Howell & Webb (1995), Pyle (1997c); PRBO data.

STREAK-BACKED ORIOLE
Icterus pustulatus

STRO
Species # 5051
Band size: 1A

Species—From Hooded Oriole (which see for separation from other orioles) by larger wg and relatively shorter tl (wg 87-106, tl 80-100; see **Age/Sex**); bill stout and straight (exp culmen 17.8-21.1, depth at tip of nares 6.0-7.4 in *I.p. microstictus*; see **Geographic variation**); back usually with dusky or blackish streaks (see **Geographic variation** & **Age/Sex**); tail less graduated (r1 – r6 7-13 mm when fresh); AHY/ASY ♂ with the back primarily orange (vs black with heavy, orange veiling in fresh-plumaged Hooded Orioles) and white edging to the ss, pp, and rects more extensive. Dull HY/SY ♀ from Bullock's and Baltimore orioles by much longer tl (81-91; see **Age/Sex**); underparts fairly uniformly yellow; back feathers with more distinct, dusky or blackish centers (forming streaks); bill black with a distinct, blue-gray base to the lower mandible.

Geographic variation—Well marked, but clinal where ranges meet. Subspecies taxonomy follows E.R. Blake *in* Paynter (1968), as modified by Phillips (1995); see also Ridgway (1902), van Rossem (1927b), Griscom (1930c, 1934a). Seven other subspecies occur in Mex-C.Am.

I.p. microstictus (br s.AZ; vag to CA): From the other subspecies by medium size (see **Age/Sex**; wg 82-118 overall); bill large (exp culmen 17.8-21.1, depth at tip of nares 6.0-7.4); back with less distinct streaks by age/sex (see **Age/Sex**); wing edging not distinctly white, s3-s5 with broader (vs narrower) white edging than the other ss and pp.

Molt—PB: HY partial-incomplete (Jul-Sep), AHY complete (Jul-Sep); PA absent-partial? (Jan-Apr). The 1st PB usually includes all med covs, 7 to 10 (~82%) inner gr covs, often (in ~65% of birds) 1-2 terts, and sometimes (in ~29% of birds) 1-2 central rects (r1), rarely other rects. Some birds may undergo eccentric replacement among the outermost 4-7 pp (see p. 208 and

Fig. 136), or arrested eccentric replacement (*e.g.*, p6-p7 only; see Fig. 172**A**); more study is needed. The PAs, if present, are limited to body feathers and include no gr covs or flight feathers.

Skull—Pneumaticization completes in HY/SY from 1 Nov through Mar.

Age/Sex—Juv (Jun-Sep) is like HY/SY ♀ in plumage coloration, but is paler, has buffier wing bars and fresher feathers at this time of year, and lacks black in the throat; juv ♀ = ♂, although juvs might be reliably sexed by rect color, as in HY/SYs (see below) and (if known *I.p. microstictus*) also by measurements (see **Geographic variation** and HY/SY ♀, below), if fully grown. CP/BP (Mar-Sep). ♀ wg(n30) 87-97, tl(n20) 80-92; ♂ wg(n30) 94-106, tl(n20) 86-100; *microstictus* only (see **Geographic variation**). The following pertains to the northern subspecies (*microstictus*) only; in certain subspecies of s.Mex-C.Am, all age/sex groups (but particularly AHY/ASY ♀♀) have much more black in the plumage, and can be more difficult to separate from ♂♂ by plumage alone.

HY/SY ♀ (Sep-Aug): Wg shorter by subspecies (see **Geographic variation** and above); body plumage dull greenish yellow with a brownish tinge and little or no dusky streaking in the back; molt limits occasionally occur among the gr covs (Fig. 133**D-E**; see **Molt**), the retained outer covs worn and brownish with buff tips, contrasting with the fresher, dusky, and whitish-tipped, replaced inner covs; 1-2 terts often replaced, contrasting with the older middle ss (s4-s6; Fig. 133**D**); outer pp covs narrow, tapered, relatively abraded (Fig. 138), and brown to dusky brown, contrasting with the slightly fresher and duskier, replaced gr covs (Fig. 134); central or other rects sometimes replaced, contrastingly fresh and washed dusky; outer rects greenish, tapered (Fig. 139**B**), and relatively abraded (especially in May-Sep). **Note: HY/SY ♀♀ and ♂♂ can resemble each other in plumage; on these the sexes are best confirmed with wg: ♀ < 94 and ♂ > 94 mm (in *microstictus*). Look also for some birds to have contrastingly fresh pp (see Molt).**

AHY/ASY ♀ (Sep-Aug): Body plumage medium-bright orange-yellow; back with moderately distinct, dusky to blackish streaks; wing covs, terts, and middle ss (s4-s6) uniformly adult (Fig. 133**F**) and dusky; outer pp covs broad, truncate, relatively fresh (Fig. 138), and dusky, not contrasting markedly in color or wear with the gr covs (Fig. 133**F**); rects uniformly adult, truncate (Fig. 139**A**), greenish with a dusky wash, and relatively fresh (especially in May-Sep).

HY/SY ♂ (Sep-Aug): Body plumage dull orange-yellow with a brownish tinge; back with moderately distinct, dusky to blackish streaks; molt-limit, wing-cov, and flight-feather criteria as in HY/SY ♀, except that the retained juvenal rects are duskier and the replaced first-basic rects are washed sooty. **Note: Caution with HY/SYs; see HY/SY ♀.**

AHY/ASY ♂ (Sep-Aug): Body plumage bright orange to reddish orange; back with distinct, black streaks; molt-limit and wing-cov criteria as in AHY/ASY ♀, except that the wing covs and flight feathers are blackish with distinct and broad white edging; rects blackish with whitish spots.

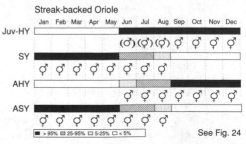

Streak-backed Oriole

Note: The graph pertains to the northern subspecies, *I.p. microstctus*, only. See text regarding other subspecies.

See Fig. 24

References—Ridgway (1902), Bent (1958), Phillips *et al.* (1964), Kaufman (1983), Hendrik (1994), Howell & Webb (1995), Pyle (1997c).

ALTAMIRA ORIOLE
Icterus gularis

ALOR
Species # 5031
Band size: 3

Species—From corresponding plumages of Hooded Oriole (which see for separation from other orioles) by much larger size (wg 103-119, tl 93-110; see **Sex**); bill large and very thick (Fig. 334; exp culmen 20.6-24.7, depth at tip of nares > 9 mm); lesser covs yellow to orange; outer pp with a distinct white patch at the bases.

Geographic variation—Moderate, but clinal where ranges meet. Subspecies taxonomy follows E.R. Blake *in* Paynter (1968); see Ridgway (1902). Five other subspecies occur in Mex-C.Am.

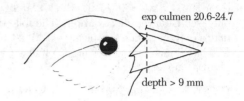

FIGURE 334. The bill shape and size in Altamira Oriole.

    I.g. tamaulipensis (res s.TX): Smaller than the other subspecies of Mex-C.Am (see **Sex**, *vs* wg 108-142, tl 91-118 in the other subspecies); bill short and stout (exp culmen 21.9-25.5, depth at tip of nares 9.3-11.8; *vs* 23.3-28.8 and 8.1-10.9, respectively, in the other subspecies); head and underparts deep orange (*vs* yellowish or reddish in the other subspecies); black on the face averages more extensive.

Molt—PB: HY partial-incomplete (Aug-Oct), AHY complete (Aug-Sep); PA absent-partial? (Jan-Apr). The 1st PB usually includes all med and gr covs, 1-3 terts, and 0 (~33%) to all 12 (~17%) rects. The PAs, if present, usually are limited to body feathers (they occasionally can include 1-2 terts but no gr covs; more study is needed), and may average more extensive in SYs than ASYs.

Skull—Pneumaticization completes in HY/SY from 1 Dec through Mar.

Age—Juv (May-Sep) resembles HY/SY, but lacks black on the throat; juv ♀ = ♂. The following applies to the subspecies of N.Am (*I.g. tamaulipensis*); some other subspecies of Mex-C.Am have yellower AHY/ASY plumages, resembling those of HY/SY more closely.

    HY/SY (Sep-Aug): Head and underparts generally greenish yellow or orangish yellow; back dusky yellow-olive; 1-3 terts replaced, contrasting with the older middle ss (s4-s6; Fig. 133**D-E**); outer pp covs narrow, tapered, relatively abraded (Fig. 138), and brown; flight feathers primarily brownish; central or other rects sometimes replaced, contrastingly fresh; some or all rects tapered (Fig. 139**C**), relatively abraded, and yellowish; throat mixed yellow and black. **Note: Beware of occasional birds that replace all rects during the 1st PB.**

    AHY/ASY (Sep-Aug): Head and underparts bright orange; back, throat, and flight feathers black; terts and middle ss (s4-s6) uniformly adult (Fig. 133**F**); outer pp covs broad, truncate, relatively fresh (Fig. 138), and black; rects uniformly adult, truncate (Fig. 139**C**), black, and relatively fresh. **Note: See HY/SY. Also, beware of some AHY/ASYs that can show yellowish rects, these having been replaced adventitiously in Mar-Jun (see p. 19). This pattern might be looked for in the other orioles, as well.**

Sex—CP/BP (Mar-Sep). Measurements are fairly useful: ♀ wg(n30) 103-113, tl(n18) 93-104; ♂ wg(n30) 108-119, tl(n18) 97-110; includes *I.g. tamaulipensis* only (see **Geographic variation**). No reliable plumage criteria are known for sexing, although ♂♂ average more black on the throat than ♀♀ (especially with HY/SYs); extremes probably are reliably sexed, with experience and consideration of age and measurements.

References—Ridgway (1902), Dickey & van Rossem (1938), Bent (1958), Oberholser (1974), Flood (1989), Pleasants (1993), Howell & Webb (1995), Pyle (1997c).

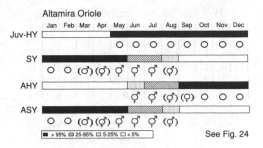

See Fig. 24

AUDUBON'S ORIOLE
Icterus graduacauda

AUOR
Species # 5030
Band size: 2

Species—HY/SY and ♀♀ from Scott's Oriole by longer tl (89-105; see **Sex**); bill thicker and shorter (Fig. 335; exp culmen 20.2-22.0, depth at tip of nares 6.0-7.5); back greenish yellow, without dusky streaks; med covs yellow or yellowish, without white tipping; tail graduated (r1 – r6 > 20 mm).

Geographic variation—Moderately well marked, but clinal where ranges meet. Subspecies taxonomy follows E.R. Blake *in* Paynter (1968); see Ridgway (1902), van Rossem (1938f), Howell & Webb (1995). Three other subspecies occur in Mex-C.Am.

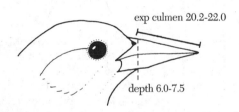

exp culmen 20.2-22.0

depth 6.0-7.5

> *I.g. audubonii* (res s.TX): Larger than the subspecies of Mex-C.Am (see **Sex**, *vs* wg 88-100, tl 88-103 in the other subspecies); edging to the terts white (*vs* yellow) and broad (> 2 mm, *vs* < 1.5 mm, when fresh); gr covs edged white (*vs* primarily or entirely black in the other subspecies).

FIGURE 335. The bill shape and size in Audubon's Oriole.

Molt—PB: HY partial-incomplete (Jul-Sep), AHY complete (Jul-Sep); PA absent. The 1st PB includes some to all med covs, 5 to 10 (~50%) inner gr covs, sometimes (in ~50% of birds) 1-3 terts, and sometimes (in ~44% of birds) 1-2 central rects (r1), occasionally up to 6 other rects (and perhaps rarely all 12).

Skull—Pneumaticization completes in HY/SY from 1 Dec through Feb.

Age—Juv (May-Aug) lacks black on the head; juv ♀ = ♂, although measurements can be useful in sexing some birds (see **Sex**).

> HY/SY (Sep-Aug): Crown mixed green and black; molt limits sometimes occur among the gr covs (Fig. 133**C-E**; see **Molt**), the retained outer covs worn and brown, contrasting with the fresher and black, replaced inner covs; 1-3 terts often replaced, contrasting with the older middle ss (s4-s6; Fig. 133**D-E**); outer pp covs narrow, tapered, relatively abraded (Fig. 138), and brown, contrasting with the slightly fresher and sootier, replaced gr covs; pp and rects brownish with greenish edging when fresh; central or other rects sometimes replaced and black, contrasting with the dusky-greenish juvenal rects; outer rects tapered (Fig. 139**C**) and brown with greenish edging.

AHY/ASY (Sep-Aug): Crown black; wing covs, terts, and middle ss (s4-s6) uniformly adult (Fig. 133**F**) and black; flight feathers black; rects uniformly truncate (Fig. 139**C**) and black.

Sex—CP/BP (Mar-Aug). Measurements are somewhat useful: ♀ wg(n35) 85-99, tl(n20) 89-101; ♂ wg(n33) 94-105, tl(n20) 96-109; includes *I.g. auduboni* only; see **Geographic variation**. ♂♂ average blacker heads (with little or no greenish mottling) and brighter and yellower backs than ♀♀, within both age groups (see **Age**), but too much overlap appears to exist for reliable sexing of single individuals; however, this can be useful for mated pairs. Otherwise, no reliable plumage criteria are known for sexing.

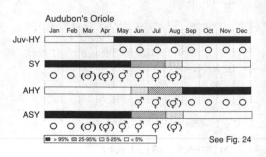

References—Ridgway (1902), Bent (1958), Oberholser (1974), Flood (1990), Howell & Webb (1995), Pyle (1997c).

BALTIMORE ORIOLE
Icterus galbula

BAOR
Species # 5070
Band size: 1A

Species— ♀♀ and HY/SY ♂♂ from most other orioles by medium size and relatively short tl (wg 83-96, tl 64-75; see **Age/Sex**); bill short, straight, and stout (Fig. 336; exp culmen 15.8-18.9, depth at tip of nares 5.3-6.6); back feathers olive with slight dusky markings (Fig. 337), not forming distinct streaks; throat usually with at least some orange; lower mandible pale horn to bluish. ♀♀ and juv-HY ♂♂ from Bullock's Oriole, with caution, by upperparts relatively dark brownish orange, scapulars and back feathers with more distinct dusky centers by age (Fig. 337); auricular olive, not contrasting markedly with the crown (Fig. 336; a capped appearance is reduced or absent); med covs with less white and more yellow by age/sex (see **Age/Sex**); throat and underparts fairly uniformly yellowish orange, the belly and flanks sometimes buffy whitish. See also differences in molt strategies for further identification clues. Beware of hybrids.

Geographic variation—No subspecies are recognized.

Molt—PB: HY partial (Jul-Sep), AHY complete (Jun-Sep); PA HY/SY limited-incomplete (Nov-May), ASY absent-limited (Mar-May). The PBs occur primarily on the summer grounds and (in some HYs) during the early stages of fall migration. The 1st PB includes no to some med covs and 0 (~55%) to 3 inner gr covs, but no terts or rects. The PA occurs more extensively in SYs than ASYs (it may not occur at all in ASYs); this

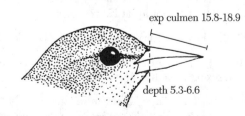

exp culmen 15.8-18.9

depth 5.3-6.6

FIGURE 336. The bill shape and size, and head pattern in ♀ and HY Baltimore Orioles.

molt is limited in Nov-Feb, accelerated in Mar-Apr, and sometimes continues through migration in May. The 1st PA includes 0 (~5%) to 10 (~24%) inner gr covs, usually (~75-81%) 1-2 terts, and 0 (~29%) to all 12 (~29%) rects.

Skull—Pneumaticization completes in HY/SY from 15 Nov through Feb. Look for windows (> 4 mm; Fig. 11**D**) in some SYs through spring.

Age/Sex—Juv (Jun-Aug) is relatively pale grayish brown with buffy wing bars; juv ♀ = ♂, although many birds can be sexed by wg (see below), if fully grown. CP/BP (Mar-Jul). ♀ wg(n100) 83-94, tl(n23) 64-72; ♂ wg(n100) 89-100, tl(n37) 68-78.

Juv-HY ♀♂ (Jul-Nov): Upperparts dark brown, without black, and with moderately indistinct, dusky streaking as in HY/SY ♀ (Fig. 337; see below); molt limits as in HY/SY ♀; rects brownish yellow without a dusky or sooty tinge. **Note: Juv-HY ♀♀ and ♂♂ (before they commence the 1st PA in Nov on the winter grounds) are similar in plumage but most juv-HYs can be separated by wg (♀ ≤ 91 mm, ♂ ≥ 91 mm). Also, occasional juv-HY ♂♂ in fall migration (Sep-Nov) can have one or more black feathers in the throat and are reliably sexed; look also for replaced inner gr covs (on some HYs only) to be sootier in ♂♂ than in ♀♀.**

HY/SY ♀ (Nov-Aug): Upperparts dark brown, without black, and with moderately indistinct, dusky streaking (Fig. 337); some or all med covs brownish with whitish tips (see Fig. 284); outer pp covs narrow, tapered, relatively abraded (Fig. 138), and brown with buff tips when fresh; molt limits usually occur among the gr covs in Mar-Aug (Fig. 133**C-E**; see **Molt**), the retained outer covs worn, brownish, and abraded, contrasting with the much fresher and duskier, replaced inner covs; 1-3 terts often replaced, contrasting with the older middle ss (s4-s6) in Mar-Aug (Fig. 133**D-E**); some or all rects yellowish, tapered (Fig. 139**B**), and abraded in Dec-Mar or (sometimes) uniformly truncate; cheeks and throat yellowish with an orange tinge and without black. **Note: Caution with HY/SY ♂♂ in Nov-Mar, some of which have acquired little or no black in the head and/or throat; always confirm sex with wg (see Juv-HY/SY ♀♂).**

AHY/ASY ♀ (Sep-Aug): Upperparts mottled brown, orange, and black, the back feathers with distinct, blackish markings (Fig. 337); med covs uniformly dusky with yellowish-white tips (see Fig. 284); outer pp covs broad, truncate, relatively fresh (Fig. 138), and dusky, without indistinct, buff tips; wing covs and inner ss uniformly adult (Fig. 133**F**) and dusky; rects uniformly adult, yellow (often tinged dusky), truncate (Fig. 139**B**), and relatively fresh; cheeks and throat yellow-orange to orange, usually with some black mottling.

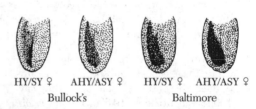

HY/SY ♀   AHY/ASY ♀   HY/SY ♀   AHY/ASY ♀

Bullock's   Baltimore

FIGURE 337. The pattern of the scapulars by age in Baltimore and Bullock's orioles.

HY/SY ♂ (Nov-Aug): Crown and back brown with dusky streaking (Nov-Feb), or blackish with orange mottling (Feb-Aug); rump brown, with some orange mottling in Mar-Aug; some or all med covs dusky with whitish to yellowish tips (see Fig. 284); molt-limit, wing-cov, and flight-feather criteria as in HY/SY ♀, except that the replaced gr covs and rects are sootier (thus, the contrast between the brown pp covs and the blackish gr covs is more distinct); cheeks and throat yellow-orange, with black feathers increasingly present in Nov-Aug. **Note: See HY/SY ♀. HY/SY ♂♂ begin acquiring black in the throat on the winter grounds, probably in Nov, but more study is needed.**

AHY/ASY ♂ (Sep-Aug): Crown, back, cheeks and throat black, the feathers edged orange in Sep-Feb; rump orange; med covs primarily or entirely yellow (see Fig. 284); gr covs uniformly black with whitish tips; pp covs and flight feathers black; rects uniformly truncate (Fig. 139**B**) and black and orange.

Hybrids reported—Bullock's Oriole (alpha code **BBOH, Species # 5078**).

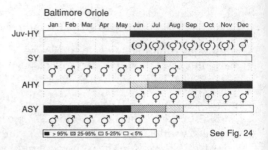

References—Stone (1896), Dwight (1900a), Ridgway (1902), Forbush (1927), Dickey & van Rossem (1938), Sutton (1938, 1968), Roberts (1955), Bent (1958), Sibley & Short (1964), Wood (1969), Rising (1970, 1973a, 1983a, 1983b, 1996b), Hubbard (1972c), Misra & Short (1974), Oberholser (1974), Fisk (1975), Sheppard & Klimkiewicz (1976), Corbin & Sibley (1977), Sealy (1979, 1986), DeBenedictis (1982), Flood (1984), Kaufman (1987b), Rohwer & Manning (1990), Rohwer & Johnson (1992), Cramp & Perrins (1994b), Howell & Webb (1995), Pyle (1997c); E.J. Fisk, J.D. Rising, J.M. Sheppard (*in litt.* to the BBL); R. Rowan (pers. comm.); IBP (MAPS) data.

BULLOCK'S ORIOLE
Icterus bullockii

BUOR
Species # 5080
Band size: 1A

Species— ♀♀ and HY/SY ♂♂ from Baltimore Oriole (which see for separation from other orioles), with caution, by bill slightly larger (Fig. 338; exp culmen 16.2-19.3, depth at tip of nares 5.5-6.7); upperparts pale grayish brown, scapulars and back feathers with smaller or no dusky centers by age (Fig. 337); auricular whitish, contrasting with the olive head (Fig. 338; giving a slight capped appearance); med covs with less yellow and more white by age/sex (see **Age/Sex**); throat and undertail covs pale yellow to orange-yellow, contrasting with the white flanks and belly. See also differences in molt strategies for further identification clues. Beware of hybrids.

Geographic variation—Weak and clinal where ranges meet. Subspecies taxonomy follows Rea (1983); see also Ridgway (1902), van Rossem (1945a), Phillips *et al.* (1964), Oberholser (1974), Browning (1978, 1990), Unitt (1984). No other subspecies occur.

exp culmen 16.2-19.3

depth 5.5-6.7

FIGURE 338. The bill shape and size, and head pattern in ♀ and HY Bullock's Orioles.

    I.b. parvus (br desert c-s.CA to s.NV-sw.AZ): Small; orange supercilium of ♂♂ usually isolated from the orange face. ♀ wg(n47) 84-94, tl(n18) 68-77; ♂ wg(n92) 90-100, tl(n50) 71-80.

    I.b. bullockii (br s.BC-c.CA to sw.ND-s.TX): Large; orange supercilium of ♂♂ often connecting with the orange face. ♀ wg(n56) 90-101, tl(n14) 72-80; ♂ wg(n56) 95-107, tl(n26) 76-84. Birds of w.OK-TX ("*eleutherus*") may average darker, but this difference, if present, is obscured by individual variation and/or due to slight mixing with Baltimore Oriole.

Molt—PB: HY partial-incomplete (Sep-Nov), AHY complete (Aug-Oct); PA absent-limited (Feb-Apr). The PBs occur primarily during migration stopover sites (especially HYs) and/or on the winter grounds (especially AHYs?). The 1st PB usually includes all med covs, 8 to 10 (~80%) inner gr covs, usually (in ~83% of birds) 1-3 terts (occasionally s6 and/or s5), and 0 (~11%) to all 12 (~46%) rects. Look for eccentric replacement patterns (see p. 208 and Fig. 136) to occur in a small (< 5%) proportion of birds, with the outermost 3-5 pp and, possibly, the outermost 1-2 pp covs replaced during the 1st PB; more study is needed. Only a very small proportion of SYs replace a few head feathers during the PA.

Skull—Pneumaticization completes in HY/SY from 15 Oct through Feb. Look for windows (> 4 mm; Fig. 11**D**) in some SYs through spring.

Age/Sex—Juv (May-Sep) is relatively pale grayish with buffy wing bars; juv ♀ = ♂, although many birds of known subspecies can be sexed by wg (see below and **Geographic variation**), if fully grown. CP/BP (Mar-Jul). Measurements are useful on known subspecies (see **Geographic variation**): ♀ wg(n100) 84-101, tl(n32) 68-80; ♂ wg(n100) 90-107, tl(n76) 71-84.

Juv-HY ♀♂ (Jul-Sep): Upperparts pale grayish brown, without black, and with little or no brownish streaking (as in HY/SY ♀, Fig. 337); throat pale yellowish to whitish, without black. **Note: Juv-HY ♀♀ and ♂♂ (before they molt at stopover sites or on the winter grounds) are similar in plumage, but many can be separated by wg, if the subspecies is known (see Geographic variation; the wg of juvs typically falls within the lower half of ranges, sex for sex). If the subspecies is unknown, only Juv-HYs with wg < 90 (♀♀) or > 96 (♂♂) can be sexed by measurements. Also, some black feathering can occur on the throats of occasional HY ♂♂ before or during migration. In both sexes, SYs in Aug-Sep are separated from HYs by extremely worn flight feathers, and SY ♂♂ during this time have extensive black in the throat, at least.**

HY/SY ♀ (Oct-Sep): Upperparts pale grayish brown, without black, and with little or no brownish streaking (Fig. 337); med covs brownish with irregular, buffy-white tips (see Fig. 284); molt limits sometimes occur among the gr covs (Fig. 133**D-E**; see **Molt**), the retained outermost 1-2 covs worn and brown with buff tips, contrasting with the fresher, dusky, and whitish-tipped, replaced inner covs; 1-3 terts (and occasionally s5 and/or s6) usually replaced, contrasting with the older middle ss (s4-s6; Fig. 133**D-E**); outer pp covs narrow, tapered, relatively abraded (Fig. 138), and brown with indistinct, buff tips when fresh, contrasting with the slightly fresher and duskier, replaced gr covs (Fig. 134); central and other rects often replaced and contrastingly fresh; some or all rects brownish yellow, tapered (Fig. 139**B**), and relatively abraded (but sometimes all rects truncate); throat pale yellowish to whitish, without black; breast and underparts primarily whitish with a dingy-yellow tinge.

AHY/ASY ♀ (Oct-Sep): Upperparts medium-pale grayish brown, without black, and with indistinct, dark brown streaking (Fig. 337); med covs dusky with distinct, whitish tips (see Fig. 284); wing covs, terts, and middle ss (s4-s6) uniformly adult (Fig. 133**F**) and dusky; outer pp covs broad, truncate, relatively fresh (Fig. 138), and dusky, without buff tipping, not contrasting markedly in color or wear with the gr covs; rects uniformly adult, yellow, truncate (Fig. 139**B**), and relatively fresh; throat yellow to yellow-orange, often with some black mottling; breast and underparts brightish yellow to orange-yellow.

HY/SY ♂ (Oct-Sep): Crown and back mixed grayish brown and black; rump grayish to yellowish; molt-limit, wing-cov, and flight-feather criteria as in HY/SY ♀, except that the med covs are duskier with broader whitish tips (see Fig. 284), and the replaced gr covs and rects are sootier (thus, the brown pp covs and pp show well-marked contrasts with the blacker gr covs); throat yellow to yellow-orange with a reduced, black patch; underparts dingy yellow to whitish.

AHY/ASY ♂ (Oct-Sep): Crown, back, and throat black, the feathers edged orange in Oct-Feb; rump orange; med covs entirely to primarily white (see Fig. 284); pp covs and ss black; rects uniformly truncate (Fig. 139**B**) and black and orange.

Hybrids reported—Baltimore Oriole (alpha code **BBOH, Species # 5078**), Black-backed Oriole (*I. abeillei*). Hooded Oriole in captivity.

References—Ridgway (1902), Dickey & van Rossem (1938), Sutton (1938, 1968), Bent (1958), Sibley & Short (1964), Rising (1970, 1973a, 1983a, 1983b, 1996b), Hubbard (1972c), Misra & Short (1974), Oberholser (1974), Corbin & Sibley (1977), DeBenedictis (1982), Kaufman (1987b), Rohwer & Manning (1990), Rohwer & Johnson (1992), Howell & Webb (1995), Pyle (1997c); J.D. Rising, (*in litt.* to the BBL); L. Elias, R. Rowan (pers. comm.); PRBO data; IBP (MAPS) data.

Bullock's Oriole

	Jan	Feb	Mar	Apr	May	Jun	Jul	Aug	Sep	Oct	Nov	Dec
Juv-HY						(♂) (♀) (♂) (♀) (♂) (♀)			♂	♂		
SY												
	♂ ♂ ♂ ♂ ♂ ♂ ♂ ♂ ♂ ♂											
AHY												
	♂ ♂ ♂ ♂ ♂ ♂ ♂ ♂											
ASY												
	♂ ♂ ♂ ♂ ♂ ♂ ♂ ♂											

■ > 95% ▨ 25-95% ▢ 5-25% □ < 5%   See Fig. 24

SCOTT'S ORIOLE
Icterus parisorum

SCOR
Species # 5040
Band size: 1A

Species— ♀♀ and HY/SY ♂♂ from Orchard, Hooded (which see for separation from other orioles), and Audubon's orioles by large size but tl relatively short (wg 92-103, tl 77-91; see **Age/Sex**); bill medium in length, straight, and slender (Fig. 339; exp culmen 20.1-23.8, depth at tip of nares 5.1-6.3); back grayish or greenish, with blackish streaking or mottling; med covs with whitish or white tips; tail relatively square to somewhat graduated (r1 – r6 6-17 mm). Black-vented Oriole (*I. wagleri*, alpha code **BVOR**, **Species # 5041**), a vagrant to sw.TX, averages larger, especially the tl (wg 95-114, tl 89-122), lacks white in the wing, and has AHYs with black undertail covs.

Geographic variation—No subspecies are recognized.

Molt—PB: HY partial-incomplete (Jul-Nov), AHY complete (Jul-Aug); PA absent-limited (Feb-Apr). The PBs occur primarily on the summer grounds, but can complete on the winter grounds in some HYs. The 1st PB is variable, including some to all med covs, 5 to 10 (~71%) inner gr covs, usually (in ~86% of birds) 1-3 terts, sometimes (in ~21% of birds) s5 and/or s6, and 0 (~57%)

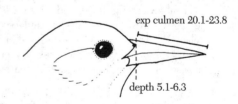

exp culmen 20.1-23.8

depth 5.1-6.3

FIGURE 339. The bill shape and size in Scott's Oriole.

to all 12 (~19%) rects. The 1st PB also occasionally (in ~14% of birds) can be eccentric (see p. 208 and Fig. 136), with the outermost 4-5 pp and occasionally (in ~10% of birds) the outermost (reduced) pp cov replaced. The PA includes no med covs, gr covs, or flight feathers and (if present at all) may be more extensive in SY ♂♂ than the other age/sex classes.

Skull—Pneumaticization completes in HY/SY from 15 Nov through Feb.

Age/Sex—Juv (May-Sep) is like HY/SY ♀♀, but is washed brownish and has broader, yellowish wing bars; juv ♀ = ♂. CP/BP (Mar-Aug). ♀ wg(n40) 92-102, tl(n20) 77-89; ♂ wg(n46) 95-107, tl(n20) 81-94.

HY/SY ♀ (Sep-Aug): Head and throat greenish olive with no (Aug-Feb), or a slight amount of (Mar-Jul), black mottling on the throat; back dull olive with indistinct to moderately distinct, blackish streaking; med covs brownish dusky with whitish tips (see Fig. 284); molt limits sometimes occur among the gr covs (Fig. 133C-E; see **Molt**), the retained outer covs worn and brownish with buff tipping, contrasting with the fresher and dusky-centered, replaced inner covs; 1-3 terts (and occasionally s5-s6) often replaced, contrasting with the older middle ss (s4-s6; Fig. 133D-E); outer pp covs narrow, tapered, relatively abraded (Fig. 138), and brown, contrasting with the slightly fresher and duskier, replaced gr covs (Fig. 134); some or all rects tapered (Fig. 139C), brownish green, and relatively abraded (or occasionally all rects truncate). **Note: In addition, look for a small proportion of HY/SYs to have 4-5 outer pp and, occasionally, the outermost (reduced) pp cov contrastingly fresh (see Molt). Beware that body plumage varies substantially within all age/sex groups, but most birds should be reliably determined when plumage is combined with skull and measurements.**

AHY/ASY ♀ (Sep-Aug): Variably plumaged; head and throat primarily olive-green, usually with some black mottling (the throat can be almost entirely black); back olive with distinct, black streaking; med covs dusky with whitish to yellowish tipping (see Fig. 284); wing covs, terts, and middle ss (s4-s6) uniformly adult (Fig. 133F) and dusky; outer pp covs broad, truncate, relatively fresh (Fig. 138), and dusky, not contrasting markedly in color or wear with the gr covs (Fig. 133F); rects uniformly adult, dusky green, truncate (Fig. 139C), and relatively fresh. **Note: See HY/SY ♀. Broad plumage overlap occurs with HY/SY ♂ in Sep-Mar; separate with caution using molt limits, rect shape, and measurements (see above).**

HY/SY ♂ (Sep-Aug): Variably plumaged; head and throat primarily greenish with black mottling on the throat (Sep-Aug), or blackish with greenish mottling (some SYs; Mar-Aug); back greenish with black streaking (Sep-Aug), or blackish with greenish streaking (some SYs; Mar-Aug); med covs brownish dusky with whitish or pale yellowish tips (see Fig. 284), sometimes mixed with primarily yellow covs (see Fig. 284) in Mar-Aug; molt-limit, wing-cov, and flightfeather criteria as in HY/SY ♀, except that the replaced rects are sootier, sometimes with dusky yellow at the bases of r4-r6. **Note: See HY/SY ♀, AHY/ASY ♀, and AHY/ASY ♂.**

AHY/ASY ♂ (Sep-Aug): Head, back, and throat black (with thin, greenish edging in Sep-Dec); med covs entirely or primarily yellow (see Fig. 284); molt-limit criteria as in AHY/ASY ♀, except that the wing covs and flight feathers are black and white; pp covs black, not contrasting in wear with the gr covs; rects truncate (Fig. 139C) and black and yellow. **Note: See HY/SY ♀. Some SY/TYs (Sep-Aug) possibly are aged by having adult body plumage and rects but a moderate amount of greenish mottling to the body, but these also may be HY/SY ♂♂ from early broods; more study is needed.**

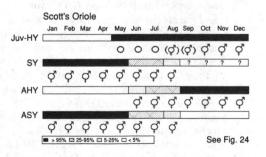

References—Brewster (1902), Ridgway (1902), Swarth (1904a), Bent (1958), Oberholser (1974), Flood (1989), Howell & Webb (1995), Pyle (1997c); J. Church, I. Tait (pers. comm.).

FINCHES

FRINGILLIDAE

Sixteen species. Family characters include relatively large, conical bills, short tails, short legs, and the presence of rictal bristles. Finches have 9 visible primaries, 9 secondaries, and 12 rectrices. The first prebasic molt is partial in many species, including a variable number of greater coverts, but no tertials or rectrices. Three species show more extensive, eccentric first prebasic molts. A prealternate molt is absent or very limited in most species, although in one species (Lesser Goldfinch) it is incomplete and eccentric. Molt limits and the shape of the rectrices generally are good ageing criteria. Most age/sex classes can be distinguished by plumage and breeding characters in spring, and males average moderately larger than females.

GRAY-CROWNED ROSY-FINCH
Leucosticte tephrocotis

GCRF
Species # 5240
Band size: 1B

Species—HY/SYs and ♀♀ from the other rosy finches by bill averages long (exp culmen 10.3-13.0, excluding the two AK Is subspecies; see **Geographic variation**); body plumage largely brownish; nape washed grayish; supercilium indistinct to distinct and grayish; belly with little to a moderate amount of dull pinkish.

Geographic variation—Moderately well marked, but clinal where ranges meet. Subspecies taxonomy follows T.R. Howell *et al. in* Paynter (1968), as modified by Browning (1990); see also Ridgway (1901), Grinnell (1913), Miller (1939b), Murie (1944), Feinstein (1958), French (1959a), Johnson (1977), Behle (1985), Pyle (1997c). No other subspecies occur. See also **Molt**.

Gray-cheeked (*L.t. littoralis*) Group.

L.t. griseonucha (br & wint Aleutian-Kodiak Is, AK): Large; bill medium long (nares to tip 9.7-11.7); auricular and hindcrown uniformly gray; throat dusky, blending into the brown breast. ♀ wg(n11) 109-120, tl(n11) 73-82; ♂ wg(n21) 112-124, tl(n21) 75-85.

L.t. umbrina (res Pribilof Is, AK): Medium large; bill long (nares to tip 10.1-12.1); auricular and hindcrown uniformly gray; throat blackish, blending into the dusky-brown breast. ♀ wg(n10) 109-118, tl(n10) 73-79; ♂ wg(n15) 112-121, tl(n10) 75-83.

L.t. littoralis (br montane wc.AK-sw.Yuk to nc.CA, wint to c.MT-n.NM): Medium small; bill short (nares to tip 7.9-9.7); auricular and hindcrown uniformly gray; throat mixed gray and black, contrasting sharply with the brownish-dusky breast. ♀ wg(n12) 96-106, tl(n10) 56-66; ♂ wg(n25) 100-110, tl(n25) 59-69.

Brown-cheeked (*L.t. tephrocotis*) Group.

L.t. tephrocotis (br montane c.Yuk-sc.BC to nw.MT, wint to ne.CA-AZ-MN): Medium small; bill thick (depth at tip of nares 6.5-7.6); longest p – p6 7-10 mm; upperparts and nape bright brown with indistinct or no grayish or dusky feather centers; auricular brown, contrasting with the gray hindcrown; breast feathers without dusky centers. ♀ wg(n54) 97-106, tl(n55) 62-71; ♂ wg(n67) 102-111, tl(n67) 64-74. Birds of nc.AK ("*irvingi*") may average brighter and with more gray in the face, but differences, if present, are largely obscured by individual variation.

L.t. wallowa (br montane ne.OR, wint to NV): Small; bill medium thick (depth at tip of nares 6.3-7.3); longest p – p6 5-10 mm; upperparts and nape dull, dark brown, the feathers often with distinct, dusky centers; auricular brown, contrasting with the gray hindcrown; breast feathers with dusky centers. ♀ wg(n10) 95-103, tl(n10) 61-69; ♂ wg(n11) 99-107, tl(n11) 63-71.

L.t. dawsoni (res montane e.CA): Medium small; bill slender (depth at tip of nares 6.0-7.0); longest p – p6 5-8 mm; upperparts and nape dull brown with a grayish wash, the feathers with indistinct or no dusky centers; auricular brown, contrasting with the gray hindcrown; breast feathers without dusky centers. ♀ wg(n50) 96-104, tl(n52) 62-71; ♂ wg(n55) 100-110, tl(n16) 65-74.

Molt—PB: HY partial (Jul-Sep), AHY complete (Jul-Sep). PA absent. The PBs occur on the summer grounds. The 1st PB includes some to most med covs and 0 (~43%) to 9 inner gr covs,

662

but no terts or rects. The longest uppertail covs often are retained (or, if replaced, they retain juvenal characters). The extent of the 1st PB averages more extensive in the AK Is subspecies (*L.t. griseonucha* and *umbrina*), usually including 1-9 gr covs and all uppertail covs, whereas in the other subspecies it includes 0-4 gr covs, and the longer uppertail covs often are retained (or retain juvenal characters).

Skull—Pneumaticization completes in HY/SY from 1 Nov through Feb.

Age—Juv (Jun-Aug) is uniformly grayish brown with dull pinkish-buff to tan wing bars (see Fig. 340); juv ♀ = ♂.

HY/SY (Aug-Jul): Molt limits occur among the med and gr covs (Fig. 133**A-D**; see **Molt**), the retained outer covs worn and brownish with dull pinkish-buff to tan edges (Fig. 340), contrasting with the fresher, duskier, and brighter, yellowish-edged (♀) or pink-edged (♂), replaced inner covs; outer pp covs narrow, tapered, relatively abraded (Fig. 138), and brownish with indistinct, narrow, or no buff or dull whitish-pink edging (Fig. 341); pp and ss brownish with whitish-pink or buff edges; outer rects tapered (Fig. 342) and relatively abraded; longest uppertail covs often tipped dull tawny to whitish, contrasting with the brighter pink-tipped, proximal uppertail covs. **Note: The uppertail-cov criterion is not as reliable in the two AK Is subspecies (see Molt); note also that the pink on these feathers varies by sex, as well (see Sex). Plumage criteria can be difficult to use with ♀♀ (use rect shape with these), but should be reliable with all ♂♂; use caution in Jun-Jul when feathers become worn.**

AHY/ASY (Aug-Jul): Wing covs uniformly adult (Fig. 133**F**) and dusky with yellowish (♀) or pink (♂) edges; outer pp covs broad, truncate, relatively fresh (Fig. 138), and dusky with relatively distinct and broad, yellowish (♀) or pink (♂) edging (Fig. 341); pp and ss dusky with pink edging; outer rects truncate (Fig. 342) and relatively fresh; uppertail covs uniformly tipped pink. **Note: See HY/SY.**

Sex—CP/BP (May-Sep). ♀ wg(n100) 95-106, tl(n100) 56-71; ♂ wg(n100) 99-111, tl(n100) 59-74; measurements exclude the two larger AK Is subspecies (see **Geographic variation**).

♀: Forecrown brownish black, the feathers with substantial (Aug-Mar), to some (Mar-Aug), grayish edging; hindcrown grayish with substantial (Aug-Mar), to some (Mar-Aug), brownish mottling; non-juvenal (see **Molt & Age**) uppertail, lesser, and med covs with indistinct, dull pinkish tips (Fig. 340); pink or pinkish of the belly reduced and duller than the pink of the rump. **Note: Some intermediates can be difficult to sex; these likely are HY/SY ♂♂ and AHY/ASY ♀♀, so compare with ageing criteria and measurements by subspecies.**

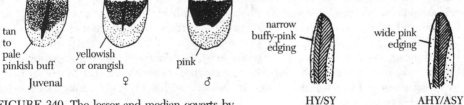

tan to pale pinkish buff

Juvenal

yellowish or orangish

♀

pink

♂

narrow buffy-pink edging

HY/SY

wide pink edging

AHY/ASY

FIGURE 340. The lesser and median coverts by age and sex in the rosy-finches. Juvenal feathers are tipped tan, basic ♀ feathers are tipped yellowish or orangish, and basic ♂ feathers are tipped pink. See the accounts for each species for slight differences in this color, especially in ♀♀. Note that most birds replace some of these during the 1st prebasic molt, allowing the sexing of HY/SYs in basic plumage.

FIGURE 341. The primary coverts by age in the rosy finches.

♂: Forecrown black, the feathers with little (Aug-Mar), to no (Mar-Aug), grayish edging; hindcrown grayish silver with little (Aug-Mar), to no (Mar-Aug), brownish mottling; non-juvenal (see **Molt & Age**) uppertail, lesser, and med covs with distinct, bright pinkish tips (Fig. 340); pink of the belly extensive, usually brighter than the pink of the rump. **Note: See ♀.**

Gray-crowned Rosy-Finch

See Fig. 24

Hybrids reported—Black Rosy-Finch.

References—Merrill (1880), Ridgway (1901), French (1959a), Bent *et al.* (1968), Behle (1973b), Johnson (1977), Clement *et al.* (1993), Pyle (1997c); J. Sarvis (*in litt.* to the BBL).

BLACK ROSY-FINCH
Leucosticte atrata

BLRF
Species # 5250
Band size: 1B

Species—HY/SYs and ♀♀ from the other rosy finches by bill averages medium in length (exp culmen 10.3-11.2); body plumage dusky; nape washed grayish; supercilium pale gray and indistinct, or lacking; belly with no to some dull pinkish.

Geographic variation—No subspecies are recognized.

Molt—PB: HY partial (Jul-Sep), AHY complete (Jul-Sep). PA absent. The PBs occur on the summer grounds. The 1st PB includes some to most lesser and med covs but few if any gr covs, and no terts or rects. The longest uppertail covs usually are retained during the 1st PB (or, if replaced, they retain juvenal characters).

Skull—Pneumaticization completes in HY/SY from 1 Nov through Feb.

Age—Juv (Jun-Aug) is uniformly blackish gray with dull pinkish-buff to tan wing bars (see Fig. 340); juv ♀ = ♂.

HY/SY (Aug-Jul): Molt limits occur among the lesser and med covs (see **Molt**; Fig. 133**A**), the retained outer covs worn and brownish with dull pinkish-buff to tan edges (Fig. 340), contrasting with the fresher, duskier, and brighter, orangish-edged (♀) or pink-edged (♂), replaced inner covs; gr covs brownish with dull pinkish-buff to tan edges; outer pp covs narrow, tapered, relatively abraded (Fig. 138), and brownish with indistinct, narrow, or no buff or dull whitish-pink edging (Fig. 341); outer rects tapered (Fig. 342) and relatively abraded; longest uppertail covs often tipped dull tawny to whitish, contrasting with the brighter pink-tipped, proximal uppertail covs. **Note: Plumage criteria can be difficult to use with ♀♀ (use rect shape with these), but should be reliable with all ♂♂; use caution in Jun-Jul when feathers become worn.**

AHY/ASY (Aug-Jul): Wing covs uniformly adult (Fig. 133**F**), dusky with orangish (♀) or pink (♂) edges; outer pp covs broad, truncate, relatively fresh (Fig. 138), and dusky with relatively distinct and broad, orangish (♀) or pink (♂) edging (Fig. 341); outer rects truncate (Fig. 342) and relatively fresh; uppertail covs uniformly tipped pink. **Note: See HY/SY.**

Sex—CP/BP (May-Sep). Measurements are useful: ♀ wg(n30) 96-106, tl(n20) 57-65; ♂ wg(n30) 100-111, tl(n20) 62-70.

♀: Hindcrown with relatively little or no grayish silver; non-juv enal (see **Molt & Age**) uppertail, lesser, and med covs with indistinct, dull orangish to pinkish tips (Fig. 340); belly without pinkish or with dull pinkish, duller than the pink of the rump.

♂: Hindcrown primarily to entirely grayish silver; non-juvenal (see **Molt & Age**) uppertail, lesser, and med covs with distinct, bright pinkish tips (Fig. 340); belly usually with extensive pink, brighter than the pink of the rump.

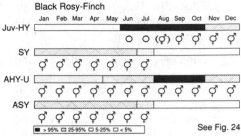

Black Rosy-Finch

See Fig. 24

Hybrids reported—Gray-crowned Rosy-Finch.

References—Ridgway (1901), French (1959a, 1959b), N.R. French *in* Bent *et al.* (1968), Behle (1973b), Johnson (1977), Clement *et al.* (1993), Pyle (1997c).

BROWN-CAPPED ROSY-FINCH
Leucosticte australis

BCRF
Species # 5260
Band size: 1B

Species—HY/SYs and ♀♀ from the other rosy finches by bill averages smaller (exp culmen 10.1-10.8); nape and supercilium usually without grayish; belly with a moderate to extensive pink wash.

Geographic variation—No subspecies are recognized.

Molt—PB: HY partial (Jul-Sep), AHY complete (Jul-Sep). PA absent. The PBs occur on the summer grounds. The 1st PB includes some to most lesser and med covs and 0 (~87%) to 3 inner gr covs, but no terts or rects. The longest uppertail covs usually are retained during the 1st PB (or, if replaced, they retain juvenal characters).

Skull—Pneumaticization completes in HY/SY from 1 Nov through Feb.

Age—Juv (Jun-Aug) is uniformly brown with dull pinkish-buff to tan wing bars (see Fig. 340); juv ♀=♂.

HY/SY (Aug-Jul): Molt limits occur among the lesser, med, and gr covs (Fig. 133**A-B**; see **Molt**), the retained outer covs worn, brownish with dull pinkish-buff or tan edges (Fig. 340), contrasting with the fresher, duskier and brighter, pinkish-edged (♀) or pink-edged (♂), replaced inner covs; outer pp covs narrow, tapered, relatively abraded (Fig. 138), and brownish with indistinct, narrow, or no buff or dull whitish-pink edging (Fig. 341); pp and ss brownish with whitish-pink or dull pink edges; outer rects tapered (Fig. 342) and relatively abraded; longest uppertail covs often tipped dull tawny to whitish, contrasting with the brighter pink-tipped, proximal uppertail covs.

AHY/ASY (Aug-Jul): Wing covs uniformly adult (Fig. 133**F**), dusky with pinkish (♀) or pink (♂) edges; outer pp covs broad, truncate, relatively fresh (Fig. 138), and dusky with relatively distinct and broad, pinkish (♀) or pink (♂) edging (Fig. 341); pp and ss dusky with brightish pink edging; outer rects truncate (Fig. 342) and relatively fresh; uppertail covs uniformly tipped pink.

Sex—CP/BP (May-Sep). ♀ wg(n30) 97-108, tl(n30) 61-70; ♂ wg(n30) 100-112, tl(n20) 62-71.

♀: Forecrown brown with black mottling; pale supercilium lacking or very indistinct; non-juvenal (see **Molt & Age**) uppertail, lesser, and med covs with indistinct, dull pinkish tips (Fig. 340); pinkish of the belly somewhat reduced, usually duller than the pink of the rump.

♂: Forecrown black, slightly mottled brown in Aug-Mar; supercilium indistinctly defined and grayish silver; non-juvenal (see **Molt & Age**) uppertail, lesser, and med covs with distinct, bright pinkish tips (Fig. 340); pink of the belly extensive and brighter than the pink of the rump.

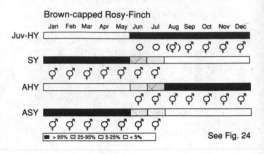

References—Ridgway (1901), F.M. Packard *in* Bent *et al.* (1968), Johnson (1977), Clement *et al.* (1993), Pyle (1997c).

PINE GROSBEAK
Pinicola enucleator

PIGR
Species # 5150
Band size: 1A

Geographic variation—Moderate and ranges fairly well defined. Subspecies taxonomy follows T.R. Howell *et al. in* Paynter (1968), as modified by Adkisson (1977); see also Ridgway (1901), Oberholser (1914a), Noble (1919), Brooks (1922), Griscom (1934b), Jenks (1938), Burleigh & Peters (1948), Sutton (1948d), Dement'ev & Gladkov (1954), Todd (1963), Phillips *et al.* (1964), Godfrey (1986), Cramp & Perrins (1994a). Three other subspecies occur in Eurasia.

P.e. kamtschatkensis (br & wint Siberia; vag to w.AK Is): Medium small; bill stout (exp culmen 14.5-16.2, depth at tip of nares 11.6-13.0); back feathers with indistinct (♀ and HY/SY ♂) to distinct (♂), dusky centers; AHY/ASY ♂ with the breast and flanks bright, dark red with little or no grayish mottling. ♀ wg(n16) 103-112, tl(n10) 80-89; ♂ wg(n27) 106-115, tl(n10) 81-90.

P.e. flammula (br coastal sc.AK-nw.BC, wint to WA-ID): Medium in size; bill large (exp culmen 14.4-16.4, depth at tip of nares 10.6-12.7); back feathers with indistinct (♀ and HY/SY ♂) to distinct (♂), dusky centers; AHY/ASY ♂ with the breast and flanks medium-bright, dark red with little or no grayish mottling. ♀ wg(n11) 106-116, tl(n10) 84-93; ♂ wg(n29) 109-119, tl(n20) 88-97.

P.e. carlottae (res wc-sw.BC Is): Small; bill medium in size (exp culmen 14.2-15.9, depth at tip of nares 10.3-11.7); back feathers with indistinct (♀ and HY/SY ♂) to distinct (♂), dusky centers; AHY/ASY ♂ with the breast and flanks dark red with little or no grayish mottling. ♀ wg(n10) 101-110, tl(n10) 77-86; ♂ wg(n12) 104-113, tl(n10) 81-91.

P.e. californicus (res montane e.CA): Medium in size; tl relatively long; bill small (exp culmen 13.8-15.8, depth at tip of nares 9.3-11.2); back feathers with no (♀ and HY/SY ♂) to indistinct (♂), dusky centers; AHY/ASY ♂ with the breast medium-dull red with gray mottling and the flanks primarily gray. ♀ wg(n20) 105-116, tl(n10) 91-101; ♂ wg(n34) 108-119, tl(n13) 92-103.

P.e. montanus (br interior BC to montane AZ-NM, wint to NE-TX): Large; bill medium in size (exp culmen 14.0-16.6, depth at tip of nares 10.2-12.1); back feathers with no (♀ and HY/SY ♂) to indistinct (♂), dusky centers; AHY/ASY ♂ with the breast medium-dark red with gray mottling and the flanks primarily gray. ♀ wg(n10) 110-120, tl(n10) 88-99; ♂ wg(n100) 112-124, tl(n45) 92-103. Birds of AZ ("*jacoti*") may average shorter-billed, longer-winged, and darker, but differences, if present, are slight and obscured by individual variation.

P.e. leucurus (br c.AK-ne.BC to Nfl-CT, wint to OR-VA): Variably large; bill variably sized (exp culmen 13.2-16.1, depth at tip of nares 10.4-13.0); back feathers with indistinct (♀ and HY/SY ♂) to distinct (♂), dusky centers; AHY/ASY ♂ with the breast and flanks medium pinkish red to red with little or no grayish mottling. ♀ wg(n27) 105-120, tl(n27) 84-99; ♂ wg(n100) 108-125, tl(n100) 87-104. Birds breeding in AK-w.NWT ("*alascensis*") average larger but with smaller bills, and birds breeding in s.Que-Nfl to CT ("*eschatosus*") average smaller, but in both cases differences are broadly clinal.

Molt—PB: HY partial (Jul-Oct), AHY complete (Jul-Sep); PA absent. The PBs occur on the summer grounds. The 1st PB includes some to all lesser and med covs and 0 (~23%) to 10 (~3%) inner gr covs, but no terts or rects.

Skull—Pneumaticization completes in HY/SY from 1 Nov through Feb.

Age/Sex—Juv (Jun-Sep) has body plumage primarily brown with buffy wing bars; juv ♀ = ♂. CP/BP (May-Sep). Measurements vary substantially by geography (see **Geographic variation**): ♀ wg(n100) 101-120, tl(n100) 77-101; ♂ wg(n100) 104-125, tl(n100) 81-104.

HY/SY ♀♂ (Oct-2nd Oct): Lower back and underparts primarily gray; crown, nape, and uppertail covs with varying amounts of olive, yellowish, or russet; molt limits occur among the med and gr covs (Fig. 133A-D; see **Molt**), the retained outer covs worn and brownish with dingy whitish tips, contrasting with the fresher, duskier, and white-tipped, replaced inner covs; outer pp covs narrow, tapered, relatively abraded, and brown with indistinct, narrow, or no pale brown edging (Fig. 138); outer rects tapered (Fig. 342) and relatively abraded; breast with or without an olive tinge. **Note: SYs in Jul-Sep are separated from HYs by abraded flight feathers. Most HY/SYs in Sep-Mar are not reliably sexed by plumage alone, although ♀♀ average duller (especially on the crown and rump) and with a lighter russet tinge to the head or olive tinge to the breast than ♂♂. In Mar-Sep some SY ♂♂ can have a few pink or reddish feathers in the body plumage and are reliably distinguished. Also, brown birds with a CP, and birds molting from brown to red in Aug-Oct are SY ♂♂. Occasional birds also may be difficult to age, and these should be sexed as unknown or ♀ as above.**

AHY/ASY ♀ (Sep-Aug): Body plumage as in HY/SY ♀♂; wing covs uniformly adult (Fig. 133F) and dusky with white tips; outer pp covs broad, truncate, relatively fresh, and dusky with relatively distinct and broad, whitish edging (Fig. 138); outer rects truncate (Fig. 342) and relatively fresh; breast tinged olive.

AHY/ASY ♂ (Oct-Sep): Body plumage primarily pink or reddish; molt-limit and flight-feather criteria as in AHY/ASY ♀, except that the pp covs often are edged pinkish.

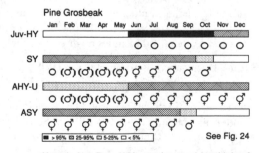

Hybrids reported—Purple Finch. Eurasian Bullfinch (*Pyrrhula pyrrhula*) in captivity.

Note: In Nov-Dec, AHYs can be sexed but birds of unknown age should be left unsexed.

References—Stone (1896), Dwight (1900a), Ridgway (1901), Forbush (1929), Jenks (1938), Roberts (1955), Todd (1963), Bent *et al.* (1968), Wood (1969), Adkisson (1977), Svensson (1992), Clement *et al.* (1993), Cramp & Perrins (1994a), Pyle (1997c); C.S. Adkisson (*in litt.* to the BBL); IBP (MAPS) data.

PURPLE FINCH
Carpodacus purpureus

PUFI
Species # 5170
Band size: 1-1C-1B

Species—From Cassin's and House finches by the combination of medium wg (71-87) and rel-atively long tl (53-62; see **Geographic variation** & **Sex**); longest p – longest s 16-25 mm; bill medium in length (nares to tip 8.2-10.1), with the culmen distinctly but not substantially decurved (Fig. 343); tail notched (r6 – r1 4-10 mm); eye ring lacking or indistinct; ♀♀ and HY/SY ♂♂ dark brown (often tinged olive), with the facial features distinct, and the undertail covs without or with distinct, dusky or blackish streaks (see **Geographic variation**); AHY/ASY ♂♂ with the head purplish to purplish red (rarely orange or yellowish) and the back strongly washed the same color; often attempts to bite; usually silent when released. Caution with juvs (especially in western populations; see **Geographic variation**), which can resemble House Finch quite closely in the bill and plumage features.

Geographic variation—Moderate and ranges fairly well defined. Subspecies taxonomy follows T.R. Howell *et al. in* Paynter (1968); see Ridgway (1901), Duvall (1945b), Rand (1946), Burleigh & Peters (1948), Dickinson (1953), Blake (1955), Phillips *et al.* (1964), Godfrey (1986), Wootton (1996). No other subspecies occur.

C.p. californicus (br & wint s.BC-w.ID to s.CA-w.AZ): Small; tl relatively long (wg – tl 22-30 mm); p9 often < p6 (p9 – p6 -4 to 2 mm); ♀♀ and HY/SY ♂♂ brown with an olive wash, the undertail covs with indistinct to distinct, blackish streaks; AHY/ASY ♂ with the head dull pinkish red to reddish, paler or duller than rump. ♀ wg(n100) 71-80, tl(n39) 53-60; ♂ wg(n100) 74-84, tl(n75) 55-62. Birds breeding in BC-OR ("*rubidus*") may average darker, but differences, if present, are slight and obscured by indi-vidual variation.

C.p. purpureus (br n-c.BC to PEI-MD, wint to AZ-c.FL): Large; tl relatively short (wg – tl 26-34 mm); p9 usually > p6 (p9 – p6 -1 to 5 mm); ♀♀ and HY/SY ♂♂ brown, sometimes tinged grayish, with indis-tinct or no dusky streaks on the undertail covs; AHY/ASY ♂ with the head bright reddish, contrasting with the pale reddish (often tinged pink or purple) rump. ♀ wg(n100) 74-83, tl(n22) 53-61; ♂ wg(n100) 77-87, tl(n51) 55-62. Birds breeding in n.BC-c.Man ("*taverneri*") may average paler, and birds breed-ing in Nfl ("*nesophilus*") may average darker and slightly larger, but in both cases differences are slight and obscured by individual variation.

Molt—PB: HY partial (Aug-Oct), AHY complete (Jul-Oct); PA limited (Mar-Apr). The PBs occur primarily on the summer grounds but can complete during fall migration. The 1st PB includes some to all med covs and 3 to 10 (~49%) inner gr covs, but no terts or rects. The PA is limited to body feathers and includes no gr covs or flight feathers.

Skull—Pneumaticization completes in HY/SY from 15 Nov. Some SYs (2-3%, primarily ♂♂) show windows on the top of the skull (> 3 mm; Fig. 11**D**) through May.

Age/Sex—Juv (Jun-Sep) is washed brown and has streaking on the throat and (loosely textured) undertail covs; juv ♀ = ♂. CP/BP (Apr-Sep); brown-plumaged birds with a CP are SY ♂♂. ♀ wg(n100) 71-83, tl(n61) 53-61; ♂ wg(n100) 74-87, tl(n100) 55-62; see **Geographic variation**.

HY/SY ♀♂ (Aug-2nd Oct): Upperparts, head, and breast brown and whitish, without reddish (some HY/SY ♂♂ can be tinged pinkish); molt limits often occur among the gr covs (Fig. 133**B-E**; see **Molt**), the retained outer covs worn and brown with buff edging, contrasting with the fresher, duskier, and tawny-edged or olive-edged, replaced inner covs; outer pp covs narrow, tapered, relatively abraded, and brown with indistinct, narrow, or no pale buff edg-ing (Fig. 138); outer rects tapered (Fig. 342) and relatively abraded. **Note: Most HY/SYs in Aug-Apr are not reliably sexed. Some HY/SYs can be reliably sexed ♂ by 1) the presence of a distinctive pinkish or yellowish tinge to the plumage (known HY/SYs only), 2) a CP in Apr-Sep (reliable for SY ♂ on brown-plumaged birds), 3) a reddish or orange gape in**

Jun-Sep (*vs* yellow to yellowish orange in ♀♀), and/or 4) a molting, brown-plumaged bird with incoming red feathers in Aug-Oct. HY/SY ♀♀ are not reliably sexed, except those with BPs in Apr-Aug. Some intermediates may not be aged and these should be sexed unknown, as well (unless they are ♀♀ by BP). HYs are separated from SYs in Aug-Oct by the skull condition and by having much fresher flight feathers.

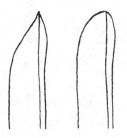

FIGURE 342. The shape of the outer rectrices (r4-r6) by age in finches.

AHY/ASY ♀ (Aug-Jul): Upperparts, head, and breast brown and whitish, without reddish (some ASY/ATYs can be tinged pinkish or yellowish); wing covs uniformly adult (Fig. 133F) and dusky brown with tawny or olive edging; outer pp covs broad, truncate, relatively fresh, and dusky brown with relatively distinct and broad, tawny edging (Fig. 138); outer rects truncate (Fig. 342) and relatively fresh. **Note: See HY/SY ♀♂.**

AHY/ASY ♂ (Oct-Sep): Upperparts, head, and breast with substantial reddish or purplish (rarely orange or yellowish); molt-limit, wing-cov, and flight-feather criteria as in AHY/ASY ♀, except that the gr covs are edged reddish.

Hybrids reported—Pine Grosbeak. Possibly House Finch. At least three other species of finches in captivity (see Gray 1958).

Purple Finch

	Jan	Feb	Mar	Apr	May	Jun	Jul	Aug	Sep	Oct	Nov	Dec
Juv-HY							○	○	○	○	○	○
SY		(♂)	(♂)	(♂)	(♀)	(♀)	♀	♀	♂	♂	♂	
AHY-U		(♂)	(♂)	(♂)	(♀)	(♀)	♀	♀	♀	♀	♀	♀
ASY	♀	♀	♀	♀	♀	♀	♀	♂	♂	♂		

■ > 95% ▨ 25-95% ▨ 5-25% □ < 5%   See Fig. 24

Note: In Nov-Dec, AHYs can be sexed but birds of unknown age should be left unsexed.

References—Stone (1896), Dwight (1900a), Ridgway (1901), Magee (1924, 1926a, 1936, 1943), Forbush (1929), Groskin (1941), Duvall (1945b), Blake (1954b, 1954c, 1955), Roberts (1955), Kennard (1959, 1962), Bent *et al.* (1968), Wood (1969), Ryan (1969), Oberholser (1974), Remsen (1975), Yunick (1975, 1979b, 1983a, 1991), Kaufman (1986, 1990a), Eckert (1988), CWS & USFWS (1991), Clement *et al.* (1993), Wootton (1996), Pyle (1997c); C.H. Blake, W. Chapman, E.H. Downs, J.H. Kennard, D. Malec, W.R. Mellancamp, J.M. Sheppard, W.P. Smith, J.S. Weske, R.P. Yunick (*in litt.* to the BBL); J.R. King, B. Principe (pers. comm.); IBP (MAPS) data, PNR data, PRBO data, R.P. Yunick data.

CASSIN'S FINCH
Carpodacus cassinii

CAFI
Species # 5180
Band size: 1B-1

Species—From Purple Finch (which see for separation from House Finch) by much larger size (wg 84-98, tl 56-68; see **Sex**); longest p – longest s 25-37 mm; bill long (nares to tip 9.6-11.8), with the culmen usually straight (Fig. 343); eye ring whitish (♀♀) to buff (AHY/ASY ♂) and indistinct to distinct; ♀♀ and HY/SY ♂♂ pale brown (without an olive tinge), with the facial features moderately indistinct and the undertail covs with distinct and heavy, blackish streaks; AHY/ASY ♂♂ with the head reddish with little or no purple tinge (rarely orange or yellowish) and the back lightly washed the same color.

FIGURE 343. The bill shape and size, and head plumage of Cassin's, Purple, and House finches.

Geographic variation—Weak and clinal where ranges meet. Subspecies taxonomy follows Monson & Phillips (1981); see also Duvall (1945b), Dickinson (1953), Phillips *et al.* (1964), Mayr & Short (1970), Burleigh (1972). No other subspecies occur.

   C.c. vinifer (br & wint s.BC-w.ID to n.CA): Bill averages longer (exp culmen 11.5-14.0); plumage darker; AHY/ASY ♂ dark red with a purple tinge.

   C.c. cassinii (br & wint e.ID-MT to se.CA-w.TX): Bill averages shorter (exp culmen 11.0-13.0); plumage paler; AHY/ASY ♂ medium red without a purple tinge.

Molt—PB: HY partial (Jul-Sep), AHY complete (Jul-Sep); PA limited (Mar-May). The PBs occur on the summer grounds. The 1st PB includes some to all med covs and 4 to 10 (~50%) inner gr covs, but no terts or rects. The PA is limited to body feathers and includes no gr covs or flight feathers.

Skull—Pneumaticization completes in HY/SY from 15 Nov through Feb. Some SYs probably show windows (> 3 mm; Fig. 11**D**) through spring.

Age/Sex—CP/BP (Apr-Sep); brown-plumaged birds with a CP are SY ♂♂. ♀ wg(n100) 84-93, tl(n44) 56-65; ♂ (n100) 88-98, tl(n48) 60-68. See Purple Finch for plumage criteria, the only difference being that rect shape (Fig. 342) may be easier with Cassin's Finch, with only 10% intermediates reported.

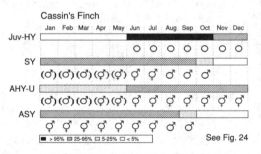

Note: See note under the graph for Purple Finch.

References—Ridgway (1901), Duvall (1945b), R.T. Orr *in* Bent *et al.* (1968), Oberholser (1974), Samson (1974a, 1974b, 1976), Remsen (1975), Balph (1977), Kaufman (1986, 1990a), Eckert (1988), CWS & USFWS (1991), Clement *et al.* (1993), Hahn (1996), Pyle (1997c); R.T. Orr (*in litt.* to the BBL); B. Principe (pers. comm.); IBP (MAPS) data.

HOUSE FINCH
Carpodacus mexicanus

HOFI
Species # 5190
Band size: 1B-1-1C

Species—From Purple Finch (which see for separation from Cassin's Finch) by smaller average wg (70-83) and relatively long tl (51-66; see **Geographic variation** & **Sex**); longest p – longest s 12-23 mm; bill short (nares to tip 6.9-9.0; see **Geographic variation**), with the culmen substantially decurved (Fig. 343); tail squared (r6 – r1 0-4 mm); ♀♀ and some HY/SY ♂♂ brown (often tinged olive), with the facial features lacking or indistinct, and the undertail covs with heavy, dusky streaks; AHY/ASY ♂♂ and most HY/SY ♂♂ with the head reddish to yellowish and the back brown with a slight or no reddish or yellowish tinge; seldom attempts to bite; usually calls when released. Use caution with separation from juv Purple Finches (which see). From Common Rosefinch (*C. erythrinus*), a vagrant to AK, by smaller average wg (70-83, *vs* 78-90 in Common Rosefinch); belly tinged buff (*vs* white); flanks and undertail covs with moderate to heavy (*vs* with little or no) streaking; ASY ♂ with little or no (*vs* with) red in the hindcrown and nape.

Geographic variation—Moderate, but clinal where most ranges meet. Subspecies taxonomy follows T.R. Howell *et al. in* Paynter (1968), as modified by Behle (1985) and evidence from delayed plumage maturation (see below and Hill 1996); see also Ridgway (1901), Brewster (1902), Thayer & Bangs (1906), Grinnell (1911d), Griscom (1928), Figgins (1930), van Rossem (1931a), Moore (1936, 1939c, 1939d, 1939e), Behle (1948), Aldrich (1949, 1982), Phillips *et al.* (1964), D.M. Power (1971, 1979, 1980, 1983), Oberholser (1974), Aldrich & Weske (1978), Browning (1978, 1990), Godfrey (1986), Hill (1993a). Nine other subspecies occur in Mex.

    C.m. frontalis (br & wint coastal sw.BC-sw.CA & MT-AZ to ME-FL): Bill averages small (exp culmen 9.7-12.7); underparts whitish with sparse brown streaking; ♂♂ (including HY/SYs) with extensive, dull orange-red to yellow on the breast. Birds of s.BC-CA and (introduced) e.N.Am ("*grinnelli*") may average redder (♂♂), birds of sw.WY-c.CO ("*smithi*") may average darker, and birds of sw.TX ("*anconophilus*") may average paler and redder, but in all cases differences are slight, broadly clinal, and obscured by individual variation and effects of diet on plumage coloration.

    C.m. solitudinus (br & wint e.WA-ID to se.CA-nw.AZ): Bill as in *frontalis*; underparts white with sparse brown streaking; HY/SY ♂♂ with little or no red (see **Age/Sex**); AHY/ASY ♂♂ with reduced, bright red on the breast.

    C.m. clementis (res Channel Is, CA): Bill averages large (exp culmen 10.4-13.1); underparts whitish with moderately heavy brown streaking; ♂♂ (including HY/SYs) with extensive, red (slightly tinged orange) on the breast.

    C.m. potosinus (res sc.TX): Bill averages large (exp culmen 10.5-13.0); underparts whitish with heavy brown streaking; ♂♂ (including HY/SYs) with extensive, deep red on the breast.

Molt—PB: HY partial-complete? (Jul-Oct), AHY complete (Jun-Oct); PA absent-limited(?). The PBs occur on the summer grounds. The 1st PB is quite variable, usually including all med and gr covs, 1-3 terts, sometimes (in ~48% of birds) other ss (of these, often s6 and s5 and/or s1 and s2), and 0 (~8%) to all 12 (~54%) rects. It also often (in ~52% of birds) can be eccentric (see p. 208, Fig. 136), with the outermost 2-7 pp, the innermost 2-7 ss, and occasionally (in ~13% of birds) the outermost 1-4 pp covs replaced. A small percentage of HYs (probably < 5%) can replace all pp, ss, and rects, although look for these birds to retain at least a few pp covs. During the adult PB, The replacement of 1-2 pp covs (usually among the 4th to the 2nd from the outside) occasionally may be suspended (until the winter grounds?), resulting in slight contrasts among these feathers (Fig. 215); more study is needed on this. A limited PA may occur in certain southern populations (reported in AZ). Note that, in ♂♂, feathers of the head and rump adventitiously replaced in Apr-Jun and Oct can be yellow and those adventitiously replaced in Nov-Mar can be brown.

Skull—Pneumaticization completes in HY/SY from 1 Oct. Look for windows (> 3 mm; Fig. 11**D**) on the top of the skull in some SYs through May.

Age—Juv (Apr-Oct) is washed brownish and has buffy wing bars, heavy streaking, and loosely textured undertail covs; juv ♀ = ♂.

    HY/SY (Sep-Aug): Most or all outer pp covs narrow, tapered, relatively abraded, and brown with indistinct, narrow, or no buff edging (Fig. 138); 1-3 terts replaced, often contrasting with the older middle ss (s4-s6); the outermost 2-7 pp, the innermost 2-7 ss (and sometimes outermost 1-2 ss), and occasionally the outermost 1-4 pp covs often replaced (see **Molt**), dark brown, contrasting with the paler brownish, retained inner pp, outer ss, and most or all pp covs (Fig. 136**A-D**); rump patch of ♂♂ often washed brownish (but can be bright) and reduced (width 10-24 mm; length 12-38 mm); some or all rects tapered (Fig. 342) and relatively abraded, or (sometimes) all rects truncate. **Note: Some HYs have a complete 1st PB and cannot be reliably separated from AHY/ASYs; examine the pp covs to detect those that have a near-complete molt. Also, molt limits can be difficult to detect, especially on worn ♀♀ in May-Jul, and many intermediates may not be reliably aged. See Sex concerning brown-plumaged ♂♂ of the subspecies *C.m. solitudinus*.**

U/AHY (Sep-Aug): Outer pp covs uniformly broad, truncate, relatively fresh, and dusky brown with relatively distinct and broad, pale (♀) or pinkish-white (♂) edging (Fig. 138); pp and ss uniformly adult (Fig. 133**F**) and dark brown; rump patch of ♂♂ bright red (or yellow) and extensive (width 17-28 mm; length 21-40 mm); rects uniformly adult, truncate (Fig. 342), and relatively fresh. **Note: See HY/SY. Look also for some birds to have contrastingly fresh pp covs, as in Figure 215; these may be aged AHY/ASY; more study is needed.**

Sex—CP/BP (Apr-Oct). ♀ wg(n100) 70-80, tl(n100) 51-63; ♂ wg(n100) 73-83, tl(n100) 54-66.

♀: Crown, breast, and rump without distinct red or gold plumage (they can be tinged yellow or orange on some AHY/ASYs). **Note: Caution is advised, as at least some ♂♂ of *C.m. solitudinus* (see Geographic variation) and of certain populations of Mex can remain in ♀-like plumage until the 2nd PB (see van Rossem 1936c; Hill 1993b, 1996). Thus, HY/SYs breeding in the range of *solitudinus* (and perhaps in a wider range in winter?) should probably be left unsexed unless they have breeding characters in Apr-Oct, or are worn SY ♂♂ molting from brown to red plumage in Jun-Oct. Some HY ♂♂ of these populations may acquire some red during the 1st PB; more study is needed to delimit the ranges of both plumage variation and geographic variation of delayed plumage maturation in this species.**

House Finch

Note: In Jul-Apr, HY/SYs of most subspecies can be reliably sexed. Only HY/SYs of the Great Basin subspecies, *C.m. solitudinus*, should be left unsexed.

See Fig. 24

♂: Crown, breast, and rump with distinct red or gold plumage. **Note: See ♀.**

Hybrids reported—Possibly Purple Finch. At least three other finch species in captivity (see Gray 1958).

References—Stone (1896), Dwight (1900a), Ridgway (1901), Forbush (1929), Michener & Michener (1931, 1932, 1940), Moore (1939e), Gill & Lanyon (1965), R.S. Woods *in* Bent *et al.* (1968), McEntee (1970a), Mott (1970), Oberholser (1974), Brush & Power (1976), Klimkiewicz (1980), Jones (1984), Stangel (1985), Kaufman (1986, 1990a), Tweit (1986b), Yunick (1987), CWS & USFWS (1991), Thompson (1991b), Hill (1992, 1993a, 1993b, 1993c, 1996), Clement *et al.* (1993), Hill *et al.* (1994a), Pyle (1997c); C.H. Blake, C.E. Cochran, J.H. Jeppson, M. Jones, E. Meese, D. Foy, M. Mutchler, R.T. Norris, R. Simpson, R.C. Tweit, M. Wood, R.P. Yunick (*in litt.* to the BBL); IBP (MAPS) data, PNR data, PRBO data.

RED CROSSBILL
Loxia curvirostra

RECR
Species # 5210
Band size: 1B

Species—Juvs and some ♀♀ of certain populations can show pale buff or whitish wing bars. These from White-winged Crossbill by longer relative tl (wg 82-101, tl 48-62; see **Geographic variation** & **Sex**); whitish tips to the gr covs absent, or ≤ 2.5 mm in width and not sharply defined.

Geographic variation—Extremely complicated by erratic nomadism and breeding; however, forms appear to be distinctly defined by vocalizations and morphology. Typical subspecies nomenclature may not be applicable in this species; therefore, subspecies taxonomy follows the "Type" system of Groth (1993a); see also Ridgway (1901), Grinnell *et al.* (1909), Bent (1912), Oberholser (1917d, 1974), van Rossem (1934b), Griscom (1937), Selander (1953), Dickerman (1957, 1986a, 1986b, 1987), Phillips *et al.* (1964), Bailey & Niedrach (1965), Phillips (1975a, 1975c, 1977), Monson & Phillips (1981), Behle (1985), Godfrey (1986), Payne (1987), Groth (1988, 1993b), Browning (1990), Benkman (1993). Thirteen other subspecies occur in Eurasia & C.Am. Note that most birds will not be identifiable to type with in-hand criteria alone (*i.e.*, without vocalizations); many birds may be identifiable to group, however. Note also that the ranges given below are incomplete until more study is undertaken; several types (especially in the Medium-sized Group) might be expected anywhere throughout the range of the species in N.Am. Birds of Greenland (*L.c. curvirostra*) may potentially occur in ne.N.Am; these are as large as Type 6 birds (see below) with thicker bills (depth 10.8-11.9).

Small (*L.c. minor*) Group.
Type 3 (= *"minor"*, *"sitkensis"*, and *"reai"*; recorded se.AK-n.CA to AZ and Ont-MI to NY): Small; bill small (nares to tip 11.7-13.9, depth at tip of nares 7.7-8.6); red of ♂♂ variable but may average deeper. ♀ wg(n17) 78-86, tl(n16) 46-52; ♂ wg(n28) 82-89, tl(n27) 48-55.

Medium-sized (*L.c. pusilla*) Group.
Type 1 (possibly = *"neogaea"* or *"vividor"*; recorded BC-WA and montane WV-GA): Medium small; bill medium small (nares to tip 13.0-15.7, depth at tip of nares 8.3-9.3); red of ♂♂ variable. ♀ wg(n33) 82-90, tl(n5) 48-55; ♂ wg(n39) 85-95, tl(n12) 50-58.

Type 2 (= *"pusilla"*, *"grinnelli"*, *"benti"* and, possibly, *"bendirei"*; recorded BC-n.CA-AZ to ME-GA): Medium in size; bill medium large (nares to tip 13.8-19.2, depth at tip of nares 8.9-10.5); red of ♂♂ variable but averages paler. ♀ wg(n100) 86-96, tl(n100) 51-58; ♂ wg(n100) 89-99, tl(n100) 53-62.

Type 4 (possibly = *"neogaea"* or *"vividor"*; recorded BC-n.CA-AZ to NS-NY): Medium in size; bill medium small (nares to tip 13.4-16.0, depth at tip of nares 7.9-9.4); red of ♂♂ variable. ♀ wg(n19) 84-90, tl(n18) 48-55; ♂ wg(n28) 86-95, tl(n27) 50-57.

Type 5 (possibly = *"bendirei"*; recorded BC-n.CA to CO-AZ): Medium large; bill medium in size (nares to tip 13.9-17.6, depth at tip of nares 8.8-10.2); red of ♂♂ variable. ♀ wg(n24) 88-95, tl(n24) 52-59; ♂ wg(n31) 92-98, tl(n29) 55-63.

Type 7 (possibly = *"bendirei"*; recorded BC-ID to n.CA): Medium in size; bill medium in size (nares to tip 13.7-15.6, depth at tip of nares 9.2-10.0); red of ♂♂ variable. ♀ wg(n2) 89-91, tl(n2) 52-53; ♂ wg(n5) 91-96, tl(n5) 53-58.

Large or Mexican (*L.c. stricklandi*) Group.
Type 6 (= *"stricklandi"*; br & wint se.AZ): Large; bill large (nares to tip 15.7-18.3, depth at tip of nares 10.3-11.7); red of ♂♂ variable but averages deeper, with less orange. ♀ wg(n10) 92-101, tl(n10) 54-61; ♂ wg(n20) 95-105, tl(n10) 56-63.

Newfoundland (*L.c. percna*) Group.
Type 8 (= *"percna"*; br & wint Nfl): Medium in size; bill medium in length but relatively stout (nares to tip 13.5-16.4, depth at tip of nares 9.6-11.4); plumage darker and duskier than the other subspecies; red of ♂♂ variable but averages darker. ♀ wg(n21) 85-93, tl(n10) 49-56; ♂ wg(n43) 89-97, tl(n10) 52-59.

Molt—PB: HY limited-incomplete (Apr-Dec), AHY complete (Apr-Nov); PA absent. The PBs often (but not always) occur in the vicinity of the summer grounds. Molts are complicated by winter breeding. Typically (summer-breeders and fledglings), the 1st PB includes some to all med covs, 0 (~15%) to 10 (~30%) inner gr covs, sometimes (in ~22% of birds) 1-3 terts, and occasionally (in ~13% of birds) 1-2 central rects (r1). Look for occasional birds (possibly winter fledglings; see below) to replace 5-7 pp, 5-6 ss, 4-12 rects (and possibly some outer pp covs?) in an eccentric pattern (see p. 208 and Fig. 136), as has been reported in Europe. During the 2nd PB, occasional birds (~6% in N.Am; up to 50% reported in Europe) can retain 1-6 inner ss in consecutive blocks (among s1-s6) and 1-4 consecutive inner pp covs. During subsequent adult PBs, a few scattered ss and/or pp covs rarely can be retained, but usually not in consecutive blocks. The PBs of Type 6 birds ("*stricklandi*" of se.AZ) are reported to occur 2-3 months earlier than those of the other types in N.Am. In winter-breeding adults and fledglings, the 1st and adult PBs can be split into two periods, the first in Apr-Jul, and the second in Aug-Oct. During the first period, HYs can replace up to 3 inner gr covs, but no terts or rects. During these molts ♂♂ (of all ages) acquire yellow or orange feathers during the first phase and red feathers during the second phase. Note that this information (on molts of winter breeders and fledglings) is based on studies in Europe (see Cramp & Perrins 1994a, Jenni & Winkler 1994); more study is needed to confirm these patterns in N.Am.

Skull—Pneumaticization may complete in HY/SY at all times of the year, but most often from Dec-Feb. AHYs are reliably aged by skull only through Jun; in Jul-Dec use plumage if skull is fully pneumaticized.

Age/Sex—Juv (Jan-Sep) is brownish with buffy wing bars and heavy streaking throughout; juv ♀ = ♂, but some birds occasionally can breed in full juvenal plumage and can be sexed by CP/BP. CP/BP (Apr-Oct, sometimes Nov-Mar). ♀ wg(n100) 82-101, tl(n100) 48-61; ♂ wg(n100) 85-105, tl(n100) 50-63; see **Geographic variation**.

HY/SY ♀ (Aug-Jul): Plumage brown or greenish, usually without substantial yellow; molt limits often occur among the med and gr covs (Fig. 133**A-E**; see **Molt**), the retained outer covs worn and pale brown with indistinct, buff or whitish tips, contrasting with the fresher and darker brown, replaced inner covs; 1-3 terts sometimes replaced, contrasting with the older middle ss (s4-s6; Fig. 133**D-E**); outer pp covs narrow, tapered, relatively abraded, and brown with little or no pale edging (Fig. 138); central rects (r1) sometimes replaced and contrastingly fresh; outer rects tapered (Fig. 342) and relatively abraded; throat grayish. **Note: Ageing and age coding in this species is potentially complicated by occasional winter breeding. In Feb-Sep HYs are separated from SYs by relative plumage wear (SYs being more abraded) and by molt replacement patterns (see Molt). Ageing by molt limits is complicated in this species by split molts in all ages (see Molt). Molt limits in the gr covs are the most reliable means of ageing; those HY/SYs that have replaced all 10 gr covs, usually have replaced 1-3 terts or 1-2 central rects (r1) and can be aged by contrasts there. In the ~5% of HY/SYs that have replaced all gr covs, look for eccentric replacement patterns (see p. 208 and Fig. 136A); AHY/ASYs should show typical replacement patterns (Fig. 137). Also, check the relationship of the pp-cov replacement to that of the pp, corresponding in AHY/ASYs, not corresponding in HY/SYs. See also SY/TY ♀.**

AHY/ASY ♀ (Aug-Jul): Plumage brown or greenish, often with some yellow, or sometimes with an orange or reddish wash (especially on the rump), but not as bright as in ♂♂; wing covs, terts, and middle ss (s4-s6) uniformly adult (Fig. 133**F**) and dark brown, without buff or whitish tips; outer pp covs broad, truncate, relatively fresh, and dusky brown, often with narrow, yellowish edging (Fig. 138); rects uniformly adult, truncate (Fig. 342), and relatively fresh; throat grayish with an olive tinge. **Note: Molt limits in Apr-Jul can occur in AHY/ASYs; see HY/SY ♀ and Molt. About 6% of AHY/ASYs can be aged SY/TY; see SY/TY ♀.**

SY/TY ♀ (Aug-Jul): Plumage as in AHY/ASY ♀, but 1-6 consecutive middle ss (among s1-s6) and/or 1-4 consecutive inner pp covs retained, worn, and brown-edged, contrasting with the much darker, fresher, and yellow-edged, remainder of the ss and pp. **Note: This plumage can be expected in only about 6% of N.Am AHY/ASYs. Retained, adult ss in irregular patterns may indicate ASY/ATY (especially in Nov-Mar) but more study is needed to separate these from AHY/ASYs with suspended summer molts, which also show contrasting feathers; see Molt.**

HY/SY ♂ (Aug-Jul): Plumage mixed dull red or yellow-orange and brownish; molt-limit, wing-cov, and flight-feather criteria as in HY/SY ♀, but the replaced feathers have reddish edging; throat orange to grayish, with dull red, orange, or yellow feathers. **Note: In ♂♂ of any age, feathers adventitiously replaced in Jan-Jun usually are yellow rather than red. HYs are separated from SYs in Feb-Oct by very worn as opposed to fresh flight feathers, molting patterns specific to that age group (see Molt), and less orange or red coloration, on average. Use consideration of molt and flight-feather criteria for ageing SY in Aug-Oct. In addition, molt limits in Apr-Jul can occur in AHY/ASYs; see HY/SY ♀ and SY/TY ♀.**

AHY/ASY ♂ (Aug-Jul): Plumage entirely red, red-orange (usually), or mixed red and yellowish; molt-limit, wing-cov, and flight-feather criteria as in AHY/ASY ♀, except that the flight-feather edging is uniformly red; throat reddish orange to red. **Note: Worn ASY ♂♂ (Apr-Jul) can lack red edging to the flight feathers. In addition, molt limits in Apr-Jul can occur in AHY/ASYs; see HY/SY ♀. About 6% of AHY/ASYs can be aged SY/TY (and possibly some birds can be aged ASY/ATY); see SY/TY ♀.**

SY/TY ♂ (Aug-Jul): Plumage as in AHY/ASY ♂, but 1-6 consecutive middle ss (among s1-s6) and/or 1-4 consecutive, inner pp covs retained, worn, and brown-edged, contrasting with the much darker, fresher, and red-edged, remainder of the ss and pp. **Note: See SY/TY ♀.**

Hybrids reported—Pine Siskin, Parrot Crossbill (*L. pytyopsittacus*). White-winged Crossbill in captivity.

Red Crossbill

See Fig. 24

References—Stone (1896), Dwight (1900a), Ridgway (1901), Forbush (1929), Tordoff (1952, 1954), Jollie (1953), Roberts (1955), Kemper (1959), Bent *et al.* (1968), Wood (1969), Oberholser (1974), Phillips (1977), Monson & Phillips (1981), Tallman & Zusi (1984), Yunick (1984), Dickerman (1986b), Svensson (1992), Clement *et al.* (1993), Groth (1993a, 1993b), Cramp & Perrins (1994a), Jenni & Winkler (1994), Adkisson (1996), Pyle (1997c); A. Knox, A.R. Phillips (pers. comm.); PRBO data.

WHITE-WINGED CROSSBILL
Loxia leucoptera

WWCR
Species # 5220
Band size: 1B

Species—From juvs of anomalous Red Crossbills (which see) by shorter relative tl (wg 80-90, tl 49-59; see **Sex**); white or whitish tips to the gr covs ≥ 2.5 mm in width and sharply defined.

Geographic variation—Moderately well marked and ranges well defined. Subspecies taxonomy follows T.R. Howell *et al. in* Paynter (1968); see Riley (1916), Dement'ev & Gladkov (1954), Parkes (1957c), Cramp & Perrins (1994a). Two other subspecies occur in Eurasia and the W.Indies.

L.l. leucoptera (br & wint throughout the range in N.Am): From the Eurasian subspecies (*bifasciata*) by shorter average wg (see **Sex**, *vs* 83-97 in *bifasciata*), bill smaller (nares to tip 12.4-15.4, depth at tip of nares 9.5-11.0, *vs* 13.9-16.0 and 9.7-12.3, respectively); plumage darker, with less white in the gr covs (width of tips 2-10 mm) and terts; from the Hispaniolian subspecies (*megaplaga*) by much smaller bill (in *megaplaga*: nares to tip 14.9-17.0, depth at tip of nares 10.8-13.0).

Molt—Not well studied, but evidence suggests it parallels that of Red Crossbill with winter and summer breeders (and fledglings) showing different strategies. Typically, PB: HY limited-incomplete (Apr-Dec), AHY complete (Apr-Nov); PA absent(?). The PBs often (but not always) occur in the vicinity of the breeding grounds. The 1st PB includes most to all med covs, 2 to 10 (~26%) inner gr covs, sometimes (in ~26% of birds) 1-3 terts (rarely s6 or other ss) and occasionally (in ~19% of birds) 1-2 central rects (r1), rarely as many as all rects. Rarely (~3-5%), eccentric replacement patterns (see p. 208 and Fig. 136) apparently can occur, with up to 8 pp and 1 or more outer pp covs replaced. Up to 6 middle ss (among s1-s6) and 1 or more pp covs can be retained during the 2nd and subsequent PBs in ~10% of AHYs, as in Red Crossbill. More study is needed on the extents of the molts in winter breeders and fledglings and whether or not they parallel those of Red Crossbill (which see). Acquisition of orange or yellow feathers by ♂♂ molting in Apr-Jun occurs, suggesting similar split molts to those of Red Crossbill.

Skull—Pneumaticization may complete at any time of year. See Red Crossbill.

Age/Sex—Juv (Jan-Sep) is brownish with reduced, dull-whitish wing bars and heavy streaking throughout; juv ♀=♂, but some birds occasionally can breed in full juvenal plumage and can be sexed by CP/BP. CP/BP (Jan-Oct). ♀ wg(n100) 80-90, tl(n26) 49-59; ♂ wg(n100) 83-93, tl(n26) 52-62. Ageing apparently follows that of Red Crossbill (which see for details).

HY/SY ♀ (Aug-Jul): Plumage brown or greenish, usually without substantial yellow; molt limits often occur among the med and gr covs (Fig. 133**A-E**; see **Molt**), the retained outer covs worn and pale brown with indistinct, whitish tips, contrasting with the fresher, dusky, and distinctly white-tipped, replaced inner covs; 1-3 terts sometimes replaced, contrasting with the older middle ss (s4-s6; Fig. 133**D-E**); outer pp covs narrow, tapered, relatively abraded, and brown with little or no pale edging (Fig. 138); central rects (r1) sometimes replaced, contrastingly fresh; outer rects tapered (Fig. 342) and relatively abraded. **Note: See HY/SY ♀ Red Crossbill.**

AHY/ASY ♀ (Aug-Jul): Plumage brown or greenish, sometimes with some yellow, or occasionally with a slight reddish tinge; wing covs, terts, and middle ss (s4-s6) uniformly adult (Fig. 133**F**) and dusky, the gr covs with distinct, white tips; outer pp covs broad, truncate, relatively fresh, and dusky (Fig. 138); rects uniformly adult, truncate (Fig. 342), and relatively fresh. **Note: See AHY/ASY ♀ Red Crossbill.**

SY/TY ♀ (Aug-Jul): Plumage as in AHY/ASY ♀, but 1-6 consecutive middle ss (among s1-s6) and/or 1-4 consecutive inner pp covs retained, worn, and brown-edged, contrasting with the much darker, fresher, and yellow-edged, remainder of the ss and pp. **Note: This plumage can be expected in only about 10% of N.Am AHY/ASYs. Retained, adult ss in irregular patterns may indicate ASY/ATY (especially in Nov-Mar), but more study is needed to separate these from AHY/ASYs with suspended summer molts, which also likely show contrasting feathers; see Molt.**

HY/SY ♂ (Aug-Jul): Plumage mixed brownish and dull pinkish red or (sometimes) yellow-orange; molt-limit, wing-cov, and flight-feather criteria as in HY/SY ♀♀, but the replaced feathers are blackish with reddish edging (thus, contrasting more distinctly with the retained pp covs); throat orange to grayish, with dull red, orange or yellow feathers. **Note: See HY/SY ♂ Red Crossbill.**

AHY/ASY ♂ (Aug-Jul): Plumage entirely pinkish red, or (sometimes) mixed red and yellowish; molt-limit, wing-cov, and flight-feather criteria as in AHY/ASY ♀ except that the flight feathers are uniformly blackish with red edging; throat reddish orange to red. **Note: See AHY/ASY ♂ Red Crossbill.**

SY/TY ♂ (Aug-Jul): Plumage as in AHY/ASY ♂, but 1-6 consecutive middle ss (among s1-s6) and/or 1-4 consecutive inner pp covs retained, worn, and brown-edged, contrasting with the much darker, fresher, and red-edged, remainder of the ss and pp. **Note: See SY/TY ♀.**

Hybrids reported—Red Crossbill in captivity.

White-winged Crossbill

	Jan	Feb	Mar	Apr	May	Jun	Jul	Aug	Sep	Oct	Nov	Dec
Juv-HY	○	○	○	○	○	(♂)	(♂)	(♀)	♂	♂	♂	♂
SY	♀♂	♀♂	♀♂	♀♂	♀♂	♀♂	♀♂	♀♂	♀♂	♀♂	♀♂	♀♂
TY	♀♂	♀♂	♀♂	♀♂	♀♂	♀♂	♀♂					
AHY	♀♂	♀♂	♀♂	♀♂	♀♂	♀♂	♀♂	♀♂	♀♂	♀♂	♀♂	♀♂
ASY	♀♂	♀♂	♀♂	♀♂	♀♂	♀♂	♀♂	?	?	?	?	?

■ > 95% ▨ 25-95% ▢ 5-25% □ < 5%   See Fig. 24

References—Stone (1896), Dwight (1900a), Ridgway (1901), Forbush (1929), Roberts (1955), Parkes (1957c), W. Taber *in* Bent *et al.* (1968), Wood (1969), Sealy *et al.* (1980), Benkman (1992), Svensson (1992), Clement *et al.* (1993), Cramp & Perrins (1994a), Pyle (1997c).

COMMON REDPOLL
Carduelis flammea

CORE
Species # 5280
Band size: 0

Species—From Hoary Redpoll, with caution (some intermediates may not be safely separable), by bill longer (nares to tip 6.8-11.4) and more acutely angled (Fig. 344); nape, back, rump, and flanks moderately pale to pale brownish white, with moderately heavy to heavy streaking; auricular moderately well defined to distinct; undertail covs with two to many broad, indistinct to distinct streaks (see **Age/Sex**; Fig. 345A-D); breast of AHY/ASY ♂♂ rosy to deep red. The difference in the streaking to the undertail covs (Fig. 345), by age/sex class, is the most reliable criterion. Beware especially of ♀ Hoary Redpolls of the subspecies *C.h. exilipes*, which can overlap with ♂ Common Redpolls in the coloration and density of the streaking; combine all criteria with those of geographic variation, age, and sex for accurate separation of most birds. See also Herremans (1990) and Seutin *et al.* (1992, 1993) for multivariate analyses, based on plumage scores and measurements of specimens, that are useful in separating the two species.

Geographic variation—Moderate, but clinal where ranges meet. Subspecies taxonomy follows T.R. Howell *et al. in* Paynter (1968); see Ridgway (1901), Salomonsen (1928), Shaub (1950), Dement'ev & Gladkov (1954), Todd (1963), Godfrey (1986), Knox (1988b), Herremans (1990), Svensson (1992), Cramp & Perrins (1994a), Czaplak (1995). Two other subspecies occur in Iceland and Eurasia.

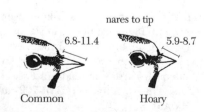

nares to tip

6.8-11.4   5.9-8.7

Common   Hoary

FIGURE 344. The bill shape and size in Common and Hoary redpolls.

C.f. flammea (br AK-Nfl, wint to n.CA-VA): Small; bill slender (depth at tip of nares 4.4-6.0); plumage medium-pale brown with moderately distinct, dusky streaking. ♀ wg(n100) 67-76, tl(n100) 50-59; ♂ wg(n100) 68-78, tl(n100) 51-61. Birds breeding in the northern part of the range ("*holboellii*") may average longer-billed, but this difference is slight and due to slight intergradation with *rostrata*.

C.f. rostrata (br n.NWT, wint to CO-NJ): Large; bill stout (depth at tip of nares 6.1-7.9); plumage medium-dark brown with heavy, dusky streaking. ♀ wg(n100) 72-82, tl(n100) 54-64; ♂ wg(n100) 75-84, tl(n100) 55-66.

Molt—PB: HY partial (Aug-Oct), AHY complete (Aug-Sep); PA absent. The PBs occur on the summer grounds. The 1st PB includes some to all med covs, 0 (~8%) to 10 (~4%) inner gr covs, rarely (in ~2% of birds) s8, and rarely (in ~2% of birds) 1-2 central rects (r1). Occasionally (in ~5% of birds) one or more middle ss (usually s6) can be retained during the adult (usually the 2nd?) PBs; also look for the occasional retention of the pp covs.

Skull—Pneumaticization completes in HY/SY from 1 Nov through Jan.

Age/Sex—Juv (Jul-Aug) lacks red in the cap and black in the throat; juv ♀ = ♂. CP/BP (May-Sep). ♀ wg(n100) 67-82, tl(n100) 50-64; ♂ wg(n100) 68-84, tl(n100) 51-66; measurements vary more by subspecies than by sex (see **Geographic variation**).

HY/SY ♀ (Sep-Aug): Molt limits usually occur among the med and gr covs (Fig. 133**A-D**; see **Molt**), the retained outer covs worn and brownish with dark buff tips, contrasting with the fresher, duskier, and whitish-tipped to pale buff-tipped, replaced inner covs; outer pp covs narrow, tapered, relatively abraded, and brown with indistinct, narrow, or no pale buffy-brownish edging (Fig. 138); outer rects tapered (Fig. 342) and relatively abraded; breast and flanks entirely without pink; longest undertail covs with heavy and distinct streaks (Fig. 345**A-B**). **Note: Molt limits in this species can be difficult to detect because the outer wing covs are buffier than the inner covs in both age groups; look more for differences in wear. Rect shape probably is the most reliable criterion for ageing. Compare with wg (by subspecies) for reliable separation from HY/SY ♂♂; many intermediates may not be reliably sexed.**

AHY/ASY ♀ (Sep-Aug): Wing covs uniformly adult (Fig. 133**F**) and dusky brown with white to dark buff tips; outer pp covs broad, truncate, relatively fresh, and dark brown with relatively distinct, grayish edging (Fig. 138); outer rects truncate (Fig. 342) and relatively fresh; breast and flanks usually tinged lightly (but sometimes without) pink; longest undertail covs with moderately heavy and distinct streaks (Fig. 345**B-C**). **Note: See HY/SY ♀. Look for a few AHY/ASYs with one or more retained middle ss (often s6) or pp covs; if these are contrastingly pale and worn, reliable ageing of SY/TY might be possible, but more study is needed.**

HY/SY ♂ (Sep-Aug): Molt-limit, wing-cov, and flight-feather criteria as in HY/SY ♀; breast and flanks usually lightly washed pink; longest undertail covs with moderately heavy and distinct streaks (Fig. 345**B-C**). **Note: See HY/SY ♀.**

AHY/ASY ♂ (Sep-Aug): Molt-limit, wing-cov, and flight-feather criteria as in AHY/ASY ♀; breast and flanks washed pink to red; longest undertail covs with moderately narrow and indistinct streaks (Fig. 345**B-C**). **Note: See HY/SY ♀ and AHY/ASY ♀.**

Hybrids reported—Pine Siskin, Eurasian Siskin (*C. spinus*). Reported hybrids with

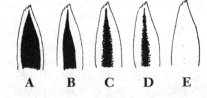

FIGURE 345. Variation in the pattern of the longest undertail covert, by species and age/sex group (see text for details), in Common and Hoary redpolls.

Hoary Redpoll in the wild may actually refer to normal variation within Hoary (which see), although these hybrids undoubtedly occur. Also, at least seven other finch species in captivity (see Gray 1958).

References—Stone (1896), Dwight (1900a), Ridgway (1901), Forbush (1929), Wetherbee (1937), Shaub (1950), Roberts (1955), Houston (1963), Todd (1963), Bergstrom (1964), R.C. Clement *in* Bent *et al.* (1968), Brooks (1968, 1973), Wood (1969), Collins & West (1974), Yunick (1979b), Troy & Brush (1983), Troy (1984, 1985), Knox (1988b), Bevier (1990), Herremans (1990), Seutin *et al.* (1992, 1993), Svensson (1992), Clement *et al.* (1993), Cramp & Perrins (1994a), Jenni & Winkler (1994), Czaplak (1995), Pyle (1997c); E.E. Burroughs, P.F. Cannell, M.K. Klimkiewicz, K.C. Parkes, L.J. Peyton, R.M. Poulin, D. Willard (*in litt.* to the BBL); A. Knox, L. Svensson (pers. comm.); IBP (MAPS) data, R.P. Yunick data.

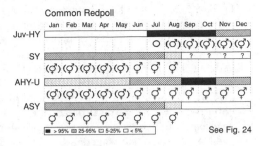

HOARY REDPOLL
Carduelis hornemanni

HORE
Species # 5270
Band size: 0

Species—From Common Redpoll, with caution (some intermediates may not be safely separable), by bill shorter (nares to tip 5.9-7.4 in *C.h. exilipes*, which resembles Common Redpoll; 7.3-8.7 in *hornemanni*; see **Geographic variation**) and broadly angled (Fig. 344); nape, back, rump, and flanks pale brownish white to whitish, with light to moderately light streaking (rump often without streaks); auricular often with little or no definition; undertail covs with 0-3 narrow, indistinct streaks by age/sex class (see **Age/Sex**; Fig 345C-E); breast of AHY/ASY ♂♂ with or without a pale rosy patch. See Common Redpoll.

Geographic variation—Well marked and ranges well defined. Subspecies taxonomy follows T.R. Howell *et al. in* Paynter (1968); see Ridgway (1901), Salomonsen (1928), Shaub (1950), Dement'ev & Gladkov (1954), Todd (1963), Troy (1984), Godfrey (1986), Knox (1988b), Herremans (1990), Svensson (1992), Cramp & Perrins (1994a), Czaplak (1995). No other subspecies occur.

  C.h. exilipes (br AK-Lab, wint to OR-MD): Small; bill small (exp culmen 7.0-9.1, depth at tip of nares 5.0-6.5, width at tip of nares 5.0-6.5); plumage pale brownish white with moderately heavy, dusky streaking; AHY/ASY ♂ with the pink of the underparts deep, usually covering most of the breast. ♀ wg(n100) 67-76, tl(n100) 51-60; ♂ wg(n100) 68-79, tl(n100) 53-62.

  C.h. hornemanni (br n.NWT, wint to MI-MD): Large; bill large (exp culmen 8.6-10.0, depth at tip of nares 5.9-7.8, width at tip of nares 6.0-7.9); plumage whitish with sparse, dusky streaking; AHY/ASY ♂ with the pink of the underparts pale, usually reduced to the sides of the breast only. ♀ wg(n76) 79-87, tl(n54) 57-67; ♂ wg(n80) 81-90, tl(n60) 59-69.

Molt—PB: HY partial (Jul-Sep), AHY complete (Jul-Sep); PA absent. The PBs occur on the summer grounds. The 1st PB includes some to all med covs and 0 (~40%) to 5 inner gr covs, but no terts or rects. See Common Redpoll concerning possible retention of middle ss (among s4-s6) and pp covs during the adult PB.

Skull—Pneumaticization completes in HY/SY from 1 Nov through Jan.

Age/Sex—Juv (Jul-Aug) lacks red in the cap and black in the throat; juv ♀ = ♂. CP/BP (May-Sep). See **Geographic variation** for measurements, which vary much more by subspecies than by sex.

HY/SY ♀♂ (Sep-Aug): Molt limits occur among the med and gr covs (see **Molt**; Fig. 133A-C), the retained outer covs worn and brownish with dark buff tips, contrasting with the fresher, duskier, and whitish-tipped or pale buff-tipped, replaced inner covs; outer pp covs narrow, tapered, relatively abraded, and brown with indistinct, narrow, or no pale buffy-brownish edging (Fig. 138); outer rects tapered (Fig. 342) and relatively abraded; breast and rump without pink; longest undertail covs usually with narrow streaks (Fig. 345C-D). **Note: A few HY/SY ♂♂ can show a slight pink tinge to the breast and rump and are reliably sexed; otherwise, HY/SY ♀=♂, although the thickness of the streaking on the undertail covs can be useful (compare with wg); more study is needed. Some intermediates will occur which are not reliably aged.**

AHY/ASY ♀ (Sep-Aug): Wing covs uniformly adult (Fig. 133F) and dusky brown with white to dark buff tips; outer pp covs broad, truncate, relatively fresh, and dark brown with relatively distinct, grayish edging (Fig. 138); outer rects truncate (Fig. 342) and relatively fresh; breast and rump usually without (sometimes slightly tinged) pink; longest undertail covs without or with narrow streaks (Fig. 345D-E). **Note: See HY/SY ♀♂. Also, reliable ageing of SY/TY might be possible by retained pp covs and ss (see Common Redpoll), but more study is needed. A few AHY/ASYs may be difficult to sex by plumage alone.**

AHY/ASY ♂ (Sep-Aug): Molt-limit, wing-cov, and flight-feather criteria as in AHY/ASY ♀; breast and rump with a light to moderate pink wash; longest undertail covs usually without streaks (Fig. 345E). **Note: See HY/SY ♀♂ and AHY/ASY ♀.**

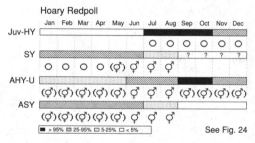

Hybrids reported—Supposed hybrids with Common Redpoll in the wild may actually refer to normal variation within Hoary Redpoll (especially *C.h. exilipes*; see **Geographic variation**), although hybrids between these two species should be expected.

Note: In Nov-Dec, some AHYs can be sexed but birds of unknown age should be left unsexed.

References—Ridgway (1901), Forbush (1929), Wetherbee (1937), Shaub (1950), Roberts (1955), Todd (1963), P.H. Baldwin *in* Bent *et al.* (1968), Brooks (1968), Troy & Brush (1983), Troy (1984, 1985), Knox (1988b), Bevier (1990), Herremans (1990), Seutin *et al.* (1992, 1993), Svensson (1992), Clement *et al.* (1993), Czaplak (1995), Pyle (1997c); P.F. Cannell, K.C. Parkes, D. Willard (*in litt.* to the BBL); A Knox, L. Svensson (pers. comm.).

PINE SISKIN
Carduelis pinus

PISI
Species # 5330
Band size: 0

Species—From HY/SY and ♀ Eurasian Siskin (*C. spinus*), a vagrant to AK and possibly ne.N.Am, by supercilium usually without (*vs* with) yellow coloration; med covs tipped buff (*vs* yellowish); rump feathers whitish (occasionally tinged yellow) with broad dusky centers (*vs* bright yellow with thin dusky streaks); flanks with heavy (*vs* light) streaking. Note that occasional "green morph" Pine Siskins can show abnormal amounts of yellow in the plumage and may be difficult to separate from Eurasian Siskin; these should have a yellow tinge to the undertail covs *vs* white in Eurasian Siskin (and most Pine Siskins).

Geographic variation—Weak and differences are obscured by individual variation, probably the result of frequent mixing. Subspecies taxonomy follows T.R. Howell *et al. in* Paynter (1968), as modified by Behle (1985); see also Ridgway (1901), Grinnell (1928d), Aldrich (1946), Phillips (1947b), Rand (1948b), Todd (1963), Phillips *et al.* (1964), Oberholser (1974), Unitt *et al.* (1992). One other subspecies occurs in Mex-C.Am. Critical analyses are needed on the amount of yellow in the wings and tail by subspecies, age, and sex (see **Sex**).

> **C.p. vagans** (br & wint s.AK-Alb to CA-w.Tx; wanders to NY-VA): Small (see **Sex**); plumage medium-pale buffy olive to whitish, with light to moderately dense, dusky streaking; yellow in flight feathers averages less extensive by age/sex.
>
> **C.p. macroptera** (br & wint nc.Mex; wanders to AZ-NM): Large; plumage pale olive to buffy whitish, with sparse, indistinct, dusky streaking; yellow in flight feathers averages more extensive by age/sex. ♀ wg(n10) 70-78, tl(n10) 42-49; ♂ wg(n11) 73-80, tl(n10) 44-51.
>
> **C.p. pinus** (br Sask to Nfl-n.ME, wint to s.TX-FL; wanders to WA): Small (see **Sex**); plumage medium-dark brownish olive to whitish olive, with moderately dense to heavy, distinct, blackish streaking; yellow in flight feathers averages less extensive by age/sex.

Molt—PB: HY partial (Jul-Dec), AHY complete (Jun-Oct); PA limited. The PBs occur primarily in the vicinity of the summer grounds but can complete on migration or on the winter grounds in some HYs. The 1st PB includes some to all med covs, 0 (~11%) to 10 (~18%) inner gr covs, sometimes (in ~36% of birds) 1-3 terts, and occasionally (in ~7% of birds) 1-2 central rects (r1; rarely up to four rects). Look for occasional birds to replace pp (often just p5-p6 or p5-p8) in an eccentric pattern (see p. 208 and Fig. 136), as occurs in Eurasian Siskin. The PA probably is limited to feathers on the throat and crown.

Skull—Pneumaticization completes in HY/SY from 15 Oct through early Mar.

Age—Juv (Apr-Sep) has a buffy or yellowish wash to the upperparts and breast (some birds are possibly sexed by the amount of yellow in the flight feathers; see **Sex**).

> HY/SY (Sep-Aug): Molt limits usually occur among the med and gr covs (Fig. 133**A-E**; see **Molt**), the retained outer covs worn and brown with dark buff tips, contrasting with the fresher, duskier, and white-tipped to pale buff-tipped, replaced inner covs; 1-3 terts sometimes replaced, contrasting with the older middle ss (s4-s6; Fig. 133**D-E**); outer pp covs narrow, tapered, relatively abraded, and brown with indistinct, narrow, or no pale grayish to brownish edging (Fig. 138); central rects (r1) occasionally replaced, contrastingly fresh; outer rects tapered (Fig. 342) and relatively abraded.
>
> AHY/ASY (Sep-Aug): Wing covs, terts, and middle ss (s4-s6) uniformly adult (Fig. 133**F**) and dusky, the gr covs with whitish to pale buff tips; outer pp covs broad, truncate, relatively fresh, and dusky with relatively distinct, yellow to buffy-yellow edging (Fig. 138); rects uniformly adult, truncate (Fig. 342), and relatively fresh.

Sex—CP/BP (Mar-Sep). ♀ wg(n100) 66-75, tl(n100) 40-48; ♂ wg(n100) 69-77, tl(n100) 42-50; includes the two subspecies of northern N.Am only (see **Geographic variation**). The amount and brightness of yellow in the flight feathers is related to sex (more and brighter yellow in ♂♂ than in ♀♀)and can be useful for separating up to 35% of birds (AHY/ASYs, at least) when combined with age and wg (see McEntee 1970b; Yunick 1970b, 1976a). The specifics for reliable sexing within age and subspecies groups have yet to be determined, however (see also **Geographic variation**).

Hybrids reported—Red Crossbill, Common Redpoll.

References—Stone (1896), Dwight (1900a), Ridgway (1901), Forbush (1929), Roberts (1955), Lowther & Walker (1967), R.S. Palmer *in* Bent *et al.* (1968), Wood (1969), McEntee (1970b), Yunick (1970b, 1976a, 1976c, 1977c, 1992b, 1995), Oberholser (1974), Sheppard & Klimkiewicz (1976), Leberman (1984), Tallman & Zusi (1984), Howard *et al.* (1989), CWS & USFWS (1991), Clement *et al.* (1993), Dawson (1997), Pyle (1997c); E.J. Fisk, M.G. Goldberg, E.B. Hurlbert, R.C. Leberman, M. McEntee, R.P. Yunick (*in litt.* to the BBL); E.J. Willoughby (pers. comm.); IBP (MAPS) data, PRBO data, R.P. Yunick data.

Pine Siskin

	Jan	Feb	Mar	Apr	May	Jun	Jul	Aug	Sep	Oct	Nov	Dec
Juv-HY				○	○	○	○	○	○	○	○	○
SY												
	○	○	(♀)	(♀)	(♀)	♂	♂	(♂)				
AHY-U												
	(♀)(♀)	(♀)(♀)	(♀)	♂	♂	(♂)	(♀)(♀)	(♀)				
ASY												
	(♀)(♀)	(♀)(♀)	(♀)	♂	♂	(♂)						

■ > 95% ▨ 25-95% ▥ 5-25% □ < 5%   See Fig. 24

Note: In Nov-Dec, AHYs can be sexed but birds of unknown age should be left unsexed.

LESSER GOLDFINCH
Carduelis psaltria

LEGO
Species # 5300
Band size: 0A-0

Species—Juvs and HYs from Lawrence's and American goldfinches by the combination of small size, especially short tl (wg 57-67, tl 36-43; see **Age/Sex**); upperparts olive, without dusky streaking; wings dull dusky; pp with white patches at the bases, usually extending beyond the pp covs (Fig. 346; see **Age/Sex**) and without yellow; outer rects (r6) without white or with the white not extending to the tips of the feathers (Fig. 347); undertail covs yellow.

Geographic variation—Well marked (AHY/ASY ♂♂) to weak (HY/SYs and ♀♀) and complicated by possible polymorphism and/or broad intergradation. Subspecies taxonomy follows Monson & Phillips (1981); see also Ridgway (1901), Brewster (1902), Grinnell (1902b), Oberholser (1903b), Phillips *et al.* (1964), Hubbard & Crossin (1974), Kaufman (1993d), Pyle (1997c), Watt & Willoughby (in press). Three other subspecies occur in Mex-S.Am. In addition to the following, see **Molt** for geographic variation in the extent of the PAs, which could prove useful for subspecies identification (especially of ♀♀), although geographic variation in replacement patterns does not currently coincide with the subspecies taxonomy, suggesting that the older taxonomy (recognizing "*hesperophilus*"; see below) may warrant further consideration (see Watt & Willoughby in press).

    C.p. psaltria (br & wint WA-UT to CA-sw.TX): AHY/ASY ♂ with the back and auricular olive with dusky streaking or black mottling (rarely almost entirely black); HY/SYs and ♀♀ with the upperparts olive, usually without a dusky tinge. Birds of WA-UT to CA-sc.AZ ("*hesperophilus*") have ♂♂ without black in the back or auricular, but differences possibly (see **Molt**) are due to polymorphism or lack of intergradation rather than true subspecific differentiation.

    C.p. mexicanus (br & wint s.TX): AHY/ASY ♂ with the back and auricular entirely black; HY/SYs and ♀♀ with the upperparts dusky olive.

Molt—PB: HY partial-incomplete (Aug-Nov), AHY incomplete-complete (Aug-Nov); PA limited-incomplete (Mar-Apr). The PBs occur during migration or on the winter grounds. The 1st PB is variable, including 0 (~3%) to 10 (~77%) inner gr covs, 1-3 terts, often one or more of s4-s6, and 0 (~23%) to 10 (~58%) rects. Also, the 1st PB often (in ~65% of birds) can show an eccentric pattern (see p. 208 and Fig. 136), with the outermost 1-7 pp, the innermost 2-6 ss, and occasionally (in ~16% of birds) the outermost (reduced) pp cov replaced. Replacement of the pp often continues from p2-p6 through the outermost pp, but can also (sometimes) arrest with, *e.g.*, just p5 or p6-p7 replaced. The extent of the 1st PB seems comparable throughout the range of the species in N.Am, and the molt apparently can suspend for migration almost anywhere within the replacement sequence. HY ♂♂ average more feathers replaced during the 1st PB than HY ♀♀. The PAs also are variable, being similar by age group but differing substantially by sex and geography, depending on the back color of ♂♂. The PAs of green-backed birds (restricted to "*hesperophilus*"; see **Geographic variation**) are partial, including 0 (~77%) to 5 inner gr covs, rarely (in ~3% of birds) 1-2 terts, and rarely (in ~3% of birds) 1-2 central rects (r1). The molt of ♀♀ averages greater than that of ♂♂, the only birds replacing gr covs, terts, or rects normally being ♀♀. The PAs of black-backed birds (including *mexicanus* and *psaltria* in sc.AZ-w.TX; see **Geographic variation**) are incomplete and eccentric (see p. 208 and Fig. 136), including 4 to 10 (~56%) outer gr covs, the innermost 3-5 ss, the outermost 4-7 pp, the outermost 0 (~55%) to 6 pp covs, and all 12 rects. The extent appears to be similar in both SYs and ASYs. Birds from intermediate populations (*e.g.*, UT-CO to n.AZ-NM) may show intermediate PA extents, and those of *mexicanus* from Mex may show complete or near-complete molts. Also, some or all black-backed birds may have an incomplete adult PB. See Willoughby (unpublished ms.).

Skull—Pneumaticization completes in HY/SY from 15 Nov through Mar. Apneumaticized areas can be difficult to see due to subtle contrasts with the pneumaticized sections.

Age/Sex—Juv (May-Aug) is like HY/SY ♀♀, but is drabber and has buffy wing bars; juvs can be sexed by the amount of white in the juvenal outer rects (r6) and inner pp, as in HY/SYs (see below). CP/BP (Mar-Oct). ♀ wg(n100) 57-65, tl(n20) 36-43; ♂ wg(n100) 61-69, tl(n21) 38-45.

HY/SY ♀ (Sep-Aug): Forehead and crown without black; some or all pp covs (see **Molt**) tapered, abraded (Fig. 138), and brown, contrasting (moderately in Sep-Mar, markedly in Mar-Aug; see **Molt**) with the duskier, replaced wing feathers; molt limits often occur among the pp and ss (see **Molt**), the inner ss and outer pp contrastingly new and dusky (Figs. 136**A-B** & 172**A**); inner pp (if juvenal) usually with white extending 0-2 mm beyond the tips of the pp covs (Fig. 346); rects varying from uniformly juvenal, tapered (Fig 342), and abraded, with little or no white in the outer rects (r6; Fig. 347**A**), to uniformly basic and truncate, with small white patches in the outer rects (r6; Fig. 347**A-C**). **Note: Plumage criteria should be reliable for ageing and sexing most birds, but ageing always should be combined with information on the extent of molts by geographic location (see Molt). In black-backed forms, both age groups can show contrasting flight feathers in Mar-Aug.**

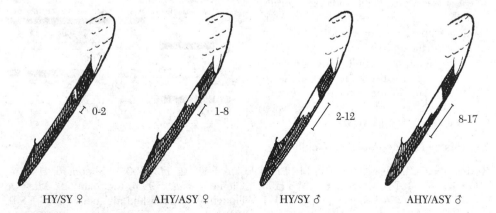

| HY/SY ♀ | AHY/ASY ♀ | HY/SY ♂ | AHY/ASY ♂ |

FIGURE 346. The extent and distinctness of the white patch at the base of the primaries, by age and sex, in Lesser Goldfinch.

AHY/ASY ♀ (Sep-Aug): Forehead and crown usually without black (occasional ASY/ATYs can have a few blackish feathers); pp covs uniformly broad, truncate, relatively fresh (Fig. 138), and dusky brown, not contrasting markedly in color or wear with the other wing feathers in Sep-Mar, and showing only moderate contrasts in Mar-Aug (see **Molt**); flight feathers uniformly adult (Fig. 133**F**) and dusky brown in Sep-Mar; inner pp with white extending 1-8 mm beyond the tips of the pp covs (Fig. 346); rects uniformly adult, truncate (Fig. 342), and relatively fresh, with small to moderately large white spots in the outer rects (r6; Fig. 347**B**). **Note: See HY/SY ♀. The flight-feather criteria are reliable in the green-backed forms throughout the year, whereas black-backed forms can show molt limits in Mar-Aug (see Molt).**

HY/SY ♂ (Oct-Sep): Forehead and crown usually mixed green and black (especially in Mar-Sep); most or all pp covs (see **Molt**) tapered, abraded (Fig. 138), and dusky brown, contrasting (moderately in Oct-Mar, markedly in Mar-Sep; see **Molt**) with the replaced, blacker wing feathers; molt limits often occur among the pp and ss (see **Molt**), the inner ss and outer pp contrastingly new and blackish (Fig. 136**A-B**); inner pp (if juvenal) usually with white extending 2-12 mm beyond the tips of the pp covs (Fig. 346); rects vary from uniformly juvenal, tapered (Fig. 342), and abraded, with small to moderately large white patches in the outer rects (r6; Fig. 347**C**), to uniformly basic and truncate, with moderately large to large white patches in the outer rects (r6; Fig. 347**B-D**); underparts dull yellow (Sep-Mar). **Note: See HY/SY ♀.**

AHY/ASY ♂ (Oct-Sep): Forehead and crown black (often with slight greenish edging in Oct-Dec); pp covs broad, truncate, relatively fresh (Fig. 138), and black, not contrasting in wear with the other wing feathers in Oct-Mar, and showing only moderate contrasts in Mar-Aug (see **Molt**); flight feathers uniformly adult (Fig. 133**F**) and black in Oct-Mar; inner pp with white extending 8-17 mm beyond the tips of the pp covs (Fig. 346); rects uniformly adult, truncate (Fig. 342), and relatively fresh, with large white spots in the outer rects (r6; Fig. 347**D**); underparts bright yellow. **Note: See HY/SY ♀ and AHY/ASY ♀.**

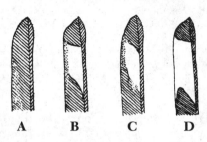

A   B   C   D

FIGURE 347. The shape and typical pattern of white in the outer rectrix (r6), by age and sex, in Lesser Goldfinch. Note that many birds replace this feather during the first prebasic or first prealternate molt, at which time this criterion is unhelpful for ageing; but some birds retain this feather until the second prebasic molt. See text for details.

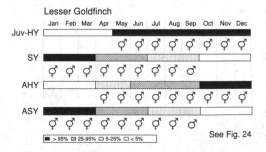

Hybrids reported—American Goldfinch.

References—Ridgway (1901), J.M. Linsdale *in* Bent *et al.* (1968), Sheppard (1972b), Oberholser (1974), CWS & USFWS (1991), Clement *et al.* (1993), Kaufman (1993d), Pyle (1997c), Watt & Willoughby (in press); E.J. Willoughby (unpublished ms., pers. comm.); S.R. Blackshaw (pers. comm.), IBP (MAPS) data, PRBO data.

LAWRENCE'S GOLDFINCH
Carduelis lawrencei

LAGO
Species # 5310
Band size: 0

Species—Juvs and HYs from Lesser and American goldfinches by the combination of medium size and relatively long tl (wg 59-69, tl 42-49; see **Sex**); upperparts brownish to gray, those of juvs with dusky streaking; pp with little or no white at the bases (not extending beyond the pp covs) but with yellow edging; outer rects (r6) with the white not extending to the tips of the feathers (Fig. 348); undertail covs white.

Geographic variation—No subspecies are recognized.

Molt—PB: HY partial-incomplete (Aug-Oct); AHY complete (Jul-Oct); PA limited-partial (Mar-Apr). The PBs occur primarily on the summer grounds. The 1st PB usually includes all med and gr covs, 1-3 terts, and 0 (~44%) to all 12 (~33%) rects. It also sometimes (in ~33% of birds) can be eccentric (see p. 208 and Fig. 136), with the outermost 2-6 pp and the innermost 2-5 ss replaced. Pp replacement often continues from p4-p7 through the outermost pp, but sometimes arrests with, *e.g.*, just p4-p5 or p5-p7 replaced. The PAs usually include few if any gr covs and no rects, but sometimes (in ~26% of birds) 1-3 terts; tert replacement appears to occur in ♀♀ only, ♂♂ having a limited molt at best. The 1st and subsequent PAs are similar in extent.

Skull—Pneumaticization completes in HY/SY from 15 Sep through Feb. The pneumaticization pattern can be difficult to see, as with Lesser Goldfinch.

Age/Sex—Juv (May-Aug) has dull yellowish-brown plumage with indistinct streaks to the upperparts; juvs can be sexed by the amount of white in the juvenal outer rects (r6), as in HY/SYs (see below). CP/BP (Mar-Sep). ♀ wg(n35) 59-68, tl(n10) 42-49; ♂ wg(n36) 62-71, tl(n10) 45-51.

HY/SY ♀ (Sep-Aug): Crown, lores, and throat without black; outer pp covs narrow, tapered, relatively abraded, and brown with indistinct, narrow, or no buffy-yellow or whitish edging (Fig. 138), contrasting with the slightly fresher, duskier, and green-edged gr covs (Fig. 134); 1-3 terts, s6, and/or s5 replaced, contrasting with the older middle ss (among s3-s6) in Sep-Mar (Fig. 133**D-E**); 2-6 middle or outermost pp sometimes replaced (see **Molt**), contrastingly fresh (Figs. 136**A** & 172**A**); rects vary from uniformly juvenal, tapered, abraded, and brownish, with small white patches in the outer rects (r6; Fig. 348**A**), to uniformly truncate and dusky, with small to moderately small white patches in the outer rects (r6; Fig. 348**A-B**). **Note: All birds should be reliably sexed and most or all should be reliably aged. Among ♀♀ (only), both HY/SY and AHY/ASY can show contrasting terts in Mar-Aug; see Molt.**

AHY/ASY ♀ (Sep-Aug): Crown, lores, and throat without black; outer pp covs broad, truncate, relatively fresh, and dusky with relatively distinct and broad, greenish edging (Fig. 138), not contrasting markedly in color or wear with the gr covs (Fig. 133**F**); terts and middle ss (s4-s6) uniformly adult and fresh in Sep-Mar (Fig. 133**F**); pp uniformly fresh (Fig. 133**F**); rects uniformly adult, truncate (Fig. 342), relatively fresh, and dusky, with moderately sized white spots in the outer rects (r6; Fig. 348**B**). **Note: See HY/SY ♀.**

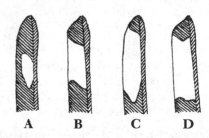

A   B   C   D

FIGURE 348. The shape and typical pattern of white in the outer rectrix (r6), by age and sex, in Lawrence's Goldfinch. Note that some birds replace this feather during the first prebasic molt, at which time this criterion is unhelpful for ageing; and some birds retain this feather until the second prebasic molt. See text for details.

HY/SY ♂ (Sep-Aug): Throat, lores, and crown partially (Sep-Mar), or primarily (Mar-Aug), black; outer pp covs narrow, tapered, relatively abraded, and brown with indistinct, narrow, or no dull buffy-yellow edging (Fig. 138), contrasting with the slightly fresher, duskier, and brighter yellow-edged gr covs (Fig. 134); 1-3 terts, s6, and/or s5 replaced, contrasting with the older middle ss (s3-s6; Fig. 133**D-E**); 2-6 middle or outermost pp sometimes replaced (see **Molt**), contrastingly fresh (Figs. 136**A** & 172**A**); rects vary from uniformly juvenal, tapered, abraded, and brownish, with a moderate amount of white in the outer rect (Fig. 348**C**), to uniformly truncate and dusky, with a moderate to substantial white patch in the outer rect (Fig. 348**C-D**; see **Molt**).

AHY/ASY ♂ (Sep-Aug): Crown, lores, and throat black; outer pp covs broad, truncate, relatively fresh, and dusky with relatively distinct, broad, and brightish yellow edging (Fig. 138), not contrasting in color or wear with the gr covs (133**F**); terts, middle ss (s4-s6), and outer pp uniformly adult (Fig. 133**F**), relatively fresh, and dusky; rects uniformly adult, truncate (Fig. 342), relatively fresh, and blackish, with substantial white spots in the outer rects (r6; Fig. 348**D**). **Note: See HY/SY ♀.**

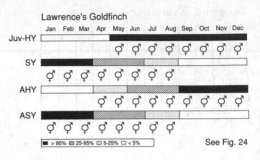

References—Ridgway (1901), Linsdale (1957), J.M. Linsdale *in* Bent *et al.* (1968), Oberholser (1974), Clement *et al.* (1993), Kaufman (1993d), Pyle (1997c); E.J. Willoughby (pers. comm.); IBP (MAPS) data.

AMERICAN GOLDFINCH
Carduelis tristis

AMGO
Species # 5290
Band size: 0-0A-1C

Species—Juvs and HYs from Lesser and Lawrence's goldfinches by the combination of large size (wg 63-77, tl 39-50; see **Age/Sex**); upperparts brownish to yellow, without dusky streaking; wings dark brown to blackish; pp with little or no white at the bases (not extending beyond the pp covs) and without yellow; outer rects (r6) with the white extending to the tips of the feathers (Fig. 349); undertail covs white.

Geographic variation—Moderately weak, although most ranges are fairly well defined. Subspecies taxonomy follows T.R. Howell *et al. in* Paynter (1968); see Ridgway (1901), Dwight (1902), Taverner (1919b), van Rossem (1943), Oberholser (1974), Godfrey (1986), Middleton (1993). No other subspecies occur. In addition to the following, the amount of white in the pp and rects averages more extensive in the western subspecies than the eastern subspecies, but this also varies by age/sex group; more study is needed.

Western (*C.t. pallida*) Group. Pale; cap of ♂♂ reduced.

C.t. jewetti (br & wint coastal sw.BC-sw.OR): Small; basic-plumaged birds and ♀♀ dark brown without an olive tinge; alternate-plumaged ♂♂ bright yellow with a reduced black cap (extending 10-14 mm from the bill); terts and undertail covs white with a brown tinge. ♀ wg(n10) 63-69, tl(n10) 39-46; ♂ wg(n10) 66-74, tl(n10) 43-48.

C.t. salicamans (br & wint coastal CA): Small; basic-plumaged birds and ♀♀ dull brown with an olive tinge; alternate-plumaged ♂♂ dull, pale yellow (sometimes tinged brown) with a reduced black cap (extending 10-14 mm from the bill); terts and undertail covs white. ♀ wg(n100) 62-70, tl(n36) 40-47; ♂ wg(n100) 65-74, tl(n64) 42-50.

C.t. pallida (br interior s.BC-NV to w.Ont-w.NE, wint to AZ-TX): Large; basic-plumaged birds and ♀♀ medium-pale brown with a gray tinge; alternate-plumaged ♂♂ pale yellow with a reduced cap (extending 10-14 mm from the bill). ♀ wg(n21) 68-75, tl(n13) 42-50; ♂ wg(n33) 70-79, tl(n17) 44-52.

Eastern (C.t. tristis) Group. Bright; cap of ♂♂ extensive.

C.t. tristis (br c.Ont-e.CO to Nfl-SC, wint to TX-FL): Medium in size; basic-plumaged birds and ♀♀ medium-dark brown with little or no olive or gray; alternate-plumaged ♂♂ bright yellow with an extensive black cap (extending 13-19 mm from the bill). ♀ wg(n100) 65-73, tl(n67) 41-50; ♂ wg(n100) 68-76, tl(n84) 43-52.

Molt—PB: HY partial (Sep-Dec), AHY complete (Aug-Dec); PA partial (Feb-Jul). The PBs commence on the summer grounds and finish on the winter grounds; continuous, limited molting occurs through the winter. The 1st PB includes most or all med covs, 4 to 10 (~22%) inner gr covs, and occasionally (in ~9% of birds) s8, but no rects. The PAs may complete on the summer grounds. The 1st PA includes 0 (~35%) to 6 inner gr covs and occasionally (in ~10% of birds) s8, but no rects. The adult PA includes 0 (~70%) to 2 inner gr covs, but no terts or rects. Both the 1st PB and the PAs average more extensive in *C.t. salicamans*, and less extensive in *tristis*, than in the other subspecies.

Skull—Pneumaticization completes in HY/SY from 15 Dec through Mar. The pattern of pneumaticization in this species is atypical (see Yunick 1979a).

Age/Sex—Juv (Jul-Oct) is brownish yellow, often with streaks in the upperparts, and has buffy-brown wing bars; some juvs can be sexed by the color of the juvenal flight feathers and the distinctness of the white patches in the outer rects (r6), as in HY/SYs (see below). CP/BP (Jun-Oct). ♀ wg(n100) 63-75, tl(n100) 39-50; ♂ wg(n100) 66-79, tl(n100) 43-52; see **Geographic variation**.

HY/SY ♀ (Oct-Sep): Crown without a distinct black patch; back greenish in Mar-Sep; lesser covs brown; molt limits usually occur among the med and/or gr covs (Fig. 133C-E; see **Molt**), the retained outer covs worn and brown with dull buffy or whitish tips, contrasting with the fresher, duskier, and whiter-tipped, replaced inner covs; s8 occasionally replaced, contrasting with the adjacent terts (Fig. 133**D**); outer pp covs narrow, tapered, relatively abraded (Fig. 138), and brownish, contrasting with the duskier, replaced gr covs; pp and ss brown; rects tapered (Fig. 342) and relatively abraded, the outer rect (r6) brownish with indistinct or no whitish (Fig. 349). **Note: Plumage criteria are reliable for sexing all birds and for ageing ♂♂; a few ♀♀ can be difficult to age, especially in Jun-Sep when plumage can become quite worn.**

AHY/ASY ♀ (Oct-Sep): Crown without a distinct black patch; back greenish in Mar-Sep; lesser covs brown; wing covs, terts, and middle ss (s4-s6) uniformly adult (Fig. 133**F**) and dusky brown; outer pp covs broad, truncate, relatively fresh (Fig. 138), and dusky brown, not contrasting markedly in color or wear with the gr covs (Fig. 133**F**); pp and ss dark brown; outer rects (r6) truncate (Fig. 342), relatively fresh, and dusky brown with a moderately distinct, whitish patch (Fig. 349). **Note: See HY/SY ♀.**

HY/SY ♂ (Oct-Sep): Crown brown, usually without black (Oct-Mar), to blackish (Mar-Sep); back yellow in Mar-Sep; lesser covs olive to yellowish olive in Oct-Mar; molt-limit, med-cov, and gr-cov criteria as in HY/SY ♀♀, except that the

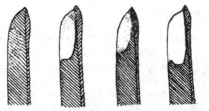

HY/SY ♀   AHY/ASY ♀   HY/SY ♂   AHY/ASY ♂

FIGURE 349. The shape and typical pattern of white in the outer rectrix (r6), by age and sex, in American Goldfinch.

replaced wing covs are black, contrasting more distinctly with the retained outer covs; outer pp covs narrow, tapered, relatively abraded (Fig. 138), and dusky blackish, contrasting with the blacker, replaced gr covs; pp and ss dull blackish; rects tapered (Fig. 342) and relatively abraded, the outer rect (r6) dusky blackish with a moderately distinct, whitish patch (Fig. 349). **Note: See HY/SY ♀.**

AHY/ASY ♂ (Oct-Sep): Crown brown, sometimes with the forehead mottled blackish (Oct-Mar), to black (Mar-Sep); back bright yellow in Mar-Sep; lesser covs partly to entirely yellow in Oct-Mar; wing covs, terts, and middle ss (s4-s6) uniformly adult (Fig. 133**F**) and black; outer pp covs broad, truncate, relatively fresh (Fig. 138), and black, not contrasting markedly in color or wear with the gr covs (Fig. 133**F**); pp and ss black; outer rects (r6) truncate (Fig. 342), relatively fresh, and black with a distinct, white patch (Fig. 349). **Note: See HY/SY ♀.**

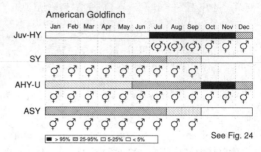

Hybrids reported—Lesser Goldfinch. Island (Common) Canary in captivity.

References—Stone (1896), Dwight (1900a, 1902), Ridgway (1901), Forbush (1929), van Rossem (1943), Groskin (1947), Roberts (1955), Bergstrom (1964), W.M. Tyler *in* Bent *et al.* (1968), Parks & Parks (1968), Wood (1969), Olyphant (1972), Fisk (1973b), Foster (1973), Middleton (1974, 1977, 1993), Oberholser (1974), Sheppard & Klimkiewicz (1976), Yunick (1979a, 1983b), Prescott (1983), CWS & USFWS (1991), Clement *et al.* (1993), Kaufman (1993d), Mulvihill (1993), Hansrote & Hansrote (1995), Pyle (1997c); D. Brewer, E.J. Fisk, E.H. Hawkin, W.A. Lamb, D.E. Miller, H. Parks, M.K. Klimkiewicz, J.S. Weske (*in litt.* to the BBL); E.J. Willoughby (pers. comm.); IBP (MAPS) data, PRBO data, R.P. Yunick data.

EVENING GROSBEAK
Coccothraustes vespertinus

EVGR
Species # 5140
Band size: 1A-2

Geographic variation—Moderately weak and clinal where ranges meet. Subspecies taxonomy follows T.R. Howell *et al. in* Paynter (1968); see Ridgway (1901), Grinnell (1917), Grinnell *et al.* (1930), van Rossem (1936c), Phillips (1961a), Phillips *et al.* (1964), Sutton (1967), Oberholser (1974). No other subspecies occur.

C.v. brooksi (br BC to n.CA-NM, wint to s.CA-sw.TX): Bill long and relatively wide (exp culmen 19.1-22.6, width at tip of nares 10.9-13.5); upperparts of HY/SYs and ♀♀ medium brown with a buff tinge; yellow on the forehead of AHY/ASY ♂ narrow (extending 3-8 mm from the bill). Birds of montane s.OR-e.CA ("*californica*") may average shorter-billed and paler, and birds of CO to AZ-NM ("*warreni*") may average paler and with narrower bills, but differences, if present, are slight and obscured by individual variation.

C.v. montanus (res se.AZ): Bill long and relatively narrow (exp culmen 19.0-22.5, width at tip of nares 10.0-12.1); upperparts of HY/SYs and ♀♀ medium-pale brown with a buff tinge; yellow on the forehead of AHY/ASY ♂ narrow (extending 3-8 mm from the bill).

C.v. vespertinus (br Alb to NB-MA, wint to TX-SC): Bill short (exp culmen 15.3-20.5); upperparts of HY/SYs and ♀♀ medium-dark brown with a gray tinge; yellow on the forehead of AHY/ASY ♂ broad (extending 7-11 mm from the bill).

Molt—PB: HY partial (Aug-Nov), AHY complete (Aug-Nov); PA absent-limited (Mar-May). The PBs occur primarily on the summer grounds. The 1st PB includes most to all med covs and 5 to 10 (~10%) inner gr covs, but no terts or rects; previous reports that the terts could be replaced probably are in error. The PAs include no gr covs or flight feathers.

Skull—Pneumaticization completes in HY/SY from 15 Nov through Feb. Look for windows (> 4 mm; Fig. 11**D**) in some SYs through spring/summer.

Age—Juv (Jun-Oct) has dingy grayish or brownish plumage, yellow inner gr covs, and a dusky bill; juvs can be sexed by the pattern of white on the pp, s5-s6, and the rects (see **Sex**).

HY/SY (Sep-Aug): Molt limits usually occur among the med and/or gr covs (Fig. 133**C-E**; see **Molt**), the retained outer covs worn and brownish, contrasting with the fresher and blacker, replaced inner covs; outer pp covs narrow, tapered, relatively abraded (Fig. 138), and brownish, contrasting with the blacker, replaced gr covs; terts of ♂♂ brownish to brownish white; outer rects (r6) tapered (Fig. 342), relatively abraded, and often with an indistinct, white patch in ♂♂.

AHY/ASY (Sep-Aug): Wing covs, terts, and middle ss (s4-s6) uniformly adult (Fig. 133**F**) and brownish black (♀) or black (♂); outer pp covs broad, truncate, relatively fresh (Fig. 138), and brownish black to black, not contrasting in color with the gr covs (Fig. 133**F**); outer rects (r6) truncate (Fig. 342), relatively fresh, and entirely black in ♂♂.

Sex—CP/BP (May-Sep). ♀ wg(n100) 100-114, tl(n100) 57-65; ♂ wg(n100) 105-117, tl(n100) 59-67.

♀: Head and body plumage grayish; p3-p6 with distinct, white bases; s5-s6 primarily brown; outer rects (r4-r6) with distinct, white patches.

♂: Head and body plumage yellow, brown, and black; p3-p6 without distinct, white bases; s5-s6 white or primarily white; outer rects (r4-r6) without white, or (in some HY/SYs) with indistinct, white patches.

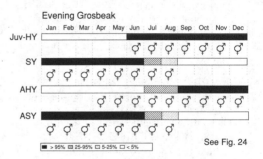

Evening Grosbeak

See Fig. 24

References—Dwight (1900a), Ridgway (1901), Magee (1926b, 1928, 1930), Forbush (1929), Brooks (1939), Parks (1951), Shaub & Shaub (1953), Roberts (1955), Shaub (1958), Bergstrom (1964), D.H. Speirs *in* Bent *et al.* (1968), Briggs (1969), Wood (1969), Oberholser (1974), Sheppard & Klimkiewicz (1976), Yunick (1973, 1977d), Lago (1979), CWS & USFWS (1991), Clement *et al.* (1993), Cramp & Perrins (1994a), Prescott (1994), Pyle (1997c); E.H. Downs, A.C. Lloyd, D.H. Speirs, M. Wood (*in litt.* to the BBL); N.J. Schmitt (pers. comm.); IBP (MAPS) data, R.P. Yunick data.

WEAVERS
PLOCEIDAE

Two species. Family characters include stout, conical bills, robust bodies, and short tails. Weavers have 10 primaries (the 10th reduced), 9 secondaries, and 12 rectrices. Both the first and the adult PBs are complete, resulting in little if any plumage variation with age. Plumage differs between the sexes in one North American species and is alike in the other.

HOUSE SPARROW
Passer domesticus

HOSP
Species # 6882
Band size: 1B

Species—Juv from juv Eurasian Tree Sparrow (which see) by larger size (wg 67-85, tl 50-61; see **Sex**); bill larger (nares to tip 8.8-10.5; see **Geographic variation**); crown brown, without chestnut; cheeks without an isolated dusky patch.

Geographic variation—Variably weak to well marked, but clinal where most ranges meet. Subspecies taxonomy follows Cramp & Perrins (1994a); see also Lack (1940), Johnston & Selander (1964, 1971, 1972, 1973), Packard (1967b), Selander & Johnston (1967), Blem (1973, 1975), Johnston (1973), Rising (1973b), Oberholser (1974), Lowther (1977), Browning (1978, 1990), Svensson (1992). Ten other subspecies occur in Eurasia.

> **P.d. domesticus** (res throughout the range in N.Am): From the other Eurasian subspecies by longer wg (see **Sex**, *vs* wg 71-82 in the other subspecies) and bill (nares to tip 8.8-10.5, *vs* 7.4-10.2); rufous of the upperparts paler; underparts grayer (less white). Birds west of Man-w.TX ("*plecticus*") may average paler, but differences, if present, are too slight for subspecies recognition. Birds of N.Am show greater size variation than in Europe (smaller in southern populations, larger in northern populations), but variation is completely clinal. Birds of CA also may average slightly larger bills than those of Europe and elsewhere in N.Am.

Molt—PB: HY complete (May-Dec), AHY complete (Aug-Nov); PA absent. Occasional birds can suspend or arrest molt, but no age-specific or other patterns have been documented.

Skull—Pneumaticization completes in HY/SY from 15 Sep; northern populations can be reliably aged AHY by skull as late as 15 Nov. Some SYs retain windows (> 3 mm; Fig. 11**D**) through the first breeding season (through Jul).

Age—Juv (May-Oct) is like HY/SY ♀♀, but is buffier and has loosely textured plumage; many juvs can be sexed by the color of the throat, whitish in ♀♀ and gray in ♂♂. Look also for a more prominent postocular patch on juv ♂♂ than juv ♀♀. Birds in active molt can be aged HY through Sep-Nov by mixed juvenal and adult plumage, *vs* mixed old and new adult plumage on AHYs. AHY/ASY ♂♂ average more gray and less brown in the cheeks, and fuller black throat patches (by season), than HY/SY ♂♂; extremes possibly are reliably aged with substantial experience, but more study is needed on populations of N.Am. Otherwise, no plumage criteria are known for ageing after the completion of the PBs.

Sex—CP/BP (Mar-Sep). ♀ wg(n100) 67-81, tl(n100) 50-59; ♂ wg(n100) 71-85, tl(n100) 52-61. The following is reliable during and after the 1st PB. Many juvs also can be reliably sexed by throat color (see **Age**).

> ♀: Throat and lores pale brownish; crown brown.

> ♂: Throat and lores partially or entirely black; crown gray and chestnut.

Hybrids reported—Eurasian Tree Sparrow, Spanish Sparrow (*P. hispaniolensis*). Several other finch and weaver species (some doubtful) in captivity (see Gray 1958).

References—Dwight (1900a), Ridgway (1901), Forbush (1929), Nero (1951), Roberts (1955), R.F. Johnston (1967), Selander & Johnston (1967), Bent *et al.* (1968), Wood (1969), Blackmore (1973), Niles (1973b), Rising (1973b), Casto (1974), Oberholser (1974), Lowther & Cink (1992), Svensson (1992), Clement *et al.* (1993), Cramp & Perrins (1994a), Jenni & Winkler (1994); D. Beimborn, M.H. Clench (*in litt.* to the BBL); IBP (MAPS) data, PRBO data.

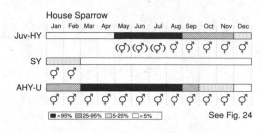

House Sparrow

See Fig. 24

EURASIAN TREE SPARROW
Passer montanus

ETSP
Species # 6883
Band size: 1-1B

Species—Juvs have the color pattern of adult, but are more subdued: from juv House Sparrow by smaller size (wg 65-74, tl 45-55; see **Sex**); bill smaller (nares to tip 7.8-8.9; see **Geographic variation**); crown with chestnut; cheeks whitish with an isolated dusky patch.

Geographic variation—Variably moderate to well marked, but clinal where ranges meet. Subspecies taxonomy follows Cramp & Perrins (1994a); see Barlow (1973), St. Louis & Barlow (1987, 1988, 1991). Nine other subspecies occur in Eurasia.

> *P.m. montanus* (res throughout the range in N.Am): From the other Eurasian subspecies by medium-small size (see **Sex**, *vs* wg 63-80 overall) and relatively large bill (nares to tip 7.8-9.3, *vs* 7.0-9.1 in the other subspecies); plumage coloration relatively dark; streaks on the back relatively distinct.

Molt—PB: HY complete (Jul-Nov); AHY complete (Jul-Oct); PA absent. See House Sparrow.

Skull—Pneumaticization completes in HY/SY from 1 Oct. Look for windows (> 3 mm; Fig. 11**D**) in some SYs through spring/summer.

Age—Juv (May-Sep) resembles adults in pattern, but is faded overall; juv ♀ = ♂. No reliable criteria are known for ageing birds after the complete PBs. See House Sparrow.

Sex—♀ = ♂ by plumage. CP/BP (Mar-Sep). ♀ wg(n62) 65-71, tl(n25) 45-53; ♂ wg(n89) 67-74, tl(n30) 47-55.

Hybrids reported—House Sparrow. Several other finch and weaver species in captivity (see Gray 1958).

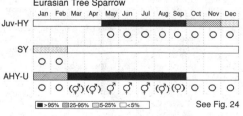

Eurasian Tree Sparrow

See Fig. 24

References—Ridgway (1901), Bent *et al.* (1968), Svensson (1992), Clement *et al.* (1993), Cramp & Perrins (1994a), Jenni & Winkler (1994).

Literature Cited

Abbott, J.M. 1959. A hybrid White-crowned × White-throated sparrow. *Wilson Bull.* 71:282-283.

Acosta, M. and O. Torres. 1984. Morfometría, reproducción, y muda de palomas del género *Zenaida* en el Jardín Botánico de Cienfuegos, Cuba. *Ciencias Biol.* 11:117-128.

Adkisson, C.S. 1977. Morphological variation in North American Pine Grosbeaks. *Wilson Bull.* 89:380-395.

____. 1996. Red Crossbill. *In* The Birds of North America, No. **256** (A. Poole and F. Gill, eds.). Acad. Nat. Sci., Philadelphia; Amer. Ornith. Union, Washington D.C.

Alatalo, R.V., L. Gustafsson, and A. Lundberg. 1983. Why do young passerine birds have shorter wings than older birds? *Ibis* 126:410-415.

Alcocer, F.J.M. 1981. Notas sobre medidas, muda de las remigeras y gónadas en Paloma Serrana. *Centzontle* 1:137-146.

Aldrich, E.C. 1935. Nesting of the Dusky Poorwill. *Condor* 37:49-55.

____. 1956. Pterylography and molt of the Allen Hummingbird. *Condor* 58:121-133.

Aldrich, J.W. 1939. Geographic variation of the Veery. *Auk* 56:338-340.

____. 1940. Geographic variation in eastern North American Savannah Sparrows (*Passerculus sandwichensis*). *Ohio J. Sci.* 40:1-8.

____. 1942. Specific relationships of the Golden and Yellow warblers. *Auk* 59:447-449.

____. 1943a. Relationships of the Canada Jays in the Northwest. *Wilson Bull.* 55:217-222.

____. 1943b. A new Fox Sparrow from the northwestern United States. *Proc. Biol. Soc. Washington* 56:163-166.

____. 1944a. Notes on the races of the White-breasted Nuthatch. *Auk* 61:592-593.

____. 1944b. Geographic variation of Bewick Wrens in the eastern United States. *Occ. Papers Mus. Zool. Louisiana State Univ.* 18:305-309.

____. 1946. New subspecies of birds from western North America. *Proc. Biol. Soc. Washington* 59:129-136.

____. 1949. A new House Finch from the Palouse country of the northwestern United States. *Proc. Biol. Soc. Washington* 62:29-30.

____. 1951. A review of the races of the Traill's Flycatcher. *Wilson Bull.* 63:192-197.

____. 1952. The source of migrant Mourning Doves in southern Florida. *J. Wildl. Manage.* 16:447-456.

____. 1968. Population characteristics and nomenclature of the Hermit Thrush. *Proc. U.S. Nat. Mus.* 124:1-33.

____. 1981. Geographic variation in White-winged Doves with reference to possible source of new Florida population. *Proc. Biol. Soc. Washington* 94:641-651.

____. 1982. Rapid evolution in the House Finch (*Carpodacus mexicanus*). *J. Yamashina Inst. Ornith.* 14:179-186.

____. 1984. Ecogeographic variation in size and proportions of Song Sparrows (*Melospiza melodia*). *Ornith. Monogr.* 35:1-134.

____ and A.J. Duvall. 1958. Distribution and migration of races of the Mourning Dove. *Condor* 60:108-128.

____ and F.C. James. 1991. Ecogeographic variation in the American Robin (*Turdus migratorius*). *Auk* 108:230-249.

____ and D.C. Nutt. 1939. Birds of eastern Newfoundland. *Sci. Pubs. Cleveland Mus. Nat. Hist.* 4:13-42.

____ and J.S. Weske. 1978. Origin and evolution of the eastern House Finch population. *Auk* 95:528-536.

Alexander, C.E. 1919. Hybrid warbler in Missouri. *Auk* 36:579.

Alexander, G. 1945. Natural hybrids between *Dendroica coronata* and *D. auduboni*. *Auk* 62:623-626.

Allen, J.M. 1963. Primary feather molt rate of wild immature doves in Indiana. *Indiana Dept. Conserv. Circ.* 4:1-5.

Alvarez, H. 1975. The social system of the Green Jay in Columbia. *Living Bird* 14:4-44.

Amadon, D. 1949. The seventy-five per cent rule for subspecies. *Condor* 51:250-258.

____. 1966. Avian plumages and molts. *Condor* 68:263-278.

____ and A.R. Phillips. 1947. Notes on Mexican birds. *Auk* 64:576-581.

____ and L.L. Short. 1976. Treatment of subspecies approaching species status. *Syst. Zool.* 25:161-167.

____ and ____. 1992. Taxonomy of lower categories - suggested guidelines. *Bull. Brit. Ornith. Club Century Suppl.* 112A:11-38.

American Ornithologists' Union. 1957. Check-list of North American birds. Fifth edition. Amer. Ornith. Union, Baltimore. 691 pp.

____. 1973. Thirty-second supplement to the American Ornithologists' Union check-list of North American birds. *Auk* 90:411-419.

____. 1976. Thirty-third supplement to the American Ornithologists' Union check-list of North American birds. *Auk* 93:875-879.

American Ornithologists' Union. 1982. Thirty-fourth supplement to the American Ornithologists' Union check-list of North American birds. Supplement to *Auk*, vol. 99.

____. 1983. Check-list of North American birds. Sixth edition. Amer. Ornith. Union, Lawrence, Kansas. 877 pp.

____. 1985. Thirty-fifth supplement to the American Ornithologists' Union check-list of North American birds. *Auk* 102:680-686.

____. 1987. Thirty-sixth supplement to the American Ornithologists' Union check-list of North American birds. *Auk* 104:591-596.

____. 1989. Thirty-seventh supplement to the American Ornithologists' Union check-list of North American birds. *Auk* 106:532-538.

____. 1991. Thirty-eighth supplement to the American Ornithologists' Union check-list of North American birds. *Auk* 108:750-754.

____. 1993. Thirty-ninth supplement to the American Ornithologists' Union check-list of North American birds. *Auk* 110:675-682.

____. 1995. Fortieth supplement to the American Ornithologists' Union check-list of North American birds. *Auk* 112:819-830.

____. 1997. Forty-first supplement to the American Ornithologists' Union check-list of North American birds. *Auk* 114:542-552.

Ammon, E.M. 1995. Lincoln's Sparrow. *In* The Birds of North America, No. **191** (A. Poole and F. Gill, eds.). Acad. Nat. Sci., Philadelphia; Amer. Ornith. Union, Washington D.C.

Anderson, B.W. and R.J. Daugherty. 1974. Characteristics and reproductive biology of grosbeaks (*Pheucticus*) in the hybrid zone in South Dakota. *Wilson Bull.* 86:1-11.

Andrews E.F. and W.H. Baltosser. 1989. First record of Allen's Hummingbird in Louisiana. *Am. Birds* 43:429-430.

Arendt, W.J. 1987. [On male-like plumage in a female American Redstart.] *N. Am. Bird Bander* 12:77.

____ and J. Faaborg. 1989. Sources of variation in measurements of birds in a Puerto Rican dry forest. *J. Field Ornith.* 60:1-11.

Armstrong, E.R. and D.L.G. Noakes. 1983. Wintering biology of Mourning Dove, *Zenaida macroura*, in Ontario. *Can. Field-Nat.* 97:434-438.

Arnold, K.A. 1983. A new subspecies of Henslow's Sparrow (*Ammodramus henslowii*). *Auk* 100:504-505.

Arny, S.A. 1952. Taxonomic status of the Bank Swallow in North America. *Condor* 54:356-357.

Arvey, M.D. 1941. A new race of Bush-tit from southern California. *Condor* 43:74-75.

____. 1951. Phylogeny of the waxwings and allied birds. *Univ. Kansas Pubs. Mus. Nat. Hist.* 3:473-530.

Atkinson, C.T. and C.J. Ralph. 1980. Acquisition of plumage polymorphism in White-throated Sparrows. *Auk* 97:245-252.

Atwood, J.L. 1988. Speciation and geographic variation in the Black-tailed Gnatcatchers. *Ornith. Monogr.* 42:1-74.

____. 1991. Subspecies limits and geographic patterns of morphological variation in California Gnatcatchers (*Polioptila californica*). *Bull. S. California Acad. Sci.* 90:118-133.

Ault, J.W. III, V.J. Heller, J.C. Lewis, and J.A. Morrison. 1976. Delayed molt of primary feathers of Mourning Doves during winter. *J. Wildl. Manage.* 40:184-187.

Austin, G.T. and A.M. Rea. 1971. Key to age and sex determination of Verdins. *W. Bird Bander* 46:41.

____ and ____. 1976. Recent southern Nevada bird records. *Condor* 78:405-408.

Avery, M.L. 1995. Rusty Blackbird. *In* The Birds of North America, No. **200** (A. Poole and F. Gill, eds.). Acad. Nat. Sci., Philadelphia; Amer. Ornith. Union, Washington D.C.

Babcock, R.E. 1975. Another instance of incubation by a male Whip-poorwill. *Wilson Bull.* 87:284.

Backstrom, P. 1992. Observations on a November 1992 Meeker County Ruby-throated Hummingbird. *Loon* 64:183-188.

Badyaev, A.V., D.D. Gibson, and B. Kessel. 1996. White Wagtail and Black-backed Wagtail. *In* The Birds of North America, Nos. **236-237** (A. Poole and F. Gill, eds.). Acad. Nat. Sci., Philadelphia; Amer. Ornith. Union, Washington D.C.

Bailey, A.M. and R.J. Niedrach. 1965. Birds of Colorado. Vols. 1 and 2. Denver Mus. Nat. Hist., Denver, CO.

Bailey, F.M. 1931. Plumage of the Black Swift. *Murrelet* 22:55.

____. 1932. Plumage of the Black Swift once more. *Murrelet* 23:22.

Bailey, H.H. 1923a. A new dove from Florida. *Wilson Bull.* 35:100.

____. 1923b. The status of the Florida crow (*Corvus brachyrhynchos pascuus*). *Wilson Bull.* 35:148-149.

____. 1928. Why a new Florida Blue Jay? *Wilson Bull.* 40:254.

Bailey, R.E. 1952. The incubation patch of passerine birds. *Condor* 54:121-136.

Bailey, R.E. 1953. Surgery for sexing and observing gonad condition in birds. *Auk* 70:497-499.

Baird, J. 1958. The postjuvenal molt of the male Brown-headed Cowbird. *Bird-Banding* 29:224-228.

———. 1964. Aging birds by skull ossification. *E. Bird Banding Assoc. News* 27:162-163.

———. 1967. Arrested molt in Tennessee Warblers. *Bird-Banding* 38:236-237.

Baker, K. 1993. Identification guide to European non-passerines. BTO Guide 24. British Trust for Ornithology, Thetford, U.K.

Bakus, G.J. 1959. Observations on the life history of the dipper in Montana. *Auk* 76:190-207.

Balch, L.G. 1979. Identification of Groove-billed and Smooth-billed anis. *Birding* 11:295-297.

———, J. Dunn, and W. Russell. 1979. Notes on field identification. *Birding* 11:8-12.

Baldridge, F.A. 1983. Plumage characteristics of juvenile Black-chinned Hummingbirds. *Condor* 85:102-103.

———, L.F. Kiff, S.K. Baldridge, and R.B. Hansen. 1983. Hybridization of a Blue-throated Hummingbird in California. *W. Birds* 14:17-30.

Baldwin, P.H. and W.F. Hunter. 1963. Nesting and nest visitors of the Vaux's Swift in Montana. *Condor* 65:400-406.

——— and N.K. Zaczkowski. 1963. Breeding biology of the Vaux Swift. *Condor* 65:400-406.

Ball, R.M. Jr. and J.C. Avise. 1992. Mitochondrial DNA phylogeographic differentiation among avian populations and the evolutionary significance of subspecies. *Auk* 109:626-636.

Balph, M.H. 1975. Wing length, hood coloration, and sex ratio in Dark-eyed Juncos wintering in northern Utah. *Bird-Banding* 46:126-130.

———. 1977. On the use of rectrix shape and wing length to determine age and sex in the Cassin's Finch. *N. Am. Bird Bander* 2:157-158.

Baltosser, W.H. 1987. Age, species, and sex determination of four North American hummingbirds. *N. Am. Bird Bander* 12:151-166.

———. 1994. Age and sex determination in the Calliope Hummingbird. *W. Birds* 25:104-109.

———. 1995. Annual molt in the Ruby-throated and Black-chinned hummingbirds. *Condor* 97:484-491.

——— and P.E. Scott. 1996. Costa's Hummingbird. *In* The Birds of North America, No. **251** (A. Poole and F. Gill, eds.). Acad. Nat. Sci., Philadelphia; Amer. Ornith. Union, Washington D.C.

Bancroft, G. 1923. Some geographic notes on the Cactus Wren. *Condor* 25:165-168.

Bancroft, G.T. 1984. Growth and sexual dimorphism of the Boat-tailed Grackle. *Condor* 86:423-432.

——— and G.E. Woolfenden. 1982. The molt of the Scrub Jays and Blue Jays in Florida. *Ornith. Monogr.* 29:1-51.

Bangs, O. 1900. A review of the three-toed woodpeckers of North America. *Auk* 17:126-139.

———. 1903. The Louisiana cardinal. *Proc. New England Zool. Club* 4:5-7.

———. 1907. A new race of the Hepatic Tanager. *Proc. Biol. Soc. Washington* 20:29-30.

———. 1912. The Florida Song Sparrow. *Proc. New England Zool. Club* 4:85-87.

———. 1918. A new race of the Black-throated Green Wood Warbler. *Proc. New England Zool. Club* 6:93-94.

———. 1925. The history and characters of *Vermivora crissalis* (Salvin and Godman). *Auk* 42:251-253.

———. 1930. The screech owls of eastern North America. *Auk* 47:403-404.

——— and T.E. Penard. 1921a. Notes on some American birds, chiefly neotropical. *Bull. Mus. Comp. Zool.* 64:365-397.

——— and ———. 1921b. Descriptions of six new subspecies of American birds. *Proc. Biol. Soc. Washington* 34:89-92.

——— and ———. 1921c. The name of the eastern Hermit Thrush. *Auk* 38:432-434.

——— and ———. 1922. The northern form of *Leptotila fulviventris* Lawrence. *Proc. New England Zool. Club* 8:29-30.

——— and J.L. Peters. 1928. A collection of birds from Oaxaca. *Bull. Mus. Comp. Zool.* 68:385-404.

Banks, R.C. 1963. Birds of Cerralvo Island, Baja California. *Condor* 65:300-312.

———. 1964. The White-crowned Sparrow, *Zonotrichia leucophrys*. *Univ. California Pubs. Zool.* 70:1-123.

———. 1970a. Re-evaluation of two supposed hybrid birds. *Wilson Bull.* 82:331-332.

———. 1970b. Molt and taxonomy of Red-breasted Nuthatches. *Wilson Bull.* 82:201-205.

———. 1978. Prealternate molt in Nuthatches. *Auk* 95:179-181.

———. 1988a. Geographic variation in the Yellow-billed Cuckoo. *Condor* 90:473-477.

———. 1988b. An old record of the Pearly-breasted Cuckoo in North America and a nomenclatural critique. *Bull. Brit. Ornith. Club* 108:87-91.

Banks, R.C. 1990. Geographic variation in the Yellow-billed Cuckoo: Corrections and comments. 92:538.

——— and J. Baird. 1978. A new hybrid warbler combination. *Wilson Bull.* 90:143-144.

——— and R. Hole Jr. 1991. Taxonomic review of the Mangrove Cuckoo, *Coccyzus minor* (Gmelin). *Caribbean J. Sci.* 27:54-62.

——— and N.K. Johnson. 1961. A review of North American hybrid hummingbirds. *Condor* 63:3-28.

Barber, R.D. 1985. A recent record of Bachman's Warbler in Florida. *Florida Field-Nat.* 13:64-66.

Barbour, T. and W.S. Brooks. 1917. Two new West Indian birds. *Pubs. New England Zool. Club* 6:51-52.

Barlow, J.C. 1973. Status of the North American population of the European Tree Sparrow. *Ornith. Monogr.* 14:10-23.

——— and D.W. Power. 1970. An analysis of character variation in Red-eyed and Philadelphia vireos (Aves: Vireonidae) in Canada. *Can. J. Zool.* 48:673-680.

——— and J.D. Rising. 1965. The summer status of wood pewees in southwestern Kansas. *Kansas Ornith. Soc. Bull.* 16:14-16.

——— and N. Williams. 1971. Colorimetric analysis of the dorsal plumage of the Red-eyed Vireo (Aves: Vireonidae) in Canada. *Can. J. Zool.* 49:417-419.

Barajas L., F.C. and A.R. Phillips. 1993. A *Haplospiza* finch in western Mexico; the lessons of an enigma. *Bull. Brit. Ornith. Club* 114:36-46.

Barrentine, C.D., M.W. Lincoln, C.E. Cochran, and P.M. Walters. 1993. Wing-length change in first postnuptial molt of Gambel's White-crowned Sparrows. *N. Am. Bird Bander* 18:148-150.

Barrowclough, G.F. 1980. Genetic and phenotypic differentiation in a wood warbler (Genus *Dendroica*) hybrid zone. *Auk* 96:655-668.

———. 1982. Geographic variation, predictiveness, and subspecies. *Auk* 99:601-603.

———. 1990. The description of geographic variation in bird populations. *Acta XX Int. Ornith. Congr.* 1:495-503.

Barrows, C.W., P.H. Bloom, and C.T. Collins. 1982. Sexual differences in the tail barring of Spotted Owls. *N. Am. Bird Bander* 7:138-139.

Bartel, K.E. 1987. [On sexing HY robins]. *Passenger Pigeon* 49:53-54.

Batchelder, C.F. 1918. Two undescribed Newfoundland birds. *Proc. New England Zool. Club* 6:81-82.

Bateman, G.C. and R.P. Balda. 1973. Growth, development and food habits of young Piñon Jays. *Auk* 90:39-61.

Baumel, J.J. 1953. Individual variation in the White-necked Raven. *Condor* 55:26-32.

———. 1953. Individual variation in the Fish Crow. *Auk* 74:73-78.

Baumgartner, A.M. 1938. Seasonal variations in the Tree Sparrow. *Auk* 55:603-613.

———. 1986a. Sex reversal in banded cardinal. *N. Am. Bird Bander* 11:11.

———. 1986b. Aberrant plumage in Downy Woodpecker. *N. Am. Bird Bander* 11:106.

———. 1989. Composition of Ruby-throated Hummingbird populations in northeast Oklahoma. *Bull. Oklahoma Ornith. Soc.* 22:3-5.

Bayer, R.D. 1989a. Are "small" crows along the Oregon coast necessarily Northwestern Crows? *Oregon Birds* 15:277-279.

———. 1989b. Measurements of possible Northwestern Crows from Oregon. *Oregon Birds* 289:281-284.

Beason, R.C. 1995. Horned Lark. *In* The Birds of North America, No. **195** (A. Poole and F. Gill, eds.). Acad. Nat. Sci., Philadelphia; Amer. Ornith. Union, Washington D.C.

Beecher, W.J. 1955. Late-Pleistocene isolation in salt marsh sparrows. *Ecology* 36:23-28.

Behle, W.H. 1938. A new race of Horned Lark from the region of the Great Salt Lake. *Condor* 40:89.

———. 1940. Distribution and characters of the Utah Red-wing. *Wilson Bull.* 52:234-240.

———. 1942a. Distribution and variation of the Horned Larks (*Otocoris alpestris*) of western North America. *Univ. California Pubs. Zool.* 46:205-316.

———. 1942b. Notes on the synonomy and distribution of the Horned Larks of Utah. *Proc. Utah Acad. Sci.* 19-20:153-156.

———. 1948. Systematic comment on some geographically variable birds occurring in Utah. *Condor* 50:71-80.

———. 1950a. A new race of Mountain Chickadee from the Utah-Idaho area. *Condor* 52:273-274.

———. 1950b. Clines in the Yellow-throats of western North America. *Condor* 52:193-219.

———. 1951. A new race of the Black-capped Chickadee from the Rocky Mountain region. *Auk* 68:75-79.

———. 1956. A systematic review of the Mountain Chickadee. *Condor* 58:51-70.

———. 1960. Problems of distribution and speciation in Utah birds. *Proc. Utah Acad. Sci.* 37:13-36.

———. 1967. Migrant races of Western Wood Pewee in Utah. *Auk* 84:133-134.

Behle, W.H. 1968. A new race of the Purple Martin from Utah. *Condor* 70:166-169.

____. 1973a. Clinal variation in White-throated Swifts from Utah and the Rocky Mountain region. *Auk* 90:299-306.

____. 1973b. Further notes on rosy finches wintering in Utah. *Wilson Bull.* 85:344-346.

____. 1976. Systematic review, intergradation, and clinal variation in Cliff Swallows. *Auk* 93:66-77.

____. 1985. Utah birds: Geographic distribution and systematics. *Occ. Papers Utah Mus. Nat. Hist.* 5:1-147.

____ and J.W. Aldrich. 1947. Description of a new yellowthroat (*Geothlypis trichas*) from the northern Rocky Mountain - Great Plains region. *Proc. Biol. Soc. Washington* 60:69-72.

____ and R.K. Selander. 1951. The systematic relationships of the Fox Sparrows (*Passerella iliaca*) of the Wasatch Mountains, Utah, and the Great Basin. *J. Washington Acad. Sci.* 41:364-367.

Beimborn, D. 1977. Possible MacGillivray's × Mourning warbler hybrid. *Passenger Pigeon* 39:257-258.

Benitez-Diaz, H. 1993. Geographic variation in coloration and morphology of the Acorn Woodpecker. *Condor* 95:63-71.

Benkman, C.W. 1992. White-winged Crossbill. *In* The Birds of North America, No. **27** (A. Poole, P. Stettenheim, and F. Gill, eds.). Acad. Nat. Sci., Philadelphia; Amer. Ornith. Union, Washington D.C.

____. 1993. Adaptation to single resources and the evolution of crossbill (*Loxia*) diversity. *Ecol. Monogr.* 63:305-325.

Benson, R.H. and K.L.P. Benson. 1988. The pocket computer: A new tool for identifying eastern *Empidonax* flycatchers in the hand. *N. Am. Bird Bander* 13:79-82.

Bent, A.C. 1912. A new subspecies of crossbill from Newfoundland. *Smithsonian Misc. Coll.* 60:1-3.

____. 1932. Life histories of North American gallinaceous birds. *U.S. Nat. Mus. Bull.* # 162:1-490.

____. 1938. Life histories of North American birds of prey. Part 2. *U.S. Nat. Mus. Bull.* # 170:1-482.

____. 1939. Life histories of North American woodpeckers. *U.S. Nat. Mus. Bull.* # 174:1-334.

____. 1940. Life histories of North American cuckoos, goatsuckers, hummingbirds, and their allies. *U.S. Nat. Mus. Bull.* 176:1-506.

____. 1942. Life histories of North American flycatchers, larks, swallows, and their allies. *U.S. Nat. Mus. Bull.* 179:1-555.

____. 1946. Life histories of North American jays, crows, titmice and their allies. *U.S. Nat. Mus. Bull.* 191:1-495.

____. 1948. Life histories of North American nuthatches, wrens, thrashers and their allies. *U.S. Nat. Mus. Bull.* 195:1-475.

____. 1949. Life histories of North American thrushes, kinglets and their allies. *U.S. Nat. Mus. Bull.* 196:1-452.

____. 1950. Life histories of North American wagtails, shrikes, vireos and their allies. *U.S. Nat. Mus. Bull.* 197:1-411.

____. 1953. Life histories of North American wood warblers. *U.S. Nat. Mus. Bull.* 203:1-734.

____. 1958. Life histories of North American blackbirds, orioles, tanagers and their allies. *U.S. Nat. Mus. Bull.* 211:1-549.

____, *et al.* 1968. Life histories of North American cardinals, buntings, towhees, finches, sparrows and their allies. O.L. Austin, ed. Parts 1-3. *U.S. Nat. Mus. Bull.* 237:1-1889.

Bergstrom, E.A. 1964. Ageing and sexing some winter finches. *E. Bird Banding Assoc. News* 27:250-251.

Berlioz, J. 1937. Note sur une collection d'oiseaux du Mexique. *Bull. Mus. Nat. Hist. Nat.* 9:170-175.

Bevier, L.R. 1990. Eleventh report of the California Bird Records Committee. *W. Birds* 21:145-176.

Binford, L.C. 1971. Identification of Northern and Louisiana waterthrushes. *California Birds* 2:1-10.

____. 1985. Re-evaluation of the "hybrid" hummingbird *Cynanthus sordidus* × *C. latirostris* from Mexico. *Condor* 87:148-150.

____ and D.F. DeSante. 1993. First Illinois record of a MacGillivray's Warbler, with a summary of eastern North American records and notes on identification. *Meadowlark* 2:47-50.

Birkehead, T.R. 1991. The magpies: The ecology and behaviour of Black-billed and Yellow-billed magpies. Academic Press Inc., San Diego, CA.

Bishop, L.B. 1900. Descriptions of three new birds from Alaska. *Auk* 17:113-120.

____. 1901. A new Sharp-tailed finch from North Carolina. *Auk* 18:269-270.

____. 1905a. Notes on a small collection of California birds with a description of an apparently unrecognized race of Hutton's Vireo. *Condor* 7:141-143.

____. 1905b. The status of *Helminthophila leucobronchialis* and *Helminthophila lawrencei*. *Auk* 22:21-24.

____. 1910. Two new subspecies of North American birds. *Auk* 27:59-63.

Bishop, L.B. 1915. Description of a new race of Savannah Sparrow and suggestions on some California birds. *Condor* 17:185-189.

____. 1926. The distributions of the races of the Ruby-crowned Kinglet. *Condor* 28:183.

____. 1931a. Three apparently undescribed owls. *Proc. Biol. Soc. Washington* 44:93-96.

____. 1931b. Sexual dichromatism in the Pygmy Owl. *Proc. Biol. Soc. Washington* 44:97-98.

____. 1933. Two apparently unrecognized races of North American birds. *Proc. Biol. Soc. Washington* 46:201-206.

____. 1938. An apparently unrecognized race of Redwing from Utah. *Trans. San Diego Soc. Nat. Hist.* 9:1-4.

Bivings, A.E. IV and N.J. Silvey. 1981. Primary feather molt of adult Mourning Doves in central Texas. *Proc. Ann. Conf. S.E. Assoc. Fish & Wild. Agencies* 34:411-414.

Blackmore, F.H. 1973. Seasonal variation and energetics of molt in captive outdoor House Sparrows (Abstract). *Ornith. Monogr.* 14:94.

Blake, C.H. 1954a. Leg color of Blackpoll and Bay-breasted warblers. *Bird-Banding* 25:16.

____. 1954b. Notes on the wing length of Eastern Purple Finch (*Carpodacus p. purpureus*). *Bird-Banding* 25:97-101.

____. 1954c. Gape color in Eastern Purple Finches (*Carpodacus p. purpureus*). *Bird-Banding* 25:133-136.

____. 1955. Notes on the Eastern Purple Finch. *Bird-Banding* 26:89-116.

____. 1956. Distinctions between the Connecticut and the Mourning warblers. *Bird-Banding* 27:185.

____. 1962a. Ageing and sexing of eastern flycatchers, thrushes, vireos, and Mimidae. *E. Bird Banding Assoc. News* 25:169-171. [Reprinted in *Inl. Bird Banding Assoc. News* 38:107-109, 1966.]

____. 1962b. Wing length of Yellow-breasted Chat. *Bird-Banding* 33:43.

____. 1962c. Wing length of Slate-colored Junco. *Bird-Banding* 33:97-99.

____. 1964. Color and wing length in the Slate-colored Junco. *Bird-banding* 35:125-126.

____. 1965a. Sexing by wing length. *E. Bird Banding Assoc. News* 28:227-228.

____. 1965b. Comments on difficult decisions. *E. Bird Banding Assoc. News* 28:179.

____. 1965c. Replaced primaries in first nuptial plumage of *Passerina cyanea*. *Bird-Banding* 36:270.

____. 1967. More on wing length of the Slate-colored Junco. *Bird-Banding* 38:234.

____. 1969. Notes on the Indigo Bunting. *Bird-Banding* 40:133-139.

____. 1971. Primary molt in juvenile cardinals. *Bird-Banding* 42:269-274.

Blake, E.R. 1950. Report on a collection of birds from Guerrero, Mexico. *Fieldiana Zool.* 31:375-393.

____. 1958. Birds of Volcán de Chiriquí, Panama. *Fieldiana Zool.* 36:499-577.

Blake, H.E. Jr. 1981. Subspecific identification of Hairy and Downy woodpeckers in Colorado. *Colorado Field Ornith. J.* 15:98-101.

Blakesley, J.A., A.B. Franklin, and R.J. Gutierrez. 1990. Sexual dimorphism in Northern Spotted Owls from Northwest California. *J. Field Ornith.* 61:320-327.

Blanchard, B.D. 1941. The White-crowned Sparrows (*Zonotrichia leucophrys*) of the Pacific seaboard: Environment and annual cycle. *Univ. California Pubs. Zool.* 46:1-178.

Blank, J.L. and V. Nolan Jr. 1983. Offspring sex ratio in Red-winged Blackbirds is dependent on maternal age. *Proc. Nat. Acad. Sci.* 80:6141-6145.

Bledsoe, A.H. 1988. A hybrid *Oporornis philadelphia* × *Geothlypis trichas*, with comments on the taxonomic interpretation and evolutionary significance of intergeneric hybridization. *Wilson Bull.* 100:1-8.

Blem, C.R. 1973. Geographic variation in the bioenergetics of the House Sparrow. *Ornith. Monogr.* 14:96-121.

____. 1975. Geographic variation in wing-loading of the House Sparrow. *Wilson Bull.* 87:543-549.

____. 1981a. Geographic variation in mid-winter body composition of starlings. *Condor* 83:370-376.

____. 1981b. A Dark-eyed Junco × White-throated Sparrow. *Raven* 52:59-61.

Bloom, P.H. 1983. Notes on the distribution and biology of the Flammulated Owl in California. *W. Birds* 14:49-52.

Bock, C.E. 1970. The ecology and behavior of the Lewis Woodpecker (*Asyndesmus lewis*). *Univ. California Pubs. Zool.* 92:1-100.

Bohlen, H.D. and V.M. Kleen. 1976. A method for aging Orange-crowned Warblers in fall. *Bird-Banding* 47:365.

Bollinger, E.K. and T.A. Gavin. 1989. The effects of site quality on breeding-site fidelity in Bobolinks. *Auk* 106:584-594.

Bond, G.M. 1962. A new Blue Jay (*Cyanocitta cristata*) from Newfoundland. *Proc. Biol. Soc. Washington* 75:205-206.

____. 1963. Geographic variation in the thrush *Hylocichla ustulata*. *Proc. U.S. Nat. Mus.* 114:373-387.

Bond, G.M. and R.E. Stewart. 1951. A new Swamp Sparrow from the Maryland coastal plain. *Wilson Bull.* 63:38-40.

Bond, J. 1931. A new nuthatch from the island of Grand Bahama. *Proc. Acad. Nat. Sci. Philadelphia* 83:389.

Borras, A., J. Cabrera, X. Colome, and J.C. Senar. 1993. Sexing fledglings of cardueline finches by plumage color and morphometric variables. *J. Field Ornith.* 64:199-204.

Bowen, R.V. 1997. Townsend's Solitaire. *In* The Birds of North America, No. 269 (A. Poole and F. Gill, eds.). Acad. Nat. Sci., Philadelphia; Amer. Ornith. Union, Washington D.C.

____. Criteria for aging Townsend's Solitaires. Unpublished ms.

Bowers, D.E. 1960. Correlation of variation in the Wrentit with environmental gradients. *Condor* 62:91-119.

Bowers, R.K. Jr. and J.B. Dunning Jr. 1986. Weights and measurements # 1 - Arizona sparrows. *North Am. Bird Bander* 11:59-60.

____ and ____. 1987. Nutting's Flycatcher (*Myiarchus nuttingi*) from Arizona. *Am. Birds* 41:5-10.

____ and ____. 1994. Buff-breasted Flycatcher. *In* The Birds of North America, No. 125 (A. Poole and F. Gill, eds.). Acad. Nat. Sci., Philadelphia; Amer. Ornith. Union, Washington D.C.

____ and ____. 1997. Buff-collared Nightjar. *In* The Birds of North America, No. 267 (A. Poole and F. Gill, eds.). Acad. Nat. Sci., Philadelphia; Amer. Ornith. Union, Washington D.C.

Boxall, P.C. and M.R. Lein. 1982. Possible courtship behavior by Snowy Owls in winter. *Wilson Bull.* 94:79-81.

Brackbill, H. Protracted prebasic head molt in the Dark-eyed Junco. *Bird-Banding* 48:370.

Bradshaw, C. 1992. Mystery photographs 183. *Brit. Birds* 85:647-649.

Brandt, H.W. 1938. Two new birds from the Chisos Mountains, Texas. *Auk* 55:269-270.

____. 1945. A new wren from Arizona. *Auk* 62:574-577.

____. 1951. Arizona and its bird life. The Bird Research Foundation, Cleveland, OH.

Braun, C.E. 1976a. Methods for locating, trapping and banding Band-tailed Pigeons in Colorado. Special report # 39, Colorado Divison of Wildlife, Denver, CO.

____. 1976b. Banding worksheet for western birds. Band-tailed Pigeon. Supplement to *N. Am. Bird Bander*, vol. 1.

____, J. Corey, J.E. Kautz, B. Petersen, L. Webster, and J.A. White. 1971. Band-tailed Pigeon investigations - plumage studies. Job final report, W-88-R-18, Colorado Division of Wildlife, Denver, CO.

____, D.E. Brown, J.C. Peterson, and T.P. Zapatka. 1975. Results of the Four Corners cooperative Band-tailed Pigeon investigation. *U.S. Fish and Wild. Serv. Resource Publ.* 126:1-20.

Braun, H.W. 1935. The semispring plumage of male Indigo Buntings. *Bird-Banding* 6:135.

Braund, B.W. and J.W. Aldrich. 1941. Notes on the birds of the Upper Peninsula of Michigan. *Oologist* 58:98-105.

Braund, F.W. and E.P. McCullagh. 1940. The birds of Anticosti Island, Quebec. *Wilson Bull.* 52:96-123.

Breckenridge, W.J. 1930. A hybrid *Passerina* (*Passerina cyanea* × *Passerina amoena*. Univ. Minnesota Mus. Nat. Hist. Occ. Papers 3:39-40.

Brennan, L.A., J.B. Buchanan, C.T. Schick, and S.G. Herman. 1991. Estimating sex ratios with discriminant function analysis: The influence of probability cutpoints and sample size. *J. Field Ornith.* 62:357-366.

Brewer, D. 1990. Ageing of White-throated Sparrow. *Brit. Birds* 83:289-290.

Brewer, R. 1961. Comparative notes on the life history of the Carolina Chickadee. *Wilson Bull.* 73:348-373.

____. 1963. Ecological and reproductive relationships of Black-capped and Carolina chickadees. *Auk* 80:9-47.

Brewster, W. 1891. Notes on the Bachman's Warbler (*Helminthophila bachmani*). *Auk* 8:149-157.

____. 1902. Birds of the Cape Region of Lower California. *Bull. Mus. Comp. Zool.* 41:1-241.

____. 1905. Notes on the breeding of Bachman's Warbler, *Helminthophila bachmani* (Aud.), near Charleston, South Carolina, with a description of the first plumage of the species. *Auk* 22:392-394.

____. 1918. An undescribed race of Henslow's Sparrow. *Proc. New England Zool. Club* 6:77-79.

Briggs, D. 1969. Notes on Evening Grosbeaks banded in 1968-1969. *E. Bird Banding Assoc. News* 32:57-59.

____. 1975. Baby Blue Jay with barred alula. *E. Bird Banding Assoc. News* 38:238.

Briskie, J.V. 1993a. Anatomical adaptations to sperm competition in Smith's Longspurs and other polyandrous passerines. *Auk* 110:875-888.

____. 1993b. Smith's Longspur. *In* The Birds of North America, No. 34 (A. Poole, P. Stettenheim, and F. Gill, eds.). Acad. Nat. Sci., Philadelphia; Amer. Ornith. Union, Washington D.C.

Briskie, J.V. 1994. Least Flycatcher. *In* The Birds of North America, No. 99 (A. Poole and F. Gill, eds.). Acad. Nat. Sci., Philadelphia; Amer. Ornith. Union, Washington D.C.

Brodkorb, P. 1934. A hybrid in the genus *Dendroica*. *Auk* 51:243.

____. 1935a. The name of the western race of Red-headed Woodpecker. *Occ. Papers Mus. Zool. Univ. Michigan* 303:1-3.

____. 1935b. Two new subspecies of the Red-shafted Flicker. *Occ. Papers Mus. Zool. Univ. Michigan* 314:1-3.

____. 1935c. A new flycatcher from Texas. *Occ. Papers Mus. Zool. Univ. Michigan* 306:1-3.

____. 1936. Geographical variation in the Piñon Jay. *Occ. Papers Mus. Zool. Univ. Michigan* 332:1-3.

____. 1940. New birds from southern Mexico. *Auk* 57:542-549.

____. 1942. Notes on some races of the Rough-winged Swallow. *Condor* 44:214-217.

____. 1943. Geographic variation in the Band-tailed Pigeon. *Condor* 45:19-20.

____. 1949. Variation in North American forms of Western Flycatcher. *Condor* 51:35-39.

____. 1950. Geographical variation in the Gray Kingbird, *Tyrannus dominicensis*. *Auk* 67:333-344.

Brooke, R.K. 1969. Age characters in swifts. *Bull. Brit. Ornith. Club* 89:78-81.

Brooks, A. 1922. Notes on the American Pine Grosbeaks with the description of a new subspecies. *Condor* 24:86-88.

____. 1923. Notes on the birds of Porcher Island, B. C. *Auk* 40:217-224.

____. 1931. On the relationships of American magpies. *Auk* 48:271-272.

____. 1934. The juvenal plumage of Townsend's Warbler (*Dendroica townsendi*). *Auk* 51:243-244.

____. 1939. Juvenal plumage of the Evening Grosbeak. *Auk* 56:191-192.

____. 1942. The status of the Northwestern Crow. *Condor* 44:166-167.

Brooks, E.S. 1980. Interspecific nesting of Clay-colored and Field sparrows. *Wilson Bull.* 92:264-265.

Brooks, W.S. 1915. Notes on birds from East Siberia and Arctic Alaska. *Bull. Mus. Comp. Zool.* 59:359-406.

____. 1919. An undescribed Song Sparrow from Alaska. *Proc. New England Zool. Club* 7:27.

____. 1920. A new jay from Anticosti Island. *Proc. New England Zool. Club* 7:49-50.

____. 1968. Comparative adaptations of the Alaskan redpolls to the arctic environment. *Wilson Bull.* 80:253-280.

____. 1973. A tentative key for sex determination of Common Redpolls (*Acanthis flammea flammea*) in the northern United States during winter. *Bird-Banding* 44:13-21.

Brown, B.T. 1993. Bell's Vireo. *In* The Birds of North America, No. 35 (A. Poole, P. Stettenheim, and F. Gill, eds.). Acad. Nat. Sci., Philadelphia; Amer. Ornith. Union, Washington D.C.

Brown, C.R. 1978. Juvenile Purple Martins: Field identification and post-fledging nest defense. *Bull. Texas Ornith. Soc.* 11:25-27.

____. 1997. Purple Martin. *In* The Birds of North America, No. 287 (A. Poole and F. Gill, eds.). Acad. Nat. Sci., Philadelphia; Amer. Ornith. Union, Washington D.C.

____ and M.B. Brown. 1995. Cliff Swallow. *In* The Birds of North America, No. 149 (A. Poole and F. Gill, eds.). Acad. Nat. Sci., Philadelphia; Amer. Ornith. Union, Washington D.C.

____, A.M. Knott, and E.J. Damrose. 1992. Violet-green Swallow. *In* The Birds of North America, No. 14 (A. Poole, P. Stettenheim, and F. Gill, eds.). Acad. Nat. Sci., Philadelphia; Amer. Ornith. Union, Washington D.C.

Brown, D.E. 1989. Arizona game birds. University of Arizona Press, Tucson, AZ.

Brown, J.L. 1963. Ecogeographic variation and introgression in an avian visual signal: The crest of the Steller's Jay, *Cyanocitta stelleri*. *Evolution* 17:23-39.

____ and E.G. Horvath. 1989. Geographic variation of group size, ontogeny, rattle calls, and body size in *Aphelocoma ultramarina*. *Auk* 106:124-128.

Brown, R.E. and J.G. Dickson. 1994. Swainson's Warbler. *In* The Birds of North America, No. 126 (A. Poole and F. Gill, eds.). Acad. Nat. Sci., Philadelphia; Amer. Ornith. Union, Washington D.C.

Browning, M.R. 1974. Taxonomic remarks on recently described subspecies of birds that occur in the northwestern United States. *Murrelet* 55:32-38.

____. 1976. The status of *Sayornis saya yukonensis* Bishop. *Auk* 93:843-846.

____. 1977a. Interbreeding members of the *Sphyrapicus varius* group (Aves: Picidae) in Oregon. *S. California Acad. Sci. Bull.* 76:38-41.

____. 1977b. Geographic variation in *Contopus sordidulus* and *C. virens* north of Mexico. *Great Basin Nat.* 37:453-456.

Browning, M.R. 1978. An evaluation of the new species and subspecies proposed in Oberholser's *Bird Life of Texas*. *Proc. Biol. Soc. Washington* 91:85-122.

____. 1979a. Type specimens of birds collected in Oregon. *Northwest Sci.* 53:132-140.

____. 1979b. A review of geographic variation in continental populations of the Ruby-crowned Kinglet (*Regulus calendula*). *Nemouria* 21:1-9.

____. 1989. The type specimens of Hekstra's owls. *Proc. Biol. Soc. Washington* 102:515-519.

____. 1990. Taxa of North American birds described from 1957 to 1987. *Proc. Biol. Soc. Washington* 103:432-451.

____. 1992a. Geographic variation in *Hirundo Pyrrhonota* (Cliff Swallow) from northern North America. *W. Birds* 23:21-29.

____. 1992b. A new subspecies of *Chamaea fasciata* (Wrentit) from Oregon (Aves: Timalinae). *Proc. Biol. Soc. Washington* 105:414-419.

____. 1993a. Comments on the taxonomy of *Empidonax traillii* (Willow Flycatcher). *W. Birds* 24:241-257.

____. 1993b. Taxonomy of the blue-crested group of *Cyanocitta stelleri* (Steller's Jay) with a description of a new subspecies. *Bull. Brit. Ornith. Club* 113:34-41.

____. 1994. A taxonomic review of *Dendroica petechia* (Yellow Warbler) (Aves: Parulinae). *Proc. Biol. Soc. Washington* 107:27-51.

____. 1995. The importance of collecting birds and preserving museum specimens. *Oregon Birds* 21:45-48.

____. 1997. Taxonomy of *Picoides pubescens* (Downy Woodpecker) from the Pacific Northwest. Pp. 25-33 *in* R.W. Dickerman, *comp.*, The era of Allan R. Phillips: A *Festshrift*. R.W. Dickerman, Albuquerque, NM.

____ and R.C. Banks. 1990. The identity of Pennant's "Wapacuthu Owl" and the subspecific name for the population of *Bubo virginianus* from the western Hudson Bay. *J. Raptor Res.* 24:80-83.

Broyd, S.J. 1985. Savannah Sparrow: New to the Western Palearctic. *Br. Birds* 78:647-656.

Brunton, D.F. and R. Pittaway Jr. 1971. Observations of the Great Gray Owl in winter range. *Can. Field-Nat.* 85:315-322.

Brush, A.H. and D.M. Power. 1976. House Finch pigmentation: Carotenoid metabolism and the effect of diet. *Auk* 93:725-739.

Buckholtz, P.G., M.H. Edwards, B.G. Ong, and R.D. Weir. 1984. Differences by age and sex in the size of Saw-whet Owls. *J. Field Ornith.* 55:204-213.

Buden, D.W. 1985. A new subspecies of Common Ground-Dove from Ile de la Tortue, Haiti, with taxonomic reappraisal of Bahaman populations (Aves: Columbidae). *Proc. Biol. Soc. Washington* 98:790-798.

Bull, E.L. and C.T. Collins. 1993a. Nesting chronology, molt, and ectoparasites of Vaux's Swifts in northeastern Oregon. *Avocetta* 17:203-207.

____ and ____. 1993b. Vaux's Swift. *In* The Birds of North America, No. 77 (A. Poole and F. Gill, eds.). Acad. Nat. Sci., Philadelphia; Amer. Ornith. Union, Washington D.C.

____ and J.A. Jackson. 1995. Pileated Woodpecker. *In* The Birds of North America, No. 148 (A. Poole and F. Gill, eds.). Acad. Nat. Sci., Philadelphia; Amer. Ornith. Union, Washington D.C.

Bunn, R.L. 1985. Field identification of Clay-colored, Chipping, & Brewer's sparrows in fall. *Colorado Field Ornith. J.* 19:13-15.

Burleigh, T.D. 1934. Description of a new subspecies of Yellowthroat, *Geothlypis trichas*, from Georgia. *Proc. Biol. Soc. Washington* 47:21-22.

____. 1935. Two new birds from the southern Appalachians. *Proc. Biol. Soc. Washington* 48:61-62.

____. 1942. A new Barn Swallow from the Gulf Coast of the United States. *Occ. Papers Mus. Zool. Louisiana State Univ.* 11:179-183.

____. 1944. Description of a new hybrid warbler. *Auk* 61:291-293.

____. 1959a. Two new subspecies of birds from western North America. *Proc. Biol. Soc. Washington* 72:15-18.

____. 1959b. Geographic variation in the Catbird *Dumetella carolinensis*. *Oriole* 24:29-32.

____. 1960a. A new subspecies of Downy Woodpecker from the Northwest. *Murrelet* 41:42-44.

____. 1960b. Geographic variation in the Western Wood Pewee (*Contopus sordidulus*). *Proc. Biol. Soc. Washington* 73:141-146.

____. 1960c. Three new subspecies of birds from western North America. *Auk* 77:210-215.

____. 1960a. A new subspecies of Downy Woodpecker from the Northwest. *Murrelet* 41:42-44.

____. 1963. Geographic variation in the Cedar Waxwing (*Bombycilla cedrorum*). *Proc. Biol. Soc. Washington* 76:177-180.

____. 1972. Birds of Idaho. Caxton Printers, Caldwell ID.

____ and A.J. Duvall. 1952. A new Ovenbird from the southeastern United States. *Wilson Bull.* 64:39-42.

____ and ____. 1959. A new subspecies of Veery from the northwestern United States. *Proc. Biol. Soc. Washington* 72:33-36.

____ and G.H. Lowery Jr. 1939. Descriptions of two new birds from western Texas. *Occ. Papers Mus. Zool. Louisiana State Univ.* 6:67-68.

____ and ____. 1942. Notes on the birds of southeastern Coahuila. *Occ. Papers Mus. Zool. Louisiana State Univ.* 12:185-212.

Burleigh, T.D. and G.H. Lowery Jr. 1944. Geographical variation in the Red-bellied Woodpecker in the southeastern United States. *Occ. Papers Mus. Zool. Louisiana State Univ.* 17:293-301.

____ and ____. 1945. Races of *Vireo griseus* in eastern United States. *Am. Midland Nat.* 34:526-530.

____ and H.S. Peters. 1948. Geographic variation in Newfoundland birds. *Proc. Biol. Soc. Washington* 61:111-126.

Burns, K.J. 1993. Geographic variation in ontogeny of the Fox Sparrow. *Condor* 95:652-661.

Burtt, E.H. Jr. 1986. An analysis of physical, physiological, and optical aspects of avian coloration with emphasis on wood-warblers. *Ornith. Monogr.* 38:1-126.

Byers, C., O. Urban, and J. Curson. 1995. Buntings and sparrows. A guide to the buntings and North American sparrows. Christopher Helm, London.

Cabe, P.R. 1993. European Starling. *In* The Birds of North America, No. 48 (A. Poole and F. Gill, eds.). Acad. Nat. Sci., Philadelphia; Amer. Ornith. Union, Washington D.C.

Calder, W.A. 1993. Rufous Hummingbird. *In* The Birds of North America, No. 53 (A. Poole and F. Gill, eds.). Acad. Nat. Sci., Philadelphia; Amer. Ornith. Union, Washington D.C.

____ and L.L. Calder. 1992. Broad-tailed Hummingbird. *In* The Birds of North America, No. 16 (A. Poole, P. Stettenheim, and F. Gill, eds.). Acad. Nat. Sci., Philadelphia; Amer. Ornith. Union, Washington D.C.

____ and ____. 1994. Calliope Hummingbird. *In* The Birds of North America, No. 135 (A. Poole and F. Gill, eds.). Acad. Nat. Sci., Philadelphia; Amer. Ornith. Union, Washington D.C.

Cameron, E.S. 1908. The birds of Custer and Dawson counties, Montana. *Auk* 25:39-56.

Camras, S. 1940. A new Savannah Sparrow from Mexico. *Zool. Ser. Field Mus. Nat. Hist.* 24:159-160.

Canadian Wildlife Service and U.S. Fish and Wildlife Service. 1991. North American Bird Banding. Vols. 1 and 2. Environment Canada, Can. Wildl. Serv., Ottawa, Canada and U.S. Fish and Wildl. Serv., Washington, D.C.

Cannell, P.F. 1984. A revised age/sex key for Mourning Doves with comments on the definition of molt. *J. Field Ornith.* 55:112-114.

____, J.D. Cherry, and K.C. Parkes. 1983. Variation and migration overlap in flight feather molt of the Rose-breasted Grosbeak. *Wilson Bull.* 95:621-627.

Carey, M., D.E. Burhans, and D.A. Nelson. 1994. Field Sparrow. *In* The Birds of North America, No. 103 (A. Poole and F. Gill, eds.). Acad. Nat. Sci., Philadelphia; Amer. Ornith. Union, Washington D.C.

Carpenter, F.L., M.A. Hixon, E.J. Temeles, R.W. Russell, and D.C. Paton. 1993. Exploitative compensation by subordinate age-sex classes of migrant Rufous Hummingbirds. *Behav. Ecol. Sociobiol.* 33:305-312.

Carpenter, T.W. 1979. An observation of an AHY Gray Catbird with a gray iris. *N. Am. Bird Bander* 4:157.

____. 1992. Utility of wing length, tail length and tail barring in determining the sex of Barred Owls collected in Michigan and Minnesota. *Condor* 94:794-795.

____ and A.L. Carpenter. 1993. Temporal differences in size of Northern Saw-whet Owls during spring migration. *Wilson Bull.* 105:356-359.

Casto, S.D. 1974. Molt schedule of House Sparrows in northwestern Texas. *Wilson Bull.* 86:176-177.

Cavanagh, J.E. Jr. 1985. North American nighthawks. *Birding* 17:212.

Chandler, R.C. and R.S. Mulvihill. 1988. The use of wing shape indices: An evaluation. *Ornis Scand.* 19:212-216.

____. 1992. Effects of age and fat level on wing loading in Dark-eyed Juncos. *Auk* 109:235-241.

Chantler, P. and G. Driessens. 1995. Swifts. A guide to the swifts and treeswifts of the world. Pica Press, Sussex, U.K.

Chapin, J.P. 1921. The abbreviated inner primary of nestling woodpeckers. *Auk* 38:531-552.

Chapman, F.M. 1900. A study of the genus *Sturnella*. *Bull. Am. Mus. Nat. Hist.* 22:297-320.

____. 1907a. The warblers of North America. D. Appleton & Co., New York.

____. 1907b. The eastern forms of *Geothlypis trichas*. *Auk* 24:30-34.

____. 1911. Description of a new oriole (*Icterus fuertesi*) from Mexico. *Auk* 28:1-4.

____. 1924. Criteria for the determination of subspecies in systematic ornithology. *Auk* 41:17-29.

____. 1925. The relationships and distribution of the warblers of the genus *Compsothlypis*: A contribution to the study of the origin of Andean bird life. *Auk* 42:193-208.

____. 1935a. Further remarks on the relationships of the grackles of the subgenus *Quiscalus*. *Auk* 52:21-29.

____. 1935b. *Quiscalus quiscula* in Louisiana. *Auk* 52:418-420.

____. 1936. Further remarks on *Quiscalus* with a report on additional specimens from Louisiana. *Auk* 53:405-417.

____. 1939a. *Quiscalus* in Mississippi. *Auk* 56:28-31.

____. 1939b. Nomenclature in the genus *Quiscalus*. *Auk* 56:364-365.

Chapman, F.M. 1940. Further studies of the genus *Quiscalus*. *Auk* 57:225-233.

____ and L. Griscom. 1924. The House Wrens of the genus *Troglodytes*. *Bull. Am. Mus. Nat. Hist.* 50:279-304.

Cherry, J.D. 1985. Early autumn movements and prebasic molt of Swainson's Thrushes. *Wilson Bull.* 97:368-370.

____ and P.F. Cannell. 1984. Rate and timing of prebasic molt of adult Boreal Chickadees. *J. Field Ornith.* 55:487-489.

Chevalier, S. 1989. Kennedy Airport Snowy Owls: An update. *N. Am. Bird Bander* 14:73-74.

Chilton, G., M.C. Baker, C.D. Barrentine, and M.A. Cunningham. 1995. White-crowned Sparrow. *In* The Birds of North America, No. **183** (A. Poole and F. Gill, eds.). Acad. Nat. Sci., Philadelphia; Amer. Ornith. Union, Washington D.C.

Cicero, C. 1996. Sibling species of titmice in the *Parus inornatus* complex (Aves: Paridae). *Univ. California Pubs. Zool.* 128:1-217.

Cimprich, D.A. and F.R. Moore. 1995. Gray Catbird. *In* The Birds of North America, No. **167** (A. Poole and F. Gill, eds.). Acad. Nat. Sci., Philadelphia; Amer. Ornith. Union, Washington D.C.

Cintra, R. 1988. Reproductive ecology of the Ruddy Ground-Dove on the central plateau of Brazil. *Wilson Bull.* 100:443-457.

Clark, R.G, P.C. James, and J.B. Morari. 1991. Sexing adult and yearling American Crows by external measurements and discriminant analysis. *J. Field Ornith.* 62:132-138.

Clement, P., A. Harris, and J. Davis. 1993. Finches and sparrows. An identification guide. Christopher Helm, London.

Clench, M.H. 1976. Possible pitfalls in museum specimen data. *N. Am. Bird Bander* 1:20-21.

____ and R.C. Leberman. 1978. Weights of 151 species of Pennsylvania birds analyzed by month, age and sex. *Bull. Carnegie Mus. Nat. Hist.* 5:1-85.

Cockrum, E.L. 1952. A check-list and bibliography of hybrid birds in North America north of Mexico. *Wilson Bull.* 64:140-159.

Coffey, B.B. 1937. Swift banding at Memphis - sixth season. *Migrant* 8:70-72.

Cohen, R.R. 1980. Color versus age in Tree Swallows. *J. Colorado-Wyoming Acad. Sci.* 12:44-45.

____. 1984. Criteria for distinguishing breeding male Tree Swallows from brightly colored females prior to capture. *N. Am. Bird Bander* 9:2-3.

Collier, B. and G.E. Wallace. 1989. Aging *Catharus* thrushes by rectrix shape. *J. Field Ornith.* 60:230-240.

Collins, C.T. 1961. Tail molt of the Saw-whet Owl. *Auk* 78:634.

____. 1972a. Banding worksheet for western birds. Tree Swallow. Supplement to *W. Bird Bander*, vol. 47.

____. 1972b. Banding worksheet for western birds. Violet-green Swallow. Supplement to *W. Bird Bander*, vol. 47.

____. 1973. Banding worksheet for western birds. Key to North American kingbirds. Supplement to *W. Bird Bander*, vol. 48.

____. 1974a. Banding worksheet for western birds. Tropical Kingbird. Supplement to *W. Bird Bander*, vol. 49.

____. 1974b. Banding worksheet for western birds. Cassin's Kingbird. Supplement to *W. Bird Bander*, vol. 49.

____. 1974c. Banding worksheet for western birds. Western Kingbird. Supplement to *W. Bird Bander*, vol. 49.

____. 1974d. Banding worksheet for western birds. Eastern Kingbird. Supplement to *W. Bird Bander*, vol. 49.

____. 1974e. Notice to kinglet banders. *W. Bird Bander* 49:19.

____. 1974f. Banding worksheet for western birds. Orange-crowned Warbler. Supplement to *W. Bird Bander*, vol. 49.

____. 1979. Banding worksheet for western birds. Roadrunner. Supplement to *N. Am. Bird Bander*, vol. 4.

____. 1983. Banding worksheet for western birds. Black-chinned Hummingbird. Supplement to *N. Am. Bird Bander*, vol. 8.

____ and L.C. Binford. 1974. Banding worksheet for western birds. Northern Waterthrush and Louisiana Waterthrush. Supplement to *W. Bird Bander*, vol. 49.

____ and S. Ervin. 1979. Banding worksheet for western birds. Bushtit. Supplement to *N. Am. Bird Bander*, vol. 4.

____ and A.R. Phillips. 1974. Banding worksheet for western birds. Black-tailed Gnatcatcher, Blue-gray Gnatcatcher, and Black-tailed Gnatcatcher. Supplement to *W. Bird Bander*, vol. 49.

____ and G.C. West. 1974. Banding worksheet for western birds. Common Redpoll. Supplement to *W. Bird Bander*, vol. 49.

Collister, D.M. and D. Wicklum. 1996. Intraspecific variation in Loggerhead Shrikes: Sexual dimorphism and implication for subspecies classification. *Auk* 113:221-223.

Confer, J.L. 1992. Golden-winged Warbler. *In* The Birds of North America, No. **20** (A. Poole, P. Stettenheim, and F. Gill, eds.). Acad. Nat. Sci., Philadelphia; Amer. Ornith. Union, Washington D.C.

Conrad, K.F. and R.J. Robertson. 1993. Relationship of age and sex to size and color of Eastern Phoebes. *Wilson Bull.* 105:597-603.

Cook, W.E. 1991. Geographic variation in wing length of the Rose-breasted Grosbeak. *Kingbird* 41:145-153.

Corbin, K.W. and C.G. Sibley. 1977. Rapid evolution in orioles of the genus *Icterus*. *Condor* 79:335-342.

____ and P.J. Wilkie. 1988. Genetic similarities between subspecies of the White-crowned Sparrow. *Condor* 90:637-647.

Cottam, C. and J.B. Trefethen, eds. 1968. Whitewings: The life history, status and management of the White-winged Dove. Van Nostrand Co., Princeton, NJ.

Courser, W.D. 1972. Variability of tail molt in the Burrowing Owl. *Wilson Bull.* 84:93-95.

Cowan, I.M. 1938. Distribution of the races of the Williamson Sapsucker in British Columbia. *Condor* 40:128-129.

Cox, G.W. 1960. A life history of the Mourning Warbler. *Wilson Bull.* 72:5-28.

____. 1973. Hybridization between Mourning and MacGillivray's warblers. *Auk* 90:190-191.

Craig, J.T. 1971. Eastern Whip-poor-will in San Diego. *California Birds* 2:37-40.

Cramp, S., ed. 1985. The birds of the western Palearctic. Vol. 4. Oxford Univ. Press, Oxford, U.K.

____, ed. 1988. The birds of the western Palearctic. Vol. 5. Oxford Univ. Press, Oxford, U.K.

____, ed. 1992. The birds of the western Palearctic. Vol. 6. Oxford Univ. Press, Oxford, U.K.

____ and C.M. Perrins, eds. 1993. The birds of the western Palearctic. Vol. 7. Oxford Univ. Press, Oxford, U.K.

____ and ____, eds. 1994a. The birds of the western Palearctic. Vol. 8. Oxford Univ. Press, Oxford, U.K.

____ and ____, eds. 1994b. The birds of the western Palearctic. Vol. 9. Oxford Univ. Press, Oxford, U.K.

Crawford, R.D. 1977. Breeding biology of year-old and older female Red-winged and Yellow-headed blackbirds. *Wilson Bull.* 89:73-80.

____ and W.L. Hohman. 1978. A method for aging female Yellow-headed Blackbirds. *Bird-Banding* 49:201-207.

Crawford, R.L. 1978. Autumn bird casualties at a northwest Florida TV tower: 1973-1975. *Wilson Bull.* 90:335-345.

Cristol, D.A. and D.C. Evers. 1992. Dominance status and latitude are unrelated in wintering Dark-eyed Juncos. *Condor* 94:539-542.

Crockett, A.B. and P.L. Hansley. 1977. Coition, nesting, and postfledging behavior of Williamson Sapsucker in Colorado. *Living Bird* 16:7-19.

Csada, R.D. and R.M. Brigham. 1992. Common Poorwill. *In* The Birds of North America, No. **32** (A. Poole, P. Stettenheim, and F. Gill, eds.). Acad. Nat. Sci., Philadelphia; Amer. Ornith. Union, Washington D.C.

Cumming, R.A. 1933. Descriptions of a proposed new race of Song Sparrow and of a Hermit Thrush. *Murrelet* 14:78-79.

Curson, J. 1992. Identification of Connecticut, Mourning and MacGillivray's warblers in female and immature plumages. *Birder's J.* 1:275-278.

____. 1993. Identification of Northern and Louisiana waterthrushes. *Birder's J.* 2:126-130.

____. 1994. Identification forum: Separation of Bicknell's and Grey-cheeked thrushes. *Birding World* 7:359-365.

____, D. Quinn, and D. Beadle. 1994. New World warblers. Christopher Helm (Publishers) Ltd., London.

Cushing, J.E. Jr. 1938. The status of the Fox Sparrows of southwestern Oregon. *Condor* 40:73-76.

Czaplak, D. 1995. Identifying Common and Hoary redpolls in winter. *Birding* 27:446-457.

____ and C. Wilds. 1986. Washington's November nighthawk: A cautionary tale. *Birding* 18:169-173.

Dater, E. 1970. Dorsal wing coverts of Blue Jay (*Cyanocitta cristata*). Guide to age. *E. Bird Banding Assoc. News* 33:125-129.

Davis, D.E. 1959. The sex and age structure of roosting Starlings. *Ecology* 40:136-140.

____. 1960. Comments on the migration of Starlings in the eastern United States. *Bird-Banding* 31:216-219.

Davis, J. 1951a. Notes on the nomenclature of the Brown Jay. *Condor* 53:152-153.

____. 1951b. Distribution and variation of the Brown Towhees. *Univ. California Pubs. Zool.* 52:1-120.

____. 1953. Birds of the Tzitzio region, Michoacan, Mexico. *Condor* 55:90-98.

____. 1954. Seasonal changes in bill length of certain passerine birds. *Condor* 56:142-149.

____. 1957. Determination of age in the Spotted Towhee. *Condor* 59:195-202.

____. 1958. Singing behavior and the gonad cycle of the Rufous-sided Towhee. *Condor* 60:308-336.

____. 1961. Some seasonal changes in morphology of the Rufous-sided Towhee. *Condor* 63:313-321.

____. 1965. Natural history, variation, and distribution of the Strickland's Woodpecker. *Auk* 82:537-590.

Davis, J. 1974a. Banding worksheet for western birds. Green-tailed Towhee. Supplement to *W. Bird Bander*, vol. 49.

____. 1974b. Banding worksheet for western birds. Spotted Towhee = Rufous-sided Towhee. Supplement to *W. Bird Bander*, vol. 49.

____. 1974c. Banding worksheet for western birds. Brown Towhee. Supplement to *W. Bird Bander*, vol. 49.

____. 1974d. Banding worksheet for western birds. Abert's Towhee. Supplement to *W. Bird Bander*, vol. 49.

Davis, J.N. 1995. Hutton's Vireo. *In* The Birds of North America, No. **189** (A. Poole and F. Gill, eds.). Acad. Nat. Sci., Philadelphia; Amer. Ornith. Union, Washington D.C.

Davis, L.I. 1958. Acoustic evidence of relationship in North American crows. *Wilson Bull.* 70:151-167.

____ and F.S. Webster Jr. 1970. An intergeneric hybrid flycatcher (*Tyrannus* × *Muscivora*). *Condor* 72:37-42.

Davis, R.S. 1969a. Northern Prairie Horned Larks. *Inl. Bird Banding News* 41:145.

____. 1969b. Lapland Longspur data. *Inl. Bird Banding News* 41:185.

Davis, T.H. 1971. A key to fall *Piranga* tanagers - females and immatures. *E. Bird Banding Assoc. News* 34:237-238.

____. 1972. How often does the Western Tanager occur in the east? *Am. Birds* 26:713-714.

Dawson, W.L. and J.H. Bowles. 1909. The birds of Washington. Vol. 1. Occidental Publishing Co., Seattle, WA.

Dawson, W.R. 1997. Pine Siskin. *In* The Birds of North America, No. **280** (A. Poole and F. Gill, eds.). Acad. Nat. Sci., Philadelphia; Amer. Ornith. Union, Washington D.C.

Deakin, A. 1936. Natural hybridization and genetics of flickers. *Am. Nat.* 70:585-590.

Dearborn, N. 1907. Catalogue of a collection of birds from Guatemala. *Field Mus. Nat. Hist. Ornith. Ser.* 1:69-138.

DeBenedictis, P. 1976. Gleanings from the technical literature. Eastern and Western meadowlarks. *Birding* 8:349-352.

____. 1979. Gleanings from the technical literature. [On sapsuckers] *Birding* 11:178-181.

____. 1982. Gleanings from the technical literature. [On orioles] *Birding* 14:51-55.

deGraw, W.A. and M.D. Kern. 1990. Postnuptial molt in Harris' Sparrows. *Condor* 92:829-838.

DeHaven, R.W. 1975a. Plumages of the Tricolored Blackbird. *W. Birds* 50:59-60.

____. 1975b. Banding worksheet for western birds. Tricolored Blackbird. Supplement to *W. Bird Bander*, vol. 50.

____, F.T. Crase, and M.R. Miller. 1974. Aging Tricolored Blackbirds by cranial ossification. *Bird-Banding* 45:156-159.

DeJong, M.J. 1996. Northern Rough-winged Swallow. *In* The Birds of North America, No. **234** (A. Poole and F. Gill, eds.). Acad. Nat. Sci., Philadelphia; Amer. Ornith. Union, Washington D.C.

de Korte, J. 1971. Birds, observed and collected by "De Nederlandse Spitsbergen Expedite" in West and East Spitsbergen, 1967 and 1968-'69; first part. *Beaufortia* 19:113-150.

Delany, M.F., C.T. Moore, and D.R. Progulske Jr. 1994. Distinguishing gender of Florida Grasshopper Sparrows using body measurements. *Florida Field Nat.* 22:48-51.

Dement'ev, G.P. and N.A. Gladkov, eds. 1951. Birds of the Soviet Union. Vol. I. Gosudarstvennoe Izdatel'stvo "Sovetskaya Nauka", Moscow.

____ and ____. eds. 1954. Birds of the Soviet Union. Vols. V and VI. Gosudarstvennoe Izdatel'stvo "Sovetskaya Nauka", Moscow.

Dennis, J.V. 1958. Some aspects of the breeding ecology of the Yellow-breasted Chat (*Icteria virens*). *Bird-Banding* 29:169-183.

____. 1967. Fall departure of the Yellow-breasted Chat (*Icteria virens*) in eastern North America. *Bird-Banding* 38:130-135.

Derrickson, K.C. and R. Breitwisch. 1992. Northern Mockingbird. *In* The Birds of North America, No. **7** (A. Poole, P. Stettenheim, and F. Gill, eds.). Acad. Nat. Sci., Philadelphia; Amer. Ornith. Union, Washington D.C.

DeSante, D.F., N.K. Johnson, R. LeValley, and R.P. Henderson. 1985. Occurrence and identification of the Yellow-bellied Flycatcher on Southeast Farallon Island, California. *W. Birds* 16:153-160.

Desrochers, A. 1990. Sex determination of Black-capped Chickadees with discriminant analysis. *J. Field Ornith.* 61:79-84.

Devillers, P. 1970a. Chimney Swifts in coastal southern California. *California Birds* 1:147-152.

____. 1970b. Identification and distribution in California of the *Sphyrapicus varius* group of sapsuckers. *California Birds* 1:47-76. [Reprinted in *Birding* 11:181-199, 1979.]

Dhondt, A.A. and J.N.M. Smith. 1980. Postnuptial molt of the Song Sparrow on Mandarte Island in relation to breeding. *Can. J. Zool.* 58:513-520.

Dick, J.A. and R.D. James. 1996. Rufous crown feathers on adult male Tennessee Warblers. *Wilson Bull.* 108:181-182.

Dickerman, R.W. 1957. Notes on the Red Crossbills in Minnesota. *Wilson Bull.* 69:367-368.

____. 1961. Hybrids among the Fringillid genera *Junco-Zonotrichia* and *Melospiza*. *Auk* 78:627-634.

____. 1962. Identification of the juvenal plumage of the Sharp-tailed Sparrow (*Ammospiza caudacuta nelsoni*). *Bird-Banding* 33:202-204.

____. 1963. The Song Sparrows of the Mexican plateau. *Occ. Papers Minnesota Mus. Nat. Hist.* 9:1-79.

____. 1964. Notes on the Horned Larks of western Minnesota and the Great Plains. *Auk* 81:430-432.

____. 1968. A hybrid Grasshopper × Savannah sparrow. *Auk* 85:312-315.

____. 1974. Review of Red-winged Blackbirds (*Agelaius phoeniceus*) of eastern, west-central and southern Mexico and Central America. *Am. Mus. Novitates* 2538:1-18.

____. 1981. Preliminary review of the Clay-coloured Robin *Turdus grayi* with redesignation of the type locality of the nominate form and a description of a new subspecies. *Bull. Brit. Ornith. Club* 101:285-289.

____. 1981. Geographic variation in the juvenal plumage of the Lesser Nighthawk (*Chordeiles acutipennis*). *Auk* 98:619-621.

____. 1982. Further notes on the juvenal plumage of the Lesser Nighthawk. *Auk* 99:764.

____. 1985. Taxonomy of the Lesser Nighthawks (*Chordeiles acutipennis*) of North and Central America. *Ornith. Monogr.* 36:356-359.

____. 1986a. A review of the Red Crossbill in New York state. Part 1. Historical and nomenclatural background. *Kingbird* 36:73-78.

____. 1986b. A review of the Red Crossbill in New York state. Part 2. Identification of specimens from New York. *Kingbird* 36:127-134.

____. 1987. The "Old Northeastern" subspecies of Red Crossbill. *Am. Birds* 41:189-194.

____. 1990. Geographic variation in the juvenal plumage of the Common Nighthawk (*Chordeiles minor*) in North America. *Auk* 107:610-613.

____. 1991a. Specimens of the subarctic nesting population of Great Horned Owl from New York, New Jersey, and Connecticut. *Kingbird* 41:154-157.

____. 1991b. On the validity of *Bubo virginianus occidentalis* Stone. *Auk* 108:964-965.

____. 1992. Additional specimens of the subarctic Great Horned Owl from New York. *Kingbird* 42:73-75.

____. 1997. Geographic variation in the southwestern U.S. and Mexican Spotted Owls, with the description of a new subspecies. Pp. 45-48 in R.W. Dickerman, *comp.*, The era of Allan R. Phillips: A *Festshrift*. R.W. Dickerman, Albuquerque, NM.

____ and K.C. Parkes. 1960. The Savannah Sparrows of Minnesota. *Flicker* 32:110-113.

____ and ____. 1997. Taxa described by Allan R. Phillips, 1939-1994: A critical list. Pp. 211-234 *in* R.W. Dickerman, *comp.*, The era of Allan R. Phillips: A *Festshrift*. R.W. Dickerman, Albuquerque, NM.

____ and A.R. Phillips. 1953. First United States record of *Myiarchus nuttingi*. *Condor* 55:101-102.

____ and ____. 1954. *Molothrus ater ater* in Arizona. *Condor* 56:312.

____ and ____. 1966. A new subspecies of the Boat-tailed Grackle from Mexico. *Wilson Bull.* 78:129-131.

____ and D.W. Warner. 1962. A new Orchard Oriole from Mexico. *Condor* 64:311-314.

Dickey, D.R. 1928. A new poor-will from the Colorado River Valley. *Condor* 30:152-153.

____ and A.J. van Rossem. 1922. Distribution of *Molothrus ater* in California with the description of a new race. *Condor* 24:206-210.

____ and ____. 1923. Additional notes from the coastal islands of southern California. *Condor* 25:126-129.

____ and ____. 1928. A new race of the White-throated Swift from Central America. *Condor* 30:193.

____ and ____. 1938. The birds of El Salvador. *Zool. Series Field Mus. Nat. Hist.* 23:1-609.

Dickinson, J.C. Jr. 1952. Geographic variation in the Red-eyed Towhee of the eastern United States. *Bull. Mus. Comp. Zool.* 107:271-352.

____. 1953. Report on the McCabe collection of British Columbian birds. *Bull. Mus. Comp. Zool.* 109:123-210.

Dieter, M.P. 1973. Sex determination of eagles, owls, and herons by analyzing plasma steroid hormones. *U.S. Fish and Wildlife Spec. Sci. Rep.* 167:1-13.

Dilger, W.C. 1956. Adaptive modifications and ecological isolating mechanisms in the thrush genera *Catharus* and *Hylocichla*. *Wilson Bull.* 68:171-199.

Dingle, E.S. and A. Sprunt Jr. 1932. A new Marsh Wren from North Carolina. *Auk* 49:454-455.

Dixon, K.L. 1955. An ecological analysis of interbreeding of Crested Titmice in Texas. *Univ. California Pubs. Zool.* 54:125-206.

____. 1962. Notes on the molt schedule of the Plain Titmouse. *Condor* 64:134-139.

Dixon, K.L. 1978. A distributional history of the Black-crested Titmouse. *Am. Midland Nat.* 100:29-42.

———. 1990. Constancy of margins of the hybrid zone in titmice of the *Parus bicolor* complex in coastal Texas. *Auk* 107:184-188.

Dobbs, R.C., T.E. Martin, and C.J. Conway. 1997. Williamson's Sapsucker. *In* The Birds of North America, No. **285** (A. Poole and F. Gill, eds.). Acad. Nat. Sci., Philadelphia; Amer. Ornith. Union, Washington D.C.

Donovan, T.M. and C.M. Stanley. 1995. A new method of determining Ovenbird age on the basis of rectrix shape. *J. Field Ornith.* 66:247-252.

Doolittle, E.A. 1929. A hybrid Field-Vesper sparrow. *Wilson Bull.* 41:41.

Dorn, R.D. and J.L. Dorn. 1994. Further data on screech-owl distribution and habitat use in Wyoming. *W. Birds* 25:35-42.

Dow, D.D. 1966. Sex determination of Slate-colored Junco by means of plumage characteristics. *Ontario Bird Banding* 2:1-14.

Drew, F.M. 1882. Notes on the plumage of *Nephoectes niger borealis. Bull. Nuttall Ornith. Club* 7:182-183.

Dugdale, M.S. Potential for ageing vireos by color of the inner upper mandible. Unpublished ms., Long Point Bird Observatory.

Dunn, J.L. 1978. The races of the Yellow-bellied Sapsucker. *Birding* 10:142-149.

———. 1981. The identification of female bluebirds. *Birding* 13:4-11.

——— and K.L. Garrett. 1987. The identification of North American gnatcatchers. *Birding* 19(1):17-29.

——— and ———. 1990. Identification of Ruddy and Common ground-doves. *Birding* 22:138-145.

——— and ———. 1997. A field guide to warblers of North America. Houghton Mifflin Co., Boston.

———, ———, and J.K. Alderfer. 1995. White-crowned Sparrow subspecies: Identification and distribution. *Birding* 27:182-200.

———. 1993b. Bachman's Sparrow. *In* The Birds of North America, No. **38** (A. Poole, P. Stettenheim, and F. Gill, eds.). Acad. Nat. Sci., Philadelphia; Amer. Ornith. Union, Washington D.C.

Dunning, J.B. Jr. 1993a. CRC handbook of avian body masses. CRC Press, Boca Raton, FL.

———. 1993b. Bachman's Sparrow. *In* The Birds of North America, No. **38** (A. Poole, P. Stettenheim, and F. Gill, eds.). Acad. Nat. Sci., Philadelphia; Amer. Ornith. Union, Washington D.C.

Dunson, W.A. 1965. Physiological aspects of the onset of molt in the Redwinged Blackbird. *Condor* 67:265-269.

Duvall, A.J. 1943. Breeding Savannah Sparrows of the southwestern United States. *Condor* 45:237-238.

———. 1945a. Distribution and taxonomy of the Black-capped Chickadees of North America. *Auk* 62:49-69.

———. 1945b. Variation in *Carpodacus purpureus* and *Carpodacus cassinii. Condor* 47:202-204.

Dwight, J. Jr. 1890. The Horned Larks of North America. *Auk* 7:138-158.

———. 1900a. The sequence of plumages and moults of the passerine birds of New York. *Ann. New York Acad. Sci.* 13:73-360.

———. 1900b. The plumage and moults of the Indigo Bunting (*Passerina cyanea*). *Science* 11:627-630.

———. 1902. Plumage-cycles and the relation between plumages and moults. *Auk* 19:248-255.

———. 1905. Plumage wear in its relation to pallid subspecies. *Auk* 22:34-38.

———. 1907. Sequence in molts and plumages with an explanation of plumage cycles. *Proc. IV Int. Ornith. Congr.* 1905:513-518.

———. 1918. The geographical distribution of color and other variable characters in the genus *Junco*: A new aspect of specific and subspecific values. *Bull. Amer. Mus. Nat. Hist.* 38:269-309.

——— and L. Griscom. 1927. A revision of the geographical races of the Blue Grosbeak (*Guiraca caerulea*). *Am. Mus. Novitates* 257:1-5.

Earhart, C.M. and N.K. Johnson. 1970. Size dimorphism and food habits of North American owls. *Condor* 72:251-264.

Eaton, S.W. 1957a. Variation in *Seiurus noveboracensis. Auk* 74:229-239.

———. 1957b. A life history study of *Seiurus noveboracensis* (with notes on *Seiurus aurocapillus* and the species of *Seiurus* compared). *Sci. Stud. St. Bonaventure Univ.* 19:7-36.

———. 1958. A life history study of the Louisiana Waterthrush. *Wilson Bull.* 70:211-236.

———. 1995. Northern Waterthrush. *In* The Birds of North America, No. **182** (A. Poole and F. Gill, eds.). Acad. Nat. Sci., Philadelphia; Amer. Ornith. Union, Washington D.C.

Eckert, K.R. 1988. Cassin's Finch: The documentation and research. *Loon* 60:6-9.

Edwards, M.H., R.D. Weir, and R.B. Stewart. 1982. Comments on sexing Saw-whet Owls by wing chord. *Wilson Bull.* 94:555-557.

Eifrig, C.W.G. 1915. Notes on some birds of the Maryland Alleganies: An anomaly in the check-list. *Auk* 32:108-110.

Eisenmann, E. 1959. South American migrant swallows of the genus *Progne* in Panama and northern South America; with comments on their identification and molt. *Auk* 76:528-532.

Eisenmann, E. 1962a. Notes on the nighthawks of the genus *Chordeiles* in southern Middle America, with a description of a new race of *Chordeiles minor* breeding in Panama. *Am. Mus. Novitates* 2094:1-21.

———. 1962b. On the genus "*Chamaethlypis*" and its supposed relationship to *Icteria. Auk* 79:265-267.

———. 1969. Wing formula as a means of distinguishing Summer Tanager, *Piranga rubra*, from Hepatic Tanager, *P. flava. Bird-Banding* 40:144-145.

Eitner, J.C. 1997. White-collared Seedeater. *In* The Birds of North America, No. **278** (A. Poole and F. Gill, eds.). Acad. Nat. Sci., Philadelphia; Amer. Ornith. Union, Washington D.C.

Ellison, W.G. 1992. Blue-gray Gnatcatcher. *In* The Birds of North America, No. **23** (A. Poole, P. Stettenheim, and F. Gill, eds.). Acad. Nat. Sci., Philadelphia; Amer. Ornith. Union, Washington D.C.

Elliston, E.P. and W.H. Baltosser. 1995. Sex ratios and bill growth in nestling Black-chinned Hummingbirds. *W. Birds* 26:76-81.

Emlen, J.T. Jr. 1936. Age determination in the American Crow. *Condor* 38:99-102.

Emlen, S.T. 1967. Migratory orientation in the Indigo Bunting, *Passerina cyanea. Auk* 84:309-342.

———, J.D. Rising, and W.L. Thompson. 1975. A behavioral and morphological study of sympatry in the Indigo and Lazuli buntings of the Great Plains. *Wilson Bull.* 87:145-179.

Engels, W.L. 1940. Structural adaptations in thrashers (Mimidae: Genus *Toxostoma*) with comments on interspecific relationships. *Univ. California Pubs. Zool.* 42:341-400.

England, A.S. and W.F. Laudenslayer. 1993. Bendire's Thrasher. *In* The Birds of North America, No. **71** (A. Poole and F. Gill, eds.). Acad. Nat. Sci., Philadelphia; Amer. Ornith. Union, Washington D.C.

Enstrom, D.A. 1992a. Delayed plumage maturation in the Orchard Oriole (*Icterus spurius*): Tests of winter adaption hypotheses. *Behav. Ecol. Sociobiol.* 30:35-42.

———. 1992b. Breeding season communication hypotheses for delayed plumage maturation in passerines: Tests in the Orchard Oriole (*Icterus spurius*). *Anim. Behav.* 43:463-472.

Erpino, M.J. 1968. Age determination in the Black-billed Magpie. *Condor* 70:91-92.

Ervin, S. 1975. Iris coloration in young Bushtits. *Condor* 77:90-91.

Evans, D.L. and R.N. Rosenfield. 1987. Remigial molt in fall migrant Long-eared and Northern Saw-whet owls. Pp. 209-214 *in* R.W. Nero, R.J. Clark, R.J. Knapton, and R.H. Hamre, eds., Biology and conservation of northern forest owls. U.S. For. Serv. Gen. Tech. Rep. RM-142.

Evans Ogden, L.J. and B.J. Stutchbury. 1994. Hooded Warbler. *In* The Birds of North America, No. **110** (A. Poole and F. Gill, eds.). Acad. Nat. Sci., Philadelphia; Amer. Ornith. Union, Washington D.C.

Ewald, P.W. and S. Rohwer. 1980. Age, coloration and dominance in non-breeding hummingbirds: A test of the asymmetry hypothesis. *Behav. Ecol. Sociobiol.* 7:273-279.

Ewert, D.N. and W.E. Lanyon. 1970. The first prebasic molt of the Common Yellowthroat (Parulidae). *Auk* 87:362-363.

Fairfield, D.M. and P.A. Shirokoff. 1978. Aging North American kinglets: A new technique. *Blue Bill* (suppl.) 25:19-21.

Falls, J.B. and J.G. Kopachena. 1994. White-throated Sparrow. *In* The Birds of North America, No. **128** (A. Poole and F. Gill, eds.). Acad. Nat. Sci., Philadelphia; Amer. Ornith. Union, Washington D.C.

Fargo, W.G. 1932. Song Sparrows of Michigan. *Auk* 49:208-211.

Fautin, R.W. 1941. Development of nestling Yellow-headed Blackbirds. *Auk* 58:215-232.

Feinstein, B. 1958. A new Gray-crowned Rosy Finch from northern Alaska. *Proc. Biol. Soc. Washington* 71:11-12.

Felt, A.C. 1967. Ageing Mountain Chickadees. *W. Bird Bander* 42:3.

ffrench, R.P. 1967. The Dickcissel on its wintering grounds in Trinidad. *Living Bird* 6:123-140.

Fiala, K.L. 1979. A laparotomy technique for nestling birds. *Bird-Banding* 50:366-367.

Ficken, M.S. 1964. Nest site selection in the American Redstart. *Wilson Bull.* 16:189-190.

——— and R.W. Ficken. 1968. Reproductive isolating mechanisms in the Blue-winged Warbler - Golden-winged Warbler complex. *Evolution* 22:166-179.

———, M.A. McLaren, and J.P. Hailman. 1996. Boreal Chickadee. *In* The Birds of North America, No. **254** (A. Poole and F. Gill, eds.). Acad. Nat. Sci., Philadelphia; Amer. Ornith. Union, Washington D.C.

——— and J. Nocedal. 1992. Mexican Chickadee. *In* The Birds of North America, No. **8** (A. Poole, P. Stettenheim, and F. Gill, eds.). Acad. Nat. Sci., Philadelphia; Amer. Ornith. Union, Washington D.C.

Ficken, R.W., M.S. Ficken, and H.D. Morse. 1968. Competition and character displacement in two sympatric pine-dwelling warblers (*Dendroica*, Parulidae). *Evolution* 22:307-314.

Figgins, J.D. 1918. A new Savannah Sparrow from James Island, South Carolina. *Proc. Colorado Mus. Nat. Hist.* 1:1-5.

Figgins, J.D. 1930. Proposals relative to certain subspecific groups of *Carpodacus mexicanus*. *Proc. Colorado Mus. Nat. Hist.* 9:1-3.

Fink, T. and J.K. DeNeal. 1993. Curve-billed Thrasher: First Illinois record. *Meadowlark* 2:87-89.

Fischer, R.B. 1958. The breeding biology of the Chimney Swift, *Chaetura pelagica*) (Linnaeus). *New York State Mus. Bull.* 368:1-141.

Fisher, D.H. 1979. Separation of Brown and Long-billed thrashers. *Birding* 11:310-312.

Fisher, W.K. 1902. The Oregon Song Sparrow. *Condor* 4:36-37.

Fisk, E.J. 1970. A note on wintering Myrtle Warblers. *E. Bird Banding Assoc. News* 33:174.

____. 1972. Bander's shoptalk. *E. Bird Banding Assoc. News* 35:58-62.

____. 1973a. Further notes on the iris color of Mockingbird eyes. *Bird-Banding* 44:124.

____. 1973b. Do not age American Goldfinch by the Olyphant system. *E. Bird Banding Assoc. News* 36:179.

____. 1973c. Further speculations on Myrtle Warblers in winter plumage. *E. Bird Banding Assoc. News* 36:38-41.

____. 1974. Wintering populations of Painted Buntings in southern Florida. *Bird-Banding* 45:353-359.

____. 1975. On Northern Oriole plumages: Questions for banders to answer. *E. Bird Banding Assoc. News* 38:146-147.

Fitch, H.S. and V.R. Fitch. 1955. Observations on the Summer Tanager in northeastern Kansas. *Wilson Bull.* 67:45-54.

Fix, D. 1988. An apparent Clay-colored Sparrow × Chipping Sparrow hybrid in Oregon. *Oregon Birds* 14:250-252.

Fleischer, R.C. and S.I. Rothstein. 1988. Known secondary contact and rapid gene flow among subspecies and dialects in the Brown-headed Cowbird. *Evolution* 42:1146-1158.

Fleming, J.H. 1916. The Saw-whet Owl of the Queen Charlotte Islands. *Auk* 33:420-423.

Fleming, T.L., J.B. Buchanan, and L.L. Irwin. 1991. Footpad dimorphism as a possible means to determine sex of adult and juvenile Northern Spotted Owls (*Strix occidentalis caurina*). *N. Am. Bird Bander* 16:66-69.

____, J.L. Haverson, and J.B. Buchanan. 1996. Use of DNA to identify sex of Northern Spotted Owls. (*Strix occidentalis caurina*). *J. Raptor Res.* 30:118-122.

Flood, N.J. 1984. Adaptive significance of delayed plumage maturation in male Northern Orioles. *Evolution* 38:267-279.

____. 1989. Coloration in New World orioles. *Behav. Ecol. Sociobiol.* 25:49-56.

____. 1990. Aspects of the breeding biology of Audubon's Oriole. *J. Field Ornith.* 61:290-302.

Folse, L.J. Jr. and K.A. Arnold. 1976. Secondary sex characteristics in road-runners. *Bird-Banding* 47:115-118.

Forbush, E.H. 1927. Birds of Massachusetts and other New England states. Vol. II. Commonwealth of Massachusetts, Boston, MA.

____. 1929. Birds of Massachusetts and other New England states. Vol. III. Commonwealth of Massachusetts, Boston, MA.

Forsman, D. 1984. Ageing and moult in western Palearctic Hawk Owls *Surnia u. ulula* L. *Ornis Fenn.* 57:73-75.

Forsman, E.D. 1981. Molt of the Spotted Owl. *Auk* 98:735-742.

Forster, R.A. 1985. Observation of a Clay-colored Sparrow in unusual plumage. *Bird Observer* 13:21-23.

Foster, D.W. 1973. Banding worksheet for western birds. American Goldfinch. Supplement to *W. Bird Bander*, vol. 48.

Foster, M.S. 1967a. Pterylography and age determination in the Orange-crowned Warbler. *Condor* 69:1-12.

____. 1967b. Molt cycles of the Orange-crowned Warbler. *Condor* 69:169-200.

____. 1975. The overlap of molting and breeding in some tropical birds. *Condor* 77:304-314.

Fowler, L.J. 1985. Color phases of the Eastern Screech-Owl in Tennessee. *Migrant* 56:61-63.

Fox, R.P. 1954. Plumages and territorial behavior of the Lucifer Hummingbird in the Chisos Mountains, Texas. *Auk* 71:465-466.

Foy, R.W. 1974a. Aging and sexing American Redstarts in fall. *E. Bird Banding Assoc. News* 37:43-44.

____. 1974b. Aging and sexing American Redstarts in the fall:a note of caution. *E. Bird Banding Assoc. News* 37:128.

Francis, C.M. and F. Cooke. 1990. Differential timing of spring migration in Rose-breasted Grosbeaks.

____ and D.S. Wood. 1989. Effects of age and wear on wing length of wood-warblers. *J. Field Ornith.* 60:495-503.

Francis, I.S., A.D. Fox, J.P. McCarthy, and C.R. McKay. 1991. Measurements and moult of the Lapland Bunting *Calcarius lapponicus* in West Greenland. *Ringing & Migr.* 12:28-37.

Franzreb, K.E. and S.A. Laymon. 1993. A reassessment of the taxonomic status of the Yellow-billed Cuckoo. *W. Birds* 24:17-28.

Freeman-Gallant, C.R. 1996. Microgeographic patterns of genetic and morphological variation in Savannah Sparrows (*Passerculus sandwichensis*). *Evolution* 50:1631-1637.

Freer, V. and B. Belanger. 1981. A technique for distinguishing the age classes of adult Bank Swallows. *J. Field. Ornith.* 52:341-343.

French, N.R. 1959a. Life history of the Black Rosy Finch. *Auk* 76:159-180.

____. 1959b. Distribution and migration of the Black Rosy Finch. *Condor* 61:18-29.

Friedmann, H. 1927. A revision of the classification of the cowbirds. *Auk* 44:495-508.

____. 1929. The Cowbirds. A study in the biology of social parasitism. Thomas Books, Springfield, IL.

____. 1946. The Red-spotted Bluethroats of northwestern Alaska. *Auk* 63:434.

Fry, C.H., K. Fry, and A. Harris. 1992. Kingfishers, bee-eaters and rollers. Princeton University Press, Princeton, New Jersey.

Fugle, G.N. and S.I. Rothstein. 1985. Age and sex related variation in size and crown plumage brightness in wintering White-crowned Sparrows. *J. Field Ornith.* 56:356-368.

Funderburg, J.B. Jr. and T.L. Quay. 1983. Distributional evolution of the Seaside Sparrow. Pp. 19-27 *in* T.L. Quay *et al.*, eds., The Seaside Sparrow, its biology and management. *Occ. Papers North Carolina Biol. Surv.*, Raleigh, NC.

Gabrielson, I.N. and F.C. Lincoln. 1951a. A new Alaskan race of the Winter Wren. *Proc. Biol. Soc. Washington* 64:73-74.

____ and ____. 1951b. The races of Song Sparrows in Alaska. *Condor* 53:250-255.

Gamble, L.R. and T.M. Bergin. 1996. Western Kingbird. *In* The Birds of North America, No. **227** (A. Poole and F. Gill, eds.). Acad. Nat. Sci., Philadelphia; Amer. Ornith. Union, Washington D.C.

Ganier, A.F. 1954. A new race of the Yellow-bellied Sapsucker. *Migrant* 25:38-41.

Garrett, K.L., M.G. Raphael, and R.D. Dixon. 1996. White-headed Woodpecker. *In* The Birds of North America, No. **252** (A. Poole and F. Gill, eds.). Acad. Nat. Sci., Philadelphia; Amer. Ornith. Union, Washington D.C.

Gavin, T.A., R.A. Howard, and B. May. 1991. Allozyme variation among breeding populations of Red-winged Blackbirds: The California conundrum. *Auk* 108:602-611.

Gayou, D.C. 1995. Green Jay. *In* The Birds of North America, No. **187** (A. Poole and F. Gill, eds.). Acad. Nat. Sci., Philadelphia; Amer. Ornith. Union, Washington D.C.

Gebhardt, S. 1971. Eye color in Blue Jays. *Inl. Bird Banding News* 43:52-53.

Gehlbach, F.R. 1994. The Eastern Screech Owl. Texas A&M University Press, College Station, TX.

____. 1995. Eastern Screech-Owl. *In* The Birds of North America, No. **165** (A. Poole and F. Gill, eds.). Acad. Nat. Sci., Philadelphia; Amer. Ornith. Union, Washington D.C.

George, W.G. 1962. The classification of the Olive Warbler, *Peucedramus taeniatus*. *Am. Mus. Novitates* 2103:1-41.

____. 1972. Age determination of Hairy and Downy woodpeckers in eastern North America. *Bird-Banding* 43:128-135.

____. 1973. Molt of juvenile White-eyed Vireos. *Wilson Bull.* 85:327-330.

Gerber, D.T. 1986. Female Golden-fronted Woodpecker or mutant female Red-bellied Woodpecker? *Am. Birds* 40:203-204.

Gibson, D.D. 1981. Migrant birds at Shemya Island, Aleutian Islands, Alaska. *Condor* 83:65-77.

____. 1986. *Calcarius lapponicus coloratus* in the Aleutian Islands, Alaska. *Auk* 103:635-636.

____. 1987. Hammond's Flycatcher (*Empidonax hammondii*) new to Maryland and the Atlantic coast. *Wilson Bull.* 99:500.

Gill, D.E. and W.E. Lanyon. 1965. Establishment, growth, and behavior of an extralimital population of House Finches in Huntington, New York. *Bird-Banding* 36:1-14.

Gill, F.B. 1980. Historical aspects of hybridization between Blue-winged and Golden-winged warblers. *Auk* 97:1-18.

____. 1987. Allozymes and genetic similarity of Blue-winged and Golden-winged warblers. *Auk* 104:444-449.

____, A.M. Mostrom, and A.L. Mack. 1993. Speciation in North American chickadees: I. Patterns in mtDNA genetic divergence. *Evolution* 47:195-212.

Gillespie, M. and J.A. Gillespie. 1932. Color of the iris in grackles. *Auk* 49:96.

Ginn, H.B. and D.S. Melville. 1983. Moult in birds. BTO Guide 19. British Trust for Ornithology, Thetford, U.K.

Glase, J.C. 1973. Ecology of social organization in the Black-capped Chickadee. *Living Bird* 12:235-267.

Gochfeld, M. 1977. Plumage variation in Black-capped Chickadees: Is there sexual dimorphism? *Bird-Banding* 48:62-66.

Godfrey, W.E. 1946. A new Carolina Wren. *Auk* 63:564-568.

____. 1947. A new Long-eared Owl. *Can. Field-Nat.* 61:196-197.

____. 1949. Distribution of the races of the Swamp Sparrow. *Auk* 66:35-38.

____. 1950. Description of a new northwestern *Geothlypis*. *Can. Field-Nat.* 64:104.

Godfrey, W.E. 1951a. Geographical variation in the Boreal Chickadee east of the Rockies. *Can. Field-Nat.* 65:22-26.

____. 1951b. A new northwestern Olive-backed Thrush. *Can. Field-Nat.* 64:104.

____. 1951c. Comments on the races of Myrtle Warbler. *Can. Field-Nat.* 65:166-167.

____. 1965. Geographic variation in the White-crowned Sparrow *Zonotrichia leucophrys.* [Review of Banks 1964.] *Auk* 82:510-511.

____. 1986. The birds of Canada. Revised edition. National Museums of Canada, Ottawa.

____ and A.L. Wilk. 1948. Birds of the Lake St. John region, Quebec. *Nat. Mus. Can. Bull.* 110:1-32.

Goetz, R.E. 1987. Illinois' first *Selasphorus* hummingbird: An identification problem. *Ill. Birds & Birding* 3:56-59.

Goodman, S.M. 1982. Age and sexual morphological variation in the Kirtland's Warbler (*Dendroica kirtlandii*). *Jack-Pine Warbler* 60:144-147.

Goodpasture, K.A. 1963. Age, sex and wing length of tower casualties: Fall migration, 1962. *Bird-Banding* 34:191-199.

____. 1972. A rarely reported sex-plumage association in a Rose-breasted Grosbeak. *Bird-Banding* 43:136.

Goodwin, D. 1967. Pigeons and doves of the world. British Museum of Natural History, U.K.

____. 1968. Notes on woodpeckers (Picidae). *Bull. Brit. Mus. (Nat. Hist.) Zool.* 17:1-44

____. 1976. Crows of the world. Comstock Publishing Associates, Ithaca, NY.

Goossen, J.P. 1986. Apparent dichromatism in juvenile Common Nighthawks (*Chordeiles minor*). *Murrelet* 67:62-63.

Gosler, A.G., J.J.D. Greenwood, J.K. Baker, and J.R. King. 1995. A comparative study of wing length and primary length as size measures for small passerines. *Ringing &Migr.* 16:65-78.

Gowaty, P.A. and M.R. Lennartz. 1985. Sex ratios and fledgling Red-cockaded Woodpeckers (*Picoides borealis*) favor males. *Am. Nat.* 126:347-353.

Graber, R.R. and J.W. Graber. 1951. Notes on the birds of southwestern Kansas. *Trans. Kansas Acad. Sci.* 54:145-174.

____ and ____. 1954. Comparative notes on Fuertes and Orchard orioles. *Condor* 56:274-282.

Grant, G.S. and T.L. Quay. 1970. Sex and age criteria in the Slate-colored Junco. *Bird-Banding* 41:274-278.

Grant, R.A. 1965. The Burrowing Owl in Minnesota. *Loon* 37:2-17.

Graves, G.R. 1988. Evaluation of *Vermivora* × *Oporornis* hybrid woodwarblers. *Wilson Bull.* 100:285-289.

____. 1993. A new intergeneric wood warbler hybrid (*Parula americana* × *Dendroica coronata*) (Aves: Fringillidae). *Proc. Biol. Soc. Washington* 106:402-409.

____. 1997. Age determination of free-living male Black-throated Blue Warblers during the breeding season. *J. Field Ornith.* 68:443-449.

____, M.A. Patten, and J.L. Dunn. 1996. Comments on a probable gynandromorphic Black-throated Blue Warbler. *Wilson Bull.* 108:178-180.

Gray, A.P. 1958. Bird hybrids. *Commonwealth Bur. Anim. Breed. Genetics Edinburg Tech. Comm.* 13:1-390.

Gray, D.R. III. 1973. Report on aging and sexing criteria for American Redstart. *E. Bird Banding Assoc. News* 36:143-146.

Green, G.H. and R.W. Summers. 1975. Snow Bunting moult in Northeast Greenland. *Bird Study* 22:9-17.

Green, H.O. 1940. Horned Larks. *Oologist* 57:8-9.

Greenberg, R. 1988. Seasonal plumage dimorphism in the Swamp Sparrow. *J. Field Ornith.* 59:149-154.

____ and S. Droege. 1990. Adaptations to tidal marshes in breeding populations of the Swamp Sparrow. *Condor* 92:393-404.

Greene, E., V.R. Muehter, and W. Davison. 1996. Lazuli Bunting. *In* The Birds of North America, No. **232** (A. Poole and F. Gill, eds.). Acad. Nat. Sci., Philadelphia; Amer. Ornith. Union, Washington D.C.

Greenlaw, J.S. 1993. Behavioral and morphological diversification in Sharp-tailed Sparrows (*Ammodramus caudacutus*) of the Atlantic Coast. *Auk* 110:286-303.

____. 1996a. Eastern Towhee. *In* The Birds of North America, No. **262** (A. Poole and F. Gill, eds.). Acad. Nat. Sci., Philadelphia; Amer. Ornith. Union, Washington D.C.

____. 1996b. Spotted Towhee. *In* The Birds of North America, No. **263** (A. Poole and F. Gill, eds.). Acad. Nat. Sci., Philadelphia; Amer. Ornith. Union, Washington D.C.

—— and J.D. Rising. 1994. Sharp-tailed Sparrow. *In* The Birds of North America, No. **112** (A. Poole and F. Gill, eds.). Acad. Nat. Sci., Philadelphia; Amer. Ornith. Union, Washington D.C.

Greenwood, H., P.J. Weatherhead, and R.D. Titman. 1983. A new age-and sex-plumage molt scheme for the Red-winged Blackbird. *Condor* 85:104-105.

Grinnell, J. 1901. The Santa Cruz Song Sparrow, with notes on the Salt Marsh Song Sparrow. *Condor* 3:92-93.

Grinnell, J. 1902a. The Monterey Fox Sparrow. *Condor* 4:44-45.

____. 1902b. Status of the "Arizona Goldfinch" in California. *Condor* 4:115-116.

____. 1903. The California Yellow Warbler. *Condor* 5:71-73.

____. 1905a. Status of the Townsend's Warbler in California. *Condor* 7:52-53.

____. 1905b. The California Sage Sparrow. *Condor* 7:18-19.

____. 1908. The southern California chickadee. *Condor* 10:29-30.

____. 1909a. Three new Song Sparrows from California. *Univ. California Pubs. Zool.* 5:265-269.

____. 1909b. A new cowbird of the genus *Molothrus.* *Univ. California Pubs. Zool.* 5:275-281.

____. 1910a. Birds of the 1908 Alexander Alaska expedition with a note on the avifaunal relationships of the Prince William Sound district. *Univ. California Pubs. Zool.* 5:361-428.

____. 1910b. Two heretofore unnamed wrens of the genus *Thryomanes.* *Univ. California Pubs. Zool.* 5:307-309.

____. 1910c. The Savannah Sparrow of the Great Basin. *Univ. California Pubs. Zool.* 5:311-316.

____. 1911a. A new Blue Grosbeak from California. *Proc. Biol. Soc. Washington* 24:163.

____. 1911b. Description of a new Spotted Towhee from the Great Basin. *Univ. California Pubs. Zool.* 7:309-311.

____. 1911c. The Modesto Song Sparrow. *Univ. California Pubs. Zool.* 5:197-199.

____. 1911d. The linnet of the Hawaiian Islands: A problem in speciation. *Univ. California Pubs. Zool* 7:179-195.

____. 1912. The northern Brown Towhee. *Condor* 14:199.

____. 1913. *Leucosticte tephrocotis dawsoni* - A new race of Rosy Finch from the Sierra Nevada. *Condor* 15:76-79.

____. 1914a. An account of the mammals and birds of the Lower Colorado Valley. *Univ. California Pubs. Zool.* 12:51-294.

____. 1914b. A new Red-winged Blackbird from the Great Basin. *Proc. Biol. Soc. Washington* 27:107-108.

____. 1915a. A new subspecies of Screech Owl from California. *Auk* 32:59-60.

____. 1915b. A distributional list of the birds of California. *Pacific Coast Avif.* 11:1-217.

____. 1917. The subspecies of *Hesperiphona vespertina.* *Condor* 19:17-22.

____. 1918a. The subspecies of the Mountain Chickadee. *Univ. California Pubs. Zool.* 17:505-515.

____. 1918b. Seven new or noteworthy birds from east-central California. *Condor* 20:86-90.

____. 1920. The California race of the Brewer Blackbird. *Condor* 22:152-153.

____. 1921. The Bryant Cactus Wren not a bird of California. *Condor* 23:169.

____. 1922. The "Anthony Vireo" not a tenable subspecies. *Condor* 24:32-33.

____. 1926a. A new race of the Say's Phoebe from Lower California. *Condor* 29:81-82.

____. 1926b. A new race of the White-breasted Nuthatch from Lower California. *Univ. California Pubs. Zool.* 22:405-410.

____. 1926c. A critical inspection of the gnatcatchers of the Californias. *Proc. California Acad. Sci.*, 4th Ser., 15:493-500.

____. 1927a. Six new subspecies of birds from Lower California. *Auk* 44:67-72.

____. 1927b. The Rock Wren of San Nicolas Island not a recognizable subspecies. *Condor* 29:165-166.

____. 1927c. Designation of a Pacific Coast subspecies of Chipping Sparrow. *Condor* 29:81-82.

____. 1928a. A new race of Screech Owl from California. *Auk* 45:213-215.

____. 1928b. Notes on the systematics of west American birds. II. *Condor* 30:153-156.

____. 1928c. Notes on the systematics of west American birds. III. *Condor* 30:185-189.

____. 1928d. Notes on the systematics of west American birds. I. *Condor* 30:121-124.

____. 1928e. The Song Sparrow of San Miguel Island, California. *Proc. Biol. Soc. Washington* 41:37-38.

____. 1929. A new race of hummingbird from southern California. *Condor* 31:226-227.

____. 1931. The type locality of the Verdin. *Condor* 33:163-168.

____. 1933. The LeConte Thrashers of the San Joaquin. *Condor* 35:107-114.

____. 1934a. The New Mexico race of Plain Titmouse. *Condor* 36:251-252.

____. 1934b. The race of cowbird in the San Francisco Bay region. *Condor* 36:218-219.

____. 1935. The subspecific status of the Hutton Vireo of Vancouver Island. *Condor* 37:40.

____. 1937. Subspecific appraisal of Red-breasted Sapsuckers. *Condor* 39:122-124.

Grinnell, J. 1939. Proposed shifts of names in *Passerculus* - a protest. *Condor* 41:112-119.

_____ and W.H. Behle. 1935. Comments upon the subspecies of *Catherpes mexicanus*. *Condor* 37:247-261.

_____ and _____. 1937a. A new race of titmouse from the Kern Basin of California. *Condor* 39:225-226.

_____ and _____. 1937b. A new race of Brown Towhee from the Kern Basin of California. *Condor* 39:177-178.

_____ and F.S. Daggett. 1903. An ornithological visit to Los Coronados Islands, Lower California. *Auk* 20:27-37.

_____, J. Dixon, and J.M. Linsdale. 1930. Vertebrate natural history of a section of northern California through the Lassen Peak region. *Univ. California Pubs. Zool.* 35:1-594.

_____, S. Stephens, J. Dixon, and E. Heller. 1909. Birds and mammals of the 1907 Alexander expedition to southeastern Alaska. *Univ. California Pubs. Zool.* 5:171-264.

_____ and T.I. Storer. 1917. A new race of Fox Sparrow from the vicinity of Mono Lake, California. *Condor* 19:165-166.

_____ and H.S. Swarth. 1913. An account of the birds and mammals of the San Jacinto area of southern California with remarks upon the behavior and geographic races on the margins of their habitats. *Univ. California Pubs. Zool.* 10:197-406.

_____ and _____. 1926a. A new race of Acorn-storing Woodpecker from Lower California. *Condor* 28:130-133.

_____ and _____. 1926b. New subspecies of birds (*Penthestes, Baelophus, Psaltriparus, Chamaea*) from the Pacific coast of North America. *Univ. California Pubs. Zool.* 30:163-175.

_____ and _____. 1926c. Systematic review of the Pacific coast Brown Towhees. *Univ. California Pubs. Zool.* 21:427-433

_____ and _____. 1926d. Geographic variation in *Spizella atrogularis*. *Auk* 43:475-478.

Griscom, L. 1928. New birds from Mexico and Panama. *Am. Mus. Novitates* 293:1-6.

_____. 1929a. Studies from the Dwight collection of Guatemala birds. I. *Am. Mus. Novitates* 379:1-13.

_____. 1929b. Notes on the Rough-winged Swallow (*Stelgidopteryx serripennis* (Aud.)) and its allies. *Proc. New England Zool. Club* 11:67-72.

_____. 1930a. Critical notes on Central American birds. *Proc. New England Zool. Club* 12:1-8.

_____. 1930b. Studies from the Dwight collection of Guatemala birds. II. *Am. Mus. Novitates* 414:1-8.

_____. 1930c. Studies from the Dwight collection of Guatemala birds. III. *Am. Mus. Novitates* 438:1-18.

_____. 1932. The distribution of bird-life in Guatemala. *Bull. Am. Mus. Nat. Hist.* 64:1-425.

_____. 1934a. The ornithology of Guerrero, Mexico. *Bull. Mus. Comp. Zool.* 75:367-422.

_____. 1934b. The Pine Grosbeaks of eastern North America. *Proc. New England Zool. Club* 14:5-12.

_____. 1935. Critical notes on Central American birds in the British Museum. *Ibis* 13th Series, 5:541-554.

_____. 1937. A monographic study of the Red Crossbill. *Proc. Boston Soc. Nat. Hist.* 41:77-210.

_____. 1944. A second revision of the Seaside Sparrows. *Occ. Papers Mus. Zool. Louisiana State Univ.* 19:313-328.

_____. 1948a. Notes on Texas Seaside Sparrows. *Wilson Bull.* 60:103-108.

_____. 1948b. A note on the western Swamp Sparrow. *Auk* 65:313.

_____ and J.T. Nichols. 1920. A revision of the Seaside Sparrows. *Abstr. Proc. Linnean Soc. New York* 32:18-30.

_____ and D.E. Snyder. 1955. The birds of Massachusetts. An annotated and revised checklist. Anthoensen Press, Portland, ME.

Groschupf, K. 1992. Five-striped Sparrow. *In* The Birds of North America, No. 21 (A. Poole, P. Stettenheim, and F. Gill, eds.). Acad. Nat. Sci., Philadelphia; Amer. Ornith. Union, Washington D.C.

Groskin, H. 1941. The invasion and wing measurements of the Purple Finch at Ardmore, Pa. *Bird-Banding* 12:8-16.

_____. 1947. Variations in color of the shoulders of the male Goldfinch. *Auk* 64:70-78.

Gross, A.O. 1921. The Dickcissel (*Spiza americana*) of the Illinois prairies. *Auk* 38:1-26.

Groth, J.G. 1988. Resolution of cryptic species in Appalachian Red Crossbills. *Condor* 90:745-760.

_____. 1993a. Evolutionary differentiation in morphology, vocalizations, and allozymes among nomadic sibling species in the North American Red Crossbill (*Loxia curvirostra*) complex. *Univ. California Pubs. Zool.* 127:1-143.

_____. 1993b. Call matching and positive assortative mating in Red Crossbills. *Auk* 110:398-401.

Grubb, T.C. Jr. 1991. A deficient diet narrows growth bars on induced feathers. *Auk* 108:725-727.

_____ and V.V. Pravosudov. 1994. Tufted Titmouse. *In* The Birds of North America, No. 86 (A. Poole and F. Gill, eds.). Acad. Nat. Sci., Philadelphia; Amer. Ornith. Union, Washington D.C.

Grzybowski, J.A. 1991. A closer look: Black-capped Vireo. *Am. Birds* 45:216-219.

_____. 1995. Black-capped Vireo. *In* The Birds of North America, No. 181 (A. Poole and F. Gill, eds.). Acad. Nat. Sci., Philadelphia; Amer. Ornith. Union, Washington D.C.

Gustafson, M. 1988. *Oporornis* eyerings. *Birding* 20:96-98.

Gutierrez, A.B., A.B. Franklin, and W.S. Lahaye. 1995. Spotted Owl. *In* The Birds of North America, No. 179 (A. Poole and F. Gill, eds.). Acad. Nat. Sci., Philadelphia; Amer. Ornith. Union, Washington D.C.

Haas, C.A. 1987. Eastern subspecies of the Loggerhead Shrike: The need for measurements of live birds. *N. Am. Bird Bander* 12:99-102.

Haas, F.C. 1990. Pacific-slope Flycatcher, *Empidonax difficilis*: Lancaster County. *Pennsylvania Birds* 5:156.

Haas, G.H. and S.R. Amend. 1976. Aging immature Mourning Doves by primary feather molt. *J. Wildl. Manage.* 40:575-578.

_____ and _____. 1979. Primary feather molt of adult Mourning Doves in North and South Carolina. *J. Wildl. Manage.* 43:202-207.

Haberman, K., D.I. MacKenzie, and J.D. Rising. 1991. Geographic variation in the Gray Kingbird. *J. Field. Ornith.* 62:117-131.

Haggerty, T.M. and E.S. Morton. 1995. Carolina Wren. *In* The Birds of North America, No. 188 (A. Poole and F. Gill, eds.). Acad. Nat. Sci., Philadelphia; Amer. Ornith. Union, Washington D.C.

Hahn, T.P. 1996. Cassin's Finch. *In* The Birds of North America, No. 240 (A. Poole and F. Gill, eds.). Acad. Nat. Sci., Philadelphia; Amer. Ornith. Union, Washington D.C.

Hailman, J.P. and S. Haftorn. 1995. Siberian Tit. *In* The Birds of North America, No. 196 (A. Poole and F. Gill, eds.). Acad. Nat. Sci., Philadelphia; Amer. Ornith. Union, Washington D.C.

Hall, G.A. 1979. Hybridization between Mourning and MacGillivray's warblers. *Bird-Banding* 50:101-107.

_____. 1994. Magnolia Warbler. *In* The Birds of North America, No. 136 (A. Poole and F. Gill, eds.). Acad. Nat. Sci., Philadelphia; Amer. Ornith. Union, Washington D.C.

_____. 1996. Yellow-throated Warbler. *In* The Birds of North America, No. 223 (A. Poole and F. Gill, eds.). Acad. Nat. Sci., Philadelphia; Amer. Ornith. Union, Washington D.C.

Haller, K.W. 1940. A new wood warbler from West Virginia. *Cardinal* 5:49-53.

Hamas, M.J. 1994. Belted Kingfisher. *In* The Birds of North America, No. 84 (A. Poole and F. Gill, eds.). Acad. Nat. Sci., Philadelphia; Amer. Ornith. Union, Washington D.C.

Hamel, P.B. 1995. Bachman's Warbler. *In* The Birds of North America, No. 150 (A. Poole and F. Gill, eds.). Acad. Nat. Sci., Philadelphia; Amer. Ornith. Union, Washington D.C.

_____, J.L. Beacham, and A.E. Ross. 1983. A laboratory study of cranial pneumatization in Indigo Buntings. *J. Field Ornith.* 54:58-66.

_____ and S.A. Gauthreaux Jr. 1982. The field identification of Bachman's Warbler (*Vermivora bachmanii* Audubon). *Am. Birds* 36:235-240.

_____ and M.K. Klimkiewicz. 1981. Standard abbreviations for common names of birds - revisited. *N. Am. Bird Bander* 6:46.

_____ and S.J. Wagner. 1990. Laboratory and field investigation of skull pneumatization in Song and Swamp sparrows. *J. Field Ornith.* 61:34-40.

Hamer, T.E., E.D. Forsman, A.D. Fuchs, and W.L. Walters. 1994. Hybridization between Barred and Spotted owls. *Auk* 111:487-492.

Hamilton, T.H. 1958. Adaptive variation in the genus *Vireo*. *Wilson Bull.* 70:307-346.

_____. 1961. The adaptive significances of intraspecific trends of variation in wing length and body size among bird species. *Evolution* 15:180-195.

Hanson, H.C. and C.W. Kossack. 1963. The Mourning Dove in Illinois. *Illinois Dept. Cons. Tech. Bull.* 2:1-133.

Hansrote, C. and M. Hansrote. 1995. Spring wing chord values for American Goldfinches. *N. Am. Bird Bander* 20:5-10.

Hardy, J.W. 1973. Age and sex differences in the black-and-blue jays of Middle America. *Bird-Banding* 44:81-90.

Harkins, C.E. 1937. Harris's Sparrow in its winter range. *Wilson Bull.* 49:286-292.

Harley, G.F. and J.W. Jones II. 1983. A presumed mixed Bay-breasted × Blackburnian nesting in West Virginia. *Redstart* 50:108-111.

Harper, F. 1926. A new Marsh Wren from Alberta. *Occ. Papers Boston Soc. Nat. Hist.* 5:221-222.

_____. 1934. The Boat-tailed Grackle of the Atlantic Coast. *Proc. Acad. Sci. Philadelphia* 86:1-2.

Harrap, S. and D. Quinn. 1995. Chickadees, tits, nuthatches and treecreepers. Christopher Helm, London.

Harris, R.D. 1944. The Chestnut-collared Longspur in Manitoba. *Wilson Bull.* 56:105-115.

Hartert, E. and A. Goodson. 1917. Notes and descriptions of South American birds. *Nov. Zool.* 24:410-419.

Hawbecker, A.C. 1948. Analysis of variation in western races of the White-breasted Nuthatch. *Condor* 50:26-39.

Hawkins, R.W. 1948. A new western race of the nighthawk. *Condor* 50:131-132.

Hawthorn, I. 1972. Some differences between juvenile, first year and adult wrens. *The Ringers Bulletin* 3:9-11. [Reprinted in *E. Bird Banding Assoc. News* 35:35-38.]

Hayward, G.D. and P.H. Hayward. 1991. Body measurements of Boreal Owls in Idaho and a discriminant model to determine sex of live specimens. *Wilson Bull.* 103:497-500.

Heimerdinger, M.A. 1955. A possible case of polymorphism in the Lead-colored Bushtit. *Wilson Bull.* 67:133.

Heindel, M.T. 1996. Field identification of the Solitary Vireo complex. *Birding* 28:458-471.

Heinrich, B. 1994. When is the Common Raven black? *Wilson Bull.* 106:571-572.

_____ and J. Marzluff. 1992. Age and mouth color in Common Ravens. *Condor* 94:549-550.

Hekstra, G.P. 1982. Descriptions of twenty-four new subspecies of North American owls (Aves: Strigidae). *Bull. Zool. Mus. Univ. Amsterdam* 9:49-63.

Hendrik, H. 1994. Oregon's first Streak-backed Oriole. *Oregon Birds* 20:39-41.

Henny, C.J. and L.F. Van Camp. 1979. Annual weight cycle in wild screech owls. *Auk* 96:795-796.

Herremans, M. 1990. Taxonomy and evolution in redpolls *Carduelis flammea-hornemanni*; a multivariate study of their biometry. *Ardea* 78:441-458.

Hertzel, A. and P. Hertzel. 1995. A possible hybrid Blackpoll Warbler in western Minnesota. *Loon* 67:166-171.

Heydweiller, A.M. 1936. Sex, age and individual variation of winter Tree Sparrows. *Bird-Banding* 7:61-68. [Reprinted in *Passenger Pigeon* 46:143-145, 1984.]

Hicks, L.E. 1934. Individual and sexual variations in the European Starling. *Bird-Banding* 5:103-118.

Hill, D.P. and L.K. Gould. 1997. Chestnut-collared Longspur. *In* The Birds of North America, No. **288** (A. Poole and F. Gill, eds.). Acad. Nat. Sci., Philadelphia; Amer. Ornith. Union, Washington D.C.

Hill, G.E. 1987. Aging and sexing Black-headed Grosbeaks in alternate plumage. *J. Field Ornith.* 58:311-317.

_____. 1988a. The function of delayed plumage maturation in male Black-headed Grosbeaks. *Auk* 105:1-10.

_____. 1988b. Age, plumage brightness, territory quality, and reproductive success in the Black-headed Grosbeak. *Condor* 90:379-388.

_____. 1992. Proximate basis of variation in carotenoid pigmentation in male House Finches. *Auk* 109:1-12.

_____. 1993a. Geographic variation in carotenoid plumage pigmentation of House Finches. *Biol. J. Linnean Soc.* 49:63-86.

_____. 1993b. House Finch. *In* The Birds of North America, No. **46** (A. Poole and F. Gill, eds.). Acad. Nat. Sci., Philadelphia; Amer. Ornith. Union, Washington D.C.

_____. 1993c. The proximate basis of inter- and intra-population variation in female plumage coloration in the House Finch. *Can. J. Zool.* 71:619-627.

_____. 1994. Testis mass and subadult plumage in Black-headed Grosbeaks. *Condor* 96:626-630.

_____. 1995. Black-headed Grosbeak. *In* The Birds of North America, No. **143** (A. Poole and F. Gill, eds.). Acad. Nat. Sci., Philadelphia; Amer. Ornith. Union, Washington D.C.

_____. 1996. Subadult plumage in the House Finch and tests of models for the evolution of delayed plumage maturation. *Auk* 113:858-874.

_____, R. Montgomerie, C. Inouye, and J. Dale. 1994. Influence of dietary carotenoids on plasma and plumage color in the House Finch: Intra- and intersexual variation. *Funct. Ecol.* 8:343-350.

Hill, R.A. 1976. Sex ratio and sex determination of immature Brown-headed Cowbirds. *Bird-Banding* 47:112-114.

Holcomb, L.C. 1975. Incubation patch fluctuations in Red-winged Blackbirds. *Condor* 77:506-509.

Holmes, R.T. 1994. Black-throated Blue Warbler. *In* The Birds of North America, No. **87** (A. Poole and F. Gill, eds.). Acad. Nat. Sci., Philadelphia; Amer. Ornith. Union, Washington D.C.

_____, T.W. Sherry, P.P. Marra and K.E. Petit. 1992. Multiple brooding and productivity of a neotropical migrant, the Black-throated Blue Warbler (*Dendroica caerulescens*), in an unfragmented temperate forest. *Auk* 109:321-333.

Hoover, E. 1973. Adult Red-headed Woodpecker retains juvenile coloration in its plumage. *Inl. Bird Banding News* 45:15.

Hopp, S.L., A. Kirby, and C.A. Boone. 1995. White-eyed Vireo. *In* The Birds of North America, No. **168** (A. Poole and F. Gill, eds.). Acad. Nat. Sci., Philadelphia; Amer. Ornith. Union, Washington D.C.

Hörnfeldt, B., B.G. Carlsson, and Ä. Nordström. 1988. Molt of primaries and age determination in Tengmalm's Owl (*Aegolius funereus*). *Auk* 105:783-789.

Houston, C.S. 1963. Redpoll identification - a problem. *Bird-Banding* 34:94-95.

Howard, D.V. 1968. Criteria for aging and sexing Bay-breasted Warblers in the fall. *Bird-Banding* 39:132.

Howard, G.E., A. McCormick, and P.B. Hamel. 1989. Measurements of 677 Pine Siskins banded one spring in South Carolina. *N. Am. Bird Bander* 14:9-10.

Howard, R. and A. Moore. 1994. A complete checklist of the birds of the world. 2nd ed. Academic Press, London.

Howe, M.A., R.C. Laybourne, and F.C. James. 1977. Morphological variation in breeding Red-winged Blackbirds, *Agelaius phoeniceus*, in Florida. *Florida Scientist* 40:273-280.

Howe, R.H. 1901. A new subspecies of *Passerculus sandwichensis*. *Contr. N. Am. Ornith.* 1:1-2.

Howell, A.H. 1913. Description of two new birds from Alabama. *Proc. Biol. Soc. Washington* 26:199-202.

_____. 1919. Description of a new Seaside Sparrow from Florida. *Auk* 36:86-87.

_____. 1930. Description of a new subspecies of the Prairie Warbler with remarks on two other unrecognized Florida races. *Auk* 47:41-43.

_____. 1932. Florida bird life. Coward-McCann Inc., New York, NY.

_____ and A.J. van Rossem. 1928. A study of the Red-winged Blackbirds of southeastern United States. *Auk* 45:155-163.

Howell, S.N.G. 1987. More about gnatcatchers. *Birding* 19(4):16-17.

_____. 1990. Identification of White and Black-backed wagtails in alternate plumage. *W. Birds* 21:41-49.

_____ and P. Pyle. 1997. Twentieth report of the California Bird Records Committee. *W. Birds* 28:117-144.

_____ and S. Webb. 1994. Field identification of *Myiarchus* flycatchers in Mexico. *Cotinga* 2:20-25.

_____ and _____. 1995. A guide to the birds of Mexico and northern Central America. Oxford Univ. Press, Oxford, U.K.

Howell, T.R. 1952. Natural history and differentiation in the Yellow-bellied Sapsucker. *Condor* 54:237-282.

_____. 1953. Racial and sexual differences in migration in *Sphyrapicus varius*. *Auk* 70:118-126.

Hoyt, J.S.Y. 1944. Preliminary notes on the development of nestling Pileated Woodpeckers. *Auk* 61:376-384.

Hoyt, S.F. 1953. Forehead color of the Pileated Woodpecker (*Dryocopus pileatus*). *Auk* 70:209-210.

Hubbard, J.P. 1965a. The summer birds of the forests of the Mogollon Mountains, New Mexico. *Condor* 67:404-415.

_____. 1965b. Migration of the Black-throated Blue Warbler in southern Michigan. *Jack-Pine Warbler* 43:162-163.

_____. 1969. The relationships and evolution of the *Dendroica coronata* complex. *Auk* 86:393-432.

_____. 1970a. Mensural separation of Black-capped and Carolina chickadees. *E. Bird Banding Assoc. News* 33:211-213.

_____. 1970b. Geographic variation in the *Dendroica coronata* complex. *Wilson Bull.* 82:355-369.

_____. 1972a. Notes on Arizona birds. *Nemouria* 5:1-22.

_____. 1972b. The nomenclature of *Pipilo aberti* Baird (Aves: Fringillidae). *Proc. Biol. Soc. Washington* 85:131-138.

_____. 1972c. Identification of wintering orioles in the northeast. *Delmarva Ornith.* 7:10-12. [Reprinted in *E. Bird Banding Assoc. News* 37:70-73, 1974.]

_____. 1974. Geographic variation in the Savannah Sparrows of the inland Southwest, Mexico, and Guatemala. *Nemouria* 12:1-21.

_____. 1975. Geographic variation in non-California populations of the Rufous-crowned Sparrow. *Nemouria* 15:1-13.

_____. 1978. The status of the Northern Shrike in New Mexico. *W. Birds* 9:159-168.

_____. 1980. The extent and sequence of the molts of the Yellow-rumped Warbler. *Nemouria* 25:1-9.

_____. 1983. The tail pattern of meadowlarks in New Mexico. *New Mexico Ornith. Soc. Bull.* 11:61-66.

_____ and R.C. Banks. 1970. The types and taxa of Harold H. Bailey. *Proc. Biol. Soc. Washington* 83:321-332.

_____ and R.S. Crossin. 1974. Notes on northern Mexican birds. *Nemouria* 14:1-41.

Huels, T.R. 1985. Cave Swallow paired with Cliff Swallows. *Condor* 87:441-442.

Huey, L.M. 1930. Comment on the Marsh Sparrows of Southern and Lower California, with the description of a new race. *Trans. San Diego Soc. Nat. Hist.* 6:203-206.

_____. 1940. A new cardinal from central Lower California, Mexico. *Trans. San Diego Soc. Nat. Hist.* 9:215-217.

_____. 1944. A hybrid Costa's × Broad-tailed hummingbird. *Auk* 61:636-637.

Hughes, J.M. 1996. Greater Roadrunner. *In* The Birds of North America, No. **244** (A. Poole and F. Gill, eds.). Acad. Nat. Sci., Philadelphia; Amer. Ornith. Union, Washington D.C.

Humphrey, P.S. and K.C. Parkes. 1959. An approach to the study of molts and plumages. *Auk* 76:1-31.

_____ and _____. 1963. Comments on the study of plumage succession. *Auk* 80:496-503.

Hunt, L.B. 1994. Wing chord differences in Common Grackles relating to sex and age. *N. Am. Bird Bander* 19:52-55.

Huntington, C.E. 1952. Hybridization in the Purple Grackle *Quiscalus quiscula. Syst. Zool.* 1:149-170.

Hussell, D.J.T. 1980. The timing of fall migration and molt in Least Flycatchers. *J. Field Ornith.* 51:65-71.

____. 1982a. The timing of fall migration in Yellow-bellied Flycatchers. *J. Field Ornith.* 53:1-6.

____. 1982b. Migrations of the Yellow-bellied Flycatcher in southern Ontario. *J. Field Ornith.* 53:223-224.

____. 1983. Age and plumage color in female Tree Swallows. *J. Field Ornith.* 54:312-318.

____. 1990. Implications for age-dependent bill length variation in *Empidonax* for identification of immature Alder and Willow flycatchers. *J. Field Ornith.* 61:54-63.

____. 1991a. Spring migrations of Alder and Willow flycatchers in southern Ontario. *J. Field Ornith.* 62:69-77.

____. 1991b. Fall migrations of Alder and Willow flycatchers in southern Ontario. *J. Field Ornith.* 62:260-270.

Hyde, A.S. 1939. The life history of Henslow's Sparrow, *Passerherbulus henslowi* (Audubon). *Misc. Pubs. Mus. Zool. Univ. Michigan* 41:1-80.

Inger, R.F. 1961. Problems in the application of the subspecies concept in vertebrate taxonomy. Pp. 262-285 *in* W.F. Blair, ed., Vertebrate speciation. Univ. Texas Press, Austin, TX.

Ingold, J.L. 1993. Blue Grosbeak. *In* The Birds of North America, No. **79** (A. Poole and F. Gill, eds.). Acad. Nat. Sci., Philadelphia; Amer. Ornith. Union, Washington D.C.

Ivor, H.R. 1944. Bird study and semi-captive birds: The Rose-breasted Grosbeak. *Wilson Bull.* 56:91-104.

Jackson, C.H.W. 1992. A cautionary note on the ageing of firecrests *Regulus ignicapillus* using rectrix shape. *Ringing & Migr.* 13:127.

Jackson, J.A. 1971. The evolution, taxonomy, past populations and current status of the Red-cockaded Woodpecker. Pp. 4-29 *in* R.L. Thompson, ed., The ecology and management of the Red-cockaded Woodpecker. Tall Timbers Research Station, Tallahassee, FL.

____. 1979. Age characteristics of Red-cockaded Woodpeckers. *Bird-Banding* 50:23-29.

____. 1994. Red-cockaded Woodpecker. *In* The Birds of North America, No. **85** (A. Poole and F. Gill, eds.). Acad. Nat. Sci., Philadelphia; Amer. Ornith. Union, Washington D.C.

Jackson, W.M., C.S. Wood, and S. Rohwer. 1992. Age-specific plumage characters and annual molt cycles of Hermit Warblers and Townsend's Warblers. *Condor* 94:490-501.

James, D. 1987. The "aberrant" Downy Woodpecker plumage was a normal juvenile. *N. Am. Bird Bander* 12:78.

James, F.C. 1970. Geographic variation in birds and its relationship to climate. *Ecology* 51:366-390.

____, R.T. Engstrom, C. NeSmith, and R.C. Laybourne. 1984. Inferences about population movements of Red-winged Blackbirds from morphological data. *Am. Midland Nat.* 111:319-331.

Janos, M. and I. Prather. 1989. A second specimen record of Lesser Nighthawk (*Chordeiles acutipennis*) from Colorado, with some notes on its occurrence and identification. *Colorado Field Ornith. J.* 23:134-138.

Jaramillo, A. 1993. Subspecific identification of Yellow-throated Warblers. *Birder's J.* 2:160.

Jehl, J.R. Jr. 1959. Identification of immature cuckoos. *E. Bird Banding Assoc. News* 22:102-103.

____. 1968a. Geographic and seasonal variation in Smith's Longspur. *Trans. San Diego Soc. Nat Hist.* 15:1-5.

____. 1968b. The breeding biology of Smith's Longspur. *Wilson Bull.* 80:123-149.

Jenks, R. 1936. A new race of Golden-crowned Kinglet from Arizona. *Condor* 38:239-244.

____. 1938. A new subspecies of Pine Grosbeak from Arizona with critical notes on other races. *Condor* 40:28-35.

Jenni, L. and R. Winkler. 1989. The feather length of small passerines: A measurement for wing length in live birds and museum skins. *Bird Study* 36:1-15.

____ and ____. 1994. Moult and ageing of European passerines. Academic Press, New York, NY.

Jeter, H.H. 1959. Cliff Swallows of mixed plumage types in a colony in southeastern Arizona. *Condor* 61:434.

Jett, G.M. 1991. Recycling road- and window-killed birds. *Birding* 23:28-29.

Jewell, S.D. 1986. Weights and wing lengths in Connecticut Blue Jays. *Connecticut Warbler* 6:47-49.

Jewett, S.G. 1943. A new Horned Lark from the state of Washington. *Auk* 60:262-263.

____. 1944a. A new wren from the state of Washington. *Auk* 61:288.

____. 1944b. Hybridization between Hermit and Townsend's warblers. *Condor* 46:23-24.

____, W.P. Taylor, W.T. Shaw, and J.W. Aldrich. 1953. Birds of Washington State. University of Washington Press, Seattle, WA.

Johnsen, T.S., J.D. Hengeveld, J.L. Blank, K. Yasukawa, and V. Nolan Jr. 1996. Epaulet brightness and condition in female Red-winged Blackbirds. *Auk* 113:356-362.

Johnson, J.C. 1972. 1970 Ruby-throated Hummingbird activities. *Inl. Bird Banding News* 44:211-224.

Johnson, L.G. and W. Moskoff. 1995. First hybridization attempt between a Violet-green Swallow and Tree Swallow. *Meadowlark* 4:2-3.

Johnson, N.K. 1963a. Biosystematics of sibling species of flycatchers in the *Empidonax hammondii-oberholseri-wrightii* complex. *Univ. California Pubs. Zool.* 66:79-238.

____. 1963b. Comparative molt cycles in the Tyrannid genus *Empidonax. Proc. XIIIth Int. Ornith. Congr.* 1963:870-883.

____. 1966a. Morphologic stability versus adaptive variation in the Hammond's Flycatcher. *Auk* 83:179-200.

____. 1966b. Bill size and the question of competition in allopatric and sympatric populations of Dusky and Gray flycatchers. *Syst. Zool.* 15:70-87.

____. 1974. Molt and age determination in Western and Yellowish flycatchers. *Auk* 91:111-131.

____. 1980. Character variation and evolution of sibling species in the *Empidonax difficilis-flavescens* complex (Aves: Tyrannidae). *Univ. California Pubs. Zool.* 112:1-151.

____. 1994. Old-school taxonomy versus modern biosystematics: Species-level decisions in *Stelgidopteryx* and *Empidonax. Auk* 111:773-780.

____. 1995. Speciation in vireos. I. Macrogeographic patterns of allozymic variation in the *Vireo solitarius* complex in the contiguous United States. *Condor* 97:903-919.

____ and C.B. Johnson. 1985. Speciation in sapsuckers (*Sphyrapicus*): II. Sympatry, hybridization, and mate preference in S. *ruber daggetti* and S. *nuchalis. Auk* 102:1-15.

____ and R.E. Jones. 1993. The Green Jay turns blue in Peru: Interrelated aspects of the annual cycle in the arid tropical zone. *Wilson Bull.* 105:389-398.

____ and J.A. Marten. 1992. Macrogeographic patterns of morphometric and genetic variation in the Sage Sparrow complex. *Condor* 94:1-19.

____ and R.M. Zink. 1983. Speciation in sapsuckers (*Sphyrapicus*): I. Genetic differentiation. *Auk* 100:871-884.

____ and ____. 1985. Genetic evidence for relationships among the Red-eyed, Yellow-green and Chivi vireos. *Wilson Bull.* 97:421-435.

Johnson, P.N. 1991. Development of talon flange and serrations in the Barn Owl *Tyto alba*: A guide to ageing. *Ringing & Migr.* 12:126-127.

Johnson, R.E. 1977. Seasonal variation in the genus *Leucosticte* in North America. *Condor* 79:76-86.

Johnson, R.R. and L.T. Haight. 1996. Canyon Towhee. *In* The Birds of North America, No. **264** (A. Poole and F. Gill, eds.). Acad. Nat. Sci., Philadelphia; Amer. Ornith. Union, Washington D.C.

Johnston, D.W. 1958. Sex and age characters and salivary glands of the Chimney Swift. *Condor* 60:73-84.

____. 1961. The biosystematics of American Crows. University of Washington Press, Seattle, WA.

____. 1967. The identification of autumnal Indigo Buntings. *Bird-banding* 38:211-214.

____. 1971. Ecological aspects of hybridizing chickadees (*Parus*) in Virginia. *Am. Midland Nat.* 85:124-134.

____. 1976. Races of Palm Warbler killed at a Florida TV tower. *Florida Field Nat.* 4:22-24.

____ and A.C. Downer. 1968. Migratory features of the Indigo Bunting in Jamaica and Florida. *Bird-Banding* 39:277-293.

Johnston, R.F. 1962. Precocious sexual competence in the Ground Dove. *Auk* 79:269-270.

____. 1966. The adaptive basis of geographic variation in color of the Purple Martin. *Condor* 68:219-228.

____. 1967. Sexual dimorphism in juvenile House Sparrows. *Auk* 84:275-277.

____. 1973. Evolution in the House Sparrow. IV. Replicate studies in phenetic covariation. *Syst. Zool.* 22:219-226.

____ and R.K. Selander. 1964. House Sparrows: Rapid evolution of races in North America. *Science* 144:548-550.

____ and ____. 1971. Evolution in the House Sparrow. II. Adaptive differentiation in North American populations. *Evolution* 25:1-28.

____ and ____. 1972. Variation, adaption, and evolution in the North American House Sparrows. Pp 301-326 *in* S.C Kendeigh and J. Pinowski, eds., Productivity, population dynamics and systematics of granivorous birds. Institute of Ecology, Warsaw, Poland.

____ and ____. 1973. Evolution in the House Sparrow. III. Variation in size and sexual dimorphism in Europe, North and South America. *Am. Nat.* 107:373-390.

Jollie, M. 1953. Plumages, molt and racial status of Red Crossbills in northern Idaho. *Condor* 55:193-197.

Jones, E.G. 1992. Color variation in maturing male Rufous Hummingbirds. *N. Am. Bird Bander* 17:119-120.

Jones, E.G. 1993. Throat patterns of female Rufous Hummingbirds. *N. Am. Bird Bander* 18:13-14.

Jones, L. 1930. The sequence of molt. *Wilson Bull.* 42:97-102.

Jones, M. 1984. A revised key for House Finches. *The Texas Bander* 6:3-4.

Jones, P.W. and T.M. Donovan. 1996. Hermit Thrush. *In* The Birds of North America, No. **261** (A. Poole and F. Gill, eds.). Acad. Nat. Sci., Philadelphia; Amer. Ornith. Union, Washington D.C.

Jones, R.E. The incubation patch of birds. *Biol. Review* 46:315-339.

Jones, S.L. and J.S. Dieni. 1995. Canyon Wren. *In* The Birds of North America, No. **197** (A. Poole and F. Gill, eds.). Acad. Nat. Sci., Philadelphia; Amer. Ornith. Union, Washington D.C.

Josephson, B. 1980. Aging and sexing Snowy Owls. *J. Field Ornith.* 51:149-160.

Jung, R.E., E.S. Morton, and R.C. Fleischer. 1994. Behavior and parentage of a White-throated Sparrow × Dark-eyed Junco hybrid. *Wilson Bull.* 106:189-202.

Kale, H.W. 1966. Plumages and molts in the Long-billed Marsh Wren. *Auk* 83:140-141.

_____. 1983. Distribution, habitat and status of breeding Seaside Sparrows in Florida. Pp. 41-48 *in* T.L. Quay *et al.*, eds., The Seaside Sparrow, its biology and management. *Occ. Papers North Carolina Biol. Surv.*, Raleigh, NC.

Katholi, C. 1966. Titmouse postjuvenal molt. *E. Bird Banding Assoc. News* 29:200.

Kaufman, K. 1979a. Field identification of the flicker forms and their hybrids in North America. *Cont. Birdlife* 1:4-15.

_____. 1979b. Field identification of Hutton's Vireo. *Cont. Birdlife* 1:62-66.

_____. 1979c. Identifying "Myrtle" and "Audubon's" warblers out of breeding plumage. *Cont. Birdlife* 1:89-92.

_____. 1979d. Comments on the Peninsular Yellowthroat. *Cont. Birdlife* 1:38-42.

_____. 1983. Identifying Streak-backed Orioles: A note of caution. *Am. Birds* 37:140-141.

_____. 1986. The practiced eye. Cassin's Finch versus Purple Finch. *Am. Birds* 40:1124-1126.

_____. 1987a. Spotted Owl and Barred Owl compared. *Am. Birds* 41:355-356.

_____. 1987b. Notes on female orioles. *Am. Birds* 41:1-3.

_____. 1988a. Red-naped Sapsucker and Yellow-bellied Sapsucker. *Am. Birds* 42:348-350.

_____. 1988b. Notes on female tanagers. *Am. Birds* 42:3-5.

_____. 1989. Cassin's and Botteri's sparrows. *Birding* 21:293-297.

_____. 1990a. Advanced birding. Houghton Mifflin Co., Boston.

_____. 1990b. Scrub Jay and Gray-breasted Jay. *Am. Birds* 44:5-6.

_____. 1991a. A flicker of recognition: Three distinct forms, and their offspring. *Am. Birds* 45:1172-1175.

_____. 1991b. Yellow Warbler and its I.D. contenders. *Am. Birds* 45:167-170.

_____. 1992a. Lucifer Hummingbird identification. *Am. Birds* 46:491-494.

_____. 1992b. Western Kingbird identification. *Am. Birds* 46:323-326.

_____. 1992c. Bluebirds. *Am. Birds* 46:159-162.

_____. 1993a. Identifying the Hairy Woodpecker. *Am. Birds* 47:311-314.

_____. 1993b. Identifying Hutton's Vireo. *Am. Birds* 47:460-462.

_____. 1993c. Answers to the August photo quiz. *Birding* 25:339-342.

_____. 1993d. Notes on goldfinch identification. *Am. Birds* 47:159-162.

_____ and R. Bowers. 1989. Comparing the screech-owls. *Am. Birds* 43:203-206.

_____ and _____. 1990. Curve-billed Thrasher and Bendire's Thrasher. *Am. Birds* 44:359-362.

Keith, L.B. 1960. Observations on Snowy Owls at Delta, Manitoba. *Can. Field-Nat.* 74:106-112.

Keith, R. 1986. Hammond's Flycatcher in Kent County, Delaware. *Cassinia* 62:64-65.

Kelso, L. 1950. The post juvenal molt of the northeastern screech owl. *Biol. Leaflet* 50:1-3.

Kemper, T. 1959. Notes on the breeding cycle of the Red Crossbill (*Loxia curvirostra*) in Montana. *Auk* 76:181-189.

Kemsies, E. 1961. Subspeciation in the Smith's Longspur, *Calcarius pictus. Can. Field-Nat.* 75:143-149.

Kennard, J.H. 1959. Occurrence of pink coloration in adult female Purple Finches. *Auk* 76:363-364.

_____. 1962. Further notes on the occurrence of pink coloration in Purple Finches. *Bird-Banding* 33:90-92.

Kerlinger, P. and M.R. Lein. 1986. Differences in winter range among age-sex classes of Snowy Owls *Nyctea scandiaca* in North America. *Ornis Scand.* 17:1-7.

Kertell, K. 1986. Reproductive biology of Northern Hawk-Owls in Denali National Park, Alaska. *Raptor Res.* 20:91-101.

Kessel, B. 1951. Criteria for sexing and aging European Starlings (*Sturnus vulgaris*). *Bird-Banding* 22:16-23.

_____. 1957. A study of the breeding biology of the European Starling (*Sturnus vulgaris* L.) in North America. *Am. Midland Nat.* 58:257-331.

Ketterson, E.D. 1979. Aggressive behavior in wintering Dark-eyed Juncos: Determinants of dominance and their possible relation to geographic variation in sex ratio. *Wilson Bull.* 91:371-383.

_____ and V. Nolan Jr. 1976. Geographic variation and its climatic correlates in the sex ratio of eastern wintering Dark-eyed Juncos. *Ecology* 57:679-693.

_____ and _____. 1982. The role of migration and winter mortality in the life history of a temperate-zone migrant, the Dark-eyed Junco, as determined from demographic analyses of winter populations. *Auk* 99:243-259.

_____ and _____. 1986. Effect of laparotomy of Tree Sparrows and Dark-eyed Juncos during winter on subsequent survival in the field. *J. Field Ornith.* 57:239-240.

Kilgore, W. and W.J. Breckenridge. 1929. Connecticut Warbler nesting in Minnesota. *Auk* 46:551-552.

King, B. 1981. The field identification of North American pipits. *Am. Birds* 35:778-788.

Kingery, H.E. 1996. American Dipper. *In* The Birds of North America, No. **229** (A. Poole and F. Gill, eds.). Acad. Nat. Sci., Philadelphia; Amer. Ornith. Union, Washington D.C.

Klimkiewicz, M.K. 1980. Notes from the BBL. *N. Am. Bird Bander* 5:96.

_____ and C.S. Robbins. 1978. Standard abbreviations for common names of birds. *N. Am. Bird Bander* 3:16-25.

Knapton, R.W. 1978. Sex and age determination in the Clay-colored Sparrow. *Bird-Banding* 49:152-156.

Knox, A. 1988a. Taxonomy of the Rock/Water pipit superspecies *Anthus petrosus, spinoletta* and *rubescens. Brit. Birds* 81:206-211.

_____. 1988b. The taxonomy of redpolls. *Ardea* 76:1-26.

_____. 1994. Species and subspecies. *Brit. Birds* 87:51-58.

_____. 1996. Gray-cheeked and Bicknell's thrushes: Taxonomy, identification and the British and Irish records. *Brit. Birds* 89:1-9.

Koelz, W.N. 1939. Three new subspecies of birds. *Proc. Biol. Soc. Washington* 52:121-122.

_____. 1954. Ornithological studies. II. A new subspecies of Red-bellied Woodpecker from Texas. *Contr. Inst. Reg. Expl.* 1:32.

Koenig, W.D. 1980. Variation and age determination in a population of Acorn Woodpeckers. *J. Field Ornith.* 51:10-16.

_____, P.B. Stacey, M.T. Stanback, and R.L. Mumme. 1995. Acorn Woodpecker. *In* The Birds of North America, No. **194** (A. Poole and F. Gill, eds.). Acad. Nat. Sci., Philadelphia; Amer. Ornith. Union, Washington D.C.

Kolb, H. 1980. Another Dark-eyed Junco with 13 rectrices. *North Am. Bird Bander* 5:51.

_____. 1986. Occurrence of white in the wing coverts of Dark-eyed Juncos. *N. Am. Bird Bander* 11:88-89.

Korpimäki, E. 1987. Sexual size dimorphism and life-history traits of Tengmalm's Owl: A review. Pp 157-161 *in* R.W. Nero, R.J. Clark, R.J. Knapton, and R.H. Hamre, eds., Biology and conservation of northern forest owls. U.S. For. Serv. Gen. Tech. Rep. RM-142.

_____. 1990. Body mass of breeding Tengmalm's Owls *Aegolius funereus*: Seasonal, between-year, site and age-related variation. *Ornis Scand.* 21:169-178.

Kowalski, M.P. 1983. Identifying Mourning and MacGillivray's warblers: Geographic variation in the MacGillivray's Warbler as a source of error. *N. Am. Bird Bander* 8:56-57.

_____. 1986. Weights and measurements of Prothonotary Warblers from southern Indiana, with a method of aging males. *N. Am. Bird Bander* 11:129-131.

Kricher, J.C. 1995. Black-and-white Warbler. *In* The Birds of North America, No. **158** (A. Poole and F. Gill, eds.). Acad. Nat. Sci., Philadelphia; Amer. Ornith. Union, Washington D.C.

Kroodsma, R.L. 1974. Hybridization in grosbeaks (*Pheucticus*) in North Dakota. *Wilson Bull.* 86:230-236.

_____. 1975. Hybridization in buntings (*Passerina*) in North Dakota and eastern Montana. *Auk* 92:66-80.

Kuenzel, W.J. and C.W. Helms. 1974. An annual cycle study of tan-striped and white-striped White-throated Sparrows. *Auk* 91:44-53.

Kuerzi, R.G. 1941. Life history studies of the Tree Swallow. *Proc. Linnean Soc.* 52-53:1-52.

Lack, D. 1940. Variation in the introduced English Sparrow. *Condor* 42:239-241.

_____. 1956. A review of the genera and nesting habits of swifts. *Auk* 73:1-32.

_____. 1957. The first primary in swifts. *Auk* 74:385-386.

LaFrance, F. 1983. Adirondack woodpeckers in unusual plumages. *Kingbird* 33:165-166.

Lago, P.K. 1979. Notes on wing length and sex ratio in Evening Grosbeaks. *Inland Bird Banding* 51:11-13.

Lamb, W.A., A.H. Kelley, and S.M. Cohen. 1978. Age determination of Blue Jays. *Bird-Banding* 49:215-217.

Lamm, D.W. 1991. Lucy's Warbler banding in southeastern Arizona. *N. Am. Bird Bander* 16:9-10.

_____ and J.C. Luepke. 1982. Iris changes in hatching year Yellow-eyed Juncos. *N. Am. Bird Bander* 7:93.

Landing, J.E. 1991. On Yellow-bellied Sapsuckers with red napes. *Birding* 23:20-22.

_____ and S. Patti. 1986. Cassin's Sparrow in Chicago, Illinois, 1983, Indiana, 1984, and notes on field identification of Cassin's, Botteri's and Bachman's sparrows. *Indiana Audubon Quart.* 64:122-126.

Lane, J. 1968. A hybrid Eastern × Mountain bluebird. *Auk* 85:684.

Langridge, H.P. 1986. More on Lesser and Common nighthawks. *Birding* 18:208.

Lanyon, W.E. 1957. The comparative biology of the meadowlarks (*Sturnella*) in Wisconsin. *Publ. Nuttall Ornith. Club* 1:1-67.

_____. 1960a. The middle American populations of the Crested Flycatcher *Myiarchus tyrannulus*. *Condor* 62:341-350.

_____. 1960b. Relationship of the House Wren (*Troglodytes aedon*) of North America and the Brown-throated Wren (*Troglodytes brunneicollis*) of Mexico. *Proc. XII Ornith. Congr.* 1958:450-458.

_____. 1961. Specific limits and distribution of Ash-throated and Nutting flycatchers. *Condor* 63:421-449.

_____. 1962. Specific limits and distribution of meadowlarks on the desert grassland. *Auk* 79:183-207.

_____. 1963. Notes on the race of the Ash-throated Flycatcher, *Myiarchus cinerascens pertinax*, of Baja California. *Am. Mus. Novitates* 2129:1-7.

_____. 1966. Hybridization in meadowlarks. *Bull. Am. Mus. Nat. Hist.* 134:1-25.

_____. 1975. Evidence of an incomplete prealternate molt in some South American *Myiarchus* flycatchers. *Condor* 77:511.

_____. 1994. Western Meadowlark. *In* The Birds of North America, No. 104 (A. Poole and F. Gill, eds.). Acad. Nat. Sci., Philadelphia; Amer. Ornith. Union, Washington D.C.

_____. 1995. Eastern Meadowlark. *In* The Birds of North America, No. 160 (A. Poole and F. Gill, eds.). Acad. Nat. Sci., Philadelphia; Amer. Ornith. Union, Washington D.C.

_____ and J. Bull. 1967. Identification of Connecticut, Mourning, and MacGillivray's warblers. *Bird-Banding* 38:187-194.

Laskey, F.C. 1963. Notes on color phases of the Screech Owl. *Migrant* 34:55-56.

Law, J.E. 1928. *Toxostoma curvirostris* [sic]: I. Description of a new subspecies from the lower Rio Grande. *Condor* 30:151-152.

_____. 1929. The spring molt of *Zonotrichia*. *Condor* 31:208-212.

Lawrence, L.deK. 1967. A comparative life-history study of four species of woodpeckers. *Ornith. Monogr.* 5:1-156.

Lawton, M.F. and C.F. Guindon. 1981. Flock composition, breeding success, and learning in the Brown Jay. *Condor* 83:27-33.

_____ and R.O. Lawton. 1985. The breeding biology of the Brown Jay in Monteverde, Costa Rica. *Condor* 87:192-204.

Leberman, R.C. 1967. The influence of fat on bird weight. *E. Bird Banding Assoc. News* 30:181-184.

_____. 1970. Pattern and timing of skull pneumatization in the Ruby-crowned Kinglet. *Bird-Banding* 41:121-124.

_____. 1972. Key to age and sex determination of Ruby-throated Hummingbirds in autumn. *Inl. Bird Banding News* 44:197-202.

_____. 1973. A study of Tufted Titmouse weights. *E. Bird Banding Assoc. News* 36:34-38.

_____. 1984. Rose underwings in female Rose-breasted Grosbeaks. *J. Field Ornith.* 55:486-487.

LeFebvre, E.A. and D.W. Warner. 1959. Molts, plumages and age groups in *Piranga bidentata* in Mexico. *Auk* 76:208-217.

Lefebvre, G., B. Poulin, and R. McNeil. 1992. Abundance, feeding behavior, and body condition of Nearctic warblers wintering in Venezuelan mangroves. *Wilson Bull.* 104:400-412.

Lehman, P. 1988. Orchard and immature Hooded orioles: A field identification nightmare. *Birding* 20:98-100.

_____. 1991. Notes on plumage variation in adult Red-naped and Red-breasted sapsuckers. *Birding* 23:23-26.

Lein, M.R. and K.W. Corbin. 1990. Song and plumage phenotypes in a contact zone between subspecies of the White-crowned Sparrow (*Zonotrichia leucophrys*). *Can. J. Zool.* 68:2625-2629.

Lenton, G.M. 1984. Moult of Malaysian Barn Owls *Tyto alba*. *Ibis* 126:188-197.

Lethaby, N. 1996. Identification of Tree, Northern Rough-winged, and Bank swallows. *Birding* 28:111-116.

Lewington, I., P. Alström, and P. Colston. 1991. A field guide to the rare birds of Britain and Europe. Harper Collins, London.

Ligon, J.D. 1968. The biology of the Elf Owl, *Micrathene whitneyi*. *Misc. Pubs. Mus. Zool. Univ. Michigan* 136:1-70.

_____. 1970. Behavior and breeding biology of the Red-cockaded Woodpecker. *Auk* 87:255-278.

_____. 1971. Late summer-autumnal breeding of the Piñon Jay in New Mexico. *Condor* 73:147-153.

_____ and J.L. White. 1974. Molt and its timing in the Piñon Jay, *Gymnorhinus cyanocephalus*. *Condor* 76:274-287.

Lincoln, F.C. 1919. Some notes on the plumage of the male Florida Redwing (*Agelaius p. floridanus*). *Proc. Biol. Soc. Washington* 32:196-197.

Linsdale, J.M. 1928. Variations in the Fox Sparrow (*Passerella iliaca*) with reference to natural history and osteology. *Univ. California Pubs. Zool.* 30:251-392.

_____. 1937. The natural history of Magpies. *Pacific Coast Avif.* 25:1-234.

_____. 1938. Geographic variation in some birds in Nevada. *Condor* 40:36-38.

_____. 1957. Goldfinches on the Hastings Natural History Reservation. *Am. Midland Nat.* 57:1-119.

Linz, G.M. 1986. Temporal, sex, and population characteristics of the first prebasic molt of Red-winged Blackbirds. *J. Field Ornith.* 57:91-98.

_____, S.B. Bolen, and J.F. Cassel. 1983. Postnuptial and postjuvenal molts of Red-winged Blackbirds in Cass County, North Dakota. *Auk* 100:206-209.

_____ and L.J. Linz. 1987. Growth rate of the primaries of captive hatching-year Red-winged Blackbirds. *J. Field Ornith.* 58:293-296.

Lloyd, J.A. 1965. Seasonal development of the incubation patch in the Starling. *Condor* 67:67-72.

Lloyd-Evans, T.L. 1983. Incomplete molt of juvenile White-eyed Vireos. *J. Field Ornith.* 54:50-57.

Longmire, J.L., M. Maltbie, R.W. Pavelka, L.M. Smith, S.M. Witte, O.A. Ryder, D.L. Ellsworth, and R.J. Baker. 1993. Gender identification in birds using microsatellite DNA fingerprint analysis. *Auk* 110:378-381.

Lowery, G.H. Jr. 1938. A new grackle of the *Cassidix mexicanus* group. *Occ. Papers Mus. Zool. Louisiana State Univ.* 1:1-11.

_____ 1940. Geographical variation in the Carolina Wren. *Auk* 57:95-104.

_____ and W.W. Dalquest. 1951. Birds from the state of Veracruz, Mexico. *Univ. Kansas Pubs. Mus. Nat. Hist.* 3:531-649.

_____ and R.J. Newman. 1949. New birds from the state of San Luis Potosi and the Tuxtla Mountains of Veracruz, Mexico. *Occ. Papers Mus. Zool. Louisiana State Univ.* 22:1-10.

Lowther, J.K. 1961. Polymorphism in the White-throated Sparrow, *Zonotrichia albicollis* (Gmelin). *Can. J. Zool.* 39:281-292.

_____ and R.E. Walker. 1967. Sex ratios and wing chord lengths of Pine Siskins (*Spinus pinus*) in Algonquin Park, Ontario. *Can. Field-Nat.* 81:220-222.

Lowther, P.E. 1977. Selection intensity in North American House Sparrows *Passer domesticus*. *Evolution* 31:649-656.

_____. 1993. Brown-headed Cowbird. *In* The Birds of North America, No. 147 (A. Poole and F. Gill, eds.). Acad. Nat. Sci., Philadelphia; Amer. Ornith. Union, Washington D.C.

_____. 1995. Bronzed Cowbird. *In* The Birds of North America, No. 144 (A. Poole and F. Gill, eds.). Acad. Nat. Sci., Philadelphia; Amer. Ornith. Union, Washington D.C.

_____. 1996. Le Conte's Sparrow. *In* The Birds of North America, No. 224 (A. Poole and F. Gill, eds.). Acad. Nat. Sci., Philadelphia; Amer. Ornith. Union, Washington D.C.

_____ and C.L. Cink. 1992. House Sparrow. *In* The Birds of North America, No. 12 (A. Poole, P. Stettenheim, and F. Gill, eds.). Acad. Nat. Sci., Philadelphia; Amer. Ornith. Union, Washington D.C.

Lunk, W.A. 1952. Notes on the variation in the Carolina Chickadee. *Wilson Bull.* 64:7-24.

_____. 1962. The Rough-winged Swallow *Stelgidopteryx ruficollis* (Vieillot). A study based on its breeding biology in Michigan. *Pubs. Nuttall Ornith. Club* 4:1-155.

Lynch, J.F. and P.L. Ames. 1970. A new hybrid hummingbird, *Archilochus alexandri* × *Selasphorus sasin*. *Condor* 72:209-212.

_____, E.S. Morton, and M.E. Van der Voort. 1985. Habitat segregation between the sexes of wintering Hooded Warblers (*Wilsonia citrina*). *Auk* 102:714-721.

Lyon, B. and R. Montgomerie. 1986. Delayed plumage maturation in passerine birds: Relative signalling by subordinate males? *Evolution* 40:605-615.

_____ and _____. 1995. Snow Bunting and McKay's Bunting. *In* The Birds of North America, Nos. 198-199 (A. Poole and F. Gill, eds.). Acad. Nat. Sci., Philadelphia; Amer. Ornith. Union, Washington D.C.

MacBriar, W.N. Jr. 1995. Wing measurement data of Bank Swallows from southeastern Wisconsin. *N. Am. Bird Bander* 20:60-62.

Madge, S.C., G.C. Hearl, S.C. Hutchings, and L.P. Williams. 1990. Varied Thrush: New to the western Palearctic. *Brit. Birds* 83:187-195.

Magee, M.J. 1924. Notes on the Purple Finch (*Carpodacus purpureus purpureus*). *Auk* 41:606-610.

_____. 1926a. Summary of trapping and banding operations in northern Michigan. *Wilson Bull.* 38:162-167.

_____. 1926b. Notes on the Evening Grosbeak. *Wilson Bull.* 38:170-172.

_____. 1928. Spring molt of the Evening Grosbeak. *Bull. NE. Bird-Banding Assoc.* 4:149-152.

_____. 1930. More notes on the spring molt of the Evening Grosbeak. *Bird-Banding* 1:43-45.

_____. 1936. The wing molt in Purple Finch. *Bird-Banding* 7:73-76.

_____. 1943. Seasonal changes in color of the gape of male Purple Finches. *Auk* 60:90.

Mailliard, J. 1912. *Passerella stephensi* in Marin County, California. *Condor* 14:63-67.

____. 1915. The Kern Redwing - *Agelaius phoeniceus aciculatus*. *Condor* 17:12-15.

____. 1918. The Yolla Bolly Fox Sparrow. *Condor* 20:138-139.

____. 1932. Observations on the head markings of the Golden-crowned Sparrow. *Condor* 34:66-70.

____. 1937. Hybridism between Myrtle and Audubon's warblers. *Condor* 39:223-225.

Mailliard, J.W. 1910. For the better determination of *Agelaius tricolor*. *Condor* 12:39-41.

Manolis, T. 1987. Juvenal plumages of *Picoides* woodpeckers. *N. Am. Bird Bander* 12:93.

Maridon, B. and L.C. Holcomb. 1971. No evidence for incubation patch changes in Mourning Doves throughout reproduction. *Condor* 73:374-375.

Marin, A.M. and F.G. Stiles. 1992. On the biology of five species of swifts (*Apodidae, Cypseloidinae*) in Costa Rica. *Proc. Western Found. Vert. Zool.* 4:287-351.

Marks, J.S. 1985. Yearling male Long-eared Owls breed near natal nest. *J. Field. Ornith.* 56:181-182.

____, D.L. Evans, and D.W. Holt. 1994. Long-eared Owl. *In* The Birds of North America, No. **133** (A. Poole and F. Gill, eds.). Acad. Nat. Sci., Philadelphia; Amer. Ornith. Union, Washington D.C.

Marra, P.P., T.W. Sherry, and R.T. Holmes. 1993. Territorial exclusion by a long-distance migrant warbler in Jamaica: A removal experiment with American Redstarts (*Setophaga ruticilla*). *Auk* 110:565-572.

Marshall, J.T. Jr. 1948a. Ecologic races of Song Sparrows in the San Francisco Bay region. Part I. Habitat and abundance. *Condor* 50:193-215.

____. 1948b. Ecologic races of Song Sparrows in the San Francisco Bay region. Part II. Geographic variation. *Condor* 50:233-256.

____. 1956. Summer birds of the Rincon Mountains, Saguaro National Monument, Arizona. *Condor* 58:81-97.

____. 1967. Parallel variation in North and Middle American screech-owls. *Western Found. Vert. Zool. Monogr.* 1:1-33.

____. 1978. Systematics of smaller Asian night birds based on voice. *Ornith. Monogr.* 25:1-58.

____. 1988. Birds lost from a Giant Sequoia forest during fifty years. *Condor* 90:359-372.

____. 1997. Allan Phillips and the Flammulated Owl. Pp. 87-91 *in* R.W. Dickerman, *comp.*, The era of Allan R. Phillips: A *Festshrift*. R.W. Dickerman, Albuquerque, NM.

____ and W.H. Behle. 1942. The Song Sparrows of the Virgin River valley, Utah. *Condor* 44:122-124.

Marti, C.D. 1990. Sex and age dimorphism in the Barn Owl and a test of mate choice. *Auk* 107:246-254.

Martin, D.J. 1973. Selected aspects of Burrowing Owl ecology and behavior. *Condor* 75:446-456.

Martin, R.F. 1980. Analysis of hybridization between the Hirundinid genera *Hirundo* and *Petrochelidon*. *Auk* 97:148-159.

____, M.W. Martin, and N.G. Lanier-Martin. 1986. Geographic variation in white facial markings of juvenile Cave Swallows. *Southwestern Nat.* 31:402-403.

____ and R.K. Selander. 1975. Morphological and biochemical evidence of hybridization between Cave and Barn swallows. *Auk* 75:362-364.

Martin, S.G. and T.A. Gavin. 1995. Bobolink. *In* The Birds of North America, No. **176** (A. Poole and F. Gill, eds.). Acad. Nat. Sci., Philadelphia; Amer. Ornith. Union, Washington D.C.

____ and K.A. Martin. 1996. Hybridization between a Mountain Chickadee and a Black-capped Chickadee in Colorado. *Colorado Field Ornith. J.* 30:60-65.

Martin, T.E. and P.M. Barber. 1995. Red-faced Warbler. *In* The Birds of North America, No. **152** (A. Poole and F. Gill, eds.). Acad. Nat. Sci., Philadelphia; Amer. Ornith. Union, Washington D.C.

Martindale, S. and D. Lamm. 1984. Sexual dimorphism and parental role switching in Gila Woodpeckers. *Wilson Bull.* 96:116-121.

Mason, E.A. 1938. Determining sex in breeding birds. *Bird-Banding* 9:46-48.

Mayfield, H. 1960. The Kirtland's Warbler. Cranbrook Institute of Science, Bloomfield Hills, MI.

____. 1992. Kirtland's Warbler. *In* The Birds of North America, No. **19** (A. Poole, P. Stettenheim, and F. Gill, eds.). Acad. Nat. Sci., Philadelphia; Amer. Ornith. Union, Washington D.C.

Maynard, C.J. 1906. Directory to the birds of North America. C.J. Maynard & Co., Newtonville, MA.

Mayr, E. 1954. Notes on nomenclature and classification. *Syst. Zool.* 3:86-89.

____. 1963. Animal species and evolution. Harvard Univ. Press, Cambridge, MA.

____. 1982. Of what use are subspecies? *Auk* 99:593-595.

____ and J.C. Greenway Jr., eds. 1960. Check-list of birds of the world. Vol. IX. Museum of Comparative Zoology, Cambridge, MA.

Mayr, E. and J.C. Greenway Jr., eds. 1962. Check-list of birds of the world. Vol. XV. Museum of Comparative Zoology, Cambridge, MA.

____ and L.L. Short. 1970. Species taxa of North American birds. *Publ. Nuttall Ornith. Club* 9:1-127.

McBriar, W.N. 1968. Comparative chart for *Empidonax* flycatchers. *Inl. Bird Banding News* 40:83-86.

McCabe, T.T. and E.B. McCabe. 1932. Preliminary studies of western Hermit Thrushes. *Condor* 34:26-40.

____ and ____. 1933. Hermit Thrushes of the northwestern states. *Condor* 35:122-123.

____ and A.H. Miller. 1933. Geographic variation in the Northern Water-thrushes. *Condor* 35:192-197.

McCallum, D.A. 1994. Flammulated Owl. *In* The Birds of North America, No. **93** (A. Poole and F. Gill, eds.). Acad. Nat. Sci., Philadelphia; Amer. Ornith. Union, Washington D.C.

McCamey, F. 1950. A puzzling hybrid warbler from Michigan. *Jack-Pine Warbler* 28:67-72.

McCaskie, G. and M.A. Patten. 1994. Status of the Fork-tailed Flycatcher (*Tyrannus savana*) in the United States and Canada. *W. Birds* 25:113-127.

McCarty, J.P. 1996. Eastern Wood-Pewee. *In* The Birds of North America, No. **245** (A. Poole and F. Gill, eds.). Acad. Nat. Sci., Philadelphia; Amer. Ornith. Union, Washington D.C.

McEntee, E. 1970a. Age determination of House Finches by plumage change. *E. Bird Banding Assoc. News* 33:70-76.

____. 1970b. Pine Siskins - some observations on color, size and sex. *E. Bird Banding Assoc. News* 33:100-101.

McGillivray, W.B. 1985. Size, sexual dimorphism, and their measurement in Great Horned Owls in Alberta. *Can. J. Zool.* 63:2364-2372.

____. 1989. Geographic variation in size and reverse size dimorphism of the Great Horned Owl in North America. *Condor* 91:777-786.

____ and G.C. Biermann. 1987. Expansion of the zone of hybridization of Northern Flickers in Alberta. *Wilson Bull.* 99:690-692.

McGregor, R.C. 1901. New Alaskan birds. *Condor* 3:8.

McIlhenny, E.A. 1937. Life history of the Boat-tailed Grackle in Louisiana. *Auk* 54:276-295.

McKinney, R.G. 1988. Bander's guide to the identification of *Empidonax* flycatchers in northeastern North America. *N. Am. Bird Bander* 13:62-65.

McKnight, B.C. 1969. Change in facial coloration in a bushtit. *Auk* 86:570.

McLaren, I.A. 1994. *Ammodramus* sparrows in Nova Scotia. *Nova Scotia Birds* 36:23-29.

____. 1995. Field identification and taxonomy of Bicknell's Thrush. *Birding* 27:358-366.

McMannama, Z. 1950. Post-juvenal molt of a Steller's Jay in captivity. *Murrelet* 31:33-34.

McMinn, S. 1995. Ageing *Catharus* thrushes. *Birding World* 8:317.

McNicholl, M.K. 1977. Measurements of Wilson's Warblers in Alberta. *N. Am. Bird Bander* 2:108-109.

Meanley, B. 1964. Origin, structure, molt, and dispersal of a late summer Red-winged Blackbird population. *Bird-Banding* 35:32-38.

____. 1967. Aging and sexing blackbirds, Bobolinks and starlings. Special report to Patuxent Wildlife Research Center; work unit F-24.1.

____. 1971. Natural history of the Swainson's Warbler. *N. Am. Fauna* 69:1-90.

____ and G.M. Bond. 1950. A new race of Swainson's Warbler from the Appalachian mountains. *Proc. Biol. Soc. Washington* 63:191-194.

____ and ____. 1970. Molts and plumages of the Red-winged Blackbird with particular reference to fall migration. *Bird-Banding* 41:22-27.

Mearns, E.A. 1902. Descriptions of three new birds from the southern United States. *Proc. U.S. Nat. Mus.* 24:915-919.

____. 1911. Description of a new subspecies of the Painted Bunting from the interior of Texas. *Proc. Biol. Soc. Washington* 24:217-218.

Mees, G.F. 1970. On some birds from southern Mexico. *Zool. Med.* 44:237-245.

Meigs, J.B., D.C. Smith, and J. Van Buskirk. 1983. Age determination of Black-capped Chickadees. *J. Field Ornith.* 54:283-286.

Meinertzhagen, R. 1926. Introduction to a review of the genus *Corvus*. *Novit. Zoologicae* 33:57-121.

Mellancamp, W.R. 1969. Skull ossification in the White-throated Sparrow. *E. Bird Banding Assoc. News* 32:109-111.

Mellink, E. and A.M. Rea. 1994. Taxonomic status of the California Gnatcatchers of northwestern Baja California, Mexico. *W. Birds* 25:50-62.

Menasco, K.A. and H.R. Perry. 1978. Errors from determining sex of Mourning Doves by plumage characteristics. *Proc. Ann. Conf. S.E. Assoc. Fish & Wild. Agencies* 32:224-227.

Mengel, R.M. 1952. Certain molts and plumages of Acadian and Yellow-bellied Flycatchers. *Auk* 69:273-283.

____. 1963. A second probable hybrid between the Scarlet and Western tanagers. *Wilson Bull.* 75:201-203.

Mengel, R.M. 1965. The birds of Kentucky. *Ornith. Monogr.* 3:1-581.

____. 1976. Rapid tail molt and temporarily impaired flight in the Chuck-will's-widow. *Wilson Bull.* 88:351-353.

____ and J.A. Jackson. 1977. Geographic variation of the Red-cockaded Woodpecker. *Condor* 79:349-355.

Merrill, J.C. 1880. Notes on the winter plumage of *Leucosticte tephrocotis*, Sw., and *L. tephrocotis* var. *littoralis*, Bd. *Auk* 5:75-77.

Merritt, P.G. 1978. Characteristics of Black-capped and Carolina chickadees at the range of interface in northern Indiana. *Jack-Pine Warbler* 56:170-179.

Mewaldt, L.R. 1952. The incubation patch of the Clark's Nutcracker. *Condor* 54:361.

____. 1958. Pterylography and natural and experimentally induced molt in Clark's Nutcracker. *Condor* 60:165-187.

____. 1973. Wing-length and age in White-crowned Sparrows. *Western Bird Bander* 48:54-56.

____. 1977. Banding worksheet for Western birds. White-crowned Sparrow. Supplement to *N. Am. Bird Bander*, vol. 2.

____, S.S. Kibby, and M.L. Norton. 1968. Comparative biology of Pacific White-crowned Sparrows. *Condor* 70:14-30.

____ and J.R. King. 1977. The annual cycle of White-crowned Sparrows (*Zonotrichia leucophrys nuttalli*) in coastal California. *Condor* 79:445-455.

____ and ____. 1978a. Latitudinal variation of postnuptial molt in Pacific coast White-crowned Sparrows. *Auk* 95:168-179.

____ and ____. 1978b. Latitudinal variation in prenuptial molt in wintering Gambel's White-crowned Sparrows. *N. Am. Bird Bander* 3:138-144.

____ and ____. 1986. Estimation of sex ratio from wing-length in birds when sexes differ in size but not coloration. *J. Field. Ornith.* 57:155-167.

Michener, H. and J.R. Michener. 1931. Variation in the color of male House Finches. *Condor* 33:12-19.

____ and ____. 1932. Colors induced in male House Finches by repeated feather removals. *Condor* 34:253-256.

____ and ____. 1940. The molt of House Finches of the Pasadena region, California. *Condor* 42:140-153.

____ and ____. 1943. The spring molt of the Gambel Sparrow. *Condor* 45:113-116.

Michener, J.R. 1953. Molt and variations in plumage pattern of Mockingbirds at Pasadena, California. *Condor* 55:75-89.

____ and H. Michener. 1951. Notes on banding records and plumages of the Black-headed Grosbeak. *Condor* 53:93-96.

Middleton, A.L.A. 1974. Age determination in the American Goldfinch. *Bird-Banding* 45:293-296.

____. 1977. The molt of the American Goldfinch. *Condor* 79:440-444.

____. 1993. American Goldfinch. *In* The Birds of North America, No. **80** (A. Poole and F. Gill, eds.). Acad. Nat. Sci., Philadelphia; Amer. Ornith. Union, Washington D.C.

Millard, S. 1988. Mysterious hybrid warbler in southeast Minnesota. *Birding* 20:252-254.

Miller, A.H. 1928. The molts of the Loggerhead Shrike *Lanius ludovicianus* Linnaeus. *Univ. California Pubs. Zool.* 30:393-417.

____. 1929. A new race of Black-chinned Sparrow from the San Francisco Bay district. *Condor* 31:205-207.

____. 1930. Two new races of the Loggerhead Shrike from western North America. *Condor* 32:155-156.

____. 1931. Systematic revision and natural history of American shrikes (*Lanius*). *Univ. California Pubs. Zool.* 38:11-242.

____. 1933a. The Canada Jays of northern Idaho. *Trans. San Diego Soc. Nat. Hist.* 7:287-298.

____. 1933b. Postjuvenal molt and appearance of sexual characters of plumage in *Phainopepla nitens*. *Univ. California Pubs. Zool.* 38:425-444.

____. 1935. Further comments on the cowbirds of the San Francisco Bay region. *Condor* 37:217-218.

____. 1936. The identification of juncos banded in the Rocky Mountain states. *Bird Lore* 38:429-433.

____. 1939a. Analysis of some hybrid populations of juncos. *Condor* 41:211-214.

____. 1939b. The breeding *Leucostictes* of the Wallowa Mountains, Oregon. *Condor* 41:34-35.

____. 1940. A hybrid between *Zonotrichia coronata* and *Zonotrichia leucophrys*. *Condor* 42:45-48.

____. 1941a. A review of centers of differentiation for birds in the western Great Basin region. *Condor* 43:257-267.

____. 1941b. Racial determination of Bewick Wrens in the western Great Basin region. *Condor* 43:250-251.

____. 1941c. Speciation in the avian genus *Junco*. *Univ. California Pubs. Zool.* 44:173-434.

____. 1942. Differentiation of the Oven-birds of the Rocky Mountain region. *Condor* 44:185-186.

Miller, A.H. 1943a. A new race of Canada Jay from coastal British Columbia. *Condor* 45:117-118.

____. 1943b. A new race of Brown-headed Chickadee from northern Washington. *Occ. Papers Mus. Zool. Louisiana State Univ.* 14:261-263.

____. 1946a. A method for determining the age of live passerine birds. *Bird-Banding* 17:33-35.

____. 1946b. Endemic birds of the little San Bernadino Mountains, California. *Condor* 48:75-79.

____. 1948. Further observations on variation in Canyon Wrens. *Condor* 50:83-85.

____. 1949. Some concepts of hybridization and intergradation in wild populations of birds. *Auk* 66:338-342.

____. 1954a. A hybrid woodpecker and its significance in speciation in the genus *Dendrocopos*. *Evolution* 8:317-321.

____. 1954b. Nomenclature of the Black-throated Sparrows of Chihuahua and western Texas. *Condor* 56:364-365.

____. 1955. The avifauna of the Sierra del Carmen of Coahuila, Mexico. *Condor* 57:154-178.

____ and T.T. McCabe. 1935. Racial differentiation in *Passerella* (*Melospiza*) *lincolnii*). *Condor* 37:144-160.

____ and L. Miller. 1951. Geographic variation of the Screech Owls of the deserts of western North America. *Condor* 53:161-177.

____ and R.W. Storer. 1950. A new race of *Parus sclateri* from the Sierra Madre del Sur of Mexico. *J. Washington Acad. Sci.* 40:301-302.

Miller, G.S., S.K. Nelson, and W.C. Wright. 1985. Two-year old female Spotted Owl breeds successfully. *W. Birds* 16:93-94.

Miller, J.H. and M.T. Green. 1987. Distribution, status, and origin of Water Pipits breeding in California. *Condor* 89:788-797.

Miller, W.D. and L. Griscom. 1925a. Descriptions of new birds from Nicaragua. *Am. Mus. Novitates* 159:1-9.

____ and ____. 1925b. Notes on Central American birds with descriptions of new forms. *Am. Mus. Novitates* 183:1-14.

Miller, W.J. and F.H. Wagner. 1955. Sexing mature Columbiformes by cloacal characters. *Auk* 72:279-285.

Mills, G.S., J.R. Silliman, K.D. Groschupf, and S.M. Speich. 1979. Life history of the Five-striped Sparrow. *Living Bird* 18:95-110.

Miskimen, M. 1980a. Red-winged Blackbirds: I. Age-related epaulet color changes in captive females. *Ohio J. Sci.* 80:232-235.

____. 1980b. Red-winged Blackbirds: II. Pigmentation in epaulets of females. *Ohio J. Sci.* 80:236-239.

Misra, R.K. and L.L. Short. 1974. A biometric analysis of oriole hybridization. *Condor* 76:137-146.

Moen, C.A., A.B. Franklin, and R.J. Gutierrez. 1991. Age determination of subadult Northern Spotted Owls in northwest California. *Wildl. Soc. Bull.* 19:489-493.

Moldenhauer, R.R. 1992. Two song populations of the Northern Parula. *Auk* 109:215-222.

____ and D.J. Regelski. 1996. Northern Parula. *In* The Birds of North America, No. **215** (A. Poole and F. Gill, eds.). Acad. Nat. Sci., Philadelphia; Amer. Ornith. Union, Washington D.C.

Monroe, B.L. Jr. 1959. Notes on the Western Meadowlark in the Southeast. *Kentucky Warbler* 35:43-49.

____. 1963. Notes on the avian genus *Arremonops* with description of a new subspecies from Honduras. *Occ. Papers Mus. Zool. Louisiana State Univ.* 28:1-12.

____. 1968. A distributional survey of the birds of Honduras. *Ornith. Monogr.* 7:1-458.

Monson, G. and A.R. Phillips. 1981. Annotated checklist of the birds of Arizona. University of Arizona Press, Tucson, AZ.

Montagna, W. 1940. The Acadian Sharp-tailed Sparrows of Popham Beach, Maine. *Wilson Bull.* 52:191-197.

____. 1942. The Sharp-tailed Sparrows of the Atlantic Coast. *Wilson Bull.* 54:107-120.

____. 1943. Weights and plumages of the Horned Larks of central New York. *Auk* 60:210-215.

Moore, R.T. 1932. A new race of *Aimophila carpalis* from Mexico. *Proc. Biol. Soc. Washington* 45:231-234.

____. 1936. Description of a new race of *Carpodacus mexicanus*. *Condor* 38:203-208.

____. 1937. New races of *Myadestes*, *Spizella*, and *Turdus* from northwestern Mexico. *Proc. Biol. Soc. Washington* 50:201-206.

____. 1939a. A new race of *Cyananthus latirostris* from Guanajuato. *Proc. Biol. Soc. Washington* 52:57-60.

____. 1939b. The Arizona Broad-billed Hummingbird. *Auk* 56:313-319.

____. 1939c. New races of the genera *Sialia* and *Carpodacus* from Mexico. *Proc. Biol. Soc. Washington* 52:125-130.

____. 1939d. Two new races of *Carpodacus mexicanus*. *Proc. Biol. Soc. Washington* 52:105-112.

____. 1939e. A review of the House Finches of the subgenus *Burrica*. *Condor* 41:177-205.

____. 1940a. Notes on Middle American *Empidonaces*. *Auk* 57:349-389.

Moore, R.T. 1940b. New races of *Empidonax* from Middle America. *Proc. Biol. Soc. Washington* 53:23-30.

____. 1941a. Three new races of the genus *Otus* from central Mexico. *Proc. Biol. Soc. Washington* 54:151-160.

____. 1941b. New races of flycatcher, warbler and wrens from Mexico. *Proc. Biol. Soc. Washington* 54:35-42.

____. 1941c. Notes on *Toxostoma curvirostre* of Mexico, with description of a new race. *Proc. Biol. Soc. Washington* 54:211-216.

____. 1941d. New form of *Toxostoma* from Hidalgo. *Proc. Biol. Soc. Washington* 54:149.

____. 1946a. A new woodpecker from Mexico. *Proc. Biol. Soc. Washington* 59:103-106.

____. 1946b. The status of *Dendroica auduboni nigrifrons* in the United States. *Auk* 63:241-242.

____. 1946c. The Rufous-winged Sparrow, its legends and taxonomic status. *Condor* 48:117-123.

____ and J.L. Peters. 1939. The genus *Otus* of Mexico and Central America. *Auk* 56:38-56.

Moore, W.S. 1987. Random mating in the Northern Flicker hybrid zone: Implications for the evolution of bright and contrasting patterns in birds. *Evolution* 41:539-546.

____. 1995. Northern Flicker. *In* The Birds of North America, No. 166 (A. Poole and F. Gill, eds.). Acad. Nat. Sci., Philadelphia; Amer. Ornith. Union, Washington D.C.

____ and D.B. Buchanan. 1985. Stability of the Northern Flicker hybrid zone in historical times: Implications for adaptive speciation theory. *Evolution* 39:135-151.

Morlan, J. 1981. Status and identification of forms of White Wagtail in western North America. *Cont. Birdlife* 2:37-50.

____. 1986. ID Point: Sage and Bendire's thrashers. *Birding* 18:328-329.

____. 1991. Identification of female Rose-breasted and Black-headed grosbeaks. *Birding* 23:220-223.

Morrison, J.A. and J.C. Lewis. 1974. Preliminary observations of overwintering Mourning Doves in southwestern Oklahoma. *Proc. Oklahoma Acad. Sci.* 54:25-33.

Morrison, M.L. 1982. The structure of western warbler assemblages: Ecomorphological analysis of the Black-throated Gray and Hermit warblers. *Auk* 99:503-513.

____. 1983. Analysis of geographic variation in the Townsend's Warbler. *Condor* 85:385-391.

____. 1990. Morphological and vocal variation in the Black-throated Gray Warbler in the Pacific Northwest. *Northwestern Nat.* 71:53-58.

____ and J.W. Hardy. 1983. Hybridization between Hermit and Townsend's warblers. *Murrelet* 64:65-72.

Morse, W.B. 1950. Observations on the Band-tailed Pigeon in Oregon. *Proc. W. Assoc. State Game & Fish Comm.* 30:102-104.

Morse, D.H. 1993. Black-throated Green Warbler. *In* The Birds of North America, No. 55 (A. Poole and F. Gill, eds.). Acad. Nat. Sci., Philadelphia; Amer. Ornith. Union, Washington D.C.

Morse, D.H. 1994. Blackburnian Warbler. *In* The Birds of North America, No. 102 (A. Poole and F. Gill, eds.). Acad. Nat. Sci., Philadelphia; Amer. Ornith. Union, Washington D.C.

Morss, N. 1926. Mendalian inheritance in hybrid warblers. *Am. Nat.* 60:384-387.

Morton, E.S. 1977. Intratropical migration in the Yellow-green Vireo and Piratic Flycatcher. *Auk* 94:97-106.

____. 1989. Female Hooded Warbler plumage does not become more male-like with age. *Wilson Bull.* 101:460-462.

Morton, G.A. and M.L. Morton. 1990. Dynamics of postnuptial molt in free-living Mountain White-crowned Sparrows. *Condor* 92:813-828.

Morton, M.L. 1991. Postfledging dispersal of Green-tailed Towhees to a subalpine meadow. *Condor* 93:466-468.

____. 1992. Control of postnuptial molt in the Mountain White-crowned Sparrow: A perspective from field data. *Ornis Scand.* 23:322-327.

____, J.R. King, and D.S. Farner. 1969. Postnuptial and postjuvenal molt in White-crowned Sparrows in central Alaska. *Condor* 71:376-385.

____ and L.R. Mewaldt. 1960. Further evidence of hybridization between *Zonotrichia atricapilla* and *Zonotrichia leucophrys*. *Condor* 62:485-486.

____ and G.A. Morton. 1987. Seasonal changes in bill length in summering Mountain White-crowned Sparrows. *Condor* 89:197-200.

____ and D.E. Welton. 1973. Postnuptial molt and its relation to reproductive cycle and body weight in Mountain White-crowned Sparrows (*Zonotrichia leucophrys oriantha*). *Condor* 75:184-189.

Mosher, J.I. and S. Lane. 1972. A method of determining the sex of captured Black-capped Chickadees. *Bird-Banding* 43:139-140.

Moskoff, W. 1995. Veery. *In* The Birds of North America, No. 142 (A. Poole and F. Gill, eds.). Acad. Nat. Sci., Philadelphia; Amer. Ornith. Union, Washington D.C.

____ and S.K. Robinson. 1995. Philadelphia Vireo. *In* The Birds of North America, No. 214 (A. Poole and F. Gill, eds.). Acad. Nat. Sci., Philadelphia; Amer. Ornith. Union, Washington D.C.

Mott, D.F. 1970. Ageing House Finches by wing covert wear. *W. Bird Bander* 45:36-37.

Mountjoy, D.J. and R.J. Robertson. 1988. Why are waxwings "waxy"? Delayed plumage maturation in the Cedar Waxwing. *Auk* 105:61-69.

Mowbray, T.B. 1997. Swamp Sparrow. *In* The Birds of North America, No. 279 (A. Poole and F. Gill, eds.). Acad. Nat. Sci., Philadelphia; Amer. Ornith. Union, Washington D.C.

Mueller, A.J. 1992. Inca Dove. *In* The Birds of North America, No. 28 (A. Poole, P. Stettenheim, and F. Gill, eds.). Acad. Nat. Sci., Philadelphia; Amer. Ornith. Union, Washington D.C.

Mueller, H.C. 1982. Comments on sexing Saw-whet Owls by wing chord. *Wilson Bull.* 94:554-555.

____. 1990. Can Saw-whet Owls be sexed by external measurements? *J. Field Ornith.* 61:339-346.

____ and D.D. Berger. 1967. Observations of migrating Saw-whet Owls. *Bird-Banding* 38:120-125.

Muller, K.A. 1971. Physical and behavioral development of a Roadrunner raised at the National Zoological Park. *Wilson Bull.* 83:186-193.

Mulvihill, R.S. 1993. Using wing molt to age passerines. *N. Am. Bird Bander* 18:1-10.

____ and C.R. Chandler. 1990. The relationship between wing shape and differential migration in the Dark-eyed Junco. *Auk* 107:490-499.

____ and ____. 1991. A comparison of wing shape between migratory and sedentary Dark-eyed Juncos. *Condor* 93:172-175.

____ and R.C. Leberman. 1985. Bird banding at Powdermill, 1985, with a summary of Ruby-throated Hummingbird banding data. *Powdermill Nat. Reserve Res. Report* 46:1-19.

____ and ____. 1988. Identification guide to North American Passerines. [Review of Pyle *et al.* 1987.] *Wilson Bull.* 100:695-607.

____, K.C. Parkes, R.C. Leberman, and D.S. Wood. 1992. Evidence supporting a dietary basis for orange-tipped rectrices in the Cedar Waxwing. *J. Field Ornith.* 63:212-216.

____ and C.C. Rimmer. 1997. Timing and extent of the molts of adult Red-eyed Vireos (*Vireo olivaceus*) on their breeding and wintering grounds. *Condor* 99:73-82.

____ and R.L. Winstead. 1997. Variation in the extent of the first prebasic wing molt of Dark-eyed Juncos (*Junco hyemalis*). *J. Field Ornith.* 68:183-199.

Mumford, R.E. 1964. The breeding biology of the Acadian Flycatcher. *Misc. Pubs. Mus. Zool. Univ. Michigan* 125:1-50.

Mundy, R. and J.D. McCracken. Ageing Yellow Warblers by bill color. Unpublished ms., Long Point Bird Observatory.

Munro, J.A. and I.M. Cowan. 1947. A review of the bird fauna of British Columbia. *Spec. Pub. British Columbia Prov. Mus.* 2:1-285.

Murie, O.J. 1944. Two new subspecies of birds from Alaska. *Condor* 46:121-123.

Murphy, B. Reliability of certain wing formula criteria in the Hermit Thrush (*Catharus guttatus*). Unpublished ms. Innis Point Bird Observatory.

Murphy, M.T. 1988. Comparative reproductive biology of kingbirds (*Tyrannus* spp.) in eastern Kansas. *Wilson Bull.* 100:357-376.

____. 1996. Eastern Kingbird. *In* The Birds of North America, No. 253 (A. Poole and F. Gill, eds.). Acad. Nat. Sci., Philadelphia; Amer. Ornith. Union, Washington D.C.

Murray, B.G. Jr. 1968. The relationships of sparrows in the genera *Ammodramus*, *Passerherbulus* and *Ammospiza* with a description of a hybrid Le Conte's x Sharp-tailed sparrow. *Auk* 85:586-593.

____. 1969. A comparative study of the Le Conte's and Sharp-tailed sparrows. *Auk* 86:199-231.

Myers, M. and J. Myers. 1967. Quantitative notes on the variation of wax on Cedar Waxwings (*Bombycilla cedrorum*). *Kansas Ornith. Soc. Bull.* 18:1.

Nakamura, K. 1985. Historical change of the geographical distribution of two closely related species of genus *Motacilla* in the Japanese Achipelago. *Bull. Kanagawa Pref. Mus.* 16:23-36.

Naugler, C.T. 1993. American Tree Sparrow. *In* The Birds of North America, No. 37 (A. Poole, P. Stettenheim, and F. Gill, eds.). Acad. Nat. Sci., Philadelphia; Amer. Ornith. Union, Washington D.C.

Neff, J.A. 1947. Habits, food, and economic status of the Band-tailed Pigeon. *N. Amer. Fauna* 58:1-76.

Nelson, E.W. 1904. A revision of the North American mainland species of *Myiarchus*. *Proc. Biol. Soc. Washington* 17:21-50.

Nero, R.W. 1951. Pattern and rate of cranial "ossification" in the House Sparrow. *Wilson Bull.* 63:84-88.

____. 1954. Plumage aberrations of the Redwing (*Agelaius phoeniceus*). *Auk* 71:137-155.

____. 1960. Additional notes on the plumage of the Redwinged Blackbird. *Auk* 77:298-305.

____. 1984. Redwings. Smithsonian Institution Press, Washington D.C.

Newfield, N. 1983. Records of Allen's Hummingbird in Louisiana and possible Rufous × Allen's Hummingbird hybrids. *Condor* 85:253-254.

Nice, M.M. 1932. Measurements of White-throated and other sparrows to determine sex. *Bird-Banding* 3:30-31.

Nice, M.M. 1937. Studies in the life history of the Song Sparrow. Vol I. A population study of the Song Sparrow. Dover Publications, New York.
____. 1943. Studies in the life history of the Song Sparrow. Vol II. The behavior of the Song Sparrow and other passerines. Dover Publications, New York.
Nichols, J.T. 1945. Annual bill-color cycle of the Starling. *Bird-Banding* 16:29-32.
____. 1953a. Eye-color in the Red-eyed Towhee. *Bird-Banding* 24:16-17.
____. 1953b. Eye-color in the Brown Thrasher. *Bird-Banding* 24:17.
____. 1955. A criterion for young-of-the-year in the Blue Jay. *Bird-banding* 26:27.
Nicholson, D.J. 1938. Discovery of a new owl for Florida. *Florida Nat.* 11:99.
____. 1957. The Bahaman Nighthawk (*Chordeiles minor vicinus*) on the Florida Keys. *Auk* 74:505-507.
Niles, D.M. 1972a. Determining age and sex of Purple Martins. *Bird-banding* 43:137-138.
____. 1972b. Molt cycles of Purple Martins (*Progne subis*). *Condor* 74:61-71.
____. 1973a. Adaptive variation in body size and skeletal proportions of Horned Larks in the southwestern United States. *Evolution* 27:405-426.
____. 1973b. Geographic and seasonal variation in the occurrence of incompletely pneumatized skulls in the House Sparrow. *Condor* 75:354-356.
Nisbet, I.C.T., W.H. Drury Jr., and J.Baird. 1963. Weight loss during migration. Part I:deposition and consumption of fat by the Blackpoll Warbler *Dendroica striata*. *Bird-Banding* 34:107-159.
____, J. Baird, D.V. Howard, and K.S. Anderson. 1970. Statistical comparison on wing lengths measured by four observers. *Bird-Banding* 41:307-308.
Noble, G.K. 1919. Note on the avifauna of Newfoundland. *Bull. Mus. Comp. Zool.* 62:543-568.
Nolan, V. Jr. 1975. External differences between newly hatched cuckoos (*Coccyzus americanus* and *C. erythropthalmus*). *Condor* 77:341.
____. 1978. The ecology and behavior of the Prairie Warbler *Dendroica discolor*. *Ornith. Monogr.* 26:1-595.
____ and E.D. Ketterson. 1983. An analysis of body mass, wing length, and visible fat deposits of Dark-eyed Juncos wintering at different latitudes. *Wilson Bull.* 95:603-620.
____ and ____. 1990. Effect of long days on molt and autumn migratory state of site-faithful Dark-eyed Juncos held at their winter sites. *Wilson Bull.* 102:469-479.
____, E.D. Ketterson, C. Ziegenfus, D.P. Cullen, and C.R. Chandler. 1992. Testosterone and avian life histories: Effects of experimentally elevated testosterone on prebasic molt and survival in male Dark-eyed Juncos. *Condor* 94:364-370.
____ and R.E. Mumford. 1965. An analysis of Prairie Warblers killed in Florida during nocturnal migration. *Condor* 67:322-338.
Norment, C.J. 1995. Prebasic (postnuptial) molt in free-ranging Harris' Sparrows, *Zonotrichia querula*, in the Northwest Territories, Canada. *Can. Field-Nat.* 109:470-472.
____ and S.A. Shackleton. 1993. Harris Sparrow. *In* The Birds of North America, No. **64** (A. Poole and F. Gill, eds.). Acad. Nat. Sci., Philadelphia; Amer. Ornith. Union, Washington D.C.
Norris, R.A. 1952. Postjuvenal molt of tail feathers in the Pine Warbler. *Oriole* 17:29-31.
____. 1954. New information on the White-crowned Sparrow in southern Georgia. *Oriole* 19:25-31.
____. 1958a. Comparative biosystematics and life history of the nuthatches *Sitta pygmaea* and *Sitta pusilla. Univ. California Pubs. Zool.* 56:119-300.
____. 1958b. Notes on a captive Wood Thrush and its prenuptial molt. *Bird-Banding* 29:245.
____. 1961. A modification of the Miller method of aging live passerine birds. *Bird-Banding* 32:55-57.
____, C.E. Connell, and D.W. Johnston. 1957. Notes on fall plumages, weights, and fat condition in the Ruby-throated Hummingbird. *Wilson Bull.* 69:155-163.
____ and G.L. Hight Jr. 1957. Subspecific variation in winter populations of Savannah Sparrows: A study in field taxonomy. *Condor* 59:40-52.
Oberholser, H.C. 1898. A revision of the wrens of the genus *Thryomanes* Sclater. *Proc. U.S. Nat. Mus.* 31:421-449.
____. 1902. A review of the larks of the genus *Otocoris. Proc. U.S. Nat. Mus.* 24:801-884.
____. 1903a. A review of the genus *Catherpes. Auk* 20:196-198.
____. 1903b. The North American forms of *Astragalinus psaltria* (Say). *Proc. Biol. Soc. Washington* 41:113-116.
____. 1904. A revision of the American Great Horned Owls. *Proc. U.S. Nat. Mus.* 27:177-192.
____. 1905. The forms of *Vermivora celata* (Say). *Auk* 22:242-247.
____. 1907. A new *Agelaius* from Canada. *Auk* 24:332-336.
____. 1911a. A revision of the forms of the Ladder-backed Woodpecker (*Dryobates scalaris* [Wagler]). *Proc. U.S. Nat. Mus.* 41:139-159.

Oberholser, H.C. 1911b. A revision of the forms of the Hairy Woodpecker (*Dryobates villosus* [Linnaeus]). *Proc. U.S. Nat. Mus.* 40:595-621.
____. 1911c. Description of a new *Melospiza* from California. *Proc. Biol. Soc. Washington* 24:251-252.
____. 1914a. Four new birds from Newfoundland. *Proc. Biol. Soc. Washington* 27:43-54.
____. 1914b. A monograph of the genus *Chordeiles* Swainson, type of a new family of goatsuckers. *U.S. Nat. Mus. Bull.* 86:1-120.
____. 1915. Critical notes on the subspecies of the Spotted Owl, *Strix occidentalis* (Xantus). *Proc. U.S. Nat. Mus.* 49:251-257.
____. 1917a. Notes on North American birds. I. *Auk* 34:191-196.
____. 1917b. Description of a new subspecies of *Perisoreus obscurus. Proc. Biol. Soc. Washington* 30:185-188.
____. 1917c. The status of *Aphelocoma cyanotis* and its allies. *Condor* 19:94-95.
____. 1917d. Notes on North American birds. II. *Auk* 34:321-329.
____. 1917e. Critical notes on the eastern subspecies of *Sitta carolinensis* Latham. *Auk* 34:182-187.
____. 1917f. Description of a new *Sialia* from Mexico. *Proc. Biol. Soc. Washington* 30:27-28.
____. 1917g. A synopsis of the races of *Bombycilla garrula* (Linnaeus). *Auk* 34:330-333.
____. 1918a. Description of a new subspecies of *Cyanolaemus clemenciae. Condor* 20:181-182.
____. 1918b. New light on the status of *Empidonax traillii* (Audubon). *Ohio J. Sci.* 18:85-97.
____. 1918c. The Common Ravens of North America. *Ohio J. Sci.* 18:213-225.
____. 1918d. A revision of the races of *Toxostoma redivivum* (Gambel). *Auk* 35:467-474.
____. 1918e. Notes on North American birds. IV. *Auk* 35:62-65.
____. 1919a. An unrecognized subspecies of *Melanerpes erythrocephalus. Can. Field-Nat.* 33:48-50.
____. 1919b. Description of a new *Otocoris* from California. *Condor* 21:119-120.
____. 1919c. Notes on North American birds. VII. *Auk* 36:81-85.
____. 1919d. Notes on North American birds. VIII. *Auk* 36:406-408.
____. 1919e. Notes on the wrens of the genus *Nannus* Billberg. *Proc. U.S. Nat. Mus.* 55:223-236.
____. 1919f. Description of another new subspecies of *Lanius ludovicianus. Wilson Bull.* 31:87-90.
____. 1919g. Description of a new subspecies of *Piranga hepatica* Swainson. *Auk* 36:74-80.
____. 1919h. The geographic races of *Hedymeles melanocephalus* Swainson. *Auk* 36:408-410.
____. 1919i. Description of a new subspecies of *Pipilo fuscus. Condor* 21:210-211.
____. 1919j. A revision of the subspecies of *Passerculus rostratus* (Cassin). *Ohio J. Sci.* 19:344-354.
____. 1919k. A description of a new Red-winged Black-bird from Texas. *Wilson Bull.* 31:20-23.
____. 1919l. Notes on the races of *Quiscalus quiscula* (Linnaeus). *Auk* 36:549-555.
____. 1920a. A new Cliff Swallow from Canada. *Can. Field-Nat.* 33:95.
____. 1920b. A synopsis of the genus *Thryomanes. Wilson Bull.* 32:18-28.
____. 1921a. The geographic races of *Cyanocitta cristata. Auk* 38:83-89.
____. 1921b. A revision of the races of *Dendroica auduboni. Ohio J. Sci.* 21:240-248.
____. 1922. Notes on North American birds. XI. *Auk* 39:72-78.
____. 1930a. Notes on a collection of birds from Arizona and New Mexico. *Sci. Pubs. Cleveland Mus. Nat. Hist.* 1:83-124.
____. 1930b. Another new subspecies of *Nannus troglodytes* from Alaska. *Proc. Biol. Soc. Washington* 43:151-152.
____. 1931a. *Ammospiza caudacuta diversa* (Bishop) a valid race. *Auk* 48:610-611.
____. 1931b. The Atlantic Coast races of *Thryospiza maritima* (Wilson). *Proc. Biol. Soc. Washington* 44:123-128.
____. 1932. Descriptions of new birds from Oregon, chiefly from the Warner Valley region. *Sci. Publ. Cleveland Mus. Nat. Hist.* 4:1-12.
____. 1934. A revision of North American House Wrens. *Ohio J. Sci.* 34:86-96.
____. 1937a. Descriptions of three new screech owls from the United States. *J. Washington Acad. Sci.* 27:354-357.
____. 1937b. Descriptions of two new passerine birds from the western United States. *Proc. Biol. Soc. Washington* 50:117-120.
____. 1937c. Description of a new chickadee from the eastern United States. *Proc. Biol. Soc. Washington* 50:219-220.
____. 1938. The bird life of Louisiana. *Bull. Dept. Cons. Louisiana* 28:1-834.
____. 1942. Description of a new race of the Grasshopper Sparrow. *Proc. Biol. Soc. Washington* 55:15-16.
____. 1946. Three new North American birds. *J. Washington Acad. Sci.* 36:388-389.

Oberholser, H.C. 1947. A new flycatcher from the western United States. *Proc. Biol. Soc. Washington* 60:77.

____. 1948. Descriptions of new races of *Geothlypis trichas* (Linnaeus). H.C. Oberholser, Cleveland, OH.

____. 1955. Description of a new Chipping Sparrow from Canada. *J. Washington Acad. Sci.* 45:59-60.

____. 1956. A new Hermit Thrush from Canada. *Proc. Biol. Soc. Washington* 69:69-70.

____. 1974. The bird life of Texas. Vols. 1 & 2. University of Texas Press, Austin, TX.

Odum, E.P. 1941. Annual cycle of the Black-capped Chickadee. *Auk* 58:518-535.

____. 1943. Some physiological variations in the Black-capped Chickadee. *Wilson Bull.* 55:178-191.

____. 1949. Weight variations in wintering White-throated Sparrows in relation to temperature and migration. *Wilson Bull.* 61:3-14.

Olyphant, J.C. 1972. A method for aging American Goldfinches. *Bird-banding* 43:173-181.

____. 1977. Bird Identification, including notes on the life history and plumage. Blue Jay. *Inl. Bird Banding News* 49:262-266.

Orians, G.H. 1963. Notes on fall-hatched Tricolored Blackbirds. *Auk* 80:552-553.

Ortega, C.P. and A. Cruz. 1992a. Differential growth patterns of nesting Brown-headed Cowbirds and Yellow-headed Blackbirds. *Auk* 109:368-376.

____ and ____. 1992b. Gene flow of the *obscurus* race into the north-central Colorado population of Brown-headed Cowbirds. *J. Field Ornith.* 63:311-317.

____, J.C. Ortega, S.A. Backensto, and C.A. Rapp. 1996. Improved methods for aging second-year male and after-second-year male Brown-headed Cowbirds. *J. Field Ornith.* 67:542-548.

Ortiz-Crespo, F.I. 1971. Winter occurrences of *Selasphorus* hummingbirds in the San Francisco Bay region. *Bird-Banding* 42:290-292.

____. 1972. A new method to separate immature and adult hummingbirds. *Auk* 89:851-857.

Ouellet, H. 1993. Bicknell's Thrush: Taxonomic status and distribution. *Wilson Bull.* 105:545-572.

Owen, D.F. 1963a. Variation in North American screech owls and the subspecies concept. *Syst. Zool.* 12:8-14.

____. 1963b. Polymorphism in the Screech Owl in eastern North America. *Wilson Bull.* 75:183-190.

Packard, F.M. 1936. Notes on plumages of the Eastern Red-wing. *Bird-banding* 7:77-80.

____. 1945. Possible intergrades between Myrtle and Audubon's warblers. *Auk* 62:623.

Packard, G.C. 1967a. Seasonal variation in bill length in House Sparrows. *Wilson Bull.* 79:345-346.

____. 1967b. House Sparrows: Evolution of populations from the Great Plains and the Colorado Rockies. *Syst. Zool.* 16:73-89.

Palmer, R.S. 1972. Patterns of molting. Pp 65-102 *in* D.S. Farner and J.R. King, eds., Avian biology. Vol. II. Academic press, New York.

Palmer, W. 1894. Plumages of the young Hooded Warbler. *Auk* 11:282-291.

Panza, R.K. and K.C. Parkes. 1992. Baja California specimens of *Parus gambeli baileyae*. *W. Birds* 23:87-89.

Parkes, K.C. 1949. Brewster's Warbler breeding in Yates County, New York. *Wilson Bull.* 61-48-49.

____. 1951. The genetics of the Golden-winged × Blue-winged warbler complex. *Wilson Bull.* 63:5-15.

____. 1952a. Wayne's Long-billed Marsh Wren in New Brunswick. *Can. Field-Nat.* 66:173-174.

____. 1952b. Post-juvenal wing molt in the Bobolink. *Wilson Bull.* 64:161-162.

____. 1953a. The incubation patch in males of the suborder Tyranni. *Condor* 55:218-219.

____. 1953b. Some bird records of importance from New York. *Wilson Bull.* 65:46-47.

____. 1953c. The Yellow-throated Warbler in New York. *Kingbird* 3:4-6.

____. 1954. Notes on some birds of the Adirondack and Catskill Mountains, New York. *Ann. Carnegie Mus.* 33:149-178.

____. 1955. Sympatry, allopatry, and the subspecies in birds. *Syst. Zool.* 4:35-40.

____. 1957a. Notes, chiefly distributional, on some Florida birds. *Wilson Bull.* 69:106-107.

____. 1957b. The juvenal plumages of the finch genera *Atlapetes* and *Pipilo*. *Auk* 74:499-502.

____. 1957c. The White-winged Crossbills of Newfoundland. *Can. Field-Nat.*

____. 1959. Systematic notes on North American birds. 3. The northeastern races of the Long-billed Marsh Wren (*Telmatodytes palustris*). *Ann. Carnegie Mus.* 35:275-281.

____. 1961. Taxonomic relationships among the American redstarts. *Wilson Bull.* 73:374-379.

Parkes, K.C. 1963. The contribution of museum collections to the study of the living bird. *Living Bird* 2:121-130.

____. 1967. Prealternate molt in the Summer Tanager. *Wilson Bull.* 79:456-458.

____. 1972. Tail molt in the family Icteridae (abstract). *Proc. XV Int. Ornith. Congr.* 1972:674.

____. 1978. Still another Parulid intergeneric hybrid (*Mniotilta × Dendroica*) and its taxonomic and evolutionary implications. *Auk* 95:682-690.

____. 1979. Plumage variation in female Black-throated Blue Warblers. *Cont. Birdlife* 1:133-135.

____. 1982a. Subspecies taxonomy: Unfashionable does not mean irrelevant. *Auk* 99:596-598.

____. 1982b. Parallel geographic variation in three *Myiarchus* flycatchers in the Yucatan Peninsula and adjacent areas (Aves: Tyrannidae). *Ann. Carnegie Mus.* 51:1-16.

____. 1982c. Further comments on the field identification of North American pipits. *Am. Birds* 36:20-22.

____. 1984. An apparent hybrid Black-billed x Yellow-billed cuckoo. *Wilson Bull.* 96:294-296.

____. 1985a. Sexing Blue-gray Gnatcatchers (*Polioptila caerulea*). *Ontario Birds* 3:104-106.

____. 1985b. Yellow-rumped Warbler in flight feather molt on Great Gull Island. *Kingbird* 35:114-115.

____. 1987a. [On juvenal plumage in Downy Woodpecker.] *N. Am. Bird-Bander* 12:78.

____. 1987b. Sorting out the chickadees in southwestern Pennsylvania. *Pennsylvania Birds* 1:105-110. [Reprinted in *Birding* 20:308-310.]

____. 1988a. [On hybrid warblers.] *Birding* 20:254-256.

____. 1988b. Identification guide to North American Passerines. [Review of Pyle *et al.* 1987.] *Auk* 105:598-601.

____. 1988c. A brown-eyed adult Red-eyed Vireo specimen. *J. Field Ornith.* 59:60-62.

____. 1988d. Color variation in male Scarlet Tanager wings. *Bird Observer* 16:324-325.

____. 1989a. Sex ratios based on museum specimens - a caution. *Colonial Waterbirds* 12:130-131.

____. 1989b. Juvenile warblers. *Birding* 21:249.

____. 1991. Family tree: Tracing the genealogy of Brewster's and Lawrence's warbler. *Birding World* 5:34-37.

____. 1992a. Ageing North American warblers. *Birding World* 5:445.

____. 1992b. The subspecies of the Sharp-tailed Sparrow and the re-identification of a Western Pennsylvania specimen. *Pennsylvania Birds* 6:13-14.

____. 1993. AHY White-throated Sparrows said to have retained juvenal plumage. *N. Am. Bird Bander* 18:164.

____. 1995a. Moult and ageing terminology. *Brit. Birds* 88:604-605.

____. 1995b. Identification of Bicknell's Thrush. *Birding World* 8:316-317.

____. 1995c. Reinterpretation of the probable parentage of a hybrid wood-warbler (*Seiurus × Dendroica*). *Auk* 112:510-511.

____. 1996. Nashville × Tennessee warbler hybrids. *Ontario Birds* 14:110-116.

____. 1997. The Northern Cardinals of the Carribean Slope of Mexico, with the description of an additional subspecies from Yucatan. Pp. 129-138 *in* R.W. Dickerman, *comp.*, The era of Allan R. Phillips: A Festschrift. R.W. Dickerman, Albuquerque, NM.

____ and E.R. Blake. 1965. Taxonomy and nomenclature of the Bronzed Cowbird. *Fieldiana Zool.* 44:207-216.

____ and R.C. Leberman. 1967. Abnormal retention of juvenal feathers by a Catbird. *Bird-Banding* 38:326.

____ and R.W. Dickerman. 1967. A new subspecies of Mangrove Warbler (*Dendroica petechia*) from Mexico. *Ann. Carnegie Mus. Nat. Hist.* 39:85-89

____ and A.R. Phillips. 1978. Two new Caribbean subspecies of Barn Owl (*Tyto alba*), with remarks on variation in other populations. *Ann. Carnegie Mus. Nat. Hist.* 47:479-492.

Parks, G.H. 1951. Plumage coloration and age of Evening Grosbeaks. *Bird-Banding* 22:23-32.

____. 1962. A convenient method of sexing and aging the Starling. *Bird-Banding* 33:148-151.

____ (Mr. and Mrs.). 1968. About the sexing and aging of wintertime American Goldfinches. *E. Bird Banding Assoc. News* 31:115-119.

Parmelee, D.F. 1992. Snowy Owl. *In* The Birds of North America, No. **10** (A. Poole, P. Stettenheim, and F. Gill, eds.). Acad. Nat. Sci., Philadelphia; Amer. Ornith. Union, Washington D.C.

Passmore, M.F. 1984. Reproduction by juvenile Common Ground-Doves in south Texas. *Wilson Bull.* 96:241-248.

____ and R.L. Jarvis. 1979. Reliability of determining sex of Band-tailed Pigeons by plumage characters. *Wildl. Soc. Bull.* 7:124-125.

Patten, M.A. 1993. A probable bilateral gynandromorphic Black-throated Blue Warbler. *Wilson Bull.* 105:695-698.

Patten, M.A. 1997. The lessons of *Catharus* thrushes revisited. Pp. 139-142 *in* R.W. Dickerman, *comp*., The era of Allan R. Phillips: A *Festshrift*. R.W. Dickerman, Albuquerque, NM.

____ and R.A. Erickson. 1994. Fifteenth report of the California Bird Records Committee. *W. Birds* 25:1-34.

Patterson, M. 1988. Possible occurrences of Allen's Hummingbird north of its recognized range. *Oregon Birds* 14:237-241.

____. 1989. [On the rictal bristles of Northwestern Crow.] *Oregon Birds* 15:286.

____. 1990. Green-backed *Selasphorus* hummingbirds in Clatsop County, Oregon. *Oregon Birds* 16:218-222.

Patterson, R.M. 1981. Latitudinal variation in length of Barn Swallow tails in North America. *N. Am. Bird Bander* 6:151-154.

Patti, S.T. and M.L. Meyers. 1976. A probable Mourning × MacGillivray's warbler hybrid. *Wilson Bull.* 88:490-491.

Paulsen, I. 1989. Northwestern Crow distinction? *Oregon Birds* 15:279-280.

____. 1995. New kinglet field mark. *Oregon Birds* 21:7.

Paulson, D. 1989. Northwestern Crow distinction? Maybe not. *Oregon Birds* 15:285.

____. 1992. Interior Song Sparrow in western Washington. *Washington Birds* 2:42-43.

Payne, R.B. 1961. Age variation and time of migration in Swainson's and Gray-cheeked thrushes. *Wilson Bull.* 73:384-386.

____. 1969. Breeding seasons and reproductive physiology of Tricolored Blackbirds and Redwinged Blackbirds. *Univ. California Pubs. Zool.* 90:1-137.

____. 1972. Mechanisms and control of molt. Pp 103-105 *in* D.S. Farner and J.R. King, eds., Avian biology. Vol. II. Academic Press, New York.

____. 1979. Two apparent hybrid *Zonotrichia* sparrows. *Auk* 96:595-599.

____. 1982. Ecological consequences of song matching: Breeding success and intraspecific song mimicry in Indigo Buntings. *Ecology* 63:401-411.

____. 1984. Sexual selection, lek and arena behavior, and sexual size dimorphism in birds. *Ornith. Monogr.* 33:1-52.

____. 1987. Populations and type specimens of a nomadic bird: Comments on the North American crossbills *Loxia pusilla* Gloger 1854 and *Crucirostra minor* Brehm 1845. *Occ. Papers Mus. Zool. Univ. Michigan* 714:1-37.

____. 1992. Indigo Bunting. *In* The Birds of North America, No. **4** (A. Poole, P. Stettenheim, and F. Gill, eds.). Acad. Nat. Sci., Philadelphia; Amer. Ornith. Union, Washington D.C.

____ and L.L. Payne. 1989. Heritability and behaviour observations: Extra-pair matings in Indigo Buntings. *Anim. Behav.* 38:457-467.

Paynter, R.A. Jr. 1957. Taxonomic notes on the New World forms of *Troglodytes*. *Brevoria* (*Mus. Comp. Zool.*) 71:1-15.

____. 1968. Check-list of birds of the world. Vol. XIV. Museum of Comparative Zoology, Cambridge, MA.

____. 1970. Check-list of birds of the world. Vol. XIII. Museum of Comparative Zoology, Cambridge, MA.

Pearson, A.M. and G.C. Moore. 1940. Feathers may reveal the age of Mourning Doves. *Alabama Cons.* 1:9-10.

Peer, B.P. and E.K. Bollinger. 1997. Common Grackle. *In* The Birds of North America, No. **271** (A. Poole and F. Gill, eds.). Acad. Nat. Sci., Philadelphia; Amer. Ornith. Union, Washington D.C.

Peeters, H.J. 1962. Nuptial behavior of the Band-tailed Pigeon in the San Francisco Bay area. *Condor* 64:445-470.

Peters, J.L. 1920. A new jay from Alberta. *Proc. New England Zool. Club* 7:51-52.

____. 1927a. Descriptions of new birds. *Proc. New England Zool. Club* 9:111-113.

____. 1927b. A revision of the Golden Warblers *Dendroica petechia* (Linne). *Proc. Biol. Soc. Washington* 40:31-42.

____. 1931. An account of the Yellow-green Vireo (*Vireosylva flavovirides* Cassin). *Auk* 48:575-587.

____. 1937. Check-list of the birds of the world. Vol. III. Harvard University Press, Cambridge, MA.

____. 1940. Check-list of the birds of the world. Vol. IV. Harvard University Press, Cambridge, MA.

____. 1942. The Canadian forms of the Sharp-tailed Sparrow, *Ammospiza caudacuta*. *Ann. Carnegie Mus.* 29:201-210.

____. 1945. Check-list of the birds of the world. Vol. V. Harvard University Press, Cambridge, MA.

____ and L. Griscom. 1938. Geographical variation in the Savannah Sparrows. *Bull. Mus. Comp. Zool.* 80:445-481.

Peterson, A.T. 1991. Geographic variation in the ontogeny of beak coloration of Gray-breasted Jays (*Aphelocoma ultramarina*). *Condor* 93:448-452.

Peterson, B.E. and C.E. Brown. 1974. Observations on the primary feather molt of immature Mourning Doves in Colorado. *J. Colorado-Wyoming Acad. Sci.* 7:58.

Petrides, G.A. 1943. Notes on a captive Redstart. *Wilson Bull.* 55:193-194.

____. 1950. Notes on determination of sex and age in the Woodcock and Mourning Dove. *Auk* 67:357-360.

Phillips, J.C. 1911. A year's collecting in the state of Tamaulipas, Mexico. *Auk* 28:67-89.

Phillips, A.R. 1939. The type of *Empidonax wrightii* Baird. *Auk* 56:311-312.

____. 1942a. Notes on the migrations of the Elf and Flammulated screech owls. *Wilson Bull.* 54:132-137.

____. 1942b. A new crow from Arizona. *Auk* 59:573-575.

____. 1943. Critical notes on two southwestern sparrows. *Auk* 60:242-248.

____. 1944a. The wing-formula in *Empidonax traillii*. *Auk* 61:293.

____. 1944b. Some differences between the Wright's and Gray flycatchers. *Auk* 61:293-294.

____. 1947a. The races of MacGillivray's Warbler. *Auk* 64:296-300.

____. 1947b. Records of occurrence of some southwestern birds. *Condor* 49:121-122.

____. 1948. Geographic variation in *Empidonax traillii*. *Auk* 65:507-514.

____. 1950a. The pale races of the Steller's Jay. *Condor* 52:252-254.

____. 1950b. The Great-tailed Grackles of the Southwest. *Condor* 52:78-81.

____. 1951. The molts of the Rufous-winged Sparrow. *Wilson Bull.* 63:323-326.

____. 1954. Western records of *Chaetura vauxi tamaulipensis*. *Wilson Bull.* 66:72-73.

____. 1958. Las peculiaridades del satrecito (*Psaltriparus paridae*) y su incubacion. *An. Inst. Biol. Mex.* 29:355-360.

____. 1959a. The nature of avian species. *J. Arizona Acad. Sci.* 1:22-30.

____. 1959b. La acrecencia de errores acerca de la ornitologia de Mexico, con notas sobre *Myiarchus*. *An. Inst. Biol. Mex.* 30:349-368.

____. 1961a. Notas sistemáticas sobre aves Mexicanas, I. *An. Inst. Biol. Mex.* 32:333-381.

____. 1961b. Notas sobre la chuparrosa *Thalurania* y ciertos plumajes de otras aves Mexicanas. *An. Inst. Biol. Mex.* 32:383-390.

____. 1962. Notas sistemáticas sobre aves Mexicanas, II. *An. Inst. Biol. Mex.* 33:331-372.

____. 1964. Notas sistemáticas sobre aves Mexicanas, III. *Rev. Soc. Mex. Hist. Nat.* 25:217-242.

____. 1966a. Further systematic notes on Mexican birds. *Bull. Brit. Ornith. Club.* 86:86-94.

____. 1966b. Biosystematics of sibling species of flycatchers in the *Empidonax hammondii-oberholseri-wrightii* complex. [Review of Johnson 1963a.] *Auk* 83:321-326.

____. 1966c. Further systematic notes on Mexican birds. *Bull. Brit. Ornith. Club.* 86:103-112.

____. 1966d. Further systematic notes on Mexican birds. *Bull. Brit. Ornith. Club.* 86:125-131.

____. 1966e. Further systematic notes on Mexican birds. *Bull. Brit. Ornith. Club.* 86:148-159.

____. 1970. A northern race of lark supposedly breeding in Mexico. *Bull. Brit. Ornith. Club* 90:115-116.

____. 1974a. The need for education and collecting. *Bird-Banding* 45:24-28.

____. 1974b. The first prebasic molt of the Yellow-breasted Chat. *Wilson Bull.* 86:12-15.

____. 1975a. Why neglect the difficult? *W. Birds* 6:69-86.

____. 1975b. The migrations of Allen's and other hummingbirds. *Condor* 77:196-205.

____. 1975c. The incredible American Red Crossbill *Loxia curvirostra* Carduelinae. *Emu* 74:282.

____. 1977. Sex and age determination of Red Crossbills (*Loxia curvirostra*). *Bird-Banding* 48:110-117.

____. 1979. The second DMNH/CFO taxonomy clinic. Part 1. *Colorado Field Ornith. J.* 13:92-100

____. 1982. Subspecies and species: Fundamentals, needs, and obstacles. *Auk* 99:612-615.

____. 1986. The known birds of North and Middle America. Part I. Allan R. Phillips, Denver, Colorado.

____. 1991. The known birds of North and Middle America. Part II. Allan R. Phillips, Denver, Colorado.

____. 1994a. The known birds of North and Middle America versus the current AOU list. *Auk* 111:770-773.

____. 1994b. A tentative key to the species of Kingbirds, with distributional notes. *J. Field Ornith.* 65:295-306.

____. 1995. The northern races of *Icterus pustulatus* (Icteridae), Scarlet-headed or Streaked-backed oriole. *Bull. Brit. Ornith. Club* 115:98-105.

____ and C. Chase III. 1982. The third annual DMNH/CFO taxonomy clinic. *Colorado Field Ornith. J.* 16:5-15.

____, ____, D. Casey, and B. Webb. 1983. Fourth annual CFO/DMNH taxonomy clinic. Parts 1 & 2. *Colorado Field Ornith. J.* 17:22-34.

____, ____, B. Webb, and D. Casey. 1984. Fourth annual CFO/DMNH taxonomy clinic. Parts 3 & 4. *Colorado Field Ornith. J.* 18:19-26.

____ and M. Holmgren. 1980. The second DMNH/CFO taxonomy clinic. Part 2. *Colorado Field Ornith. J.* 14:4-10.

Phillips, A.R., M.A. Howe, and W.E. Lanyon. 1966. Identification of the flycatchers of eastern North America, with special emphasis on the genus *Empidonax*. *Bird-Banding* 37:153-171.

____ and W.E. Lanyon. 1970. Additional notes on the flycatchers of eastern North America. *Bird-Banding* 41:190-197.

____, J. Marshall, and G. Monson. 1964. The birds of Arizona. Univ. Arizona Press, Tucson. 220 pp.

____ and K.C. Parkes. 1955. Taxonomic comments on the Western Wood Pewee. *Condor* 57:244-246. clinic. Parts 3 & 4. *Colorado Field Ornith. J.* 18:19-26.

____ and R. Phillips F. 1993. Distribution, migration, ecology, and relationships of the Five-striped Sparrow, *Aimophila quinquestriata*. *W. Birds* 24:65-72.

____ and L.L. Short. 1968. A probable intergeneric hybrid pewee (Tyranidae: *Contopus*) from Mexico. *Bull. Brit. Ornith. Club* 88:90-93.

____, S. Speich, and W. Harrison. 1973. Black-capped Gnatcatcher, a new breeding bird for the United States; with a key to the North American species of *Polioptila*. *Auk* 90:257-262.

____ and J.D. Webster. 1957. The Vaux Swift in Western Mexico. *Condor* 59:140-141.

____ and ____. 1961. Grace's Warbler in Mexico. *Auk* 78:551-553.

Pinkowski, B.C. 1974. Criteria for sexing Eastern Bluebirds in juvenile plumage. *Inl. Bird Banding News* 46:88-91.

____. 1976. Photoperiodic effects on the postjuvenal molt of the Eastern Bluebird. *Ohio J. Sci.* 76:268-273.

Piper, W.H. and R.H. Wiley. 1989a. Distinguishing morphs of the White-throated Sparrow in basic plumage. *J. Field Ornith.* 60:73-83.

____ and ____. 1989b. Correlates of dominance in wintering White-throated Sparrows. *Anim. Behav.* 37:298-310.

____ and ____. 1991. Effects of laparotomies on wintering White-throated Sparrows and the usefulness of wing chord as a criterion for sexing. *J. Field Ornith.* 62:40-45.

Pitelka, F.A. 1945a. Differentiation of the Scrub Jay, *Aphelocoma coerulescens*, in the Great Basin and Arizona. *Condor* 47:23-26.

____. 1945b. Pterylography, molt and age determination of American jays of the genus *Aphelocoma*. *Condor* 47:229-260.

____. 1946. Age in relation to migration in the Blue Jay. *Auk* 63:82-84

____. 1948. Notes on the distribution and taxonomy of Mexican game birds. *Condor* 50:113-123.

____. 1951a. Ecologic overlap and interspecific strife in breeding populations of Anna and Allen hummingbirds. *Ecology* 32:641-661.

____. 1951b. Speciation and ecologic distribution in American jays of the genus *Aphelocoma*. *Univ. California Pubs. Zool.* 50:195-464.

____. 1958. Timing of molt in Steller Jays of the Queen Charlotte Islands, British Columbia. *Condor* 60:38-49.

____. 1961a. A curtailed postjuvenal molt in the Steller Jay. *Auk* 78:634-636.

____. 1961b. Comments on types and taxonomy in the jay genus *Aphelocoma*. *Condor* 63:234-245.

____, R.K. Selander, and M. Alvarez de Toro. 1956. A hybrid jay from Chiapas, Mexico. *Condor* 58:98-106.

Pitocchelli, J. 1990. Plumage, morphometric, and song variation in Mourning (*Oporornis philadelphia*) and MacGillivray's (*O. tolmiei*) warblers. *Auk* 107:161-171.

____. 1992. Plumage and size variation in the Mourning Warbler. *Condor* 94:198-209.

____. 1993. Mourning Warbler. *In* The Birds of North America, No. **72** (A. Poole and F. Gill, eds.). Acad. Nat. Sci., Philadelphia; Amer. Ornith. Union, Washington D.C.

____. 1995. MacGillivray's Warbler. *In* The Birds of North America, No. **159** (A. Poole and F. Gill, eds.). Acad. Nat. Sci., Philadelphia; Amer. Ornith. Union, Washington D.C.

Pitts, D.T. 1985. Identification of second-year and after-second-year Eastern Bluebirds. *J. Field Ornith.* 56:422-424.

Pleasants, B.Y. 1993. Altamira Oriole. *In* The Birds of North America, No. **56** (A. Poole and F. Gill, eds.). Acad. Nat. Sci., Philadelphia; Amer. Ornith. Union, Washington D.C.

Plissner, J.H., S.J. Wagner, and P.A. Gowaty. 1994. Reliability of aging criteria by feather characteristics of Eastern Bluebirds. *J. Field Ornith.* 65:504-507.

Plumpton, D.L. and R.S. Lutz. 1994. Sexual size dimorphism, mate choice, and productivity of Burrowing Owls. *Auk* 111:724-727.

Post, W. 1994. Banding confirmation that some middle Atlantic Coast Boat-tailed Grackles visit Florida in the winter. *Florida Field Nat.* 22:51-52.

____ and J.S. Greenlaw. 1994. Seaside Sparrow. *In* The Birds of North America, No. **127** (A. Poole and F. Gill, eds.). Acad. Nat. Sci., Philadelphia; Amer. Ornith. Union, Washington D.C.

____, J.P. Poston, and G.T. Bancroft. 1996. *In* The Birds of North America, No. **207** (A. Poole and F. Gill, eds.). Acad. Nat. Sci., Philadelphia; Amer. Ornith. Union, Washington D.C.

Potter, E.F. 1980. Notes on nesting Yellow-billed Cuckoos. *J. Field Ornith.* 51:17-29.

Poulin, R.G., S.D. Grindal, and R.M. Brigham. 1996. Common Nighthawk. *In* The Birds of North America, No. **213** (A. Poole and F. Gill, eds.). Acad. Nat. Sci., Philadelphia; Amer. Ornith. Union, Washington D.C.

Power, D.M. 1969. Evolutionary implications of wing and size variation in the Red-winged Blackbird in relation to certain geographic and climatic factors: A multiple regression analysis. *Syst. Zool.* 18:363-373.

____. 1970a. Geographic variation of Red-winged Blackbirds in central North America. *Univ. Kansas Pubs. Mus. Nat. Hist.* 19:1-83.

____. 1970b. Geographic variation in the surface/volume ratio of the bill of Red-winged Blackbirds in relation to certain geographic and climatic factors. *Condor* 72:299-304.

____. 1971. Evolution of the House Finch on Santa Cruz Island, California. *Can. J. Zool.* 49:675-684.

____. 1979. Evolution in peripheral isolated populations: *Carpodacus* finches on the California islands. *Evolution* 33:834-847.

____. 1980. Evolution of land birds on the California islands. Pp. 613-642 *in* D.M. Power, ed., The California Islands: Proceedings of a multidisciplinary symposium. Santa Barbara Museum of Natural History, Santa Barbara, CA.

____. 1983. Variability in island populations of the House Finch. *Auk* 100:180-187.

Power, H.W. 1980. The foraging behavior of Mountain Bluebirds with emphasis on sexual foraging differences. *Ornith. Monogr.* 28:1-72.

____ and M.P. Lombardo. 1996. Mountain Bluebird. *In* The Birds of North America, No. **222** (A. Poole and F. Gill, eds.). Acad. Nat. Sci., Philadelphia; Amer. Ornith. Union, Washington D.C.

Powers, D.R. 1996. Magnificent Hummingbird. *In* The Birds of North America, No. **221** (A. Poole and F. Gill, eds.). Acad. Nat. Sci., Philadelphia; Amer. Ornith. Union, Washington D.C.

Pratt, H.D. 1974. Field identification of Great-tailed and Boat-tailed grackles in their zone of overlap. *Birding* 6:217-223.

____. 1991. Hybridization of Great-tailed and Boat-tailed grackles (*Quiscalus*) in Louisiana. *J. Louisiana Ornith.* 2:2-14.

Pravosudov, V.V. and T.C. Grubb. 1993. White-breasted Nuthatch. *In* The Birds of North America, No. **54** (A. Poole and F. Gill, eds.). Acad. Nat. Sci., Philadelphia; Amer. Ornith. Union, Washington D.C.

Preble, E.A. 1908. A biological investigation of the Athabaska-Mackenzie region. *N. Am. Fauna* 27:1-574.

Prescott, D.C. 1994. Intraspecific and geographical trends in body size of a differential migrant, the Evening Grosbeak. *Auk* 111:693-702.

Prescott, K.W. 1972. An adult Mockingbird with a pale white iris. *Bird-Banding* 43:219-220.

____. 1979. Weight, fat class and wing measurements of living Dark-eyed Juncos (*Junco hyemalis*) *Inl. Bird Banding* 52:1-7.

____. 1980a. Weight, fat class and wing measurements of Ruby-crowned Kinglets during migration. *Inl. Bird Banding* 52:1-7.

____. 1980b. Weight, fat class, and wing measurements of Golden-crowned Kinglets during migration. *Inl. Bird Banding* 52:41-48.

____. 1981. Weight, fat class, and wing measurements of Yellow-rumped Warblers during migration. *Inl. Bird Banding* 53:39-48.

____. 1982. Weight, fat class and wing measurement of Gray Catbirds during migration. *N. Am. Bird Bander* 7:146-149.

____. 1983. Weight, fat, and wing measurement variations of adult American Goldfinches in New Jersey. *N. Am. Bird Bander* 8:149-152.

____. 1986. Weight, fat, and wing measurement variations during migration and overwintering of White-throated Sparrows in New Jersey. *N. Am. Bird Bander* 11:46-51.

Prowse, A. 1993. Identification of Tennessee Warbler. *Brit. Birds* 86:541.

Pulich, W.M. and R.M. Dellinger. 1981. An example of a hybrid Green Jay × Blue Jay. *Wilson Bull.* 93:538-540.

Pustmueller, C.J. 1975. New method for sexing Steller's Jays. *Bird-banding* 46:342-343.

Pyle, P. 1995a. Incomplete flight-feather molts and age in certain North American non-passerines. *N. Am. Bird Bander* 20:15-26.

____. 1995b. Age of Norfolk Red-breasted Nuthatch. *Br. Birds*. 88:611.

____. 1997a. A further examination of wing and tail formulae in *Empidonax* and *Contopus* flycatchers. Pp. 147-154 *in* R.W. Dickerman, *comp.*, The era of Allan R. Phillips: A *Festshrift*. R.W. Dickerman, Albuquerque, NM.

____. 1997b. Flight-feather molt patterns and age in North American owls. *Monogr. Field Ornith.* 2:1-32.

____. 1997c. Molt limits in North American passerines. *N. Am. Bird Bander* 22:49-90.

____. In press. Eccentric first-year molt patterns in certain tyrannid flycatchers. *W. Birds*.

____ and P. Henderson. 1990. On separating female and immature *Oporornis* warblers in fall. *Birding* 22:222-229.

____ and S.N.G. Howell. 1995. Flight-feather molt patterns and age in North American woodpeckers. *J. Field Ornith.* 66:564-581.

Pyle, P. and S.N.G. Howell. 1996. *Spizella* sparrows. Intraspecific variation and identification. *Birding* 28:374-387.

____, S.N.G. Howell, and G.M. Yanega. 1997. Molt, retained flight feathers and age in North American hummingbirds. Pp. 155-166 *in* R.W. Dickerman, *comp.*, The era of Allan R. Phillips: A *Festshrift*. R.W. Dickerman, Albuquerque, NM.

____, S.N.G. Howell, R.P. Yunick, and D.F. DeSante. 1987. Identification guide to North American passerines. Slate Creek Press, Bolinas, CA.

____ and G. McCaskie. 1992. Thirteenth report of the California Bird Records Committee. *W. Birds* 23:97-132.

____ and D.A. Sibley. 1992. Juvenal-plumaged Le Conte's Sparrows on migration. Are they being overlooked? *Birding* 24:70-76.

____ and P. Unitt. In press. Molt and plumage variation by age and sex in the California and Black-tailed gnatcatchers. *Studies Avian Biol.*

Quay, W.B. 1987. Physical characteristics and arrival times of Indigo Buntings in eastern Missouri. *N. Am. Bird Bander* 12:2-7.

____. 1989. Insemination of Tennessee Warblers during spring migration. *Condor* 91:660-670.

Radke, E.L., A.M. Craig, and R.G. McCaskie. 1968. Bushtit (*Psaltriparus minimus*). *W. Bird Bander* 43:5.

Raitt, R.J. 1967. Relationships between black-eared and plain-eared forms of Bushtits. *Auk* 84:503-528.

Ralph, C.J. and C.A. Pearson. 1971. Correlation of age, size of territory, plumage, and breeding success in White-crowned Sparrows. *Condor* 73:77-80.

Ramos, M.A. and D.W. Warner. 1980. Analysis of North American subspecies of migrant birds wintering in Los Tuxtlas, southern Veracruz, Mexico. Pp. 173-180 *in* A. Keast and E.S. Morton, eds., Migrant birds in the Neotropics: ecology, behavior, distribution, and conservation. Smithsonian Institution Press, Washington D.C.

Rand, A.L. 1944a. A northern record of the Flicker and a note on the cline *Colaptes auratus* cl. *auratus-luteus*. *Can. Field-Nat.* 58:183-184.

____. 1944b. Notes on the Palm Warbler, *Dendroica palmarum* (Gmelin) in Canada. *Can. Field-Nat.* 58:181-182.

____. 1946. A new race of the Purple Finch *Carpodacus purpureus* (Gmelin). *Can. Field-Nat.* 60:95-96.

____. 1948a. Probability in subspecific identification of single specimens. *Auk* 65:416-432.

____. 1948b. Birds of southern Alberta. *Nat. Mus. Canada Bull.* 111:1-105.

____. 1948c. Distributional notes on Canadian birds. *Can. Field-Nat.* 62:175-180.

____. 1957. *Lanius ludovicianus miamensis* Bishop, a valid race from southern Florida. *Auk* 74:503-505.

____ and H. Traylor. 1949. Variation in *Dumetella carolinensis*. *Auk* 66:25-28.

____ and ____. 1950. The amount of overlap allowable for subspecies. *Auk* 67:169-183.

Rappole, J.H. 1983. Analysis of plumage variation in the Canada Warbler. *J. Field Ornith.* 54:152-159.

____, E.C. Rappole, and C. P. Barkan. 1979. Basic plumage in the male Blue-gray Gnatcatcher. *Bird-Banding* 50:71.

Rathbun, S.F. 1917. Description of a new subspecies of the Western Meadowlark. *Auk* 34:68-70.

____. 1925. The Black Swift and its habits. *Auk* 42:497-516.

Ratti, J.T. 1984. Selected avian systematic problems in the Northwest: The 1983 A.O.U. Check-list. *Northwest Sci.* 58:237-242.

Raveling, D.G. 1965. Geographic variation and measurements of Tennessee Warblers killed at a TV tower. *Bird-Banding* 36:89-101.

____ and D.W. Warner. 1965. Plumages, molts and morphometry of Tennessee Warblers. *Bird-Banding* 36:169-179.

____ and ____. 1978. Geographic variation of Yellow Warblers killed at a TV tower. *Auk* 95:73-79.

Raynor, G.S. 1979. Weight and size variation in the Gray Catbird. *Bird-Banding* 50:124-144.

Rea, A.M. 1967. Age determination of Corvidae. Part 1:Common Crow. *W. Bird Bander* 42:44-47.

____. 1968. Age, sex, and race determination of Yellow-bellied Sapsuckers. *W. Bird Bander* 43:46-47.

____. 1969. Species, age and sex determination in the genus *Tyrannus*. *W. Bird Bander* 44:32-35.

____. 1970a. Age determination of Red-shafted Flickers. *W. Bird Bander* 45:52-54.

____. 1970b. Status of the Summer Tanager on the Pacific Slope. *Condor* 72:230-232.

____. 1972a. Notes on the Summer Tanager. *W. Bird Bander* 47:52-53.

____. 1972b. Banding worksheet for western birds. Summer Tanager. Supplement to *W. Bird Bander*, vol. 47.

____. 1983. Once a River. University of Arizona Press, Tucson, Arizona.

____ and D. Kanteena. 1968. Age determination of Corvidae. Part 2. Common and White-necked ravens. *W. Bird Bander* 43:6-9.

____ and K.L. Weaver. 1990. The taxonomy, distribution, and status of coastal California Cactus Wrens. *W. Birds* 21:81-119.

Reese, J.G. 1975. Fall remix and rectrix molt in the Cardinal. *Bird-banding* 46:305-310.

Reese, K.P. and J.A. Kadlec. 1982. Determining the sex of Black-billed Magpies by external measurements. *J. Field Ornith.* 53:417-418.

Reeves, H.M., A.D. Geis, and F.C. Kniffin. 1968. Mourning Dove capture and banding. *Special Sci. Report. Wildl.* #117. U.S. Fish and Wildl. Serv., Washington D.C.

Regelski, D.J. and R.R. Moldenhauer. 1997. Tropical Parula. *In* The Birds of North America, No. **293** (A. Poole and F. Gill, eds.). Acad. Nat. Sci., Philadelphia; Amer. Ornith. Union, Washington D.C.

Regosin, J.V. and S. Pruett-Jones. 1995. Aspects of breeding biology and social organization in the Scissor-tailed Flycatcher. *Condor* 97:154-164.

Reichenow, A. 1908. Neue Vogelarten. *Orn. Monatsb.* 16:191.

Releya, G.M. 1936. An attempt to measure statistically the differences between eastern and western subspecies of the same species. *Auk* 53:22-27.

Remsen, J.V. Jr. 1975. Identification of Purple and Cassin's finches. *Colorado Field Ornith. J.* 25:4-7. [Reprinted in *Birding* 8:231-234, 1976.]

____. 1995. The importance of continued collecting of bird specimens to ornithology and bird conservation. *Bird Conserv. Int.* 5:145-180.

____, S.W. Cardiff, and D.L. Dittmann. 1996. Timing of migration and status of vireos (Vireonidae) in Louisiana. *J. Field Ornith.* 67:119-140.

Reynolds, M.D. 1995. Yellow-billed Magpie. *In* The Birds of North America, No. **187** (A. Poole and F. Gill, eds.). Acad. Nat. Sci., Philadelphia; Amer. Ornith. Union, Washington D.C.

Reynolds, R.T. and B.D. Linkhart. 1984. Methods and materials for capturing and monitoring Flammulated Owls. *Great Basin Nat.* 44:49-51.

____ and ____. 1987. The nesting biology of the Flammulated Owl in Colorado. Pp. 239-248 *in* R.W. Nero, R.J. Clark, R.J. Knapton, and R.H. Hamre, eds., Biology and conservation of northern forest owls. U.S. For. Serv. Gen. Tech. Rep. RM-142.

Rhoads, S.N. 1893. Notes on certain Washington and British Columbia birds. *Auk* 10:16-24.

Richards, G.L. 1971. The Common Crow, *Corvus brachyrhynchos*, in the Great Basin. *Condor* 73:116-118.

Richardson, M. and D.W. Brauning. 1995. Chestnut-sided Warbler. *In* The Birds of North America, No. **190** (A. Poole and F. Gill, eds.). Acad. Nat. Sci., Philadelphia; Amer. Ornith. Union, Washington D.C.

Richmond, M.L., L.R. DeWeese, and R.E. Pillmore. 1980. Brief observations on the breeding biology of the Flammulated Owl in Colorado. *W. Birds* 11:35-46.

Richner, H. 1989. Avian laparoscopy as a field technique for sexing birds and an assessment of its effects on wild birds. *J. Field Ornith.* 60:137-142.

Ricklefs, R.E. 1972. Latitudinal variation in breeding productivity of the Rough-winged Swallow. *Auk* 89:826-836.

Ridgway, R. 1901. The birds of Middle and North America. Part I. *Bull. U.S. Nat. Mus.* 50(1):1-715.

____. 1902. The birds of Middle and North America. Part II. *Bull. U.S. Nat. Mus.* 50(2):1-834.

____. 1904. The birds of Middle and North America. Part III. *Bull. U.S. Nat. Mus.* 50(3):1-801.

____. 1906. "*Attratus* versus *megalonyx*. *Condor* 8:100.

____. 1907. The birds of Middle and North America. Part IV. *Bull. U.S. Nat. Mus.* 50(4):1-973.

____. 1911. The birds of Middle and North America. Part V. *Bull. U.S. Nat. Mus.* 50(5):1-859.

____. 1912. Color standards and color nomenclature. R.S. Ridgway, Washington D.C.

____. 1914. The birds of Middle and North America. Part VI. *Bull. U.S. Nat. Mus.* 50(6):1-882.

____. 1916. The birds of Middle and North America. Part VII. *Bull. U.S. Nat. Mus.* 50(7):1-543.

Riggins, J. and H. Riggins. 1974. Aging Swamp Sparrows by plumage. *Inl. Bird Banding News* 46:5-9.

____ and ____. 1977. Characteristics of Canada Warblers. *N. Am. Bird Bander* 2:117.

Righter, R. 1990. A discussion of the juvenile plumages of *Melospiza* sparrows as seen in the field in the Rocky Mountain area. *Colorado Field Ornith. J.* 24:73-75.

Riley, J.H. 1911. Descriptions of three new birds from Canada. *Proc. Biol. Soc. Washington* 24:233-236.

____. 1916. Three remarkable new species of birds from Santo Domingo. *Smithsonian Misc. Coll.* 16(15):1-2.

Rimmer, C.C. 1986. Identification of juvenile Lincoln's and Swamp sparrows. *J. Field Ornith.* 57:114-125.

____. 1988. Timing of the definitive prebasic molt in Yellow Warblers at James Bay, Ontario. *Condor* 90:141-156.

Rising, J.D. 1968. A multivariate assessment of interbreeding between the chickadees *Parus atricapillus* and *P. carolinensis*. *Syst. Zool.* 17:160-169.

____. 1970. Morphological variation and evolution in some North American orioles. *Syst. Zool.* 19:315-351.

Rising, J.D. 1973a. Morphological variation and status of the oriole *Icterus galbula, I. bullockii,* and *I. abeillei,* in the northern Great Plains and in Durango, Mexico. *Can. J. Zool.* 51:1267-1273.

____. 1973b. Age and seasonal variation in dimensions of House Sparrow, *Passer domesticus* (L.), from a single population in Kansas. Pp 327-336 *in* S.C Kendeigh and J. Pinowski, eds., Productivity, population dynamics and systematics of granivorous birds. Institute of Ecology, Warsaw, Poland.

____. 1983a. The Great Plains hybrid zones. *Current Ornith.* 1:131-157.

____. 1983b. The progress of oriole hybridization in Kansas. *Auk* 100:885-897.

____. 1987. Geographic variation of sexual dimorphism in size of Savannah Sparrow (*Passerculus sandwichensis*): A test of hypotheses. *Evolution* 41:514-524.

____. 1988. Geographic variation in sex ratios and body size in wintering flocks of Savannah Sparrows. *Wilson Bull.* 100:183-203.

____. 1996a. A guide to the identification and natural history of the sparrows of the United States and Canada. Academic Press, San Diego, CA.

____. 1996b. The stability of the oriole hybrid zone in western Kansas. *Condor.* 98:658-663.

____ and J.C. Avise. 1993. Application of genealogical-concordance principles to the taxonomy and evolutionary history of the Sharp-tailed Sparrow (*Ammodramus caudacutus*). *Auk* 110:844-856.

____ and D. Beadle. 1995. Taxonomy and identification of Fox Sparrows. *Birder's J.* 4:159-166.

____ and F.W. Schueler. 1980. Identification and status of wood pewees (*Contopus*) from the Great Plains:what are sibling species? *Condor* 82:301-308.

____ and G.F. Shields. 1980. Chromosomal and morphological correlates in two New World sparrows (*Emberizidae*). *Evolution* 34:654-662.

Risser, A.C. Jr. 1971. A technique for performing laparotomy on small birds. *Condor* 73:376-379.

Robbins, C.S. 1964. A guide to the aging and sexing of wood warblers (Parulidae) in fall. *E. Bird Banding Assoc. News* 27:199-215.

____. 1972. Identify, sex, and age it. Eastern *Empidonax* flycatchers. *Inl. Bird Banding News* 44:72-76.

____. 1975. Atlantic Flyway review - region V. *E. Bird Banding Assoc. News* 38:31-35.

Robbins, M.B., M.J. Braun, and E.A. Tobey. 1986. Morphological and vocal variation across a contact zone between the chickadees *Parus atricapillus* and *P. carolinensis. Auk* 103:655-666.

Roberts, C. 1990. More on the Northwestern Crow in Oregon. *Oregon Birds* 16:223-224.

Roberts, T.S. 1955. A manual for the identification of the birds of Minnesota and neighboring states. Univ. Minnesota Press, Minneapolis.

Robertson, R.J., B.J. Stutchbury, and R.R. Cohen. 1992. Tree Swallow. *In* The Birds of North America, No. 11 (A. Poole, P. Stettenheim, and F. Gill, eds.). Acad. Nat. Sci., Philadelphia; Amer. Ornith. Union, Washington D.C.

Robinson, T.R., R.R. Sargent, and M.B. Sargent. 1996. Ruby-throated Hummingbird. *In* The Birds of North America, No. 204 (A. Poole and F. Gill, eds.). Acad. Nat. Sci., Philadelphia; Amer. Ornith. Union, Washington D.C.

Robinson, W.D. 1995. Louisiana Waterthrush. *In* The Birds of North America, No. 151 (A. Poole and F. Gill, eds.). Acad. Nat. Sci., Philadelphia; Amer. Ornith. Union, Washington D.C.

____. 1996. Summer Tanager. *In* The Birds of North America, No. 248 (A. Poole and F. Gill, eds.). Acad. Nat. Sci., Philadelphia; Amer. Ornith. Union, Washington D.C.

Rodewald, P.G. and R.D. James. 1996. Yellow-throated Vireo. *In* The Birds of North America, No. 247 (A. Poole and F. Gill, eds.). Acad. Nat. Sci., Philadelphia; Amer. Ornith. Union, Washington D.C.

Rogers, D.I. 1990. The use of feather abrasion in molt studies. *Corella* 14:141-147.

Rogers, C.H. 1939. A new swift from the United States. *Auk* 56:465-468.

Rogers, C.M. 1991. An evaluation of the method of estimating body fat in birds by quantifying visible subcutaneous fat. *J. Field Ornith.* 62:349-356.

Rohwer, S.A. 1971. Molt and the annual cycle of the Chuck-will's-widow (*Caprimulgus carolinensis*). *Auk* 88:485-519.

____. 1972. A multivariate assessment of interbreeding between the meadowlarks, *Sturnella. Syst. Zool.* 21:313-338.

____. 1973. Plumage variability in Harris Sparrows. *Inl. Bird Banding News* 45:163-169.

____. 1976. Specific distinctness and adaptive differences in southwestern meadowlarks. *Occ. Papers Mus. Nat. Hist. Univ. Kansas* 44:1-14.

____. 1986. A previously unknown plumage of first-year Indigo Buntings and theories of delayed plumage maturation. *Auk* 103:281-292.

____. 1994. Two new hybrid *Dendroica* warblers and a new methodology for inferring parental species. *Auk* 111:441-449.

Rohwer, S.A. and J. Butler. 1977. Ground foraging and rapid molt in the Chuck-will's-widow. *Wilson Bull.* 89:165-166.

____, P.W. Ewald, and F.C. Rohwer. 1981. Variation in size, appearance and dominance within and among the sex and age classes of Harris' Sparrows. *J. Field Ornith.* 52:291-303.

____, S.D. Fretwell, and D.M. Niles. 1980. Delayed maturation in passerine plumages and the deceptive acquisition of resources. *Am. Nat.* 115:400-437.

____ and M.S. Johnson. 1992. Scheduling differences of molt and migration for Baltimore and Bullock's orioles persist in a common environment. *Condor* 94:992-994.

____, W.P. Klein Jr., and S. Heard. 1983. Delayed plumage maturation and the presumed prealternate molt in American Redstarts. *Wilson Bull.* 95:199-208.

____ and J. Manning. 1990. Differences in timing and number of molts for Baltimore and Bullock's orioles: Implications to hybrid fitness and theories of delayed plumage maturation. *Condor* 95:125-140.

____ and D.M. Niles. 1979. The subadult plumage of male Purple Martins: Variability, female mimicry and recent evolution. *Z. Tierpsychol.* 51:282-300.

____ and F.C. Rohwer. 1978. Status signalling in Harris Sparrows: Experimental deceptions achieved. *Anim. Behav.* 26:1012-1022.

____, C.W. Thompson, and B.E. Young. 1992. Clarifying the Humphrey-Parkes molt and plumage terminology. *Condor* 94:297-300.

Roth, R.R., M.S. Johnson, and T.J. Underwood. 1996. Wood Thrush. *In* The Birds of North America, No. 246 (A. Poole and F. Gill, eds.). Acad. Nat. Sci., Philadelphia; Amer. Ornith. Union, Washington D.C.

Rothstein, S.I. 1978. Geographical variation in the nestling coloration of parasitic cowbirds. *Auk* 95:152-160.

Rounds, R.C. and H.L. Munro. 1982. A review of hybridization between *Sialia sialis* and *S. currucoides. Wilson Bull.* 94:219-223.

Russell, S.M. 1996. Anna's Hummingbird. *In* The Birds of North America, No. 226 (A. Poole and F. Gill, eds.). Acad. Nat. Sci., Philadelphia; Amer. Ornith. Union, Washington D.C.

____, R.O. Russell, and S. Wethington. 1994. Lucifer Hummingbirds banded in Southeastern Arizona. *N. Am. Bird Bander* 19:96-98.

Ryan, L.S. 1969. Sexing Purple Finches. *Inl. Bird Banding News* 41:123-125.

____. 1978. Dark-eyed Junco wing chord lengths. *Inl. Bird Banding News* 50:43-45.

Sadler, K.C., R.E. Tomlinson, and H.M. Wight. 1970. Progress of primary feather molt of adult Mourning Doves in Missouri. *J. Wildl. Manage.* 34:783-788.

Saiza, A. 1968. Age determination of Corvidae. Part III. Juveniles. *W. Bird Bander* 43:20-23.

Salomonsen, F. 1928. Bemerkungen über die Verbreitung der *Carduelis linaria* Gruppe und Ihre Variationen. *Vidensk. medd. Dansk Naturalh. Foren.* 86:123-202.

____. 1931. On the geographical variation in the Snow Bunting (*Plectrophenax nivalis*). *Ibis* 13th Series, 1:57-70.

Salomonsen, M.G. and R.P. Balda. 1977. Winter territoriality of Townsend's Solitaires (*Myadestes townsendi*) in a piñyon-juniper-ponderosa pine ecotone. *Condor* 79:148-161.

Salt, W.R. 1954. The structure of the cloacal protuberance of the Vesper Sparrow (*Pooecetes gramineus*) and certain other passerine birds. *Auk* 71:64-73.

Samson, F.B. 1974a. On determining sex and age in the Cassin's Finch. *W. Bird Bander* 49:4-7.

Samson, F.B. 1974b. Banding worksheet for western birds. Cassin's Finch. Supplement to *W. Bird Bander,* vol. 49.

____. 1976. Pterylosis and molt in Cassin's Finch. *Condor* 78:505-511.

Samuel, D.E. 1971a. The breeding biology of Barn and Cliff swallows in West Virginia. *Wilson Bull.* 83:284-301.

____. 1971b. Field methods for determining the sex of Barn Swallows (*Hirundo rustica*). *Ohio J. Sci.* 71:125-128.

Sanders, M. 1979. In Detail. Acorn Woodpecker. *Cont. Birdlife* 1:43.

Saner, G.P. 1975. Some differences between mature and immature Purple Martins. *Inl. Bird Banding News* 47:187-189.

Saunders, G.B. 1968. Seven new White-winged Doves from Mexico, Central America and southwestern United States. *N. Am. Fauna* 65:1-30.

Sawyer, P.J. 1961. Report on the cause of mortality and the morphometry of seventy Ruby-crowned Kinglets killed at the WENH-TV tower in Deerfield, New Hampshire. *Bird-Banding* 32:162-168.

Schaeffer, F.S. 1968. The Barn Swallow: Observations during breeding season. *E. Bird Banding Assoc. News* 31:250-252.

____. 1974. Chin spots in Louisiana Waterthrush. *E. Bird Banding Assoc. News* 37:128.

Scharf, C.S. 1987. Sex determination of the Black-billed Magpie. *Can. Field-Nat.* 101:111-114.

Scharf, W.S. and J. Kren. 1996. Orchard Oriole. *In* The Birds of North America, No. 255 (A. Poole and F. Gill, eds.). Acad. Nat. Sci., Philadelphia; Amer. Ornith. Union, Washington D.C.

Schlinger, B.A. and G.H. Adler. 1990. A nonparametric aid in identifying sex of cryptically dimorphic birds. *Wilson Bull.* 102:545-550.

Schneider, K.J. 1981. Age determination by skull pneumatization in the Field Sparrow. *J. Field Ornith.* 52:57-59.

Schulz, J.H., S.L. Sheriff, Z. He, C.E. Braun, R.D. Drobney, R.E. Tomlinson, D.D. Dolton, and R.A. Montgomery. 1995. Accuracy of techniques used to assign Mourning Dove age and gender. *J. Wildl. Manage.* 59:759-765.

Schussler, G.W. 1918. The salt marsh yellowthroats of San Francisco. *Condor* 20:62-64.

Schwab, R.G. and R.E. Marsh. 1967. Reliability of external sex characteristics of the Starling in California. *Bird-Banding* 38:143-147.

Schwartz, A. 1970. Subspecific variation in two species of Antillean birds. *Quart. J. Florida Acad. Sci.* 33:221-236.

Sclater, W.L. 1939. A note on some American orioles of the family Icteridae. *Ibis* 14th Series, 3:140-145.

Scott, D.M. 1967. Postjuvenal molt and determination of age of the Cardinal. *Bird-Banding* 38:37-51.

_____, C.D. Ankney, and C.H. Jarosch. 1976. Sapsucker hybridization in British Columbia: Changes in 25 years. *Condor* 78:253-257.

Scott, P.E. 1994. Lucifer Hummingbird. *In* The Birds of North America, No. 134 (A. Poole and F. Gill, eds.). Acad. Nat. Sci., Philadelphia; Amer. Ornith. Union, Washington D.C.

Sealy, S.G. 1969. Apparent hybridization between Snow Bunting and McKay's Bunting on St. Lawrence Island, Alaska. *Auk* 86:350-351.

_____. 1979. Prebasic molt of the Northern Oriole. *Can J. Zool.* 57:1473-1478.

_____. 1985. Analysis of a sample of Tennessee Warblers window killed during spring migration in Manitoba. *N. Am. Bird Bander* 10:121-124.

_____. 1986. Fall migration of Northern Orioles: An analysis of tower-killed individuals. *N. Am. Bird Bander* 11:43-45.

_____ and G.C. Biermann. 1983. Timing of breeding and migrations in a population of Least Flycatchers in Manitoba. *J. Field Ornith.* 54:113-124.

_____, D.A. Sexton, and K.M. Collins. 1980. Observations of a White-winged Crossbill invasion of southeastern Manitoba. *Wilson Bull.* 92:114-116.

Searcy, W.A. 1979. Size and mortality in male Yellow-headed Blackbirds. *Condor* 81:304-305.

Sedgwick, J.A. 1993. Dusky Flycatcher. *In* The Birds of North America, No. 78 (A. Poole and F. Gill, eds.). Acad. Nat. Sci., Philadelphia; Amer. Ornith. Union, Washington D.C.

_____. 1994. Hammond's Flycatcher. *In* The Birds of North America, No. 109 (A. Poole and F. Gill, eds.). Acad. Nat. Sci., Philadelphia; Amer. Ornith. Union, Washington D.C.

Selander, R.K. 1953. Notes on the Red Crossbills of the Uinta and Wasatch Mountains, Utah. *Condor* 55:158-160.

_____. 1954. A systematic review of the booming nighthawks of western North America. *Condor* 56:57-82.

_____. 1958. Age determination and molt in the Boat-tailed Grackle. *Condor* 62:355-375.

_____. 1959. Polymorphism in Mexican Brown Jays. *Auk* 76:385-417.

_____. 1964. Speciation in Wrens of the genus *Campylorhynchus*. *Univ. California Pubs. Zool.* 74:1-305.

_____. 1966. Sexual dimorphism and differential niche utilization in birds. *Condor* 68:113-151.

_____. 1971. Systematics and speciation in birds. *Avian Biology* 1:57-147.

_____. 1972. Sexual selection and dimorphism in birds. Pp. 180-230 *in* B.G. Campbell, ed., Sexual selection and the ascent of man (1871-1971). Aldine-Atherton, Chicago, IL.

_____ and M. Alvarez de Toro. 1955. A new race of the Booming Nighthawk from southern Mexico. *Condor* 57:144-147.

_____ and J.K. Baker. 1957. The Cave Swallow in Texas. *Condor* 59:345-363.

_____ and D.R. Giller. 1959. Interspecific relations of woodpeckers in Texas. *Wilson Bull.* 71:107-124.

_____ and _____. 1960. First-year plumages of the Brown-headed Cowbird and Red-winged Blackbird. *Condor* 62:202-214.

_____ and _____. 1961. Analysis of sympatry of Great-tailed and Boat-tailed grackles. *Condor* 63:29-86.

_____ and _____. 1963. Species limits in the woodpecker genus *Centurus* (Aves). *Bull. Am. Mus. Nat. Hist.* 124:213-274.

_____ and R.F. Johnston. 1967. Evolution in the House Sparrow. I. Intrapopulation variation in North America. *Condor* 69:217-258.

Seutin, G. 1991. Morphometric identification of Traill's Flycatchers: An assessment of Stein's formula. *J. Field Ornith.* 62:308-313.

_____, P.T. Boag, and L.M. Ratcliffe. 1992. Plumage variability in redpolls from Churchill, Manitoba. *Auk* 109:771-785.

_____, P.T. Boag, and L.M. Ratcliffe. 1993. Morphometric variability in redpolls from Churchill, Manitoba. *Auk* 110:832-843.

Shaub, B.M. 1950. Weight variation of Greater Redpolls. *Bird Banding* 21:105-111.

Shaub, B.M. 1958. A juvenal Evening Grosbeak appears in Northampton, Massachusetts, in late October 1957. *Bird Banding* 29:31-34.

_____. and M.S. Shaub. 1953. Adult and young Evening Grosbeaks at Saranac Lake, New York: Summer of 1952. *Bird-Banding* 24:135-141.

Sheppard, J.M. 1972a. Banding worksheet for western birds. Lazuli Bunting. Supplement to *W. Bird Bander*, vol. 47.

_____. 1972b. Banding worksheet for western birds. Lesser Goldfinch. Supplement to *W. Bird Bander*, vol. 47.

_____. 1996. Le Conte's Thrasher. *In* The Birds of North America, No. 230 (A. Poole and F. Gill, eds.). Acad. Nat. Sci., Philadelphia; Amer. Ornith. Union, Washington D.C.

_____ and C.T. Collins. 1971a. Banding worksheet for western birds. Western Tanager. Supplement to *W. Bird Bander*, vol. 46.

_____ and _____. 1971b. Banding worksheet for western birds. Black-headed Grosbeak. Supplement to *W. Bird Bander*, vol. 46.

_____ and M.K. Klimkiewicz. 1976. An update to Wood's Bird Bander's Guide. *N. Am. Bird Bander* 1:25-27. [Reprinted in *Inl. Bird Banding News* 48:88-91.]

Sherry, T.W. and R.T. Holmes. 1997. Black-throated Blue Warbler. *In* The Birds of North America, No. 271 (A. Poole and F. Gill, eds.). Acad. Nat. Sci., Philadelphia; Amer. Ornith. Union, Washington D.C.

Shields, K. 1993. Early skull pneumatization in the Black Phoebe (*Sayornis nigricans*). *N. Am. Bird Bander* 18:164.

Short, L.L. Jr. 1963. Hybridization in the wood-warblers *Vermivora pinus* and *V. chrysoptera*. *Proc. XIII Int. Ornith. Congr.* 1962:147-160.

_____. 1965. Hybridization in the flickers (*Colaptes*) of North America. *Bull. AM. Mus. Nat. Hist.* 129:307-428.

_____. 1968a. Variation of Ladder-backed Woodpeckers in southwestern North America. *Proc. Biol. Soc. Washington* 81:1-10.

_____. 1968b. Sympatry of Red-breasted Meadowlarks in Argentina, and the taxonomy of meadowlarks (Aves: *Leistes, Pezites, Sturnella*). *Am. Mus. Novitates* 2349:1-30.

_____. 1969a. Taxonomic aspects of avian hybridization. *Auk* 86:84-105.

_____. 1969b. "Isolating mechanisms" in the Blue-winged Warbler - Golden-winged Warbler complex. *Evolution* 23:355-356.

_____. 1971a. Systematics and behavior of some North American woodpeckers, genus *Picoides* (Aves). *Bull. Am. Mus. Nat. Hist.* 145:1-118.

_____. 1971b. Hybridization and introgression in flickers. *E. Bird Banding Assoc. News* 34:4-8.

_____. 1982. Woodpeckers of the World. *Monogr. Delaware Mus. Nat. Hist.* 4:1-676.

_____ and R.C. Banks. 1965. Notes on birds of northwestern Baja California. *Trans. San Diego Soc. Nat. Hist.* 14:41-52.

_____ and T.D. Burleigh. 1965. An intergeneric hybrid flycatcher (*Contopus* × *Empidonax*) from Idaho. *Proc. Biol. Soc. Washington* 78:33-37.

_____ and J.J. Morony Jr. 1970. A second hybrid Williamson's × Red-naped Sapsucker and an evolutionary history of sapsuckers. *Condor* 72:310-315.

_____ and A.R. Phillips. 1966. More hybrid hummingbirds from the United States. *Auk* 83:253-265.

_____ and C.S. Robbins. 1967. An intergeneric hybrid wood warbler (*Seiurus* × *Dendroica*). *Auk* 84:534-543.

_____ and S.W. Simon. 1965. Additional hybrids of the Slate-colored Junco and White-throated Sparrow. *Condor* 67:438-442.

Shortt, T.M. 1951. On the juvenal plumages of North American pipits. *Auk* 68:265.

Sibley, C.G. 1940. The Warbling Vireo of the Cape District of Lower California. *Condor* 42:255-258.

_____. 1950. Species formation in the Red-eyed Towhees of Mexico. *Univ. California Pubs. Zool.* 50:109-194.

_____. 1954. Hybridization in the red-eyed towhees of Mexico. *Evolution* 8:252-290.

_____. 1956. A white-throated Golden-crowned Sparrow. *Condor* 58:294-295.

_____. 1957a. The evolutionary and taxonomic significance of sexual dimorphism and hybridization in birds. *Condor* 59:166-191.

_____. 1957b. The abbreviated inner primaries of nestling woodpeckers. *Auk* 74:102-103.

_____ and O.S. Pettingill Jr. 1955. A hybrid longspur from Saskatchewan. *Auk* 72:423-425.

_____ and L.L. Short Jr. 1959. Hybridization of the buntings (*Passerina*) of the Great Plains. *Auk* 76:443-463.

_____ and _____. 1964. Hybridization of the orioles of the Great Plain. *Condor* 66:130-150.

_____ and D.A. West. 1959. Hybridization in the Rufous-sided Towhees of the Great Plains. *Auk* 76:326-338.

_____ and _____. 1964. Hybridization in the red-eyed towhees of Mexico: The populations of the southeastern plateau region. *Auk* 81:479-504.

Sibley, D.A. 1994. A guide to finding and identifying hybrid birds. *Birding* 26:162-177.

_____. 1996. Field identification of the Sharp-tailed Sparrow complex. *Birding* 28:196-208.

Sibley, D.A. and S.N.G. Howell. Identification of White and Black-backed wagtails in basic plumage. Unpublished ms.

Silovsky, G.D., H.M. Wright, L.H. Sisson, T.L. Fox, and S.W. Harris. 1968. Methods of determining age of Band-tailed Pigeons. *J. Wildl. Manage* 32:421-424.

Simon, D. 1977. Identification of Clay-colored, Brewer's and Chipping sparrows in fall plumage. *Birding* 9:189-191.

Simon, S.W. 1959. Occurrence and measurements of Black-capped Chickadees at Monkton, Md. *Maryland Birdlife* 15:3-4. [Reprinted in *E. Bird Banding Assoc. News* 23:11-12.]

Slack, H.E. III. 1994. Age and sex related characteristics of the Loggerhead Shrike (*Lanius l. ludovicianus*) in coastal Mississippi. *N. Am. Bird Bander* 19:84-89.

Slack, R.S. 1992a. An unexpected sex ratio in a sample of Northern Saw-whet Owls. *N. Am. Bird Bander* 17:1-5.

____. 1992b. Primary molt patterns of Northern Saw-whet Owls (*Aegolius acadicus*) captured during spring migration. *N. Am. Bird Bander* 17:97-101.

Smith, C.E. 1966. Preliminary notes on a six-year study of Rose-breasted Grosbeak plumages. *Bird-Banding* 37:49-51.

Smith, D.G. and S.N. Wiemeyer. 1992. Determining sex of Eastern Screech-Owls using discriminant function analysis. *J. Raptor Res.* 26:24-26.

Smith, H.M. and F.N. White. 1956. A case for the trinomen. *Syst. Zool.* 5:183-190.

Smith, J.N.M. and R. Zach. 1979. Heritability of some morphological characters in a Song Sparrow population. *Evolution* 33:460-467.

Smith, J.I. 1987. Evidence of hybridization between Red-bellied and Golden-fronted woodpeckers. *Condor* 89:377-386.

Smith, P.W., D.S. Evered, L.R. Messick, and M.C. Wheeler. 1990. First verifiable records of the Thick-billed Vireo from the United States. *Am. Birds* 44:372-376.

____ and A. Sprunt IV. The Shiny Cowbird reaches the United States. *Am. Birds.* 41:370-371.

Smith, S.M. 1991. The Black-capped Chickadee. Behavioral ecology and natural history. Cornell University Press, Ithaca, NY.

____. 1993. Black-capped Chickadee. *In* The Birds of North America, No. 39 (A. Poole, P. Stettenheim, and F. Gill, eds.). Acad. Nat. Sci., Philadelphia; Amer. Ornith. Union, Washington D.C.

Smith, W.A. 1968. The Band-tailed Pigeon in California. *California Fish & Game* 54:4-16.

Smith, W.P. 1979. Timing of skull ossification in Kinglets. *N. Am. Bird Bander* 4:103-105.

____ and W.B. Robertson Jr. 1988. West Indian Cave Swallows nesting in Florida with comments on the taxonomy of *Hirundo fulva. Florida Field Nat.* 16:86-90.

Smithe, F.B. 1975 and 1981. Naturalist's color guide. 3 parts. American Museum of Natural History, New York.

Snow, D.W. and B.K. Snow. 1964. Breeding seasons and annual cycles of Trinidad land-birds. *Zoologica* 49:1-35.

Snyder, L.L. 1923. On the crown markings of juvenile Hairy and Downy woodpeckers. *Can. Field-Nat.* 37:167-168.

____. 1937. Some measurements and observations from Bronzed Grackles. *Can. Field-Nat.* 51:37-39.

____. 1953. On eastern empidonaces with particular reference to variation in *E. traillii. Contr. Royal Ontario Mus. Zool. Paleo.* 35:1-26.

____. 1954. Another hybrid *Zonotrichia albicollis* × *Junco hyemalis. Auk* 71:471.

____. 1961. On an unnamed population of the Great Horned Owl. *Cont. Royal Ont. Mus.* 54:J-7.

____ and E.D. Lapworth. 1953. A comparative study of adults of two Canadian races of Red-wings. *Can. Field-Nat.* 67:143-147.

Sogge, S.K., W.M. Gilbert, and C. van Riper III. 1994. Orange-crowned Warbler. *In* The Birds of North America, No. 101 (A. Poole and F. Gill, eds.). Acad. Nat. Sci., Philadelphia; Amer. Ornith. Union, Washington D.C.

Sorrie, B.A. 1977. Banding worksheet for western birds. Varied Thrush. Supplement to *N. Am. Bird Bander*, vol. 2.

____. 1980. Notes on the identification of *Selasphorus* and *Archilochus* hummingbirds. *Bird Observer E. Massachusetts* 8:143-146.

Southern, W.E. 1961. Dichromatism in juvenal Yellow Warblers. *Auk* 78:440-441.

Spellman, C.B., R.E. Lemon, and M.M.J. Morris. 1987. Color dichromatism if female American Redstarts. *Wilson Bull.* 99:257-261.

Spencer, R. 1984. The ringer's manual. 3rd edition. British Trust for Ornithology, Thetford, U.K.

Spray, C.J. and M.H. MacRoberts. 1975. Notes on molt and juvenal plumage in the Acorn Woodpecker. *Condor* 77:342-344.

Sprunt, A. 1934. A new grackle from Florida. *Leaflet Charleston Mus.* 6:1-5.

Stallcup, R. 1984. Identification quiz. *W. Birds* 15:95-96.

Stangel, P.W. 1985. Incomplete first prebasic molt of Massachusetts House Finches. *J. Field Ornith.* 56:1-8.

Stanley, A.J. 1941. Sexual dimorphism in the cowbird *Molothrus ater. Wilson Bull.* 53:33-36.

Stavy, M., D. Gilbert, and R.D. Martin. 1979. Routine determination of sex in monomorphic bird species using faecal steroid analysis. *Int. Zoo Yearb.* 19:209-214.

Stedman, S. and A. Stedman. 1989. Notes on waxy appendages on Cedar Waxwings at an Ohio and a Florida banding station. *N. Am. Bird Bander* 14:75-77.

Stein, R.C. 1963. Isolating mechanisms between populations of Traill's Flycatchers. *Proc. Am. Phil. Soc.* 107:21-50.

Stephens, F. 1904. Cactus Wrens. *Condor* 6:51-52.

Stevenson, H.M. 1973. An undescribed insular race of the Carolina Wren. *Auk* 90:35-38.

____. 1978. The populations of Boat-tailed Grackles in the southeastern United States. *Proc. Biol. Soc. Washington* 91:27-51.

____. 1982. Comments on the identification of Stoddard's Yellow-throated Warbler. *Florida Field Nat.* 10:37-38.

____ and B.H. Anderson. 1994. The birdlife of Florida. University Press of Florida, Gainesville, FL.

____, E. Eisenmann, C. Winegarner, and A. Karlin. 1983. Notes on the Common and Antillean Nighthawks of the Florida keys. *Auk* 100:983-988.

Stevenson, J.O. 1934. Comments upon the systematics of Pacific Coast jays of the genus *Cyanocitta. Condor* 36:72-78.

____. 1940. Two new birds from northwestern Texas. *Proc. Biol. Soc. Washington* 53:15-18.

Stewart, R.E. 1952. Molting of Northern Yellow-throat in southern Michigan. *Auk* 69:50-59.

Stewart, R.M. 1971. Application of an analysis of wing length in Swainson's Thrushes. *W. Bird Bander* 46:52-53.

____. 1972a. The reliability of aging some fall migrants by skull pneumatization. *Bird-Banding* 43:9-14.

____. 1972b. Age and crown types in the Golden-crowned Sparrow. *W. Bird Bander* 47:32-33.

____. 1972c. Determining sex in western races of adult Wilson's Warbler: A reexamination. *W. Bird Bander* 47:45-48.

Stiles, F.G. 1971. On the field identification of California hummingbirds. *California Birds* 2:41-54.

____. 1972. Age and sex determinations in Rufous and Allen's Hummingbirds. *Condor* 74:25-32.

____. 1973. Food supply and the annual cycle of the Anna Hummingbird. *Univ. California Pubs. Zool.* 97:1-109.

____. 1981. The taxonomy of Rough-winged Swallows (*Stelgidopteryx*; Hirundinidae) in southern Central America. *Auk* 98:282-293.

____. 1982. Agressive and courtship displays of the male Anna's Hummingbird. *Condor* 84:208-225.

____ and R.G. Campos. 1983. Identification and occurrence of Blackpoll Warblers in southern Middle America. *Condor* 85:254-255.

St. Louis, V.L. and J.C. Barlow. 1987. Comparisons between morphometric and genetic differentiation among populations of the Eurasian Tree Sparrow (*Passer montanus*). *Wilson Bull.* 99:628-641.

____ and ____. 1988. Genetic differentiation among ancestral and introduced populations of the Eurasian Tree Sparrow (*Passer montanus*). *Evolution* 42:266-276.

____ and ____. 1991. Morphometric analyses of introduced and ancestral populations of the Eurasian Tree Sparrow. *Wilson Bull.* 103:1-12.

Stone, W. 1896. The molting of birds with special reference to the plumages of the smaller landbirds of eastern North America. *Proc. Acad. Nat. Sci. Philadelphia* 1896:108-167.

Storer, R.W. 1951. Variation in the Painted Bunting (*Passerina ciris*) with special reference to wintering populations. *Occ. Papers Mus. Zool. Univ. Michigan* 532:1-11.

____. 1954. A hybrid between the Chipping and Clay-colored sparrows. *Wilson Bull.* 66:143-144.

____. 1961. A hybrid between the Painted and Varied buntings. *Wilson Bull.* 73:209.

____ and D.A. Zimmerman. 1959. Variation in the Blue Grosbeak (*Guiraca caerulea*) with special reference to the Mexican populations. *Occ. Papers Mus. Zool. Univ. Michigan* 609:1-13.

Stresemann, E. 1963. The nomenclature of plumages and molts. *Auk* 80:1-8.

____ and V. Stresemann. 1966. Die Mauser der Vogel. *J. Ornith.* 107:1-447.

Stresemann, V. and E. Stresemann. 1961. Die Handschwingen-Mauser der Eisvogel. *J. Ornith.* 102:439-455.

Strickland, D. and H. Ouellet. 1993. Gray Jay. *In* The Birds of North America, No. 40 (A. Poole, P. Stettenheim, and F. Gill, eds.). Acad. Nat. Sci., Philadelphia; Amer. Ornith. Union, Washington D.C.

Studd, M.V. and R.J. Robertson. 1985. Sexual selection and variation in reproductive strategy in male Yellow Warblers (*Dendroica petechia*). *Behav. Ecol. Sociobiol.* 17:101-109.

Stutchbury, B.J. 1991a. Coloniality and breeding biology of Purple Martins (*Progne subis hesperia*) in saguaro cacti. *Condor* 93:666-675.

Stutchbury, B.J. 1991b. The adaptive significance of male subadult plumage in Purple Martins: Plumage dying experiments. *Behav. Ecol. Sociobiol.* 29:297-306.

____. 1994. Competition for winter territories in a Neotropical migrant: The role of age, sex and color. *Auk* 111:63-69.

____ and J.S. Howlett. 1995. Does male-like coloration of female Hooded Warblers increase nest predation? *Condor* 97:559-564.

____ and R.J. Robertson. 1987. Two methods of sexing adult Tree Swallows before they begin breeding. *J. Field Ornith.* 58:236-242.

____ and S. Rohwer. 1990. Molt patterns in the Tree Swallow (*Tachycineta bicolor*). *Can. J. Zool.* 68:1468-1472.

Sullivan, J.O. 1965. "Flightlessness" in the Dipper. *Condor* 67:535-536.

Sumner, L.E. Jr. 1933. The growth of some raptorial birds. *Univ. California Pubs. Zool.* 40:277-308.

Suthers, H.B. 1978. Analysis of a resident flock of starlings. *Bird-banding* 49:35-46.

____. 1993. Effect of age class separation on sex determination by wing and tail in Veery and Wood Thrush. *N. Am. Bird Bander* 18:142-147.

____. 1994. Sex determination by wing and tail measurements in the Song Sparrow and Field Sparrow. *N. Am. Bird Bander* 19:77-83.

____ and D.D. Suthers. 1990. Aging and sexing Gray Catbirds by external characteristics. *N. Am. Bird Bander* 15:45-52.

Sutton, G.M. 1934. A new Bewick's Wren from the western panhandle of Oklahoma. *Auk* 51:217-220.

____. 1935a. The juvenal plumage and postjuvenal molt in several species of Michigan sparrows. *Cranbrook Inst. Sci.* 3:1-36.

____. 1935b. A new Blue Jay from the western border of the Great Basin. *Auk* 52:176-177.

____. 1936. The postjuvenal molt of the Grasshopper Sparrow. *Occ. Papers Mus. Zool. Univ. Michigan* 336:1-9.

____. 1937. The juvenal plumage and postjuvenal molt of the Chipping Sparrow. *Occ. Papers Mus. Zool. Univ. Michigan* 355:1-5.

____. 1938. Oddly plumaged orioles from western Oklahoma. *Auk* 55:1-6.

____. 1941a. The plumages and molts of the young eastern Whip-poor-will. *Occ. Papers Mus. Zool. Univ. Michigan* 446:1-7.

____. 1941b. A new race of *Chaetura vauxi* from Tamaulipas. *Wilson Bull.* 53:231-233.

____. 1941c. The juvenal plumage and postjuvenal molt of the Vesper Sparrow. *Occ. Papers Mus. Zool. Univ. Michigan* 445:1-11.

____. 1947. Eye-color in the Green Jay. *Condor* 49:196-198.

____. 1948a. The Curve-billed Thrasher in Oklahoma. *Condor* 50:40-43.

____. 1948b. The juvenal plumage of the Eastern Warbling Vireo (*Vireo gilvus gilvus*). *Occ. Papers Mus. Zool. Univ. Michigan* 511:1-7.

____. 1948c. Comments on *Icterus cucullatus cucullatus* Swainson in the United States. *Condor* 50:257-258.

____. 1948d. Small Pine Grosbeaks collected in Tompkins County, New York. *Auk* 65:125-126.

____. 1949. Studies of the nesting birds of the Edwin S. George Reserve. Part 1. The vireos. *Misc. Pubs. Mus. Zool. Univ. Michigan* 74:1-37.

____. 1951a. A subspecific status of the Green Jays of northeastern Mexico and southern Texas. *Condor* 53:124-128.

____. 1951b. A new race of Yellow-throated Warbler from northwestern Florida. *Auk* 68:27-29.

____. 1967. The birds of Oklahoma. University of Oklahoma Press, Norman, Oklahoma.

____. 1968. Oriole hybridization in Oklahoma. *Bull. Oklahoma Ornith. Soc.* 1:1-7.

____. 1980. Subspecies of Savannah Sparrow found in Oklahoma. *Bull. Oklahoma Ornith. Soc.* 13:6-8.

____ and T.D. Burleigh. 1939. A new screech owl from Nuevo Leon. *Auk* 56:174-175.

____ and ____. 1940. A new Warbling Vireo from Hidalgo. *Auk* 57:398-400.

____ and ____. 1941. Birds recorded in the state of Hidalgo, Mexico, by the Semple expedition of 1939. *Ann. Carnegie Mus.* 28:169-186.

____, R.B. Lea, and E.P. Edwards. 1950. Notes on the ranges and breeding habits of certain Mexican birds. *Bird-Banding* 21:45-59.

____ and A.R. Phillips. 1942. The northern races of *Piranga flava*. *Condor* 44:277-279.

Svensson, L. 1992. Identification guide to European Passerines. 4th ed. L. Svensson, Stockholm.

Svingen, P. and K. Risen. 1991. First Minnesota record of the Ash-throated Flycatcher identification. *Loon* 63:4-11.

Swank, W.G. 1955. Feather molt as an ageing technique for Mourning Doves. *J. Wildl. Manage.* 19:412-414.

Swanson, D.A. and J.H. Rappole. 1992. Determining the sex of adult White-winged Doves by cloacal characteristics. *N. Am. Bird Bander* 17:137-139.

Swarth, H.S. 1902. Winter plumage in the Black-tailed Gnatcatcher. *Condor* 4:86-87.

____. 1904a. Birds of the Huachuca Mountains, Arizona. *Pacific Coast Avif.* 4:1-70.

Swarth, H.S. 1904b. The status of the southern California Cactus Wren. *Condor* 6:17-19.

____. 1905. *Atratus* versus *megalonyx*. *Condor* 7:171-174.

____. 1910. Two new owls from Arizona with description of the juvenal plumage of *Strix occidentalis occidentalis* (Xantus). *Univ. California Pubs. Zool.* 7:1-8.

____. 1911. Birds and mammals of the 1909 Alexander Alaska expedition. *Univ. California Pubs. Zool.* 7:9-172.

____. 1912a. Differences due to sex in the Black Swift. *Auk* 29:241-242.

____. 1912b. Report on a collection of birds and mammals from Vancouver Island. *Univ. California Pubs. Zool.* 10:1-124

____. 1913a. The status of Lloyd's Bush-tit as a bird of Arizona. *Auk* 30:399-401.

____. 1913b. A revision of the California forms of *Pipilo maculatus* Swainson, with description of a new subspecies. *Condor* 15:167-175.

____. 1914a. The California forms of the genus *Psaltriparus*. *Auk* 31:498-526.

____. 1914b. A study of the status of certain island forms of the genus *Salpinctes*. *Condor* 16:211-217.

____. 1915. The status of the Arizona Spotted Owl. *Condor* 17:15-19.

____. 1916a. The Sahuaro Screech Owl as a recognizable race. *Condor* 18:163-165.

____. 1916b. The Pacific Coast races of the Bewick Wren. *Proc. California Acad. Sci.*, 4th Ser., 6:53-85.

____. 1917a. Geographical variation in *Sphyrapicus thyroideus*. *Condor* 19:62-65.

____. 1917b. A revision of the Marsh Wrens of California. *Auk* 34:308-318.

____. 1918a. The subspecies of the Oregon Jay. *Condor* 20:83-84.

____. 1918b. The Pacific coast jays of the genus *Aphelocoma*. *Univ. California Pubs. Zool.* 17:405-422.

____. 1918c. The distribution of the subspecies of the Brown Towhee (*Pipilo crissalis*). *Condor* 20:117-121.

____. 1918d. Three new subspecies of *Passerella iliaca*. *Proc. Biol. Soc. Washington* 31:161-164.

____. 1920. Revision of the avian genus *Passerella*, with special reference to the distribution and migration of the races in California. *Univ. California Pubs. Zool.* 21:75-224.

____. 1922. Birds and mammals of the Sitkine River region of northern British Columbia and southeastern Alaska. *Univ. California Pubs. Zool.* 24:125-314.

____. 1923. The systematic status of some northwestern Song Sparrows. *Condor* 25:214-223.

____. 1926a. Report on a collection of birds and mammals from the Atlin region, northern British Columbia. *Univ. California Pubs. Zool.* 30:51-162.

____. 1926b. Northern Say Phoebe in California. *Condor* 28:45-46.

____. 1929. The faunal areas of southern Arizona: A study of animal distribution. *Proc. California Acad. Sci.*, 4th Ser., 18:267-383.

____. 1933. The Savannah Sparrows of northwestern North America. *Condor* 35:243-245.

____. 1934a. Problems in the classification of northwestern Horned Owls. *Condor* 36:38-40.

____. 1934b. Birds of Nunivak Island Alaska. *Pacific Coast Avif.* 22:1-64.

____. 1935. Systematic status of some northwestern birds. *Condor* 37:199-204.

____ and A. Brooks. 1925. The Timberline Sparrow a new species from northwestern Canada. *Condor* 27:67-69.

Swenk, M.H. 1930a. The Rose-breasted and Black-headed grosbeaks hybridize. *Wilson Bull.* 42:289.

____. 1930b. The crown sparrows (*Zonotrichia*) of the Middle West. *Wilson Bull.* 37:81-97.

____. 1936. A study of the distribution, migration, and hybridism of the Rose-breasted and Rocky Mountain Black-headed grosbeaks in the Missouri Valley region. *Nebraska Bird Rev.* 4:27-40.

____ and O.A. Stevens. 1929. Harris's Sparrow and the study of it by trapping. *Wilson Bull.* 41:129-177.

Sykes, P.W., C.I. Bocetti, and L.A. Moore. 1993. Male Kirtland's Warbler with incubation patch. *Wilson Bull.* 105:354-356.

____, C.B. Kepler, D.A. Jett, and M.E. DeCapita. 1989. Kirtland's Warbler on the nesting grounds during the post-breeding period. *Wilson Bull.* 101:545-558.

Szijj, L.J. 1963. Morphological analysis of the sympatric populations of meadowlarks in Ontario. *Proc. XIII Ornith. Congr.* 1962:176-188.

____. 1966. Hybridization and the nature of the isolating mechanism in sympatric populations of meadowlarks (*Sturnella*) in Ontario. *Z. Tierpsychol.* 6:677-690.

Tallman, D.A. and R.L. Zusi. 1984. A hybrid Red Crossbill - Pine Siskin (*Loxia curvirostra* × *Carduelis pinus*) and speculations on the evolution of *Loxia*. *Auk* 101:155-158.

Tanner, J.T. 1952. Black-capped and Carolina Chickadees in the southern Appalachian Mountains. *Auk* 69:407-424.

Taverner, P.A. 1919a. The summer birds of Hazelton, British Columbia. *Condor* 21:80-86.

Taverner, P.A. 1919b. The birds of the Red Deer River, Alberta. *Auk* 36:248-265.

___. 1932. A partial study of the Canadian Savanna (*sic.*) Sparrows, with description of *Passerculus sandwichensis campestris*, subsp. nov. the Prairie Savannah Sparrow. *Proc. Biol. Soc. Washington* 45:201-206.

___. 1934. Flicker hybrids. *Condor* 36:34-35.

___. 1939. The Red-winged Blackbirds of the Canadian prairie provinces. *Condor* 41:244-246.

___. 1940. Canadian status of the Long-tailed Chickadee. *Auk* 57:536-541.

___. 1942. Canadian races of the Great Horned Owls. *Auk* 59:234-245.

___ and G.M. Sutton. 1934. The birds of Churchill, Manitoba. *Ann. Carnegie Mus.* 23:1-84.

Taylor, I.R. 1993. Age and sex determination of Barn Owls *Tyto alba alba. Ringing & Migr.* 14:94-102.

Taylor, W.K. 1970. Molts of the Verdin, *Auriparus flaviceps. Condor* 72:493-496.

___. 1972. Analysis of Ovenbirds killed in central Florida. *Bird-banding* 43:15-19.

___. 1973. Aging of Ovenbirds by rusty-tipped tertials and skull ossification. *E. Bird Banding Assoc. News* 36:71-72.

___. 1974. A new hybrid bunting (*Passerina cyanea × Passerina ciris*). *Auk* 91:485-487.

___. 1976. Variations in the black mask of the Common Yellowthroat. *Bird-Banding* 47:72-73.

Taylor, W.P. 1911. An apparent hybrid in the genus *Dendroica. Univ. California Pubs. Zool.* 7:173-177.

Tenney, C.R. 1997. Black-chinned Sparrow. *In* The Birds of North America, No. 270 (A. Poole and F. Gill, eds.). Acad. Nat. Sci., Philadelphia; Amer. Ornith. Union, Washington D.C.

Terrill, S.B. and L.S. Terrill. 1981. On the field identification of Yellow-green, Red-eyed, Philadelphia and Warbling vireos. *Cont. Birdlife* 2:144-149.

Test, F.H. 1945. Molt in flight feathers of flickers. *Condor* 47:63-72.

Teulings, E. 1973. Plumage variations in the Summer Tanager. *Chat* 37:40-42.

Thayer, J.E. and O. Bangs. 1906. Breeding birds of the Sierra de Antonez, north central Sonora. *Proc. Biol. Soc. Washington* 19:17-22.

___ and ___. 1914. A new Song Sparrow from Nova Scotia. *Proc. New England Zool. Club* 5:67-68.

Thompson, C.F. 1973. Postjuvenal molt in the White-eyed Vireo. *Bird-banding* 44:63-65.

Thompson, C.W. 1991a. Is the Painted Bunting actually two species? Problems determining species limits between allopatric populations. *Condor* 93:987-1000.

___. 1991b. The sequence of molts and plumages in Painted Buntings and implications for theories of delayed plumage maturation. *Condor* 93:209-235.

___. 1992. A key to aging and sexing Painted Buntings. *J. Field Ornith.* 63:445-454.

___ and M. Leu. 1994. Determining homology of molts and plumages to address evolutionary questions: A rejoinder regarding Emberizid finches. *Condor* 96:769-782.

Thompson, D.R. 1950. Foot-freezing and arrestment of post-juvenal wing molt in the Mourning Dove. *Wilson Bull.* 62:212-213.

Thomsen, L. 1971. Behavior and ecology of Burrowing Owls on the Oakland municipal airport. *Condor* 73:177-192.

Tiersch, T.R. and R.L. Mumme. 1993. An evaluation of the use of flow cytometry to identify sex in the Florida Scrub Jay. *J. Field Ornith.* 64:18-26.

Tipton, S.R. and I.H. Tipton. 1978. Some notes on Painted Buntings. *N. Am. Bird Bander* 3:26.

Todd, W.E.C. 1922. A new sparrow from southern California. *Condor* 24:126-127.

___. 1923. A synopsis of the genus *Arremonops. Proc. Biol. Soc. Washington* 36:35-44.

___. 1924. A new Song Sparrow from Virginia. *Auk* 41:147-148.

___. 1928. A new Blue Jay from southern Florida. *Auk* 45:364-365.

___. 1929. A revision of the wood-warbler genus *Basileuterus* and its allies. *Proc. U.S. Nat. Mus.* 74(7):1-95.

___. 1930. Note on the eastern Song Sparrow. *Auk* 47:257.

___. 1931. On *Vireo chivi* and its allies. *Auk* 48:407-412.

___. 1933. The races of the White-eyed Vireo. *Auk* 50:115-116.

___. 1935. Geographical variation in the American Titlark. *Proc. Biol. Soc. Washington* 48:63-66.

___. 1937. Critical remarks on the Long-billed Marsh Wren. *Proc. Biol. Soc. Washington* 50:23.

___. 1938. Two new races of North American birds. *Auk* 55:116-118.

___. 1942. Critical remarks on the races of the Sharp-tailed Sparrow. *Ann. Carnegie Mus.* 29:197-199.

___. 1946. Critical notes on the woodpeckers. *Ann. Carnegie Mus.* 30:297-317.

Todd, W.E.C. 1948. Systematics of the White-crowned Sparrow. *Proc. Biol. Soc. Washington* 61:19-20.

___. 1950. A new race of Hudsonian Chickadee. *Ann. Carnegie Mus.* 31:333-334.

___. 1953. Further taxonomic notes on the White-crowned Sparrow. *Auk* 70:370-372.

___. 1958. The Newfoundland race of the Gray-cheeked Thrush. *Can. Field-Nat.* 72:159-161.

___. 1963. Birds of the Laborador peninsula and adjacent areas. University of Toronto Press, Toronto.

___ and M.A. Carriker Jr. 1922. The birds of the Santa Marta region of Columbia: A study in altitudinal distribution. *Ann. Carnegie Mus.* 14:3-611.

___ and G.M. Sutton. 1936. Taxonomic remarks on the Carolina Chickadee, *Penthestes carolinensis Proc. Biol. Soc. Washington* 49:69-70.

Tobalske, B.W. 1997. Lewis' Woodpecker. *In* The Birds of North America, No. 284 (A. Poole and F. Gill, eds.). Acad. Nat. Sci., Philadelphia; Amer. Ornith. Union, Washington D.C.

Tomback, D.F. 1978. Banding worksheet for western birds. Clark's Nutcracker. Supplement to *N. Am. Bird Bander*, no. 3.

Tomer, J.S. 1982. Smith's Longspur in breeding plumage in Oklahoma in December. *Bull. Oklahoma Ornith. Soc.* 15:27-29.

Tomkins, I.R. 1937. The status of the MacGillivray's Seaside Sparrow. *Auk* 54:185-188.

___. 1941. Notes on Macgillivray's Seaside Sparrow. *Auk* 58:38-51.

Tordoff, H.B. 1950. A hybrid tanager from Minnesota. *Wilson Bull.* 62:3-4.

___. 1952. Notes on plumages, molts, and age variation of the Red Crossbill. *Condor* 54:200-203.

___. 1954. Further notes on molts and plumages of Red Crossbills. *Condor* 56:108-109.

___ and R.M. Mengel. 1951. The occurrence and possible significance of a spring molt in Le Conte's Sparrow. *Auk* 68:519-522.

Townsend, C.W. 1916. A new subspecies of Hudsonian Chickadee from the Labrador Peninsula. *Auk* 33:74.

Traylor, M.A. Jr. 1949. Notes on some Veracruz birds. *Fieldiana Zool.* 31:269-275.

___. 1968. Winter molt in the Acadian Flycatcher, *Empidonax virens. Auk* 85:691.

___, ed. 1979a. Check-list of the birds of the world. Vol. VIII. Museum of Comparative Zoology, Cambridge, MA.

___. 1979b. Two sibling species of *Tyrannus* (Tyrannidae). *Auk* 96:221-233.

Troetschler, R.G. 1974. Ageing Acorn Woodpeckers. *W. Bird Bander* 49:67-69.

Troy, D.M. 1984. Holboell's Redpolls: Do they exist? *Can. J. Zool.* 62:2302-2306.

___. 1985. A phenetic analysis of the redpolls *Carduelis flammea flammea* and *C. hornemanni exilipes. Auk* 102:82-96.

___ and A.H. Brush. 1983. Pigments and feather structure of the redpolls, *Carduelis flammea* and *C. hornemanni. Condor* 85:443-446.

Turner, A. and C. Rose. 1989. A handbook to the swallows and martins of the world. Christopher Helm (Publishers) Ltd., Kent, U.K.

Twedt, D.J. and W.J. Bleier. 1994. Geographic variation in Yellow-headed Blackbirds from the northern Great Plains. *Condor* 96:1030-1036.

___ and R.D. Crawford. 1995. Yellow-headed Blackbird. *In* The Birds of North America, No. 192 (A. Poole and F. Gill, eds.). Acad. Nat. Sci., Philadelphia; Amer. Ornith. Union, Washington D.C.

Tweit, R.C. 1986a. Banding worksheet for western birds. Inca Dove. Supplement to *N. Am. Bird Bander*, vol. 11.

___. 1986b. Banding worksheet for western birds. House Finch. Supplement to *N. Am. Bird Bander*, vol. 11.

___. 1996. Curve-billed Thrasher. *In* The Birds of North America, No. 235 (A. Poole and F. Gill, eds.). Acad. Nat. Sci., Philadelphia; Amer. Ornith. Union, Washington D.C.

___ and D.M. Finch. 1994. Abert's Towhee. *In* The Birds of North America, No. 111 (A. Poole and F. Gill, eds.). Acad. Nat. Sci., Philadelphia; Amer. Ornith. Union, Washington D.C.

Twomey, A.C. 1942. The birds of Uinta Basin, Utah. *Ann. Carnegie Mus.* 28:341-490.

___. 1947. Critical notes on some western Song Sparrows. *Condor* 49:127-128.

Tyler, J.D. and K.C. Parkes. 1992. A hybrid Scissor-tailed Flycatcher × Western Kingbird specimen from southwestern Oklahoma. *Wilson Bull.* 194:178-181.

Unitt, P. 1984. The birds of San Diego County. *Mem. San Diego Soc. Nat. Hist.* 13:1-276.

___. 1985. Plumage wear in *Vireo belli. W. Birds* 16:189-190.

___. 1986. Another hybrid Downy × Nuttall's Woodpecker from San Diego County. *W. Birds* 17:43-44.

___. 1987. *Empidonax traillii extimus*: An endangered subspecies. *W. Birds* 18:137-162.

Unitt, P., and R.R. Estrella. 1996. Winter specimens of Hermit Thrush subspecies in the Sierra de la Laguna, Baja California Sur. *W. Birds* 27:65-69.

____ and R.R. Estrella, and A.C. Vera. 1992. Ferruginous Hawk and Pine Siskin in the Sierra de la Laguna, Baja California; subspecies of the Pine Siskin in Baja California. *W. Birds* 23:171-172.

____ and A.M. Rea. 1997. Taxonomy of the Brown Creeper in California. Pp. 177-185 *in* R.W. Dickerman, *comp.*, The era of Allan R. Phillips: A *Festshrift*. R.W. Dickerman, Albuquerque, NM.

United States Fish and Wildlife Service and Canadian Wildlife Service. 1977. Bird Banding Manual. Vol. II. Bird Banding Techniques. Can. Wildl. Serv., Ottawa. (Parts revised, 1981).

Van Horn, M.A. and T.M. Donovan. 1994. Ovenbird. *In* The Birds of North America, No. **88** (A. Poole and F. Gill, eds.). Acad. Nat. Sci., Philadelphia; Amer. Ornith. Union, Washington D.C.

van Rossem, A.J. 1924. A survey of the Song Sparrows of the Santa Barbara Islands. *Condor* 26:217-220.

____. 1926. The California forms of *Agelaius phoeniceus*. *Condor* 28:215-230.

____. 1927a. The Arizona race of the Sulfur-bellied Flycatcher. *Condor* 29:126.

____. 1927b. A new race of Sclater Oriole. *Condor* 29:75-76.

____. 1928. A northern race of the Mountain Chickadee. *Auk* 45:104-105.

____. 1929. The races of *Sitta pygmaea* Vigors. *Proc. Biol. Soc. Washington* 42:175-178.

____. 1930a. Two new subspecies of birds from Sonora. *Trans. San Diego Soc. Nat. Hist.* 6:197-198.

____. 1930b. A new race of Gilded Flicker from Sonora. *Trans. San Diego Soc. Nat. Hist.* 6:171-172.

____. 1930c. The Sonora races of *Camptostoma* and *Platypsaris*. *Proc. Biol. Soc. Washington* 43:129-131.

____. 1930d. The races of *Auriparus flaviceps* (Sundevall). *Trans. San Diego Soc. Nat. Hist.* 6:199-202.

____. 1930e. Critical notes on some yellowthroats of the Pacific Southwest. *Condor* 32:297-300.

____. 1930f. Four new birds from north-western Mexico. *Trans. San Diego Soc. Nat. Hist.* 6:213-226.

____. 1931a. Report on a collection of land birds from Sonora, Mexico. *Trans. San Diego Soc. Nat. Hist.* 6:237-304.

____. 1931b. Descriptions of new birds from the mountains of southern Nevada. *Trans. San Diego Soc. Nat. Hist.* 6:327-332.

____. 1931c. Concerning some western races of *Polioptila melanura*. *Condor* 33:35-36.

____. 1931d. Concerning some Polioptilae of the west coast of Middle America. *Auk* 48:33-39.

____. 1932a. A southern race of the Spotted Screech Owl. *Trans. San Diego Soc. Nat. Hist.* 7:183-186.

____. 1932b. On the validity of the San Clemente Island Bell's Sparrow. *Auk* 49:490-491.

____. 1933. The types of three birds described from California. *Trans. San Diego Soc. Nat. Hist.* 7:345-366.

____. 1934a. Critical notes on Middle American birds. *Bull. Mus. Comp. Zool.* 77:387-490.

____. 1934b. Notes on some types of North American birds. *Trans. San Diego Soc. Nat. Hist.* 7:349-361.

____. 1934c. The avifauna of Tiburon Island, Sonora, Mexico, with descriptions of four new races. *Trans. San Diego Soc. Nat. Hist.* 7:119-150.

____. 1934d. A northwestern race of the Varied Bunting. *Trans. San Diego Soc. Nat. Hist.* 7:369-370.

____. 1934e. A subspecies of the Brown Towhee from south-central Texas. *Trans. San Diego Soc. Nat. Hist* 7:371-372.

____. 1935a. A note on the color of the eye of the Bush-tit. *Condor* 37:254.

____. 1935b. A new race of Brown Towhee from the Inyo region of California. *Trans San Diego Soc. Nat. Hist.* 8:69-72.

____. 1935c. Notes on the forms of *Spizella atrogularis*. *Condor* 37:282-284.

____. 1936a. Notes on birds in relation to the faunal areas of south-central Arizona. *Trans. San Diego Soc. Nat. Hist.* 8:121-148.

____. 1936b. Remarks stimulated by Brodkorb's "Two subspecies of the Red-shafted Flicker". *Condor* 38:40.

____. 1936c. Birds of the Charleston Mountains, Nevada. *Pacific Coast Avif.* 24:1-65.

____. 1936d. The Bush-tit of the southern Great Basin. *Auk* 53:85-86.

____. 1937a. The Ferruginous Pygmy Owl of north-western Mexico and Arizona. *Proc. Biol. Soc. Washington* 50:27-28.

____. 1937b. A race of the Derby Flycatcher from northwestern Mexico. *Proc. Biol. Soc. Washington* 50:25-26.

____. 1938a. The Groove-billed Ani of Lower California and northwestern Mexico. *Condor* 40:91.

____. 1938b. A new Spotted Screech Owl from Guerrero, Mexico. *Condor* 40:258.

van Rossem, A.J. 1938c. A new race of becard from northeastern Mexico. *Condor* 40:262-263.

____. 1938d. Notes on some Mexican and Central American wrens of the genera *Heleodytes*, *Troglodytes*, and *Nannorchilus*; and four new races. *Bull. Brit. Ornith. Club* 59:10-15.

____. 1938e. A Colorado Desert race of the Summer Tanager. *Trans. San Diego Nat. Hist.* 9:13-14.

____. 1938f. [Descriptions of twenty-one new races of Fringillidae and Icteridae from Mexico and Guatemala.] *Bull. Brit. Ornith. Club* 58:124-138.

____. 1939a. A race of the Rivoli Humming bird from Arizona. *Proc. Biol. Soc. Washington* 52:7-8.

____. 1939b. Four new races of Sittidae and Certhidae from Mexico. *Proc. Biol. Soc. Washington* 52:3-6.

____. 1939c. A race of the Yellow-breasted Chat from the tropical zone of Sonora. *Wilson Bull.* 51:156.

____. 1940. Notes on some North American birds of the genera *Myiodynastes*, *Pitangus*, and *Myiochanes*. *Trans. San Diego Nat. Hist.* 9:79-86.

____. 1941a. A race of the Poor-will from Sonora. *Condor* 43:247.

____. 1941b. The Thick-billed Kingbird of northern Sonora. *Condor* 43:249-250.

____. 1941c. Further notes on some southwestern yellowthroats. *Condor* 43:291-292.

____. 1942a. The Lower California Nighthawk not a recognizable race. *Condor* 44:73-74.

____. 1942b. Four new woodpeckers from the western United States and Mexico. *Condor* 44:22-26.

____. 1942c. Notes on some Mexican and Californian birds, with descriptions of six undescribed races. *Trans. San Diego Soc. Nat. Hist.* 9:377-384.

____. 1942d. A western race of the Tooth-billed Tanager. *Auk* 59:87-89.

____. 1943. Description of a race of goldfinch from the Pacific Northwest. *Condor* 45:158-159.

____. 1944. The Santa Cruz Island Flicker. *Condor* 46:245-246.

____. 1945a. A distributional summary of the birds of Sonora, Mexico. *Occ. Papers Mus. Zool. Louisiana State Univ.* 21:1-379.

____. 1945b. The Golden-crowned Kinglet of California. *Condor* 47:77-78.

____. 1946a. Two new races of birds from the lower Colorado River Valley. *Condor* 48:80-82.

____. 1946b. Two new races of birds from the Harquahala Mountains, Arizona. *Auk* 63:560-563.

____. 1947a. Comment on certain birds of Baja California, including descriptions of three new races. *Proc. Biol. Soc. Washington* 60:51-58.

____. 1947b. Two races of the Bridled Titmouse. *Fieldiana Zool.* 31:87-92.

____. 1947c. A synopsis of the Savannah Sparrows of northwestern Mexico. *Condor* 49:97-107.

____ and the M. Hachisuka. 1937a. The Blue-gray Gnatcatcher of southern Sonora. *Proc. Biol. Soc. Washington* 50:109-110.

____ and ____. 1937b. The Yellow-green Vireo of northwestern Mexico. *Proc. Biol. Soc. Washington* 50:159-160.

____ and ____. 1938a. A race of the Green Kingfisher from northwestern Mexico. *Condor* 40:227-228.

____ and ____. 1938b. A new race of the Cliff Swallow from northwestern Mexico. *Trans. San Diego Soc. Nat. Hist.* 9:5-6.

____ and ____. 1938c. A dimorphic subspecies of the Bush-tit from northwestern Mexico. *Trans. San Diego Soc. Nat. Hist.* 9:7-8.

Van Tyne, J. 1925. An undescribed race of Phainopepla. *Occ. Papers Boston Soc. Nat. Hist.* 5:149-150.

____. 1929. Notes on some birds of the Chisos Mountains of Texas. *Auk* 46:204-206.

____. 1933. Some birds of the Rio Grande delta of Texas. *Occ. Papers Mus. Zool. Univ. Michigan* 255:1-5.

____. 1953. Geographic variation in the Blue-throated Hummingbirds (*Lampornis clemenciae*). *Condor* 70:207-209.

____. 1954. The Black-crested Titmouse of Trans-Pecos Texas. *Auk* 71:201-202.

____ and G.M. Sutton. 1937. The birds of Brewster County, Texas. *Misc. Pubs. Mus. Zool. Univ. Michigan* 37:1-119.

Van Wynsberghe, N.R., J.D. Rising, and D.I. MacKenzie. 1992. Geographic variation in size of the Eastern Kingbird. *Wilson Bull.* 104:612-629.

Vardy, L.E. 1971. Color variation in the crown of the White-throated Sparrow (*Zonotrichia albicollis*). *Condor* 73:401-414.

Vehrencamp, S.L. 1978. The adaptive significance of communal nesting in Groove-billed Anis (*Crotophaga sulcirostris*). *Behav. Ecol. Sociobiol.* 4:1-33.

____. 1985. Male incubation and communal nesting in anis. *Nat. Geo. Soc. Res. Reports* 19:617-623.

____, B.S. Bowen, and R.R. Koford. 1986. Breeding roles and pairing patterns within communal groups of Groove-billed Anis. *Anim. Behav.* 34:347-366.

Verbeek, N.A.M. 1973a. The exploitation system of the Yellow-billed Magpie. *Univ. California Pubs. Zool.* 99:1-58.
____. 1973b. Pterylosis and timing of molt in the Water Pipit. *Condor* 75:287-292.
____. 1976. Banding worksheet for western birds. Yellow-billed Magpie. Supplement to *N. Am. Bird Bander*, vol. 1.
____. 1991. Natal pterylosis of the Northwestern Crow, *Corvus caurinus*. *Can. J. Zool.* 69:1534-1537.
____ and P. Hendricks. 1994. Water Pipit. *In* The Birds of North America, No. 95 (A. Poole and F. Gill, eds.). Acad. Nat. Sci., Philadelphia; Amer. Ornith. Union, Washington D.C.
Vickery, P.D. 1996. Grasshopper Sparrow. *In* The Birds of North America, No. 239 (A. Poole and F. Gill, eds.). Acad. Nat. Sci., Philadelphia; Amer. Ornith. Union, Washington D.C.
Voous, K.H. 1983. Birds of the North Antilles. 2nd ed. De Walburg Pers, Utrecht, Netherlands.
Wagner, H.O. 1946. Observaciónes sobre la vida de *Calothorax lucifer*. *An. Inst. Biol. Mex.* 17:283-299.
____. 1948. Die balz des kolibris *Selasphorus platycercus*. *Zool. Jahrb. Jena (Syst.)* 77:267-278.
____. 1955. The molt of hummingbirds. *Auk* 72:286-291.
____. 1957. The molting periods of Mexican hummingbirds. *Auk* 74:251-257.
Waite, T.A. 1990. Effects of caching supplemental food on induced feather regeneration in wintering Gray Jays *Perisoreus canadensis*: A ptilochronology study. *Ornis Scand.* 21:122-128.
Walker, C.F. and M.B. Trautman. 1936. Notes on the Horned Larks of the central Ohio region. *Wilson Bull.* 48:151-155.
Walkinshaw, L.H. 1944. Clay-colored Sparrow notes. *Jack-Pine Warbler* 22:119-131.
Wallace, D.I.M. 1976. A review of waterthrush identification with particular reference to the 1968 British record. *Brit. Birds* 69:27-33.
Wallace, G.J. 1939. The Bicknell's Thrush, its taxonomy, distribution, and life history. *Proc. Boston Soc. Nat. Hist.* 41:211-402.
Wallace, R.M. 1974. Ecological and social implications of sexual dimorphism in five melanerpine woodpeckers. *Condor* 76:238-248.
Walters, P.M. 1981. Notes on the body weight and molt of the Elf Owl (*Micrathene whitneyi*) in southeastern Arizona. *N. Am. Bird Bander* 6:104-105.
____. 1983a. Notes on the mist-netting of seven Elf Owls (*Micrathene whitneyi*) and two Western Screech-Owls (*Otus kennecotti* [*sic.*]) on 15 July 1982. *N. Am. Bird Bander* 8:13.
____. 1983b. Notes on the first banding of the Cave Swallow (*Hirundo fulva*) in Arizona. *N. Am. Bird Bander* 8:103.
____ and D.W. Lamm. 1980. A Hooded Warbler (*Wilsonia citrina*) in South-east Arizona. *N. Am. Bird Bander* 5:15.
____ and ____. 1986. Notes on the ageing and sexing of the Curve-billed Thrasher (*Toxostoma curvirostre*). *N. Am. Bird Bander* 11:2-3.
Wander, W. and S.A. Brady. 1984. Probable Hammond's Flycatcher in New Jersey. *Records New Jersey Birds* 10:27-28.
Watson, G.E. 1963. The mechanism of feather replacement during natural molt. *Auk* 80:486-495.
Watt, D.J. 1986. Plumage brightness index for White-throated Sparrows. *J. Field Ornith.* 57:105-113.
____ and E.J. Willoughby. In press. Lesser Goldfinch. *In* The Birds of North America (A. Poole and F. Gill, eds.). Acad. Nat. Sci., Philadelphia; Amer. Ornith. Union, Washington D.C.
Weatherhead, P.J. 1980. Sexual dimorphism in two Savannah Sparrow populations. *Can. J. Zool.* 58:412-415.
Webb, E.A. and C.E. Bock. 1996. Botteri's Sparrow. *In* The Birds of North America, No. 216 (A. Poole and F. Gill, eds.). Acad. Nat. Sci., Philadelphia; Amer. Ornith. Union, Washington D.C.
Webster, J.D. 1950. Notes on the birds of Wrangell and vicinity, southeastern Alaska. *Condor* 52:32-38.
____. 1957. A new race of the Western Wood-Pewee. *Indiana Acad. Sci.* 66:337-340.
____. 1958a. Further ornithological notes from Zacatecas, Mexico. *Wilson Bull.* 70:243-256.
____. 1958b. Systematic notes on the Olive Warbler. *Auk* 75:469-472.
____. 1959a. The taxonomy of the Robin in Mexico. *Wilson Bull.* 71:278-280.
____. 1959b. A revision of the Botteri's Sparrow. *Condor* 61:136-146.
____. 1961. A revision of the Grace's Warbler. *Auk* 78:554-566.
____. 1962. Systematic and ecological notes on the Olive Warbler. *Wilson Bull.* 74:417-425.
____. 1963. A revision of the Rose-throated Becard. *Condor* 65:383-399.
____. 1973. Middle American races of the Eastern Bluebird. *Auk* 90:579-590.
____. 1978. Notes on the birds of the Haines area of southeastern Alaska. *Condor* 80:111-112.
____. 1983. A new subspecies of Fox Sparrow from Alaska. *Proc. Biol. Soc. Washington* 96:664-668.

Webster, J.D. 1984. Richardson's Mexican collection: Birds from Zacatecas and adjoining states. *Condor* 86:204-207.
____ and R.T. Orr. 1958. Variation in the Great Horned Owls of Middle America. *Auk* 75:134-142.
Weeks, H.P. Jr. 1994. Eastern Phoebe. *In* The Birds of North America, No. 94 (A. Poole and F. Gill, eds.). Acad. Nat. Sci., Philadelphia; Amer. Ornith. Union, Washington D.C.
Weinberg, H.J. and R.B. Roth. 1994. Rectrix shape as an indicator of age in the Wood Thrush. *J. Field Ornith.* 65:115-121.
Weintraub, J. and T. Ryan. Black-backed Wagtail (*Motacilla lugens*) at Doheny State Beach, Orange County, California, 25 January to 12 April 1996. Unpublished ms.
Weir, R.D., F. Cooke, M.H. Edwards, and R.B. Stewart. 1980. Fall migration of Saw-whet Owls at Prince Edwards Point, Ontario. *Wilson Bull.* 92:475-488.
Weise, C.M. 1979. Sex identification in Black-capped Chickadees. *Univ. Wisconsin-Milwaukee Field Sta. Bull.* 12:16-19.
Weller, M.W. 1965. Bursa regression, gonad cycle, and molt of the Great-horned Owl. *Bird-Banding* 36:102-112.
Wells, S. and L.F. Baptista. 1979a. Displays and morphology of an Anna × Allen hummingbird hybrid. *Wilson Bull.* 91:524-532.
____ and ____. 1979b. Breeding of Allen's Hummingbird (*Selasphorus sasin sedentarius*) on the southern California mainland. *W. Birds* 10:83-85.
____, L.F. Baptista, S.F. Bailey, and H.M. Horblit. 1996. Age and sex determination in Anna's Hummingbird by means of tail pattern. *W. Birds* 27:204-206.
____, R.A. Bradley, and L.F. Baptista. 1978. Hybridization in *Calypte* hummingbirds. *Auk* 95:537-549.
Welter, W.A. 1935. The natural history of the Long-billed Marsh Wren. *Wilson Bull.* 47:3-34.
____. 1936. Feather arrangement, development, and molt of the Long-billed Marsh Wren. *Wilson Bull.* 48:256-269.
Werner, H.W. and G.E. Woolfenden. 1983. The Cape Sable Sparrow: Its habitat, habits and history. Pp. 55-75 *in* T.L. Quay *et al.*, eds., The Seaside Sparrow, its biology and management. *North Carolina Biol. Surv. and North Carolina State Mus.*
Weske, J.S. 1976. Western Flycatcher in Oklahoma. *Auk* 93:655-656.
West, D.A. 1962. Hybridization in grosbeaks (*Pheucticus*) of the Great Plains. *Auk* 79:399-424.
West, S. 1995. Cave Swallow. *In* The Birds of North America, No. 141 (A. Poole and F. Gill, eds.). Acad. Nat. Sci., Philadelphia; Amer. Ornith. Union, Washington D.C.
Weston, F.M. 1952. Hybrid (?) thrasher near Pensicola. *Florida Nat.* 25:39.
Wetherbee, O.P. 1937. A study of wintering Hoary, Common and Greater Redpolls and various intermediates and hybrids. *Bird Banding* 8:1-10.
____. 1951. Molt of remiges and rectrices of immature Song Sparrows. *Bird Banding* 22:82.
Wetmore, A. 1936. A new race of Song Sparrow from the Appalachian region. *Smithsonian Misc. Coll.* 95(17):1-3.
____. 1937. Observations on the birds of West Virginia. *Proc. U.S. Nat. Mus.* 84:401-441.
____. 1939. Notes on the birds of Tennessee. *Proc. U.S. Nat. Mus.* 86:175-243.
____. 1940. Notes on the birds of Kentucky *Proc. U.S. Nat. Mus.* 88:529-574.
____. 1941. Notes on the birds of North Carolina. *Proc. U.S. Nat. Mus.* 90:483-530.
____. 1943. The birds of southern Veracruz, Mexico. *Proc. U.S. Nat. Mus.* 93:215-340.
____. 1944. A collection of birds from northern Guanacaste, Costa Rica. *Proc. U.S. Nat. Mus.* 95:25-80.
____. 1947. The races of the Violet-crowned Hummingbird, *Amazilia violiceps*. *J. Washington Acad. Sci.* 37:103-104.
____. 1948. The Golden-fronted Woodpeckers of Texas and northern Mexico. *Wilson Bull.* 60:185-186.
____. 1949. Geographical variation in the American Redstart (*Setophaga ruticilla*). *J. Washington Acad. Sci.* 39:137-139.
____. 1953. The application of the name *Emberiza leucophrys* Forster. *Auk* 70:372-373.
____. 1957. Species limitation in certain groups of the swift genus *Chaetura*. *Auk* 74:383-385.
____. 1968. The birds of the Republic of Panama. Part 2. Smithsonian Institution Press, Washington D.C.
____. 1972. The birds of the Republic of Panama. Part 3. Smithsonian Institution Press, Washington D.C.
____, R.F. Pasquier, and S.L. Olson. 1984. The birds of the Republic of Panama. Part 4. Smithsonian Institution Press, Washington D.C.
Wheat, P. 1981. Hybridization of the Blue and Steller's jays. *Colorado Field Ornith. J.* 15:9-23.

Wheeler, H.E. 1931. The status, breeding range, and habits of Marian's Marsh Wren. *Wilson Bull.* 43:247-267.

Wheelwright, N.T. and J.D. Rising. 1993. Savannah Sparrow. *In* The Birds of North America, No. **45** (A. Poole and F. Gill, eds.). Acad. Nat. Sci., Philadelphia; Amer. Ornith. Union, Washington D.C.

____, G. Trussell, J.P. Devine, and R. Anderson. 1994. Sexual dimorphism and population sex ratios in juvenile Savannah Sparrows. *J. Field Ornith.* 65:520-529.

White, J.A. and C.E. Braun. 1978. Age and sex determination of juvenile Band-tailed Pigeons. *J. Wildl. Manage.* 42:564-569.

Whitman, C.O. 1919. Orthogenetic evolution in pigeons. Vol. 1. *Pubs. Carnegie Inst. Washington* 257:1-194.

Whitney, B. 1983. Bay-breasted, Blackpoll and Pine warblers in fall plumage. *Birding* 15:219-222.

____ and K. Kaufman. 1985a. The *Empidonax* challenge. Part I: Introduction. *Birding* 17:151-158.

____ and ____. 1985b. The *Empidonax* challenge. Part II: Least, Hammond's, and Dusky flycatchers. *Birding* 17:277-287.

____ and ____. 1986a. The *Empidonax* challenge. Part III: "Traill's" Flycatcher: The Alder/Willow problem. *Birding* 18:152-159.

____ and ____. 1986b. The *Empidonax* challenge. Part IV: Acadian, Yellow-bellied, and Western flycatchers. *Birding* 18:315-327.

____ and ____. 1987. The *Empidonax* challenge. Part V: Gray and Buff-breasted flycatchers. *Birding* 19(5):7-15.

Whitson, M. 1975. Courtship behavior of the Greater Roadrunner. *Living Bird* 14:215-255.

Whittles, C.L. 1938. An estimate of the sex ratio of the Rose-breasted Grosbeak (*Hedymeles ludovicianus*) with comments on the species. *Bird-banding* 9:196-197.

Wiedenfeld, D.A. 1991. Geographic morphology of male Yellow Warblers. *Condor* 93:712-723.

Wiggins, D.A. and T. Pärt. 1995. Sexual dimorphism and breeding success in Tree Swallows and Collared Flycatchers. *Condor* 97:267-271.

Wight, H.M. 1956. A field technique for bursal inspection of Mourning Doves. *J. Wildl. Manage.* 20:94-95.

____, L.H. Blankenship, and R.E. Tomlinson. 1967. Aging Mourning Doves by outer primary wear. *J. Wildl. Manage.* 31:832-835.

Wijnandts, H. 1984. Ecological energetics of the Long-eared Owl (*Asio otus*). *Ardea* 72:1-92.

Wilds, C. 1985a. North American nighthawks. *Birding* 17:212-213.

____. 1985b. Unraveling the mysteries of brown swallows. *Birding* 17:209-211.

____. 1989. The terminology of plumage and molt. *Birding* 21:148-154.

Wiley, R.H. and W.H. Piper. 1992. Timing of cranial pneumatization in White-throated Sparrows. *Condor* 94:336-343.

Willett, G. 1912. Birds of the Pacific slope of southern California. *Pacific Coast Avif.* 7:1-122.

____. 1933. A revised list of the birds of southwestern California. *Pacific Coast Avif.* 21:1-204.

____. 1941. Variation in American ravens. *Auk* 58:246-249.

Williams, J.B. 1980. Intersexual niche partitioning in Downy Woodpeckers. *Wilson Bull.* 92:439-451.

Williams, J.M. 1996a. Nashville Warbler. *In* The Birds of North America, No. **205** (A. Poole and F. Gill, eds.). Acad. Nat. Sci., Philadelphia; Amer. Ornith. Union, Washington D.C.

____. 1996b. Bay-breasted Warbler. *In* The Birds of North America, No. **206** (A. Poole and F. Gill, eds.). Acad. Nat. Sci., Philadelphia; Amer. Ornith. Union, Washington D.C.

Williams, O. and P. Wheat. 1971. Hybrid jays in Colorado. *Wilson Bull.* 83:343-346.

Williamson, K. 1957. The annual post-nuptial molt in the Wheatear (*Oenanthe oenanthe*). *Bird-Banding* 28:129-135.

Williamson, F.S.L. 1956. The molt and testis cycle of the Anna Hummingbird. *Condor* 58:342-366.

____. 1957. Hybrids of the Anna and Allen hummingbirds. *Condor* 59:118-123.

Willoughby, E.J. 1986. An unusual sequence of molts and plumages in Cassin's and Bachman's sparrows. *Condor* 88:461-472.

____. 1989. The molts of Chipping Sparrows and Field Sparrows in Maryland. *Maryland Birdlife* 45:127-134.

____. 1991. Molt of the genus *Spizella* (Passeriformes, Emberizidae) in relation to ecological factors affecting plumage wear. *Proc. Western Found. Vert. Zool.* 4:247-286.

____. 1992. Incorrect use of the Humphrey-Parkes molt and plumage terminology for buntings of the genus *Passerina*. *Condor* 94:295-297.

____. Geographic and sexual differences in molting of the Lesser Goldfinch, *Carduelis psaltria*, in North America. Unpublished ms.

Wilson, B.L. 1983. Identifying meadowlarks in Iowa. *Iowa Bird Life* 53:83-86.

Wilson, E.O. and W.L. Brown Jr. 1953. The subspecies concept and its taxonomic application. *Syst. Zool.* 2:97-111.

Wilson, W.H. Jr. 1996. Palm Warbler. *In* The Birds of North America, No. **238** (A. Poole and F. Gill, eds.). Acad. Nat. Sci., Philadelphia; Amer. Ornith. Union, Washington D.C.

Wingfield, J.C. and D.S. Farner. 1976. Avian endocrinology - field investigations and methods. *Condor* 78:570-573.

Winker, K. 1991. Problems with resolving our ignorance concerning some *Empidonax* flycatchers of the northcentral region. *Loon* 63:113-115.

____. 1993. Specimen shrinkage in Tennessee Warblers and "Traill's" Flycatchers. *J. Field Ornith.* 64:331-336.

____, B.A. Fall, J.T. Klicka, D.F. Parmelee, and H.B. Tordoff. 1991. The importance of avian collections and the need for continued collecting. *Loon* 63:238-246.

____, J.H. Rappole, and M.A. Ramos. 1990. Population dynamics of the Wood Thrush in southern Veracruz, Mexico. *Condor* 92:444-460.

____, D.W. Warner, and A.R. Weisbrod. 1992. The Northern Waterthrush and Swainson's Thrush as transients at a temperate inland stopover site. Pp. 384-402 *in* J.M. Hagan III and D.W. Johnston, eds., Ecology and conservation of neotropical migrant landbirds. Smithsonian Institution Press, Washington D.C.

Winkler, K.P. 1988. Note on a Hammond's Flycatcher. *Bird Observer* 16:133-137.

Winkler, R. and L. Jenni. 1996. Terminology in molt and wing feathers: Use of descendent, ascendent, and lesser coverts. *Auk* 113:968-969.

Wiseman, A.J. 1968a. Ageing by skull ossification. *Inl. Bird Banding News.* 40:47-52.

____. 1968b. Ageing Cardinals by juvenal secondaries and secondary coverts. *Inl. Bird Banding News* 40:172-173.

____. 1969. The geographically erratic chickadees. *Inl. Bird Banding News* 41:164-168.

____. 1977. Interrelation of variables in postjuvenal molt of Cardinals. *Bird-Banding* 48:206-223.

With, K.A. 1994. McCown's Longspur. *In* The Birds of North America, No. **96** (A. Poole and F. Gill, eds.). Acad. Nat. Sci., Philadelphia; Amer. Ornith. Union, Washington D.C.

Witmer, E. 1991. Second state record of Pacific-slope Flycatcher (*Empidonax difficilis*): Lancaster County. *Pennsylvania Birds* 4:142.

Witmer, M.C. 1996. Consequences of an alien shrub on the plumage coloration and ecology of Cedar Waxwings. *Auk* 113:735-743.

Wolcott, M.J. 1975. Can a Yellow-bellied Sapsucker continue to wear HY plumage into early May? *E. Bird Banding Assoc. News* 38:9-10.

Wolf, B.O. 1997. Black Phoebe. *In* The Birds of North America, No. **268** (A. Poole and F. Gill, eds.). Acad. Nat. Sci., Philadelphia; Amer. Ornith. Union, Washington D.C.

Wolf, L.L. 1977. Species relationships in the avian genus *Aimophila*. *Ornith. Monogr.* 23:1-220.

Wolfson, A. 1952. The cloacal protuberance - a means for determining breeding condition in live male passerines. *Bird-Banding* 23:159-165.

Wood, D.L. and D.S. Wood. 1972. Numerical color specification for bird identification:iris color and age in fall migrants. *Bird-Banding* 43:182-190.

Wood, D.S. 1973. A numerical criterion for aging by iris color in the Gray Catbird. *E. Bird Banding Assoc. News* 36:147-149.

____. 1992. Color and size variation in eastern White-breasted Nuthatches. *Wilson Bull.* 104:599-611.

____ and D.L. Wood. 1973. Quantitative iris color change with age in Downy Woodpeckers. *Bird-Banding* 44:100-101.

Wood, H.B. 1945. The sequence of molt in Purple Grackles. *Auk* 62:455-456.

____. 1950. Growth bars in feathers. *Auk* 67:486-491.

____. 1951. Development of white in the tails of juncos, *Junco hyemalis*. *Auk* 68:522-523.

Wood, M. 1969. A bird-Bander's guide to determination of age and sex of selected species. College of Agriculture, The Pennsylvania State Univ., University Park, PA.

____. 1970. Corrections by the author for "A bird-Bander's guide to the determination of age and sex of selected species". *W. Bird Bander* 45:43. [Reprinted in *E. Bird Banding Assoc. News* 33:107-108 and *Inl. Bird Banding News* 42:66-67]

Wood, N.A. 1904. Discovery of the breeding area of Kirtland's Warbler. *Bull. Michigan Orn. Club* 5:3-13.

Woodford, J. and F.T. Lovesy. 1958. Weights and measurements of wood warblers at Pelee Island. *Bird-Banding* 29:109-110.

Woodward, J. 1975. [On the use of roof-of-mouth color for ageing Tufted Titmice.] *E. Bird Banding Assoc. News* 38:19.

Woolfenden, G.E. 1955. Spring molt of the Harris Sparrow. *Wilson Bull.* 67:212-213.

____ and J.W. Fitzpatrick. 1996. Florida Scrub-Jay. *In* The Birds of North America, No. **228** (A. Poole and F. Gill, eds.). Acad. Nat. Sci., Philadelphia; Amer. Ornith. Union, Washington D.C.

Wootton, J.T. 1996. Purple Finch. *In* The Birds of North America, No. **208** (A. Poole and F. Gill, eds.). Acad. Nat. Sci., Philadelphia; Amer. Ornith. Union, Washington D.C.

Worthington, W.W. and W.E.C. Todd. 1926. The birds of the Choctawhatchee Bay region of Florida. *Wilson Bull.* 38:204-229.

Wright, P.L. and M.H. Wright. 1944. The reproductive cycle of the male Red-winged Blackbird. *Condor* 46:46-59.

Yanega, G.M., P. Pyle, and G.R. Geupel. 1997. The timing and reliability of bill corrugations for ageing hummingbirds. *W. Birds* 28:13-18.

Yang, S.Y. and R.K. Selander. 1968. Hybridization in the grackle *Quiscalus quiscula* in Louisiana. *Syst. Zool.* 17:107-143.

Yarbrough, C.G. and D.W. Johnston. 1965. Lipid deposition in wintering and premigratory Myrtle Warblers. *Wilson Bull.* 77:175-191.

Yasukawa, K. and W.A. Searcy. 1995. Red-winged Blackbird. *In* The Birds of North America, No. **184** (A. Poole and F. Gill, eds.). Acad. Nat. Sci., Philadelphia; Amer. Ornith. Union, Washington D.C.

Yen, C.W. 1989. A plumage study of the cardinal (*Cardinalis cardinalis cardinalis*) of western Pennsylvania. *Bull. Nat. Mus. Nat. Sci., Taichung, Taiwan* 1:11-21.

Yong, W. and F.R. Moore. 1994. Flight morphology, energetic condition, and stopover biology of migrating thrushes. *Auk* 111:683-692.

Yosef, R. 1996. Loggerhead Shrike. *In* The Birds of North America, No. **231** (A. Poole and F. Gill, eds.). Acad. Nat. Sci., Philadelphia; Amer. Ornith. Union, Washington D.C.

Young, B.E. 1989. First specimen record of the Indigo Bunting, *Passerina cyanea*, in British Columbia. *Can. Field-Nat.* 103:415.

____. 1991. Annual molt and interruption of the fall migration for molting in Lazuli Buntings. *Condor* 93:236-250.

Yunick, R.P. 1970a. On Bank Swallow banding. *E. Bird Banding Assoc. News* 33:85-96.

____. 1970b. The Pine Siskin wing stripe and its relation to age and sex. *E. Bird Banding Assoc. News* 33:267-274.

____. 1970c. An examination of certain aging criteria for the Cedar Waxwing (*Bombycilla cedrorum*). *Bird-Banding* 41:291-299.

____. 1972. Variations in the tail spotting of the Slate-colored Junco. *Bird-Banding* 43:38-46.

____. 1973. An age technique for female Evening Grosbeaks. *E. Bird Banding Assoc. News* 36:69-70.

____. 1975. Very few Purple Finches can be sexed by wing chord length. *Inl. Bird Banding News* 47:86-88.

____. 1976a. Further examination of the wing stripe of the Pine Siskin. *N. Am. Bird Bander* 1:63-66.

____. 1976b. Incomplete prebasic molt in a Dark-eyed Junco. *Bird-banding* 47:276-277.

____. 1976c. Delayed molt in the Pine Siskin. *Bird-Banding* 47:306-309.

____. 1977a. Eye color changes in the Dark-eyed Junco and White-throated Sparrow. *N. Am. Bird Bander* 2:155-156.

____. 1977b. Dark-eyed Junco with 13 rectrices. *N. Am. Bird Bander* 2:6.

____. 1977c. Timing of completion of skull pneumatization in the Pine Siskin. *Bird-Banding* 48:67-71.

____. 1977d. Evening Grosbeak age-sex determining criteria. *N. Am. Bird Bander* 2:12-13.

____. 1979a. Variation in skull pneumatisation patterns of certain passerines. *N. Am. Bird Bander* 4:145-147.

____. 1979b. Timing of completion of skull pneumatization of the Purple Finch and the Common Redpoll. *N. Am. Bird Bander* 4:49-51.

____. 1980. Timing of completion of skull pneumatization of the Black-capped Chickadee and the Red-breasted Nuthatch. *N. Am. Bird Bander* 5:43-46.

____. 1981a. Further observations on skull pneumatization. *N. Am. Bird Bander* 6:40-43.

____. 1981b. Skull pneumatization rates in three invading populations of Black-capped Chickadees. *North Am. Bird Bander* 6:6-7.

____. 1981c. Age determination of winter and spring Dark-eyed Juncos. *N. Am. Bird Bander.* 6:97-100.

____. 1983a. Age and sex determination of Purple Finches during the breeding season. *N. Am. Bird Bander* 8:48-51.

____. 1983b. Age determination of female American Goldfinches. *N. Am. Bird Bander* 8:152.

Yunick, R.P. 1984. Toward more effective age determination of banded birds. *N. Am. Bird Bander* 9:2-4.

____. 1986. Carpal compression as a variable in taking wing chord measurements. *N. Am. Bird Bander* 11:78-83.

____. 1987. Age determination of male House Finches. *N. Am. Bird Bander* 12:8-11.

____. 1989. Some comments on Yellow-rumped Warbler molt. *Kingbird* 39:100-101.

____. 1990. Identification criteria for some Emberizid sparrows. *N. Am. Bird Bander* 15:1-5.

____. 1991. Another assessment of gape color in the Purple Finch. *N. Am. Bird Bander* 16:109-113.

____. 1992a. A method for age determination of Blue Jays in northeastern United States and southeastern Canada. *N. Am. Bird Bander* 17:10-15.

____. 1992b. Further observations on the timing of skull pneumatization in the Pine Siskin. *N. Am. Bird Bander* 17:93-96.

____. 1995. Rectrix shape as a criterion for determining age of the Pine Siskin. *N. Am. Bird Bander* 20:101-105.

Yuri, T. and S. Rohwer. 1997. Molt and migration in the Northern Rough-winged Swallow. *Auk* 114:249-262.

Zaias, J. and R. Breitwisch. 1990. Molt-breeding overlap in Northern Mockingbirds. *Auk* 107:414-416.

Zammuto, R.M. and E.C. Franks. 1979. Trapping flocks of Chimney Swifts in Illinois. *Bird-Banding* 50:201-209.

Zimmer, K.J. 1984. ID point: Eastern vs. Western meadowlarks. *Birding* 16:155-156.

____. 1988. The Brown Towhee complex. *Birding* 20:129-136.

Zimmer, J.T. 1929. A study of the Tooth-billed Red Tanager, *Piranga flava*. *Field Mus. Nat. Hist. Zool.* 17:169-219.

____. 1937a. Studies of Peruvian birds. No. XXVIII. Notes on the genera *Myiodynastes, Conopias, Myiozetetes,* and *Pitangus*. *Am. Mus. Novitates* 963:1-28.

____. 1937b. Studies of Peruvian birds no. XXVII. Notes on the genera *Muscivora, Tyrannus, Empidonomus,* and *Sirystes*, with further notes on *Knipolegus*. *Am. Mus. Novitates* 962:1-28.

____. 1939. Studies of Peruvian birds. No. XXXI. *Am. Mus. Novitates* 1043:1-15.

____. 1941. Studies of Peruvian birds. No. XXXIX. The genus *Vireo*. *Am. Mus. Novitates* 1127:1-20.

____. 1945. A new swift from Central and South America. *Auk* 62:586-592.

Zimmerman, D. 1972. Age and sex determination in game birds. *Pennsylvania Game News* 43(11):17-21.

Zimmerman, D.A. 1955. Notes on field identification and comparative behavior of shrikes in winter. *Wilson Bull.* 67:200-208.

Zimmerman, J.L. 1965. Carcass analysis of wild and theral-stressed Dickcissels. *Wilson Bull.* 77:55-70.

Zink, R.M. 1983. Evolutionary and systematic significance of temporal variation in the Fox Sparrow. *Syst. Zool.* 32:223-238.

____. 1986. Patterns and evolutionary significance of geographic variation in the Schistacea group of the Fox Sparrow (*Passerella iliaca*). *Ornith. Monogr.* 40:1-119.

____. 1994. The geography of mitochondrial DNA variation, population structure, hybridization, and species limits in the Fox Sparrow (*Passerella iliaca*). *Evolution* 48:96-111.

____, R.C. Blackwell, and O. Rojas-Soto. 1997. Species limits in the Le Conte's Thrasher. *Condor* 99:132-138.

____ and D.L. Dittmann. 1993. Population structure and gene flow in the Chipping Sparrow. *Wilson Bull.* 105:399-413.

____, ____, S.W. Cardiff, and J.D. Rising. 1991. Mitochondrial DNA variation and the taxonomic status of the Large-billed Savannah Sparrow. *Condor* 93:1016-1019.

____ and J.V. Remsen Jr. 1986. Evolutionary processes and patterns of geographic variation in birds. *Current Ornith.* 4:1-69.

Index

Notes

SOME ABBREVIATIONS AND INTERPRETATIONS

MONTHS (see also p. 29)

All months are abbreviated to the first 3 letters. Parentheses surrounding the months indicate that the plumage or condition described may be encountered between and/or within the months listed, but is usually not found or can't be reliably used outside of them.

FEATHERS (see also pp. 2 and 14)

p (pp) — primary (primaries).

pN — (ex. p10) the Nth (10th or outermost) primary.

s (ss) — secondary (secondaries).

terts — tertials.

covs — coverts.

pp covs — (greater) primary coverts.

gr covs — greater (secondary) coverts.

med covs — median (secondary) coverts.

rect(s) — rectrix (rectrices).

flight feathers — collective for pp, pp covs, ss, and rects.

MEASUREMENTS (see also p. 4)

wg — length of wing chord (unflattened) in mm.

wg (flat) — length of flattened wing in mm.

p6-p10 (example) — distance from the tip of p6 to the tip of p10 in mm. If p10 > p6 the value is negative.

tl — tail length in mm.

bill nares to tip — length of the bill along the culmen (anteior end of nares to the bill tip) in mm.

exp culmen — exposed culmen (bill from edge of feathers on ridge, to tip) in mm.

MOLT (see also pp. 12 and 31)

PB — Prebasic (often = postjuvenal and/or postnuptial) molt.

1st PB — First prebasic (often = postjuvenal) molt.

Adult PB — Adult prebasic (often = postnuptial or pre-breeding) molt.

1st PA — Prealternate molt in first-year birds.

PA — Prealternate (often = prenuptial or pre-breeding) molt.

Adult PA — Prealternate molt in adults (at least 1-1/2 years old).

Absent — No molt or feather replacement occurs (many PAs).

Limited — Some, but not all, body feathers and no flight feathers are replaced (some PAs).

Partial — Most or all body feathers but no flight feathers (except, sometimes, 1-3 terts and 1-2 central rects) are replaced (many 1st PBs, some PAs).

Incomplete —Usually all body feathers and some, but not all, flight feathers are replaced (some 1st PBs, a few PAs).

Complete — All body and flight feathers are replaced (virtually all adult PBs, some 1st PBs, a few PAs).

AGE/SEX (see also p. 32)

CP/BP — Cloacal protuberance and brood patch are reliable indicators of sex within the months given.

Juv — Juvenile. A bird in juvenal plumage, before the first prebasic molt.

HY — A bird in first-basic plumage and in its first calendar year (i.e. from the first prebasic molt until December 31st of the year it fledged).

SY — A bird in its second calendar year (i.e. January 1st of the year following fledging through December 31st of the same year).

AHY — A bird in at least its second calendar year (at least an SY).

TY — A bird in its third calendar year.

ASY — A bird in at least its third calendar year (i.e. a bird in at least the year following its first breeding season and 2nd prebasic molt).

ATY — An adult in at least its fourth calendar year.

4Y — A bird in its fourth calendar year (not accepted by BBL/CWS).

A4Y — A bird in at least its fourth calendar year (not accepted by BBL/CWS).